PRENTICE HALL
is now making
teachers' lives easier!

PRENTICE HALL
TeacherEXPRESS™

Plan • Teach • Assess

Teacher Express CD-ROM is a new suite of instructional tools to help teachers plan, teach, and assess. Powerful lesson planning, resource management, testing, and an interactive Teacher's Edition, all in one place, make class preparation quick and easy!

Show students how geography affects their lives.

World Geography Program Components

Student Edition
Teacher's Edition

Classroom Resources

Teaching Resources
  Program Overview
  Unit Books
    Guided Reading and Review
    Section Quizzes
    Reviewing Main Ideas
    Regional Atlas Resources
    Regional Atlas Database Skills
    Map and Graph Skills
    Outline Maps
    Critical Thinking
    Geography and World Literature
    Test Forms A and B
  Mental Mapping Activities
  Simulations, Games, and Lab Activities
  People and Geography
  Creative Teaching Activities
  Spanish Resources

Teaching Resources (continued)
  Guide to the Essentials of World Geography (English)
  Guide to the Essentials of World Geography (Spanish)
  Guide to the Essentials of World Geography
    Teacher's Manual
  Global Issues Posters
  Nystrom Desk Atlas
Guided Reading and Review Workbook (English)
Guided Reading and Review Workbook (Spanish)
Guided Reading and Review Workbook
  Teacher's Manual (English)
Guided Reading and Review Workbook
  Teacher's Manual (Spanish)
Map and Photo Transparencies
Section Reading Support Transparency System

Component Showcase

Interactive Textbook Online and on CD-ROM offers the same trusted content as the printed textbook with interactive activities, an audio glossary, and instant feedback on self-assessments to engage all learners.

TeacherEXPRESS™ CD-ROM is a new suite of instructional tools to help teachers plan, teach, and assess. Powerful lesson planning, resource management, testing, and an interactive Teacher's Edition—all in one place—make class preparation quick and easy!

PH SuccessNet™—featuring Teacher Center—is a convenient, all-in-one online resource that helps you plan, teach, assess, and manage your clas

PRENTICE HALL
TeacherEXPRESS™
Plan · Teach · Assess

featuring Teacher Center

TEACHER'S EDITION

PRENTICE HALL

WORLD GEOGRAPHY

BUILDING A GLOBAL PERSPECTIVE

Authors THOMAS J. BAERWALD • CELESTE FRASER

Academic Consultant SARAH WITHAM BEDNARZ

PEARSON

Prentice
Hall

Upper Saddle River, New Jersey
Needham, Massachusetts

In Association With DK Publishing

ISBN 0-13-181704-3
2 3 4 5 6 7 8 9 10   07 06 05 04

Assessment

Prentice Hall Assessment System
  Program Assessment
    Chapter Tests with **Exam**_View_® Test Bank CD-ROM
    Alternative Assessment
  Test Prep
    Diagnose and Prescribe
      Diagnostic Tests for High School
        Social Studies Skills
    Review and Reteach
      Review Book for World Geography
    Practice and Assess
      Test Prep Book for World Geography
      Test-Taking Strategies With
        Transparencies for High School
      Test-Taking Strategies Posters
Exam_View_® Test Bank CD-ROM

Technology

The Interactive Textbook Online and on CD-ROM
TeacherEXPRESS™ CD-ROM
Guided Reading Audiotapes (English)
Guided Reading Audiotapes (Spanish)
Student Edition on Audio CD
World Geography Video Collection
Passport to the World CD-ROM
Social Studies Skills Tutor CD-ROM
Prentice Hall Presentation Pro CD-ROM
Companion Web site

Go Online Web links at point-of-use in the student text provide instant access to Internet content.

DK Online World Desk Reference explores topics in physical and human geography for every country in the world, and practices critical-thinking skills—brought to you through an exclusive partnership between DK and Prentice Hall.

Passport to the World CD-ROM lets students explore the geography, culture, economy, and government of key places through an interactive game.

Putting the Standards Into Practice

National Geography Standards

Prentice Hall's *World Geography: Building a Global Perspective* program has been designed to help your students meet the standards established in *Geography for Life: National Geography Standards* (1994). That publication was produced by the Geography Education Standards Project on behalf of the American Geographical Society, Association of American Geographers, National Council for Geographic Education, and National Geographic Society. The standards present a detailed composite of what students in grades K–4, 5–8, and 9–12 should know and be able to demonstrate in the area of geography. Each of the 18 National Geography Standards has been correlated to the sections, features, and lessons in the Student Edition and Teacher's Edition of *World Geography: Building a Global Perspective*.

The National Geography Standards

The geographically informed person knows and understands . . .

1. How to use maps and other geographic representations, tools, and technologies to acquire, process, and report information from a spatial perspective.

2. How to use mental maps to organize information about people, places, and environments in a spatial context.

3. How to analyze the spatial organization of people, places, and environments on Earth's surface.

4. The physical and human characteristics of places.

5. That people create regions to interpret Earth's complexity.

6. How culture and experience influence people's perceptions of places and regions.

7. The physical processes that shape the patterns of Earth's surface.

8. The characteristics and spatial distribution of ecosystems on Earth's surface.

9. The characteristics, distribution, and migration of human populations on Earth's surface.

10. The characteristics, distribution, and complexity of Earth's cultural mosaics.

11. The patterns and networks of economic interdependence on Earth's surface.

12. The processes, patterns, and functions of human settlement.

13. How the forces of cooperation and conflict among people influence the division and control of Earth's surface.

14. How human actions modify the physical environment.

15. How physical systems affect human systems.

16. The changes that occur in the meaning, use, distribution, and importance of resources.

17. How to apply geography to interpret the past.

18. How to apply geography to interpret the present and plan for the future.

Concepts of Geography

For ease of student reference, *World Geography: Building a Global Perspective* focuses on 21 concepts of geography, which are derived from the National Geography Standards and state standards. Students can apply these concepts to gain a fuller understanding of the patterns and processes that shape the world and its people.

Concepts of Geography

Climates	Geographic Tools	Physical Characteristics
Cooperation and Conflict	Global Trade Patterns	Physical Processes
Cultures	Government and Citizenship	Planning for the Future
Economic Activities	Migration	Population Growth
Economic Systems	Natural Hazards	Science and Technology
Ecosystems	Natural Resources	Understanding the Past
Environmental Change	Patterns of Settlement	Urbanization

These concepts are woven throughout the text. By examining subsection headings, captions, and assessment questions, students can draw comparisons across cultures and regions.

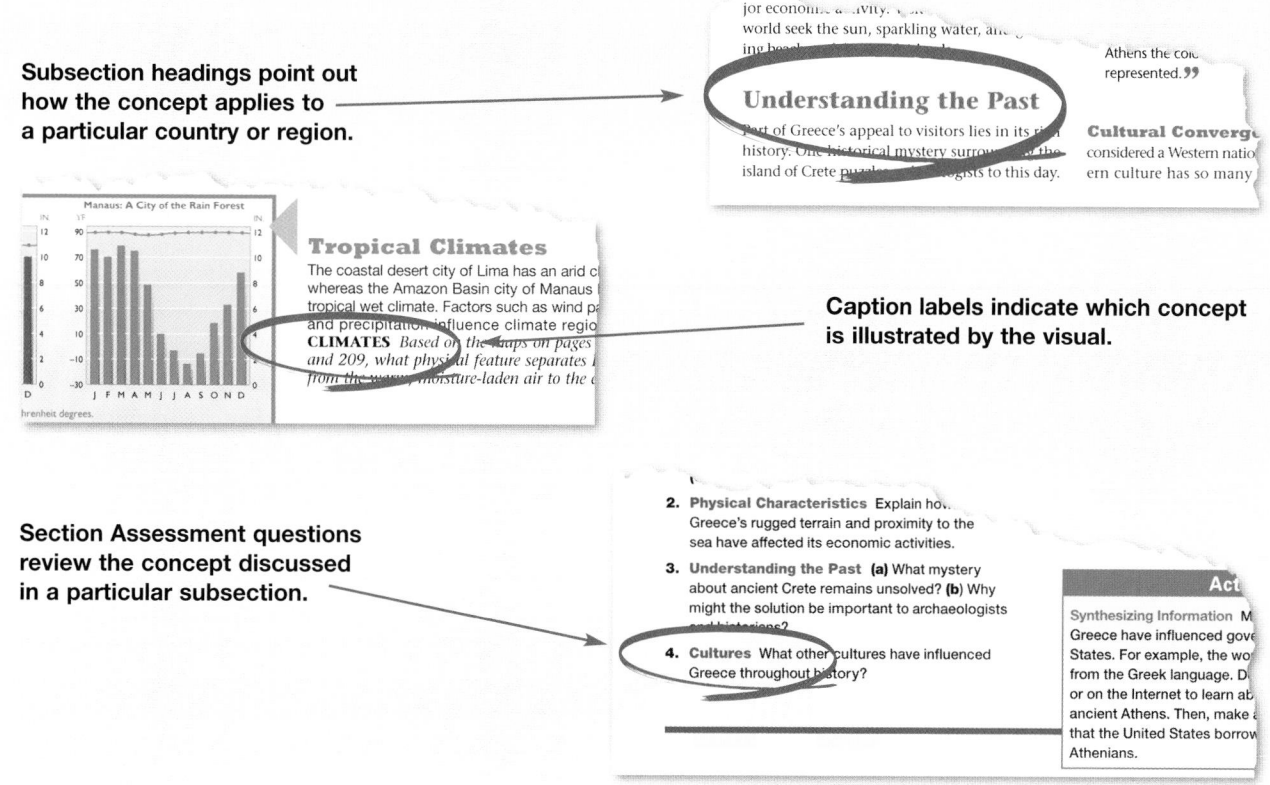

Subsection headings point out how the concept applies to a particular country or region.

Understanding the Past

.ajor econom.. ..ivity. ...
world seek the sun, sparkling water, an...
ing bea...

Athens the co...
represented. "

...art of Greece's appeal to visitors lies in its ri...
history. One historical mystery surrou... ...the
island of Crete puzzl... ...ogists to this day.

Cultural Converg...
considered a Western natio...
ern culture has so many...

Manaus: A City of the Rain Forest

Tropical Climates

The coastal desert city of Lima has an arid cl...
whereas the Amazon Basin city of Manaus ...
tropical wet climate. Factors such as wind p...
and precipitation influence climate regio...
CLIMATES *Based on the maps on pages*
and 209, what physical feature separates...
from the war... moisture-laden air to the ...

Caption labels indicate which concept is illustrated by the visual.

Section Assessment questions review the concept discussed in a particular subsection.

2. **Physical Characteristics** Explain ho...
Greece's rugged terrain and proximity to the
sea have affected its economic activities.

3. **Understanding the Past (a)** What mystery
about ancient Crete remains unsolved? **(b)** Why
might the solution be important to archaeologists
...

4. **Cultures** What other cultures have influenced
Greece throughout history?

Act...

Synthesizing Information M...
Greece have influenced gove...
States. For example, the wo...
from the Greek language. D...
or on the Internet to learn ab...
ancient Athens. Then, make ...
that the United States borro...
Athenians.

But I'm Not a Reading Teacher!

*F*ew people choose to be social studies teachers in order to focus on reading. Yet a significant number of today's students lack reading proficiency. Without it, they cannot access the wealth of social studies content they need to absorb from textbooks, primary sources, literature, and more. When students can't read well, they don't read and won't read.

Best Practices in Reading

Instead of plunging in and plodding through a section, students need a plan of action, a strategy. Best practices for teaching reading in social studies focus on **comprehension strategies**—teaching students what to do *before reading, during reading,* and *after reading.*

Reading Proficiency in Secondary Students

Source: NAEP Reading Report Card, 1998

Here are some ways to implement these strategies with struggling readers:

Before Reading Both teacher and student preparations precede reading.

- Use an anecdote, photo, artifact, or audio to set the scene.
- Display a map or other visual aid to encourage students to identify what they already know and to make predictions to apply this knowledge to a new situation.
- Model for students how to look at pictures, captions, and headings in order to predict what they will be learning.

During Reading Student-directed, individual activities take place during reading. Providing guided practice will help students develop these habits.

- Show students how to take notes, using graphic organizers that match the type of information they are reading. For example, use a Venn diagram for comparing and contrasting, a flowchart for sequencing, and a concept web for finding main idea and supporting details.
- Teach students to ask themselves questions as they read.
- Demonstrate for students how to make connections between what they read and what they already know.

After Reading Both student-directed and teacher-directed activities can follow reading.

- Conduct a sample self-check for students—"What have I learned?"
- Teach students to ask themselves, "How does this relate to what I already know?"
- Demonstrate both formal and informal assessments that students will encounter.

Comprehension Strategies

Before Reading
- Activate prior knowledge
- Build needed prior knowledge
- Focus attention
- Set purpose for reading
- Make predictions

During Reading
- Confirm predictions
- Read and self-monitor
- Take notes and ask questions

After Reading
- Recall information
- Respond to new learning
- Extend and transfer new learning
- Assess reading success

Reading success happens when students can construct meaning from information.

Prentice Hall Support Throughout the Program

The structure of each Prentice Hall program embeds the development of solid reading skills in the Student Edition. Each section of the text enables students to organize information *before reading* and *during reading*.

At the end of each section, students will find opportunities to recall and apply information and construct meaning from it.

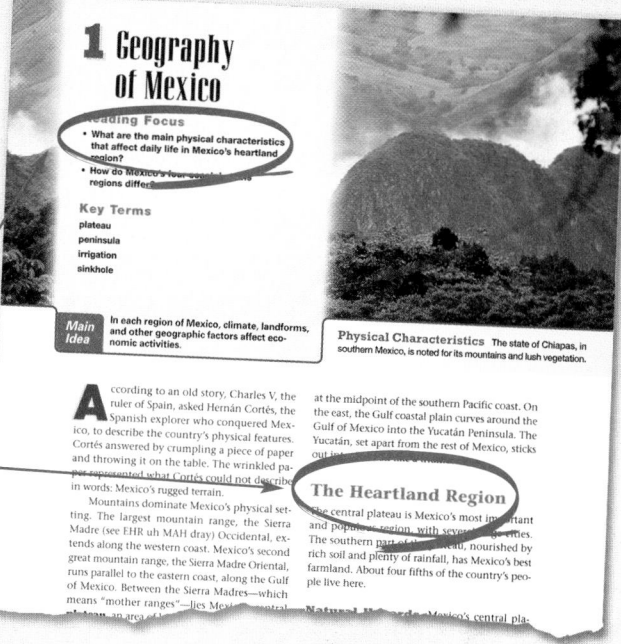

Notice that the *Reading Focus* questions align with the sub-headings in the section.

Teacher's Edition

Additional reading strategies as well as ways to customize instruction for less proficient readers and English language learners give you focused strategies to improve students' comprehension.

📖 Section Reading Support Transparency System

Every section of the text has a companion reading support transparency that delivers the main points through a graphic organizer.

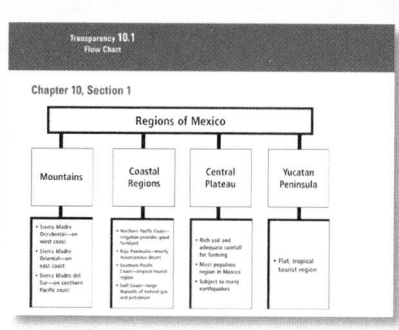

📕 Guide to the Essentials

Look in the Teaching Resources box for the *Guide to the Essentials* in both English and Spanish. Students use this book to review and master new content through summaries written below grade level.

🔊 Student Edition on Audio

Auditory learners, less proficient readers, and English language learners can benefit from listening to the book on CD as they read the text.

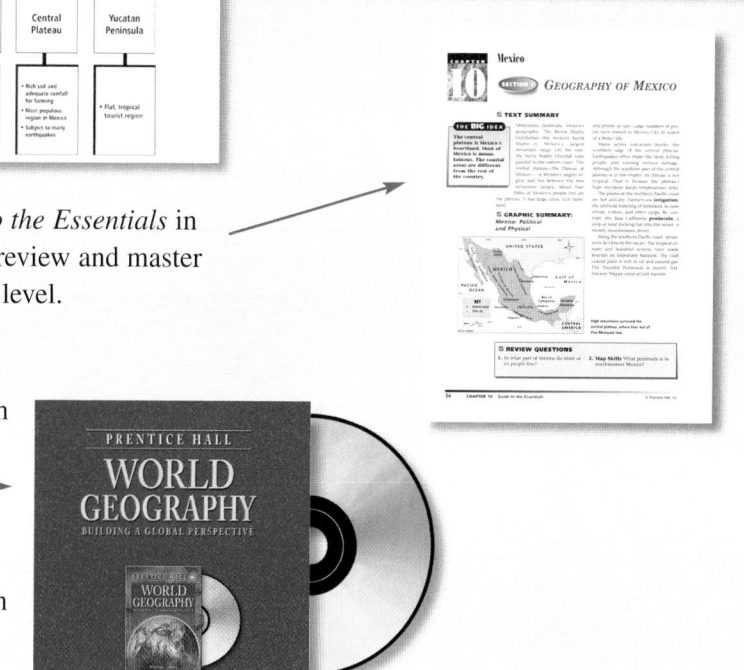

📼 Guided Reading Audiotapes

Auditory learners, less proficient readers, and English language learners can listen to section summaries provided on the Guided Reading Audiotapes in English and in Spanish.

Why Should I Teach Skills?

> **"**Give a man a fish, and he eats for a day. Teach a man to fish, and he eats for a lifetime.**"**
>
> — Author Unknown

Following this advice, if we present our students with only content, we are, in essence, giving them the fish. If we are to prepare students for life, we need to teach the skills needed to make sense out of the increasing volume of information in the world. To help students become lifelong learners, we need to develop their abilities to question, read, analyze, interpret, and evaluate information, as well as to communicate their ideas to others.

Best Practices in Skills Integration

These guidelines will help you to embed skills development within content instruction.

Topic: Foreign Relations		
	Example	**Skill**
Facts	Region divided among colonial powers	Map reading
Concepts	Cooperation and conflict	Cause and effect
Big Ideas	Political independence brought both opportunities and challenges	Predicting consequences

1. **Plan each unit around an enduring understanding or big idea.** For example, if the chapter you are about to teach is Southeast Asia, the big idea might be "political independence brought both opportunities and challenges."

2. **Develop each lesson around the facts, concepts, the big idea, and the skills students need to be able to connect the content to the big idea.** For part of a lesson on cooperation and conflict, you might want to focus on the effects of colonialism in the region.

3. **Teach skills that are new or that add another level of complexity to a previously mastered skill.** Follow the elements of good skill instruction:

   - Set a purpose for using the skill.
   - Present the steps to follow.
   - Model the process for using the skill.
   - Guide practice and provide feedback.
   - Apply to a prompt such as a picture, map, or reading passage.

4. **Reinforce skills whenever possible.** Ask critical thinking questions about maps, photos, graphs, charts, and primary sources.

Elements of Skill Instruction

Teach the skill

Model applying the skill often

Guide practice of the skill

Give feedback and correction

Have students apply the skill independently

5. **Assess both content and skills mastery regularly.** It is important to determine whether students are remembering important information, but it is equally as important to determine whether they are internalizing skills as lifelong learners.

Prentice Hall Support for Skills

Skills mastery means developing habits of mind that enable us to turn information into meaning. Every Prentice Hall social studies program contains a wealth of resources to build skills for life.

Skills pages in the Student Edition provide a three-step instruction strategy.

Learn | **Practice** | **Apply**

Skills reinforcement appears in caption questions.

Social Studies Skills Tutor CD-ROM provides two levels of interactive instruction and practice in 20 core social studies skills.

Prentice Hall Vertical Alignment System

Mastery also requires that students learn skills at increasing levels of complexity as they progress through school. Prentice Hall programs take the guesswork out of aligning skills instruction by developing 20 core social studies skills with increasing difficulty from grade to grade.

The 20 Core Social Studies Skills

1. Using the Cartographer's Tools	**11.** Comparing and Contrasting
2. Using Special-Purpose Maps	**12.** Analyzing Primary Sources
3. Analyzing Graphic Data	**13.** Recognizing Bias and Propaganda
4. Analyzing Images	**14.** Identifying Frame of Reference and Point of View
5. Identifying Main Ideas/Summarizing	**15.** Decision Making
6. Sequencing	**16.** Problem Solving
7. Identifying Cause and Effect/Making Predictions	**17.** Using Reliable Information
8. Drawing Inferences and Conclusions	**18.** Transferring Information From One Medium to Another
9. Making Valid Generalizations	**19.** Synthesizing Information
10. Distinguishing Fact and Opinion	**20.** Supporting a Position

Should I Teach to the Test?

*T*he increasing importance of state standards and student accountability leads many teachers to wonder whether they must limit their classes to the content of high-stakes exams. While based on state standards and student needs, a truly effective social studies program requires **alignment of curriculum, instruction, and assessment.** When each of these elements dovetails with the others, *all* instruction prepares students for assessment based on curriculum objectives.

In an aligned system, both teacher and student know what is expected. There are no secrets or surprises. To ensure alignment:

- Teach the objectives in your standards to the specified level of understanding.
- Make sure that students know what they should learn before you teach.
- Test those same objectives as precisely as possible to the same depth of understanding that the standards require.

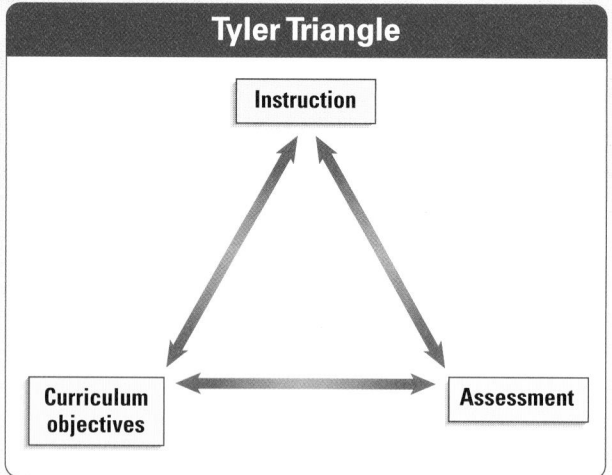

Tyler Triangle

Instruction

Curriculum objectives — Assessment

Best Practices in Assessment

Here are some ways to integrate ongoing assessment with instruction:

Assessment Techniques	
Diagnose and Prescribe	Evaluate student abilities at the beginning of the year.
Plan and Align Plan instruction to align with assessment.	• Examine objectives carefully and choose activities where more than a knowledge level (or memorized level) is expected of students. • Test students on all of the objectives, omitting none. • Test skill development at the same time you assess content.
Review and Reteach Weave ongoing review into aligned instruction and assessment.	Connect instruction to prior learning and include review questions on each test.
Practice and Assess Apply assessment results to improve teaching and learning.	• Use individual student information for tutoring and devising individualized plans. • Use whole-class data to determine if your teaching was aligned to the assessment.

Prentice Hall Assessment System

The Prentice Hall Assessment System provides comprehensive support for both program content assessment and preparation for high-stakes standardized tests.

Program Assessment

Use the Chapter Tests to assess core content for every chapter.

💿 Develop your own customized tests and practice worksheets with the ExamView® Test Bank CD-ROM, selecting from hundreds of test questions and using the word-processing and editing capabilities. Create online tests and study guides and receive instant feedback on student progress.

Standardized Test Preparation

Prentice Hall Assessment System gives you the tools to help your students succeed on standardized tests, from the beginning of the year to the culminating high-stakes exam.

Diagnose and Prescribe

📖 Profile student skills with Diagnostic Tests A & B.

📖 Address student needs with program resources correlated to diagnostic test questions.

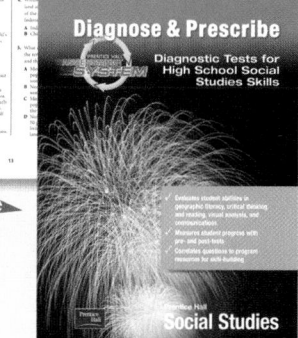

Review and Reteach

📖 Provide cumulative content review with unit-level questions and study sheets.

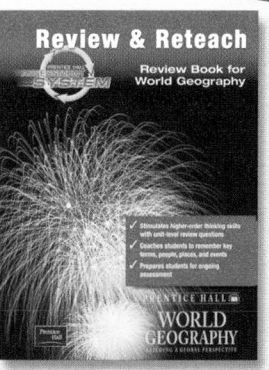

Practice and Assess

📖 Build assessment skills using Test-Taking Strategies With Transparencies.

Reinforce assessment skills with Test-Taking Posters.

📖 Practice taking tests and improve scores on standardized tests with the Test Preparation Workbook.

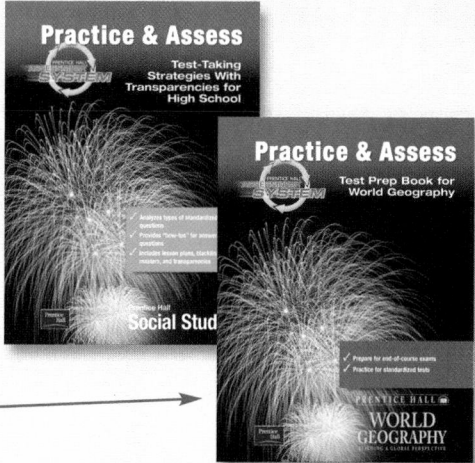

How Am I Doing?

*P*aired with the demand for high student achievement has come the drive for greater teacher accountability. More and more states and districts are establishing standards for teaching and new systems of teacher evaluation.

In the past, professional appraisals focused on teacher behaviors. Nationwide, the focus of teacher evaluation is now shifting to what students are able to do. Student success emerges as the most critical measure of teaching—the teacher has not taught if students have not learned. The goal is becoming the learner-centered class, alive with critical thinking, problem-solving activities, collaborative learning, projects, and investigations. Evaluation criteria now measure how well teachers promote this kind of learning.

Prentice Hall social studies programs provide a variety of ways to support learner-centered instruction. Below you will find a guide to program resources to help you address criteria commonly found in teacher evaluations.

Common Criteria	Where to Look for Support
Active, successful student participation in the learning process	• Structured reading support • Activities at section and chapter levels • Group and individual activities
Learner-centered instruction	• Critical thinking questions in every caption • Strategies for different learner needs • Technology for students: Social Studies Skills Tutor CD-ROM, Companion Web Site
Evaluation and feedback on student progress	• Section and chapter assessments in Student Edition • Test Bank CD-ROM
Classroom management of students, time, and materials	• Pacing charts • Chapter interleaves • Resource Pro®
Professional communications	• Letters to families • Resource Pro® lesson plans for supervisors
Improvement of student performance	• Prentice Hall Assessment System
Professional development	• eTeach • Skylight • PHSuccessNet.com

PRENTICE HALL

IN ASSOCIATION WITH

WORLD GEOGRAPHY

BUILDING A GLOBAL PERSPECTIVE

THOMAS J. BAERWALD • CELESTE FRASER

PEARSON

Prentice
Hall

Upper Saddle River, New Jersey
Needham, Massachusetts

In Association With DK Publishing

Authors

Thomas J. Baerwald received a B.A. degree in geography and history from Valparaiso University in Indiana and earned his M.A. and Ph.D. degrees in geography at the University of Minnesota. He has served on the boards of the Association of American Geographers and the National Council for Geographic Education and has lectured at many universities across the country. Currently Dr. Baerwald is Program Director for Geography at the National Science Foundation in Arlington, Virginia.

Celeste Fraser received her B.A. and M.A. degrees at the University of Colorado. Ms. Fraser has taught at the middle, high school, and college levels and has served as Geography Specialist and Exhibit Developer at the Chicago Children's Museum. She currently owns her own company, which provides geography enrichment programs for K–8 schools.

Dorling Kindersley is an international publishing company specializing in the creation of high-quality reference content for books, CD-ROMs, online, and video. The hallmark of DK content is its unique combination of educational value and strong visual style. This combination allows DK to deliver appealing, accessible, and engaging educational content that delights children, parents, and teachers around the world.

Academic Consultants

Dr. Sarah Witham Bednarz
Associate Professor of Geography
Texas A&M University

Dr. Diane Doser
Professor of Geological Sciences
University of Texas at El Paso

Leonard A. Gordon
Professor of History
Brooklyn College
City University of New York

Dr. Sam Sheldon
Professor of Geography
St. Bonaventure University, New York

John Voll
Professor of Islamic History
Associate Director,
  Center for Muslim-Christian
  Understanding
Georgetown University, Washington, D.C.

Teacher Reviewers

Michael Acuff
Fort Worth ISD
Fort Worth, Texas

Mel Bacon
Brighton High School
Brighton, Colorado

Henry Dircks
Mepham High School
Long Island, New York

Karen Hausdorf
North Cobb High School
Kennesaw, Georgia

Bette LaRue North
Perryville High School
Perryville, Missouri

Peggy Sorenson
Freestate High School
Lawrence, Kansas

Juliann Warner
James Martin High School
Arlington, Texas

Robert Weaver
Snider High School
Fort Wayne, Indiana

Acknowledgments appear on page 799, which constitutes an extension of this copyright page.

 is a registered trademark of Dorling Kindersley Limited.

ISBN 0-13-181707-8

1 2 3 4 5 6 7 8 9 10   07 06 05 04 03

TABLE OF CONTENTS

UNIT 1 — Physical and Human Geography — 32

iii

UNIT 3 Latin America 202

Unit 5 Central Europe and Northern Eurasia 370

Unit 6 Central and Southwest Asia 436

UNIT 9 East Asia and the Pacific World — 632

SPECIAL FEATURES

 How the Earth Works

Visualize forces and concepts in physical geography.

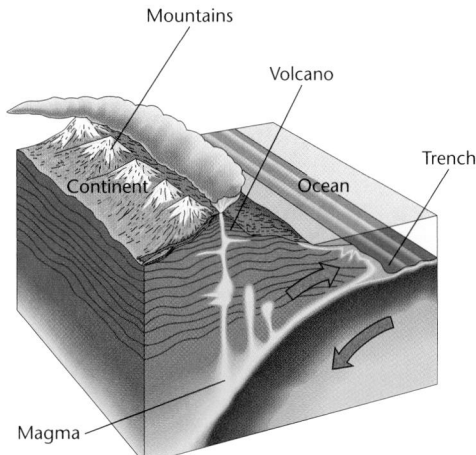

Subduction

REGIONAL DATABASES

Explore issues by analyzing data from each region.

Change Over Time

Witness how a place changes over time.

People and Geography

Investigate case studies in human geography.

SPECIAL FEATURES

Master essential social studies skills.

Organize data like real geographers.

TEST PREPARATION

Practice your test-taking skills.

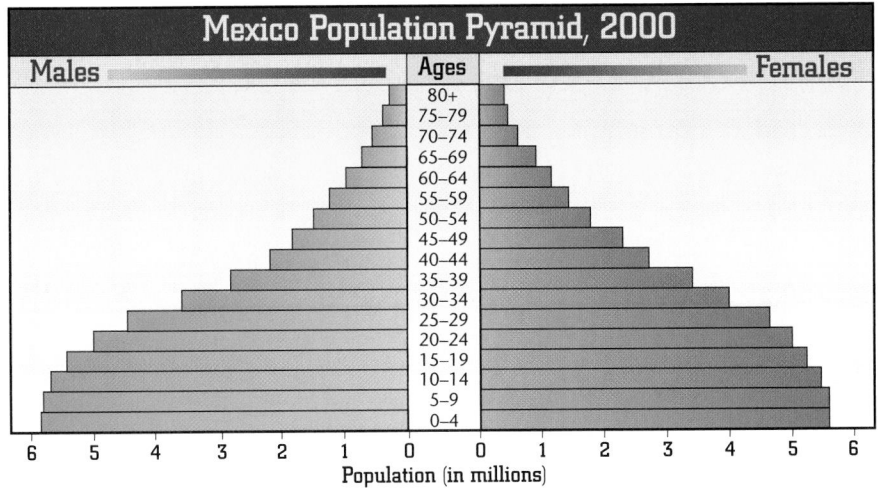

Mexico Population Pyramid, 2000

MAPS

Russia: PHYSICAL

MAPS

East Asia: MAJOR RELIGIONS

KEY
- Buddhism
- Buddhism and Shinto
- Buddhism and Daoism
- Islam
- Christianity
- Traditional religions

Lambert Azimuthal Equal-Area Projection

CHARTS, GRAPHS, AND DIAGRAMS

CHARTS, GRAPHS, AND DIAGRAMS

Ethnic Composition of Canada

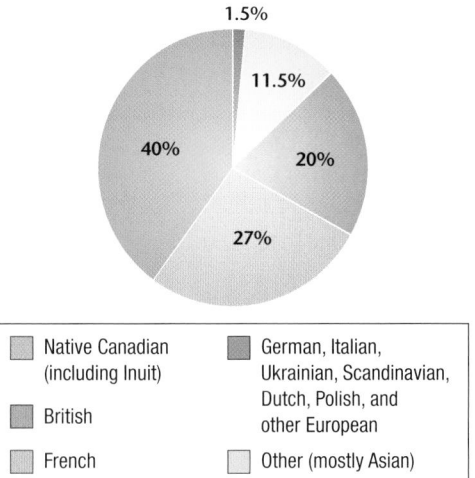

1.5%
11.5%
40%
20%
27%

Native Canadian (including Inuit)		German, Italian, Ukrainian, Scandinavian, Dutch, Polish, and other European
British		
French		Other (mostly Asian)

Introducing
Geography

What does it mean to learn world geography? It means more than gathering the facts, names, and data about the nations and lands of the earth. It means gaining a feel for, or an appreciation of, the richness and variety of the face of our planet.

Use This Program for Success

This program will help you learn content, develop skills, and apply what you know. Examine these pages to understand how this textbook and its online resources can guide you through the study of world geography.

Read to Learn

Organize Your Reading. Before you read, preview each section.

- *Reading Focus* questions identify key ideas.
- Red subsection headings indicate where the answers to Reading Focus questions can be found.
- *Section Assessment* questions enable you to demonstrate your understanding of the ideas introduced by the Reading Focus questions.

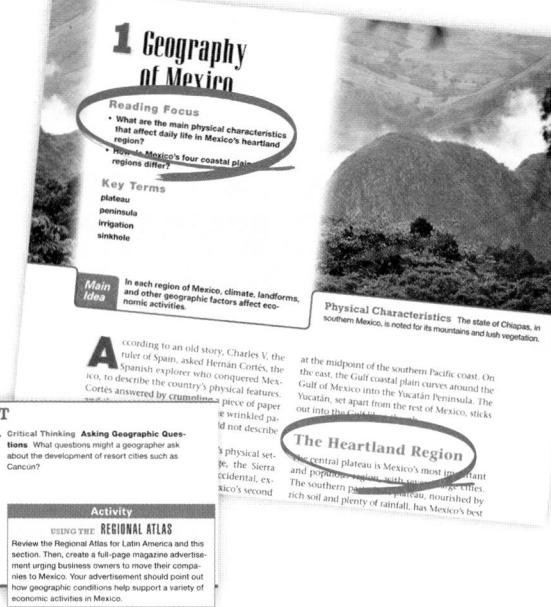

Learn in Many Ways. Understanding world geography requires more than reading the text. Examine all parts of this book—charts, graphic organizers, maps, photographs, and more—to learn about the world. Get a sense of each region by analyzing its Regional Atlas. Study the Global Connections features to see how places and people around the world share common characteristics.

xviii   Use This Program for Success

xviii

Develop Your Skills

Success in world geography requires you to master social studies skills. In each chapter, you will find a *Skills for Life* lesson or a *Do-It-Yourself Skills* lesson. Learn and practice skills covering geographic literacy, visual analysis, critical thinking and reading, and communications. You can also practice your skills by answering critical thinking questions on maps, pictures, charts, and graphs. Apply what you have learned by completing the *Applying Skills* questions at the end of every chapter.

Go online at **PHSchool.com** and discover a high-tech world of Internet resources. You can travel the globe on virtual field trips, learn through Internet activities, or prepare for exams with online self-tests. The resource center has primary sources, biographies, Web links, and more. For news, data, and maps, link to Prentice Hall NewsTracker, *Dorling Kindserley World Desk Reference* Online, or Infoplease®. And don't forget the Interactive Textbook, where you will find animations, video, and help with reading, homework, and tests.

For Internet activities, primary sources, current events, maps, and more, use Web Code mjk–1000.

Get up-to-date information about any country in the world.

Through an exclusive association with Dorling Kindersley, Prentice Hall brings you the *World Desk Reference* Online. Follow these step-by-step instructions to learn about the world, research specific countries, practice critical-thinking skills, and get updated statistics and data.

1 Access the *Dorling Kindersley World Desk Reference* Online using the Web Code on the chapter opening pages in this textbook. Click the *Dorling Kindersley World Desk Reference* Online link. Then, click the globe to begin your search.

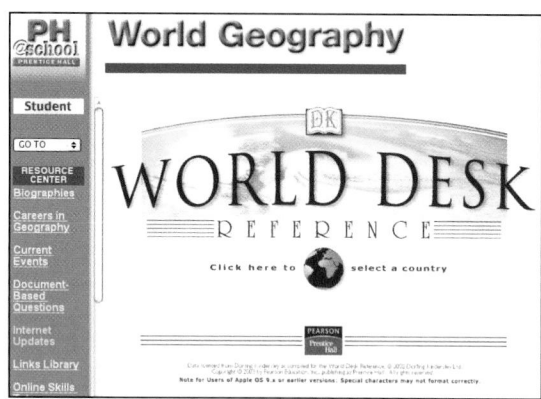

2 Select a country from the Country List.

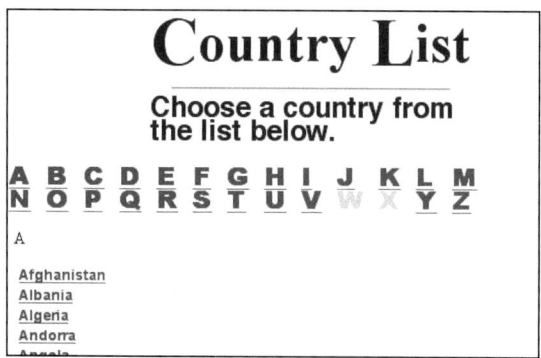

3 Review the country's introduction and the map.

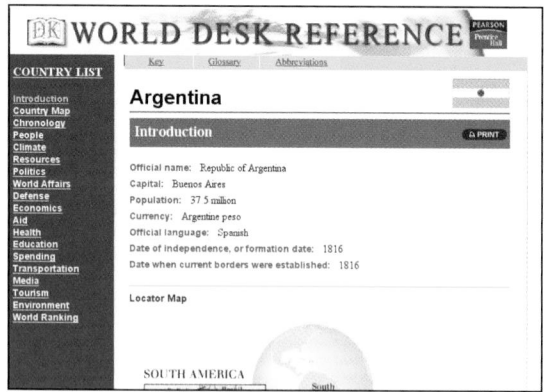

4 In the left navigation column, click each of the categories to learn more.

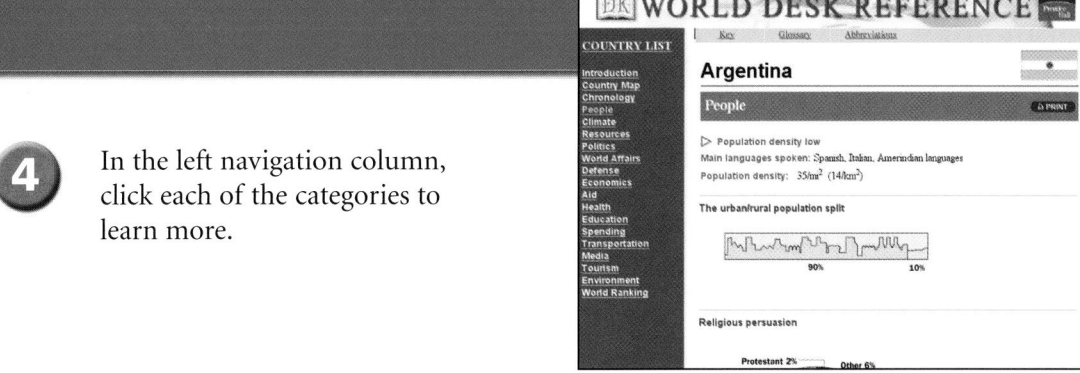

5 You are now ready to gather in-depth information. Print out any screens that you will need.

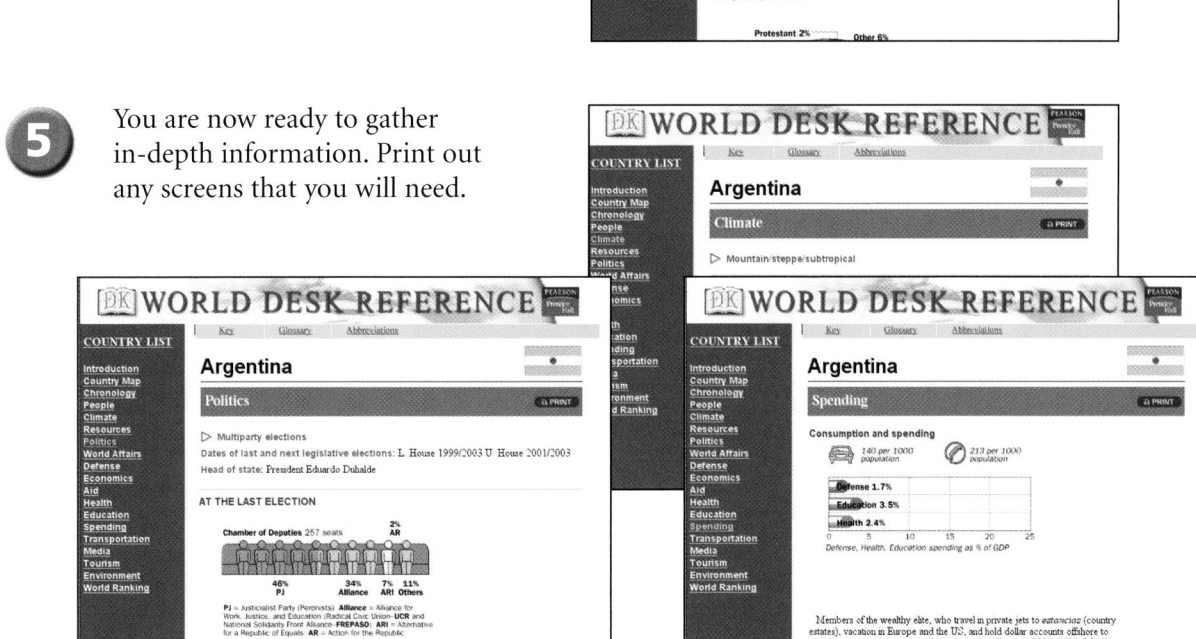

Applying Your Skills

Compare and contrast the populations of any two countries of the world. Select a country, then click the "People" category in the left navigation column. Copy the table below and then complete it. Write a brief paragraph comparing the populations of the two countries you have selected.

Category	Country #1	Country #2
Population Density		
Rural/Urban Population		
Major Religions		
Major Ethnic Groups		

Dorling Kindersley World Desk Reference Online **xxi**

Prentice Hall NewsTracker

Find information on global issues.

NewsTracker, powered by FT.com, delivers dynamic current events and global issues to you. Follow these step-by-step instructions to research a particular topic or country.

1 Access NewsTracker using the Web Code on the unit opening pages in this textbook. Click the NewsTracker link. From here, you will be able to choose News in Depth, Country Surveys, and Lesson Support.

2 If you choose News in Depth, scan the subjects and select your topic. Enter your password to access your selection.

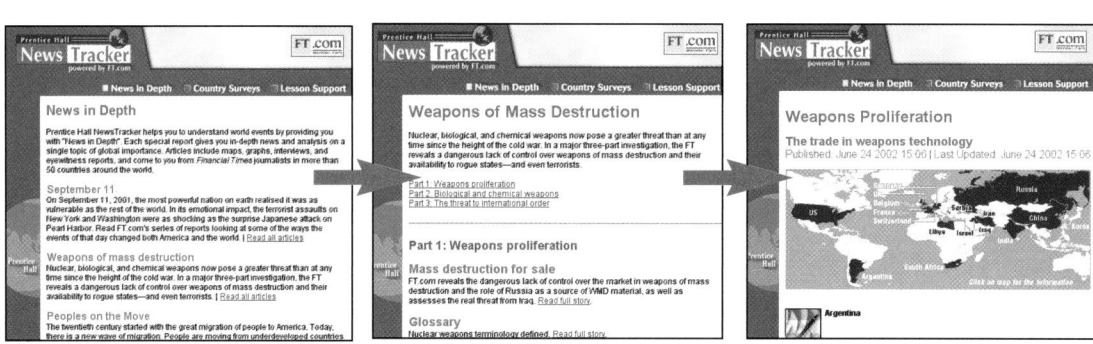

3 If you choose Country Surveys, scan the subjects and select your topic. Enter your password to access your selection.

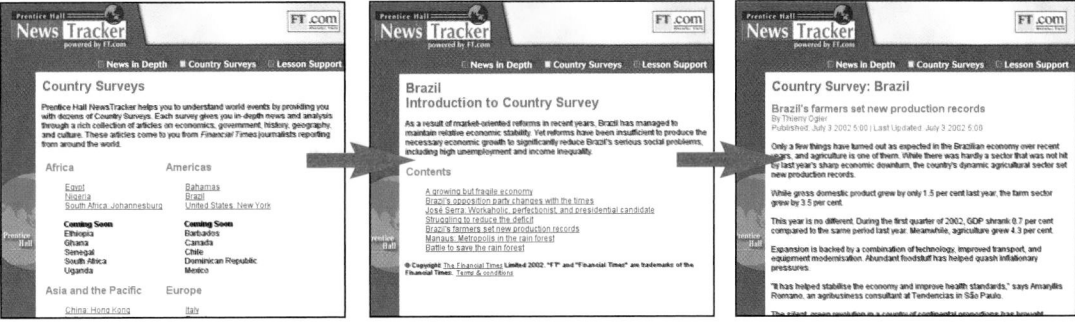

4 Choose Lesson Support for guidelines on how to gather information and for graphic organizers. Record your information on an appropriate graphic organizer.

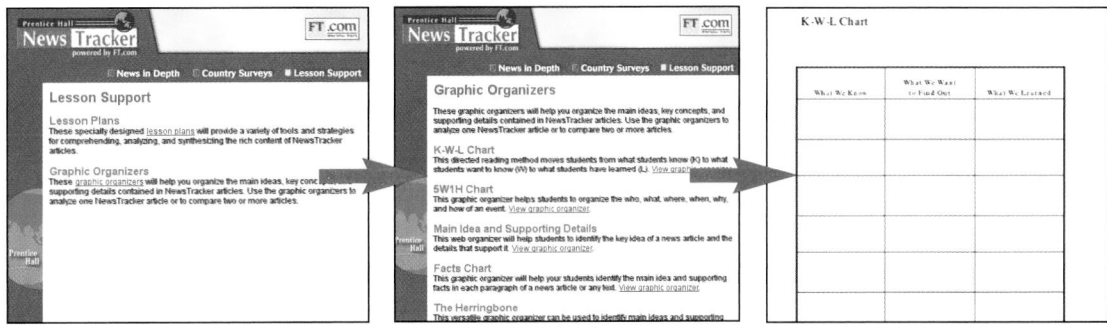

Applying Your Skills

Follow the steps above to find information in Country Surveys. Choose a country in the region of the world you are currently studying. Select an appropriate graphic organizer for arranging your information and write a brief report on what you've learned about the country you selected.

Infoplease®

Keep up-to-date on world events.

Prentice Hall brings you all the resources of Infoplease®. This rich online reference source puts news stories and the facts behind them at your fingertips. Follow these step-by-step instructions to stay on top of breaking news.

1 Access Reuters news summaries on Infoplease® using the Web Code on the unit opening pages in this textbook. Click the link to Infoplease®.

2 Click the link to News in the left column of the page to bring up Reuters news summaries.

3 Click "Facts Behind the News" and choose one of the stories under News Headlines. Click the links under that headline.

4 You are now ready to read about stories in the news. Print out any screens that you will need for background information.

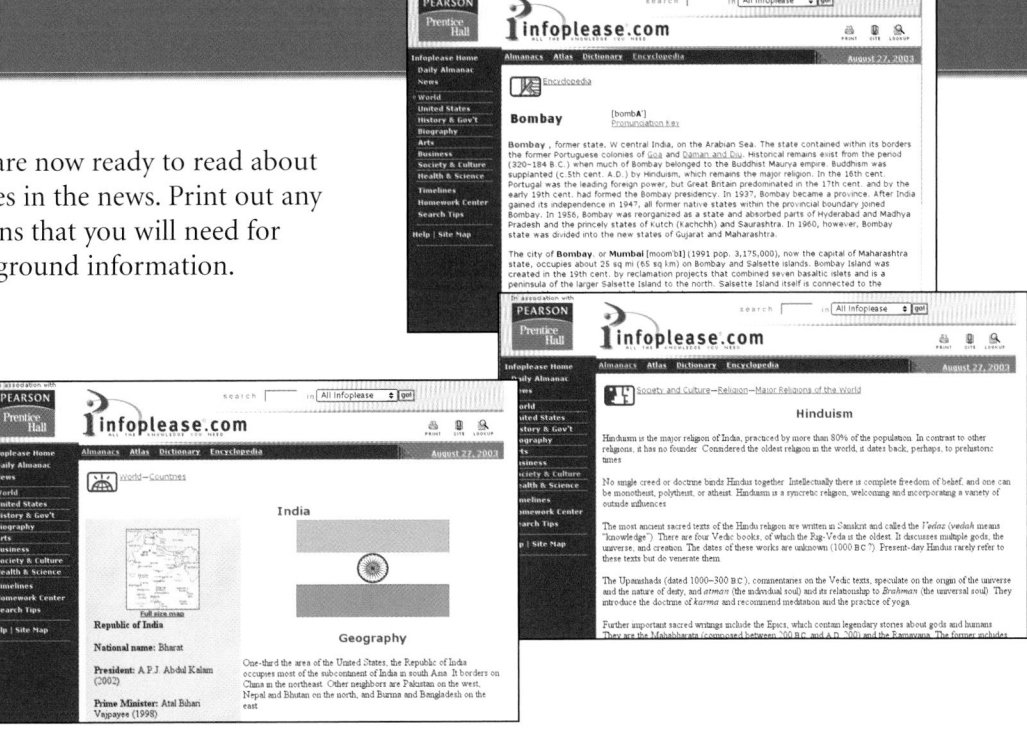

Applying Your Skills

Follow the steps above to read about a prominent issue or event covered by daily news services. What is the significance of this issue or event? How might it affect the United States or the region you are studying? Prepare an oral report about the subject. Use the following rubric to evaluate your presentation.

Rating System			
Content	**+ = Excellent**	**✓ = Average**	**– = Weak**
Defines the topic of the subject			
Establishes and maintains context			
Establishes a point of view on the subject			
Uses effective, factual descriptions of appearance and concrete images			
Uses comparison as a means for showing relevance			
Delivery	**+ = Excellent**	**✓ = Average**	**– = Weak**
Uses appropriate verbal techniques			
Uses appropriate nonverbal techniques			
Gauges audience reaction and adjusts accordingly			
Achieves a focused and coherent presentation			
Presentation Summary	**+ = Excellent**	**✓ = Average**	**– = Weak**
Attitude toward subject is apparent and appropriate			
Attitude toward audience is apparent and appropriate			
Preparation is evident and thorough			
Organization is discernible and effective			

Infoplease® xxv

Infoplease®

Gather in-depth information about the history of a region and its physical and human geography.

Infoplease® offers time lines, maps, biographies, and several other reference tools to help you learn more about world regions. Follow these step-by-step instructions to find additional historical and geographic information about a specific country.

1 Access Infoplease® using the Web Code on the unit opening pages in this textbook.

2 Scroll to the bottom of the page and note the Infoplease® search engine in the left margin. After you enter the name of a country in the region you are studying, you will be shown your search results. Articles or items with the highest correlation to your search request will be listed first.

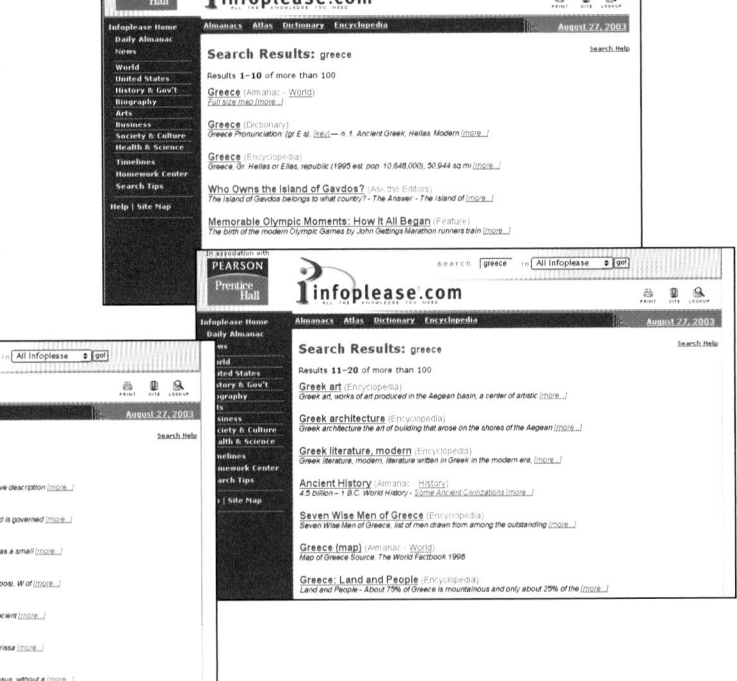

3 For more information about the history or physical and human geography of the country you selected, click the search results.

4 To record the source of your information, click **PRINT** to print the article. Click **CITE** for footnote and bibliography information.

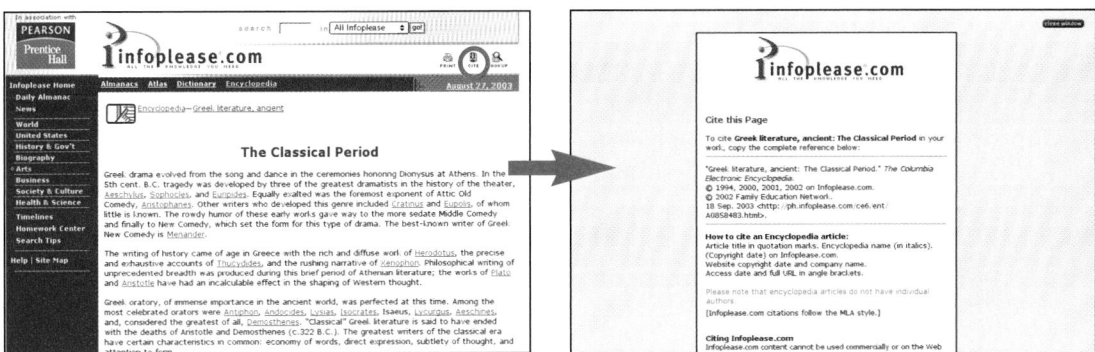

Applying Your Skills

Follow the steps above to conduct thorough research about a country in the region you are studying. Use the information you find to construct a time line showing major events in the history of that country.

World Geography Companion Web Site

Access content resources from your textbook.

The *Prentice Hall World Geography: Building a Global Perspective Companion Web Site* includes a wealth of Internet activities, self-assessment tests, skills tutorials, and libraries of subject-related Internet links. Follow these step-by-step instructions to tap into the resources maintained on the *World Geography* site.

1 Access the *World Geography Companion Web Site* at **www.PHSchool.com.** Enter the Web Code mjk-1000 to proceed to the *World Geography* home page.

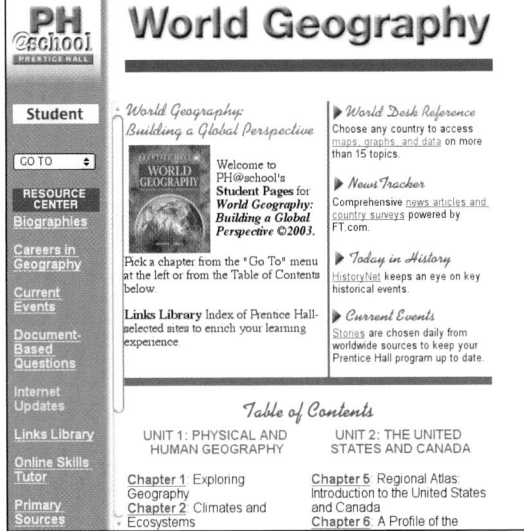

2 Click the Links Library link in the left column. You will find a list of reference Web sites that will aid you in searches for information on various topics.

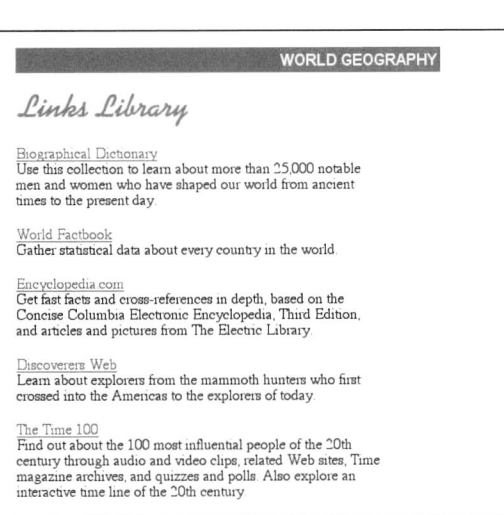

3 Click the Primary Sources link in the left column. Select a unit from the list of regions covered in *World Geography.* You will find a detailed menu of images, maps, and news items from the region.

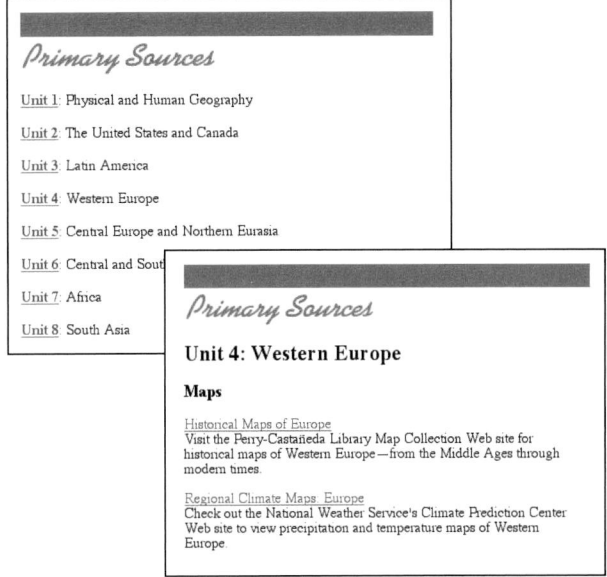

4 Click the Online Skills Tutor link in the left column. You will access a tutorial program to practice and apply Social Studies skills.

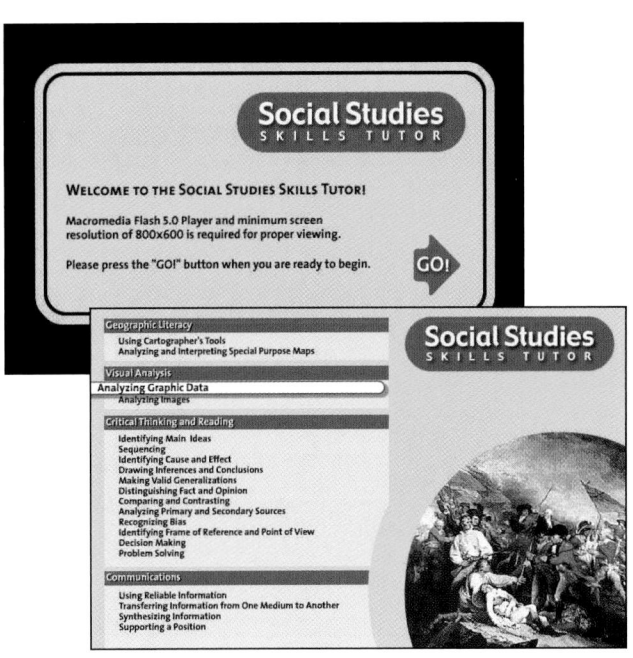

Applying Your Skills

Follow the steps above to access the resources available on the *World Geography Companion Web Site.*

1. Where should you go to find reports on deforestation in the Amazon?

2. Where should you go to practice map skills?

3. Where should you go to find photographs of Mt. Everest?

Go Online

Go Online and discover a vast array of Internet resources for *World Geography: Building a Global Perspective.* Enter the Web Codes from the unit and chapter opening pages in this textbook to access a virtual library of current events, country profiles, and skills activities.

1 Go to **www.PHSchool.com** and insert the Web Code from a unit or chapter opening page in the book.

2 Click the yellow button next to the Web Code to reach a page of links to valuable resources. Among these key resources is a link to the *World Geography Companion Web Site* that features help for each chapter in the book.

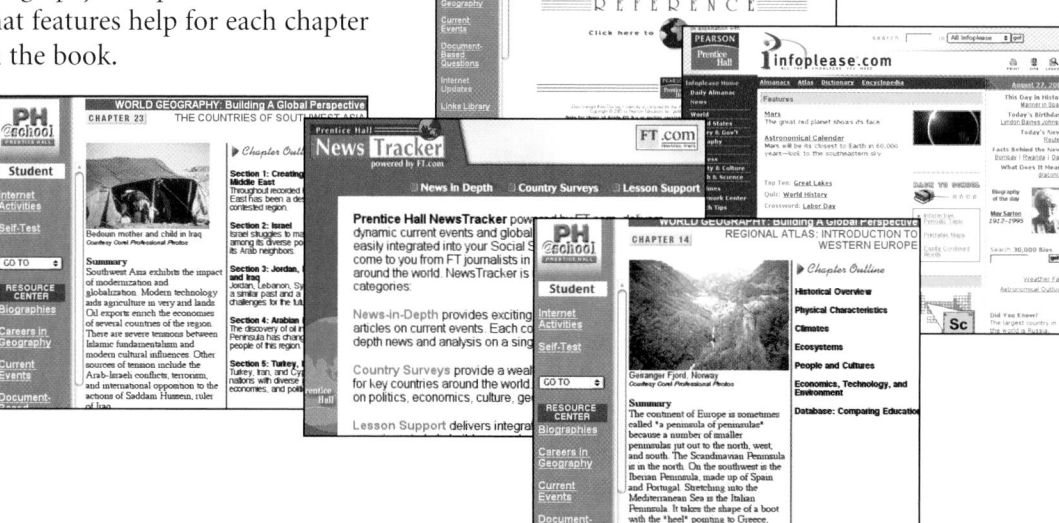

3 Review the list of links. Each unit opener and chapter opener Web Code will give you access to links for all Take It to the Net activities.

Take It to the NET

Interactive Textbook

Available online and on CD-ROM, the *World Geography: Building a Global Perspective* Interactive Textbook features the same trusted content as the printed textbook in an engaging, dynamic format. This bountiful resource delivers audio glossaries, interactive maps, and study aids to enhance your understanding of world geography.

You will need a user ID and a password to access the Interactive Textbook. Obtain these from your teacher and log in.

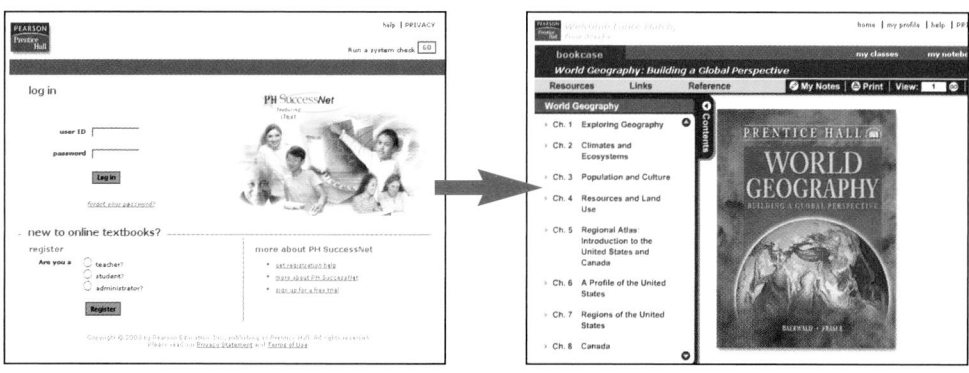

English and Spanish audio glossaries provide definitions and pronunciations of key terms.

The map viewer utilizes a zoom feature for detailed analysis of regional and historical maps.

Chapter and Section Assessments offer homework assistance with **HINT** buttons for answering strategies.

Reading Informational Texts

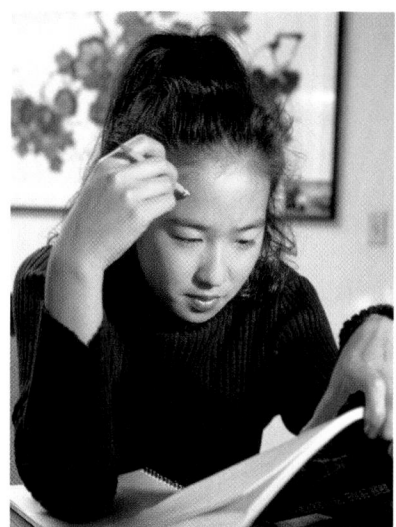

Reading and understanding the material in a textbook is not the same as reading a novel or magazine article. The purpose of reading a textbook is to acquire information. There are many reading strategies that can help you get the most out of reading informational texts. You can use these strategies before, while, and after you read to increase your comprehension of information in your textbook.

The reading strategies introduced on these pages will help you understand the words and ideas in your textbook. The graphic organizer paired with each skill helps you visualize and organize the content you are reading.

Good readers develop a bank of reading strategies. Then, they draw on those that will help them understand what they are reading.

Previewing: Preparing to Read

Before you begin reading a chapter or a section, take a few minutes to preview the text to get an idea of what you will be reading about. Previewing will give you an overview of the chapter or section, help you consider what you already know, and give you some idea of what you are supposed to learn.

- **Setting a Purpose** When you set a purpose for reading, you give yourself a focus. Before you read a section, study the objectives and look at headings and visuals to see what the section is about.

- **Predicting** Making predictions about what is about to happen next helps you remember what you read. After studying the objectives, headings, and visuals, predict what the text might discuss. Read to find out whether your predictions were accurate.

- **Asking Questions** Before you read a section, write down one or two questions that will help you understand or remember something important in the section. Read to answer your questions.

- **Using Prior Knowledge** Your prior knowledge is what you already know about a topic before you read. Building on what you already know gives you a head start on learning new information.

Reading: Being an Active Reader

Become an active reader by learning to think about the meaning of new terms, main ideas, and the details that support the main ideas. Use these strategies as you read. They will help you interact with your text.

- **Building Vocabulary** Good readers try to increase their vocabulary. Using strategies that help you learn new words as you read will help you become a better reader.

  Context When you come across an unfamiliar word, you can sometimes figure out its meaning from context clues. The context refers to the surrounding words and sentences. The surrounding words might define the word or explain it in another way.

  Word Analysis Word analysis refers to strategies you can use to figure out the meaning of unfamiliar words by breaking them into parts. Many words have a root and a prefix or a suffix. A root is the base of a word—it is a word that has meaning by itself. A prefix is placed at the beginning of a root and changes the meaning of the root.

  Think about the word *justice.* If you add *in-* as a prefix to *justice,* it becomes *injustice. Justice* means "fairness, or correctness," while *injustice* is "the quality of being unfair."

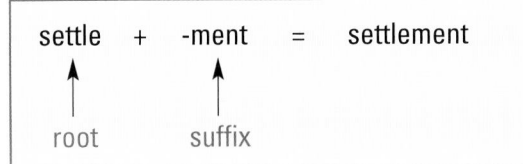

A suffix is placed at the end of a root, which changes the word's part of speech. If you add *-ment* to the root *settle,* it becomes *settlement. Settle* is a verb. *Settlement* is a noun.

```
settle   +   -ment   =   settlement
   ↑           ↑
  root       suffix
```

- **Clarifying Meaning** There are several strategies to help clarify, or make clear, the meaning of what you read. Sometimes you might reread difficult passages and paraphrase, or restate in your own words, what those passages mean. Summarizing is another good technique to help you comprehend what you have read. When you summarize, you state in the correct order the main points you have read. Outlining and filling in charts or tables or concept webs can help you clarify the meaning of a chapter or section.

  I. Differences Between North Korea and South Korea
  - **A.** Physical Characteristics
    - **1.** North Korea: colder climate, mountainous
    - **2.** South Korea: warmer climate, rolling plains
  - **B.** Political Characteristics
    - **1.** North Korea: Communist state
    - **2.** South Korea: capitalist state

- **Identifying Main Ideas** It is impossible to remember every detail that you read. So, good readers identify the main idea in every paragraph or section. The main idea is the most important point in a reading passage. Remember that a main idea is supported by details that give more information about it. You can use outlines or concept webs to make note of main ideas and supporting details.

- **Comparing and Contrasting** Comparing and contrasting can help you sort out and analyze information. When you compare, you examine the similarities between things. When you contrast, you look at the differences. A Venn diagram is a good tool for comparing and contrasting people, places, events, or ideas.

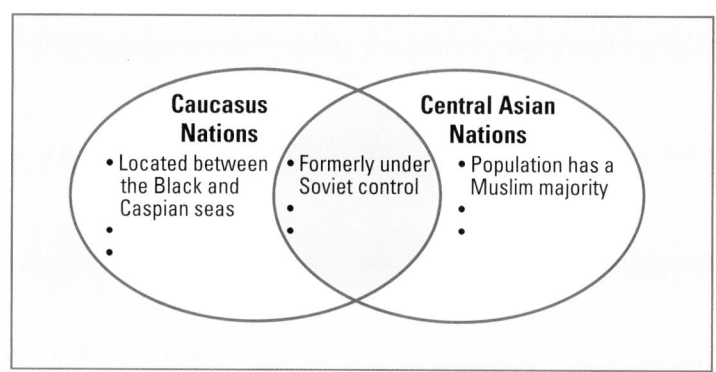

- **Sequencing** A sequence is the order in which a series of events occurs. Noting the sequence of important events can help you understand and remember the events. You can track the order of events by making a flowchart. Write the first event, or thing that sets the other events in motion, in the first box. Then write each additional event in a box. Use arrows to show how one event leads to the next.

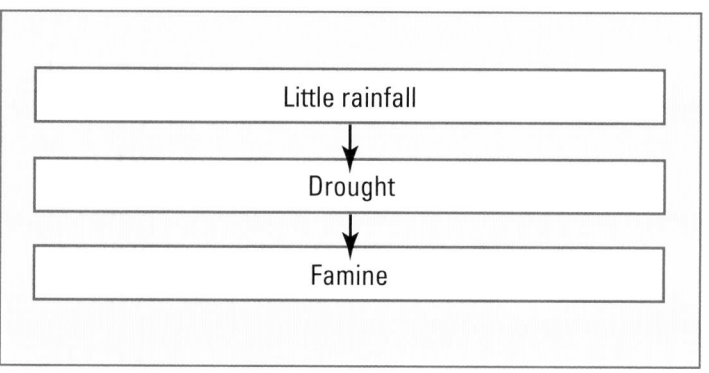

• Identifying Cause and Effect

Determining causes and effects helps you understand relationships among situations or events. A cause makes something happen. An effect is what happens. Remember that there can be more than one cause for an event and more than one effect. Fill in a cause-and-effect chart to help you understand how causes lead to events and how effects are the results of events.

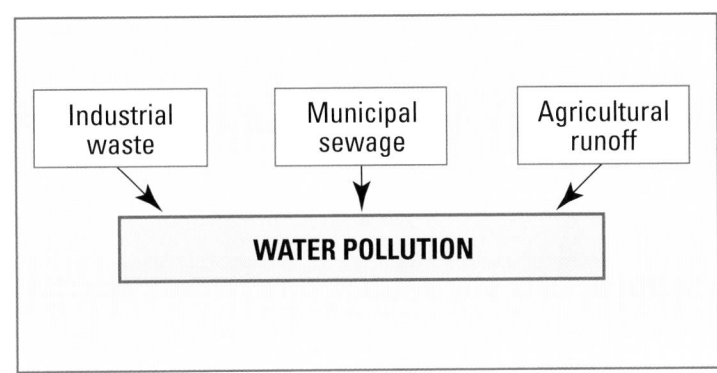

After Reading

Take time to be sure you understand and can remember what you read.

- Review the headings and subheadings.

- Summarize the main ideas and recall supporting details.

- Check the notes you took.

- Informational text often requires reading more than once. If you need to, read part or all of the section again.

- Look over the questions in your textbook to make sure you can answer them.

- Review the visuals.

If you still have questions about the content, get help from a classmate or your teacher.

Analyzing Informational Texts

Here are several reading strategies to help you think about and analyze informational text. They include analyzing the author's purpose, distinguishing between facts and opinions, identifying evidence, and evaluating credibility. These strategies will help you read your textbook, as well as other informational texts such as newspapers, journals, Web sites, and more.

Analyzing the Author's Purpose

Different types of materials are written with a different purpose in mind. For example, a textbook is written to teach students information about a subject. The purpose of a technical manual is to teach someone how to use something, such as a computer. A newspaper editorial might be written to persuade the reader to a particular point of view. A writer's purpose influences how the material is presented.

Distinguishing Between Facts and Opinions

It is important when reading informational texts to read actively and to distinguish between fact and opinion. A fact can be proven or disproven. An opinion reveals someone's personal viewpoint or evaluation.

For example, the editorial pages in a newspaper offer opinions on topics that are currently in the news. You need to read newspaper editorials with an eye for bias and faulty logic. For example, the newspaper editorial shown here shows factual statements in blue and opinion statements in red. The underlined words are examples of highly charged words and exaggerations. They reveal bias on the part of the writer.

More than 5,000 people voted last week in favor of building a new shopping center, but the opposition won out. The margin of victory is irrelevant. Those radical voters who opposed the center are obviously self-serving elitists who do not care about anyone but themselves.

This month's unemployment figures for our area are 10 percent, which represents an increase of about 5 percent over the figures for last year. These figures mean that unemployment is worsening. But the people who voted against the mall probably do not care about creating new jobs.

Identifying Evidence

Before you accept an author's conclusions, you need to make sure that the author has based the conclusion on enough evidence and on an accurate portrayal of the evidence. An author may present a whole series of facts to support a claim, but the facts may not tell the whole story.

For example, what evidence does the author in the newspaper editorial (on the previous page) provide to support his claim that shopping centers would create more jobs? Isn't it possible that the shopping center might have put some stores out of business? This would increase unemployment rather than decrease it.

Evaluating Credibility

Anytime you are reading informational texts, you need to assess the credibility of the author. This is especially true of Web sites you may visit on the Internet. All Internet sources are not created equal. Here are some questions to ask yourself when evaluating the credibility of a Web site.

- ❏ Is the Web site created by a respected organization, a discussion group, or an individual?
- ❏ Does the creator of the Web site include his or her name as well as credentials and the sources he or she used to write the material?
- ❏ Is the information on the site balanced or biased?
- ❏ Can you verify the information using two other sources?
- ❏ Is there a date telling when the Web site was created or last updated?

Writing for Social Studies

When you face a writing assignment, do you think, "How will I ever get through this?" Research shows that writing about what you read helps you remember new content. And, of course, good writing skills are important for doing well on tests. Here are some tips to guide you through your social studies writing assignments, whether they be writing a variety of different essays or writing research papers.

① Narrative Essays

Writing a narrative essay is essentially telling a good story.

Step 1: Select and Narrow Your Topic

A narrative is a good story. In social studies, a narrative essay might focus on how a historical event affected you or your family.

Step 2: Gather Details

Brainstorm a list of details you would like to include in your narrative. Keep in mind who your audience will be.

Step 3: Write a First Draft

Start by writing a sample opening sentence that will catch your reader's attention while conveying the main idea of your essay. Continue by writing a colorful story that has interesting details as well as a beginning, a middle, and an end. Write a conclusion that sums up the significance of the event or situation described in your essay.

Step 4: Revise and Edit

Consider adding dialogue to convey a person's thoughts or feelings in his or her own words. Then check to make sure you have not begun too many sentences with the word *I*. Replace general words with more specific, colorful ones.

Main idea

Details

Significance of narrative

In my last year of college, I volunteered for an organization called Amigos De Las Americas (Friends of the Americas). I was sent to a remote village in Brazil and worked with villagers to improve the community's water supply and sanitation systems. The experience made me realize I wanted to work in the field of public health. When I went to Brazil, I never imagined what an incredible sense of purpose it would add to my life.

② Persuasive Essays

A persuasive essay is writing in which you support an opinion or position. In it, you attempt to convince the reader that your point of view or course of action is valid.

Step 1: Select and Narrow Your Topic

Choose a topic that provokes an argument and has at least two sides. Your task will be to persuade most of your readers to understand your point of view.

Step 2: Consider Your Audience

The argument that you make in your writing should be targeted to the specific audience for your writing. Which argument is going to persuade your readership to understand your point of view? If there are too many pros and cons for the argument, consider narrowing your topic to cover only part of the debate.

Step 3: Gather Evidence

You will need to include convincing examples in your essay. Begin by creating a table that states your position at the top and lists the pros and cons for your position below, in two columns. Consider interviewing experts on the topic.

Even though your essay may focus on the pro arguments, it is important to address the strongest arguments against your stand.

Step 4: Write a First Draft

Begin by writing a strong thesis statement that clearly states the position you will prove. Continue by presenting the strongest arguments in favor of your position. Take time to acknowledge and refute opposing arguments, too. Build a strong case by including facts, statistics, and comparisons, and by sharing personal experiences.

Step 5: Revise and Proof

Check to make sure you have made a logical argument and that you have not oversimplified the argument. Try adding the following transition words to make your reasoning more obvious:

To show a contrast — use *however, although, despite*

To point out a reason — use *since, because, if*

To signal a conclusion — use *therefore, consequently, so, then*

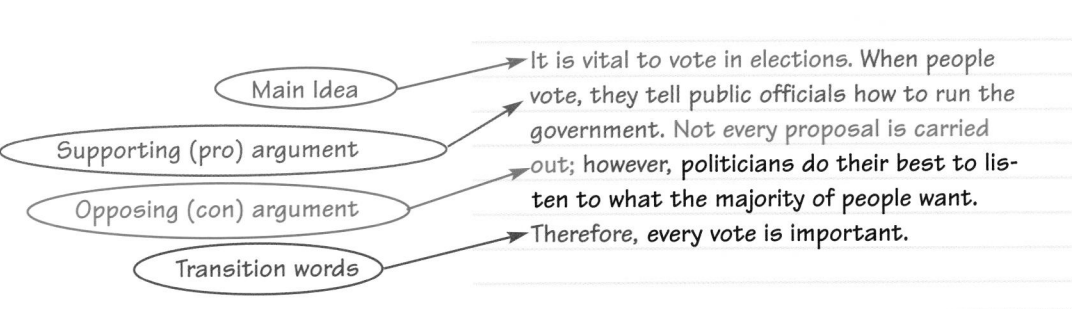

Main Idea
Supporting (pro) argument
Opposing (con) argument
Transition words

It is vital to vote in elections. When people vote, they tell public officials how to run the government. Not every proposal is carried out; however, politicians do their best to listen to what the majority of people want. Therefore, every vote is important.

③ Expository Essays

An expository essay is writing in which you explain a process, compare and contrast, explain causes and effects, or explore solutions to a problem. Expository essays often use facts and statistical information in the form of charts.

Step 1: Identify and Narrow Your Topic

Expository writing is writing that explains some-thing in detail. An essay might explain the similar-ities and differences between two or more subjects (compare and contrast). It might explain how one event causes another (cause and effect), or it might explain a problem and describe a solution.

Step 2: Gather Evidence

Create a graphic organizer that identifies details to include in your essay. You might create a Venn diagram for a compare-and-contrast essay, a dia-gram showing multiple causes and effects for a cause-and-effect essay, or a web for defining all the aspects of a problem and possible solutions.

Cause 1	Cause 2	Cause 3
Most people in the Mexican countryside work on farms.	The population in Mexico is growing at one of the highest rates in the world.	There is not enough farm work for so many people.

Effect
As a result, many rural families are moving from the countryside to live in Mexico City.

Step 3: Write a First Draft

Write a strong topic sentence and then organize the body of your essay around the similarities and differences, causes and effects, or problems and solutions. Be sure to include convincing details, facts, and examples.

Step 4: Revise and Proof

Be sure you have included transition words between sentences and paragraphs:

Here are some transition words to show similarities — *all, similarly, both, in the same way, closely related, equally*

Here are some transition words that show differences — *on the other hand, in contrast, however, instead, yet*

④ Research Papers

A research paper is writing in which you conduct research and write about a specific topic. Research papers are very different from other types of writing. People who enjoy creative writing may find this form of writing more challenging. Others who do not enjoy creative writing may excel at writing research papers.

Step 1: Identify and Narrow Your Topic

Choose something you are interested in, and make sure that it is not too broad. For example, instead of writing a paper on ancient Rome, write about the Colosseum, a building in ancient Rome. Ask yourself, What do I want to know about the topic?

Step 2: Acquire Information

Use several sources of information about the topic from the library, Internet, or an interview with someone knowledgeable. Before you use a source, make sure that it is reliable and up-to-date. Take notes using an index card for each detail or subtopic and note from which source the information was taken. Use quotation marks when you copy the exact words from a source. Create a source index card for each resource listing the author, the title, the publisher, and the place and date of publication.

Step 3: Make an Outline

Decide how to organize your report by creating an outline. Sort your index cards into the same order as the outline you create.

Step 4: Write a First Draft

Write an introduction, body, and conclusion. Leave plenty of space between lines so you can go back and add details that you may have left out. Make sure that you have at least one new paragraph on each double-spaced page. If you don't, your paragraphs are probably too long and your reader may get confused or lose interest.

Source #1
McCullough, David. *The Path Between the Seas: The Creation of the Panama Canal, 1870–1914.* New York: Simon and Schuster, 1977.

Outline
I. Introduction
II. Why the Canal Was Built
III. How the Canal Was Built
    A. Physical Challenges
    B. Medical Challenges
IV. Conclusion

Introduction
Building the Panama Canal
Ever since Christopher Columbus first explored the Isthmus of Panama, the Spanish had been looking for a water route through it. They wanted to be able to sail west from Spain to Asia without sailing around South America. However, it was not until 1914 that the dream became a reality.

Conclusion
It took eight years and more than 70,000 workers to build the Panama Canal. It remains one of the greatest engineering feats of modern times.

Teaching the Skills

After students have examined the directional indicator, legend, and scales on the maps on this page, ask them the following question: **Which map shows a smaller area?** (the map on the right)

Tell students that latitude and longitude are used to designate a place's absolute location, or its position on the globe. Point out to students that lines of latitude are parallel; that is, they are always equally spaced apart. Lines of longitude, however, are farthest apart at the Equator and converge at the poles. The Equator is designated as 0° latitude, and the poles are 90° North (N) and 90° South (S). The Prime Meridian is designated as 0° longitude. Lines of longitude are measured in degrees from 0 to 180 east (E) or west (W) of Greenwich, England.

Using Maps
Basic Map Components

Most maps have basic map components that help you interpret the contents of the map: a legend or key, a scale, and a directional indicator.

Compass Rose

The compass rose, or directional indicator, shows where the cardinal directions (north, east, south, and west) lie on the map.

Legend

The legend, or key, tells the user about the symbols used on the map. In this map, the legend tells you that highways are symbolized by a red line and railroads by a crosshatched black line.

Scale

A scale tells the user about the size of a map in relation to the size of the real world by giving the ratio between distances on the map and actual distances on the earth. The map on the left shows the state of Georgia. The map on the right shows a more detailed view of the area surrounding Atlanta.

RESOURCE DIRECTORY

Teaching Resources
Social Studies Skills Handbook
• Using the Parts of a Map, pp. 3–11

Global Grid

Parallels of Latitude

Meridians of Longitude

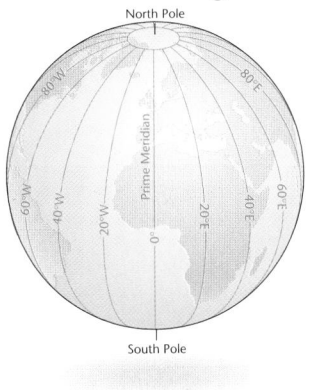

Latitude and Longitude

Lines of latitude and longitude are imaginary lines that form a grid covering the whole globe. This grid helps geographers find the location of places anywhere in the world.

The Grid

Lines of latitude, like the Equator, run east to west around the globe. Lines of longitude, like the Prime Meridian, run north to south, meeting at the poles. Taken together, latitude and longitude lines form a grid. Every place on earth has a unique position on this grid, like a street address in a big city.

Parallels

Lines of latitude are often called parallels because they run parallel to the Equator. Although not every line of latitude is shown on a map, every place does have a specific latitude.

Meridians

Lines of longitude, also called meridians, run from pole to pole, crossing the lines of latitude. Every place on earth is located at a specific longitude.

skills
PRACTICE

1. **What does a map scale indicate?**

2. **What are the four cardinal directions?**

3. **In what direction do lines of longitude run?**

Enrichment

Determining Latitude and Longitude Ask students to use maps in the text to estimate the latitude and longitude of their city or town. They can check the exact latitude and longitude using an atlas, gazetteer, geographical dictionary, or Global Positioning System (GPS). (Visual/Spatial)

The Physical World

The Tropics Because the earth is tilted 23 1/2° as it revolves around the sun, the Tropic of Cancer at 23 1/2°N and the Tropic of Capricorn at 23 1/2°S mark the boundaries of the places on the earth that receive the most direct sunlight and the greatest heat energy from the sun.

Answers to Skills Practice

1. the ratio between distances on the map and the actual distances on the earth
2. north, south, east, and west
3. north and south

11

Displaying
INFORMATION

Teaching the Skills

Point out to students that because maps are flat pictures of the earth's curved surface, it is impossible for them to capture the correct size and shape of every landmass or body of water. Ask students to imagine trying to flatten out an orange peel—assuming that you could get the peel off in one piece. The sides would split, the shape would change, and you would find it necessary to cut pieces of the peel away to get it to lie flat.

These are the problems that cartographers face when they try to map the earth. It cannot be done without stretching some places and shrinking others. This shrinking or stretching is called distortion. Cartographers draw the earth's surface using different map projections—ways of showing the round earth on flat paper. No projection is completely accurate, but each has advantages and disadvantages. Cartographers choose the projection that least distorts the data they are interested in studying.

Displaying Information

A globe is the most accurate method of showing the entire surface of the earth. However, globes are bulky and you can't carry one in your pocket. Cartographers, or mapmakers, face a difficult problem: How do you represent the features of our round planet on a flat page? Different map projections, ways of showing the earth on a flat page, are efforts to make the best possible representation with the least distortion.

Mercator Projection   Orthographic Projection

Great Circle Route

A globe provides accurate information about distances and directions between two points. A round globe is the best tool to help you find the shortest distance between two places. If you stretched a string around the entire globe, it would make a **great circle,** or an imaginary line that circles the earth. Airplanes flying a great distance use great circle routes to save fuel and to reduce travel time.

Global Gores

With the help of mathematics, cartographers can take the information from a globe and flatten the surface of the earth. Size, shape, and distance are distorted when curves become straight lines.

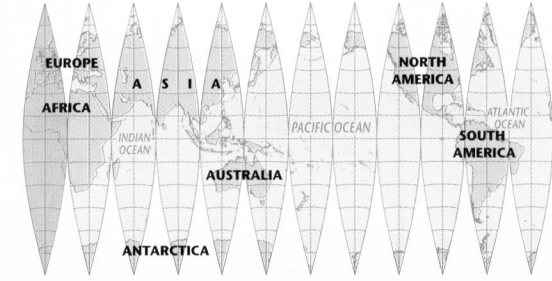

Mercator Projection

This is one of the simplest projections, but also one of the more distorted. The Mercator projection spreads the image near the poles in order to flatten the representation of the globe. This makes images near the poles appear much bigger than they really are. However, all images on a Mercator map have accurate, well-defined shapes. In short, shapes are more accurate but areas or sizes are not.

Robinson Projection

Shape and size on a map using a Robinson projection are both somewhat distorted, but not so much as on a Mercator projection map. Areas near the poles appear flatter than they really are. Land on the western and eastern edges of the map are fairly accurate in size and shape.

skills
PRACTICE

1. What is the most accurate way to display information about the earth?

2. Compare a straight route with a great circle route. How much shorter is the great circle route?

3. What is the advantage of a Robinson projection?

Types
OF MAPS

Teaching the Skills

Point out to students that maps are the geographer's most important tool because of their ability to show many different types of information. Many commonly used maps show topography—features of the earth's surface—and political boundaries. Special-purpose maps are used to provide information about nearly every topic imaginable. A land-use map of the world can show you at a glance which areas of the world are devoted to commercial farming, manufacturing, or forestry. A look at a population-density map shows which areas of the earth are most heavily populated and which are uninhabited. In addition, maps are often used in combination with one another. Transparent map overlays can be used to show data from two or more maps of the same area simultaneously.

Types of Maps

General-purpose maps show the information that is most often used by readers. Special-purpose maps relay information about specific types of data.

Physical Maps

Physical maps depict many kinds of physical features, including mountains, rivers, and lakes. Areas of water are usually colored blue. Relief—the changing elevation of the land—is represented either by shading or by changing colors, usually green at lower elevations and orange and brown at the higher elevations.

Political Maps

Political maps show political features. These are not natural or physical features, but rather features that are determined by people. Political features that are depicted on maps include state and national boundaries and capital cities. A capital is often represented by a star within a circle.

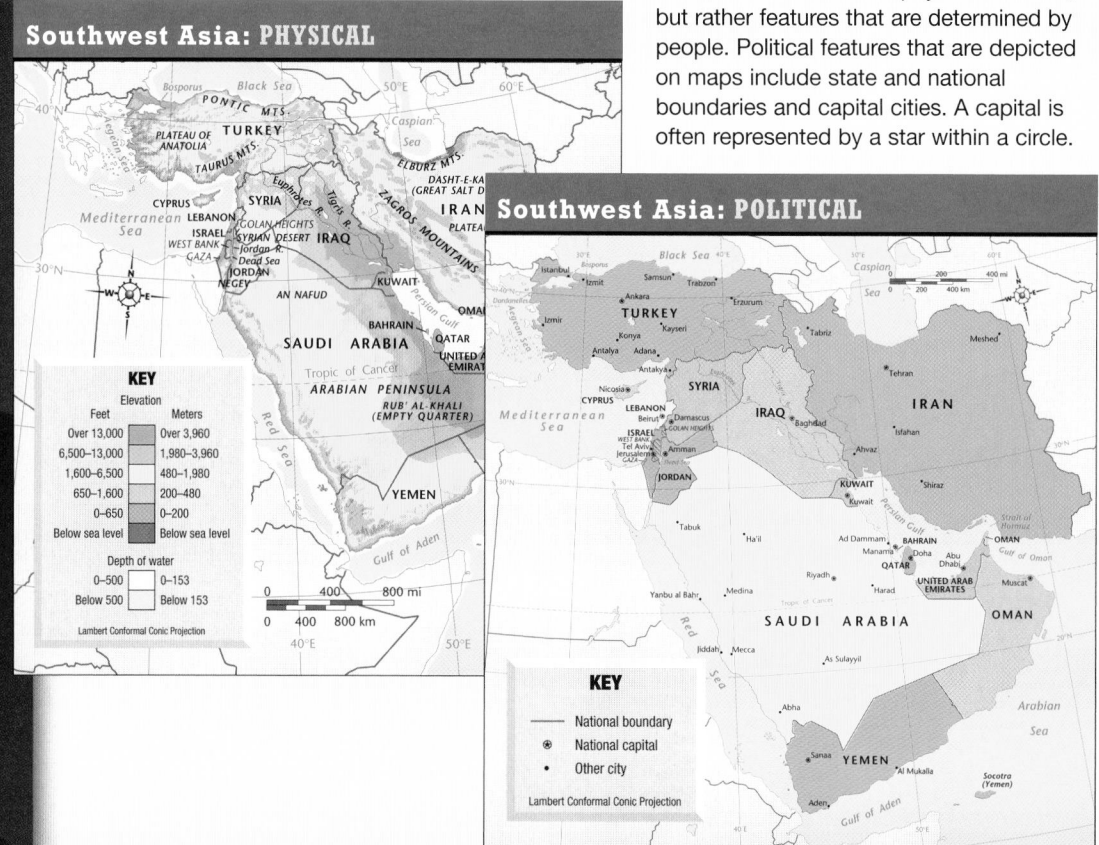

Special-Purpose Maps

Some maps are designed to display very specific data or information. These are called special-purpose maps. Road maps, which show the roads in a given region, are one example. There are many other kinds, including climate, vegetation, natural resources, and population-density maps.

Climate Maps

Climate maps show information about general temperature and precipitation patterns in a region. This map is shaded to show seven different climate zones.

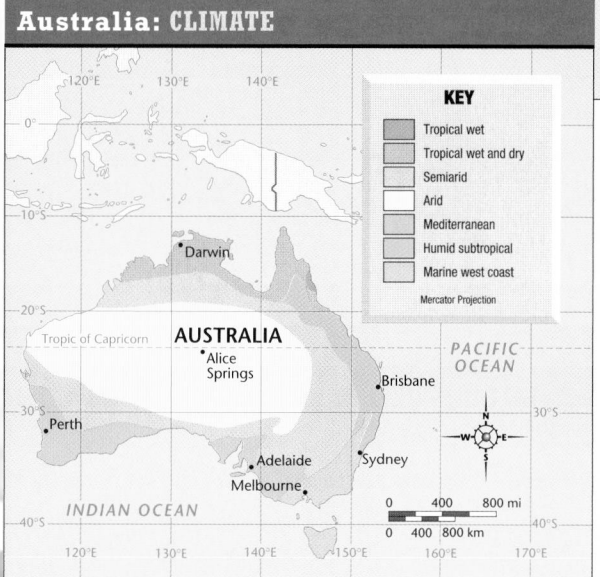

Australia: CLIMATE

KEY

Tropical wet
Tropical wet and dry
Semiarid
Arid
Mediterranean
Humid subtropical
Marine west coast

Mercator Projection

Australia: ECONOMIC ACTIVITIES AND RESOURCES

KEY

Hunting and gathering
Livestock raising
Commercial farming
Subsistence farming
Manufacturing and trade
Commercial fishing
Little or no activity

Coal
Bauxite
Tungsten
Iron
Copper
Petroleum

Gold
Silver
Uranium
Lead
Nickel
Hydroelectric power

Mercator Projection

Economic Activities and Resources Maps

Economic activities are ways in which people produce and distribute goods and services. Natural resources are items in the environment that people need and value. On an economic activities and natural resources map, symbols show key locations of activities and resources.

skills PRACTICE

1. How does a natural resources map show where different resources are found?

2. What is the climate zone found in Brisbane?

3. What is the difference between an economic activity and a natural resource?

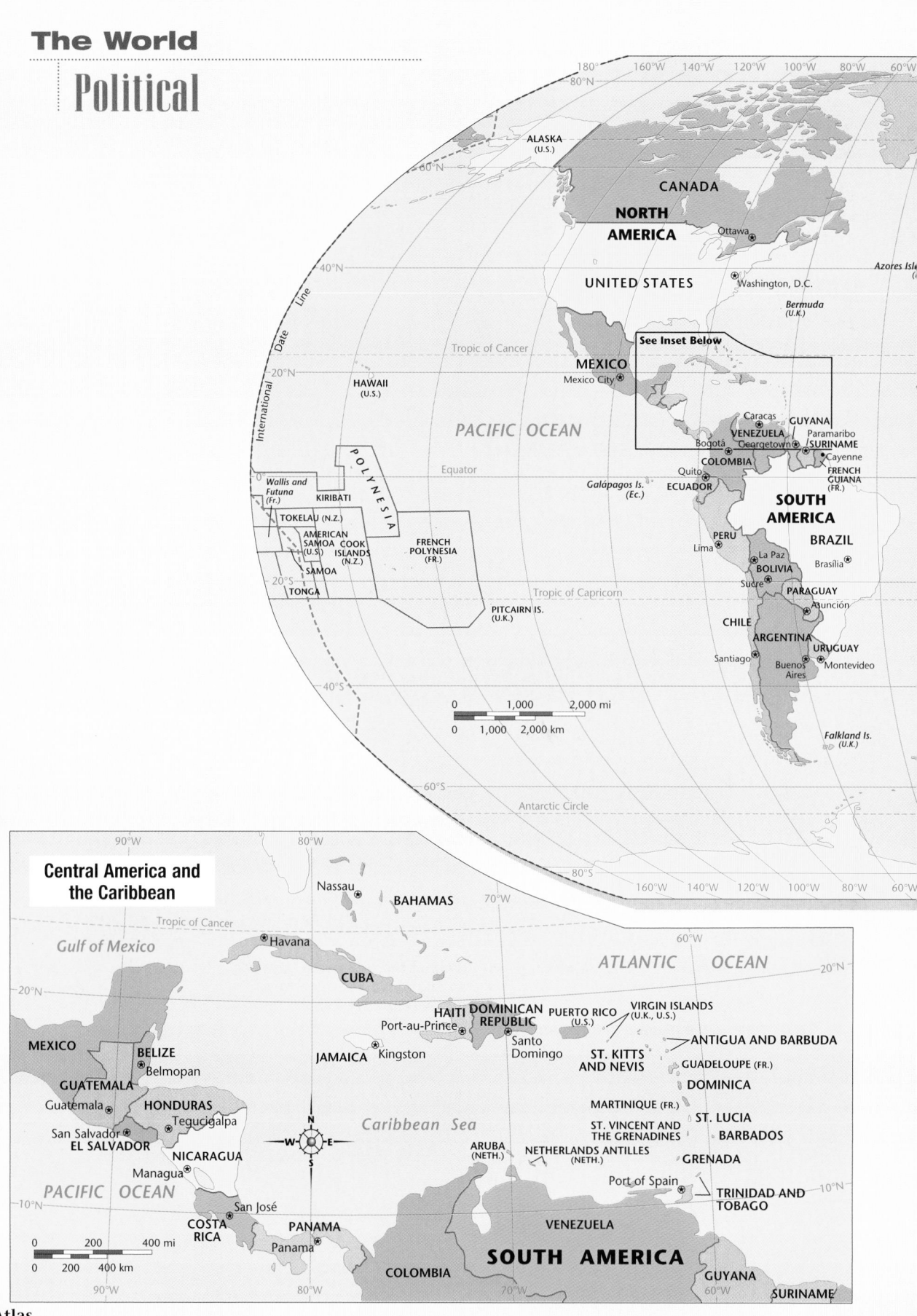

International Date Line

ALASKA (U.S.)

CANADA

NORTH AMERICA

Ottawa

UNITED STATES

Washington, D.C.

Azores Isl.

Bermuda (U.K.)

Tropic of Cancer

See Inset Below

MEXICO

Mexico City

HAWAII (U.S.)

PACIFIC OCEAN

Caracas

VENEZUELA

GUYANA

Georgetown

Paramaribo

SURINAME

Bogotá

Cayenne

COLOMBIA

FRENCH GUIANA (FR.)

Quito

Equator

Galápagos Is. (Ec.)

ECUADOR

Wallis and Futuna (Fr.)

KIRIBATI

POLYNESIA

PERU

Lima

SOUTH AMERICA

BRAZIL

TOKELAU (N.Z.)

AMERICAN SAMOA (U.S.)

COOK ISLANDS (N.Z.)

FRENCH POLYNESIA (FR.)

La Paz

BOLIVIA

Brasília

SAMOA

Sucre

PARAGUAY

TONGA

Tropic of Capricorn

Asunción

PITCAIRN IS. (U.K.)

CHILE

ARGENTINA

URUGUAY

Santiago

Buenos Aires

Montevideo

0   1,000   2,000 mi

0   1,000   2,000 km

Falkland Is. (U.K.)

Antarctic Circle

Central America and the Caribbean

Nassau

BAHAMAS

Gulf of Mexico

Havana

CUBA

ATLANTIC OCEAN

Tropic of Cancer

HAITI

DOMINICAN REPUBLIC

PUERTO RICO (U.S.)

VIRGIN ISLANDS (U.K., U.S.)

MEXICO

BELIZE

Belmopan

Port-au-Prince

Santo Domingo

ANTIGUA AND BARBUDA

GUATEMALA

JAMAICA

Kingston

ST. KITTS AND NEVIS

GUADELOUPE (FR.)

Guatemala

DOMINICA

HONDURAS

Tegucigalpa

MARTINIQUE (FR.)

ST. LUCIA

San Salvador

EL SALVADOR

Caribbean Sea

ST. VINCENT AND THE GRENADINES

BARBADOS

NICARAGUA

ARUBA (NETH.)

NETHERLANDS ANTILLES (NETH.)

GRENADA

Managua

Port of Spain

PACIFIC OCEAN

TRINIDAD AND TOBAGO

San José

VENEZUELA

0   200   400 mi

COSTA RICA

PANAMA

0   200   400 km

Panama

SOUTH AMERICA

COLOMBIA

GUYANA

SURINAME

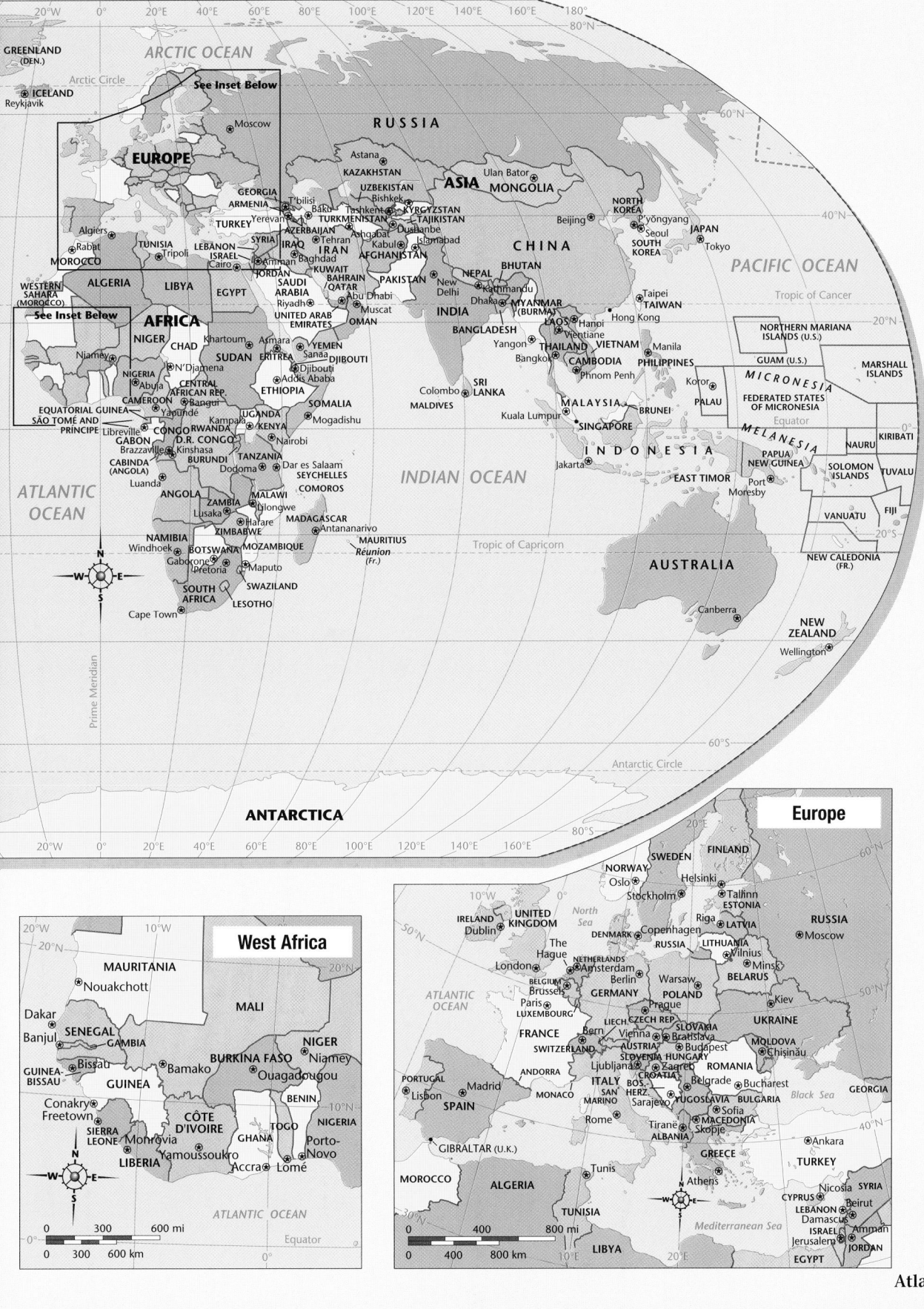

ATLAS

Europe

West Africa

The World

Physical

ARCTIC OCEAN

Greenland

Beaufort
Sea

Yukon R.

Bering
60°N
Sea

Aleutian Islands

Baffin
Island

Hudson
Bay

ROCKY MOUNTAINS

NORTH
AMERICA

CANADIAN SHIELD

GREAT PLAINS

Missouri

Great
Lakes

St. Lawrence R.

APPALACHIAN MTS.

Mississippi R.

ATLANTIC
OCEAN

Hawaiian Islands

Tropic of Cancer

SIERRA MADRE ORIENTAL

SIERRA MADRE OCCIDENTAL

Colorado

Gulf of
Mexico

West Indies

Caribbean Sea

PACIFIC OCEAN

Equator

Orinoco R.

GUIANA HIGHLANDS

AMAZON

Amazon R.

BASIN

SOUTH
AMERICA

P O L Y N E S I A

20°S

Tropic of Capricorn

ANDES MOUNTAINS

BRAZILIAN
HIGHLANDS

PAMPAS

Rio de
la Plata

40°S

PATAGONIA

Cape Horn

Drake Passage

60°S

Antarctic Circle

ANTARCTIC
PENINSULA

80°S

KEY

Elevation

Feet		Meters
14,000		4,270
7,000		2,135
1,500		457
700		213
(sea level) 0		0 (sea level)

Ice pack

Ice shelf

Orthographic Projection

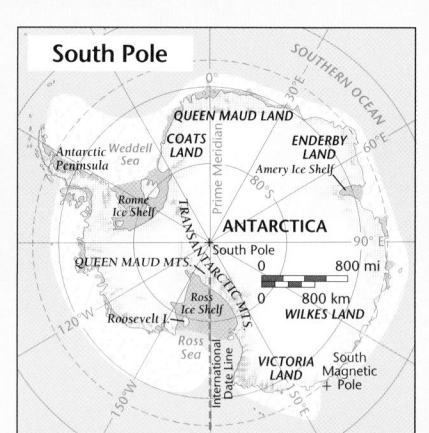

South Pole

SOUTHERN OCEAN

QUEEN MAUD LAND

Antarctic
Peninsula

Weddell
Sea

COATS
LAND

ENDERBY
LAND

Amery Ice Shelf

Ronne
Ice Shelf

Prime Meridian

ANTARCTICA

South Pole

QUEEN MAUD MTS.

TRANSANTARCTIC MTS.

Roosevelt I.

Ross
Ice Shelf

Ross
Sea

0   800 mi

0   800 km

WILKES LAND

International Date Line

VICTORIA
LAND

South
Magnetic
+ Pole

ARCTIC   OCEAN

80°N

Arctic Circle

Iceland

SCANDINAVIAN

URAL MTS.

SIBERIA

KOLYMA MTS.

60°N

British
Isles

North
Sea

NORTH EUROPEAN PLAIN

Ob R.

Yenisei R.

WEST
SIBERIAN
PLAIN

A S I A

Lena R.

Amur R.

KAMCHATKA
PENINSULA

EUROPE

ALPS

CAUCASUS

Volga R.

Aral
Sea

HIMLA.

Baikal

40°N

IBERIAN
PEN.

BALKAN
PEN.

Black Sea

MTS.

Caspian
Sea

TIEN SHAN

GOBI
DESERT

NORTH
CHINA
PLAIN

Sea of
Japan

ATLAS MTS.

Mediterranean Sea

ZAGROS MTS.

PLATEAU
OF IRAN

HINDU KUSH

KUNLUN SHAN

TIBETAN
PLATEAU

PACIFIC OCEAN

SAHARA

ARABIAN
PENINSULA

Persian
Gulf

HIMALAYAS

Mt. Everest
29,035 ft
(8,850m)

Yangtze R.

Tropic of Cancer

20°N

AFRICA

Nile R.

Red Sea

Arabian
Sea

DECCAN
PLATEAU

Bay of
Bengal

Ganges R.

Philippine
Sea

MICRONESIA

SUDAN

ETHIOPIAN
PLATEAU

South
China
Sea

Philippine
Islands

Congo R.

Lake
Victoria

INDIAN OCEAN

Sumatra

Borneo

East Indies

Celebes

Equator

MELANESIA

0°

New
Guinea

ATLANTIC
OCEAN

ZAMBEZI R.

Madagascar

Tropic of Capricorn

AUSTRALIA

20°S

KALAHARI

GREAT DIVIDING RANGE

Darling R.

North
Island

Cape of
Good Hope

N
W   E
S

0   1,000   2,000 mi

0   1,000   2,000 km

South
Island

40°S

60°S

Antarctic Circle

A N T A R C T I C A

80°S

20°W   0°   20°E   40°E   60°E   80°E   100°E   120°E   140°E   160°E

North Pole

A S I A

TAIMYR
PEN.

Kara Sea

Laptev Sea

Severnaya
Zemlya

Novaya
Zemlya

Barents
Sea

New
Siberian
Islands

90°E

Franz Josef
Land

East
Siberian
Sea

ARCTIC OCEAN

North Pole

Svalbard

International Date Line

Prime Meridian

Chukchi
Sea

0   500 mi

0   500 km

North
Magnetic Pole

Ellesmere
Island

NORTH
AMERICA

Queen
Elizabeth
Islands

Baffin
Bay

North and South America
Political

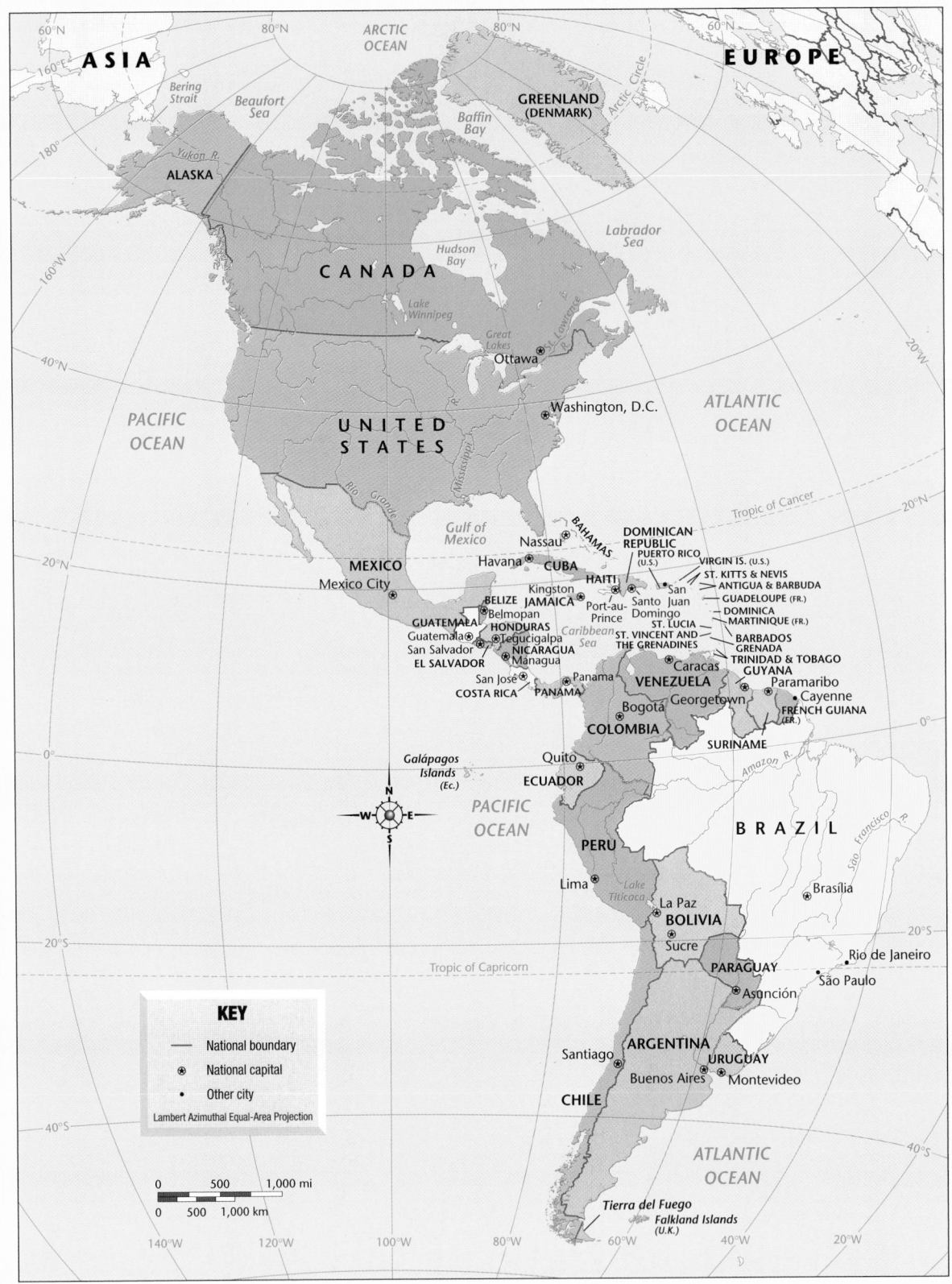

ASIA

ARCTIC OCEAN

EUROPE

Bering Strait

Beaufort Sea

GREENLAND (DENMARK)

ALASKA

Baffin Bay

Yukon R.

Labrador Sea

Hudson Bay

C A N A D A

Lake Winnipeg

Great Lakes

PACIFIC OCEAN

40°N

Ottawa

U N I T E D S T A T E S

Washington, D.C.

ATLANTIC OCEAN

Mississippi R.

Tropic of Cancer

20°N

Gulf of Mexico

BAHAMAS

Nassau

DOMINICAN REPUBLIC

PUERTO RICO (U.S.)

VIRGIN IS. (U.S.)

MEXICO

Havana

CUBA

HAITI

ST. KITTS & NEVIS

ANTIGUA & BARBUDA

Mexico City

Kingston

Port-au-Prince

Santo Domingo

San Juan

GUADELOUPE (FR.)

DOMINICA

BELIZE

JAMAICA

MARTINIQUE (FR.)

GUATEMALA

Belmopan

HONDURAS

Caribbean Sea

ST. LUCIA

Guatemala

Tegucigalpa

ST. VINCENT AND THE GRENADINES

BARBADOS

San Salvador

NICARAGUA

GRENADA

EL SALVADOR

Managua

TRINIDAD & TOBAGO

San José

Panama

VENEZUELA

GUYANA

COSTA RICA

PANAMA

Caracas

Paramaribo

Bogotá

Georgetown

Cayenne

FRENCH GUIANA (FR.)

COLOMBIA

SURINAME

Galápagos Islands (Ec.)

Quito

ECUADOR

Amazon R.

0°

B R A Z I L

N

W E

S

PACIFIC OCEAN

PERU

São Francisco R.

Lima

Lake Titicaca

Brasília

La Paz

BOLIVIA

20°S

Sucre

Rio de Janeiro

Tropic of Capricorn

PARAGUAY

São Paulo

Asunción

KEY

— National boundary

⊛ National capital

• Other city

Lambert Azimuthal Equal-Area Projection

ARGENTINA

Santiago

URUGUAY

Buenos Aires

Montevideo

CHILE

0   500   1,000 mi

0   500 1,000 km

ATLANTIC OCEAN

40°S

Tierra del Fuego

Falkland Islands (U.K.)

140°W   120°W   100°W   80°W   60°W   40°W   20°W

Physical

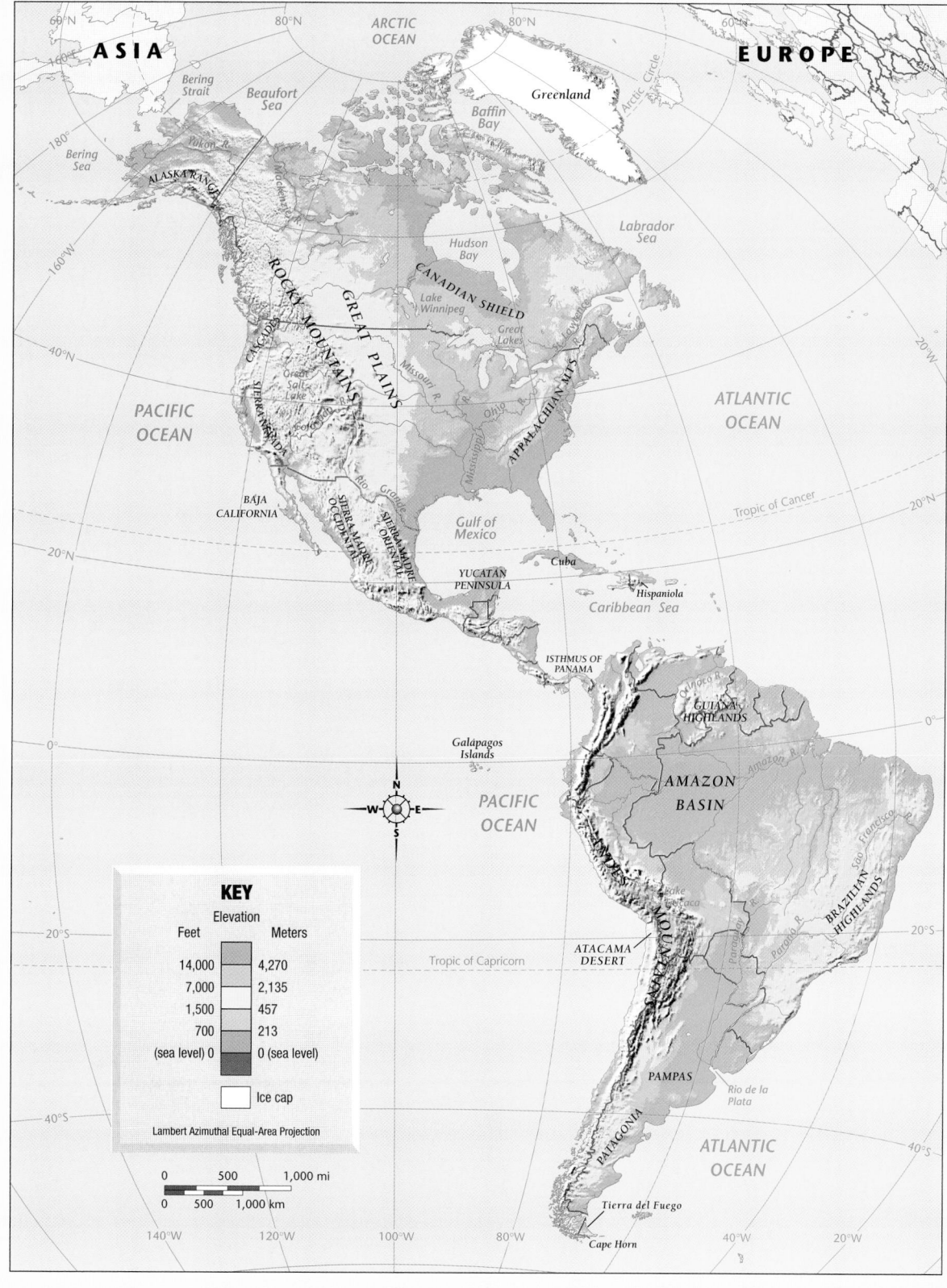

KEY

Elevation

Feet		Meters
14,000		4,270
7,000		2,135
1,500		457
700		213
(sea level) 0		0 (sea level)

☐ Ice cap

Lambert Azimuthal Equal-Area Projection

0   500   1,000 mi
0   500 1,000 km

ASIA

EUROPE

ARCTIC OCEAN

Bering Strait

Beaufort Sea

Greenland

Baffin Bay

Bering Sea

Yukon R.

ALASKA RANGE

Rockies

Labrador Sea

Hudson Bay

CANADIAN SHIELD

ROCKY MOUNTAINS

GREAT PLAINS

CASCADES

SIERRA NEVADA

Great Salt Lake

Lake Winnipeg

Great Lakes

Missouri R.

Ohio

Mississippi R.

APPALACHIAN MTS.

PACIFIC OCEAN

ATLANTIC OCEAN

BAJA CALIFORNIA

SIERRA MADRE OCCIDENTAL

SIERRA MADRE ORIENTAL

Rio Grande

Gulf of Mexico

Cuba

YUCATÁN PENINSULA

Hispaniola

Caribbean Sea

Tropic of Cancer

ISTHMUS OF PANAMA

Galápagos Islands

Orinoco R.

GUIANA HIGHLANDS

AMAZON BASIN

Amazon R.

PACIFIC OCEAN

ANDES MOUNTAINS

Lake Titicaca

São Francisco R.

BRAZILIAN HIGHLANDS

ATACAMA DESERT

Paraguay R.

Paraná R.

Tropic of Capricorn

PAMPAS

Rio de la Plata

PATAGONIA

ATLANTIC OCEAN

Tierra del Fuego

Cape Horn

Political

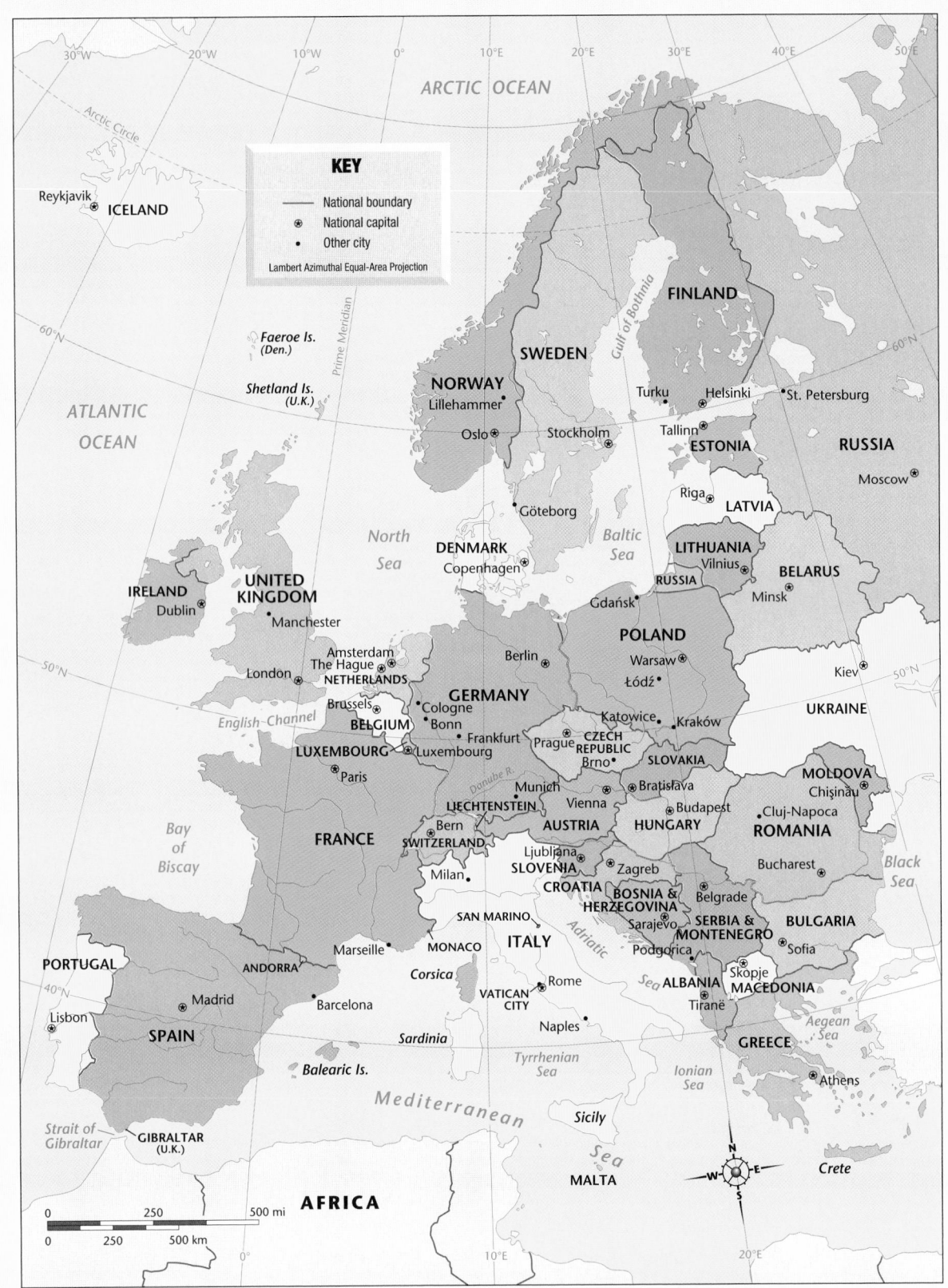

KEY

— National boundary
⊛ National capital
• Other city

Lambert Azimuthal Equal-Area Projection

ARCTIC OCEAN

Arctic Circle

Reykjavik ⊛ ICELAND

ATLANTIC OCEAN

Faeroe Is. (Den.)

Shetland Is. (U.K.)

Prime Meridian

FINLAND

SWEDEN

NORWAY
Lillehammer •
Oslo ⊛
Stockholm ⊛

Turku • Helsinki ⊛ • St. Petersburg

Tallinn ⊛ ESTONIA

RUSSIA
Moscow ⊛

Göteborg •

Riga ⊛ LATVIA

Baltic Sea

North Sea

DENMARK
Copenhagen ⊛

LITHUANIA
Vilnius ⊛

BELARUS
Minsk ⊛

IRELAND
Dublin ⊛

UNITED KINGDOM

• Manchester

RUSSIA
Gdańsk •

POLAND
Warsaw ⊛
Łódź •

Kiev ⊛

Amsterdam ⊛
The Hague ⊛
NETHERLANDS
London •

Berlin ⊛

UKRAINE

Brussels ⊛
BELGIUM

GERMANY
• Cologne
Bonn •
Frankfurt •

Katowice •
Kraków •

English Channel

LUXEMBOURG
⊛ Luxembourg

Prague ⊛
CZECH REPUBLIC
Brno •

SLOVAKIA

MOLDOVA
Chișinău ⊛

• Paris

Danube R.

Munich •

Vienna ⊛

⊛ Bratislava

Cluj-Napoca •

Bay of Biscay

LIECHTENSTEIN
Bern ⊛
SWITZERLAND

AUSTRIA

HUNGARY
⊛ Budapest

ROMANIA

FRANCE

Ljubljana ⊛
SLOVENIA
Milan •

⊛ Zagreb
CROATIA

Bucharest ⊛

Black Sea

Marseille •

SAN MARINO

BOSNIA & HERZEGOVINA
Sarajevo •

Belgrade ⊛

SERBIA & MONTENEGRO

BULGARIA
Sofia ⊛

MONACO
ANDORRA

Corsica

ITALY

Adriatic Sea

Podgorica ⊛

PORTUGAL

Barcelona •

Rome ⊛

Skopje ⊛
ALBANIA
Tiranë ⊛
MACEDONIA

Madrid ⊛

VATICAN CITY

Lisbon ⊛

SPAIN

Sardinia

Naples •

Aegean Sea

Balearic Is.

Tyrrhenian Sea

GREECE

Strait of Gibraltar

GIBRALTAR (U.K.)

Mediterranean Sea

Sicily

Ionian Sea

Athens ⊛

Crete

MALTA

N
W   E
S

AFRICA

0   250   500 mi
0   250   500 km

Europe

Physical

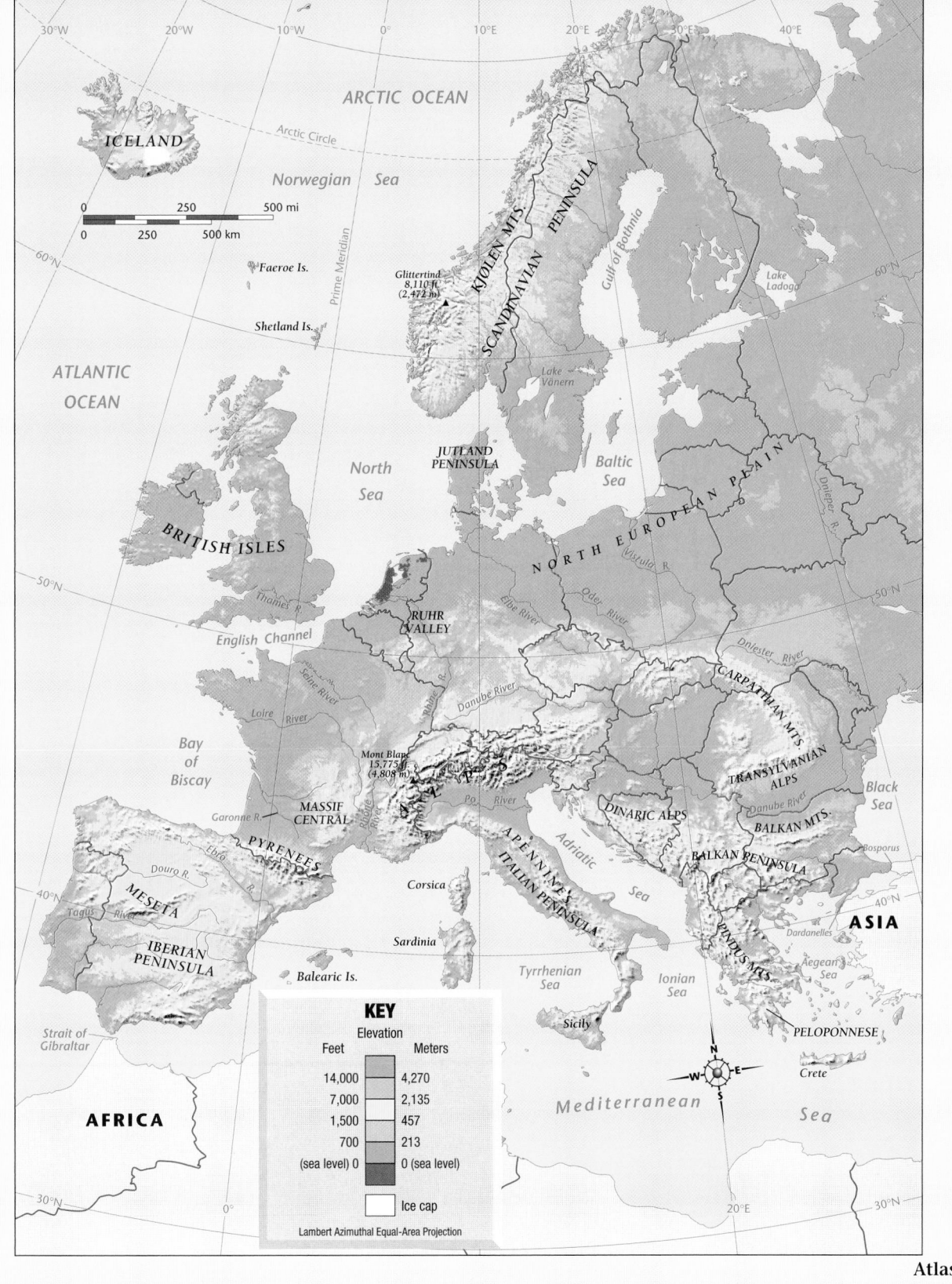

ARCTIC OCEAN

Arctic Circle

ICELAND

Norwegian Sea

0 250 500 mi
0 250 500 km

Faeroe Is.

Prime Meridian

Glittertind
8,110 ft
(2,472 m)

Shetland Is.

Gulf of Bothnia

Lake Ladoga

KJØLEN MTS.
SCANDINAVIAN PENINSULA

ATLANTIC
OCEAN

Lake Vänern

Baltic Sea

North Sea

JUTLAND PENINSULA

BRITISH ISLES

NORTH EUROPEAN PLAIN

Dnieper R.

Thames R.

Vistula R.

Elbe River

Oder River

English Channel

RUHR VALLEY

Dniester River

Seine River

Loire River

CARPATHIAN MTS.

Danube River

Bay
of
Biscay

Mont Blanc
15,775 ft
(4,808 m)

MASSIF
CENTRAL

Rhône River

Po River

Danube River

TRANSYLVANIAN ALPS

Black
Sea

Garonne R.

PYRENEES

DINARIC ALPS

BALKAN MTS.

BALKAN PENINSULA

Bosporus

MESETA

Ebro R.

Douro R.

Adriatic
Sea

APENNINES
ITALIAN PENINSULA

Corsica

ASIA

Tagus River

Dardanelles

IBERIAN
PENINSULA

Sardinia

Tyrrhenian
Sea

Ionian
Sea

PINDUS MTS.

Aegean
Sea

Balearic Is.

Mediterranean

Sicily

PELOPONNESE

Strait of
Gibraltar

Crete

AFRICA

KEY

Elevation

Feet	Meters
14,000	4,270
7,000	2,135
1,500	457
700	213
(sea level) 0	0 (sea level)
	Ice cap

Lambert Azimuthal Equal-Area Projection

N
W E
S

Africa

Political

Algiers
Tunis
TUNISIA
Mediterranean Sea
Tripoli
Alexandria
Giza Cairo

Strait of Gibraltar
Rabat
Casablanca
MOROCCO

CANARY ISLANDS (SP.)

WESTERN SAHARA (MOROCCO)

Tropic of Cancer

ALGERIA
LIBYA
EGYPT
Lake Nasser

MAURITANIA
Nouakchott
MALI
NIGER
CHAD
Khartoum
ERITREA
Asmara
DJIBOUTI

CAPE VERDE
Praia
Dakar
SENEGAL
Bamako
Niamey
Ouagadougou
Kano
N'Djamena
SUDAN
Blue Nile
L. Tana
Djibouti
Gulf of Aden

GAMBIA
Banjul
GUINEA BISSAU
Bissau
GUINEA
BURKINA FASO
NIGERIA
Abuja

White Nile
Red Sea

Conakry
Freetown
SIERRA LEONE
Monrovia
LIBERIA
CÔTE D'IVOIRE
Yamoussoukro
Abidjan
GHANA
Lomé
TOGO
BENIN
Accra
Porto-Novo
Lagos
Malabo
Gulf of Guinea
CAMEROON
Yaoundé
CENTRAL AFRICAN REPUBLIC
Bangui
Addis Ababa
ETHIOPIA
SOMALIA
L. Turkana

EQUATORIAL GUINEA
SÃO TOMÉ AND PRÍNCIPE
São Tomé
Libreville
GABON
CONGO
Congo R.
Kisangani
DEMOCRATIC REPUBLIC OF THE CONGO
Kampala
UGANDA
RWANDA
Kigali
BURUNDI
Bujumbura
KENYA
Nairobi
Mogadishu

Equator

ATLANTIC OCEAN

Brazzaville
Kinshasa
CABINDA (ANGOLA)
Lake Victoria
Dodoma
TANZANIA
Mombasa
INDIAN OCEAN
SEYCHELLES
L. Tanganyika
Dar es Salaam

Luanda
ANGOLA
Lubumbashi
L. Nyasa
COMOROS
Moroni

ZAMBIA
Lusaka
Zambezi R.
MALAWI
Lilongwe
Harare
ZIMBABWE
MOZAMBIQUE
Mozambique Channel
Antananarivo
MADAGASCAR
MAURITIUS
Port Louis
RÉUNION (FR.)

NAMIBIA
BOTSWANA
Windhoek
Gaborone
Limpopo R.
Pretoria
Maputo
Johannesburg
Mbabane
SWAZILAND
Durban

Tropic of Capricorn

Orange R.
Maseru
LESOTHO
SOUTH AFRICA

Cape Town

KEY

— National boundary
⊛ National capital
• Other city

Lambert Azimuthal Equal-Area Projection

0   400   800 mi
0   400   800 km

EUROPE
ASIA

Africa

Physical

EUROPE

ASIA

Strait of Gibraltar

Mediterranean Sea

ATLAS MOUNTAINS

Canary Islands

QATTARA DEPRESSION

Suez Canal

Tropic of Cancer

AHAGGAR MOUNTAINS

ARABIAN DESERT

Nile R.

Lake Nasser

S A H A R A

LIBYAN DESERT

Cape Verde Islands

Senegal R.

Red Sea

Niger R.

S A H E L

Gulf of Aden

L. Chad

FOUTA DJALLON

White Nile

Blue Nile

Tana

ETHIOPIAN PLATEAU

MANDARA MTS.

Benue R.

SUDD

Gulf of Guinea

Ubangi R.

Congo R.

L. Albert

L. Turkana

CONGO BASIN

L. Edward

GREAT RIFT VALLEY

Kilimanjaro 19,341 ft (5,895 m)

Equator

Lake Victoria

ATLANTIC OCEAN

L. Maï-Ndombe

SERENGETI PLAIN

INDIAN OCEAN

Kasai R.

Tanganyika

Zanzibar

Lake Nyasa

Comoros Islands

Zambezi R.

Mauritius

Réunion

NAMIB DESERT

Okavango Basin

Mozambique Channel

Tropic of Capricorn

Limpopo R.

KALAHARI DESERT

Orange R.

Cape of Good Hope

Cape Agulhas

KEY

Elevation

Feet	Meters
Over 13,000	Over 3,960
6,500–13,000	1,980–3,960
1,600–6,500	480–1,980
650–1,600	200–480
0–650	0–200
Below sea level	Below sea level

Lambert Azimuthal Equal-Area Projection

0   400   800 mi

0   400   800 km

Atlas

Asia
Political

KEY

European Russia
National boundary
National capital
Other city
Two-Point Equidistant Projection

EUROPE

(RUSSIA)

RUSSIA

ARCTIC OCEAN

North Pole

Arctic Circle

Barents Sea

St. Petersburg
Moscow
Samara
Yekaterinburg

East Siberian Sea

Verkhoyansk

Bering Sea

Sea of Okhotsk

Sakhalin Island

Kuril Islands (Russia)

Ob R.
Irtysh R.
Yenisei R.
Lena R.

Omsk
Astana
Qaraghandy
KAZAKHSTAN
Aral Sea
Lake Balkhash

Bratsk
Irkutsk
Lake Baikal

Ulan Bator
MONGOLIA

Amur R.

Vladivostok
Sea of Japan
JAPAN
Tokyo

N. KOREA
Pyŏngyang
Seoul
S. KOREA

Harbin
Beijing
Yellow Sea

Huang He
Xi'an
Xi Jiang

CHINA

Fuzhou
East China Sea
Taipei
TAIWAN

Hong Kong
Macau
South China Sea

Philippine Sea

Ryukyu Islands

PALAU
Koror

PACIFIC OCEAN

GEORGIA
Tbilisi
Black Sea
Caspian Sea
TURKEY
Ankara
Nicosia
CYPRUS
LEBANON
Beirut
ISRAEL
Jerusalem
Damascus
SYRIA
Amman
JORDAN
Baghdad
IRAQ
ARMENIA
Yerevan
AZERBAIJAN
Baku
TURKMENISTAN
Ashgabat
Tehran
IRAN
Shiraz

UZBEKISTAN
Tashkent
Bishkek
KYRGYZSTAN
Almaty
Dushanbe
TAJIKISTAN
AFGHANISTAN
Kabul
PAKISTAN
Islamabad

NEPAL
Kathmandu
BHUTAN
Thimphu
New Delhi
Ganges R.
BANGLADESH
Dhaka
INDIA

MYANMAR (BURMA)
Yangon
Bay of Bengal

LAOS
Vientiane
Hanoi
VIETNAM
THAILAND
Bangkok
CAMBODIA
Phnom Penh

Mediterranean Sea

SAUDI ARABIA
Riyadh
KUWAIT
Kuwait
BAHRAIN
QATAR
UNITED ARAB EMIRATES
Abu Dhabi
Persian Gulf
OMAN
Muscat

YEMEN
Sanaa
Mecca
Red Sea
Gulf of Aden

Socotra (Yemen)

Arabian Sea

Mumbai (Bombay)

Chennai (Madras)

Colombo
SRI LANKA

Male
MALDIVES

INDIAN OCEAN

AFRICA

Tropic of Cancer

Equator

MALAYSIA
Kuala Lumpur
SINGAPORE
Singapore
Sumatra
Jakarta
Java
INDONESIA

BRUNEI
Bandar Seri Begawan
Borneo
Celebes
Java Sea
Celebes Sea

PHILIPPINES
Manila

Tropic of Cancer

Tanimbar
EAST TIMOR

PAPUA NEW GUINEA
Port Moresby
New Guinea

0   500   1,000 mi
0   500 1,000 km

Atlas

KEY

Feet	Meters
14,000	4,270
7,000	2,135
1,500	457
700	213
(sea level) 0	0 (sea level)

Two-Point Equidistant Projection

ARCTIC OCEAN

North Pole

PACIFIC OCEAN

Bering Sea

Equator

AUSTRALIA

New Guinea

KAMCHATKA PENINSULA

Sea of Okhotsk

Kuril Islands

Sakhalin Island

Hokkaido

Honshu

Shikoku

Kyushu

Sea of Japan

Ryukyu Islands

East China Sea

Yellow Sea

Philippine Sea

Luzon

Mindanao

Tanimbar

Timor

Celebes

Borneo

Java Sea

Sumatra

South China Sea

MALAY PENINSULA

INDOCHINA PENINSULA

KOLYMA MTS.

East Siberian Sea

STANOVOI RANGE

Amur

NORTH SIBERIAN LOWLAND

CENTRAL SIBERIAN PLATEAU

Lake Baikal

MONGOLIAN PLATEAU

GOBI DESERT

Yenisei R.

Ob R.

Irtysh

Lake Balkhash

URAL MOUNTAINS

Aral Sea

TIAN SHAN

KUNLUN SHAN

PLATEAU OF TIBET

HIMALAYAS

Ganges R.

INDIAN PENINSULA

DECCAN PLATEAU

EASTERN GHATS

WESTERN GHATS

Bay of Bengal

INDIAN OCEAN

Caspian Sea

CAUCASUS MTS.

ZAGROS MTS.

Persian Gulf

Arabian Sea

Socotra

ARABIAN PENINSULA

Gulf of Aden

Red Sea

PLATEAU OF ANATOLIA

Black Sea

Mediterranean Sea

EUROPE

AFRICA

Equator

Arctic Circle

Barents Sea

Tropic of Cancer

Tropic of Cancer

N
E
S
W

| 0 | 500 | 1,000 mi |
| 0 | 500 | 1,000 km |

PACIFIC OCEAN

20°N

0°

20°S

140°W

Hawaiian
Islands
(U.S.)

160°W

Line Islands

Equator

160°W

FRENCH POLYNESIA
(Fr.)

Society
Islands — Tahiti

Tropic of Capricorn

PITCAIRN ISLAND
(U.K.)

KEY

Elevation
Feet   Meters
14,000   4,270
7,000   2,135
1,500   457
700   213
(sea level) 0   0 (sea level)

⊛ National capital
✪ State or territorial
    capital
• Other city

Mercator Projection

Midway Islands
(U.S.)

Tropic of Cancer

Wake Island (U.S.)

MARSHALL ISLANDS

Gilbert Islands

KIRIBATI

TUVALU
Funafuti ⊛

SAMOA
⊛ Apia

AMERICAN
SAMOA (U.S.)

COOK
ISLANDS
(N.Z.)

NORTHERN
MARIANA
ISLANDS
(U.S.)

GUAM (U.S.)

CAROLINE ISLANDS

FEDERATED STATES OF MICRONESIA

Palikir ⊛

Tarawa ⊛

⊛ Yaren
NAURU

FIJI
Suva ⊛

Nukualofa ⊛
TONGA

International Date Line

VANUATU
Port-Vila ⊛
New Hebrides

NEW CALEDONIA
(Fr.)

SOLOMON
ISLANDS

Honiara ⊛

Philippine
Sea

140°E

160°E

Coral Sea

Great Barrier Reef

Auckland
North Island

Wellington ⊛
Christchurch
Dunedin •
Cook Strait
NEW
ZEALAND
South Island

Tasman
Sea

Stewart
Island

AUCKLAND ISLANDS
(N.Z.)

180°

Arafura Sea

Timor Sea

Darwin •

ARNHEM
LAND

KIMBERLEY
PLATEAU

GREAT SANDY
DESERT

GIBSON DESERT

WESTERN
AUSTRALIA

GREAT VICTORIA
DESERT

Perth ✪
DARLING
RANGE

BARKLY
TABLELAND

NORTHERN
TERRITORY

SIMPSON
DESERT

SOUTH
AUSTRALIA

NULLARBOR PLAIN

Great
Australian Bight

CAPE
YORK
PENINSULA

QUEENSLAND

GREAT DIVIDING RANGE

Brisbane ✪

GREAT
ARTESIAN
BASIN

Lake
Eyre

AUSTRALIA

Adelaide ✪

Sydney ✪
NEW SOUTH
WALES

Canberra ⊛

Murray R.
Darling R.

VICTORIA
Melbourne ✪

Bass Strait

TASMANIA

Hobart ✪

INDIAN OCEAN

20°S

40°S

120°E

140°E

0   500   1,000 mi
0   500   1,000 km

The Arctic

150°E

Sea of
Okhotsk

VERKHOYANSKI RANGE

CHERSKOGO RANGE

KOLYMA MTS.

International Date Line

180°

ANADYR
RANGE

Bering Sea

CHUKOTSKI
PEN.

St. Lawrence
Island

Bering Strait

Nunivak
Island

BROOKS RANGE

ALASKA RANGE

Kodiak I.

Gulf of
Alaska

0   250   500 mi
0   250   500 km

120°E

Lena R.

ASIA

TAIMYR
PEN.

Laptev Sea

Severnaya
Zemlya

New
Siberian
Islands

Arctic Circle

70° N

East
Siberian
Sea

Wrangel
Island

Chukchi
Sea

Pt. Barrow

Beaufort
Sea

North
Magnetic Pole

Banks
Island

Amundsen Gulf

Mackenzie R.

Victoria
Island

NORTH AMERICA

90° E

Kara Sea

80° N

Novaya
Zemlya

Franz Josef
Land

A R C T I C   O C E A N

North Pole

Svalbard

80° N

Ellesmere
Island

Queen
Elizabeth
Islands

Baffin
Bay

Baffin I.

Davis Strait

60° W

EUROPE

KOLA
PEN.

Barents
Sea

North
Cape

SCANDINAVIAN PENINSULA

Baltic
Sea

Norwegian Sea

Greenland Sea

Prime Meridian

0°

North
Sea

Denmark Strait

Iceland

Greenland

70° N

60° N

Arctic Circle

60° N

Cape Farewell

30° W

ATLANTIC
OCEAN

Antarctica

Antarctic Circle

30° W

60° W

South Shetland
Is.

**SOUTH
AMERICA**

Antarctic
Peninsula

60° W

Alexander I.

Bellingshausen
Sea

Vinson Massif ▲
16,067 ft.
(4,897 m)

90°W

QUEEN MAUD MTS.

Amundsen
Sea

SOUTHERN OCEAN

60° S

120°W

150°W

Weddell
Sea

**COATS
LAND**

Filchner
Ice Shelf

Ronne
Ice Shelf

Berkner I.

SOUTH
POLAR
PLATEAU

South Pole

Ross
Ice Shelf

Roosevelt I.

Ross
Sea

International Date Line

180°

70° S

QUEEN MAUD LAND

Prime Meridian

TRANSANTARCTIC MTS.

ANTARCTICA

30° E

80° S

**ENDERBY
LAND**

Amery Ice Shelf

WILKES LAND

SOUTHERN OCEAN

90° E

60° S

120°E

**VICTORIA
LAND**

+ South Magnetic
Pole

0   400   800 mi
0   400   800 km

KEY

Elevation

Feet		Meters
14,000		4,270
7,000		2,135
1,500		457
700		213
(sea level) 0		0 (sea level)

Ice pack

Ice shelf

Orthographic Projection

ARCTIC
OCEAN

ALEUTIAN TRENCH

**NORTH
AMERICA**

*MID-ATLANTIC
RIDGE*

*NORTH AMERICAN
BASIN*

*PUERTO RICO
TRENCH*

*PACIFIC
OCEAN*

*MID-PACIFIC
BASIN*

Equator

| 0 | 1,000 | 2,000 mi |
| 0 | 1,000 | 2,000 km |

Robinson Projection

**SOUTH
AMERICA**

PERU-CHILE TRENCH

EAST PACIFIC RISE

*ATLANTIC
OCEAN*

*SOUTHWEST
PACIFIC
BASIN*

*PACIFIC-ANTARCTIC
RIDGE*

*SOUTHEAST
PACIFIC BASIN*

Feet

20,000
15,000
10,000
5,000
Sea Level
5,000
10,000
15,000
20,000

Baker Island

ANDES
MOUNTAINS

Galápagos
Islands

São Tom

PACIFIC OCEAN

SOUTH AMERICA

ATLANTIC OCEAN

MID-ATLANTIC
RIDGE

MID-PACIFIC
BASIN

Profile drawn along the Equator

ARCTIC OCEAN

EUROPE

ASIA

AFRICA

KURIL TRENCH

PACIFIC OCEAN

MID-PACIFIC MOUNTAINS

CHAGOS-LACCADIVE PLATEAU

PHILIPPINE TRENCH

MARIANA TRENCH

Equator

INDIAN OCEAN

NINETY EAST RIDGE

WALVIS RIDGE

AUSTRALIA

SOUTHWEST INDIAN RIDGE

SOUTHEAST INDIAN RIDGE

ANTIC-INDIAN RIDGE

PACIFIC-ANTARCTIC RIDGE

ANTARCTICA

N
W   E
S

Lake Victoria   Mt. Kenya

Sumatra   Borneo   Celebes   Gilbert Islands

Maldives

INDIAN   OCEAN   PACIFIC OCEAN

AFRICA

CHAGOS-LACCADIVE PLATEAU   NINETY EAST RIDGE

6,100
4,570
3,050
1,520
Sea Level
1,520
3,050
4,570
6,100

Meters

0   1,500   3,000 mi

0   1,500   3,000 km

Physical and Human Geography

Activating Prior Knowledge

Ask students how they picture the world. Do they envision a flat, one-dimensional picture, or do they see things in three dimensions, the way astronauts view the earth from space? Do they know that water covers more than two thirds of the earth's surface? Ask students to identify the continents and the oceans. Have them brainstorm a list of geographic features. Finally, refer students to the Atlas in the front of this book and encourage them to use it.

Photo Study

Machu Picchu, Peru
The Andes dominate the landscape of western South America. Machu Picchu, the site of an ancient Incan city, is located northwest of Cuzco, Peru, on a mountain in the Andes.
Drawing Conclusions Ask students to describe some of the physical and cultural aspects of this place. Then ask them to speculate why a group of people would build a city high in the mountains. (for religious reasons; for political reasons, for example, if they were forced to move away from the coasts; or for protection from enemies)

eTeach

Be sure to check out this month's online forum with a Master Teacher to join in an exchange of teaching ideas. **www.phschool.com**

UNIT

one

Physical and Human Geography

A Global Perspective

Geography allows people to find answers to questions about the world. Through the study of geography, you will explore and discover the processes that shape the earth, the relationships between people and environments, and the links between people and places. Geography will help you to build a global perspective and to understand the connections between global and local events.

Robinson Projection

RESOURCE DIRECTORY

Teaching Resources
Unit 1
- Geography and World Literature, The Other Side of the Sky: Special Delivery, p. 56

Mental Mapping booklet
- Unit 1 Checklist, p. 5
- Unit 1 Map Test, p. 8

Simulations, Games, and Lab Activities
- Where on Earth? Games, pp. 64–65

Global Environmental Posters

Technology
TeacherExpress™ CD-ROM
World Geography: Building a Global Perspective
Teaching Resources on CD-ROM offers lesson planning flexibility, test-generation capability, and resource manageability.

Prentice Hall Presentation Pro CD-ROM
This CD-ROM allows you to create custom lessons for instruction or review for every chapter.

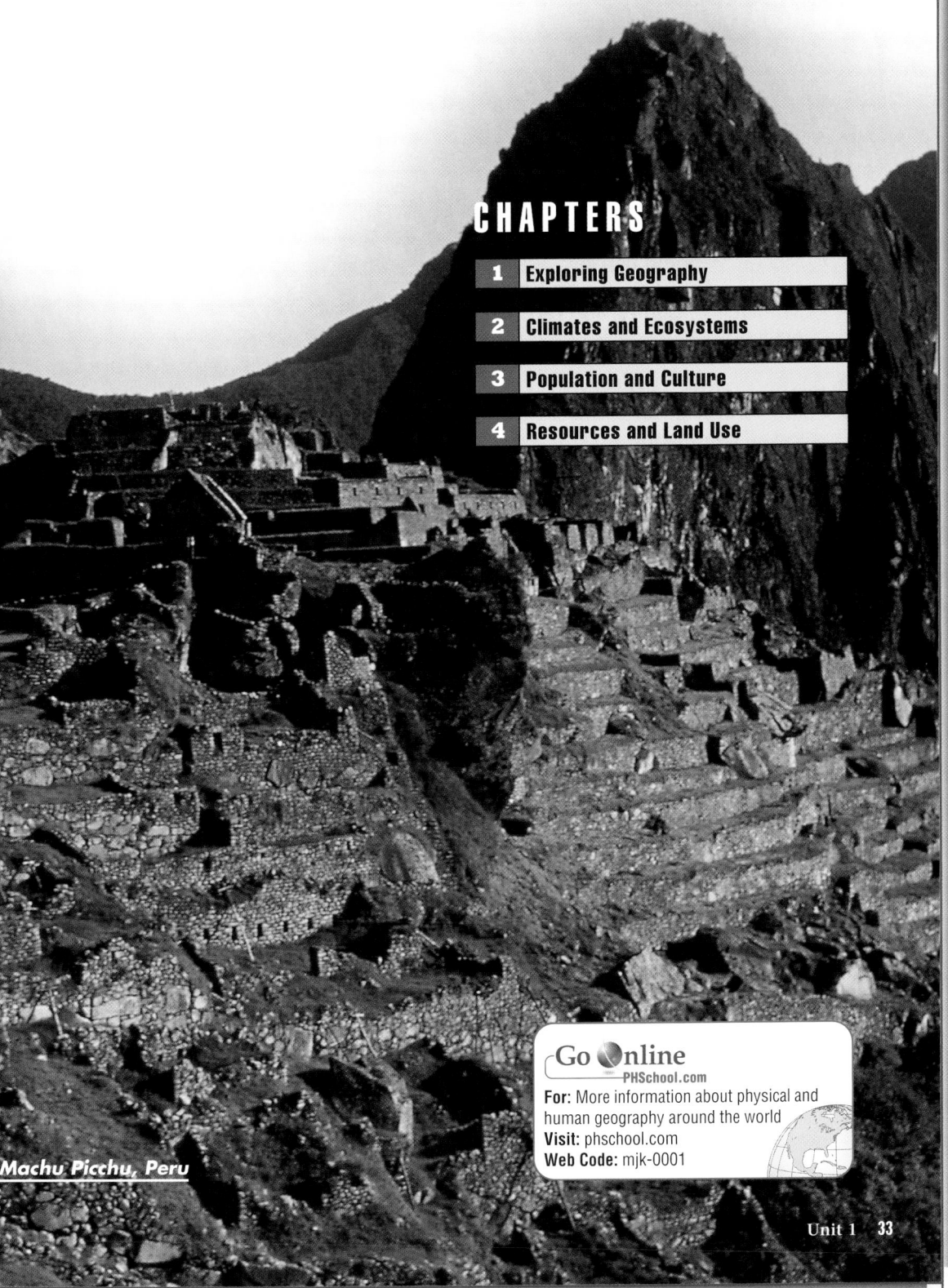

CHAPTERS

1 **Exploring Geography**

2 **Climates and Ecosystems**

3 **Population and Culture**

4 **Resources and Land Use**

Machu Picchu, Peru

Go Online
PHSchool.com
For: More information about physical and human geography around the world
Visit: phschool.com
Web Code: mjk-0001

Unit 1 **33**

Promoting Geographic Understanding

Introduce the unit by using the themes below.

1. Place Point out that all people live in a particular place. The physical and human characteristics of that place influence their lives. Ask students to brainstorm a list of various physical attributes a place might have. (hills, mountains, plains, forests, islands, streams, rivers, grasslands, deserts; hot, moderate, or cold climate)

2. Interaction Explain to students that people interact with the world around them in countless ways. For example, people build settlements and structures using the earth's natural resources. Discuss ways in which people might interact with the environment. (Examples: People might enjoy the scenic beauty of mountains; they might climb them or ski down them. People might cut forests to use the wood for paper or for building, etc.) As a follow-up activity, you may wish to briefly discuss how the environment has affected students so far today. For example, they may have worn raincoats to school or turned on the air conditioning at home.

Unit 1 **33**

Chapter 1 Planning Guide

Resource Manager

	CORE INSTRUCTION	READING/SKILLS
Chapter-Level Resources	**Teaching Resources** Unit 1/Ch. 1 • Reviewing Main Ideas, p. 8 **Mental Mapping booklet** • Unit 1 Checklist, p. 5 **Simulations, Games, and Lab Activities** • Place Location Review Games, pp. 58–63 **TeacherExpress™ CD-ROM,** Ch. 1 **Companion Web site,** **www.phschool.com** • eTeach	**Teaching Resources** Unit 1/Ch. 1 • Map/Graph Skills, p. 10 **Social Studies Skills Handbook** • Asking Questions While You Read, p. 70 • Reading a Table, p. 62 **Book on CD,** Ch. 1 **Social Studies Skills Tutor CD-ROM**
1 The Study of Geography 1. Explain how geographers use tools to understand the world. 2. Identify the five themes of geography. 3. Discuss how geographers identify location, place, and region. 4. Explain the importance of studying movement and human-environment interaction.	**Teaching Resources** Unit 1/Ch. 1 • Guided Reading and Review, p. 2 **Creative Teaching Activities** • Using Maps to Follow Directions, p. 3 **Simulations, Games, and Lab Activities** • Exploring Local Geography, Defining a Region, p. 2 **Prentice Hall Presentation Pro CD-ROM,** Ch. 1, Sec. 1	**Teaching Resources** **Guide to the Essentials (English/Spanish)** • Section Summary, Ch. 1, Sec. 1 **Mental Mapping booklet** • Outline Map 1, p. 6 **Guided Reading Audiotapes (English/Spanish),** Ch. 1, Sec. 1 **Section Reading Support Transparencies,** Ch. 1, Sec. 1
2 Changes Within the Earth 1. Explain how scientists classify the earth's major physical characteristics. 2. Describe the physical processes that affect the earth's crust. 3. Explain the theories that help scientists understand the earth's past.	**Teaching Resources** Unit 1/Ch. 1 • Guided Reading and Review, p. 4 **Prentice Hall Presentation Pro CD-ROM,** Ch. 1, Sec. 2	**Teaching Resources** **Guide to the Essentials (English/Spanish)** • Section Summary, Ch. 1, Sec. 2 **Social Studies Skills Handbook** • Reading a Diagram, p. 56 **Guided Reading Audiotapes (English/Spanish),** Ch. 1, Sec. 2 **Section Reading Support Transparencies,** Ch. 1, Sec. 2
3 Changes on the Earth's Surface 1. Explain how mechanical and chemical weathering affect a place's physical landscape. 2. Describe how the physical process of erosion alters the landscape.	**Teaching Resources** Unit 1/Chapter 1 • Guided Reading and Review, p. 6 **Simulations, Games, and Lab Activities** • Exploring Local Geography, Environmental Problems, p. 4 **Prentice Hall Presentation Pro CD-ROM,** Ch. 1, Sec. 3	**Teaching Resources** **Guide to the Essentials (English/Spanish)** • Section Summary, Ch. 1, Sec. 3 **Guided Reading Audiotapes (English/Spanish),** Ch. 1, Sec. 3 **Section Reading Support Transparencies,** Ch. 1, Sec. 3

ENRICHMENT/HONORS/PREAP®

Teaching Resources
Mental Mapping booklet
• Atlas Activity, p. 7
Social Studies Skills Handbook
• Study and Research Skills, pp. 94–108
World Geography Map and Photo Transparencies
• World Maps
• Tectonic Plates
World Geography Videos
• Exploring Geography: Geographic Tools, Tape 1
Companion Web site,
www.phschool.com
• Chapter 1 Activities

Teaching Resources
Unit 1/Ch. 1
• Critical Thinking, p. 9
Simulations, Games, and Lab Activities
• Geographer's Lab, Making and Using a Compass, p. 82
Companion Web site,
www.phschool.com
• Chapter 1 Activities

Teaching Resources
Unit 1/Ch. 1
• Geography and World Literature, p. 56
Social Studies Skills Handbook
• Drawing Conclusions, p. 52
Companion Web site,
www.phschool.com
• Chapter 1 Activities

Companion Web site,
www.phschool.com
• Chapter 1 Activities

ASSESSMENT

PRENTICE HALL ASSESSMENT SYSTEM

Core Assessment
ExamView Test Bank booklet, Ch. 1
ExamView Test Bank CD-ROM, Ch. 1

Standardized Test Preparation
Diagnose and Prescribe
Diagnostic Tests for High School Social Studies Skills

Review and Reteach
Review Book for World Geography, pp. 3–4

Practice and Assess
Test-taking Strategies With Transparencies for High School
Test-taking Strategy Poster
Alternative Assessment booklet
Test Prep Book for World Geography

Teaching Resources
Unit 1/Ch. 1
• Section Quizzes, pp. 3, 5, 7
• Test Forms A and B, pp. 11–16
Guide to the Essentials (English/Spanish)
• Chapter 1 Test
Spanish Resources, Ch. 1
• Section Quizzes, pp. 4–6
Mental Mapping booklet
• Chapter 1 Map Test, p. 8
Companion Web site, www.phschool.com
• Chapter 1 Self-Test

CUSTOMIZE FOR INDIVIDUAL NEEDS

Honors/PreAP
• Teacher's Edition, Customize for . . . , p. 55
Less Proficient Readers
• Guide to the Essentials (English), Ch. 1, Section Summaries
• Social Studies Skills Handbook, p. 68
• Guided Reading Audiotapes (English), Ch. 1
• Section Reading Support Transparencies, Ch. 1
• Book on CD, Ch. 1
• Teacher's Edition, Reading Strategy, pp. 41, 47, 55
• Teacher's Edition, Activity: Vocabulary, pp. 45, 53
Students Acquiring English/ESL
• Guide to the Essentials (English/Spanish), Ch. 1
• Guided Reading Audiotapes (English/Spanish), Ch. 1
• Section Reading Support Transparencies, Ch. 1
• Book on CD, Ch. 1
• Teacher's Edition, Customize for . . . , pp. 39, 51
Less Proficient Writers
• Social Studies Skills Handbook, p. 77
• Alternative Assessment, Writing Assignment Rubric, p. 6
• Teacher's Edition, Customize for . . . , p. 43

MENTAL MAPPING

Ask students to write five questions about a place they have never visited. Use student questions to develop a working definition of *geography*.

Unit Checklist Distribute the Unit 1 Checklist on page 5 of the Mental Mapping booklet in the Teaching Resources. This list includes all of the place names that students should learn in this unit. Ask students to store the Unit Checklist and maps they create in an Atlas Portfolio.

Mapping the World Direct students to create a map like the one on this page, lightly shading each continent. Have students label continents, oceans, and seas as they are shown on this map. Students may sketch their own maps or use the Chapter 1 Outline Map on page 6 of the Mental Mapping booklet in the Teaching Resources. Ask students to label the places listed under Part 1 of the Unit 1 Checklist. Students should keep their maps in their Atlas Portfolios in order to prepare for the Chapter 1 Map Test.

eTeach

Be sure to check out this month's online forum with a Master Teacher to join in an exchange of teaching ideas. **www.phschool.com**

C H A P T E R

1

Exploring **Geography**

SECTIONS

1 The Study of Geography

2 Changes Within the Earth

3 Changes on the Earth's Surface

The World: CONTINENTS, OCEANS, AND SEAS

Robinson Projection

Go Online
PHSchool.com

For: More geographic information about the earth and access to the Take It to the Net activities
Visit: phschool.com
Web Code: mjk-0002

RESOURCE DIRECTORY

Teaching Resources
Unit 1, Chapter 1
• Section 1 Guided Reading and Review, p. 2
Guide to the Essentials (English/Spanish)
• Section Summary, Chapter 1, Section 1
Mental Mapping booklet
• Atlas Activity, p. 7
• Unit 1 Checklist, p. 5
• Outline Map 1, p. 6

Technology
Guided Reading Audiotapes (English/Spanish),
Chapter 1, Section 1

Section Reading Support Transparencies,
Chapter 1, Section 1
World Geography Map and Photo Transparencies
• World Maps
Book on CD, Chapter 1
World Geography Videos
• Exploring Geography: Geographic Tools, Tape 1
TeacherExpress™ CD-ROM, Chapter 1
Prentice Hall Presentation Pro CD-ROM, Chapter 1
Social Studies Skills Tutor CD-ROM
Companion Web site, www.phschool.com
• Chapter 1 Activities

1 The Study of Geography

Reading Focus

- How do geographers use tools to understand the world?
- What are the five themes of geography?
- How do geographers identify location, place, and region?
- Why do geographers study movement and human-environment interaction?

Key Terms

geography	character of a place
GIS	perception
absolute location	formal region
hemisphere	functional region
relative location	perceptual region

Main Idea Geographers use a variety of methods to collect, organize, and analyze information about the world.

Environmental Change Hang gliding provides a unique view of how people have modified the environment.

Your world changes constantly. It changes as you move from one place to another and do different things. Your world may be the small area where you spend most of your time—your home, school, favorite hangout, stores, and the routes that connect them. At other times, your world grows to include other places you have visited, read about, or seen on television. Sometimes your world is the entire earth, a planet where different people interact with each other and their environments.

The size and scope of your world constantly change, and so does its character. Each school year takes you into new classrooms, where you meet new teachers and students. The weather and seasons change. Families move as their sizes change, or as members find new jobs. Some stores close, and new ones open. Over days and weeks and years, your world changes.

Geographic Tools

Geography allows you to examine and understand the constantly changing world in which you live. Through the study of geography you learn to see your world from many different perspectives. By using geographic maps, graphs, and charts, you can see global patterns or changes in your own neighborhood. Geography can help you develop valuable insights about the earth, its people, and the many different relationships between them.

Geography comes from a Greek word meaning "writing about" or "describing" the earth. **Geography** is the study of where people, places, and things are located and how they relate to each other. People always have been geographers, because they always have been curious about their world.

Technology Geography uses scientific approaches to examine and understand where things are located. One tool that has been used for decades is sonar. Sonar stands for SOund, NAvigation, and Ranging, and analyzes sounds to determine distance and direction. Originally developed in 1906 to detect icebergs, sonar became an important military tool during World

◀ Signpost in Canada's Yukon Territory *(photo left)*

Objectives

Upon completion of Section 1, students should be able to:

- explain how geographers use tools to understand the world;
- identify and discuss the importance of the five themes of geography.

 National Geography Standards

The following National Geography Standards are highlighted in this section: 1, 2, 4, 5, 11, 14, 16, 18

Bellringer

Read aloud a newspaper article that mentions landforms, climate, or features of culture. Omit references to the place's name. Have students guess its identity and describe how they made their guesses.

LESSON PLAN

1. Focus Write the following questions on the board: *Why is Texas among the fastest-growing states?* (movement) *How many professional sports teams does San Francisco have?* (place) *Is Michigan part of the Rust Belt?* (region) *Where is Zanzibar?* (location) *How did the invention of the refrigerated train car affect farmers?* (interaction) Ask students which of these is a "geographic" question. (all of them) Explain that in this section students will learn how questions such as these are linked to geography.

2. Instruct Help students compare relationships among the five themes. Ask what themes are linked to questions about the effects of locating a town near a major waterway or railroad. (relative location, movement, human-environment interaction)

3. Close/Reteach Make a two-column chart on the board. Title the first column *Geographic Themes*. List the five themes of geography under this heading. Use the name of your community for the title of the second column. Have volunteers fill the second column with examples of each of the five themes.

TEACHING TIP
From A Master Teacher

Earth's Physical Processes Physical processes such as earthquakes, erosion, and plate tectonics constantly shape and change the earth's features and environments. Although many of these processes occur in the earth's different spheres (hydrosphere, atmosphere, lithosphere, biosphere), they are interconnected in one complex global system. As students study geography, help them identify the short-term and long-term effects of physical processes on people and the environment in regions throughout the world.

Pacing Suggestions

 For 90-minute Blocks

You will want to vary activities.

- Use the Creative Teaching Activity for Chapter 1 as the basis for a 90-minute lesson. After completing the lesson, ask students to use the map on page 158 to write directions from Pittsburgh, Pennsylvania, to Mt. Katahdin in Maine. Students should include at least three stops and use geographic descriptions, but not place names, in their directions. When the directions are complete, have students swap their work and try to trace the paths that their classmates have laid for them.

Reteach

Quiz Game Have students work in pairs, using the World Geography Concepts on this page as the basis for a quiz game. One partner provides the answer. (For example, "These are networks of plants and animals interacting with the environment.") The other partner provides the question. ("What are ecosystems?") Partners may switch roles after each correct response. (Verbal/Linguistic)

 Alternative Assessment

Introduce the Activity

Participating in a Classroom Discussion Ask students to prepare for a discussion of the following: Which is greater, the impact of the earth on people or the impact of people on the earth? Distribute the Classroom Discussion Rubric on page 22 of the Alternative Assessment booklet in the Prentice Hall Assessment System for student reference.

World Geography Concepts

CONCEPT	DESCRIPTION
Geographic Tools	Instruments used to collect, organize, store, or display geographic information
Physical Characteristics	Features of the earth's surface, such as landforms, water systems, climate patterns, and plant and animal life
Physical Processes	Actions of nature that change the physical environment
Climates	Regional long-term trends in weather and atmospheric conditions
Ecosystems	Networks of plants and animals interacting with the environment
Patterns of Settlement	Distribution of populations among urban and rural communities
Urbanization	Increase in the percentage of people living in cities
Migration	Movement of people, often influenced by push-and-pull factors
Population Growth	Increase in the number of people in a specific area
Cultures	Learned behavior of people, including their belief systems, languages, governments, and material goods
Science and Technology	Discoveries and inventions that help people to change or adapt to their environments
Government and Citizenship	How different viewpoints influence political decisions, divisions, and policies connected to geographic issues
Cooperation and Conflict	Methods used by countries and organizations to pursue goals, such as maintaining or expanding control over territory
Economic Systems	Ways in which a society satisfies basic needs through the production and distribution of goods and services
Economic Activities	Use of natural resources, production of goods, provision of services, and distribution of information
Global Trade Patterns	International networks for exchanging goods and services
Natural Resources	Any part of the natural environment that people need and value
Natural Hazards	Natural events in the physical environment that are destructive, such as volcanoes and hurricanes
Environmental Change	Natural or human alterations to the environment
Understanding the Past	Analysis of how geography has affected historic events and how places, environments, and cultures have changed over time
Planning for the Future	Use of geographic knowledge and skills to analyze problems and make decisions that affect the future

CHART SKILLS

Geographic Tools Geographic concepts can be used to organize and interpret information about the earth. By understanding the concepts, you can recognize the geographic patterns and processes that shape your world.

- *Which of these concepts can be used to discuss how people affect their environment?*
- *Whether or not a person lives in the city or in the country is a characteristic of which concept?*

36   Chapter 1 ▪ Exploring Geography

Answers to Chart Skills

Possible answers: science and technology, environmental change, planning for the future

patterns of settlement

RESOURCE DIRECTORY

Teaching Resources
Mental Mapping booklet
• Atlas Activity, p. 7

Prentice Hall Assessment System
Alternative Assessment booklet
• Classroom Discussion Rubric, p. 22

Deforestation in Brazil

Science and Technology
This aerial photograph shows part of the Amazon region of Brazil. The brown areas represent bare patches of earth, where rain forest has disappeared.

Human-Environment Interaction *How might human activities contribute to disappearance of the rain forest?*

War I as surface ships tried to identify and avoid submarines. In geography, sonar is used to study the ocean floor.

Geographers also use remote-sensing technology, such as satellites. The Landsat Program has provided the United States with information since 1972. *Landsat 7* was launched in 1999 and records images of the earth's surface, which are downloaded to computers. Scientists can compare older and more recent images to identify changes in land use, vegetation, and urban growth.

Technological advances are always providing new opportunities for studying the earth. Recently, geographers have come to rely on the global positioning system (GPS). This system relies on a network of 24 satellites orbiting the earth. Using atomic clocks, the satellites broadcast extremely accurate time measurements. Back on earth, GPS units analyze these time signals to provide information about location.

Another recent innovation is the growing importance of geographic information systems (GIS). A **GIS** uses computer technology to collect, manipulate, analyze, and display data about the earth's surface in order to solve geographic problems. It might combine data from satellite photos, census results, or tax assessors. This information is then "layered" by computers to show relationships among data. For example, an urban planner might develop a GIS that shows the number and location of schools, sirens, and highways within several miles of a nuclear power plant. This information would be used to determine if the community was well-prepared for dealing with a nuclear accident. A GIS can be used to study topics as different as public health, road construction, and retail market size.

Many people think about geography only when deciding where to live or how to travel from one place to another. You may find, however, that well-developed geographic skills will enable you to be more successful in your career. Perhaps you will help preserve a wildlife habitat or find new energy sources. Your understanding of geography also will help you be a better citizen, because you can vote for elected leaders who will use geographic information at the local, state, national, and global levels.

Geographic Concepts You have learned how geographically informed people use tools

Critical Thinking

Analyzing Information Ask students to assess the accuracy of the following statements: "Geography is the study of where places are. The geographer's tools are a map and a compass." Provide time for several students to respond. Then ask students to rewrite the statements to reflect their concept of geography. (Geographers use different tools to study places. They are concerned with location, human and physical characteristics of places, human-environment interaction, movement, and regions.)

such as maps, charts, and graphs. Another kind of tool is the geographic concept. We use ideas as tools to help organize the way we think about geography. Some of these geographic concepts are *physical characteristics, patterns of settlement, science and technology,* and *economic activities.* (See the chart on page 36.)

All of the concepts help us to recognize and understand geographic patterns and processes that we can relate to real-life situations around us. For example, *physical processes,* such as volcanoes, earthquakes, and erosion, have all shaped our world and continue to do so today. *Economic activities,* such as agriculture, industry, and mining, affect both the environment and society. Another geographic concept is *cooperation and conflict.* You can see examples of this concept in the news every day as individuals, organizations, and countries work together and compete for natural resources.

As you study geography, you will use these and other concepts to study how people, places, and environments are related. You will learn how to use geography to interpret the past and present. By recognizing and understanding geographic patterns and processes, you will be better able to make informed decisions that will affect your future.

Geography's Five Themes

The study of geography is fueled by human curiosity. Why are places on the earth so amazingly different from each other? Five important questions can help organize information about places:

- What is the location of a place?
- What is the character of a place?
- How are places similar to and different from other places?
- How do people, goods, and ideas move between places?
- How do people interact with the natural environment of a place?

Each of these questions is related to one of five themes that you can use to organize your study of the world. The five themes are location, place, region, movement, and human-environment interaction. Each theme offers a way of looking at the world and its people. The themes are not mutually exclusive. To thoroughly understand a place or problem, you need to know how the different themes relate to each other.

For example, the tiny principality of Monaco occupies steep hillsides on three sides of a beautiful natural harbor of the Mediterranean Sea.

A Mediterranean Location

Physical Characteristics Monaco's natural beauty and cultural attractions draw tourists from all over the world.

Place *Describe one physical characteristic and one human characteristic of Monaco.*

38

Answer to Photo Caption

Possible answer: physical characteristic—steep, hilly terrain; human characteristic—popular tourist destination

Monaco's location makes it a popular destination for thousands of tourists who flock yearly to the sunny beaches of southern France. This movement, however, threatens the very beauty that attracts visitors to the area.

Location

Geographers studying a place usually begin by finding its location. A place's location can be described in either absolute or relative terms.

Absolute Location Where is a place? One way to answer this question is by describing its **absolute location**—its position on the globe.

The most common way to find a place's absolute location is by using the imaginary lines marking positions on the surface of the earth. The Equator is one such line. It circles the globe halfway between the North and South poles. The Equator divides the world into two **hemispheres,** or halves. All land and water between the Equator and the North Pole is located in the Northern Hemisphere. Likewise, everything that lies between the Equator and the South Pole is located in the Southern Hemisphere.

Imaginary lines that run parallel to the Equator are called lines of latitude, or parallels. They measure distances north or south of the Equator. The Equator is designated 0°, whereas the poles are 90° north (N) and 90° south (S).

Because the earth is tilted about 23½° as it revolves around the sun, the Tropic of Cancer at 23½°N and the Tropic of Capricorn at 23½°S mark the boundaries of the places on the earth that receive the most direct sunlight and the greatest heat energy from the sun. Find the Equator and the tropics in the diagram on page 11.

Another set of imaginary lines are lines of longitude, or meridians, which run north and south between the two poles. The Prime Meridian, at 0°, runs through the Royal Observatory in Greenwich, England. Other meridians are measured in degrees from 0 to 180 east (E) or west (W) from Greenwich. Unlike lines of latitude, meridians are not parallel to each other. As you can see on the diagram on page 11, the distance between meridians is greatest at the Equator and decreases until they come together at the poles.

Using the grid formed by lines of latitude and longitude, you can name the precise or absolute

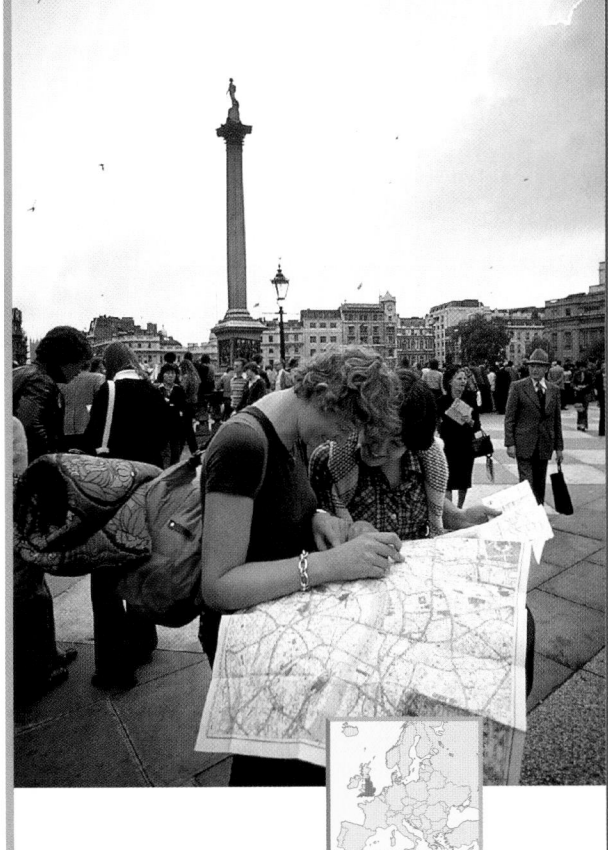

Finding Location

Geographic Tools A map is a flat drawing representing all or part of the earth's surface. These tourists at Trafalgar Square are using a city map to find their way around London.

Location *How can a map help you find both absolute location and relative location?*

location of any place on earth. Mogadishu, Somalia, is located at 2°N latitude and 45°E longitude. New Orleans, Louisiana, is at 30°N and 90°W. See page 11 to read more about this grid system.

Relative Location Another way to locate a place is to describe its **relative location,** or its relation compared to other places. New Orleans, for example, is several hundred miles south of Memphis, Tennessee, which is the next major city as you move up the Mississippi.

Although a place may have one fixed absolute location, it has many relative locations.

ACTIVITY

Group Work

Activity: Group writing

Purpose: Assign each group a well-known city, state, or country. Instruct groups to compose a written description of their assigned place, using the five themes as an organizing tool.

Roles: Have the first member of each group write one or more sentences describing the location of the assigned place. The next member adds information about its physical and human characteristics, the third describes human-environment interaction, and so on until all five themes have been covered. Have group members work together to create a short introductory sentence.

Result: A spokesperson from each group reads the group's description to the class.

BACKGROUND

History

Past Influences on Place Often the character of a place mingles its present with its past. Tourists to the modern city of Athens, Greece, for example, are sure to visit the Acropolis, a flat-top hill on which the Parthenon and other ancient structures have stood for more than two thousand years. For visitors and Athenians alike, the Acropolis injects a note of serenity amid the noise, neon lights, traffic jams, and crowds of today's booming, twenty-first–century city.

Answer to Photo Caption

Possible answer: They are European-style buildings with domes and clock towers. They stand in contrast to the tall modern buildings.

GEOFacts

Singapore has a tropical climate, with thunderstorms on 40 percent of all days in a year.

These can change over time. For example, in the 1800s a journey from New Orleans to Memphis took many days by boat. Today the cities are just over an hour apart travelling by airplane.

Place

Every place on the earth has features that distinguish it from other places. One challenge of geography is to understand how the character of a place is similar to and distinct from the character of other places. The **character of a place** consists of the place's physical characteristics and human characteristics.

Physical Characteristics Places have unique physical characteristics, such as landforms, ecosystems, and climate. A place's terrain may be mountainous, flat, or anywhere in between. Ecosystems range from leafy tropical rain forests to sparse, moss-covered tundra. Climate includes not only normal weather patterns but dramatic occurrences like hurricanes, blizzards, droughts, and floods.

Human Characteristics Places can also be described in terms of their human characteristics. How many people live, work, and visit a place? What are their languages, customs, and beliefs? How does their economy work? How are they governed?

Each place on the earth has a unique combination of physical and human characteristics. When travelers return from a vacation, they rarely talk about the places they visited in terms of latitude and longitude. Instead, they talk about the unfamiliar people, sites, and experiences that made their visit memorable. In addition to discussing new and different characteristics, they may also report that its residents speak the same language, use the same credit cards, and listen to the same music as do people at home. This mix of unique and common features is what geographers mean when they talk about "place."

Regions

A third geographic theme deals with regions. A region is a group of places with at least one common characteristic. The common elements may be physical or human characteristics. Sometimes a region is determined by people's perceptions.

An Island Nation

Urbanization In Singapore, an island nation of Southeast Asia, modern skyscrapers tower over buildings constructed during the British colonial era.

Place *How do the residential buildings at right preserve the architectural style of the colonial era?*

RESOURCE DIRECTORY

Teaching Resources
Simulations, Games, and Lab Activities
• Exploring Local Geography, Defining a Region, p. 2

Perception is a viewpoint that is influenced by one's own culture and experiences.

Formal regions are areas in which certain characteristics are found throughout the area. For example, states, countries, and cities are all political regions. Within these formal regions, all people are subject to the same laws and are ruled by the same government. Formal regions can also be defined using other characteristics. The steppe region in Northern Eurasia consists of temperate grasslands with rich soils. The Corn Belt is the part of the United States where corn is grown in abundance. Chinatown is a part of San Francisco, California, containing many Chinese American people, restaurants, and stores.

Functional regions consist of a central place and the surrounding places affected by it. The places that make up a functional region are often linked by the flow or movement of something. The Amazon drainage basin in South America is the region drained by the Amazon River and its tributaries. The Dallas–Fort Worth metropolitan area is a functional region in that Dallas and Fort Worth share a common airport located between the two cities.

Perceptual regions are defined by people's feelings and attitudes about areas. Regions such as Dixie, the upper Midwest, and the Middle States have no precise borders. For example, if you ask people in the city of St. Louis whether Missouri is a southern state or a western state, the answers will vary depending on each person's individual perception.

Because various criteria can be used to define regions, the same place may be found in several different regions. From a physical perspective, Mexico is part of the North American continental region. Culturally, however, Mexico is linked to the Spanish-speaking nations of Central and South America.

Movement

Places do not exist in isolation. Because places have different characteristics, it follows that people, goods, and ideas will move between them.

New Orleans's history illustrates the importance of movement. The city was established by the French in the early 1700s, and it became a bustling port where goods brought down the Mississippi were loaded onto ocean-going ships.

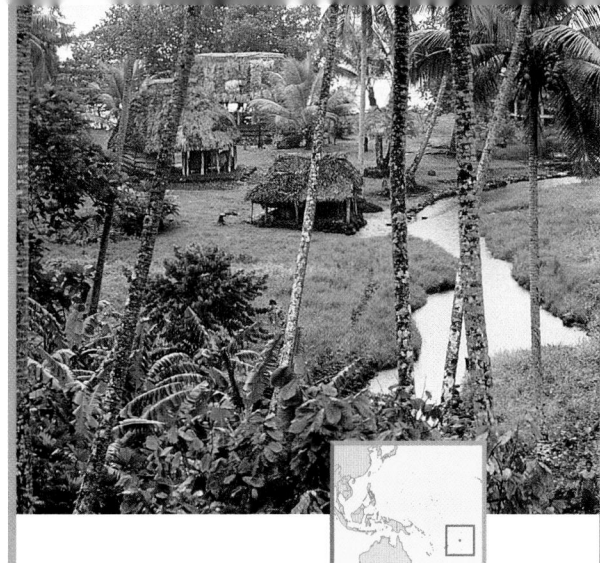

South Pacific Region

Climates The village of Luatuanuu is located in Samoa. This region of the Pacific Ocean is known for its scenic beauty and warm tropical climate.

Regions *What does this photo suggest about rainfall in Samoa?*

When the United States purchased Louisiana a century later, New Orleans became one of the young nation's five largest cities. During the mid-1800s, however, the east-west expansion of railroads throughout the nation cut into New Orleans's river trade. By the first part of the 1900s, the city's importance generally was limited to the states of Louisiana and Mississippi. As the twentieth century progressed, however, New Orleans transformed itself into a tourist hub and an important center for oil and gas production. Today, millions of people come from nations throughout the world to enjoy the distinctive charm and character of New Orleans.

Human-Environment Interaction

The final geographic theme involves how people use their environment. How have they changed it? What are the consequences of those changes? How have people responded to changes in their environment?

READING STRATEGY

Building Vocabulary

Ask a volunteer to read aloud the definitions of *formal region* and *functional region* from the Glossary. Then ask students to identify the formal and functional regions in which they live.

BACKGROUND

Environmental Issues

Human-Environment Interaction The impact of human interaction may have both positive and negative results. Overgrazing may produce larger herds, but it may also cause soil erosion. Development of property, construction of dams, and communication and transportation networks may improve the land for people. These activities also may result in the destruction of wildlife habitat, causing species to become endangered.

TEST PREPARATION

Have students read the subsection Place on the opposite page to answer the following question.

Which one of the following is an example of a human characteristic of a place?
 A Soil
 B River
 Ⓒ Language
 D Ecosystem

Answer to Photo Caption

The lush vegetation suggests that there is abundant rainfall.

Answers to Section 1 Assessment

1. **(a)** geography, p. 35 **(b)** GIS, p. 37 **(c)** absolute location, p. 39 **(d)** hemisphere, p. 39 **(e)** relative location, p. 39 **(f)** character of a place, p. 40 **(g)** perception, p. 41 **(h)** formal region, p. 41 **(i)** functional region, p. 41 **(j)** perceptual region, p. 41

2. Geographers use sonar, satellites, GPS, and GIS to gather information about the earth.

3. The five themes help geographers organize information about the world and its people.

4. **(a)** Location describes where a place is, in both absolute and relative terms. **(b)** Place identifies the unique combination of physical and human characteristics. **(c)** Region deals with the common characteristics of a group of places.

5. Possible answer: When people move to an area, they may change the environment by bringing in new plants, irrigating, and building roads and structures. Migration can strain an area's natural resources.

6. **(a)** to convey the precise location of a place **(b)** to plan a journey or determine how long it takes to get from one place to another

Activity Rubrics Share rubrics with students before they begin their concept webs and paragraphs.

Attempted The concept web and paragraph are incomplete, not providing enough detail about the five themes.

Minimal The concept web and paragraph are complete and show a general understanding of the five themes but do not provide enough detail.

Adequate The concept web shows good understanding of the five themes and provides sufficient detail. The paragraph is well organized and well written.

Exemplary The concept web and paragraph show thorough understanding of the five themes, and the paragraph provides a good description of the neighborhood in terms of the five themes.

Answer to Photo Caption

Possible answers: Positive: Dry regions can be transformed into farmland through irrigation. Negative: Bringing in plants from other regions may lead to the loss of native vegetation.

42 Chapter 1

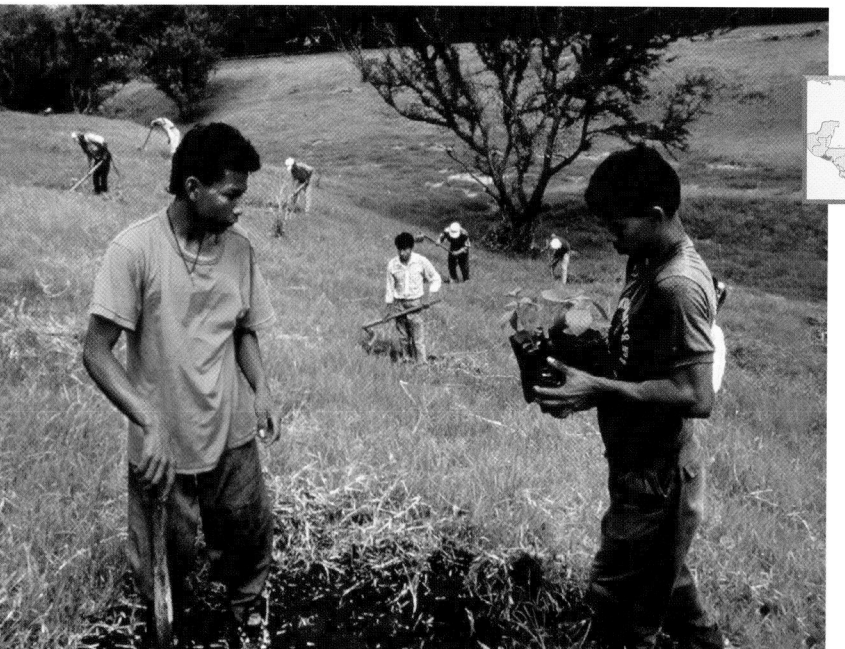

Reforestation

Environmental Change Workers plant saplings in a reforestation project in El Salvador.

Human-Environment Interaction *What types of positive and negative effects can people have on their environment?*

Human beings have made enormous changes in their environment. Some changes are intentional and others are accidental. Some changes are favorable and others are destructive. The American Southwest provides examples of positive and negative changes. Before the era of swimming pools, air conditioning, massive irrigation, and automobiles, this hot, dry region had few residents.

Today, the region's population and economy are among the fastest-growing in the country.

New growth also has brought new challenges, however. Plants and wildlife brought in from other areas have altered the region's ecosystems. Furthermore, the rapid growth in the region's population is putting a strain on the already limited supplies of water.

SECTION 1 ASSESSMENT

1. Key Terms Define **(a)** geography, **(b)** GIS, **(c)** absolute location, **(d)** hemisphere, **(e)** relative location, **(f)** character of a place, **(g)** perception, **(h)** formal region, **(i)** functional region, **(j)** perceptual region.

2. Geographic Tools How do geographers use technology to study the earth?

3. Geographic Tools Why do geographers use the five themes of geography?

4. Geographic Tools What can geographers learn from **(a)** location, **(b)** place, and **(c)** region?

5. Migration How can human movement affect the environment?

6. Critical Thinking Making Comparisons (a) When might absolute location be of interest to a geographer? **(b)** When might relative location be more useful?

Activity

Organizing Information Create a concept web that identifies characteristics of each of the five themes of geography. Write a brief paragraph that describes your neighborhood in terms of the five themes.

RESOURCE DIRECTORY

Teaching Resources
Unit 1, Chapter 1
• Section 1 Quiz, p. 3
• Critical Thinking, p. 9

Spanish Resources
• Section 1 Quiz, p. 4

Social Studies Skills Handbook
• Asking Questions While You Read, p. 70

Asking Questions

The ability to ask and answer questions is a very essential geographic skill. By asking questions, you can become an active thinker rather than a passive observer. As you become more practiced in this skill, you will be better able to understand geographic issues, identify geographic problems, and determine possible solutions.

Learn the Skill Study the chart below and the photograph on page 42. Then, follow the steps to learn some of the techniques involved in asking useful questions.

1 *Ask comprehension questions.* Questions such as those in the first column of the chart can help you to summarize or define basic information. **(a)** *What is one comprehension question you could ask about the photograph on page 42?* **(b)** *What word in your question signals that it is a comprehension question?*

2 *Think of analytical questions.* Sample analytical questions are in the second column of the chart. Unlike comprehension questions, analytical questions involve some higher-level critical thinking. You could ask, Why are these people planting trees? **(a)** *What other analytical question could you ask about the photograph on page 42?* **(b)** *What word or phrase in your question signals that it is analytical?*

3 *Pose questions that evaluate.* Examples of these questions are in the third column of the chart. With evaluation questions, you make judgments and form opinions. You also look for evidence to support your thinking. An evaluation question might be, Is planting trees beneficial to the environment? **(a)** *What other evaluation question could you ask about the photograph on page 42?* **(b)** *Write an answer to your question.*

4 *Form prediction questions.* These questions, such as those in the fourth column of the chart, usually involve the word *if*. They lead one to use information to make predictions. Each prediction takes the form of a hypothesis or theory about what might happen or what might have happened. An example of a prediction question is, If a drought occurs, how might the recently planted trees be affected? **(a)** *What is another prediction question you can ask about the photograph on page 42?* **(b)** *Write an answer to your question.* **(c)** *What key word signals a prediction question?*

Do It Yourself

Practice the Skill Select another photograph from this book or find an article about an environmental issue in a newspaper or newsmagazine. Carefully study the photograph or the news article. Then, write at least four questions about it. Include one or more questions from each of the following four categories: comprehension question; analysis question; evaluation question; and prediction question. Try to write an answer to each of your questions.

Apply the Skill See Chapter 1 Review and Assessment.

Four Kinds of Questions

Comprehension	Analysis	Evaluation	Prediction
• Who? • What? • Where? • When? • How much? • What are the examples?	• How? • Why? • What are the different points of view? • How does this compare with this or that? • What is the problem?	• Is it beneficial or harmful? • Is it ethical or not? • Is it logical or not? • What are some advantages and disadvantages? • What is the best solution?	• If this occurs, then what might happen? • If this does not occur, then what might happen? • If this had or had not happened, then what might be different? • If this solution is used, how might the outcome be affected?

Teaching the Skill

Ask students to formulate one or two questions based on information they would like to learn in their study of geography. Call on volunteers to write their questions on the chalkboard. Help students classify the questions according to the four kinds of questions explained in the chart on this page. Choose one or two questions and challenge students to formulate another kind of question on the same topic, perhaps at a higher level than the one on the chalkboard. Remind students that great discoveries can begin with good questions. Then work with students to complete the steps in the lesson.

Answers to Learn the Skill

1. (a) Possible answer: What are the men in the photograph doing? **(b)** what
2. (a) Possible answer: How will planting trees affect the environment? **(b)** How will it affect?
3. (a) Possible answer: What are some advantages and disadvantages of reforestation? **(b)** Answers will vary.
4. (a) Possible answer: If the trees are not replanted, what might happen? **(b)** Answers will vary. **(c)** if

Answer to Practice the Skill

Students' questions should reflect their pictures or articles. Students should write questions from each category.

Objectives

Upon completion of Section 2, students should be able to:

◆ explain how scientists classify the earth's major physical characteristics;

◆ describe the physical processes that affect the earth's crust;

◆ explain the theories that help scientists understand the earth's past.

National Geography Standards

The following National Geography Standards are highlighted in this section: 4, 7, 17

Bellringer

Write the words *earthquake* and *volcano* on the board. Ask: **Where do earthquakes and volcanoes occur?** Have students write their responses. Then have them verify their answers after reading Section 2.

LESSON PLAN

1. Focus Ask students: **Do you agree or disagree that the earth's landmasses are "solid ground"?** Have students share their ideas. Then point out that most scientists today believe that the continents are actually floating like giant rafts on the earth's surface.

2. Instruct Divide students into three groups and assign each group one of the following questions: (1) How do hills, mountains, and plateaus differ? (2) Why do earthquakes occur most frequently along plate boundaries? (3) How do plate movements create mountains? Have members of each group study the section to answer their assigned question. Then have the groups share answers to their questions.

3. Close/Reteach List the following geographic features on the board: Andes Mountains, Himalayas, Alps, Aleutian Islands, and Polynesia. Have students find each feature on the World Physical map in the Atlas. Then refer students to the map of plate boundaries on page 47 to explain which plate movement created each feature.

2 Changes Within the Earth

Reading Focus

- How do scientists classify the earth's major physical characteristics?
- What physical processes affect the earth's crust?
- What theories help scientists understand the earth's past?

Key Terms

core	biosphere
mantle	continent
crust	relief
lithosphere	plate tectonics
atmosphere	continental drift theory
hydrosphere	Ring of Fire

Main Idea Physical processes that originate within the earth shape the world on which we live.

Natural Hazards Volcanic eruptions betray the dynamic forces at work within the earth.

One of a geographer's biggest tasks is to understand the earth's constant changes. Earth is not a quiet planet. Earthquakes topple buildings and open up great cracks in the ground. Volcanoes erupt with red-hot lava and dangerous gases. Floods pour down from mountains after rainstorms. Many of the physical processes that shape the earth are spectacular, while others act gradually over very long periods of time.

Physical Characteristics

Geology—the study of the earth's physical structure and history—is a relatively new science. It deals, however, with very ancient history—that of the earth itself. This history, scientists now think, goes back about 4.6 billion years. Since it began, the earth has been changing. Geologists try to identify those changes, explain the causes and effects, and predict future changes.

The Earth's Layers Scientists have developed an idea of what the interior of the earth is like. The diagram on page 45 shows the earth's layers as geologists envision them.

The **core,** or center, of the earth consists of very hot metal, mainly iron mixed with some nickel. The inner core is thought to be dense and solid, whereas the metal of the outer core is molten, or liquid. Around the core is the **mantle,** a thick layer of rock. Scientists speculate that the mantle is about 1,800 miles (2,896 km) thick. Mantle rock is mostly solid, but some upper layers may be flexible.

The rocky surface layer, called the **crust,** is surprisingly thin, like frosting on a cake. The thinner parts of the crust, which are only about 5 miles (8 km) thick, are below the oceans. The crust beneath the continents is thicker and very uneven, averaging about 22 miles (35 km) in thickness. Natural forces interact with the earth's crust, creating the landforms, or natural features, found on the surface of the earth.

Land, Air, and Water Geographers often talk of the different elements of the earth's natural environment as a set of related "spheres" dominated by different physical forms. Soil,

RESOURCE DIRECTORY

Teaching Resources

Unit 1, Chapter 1
- Section 2 Guided Reading and Review, p. 4

Guide to the Essentials (English/Spanish)
- Section Summary, Chapter 1, Section 2

Mental Mapping booklet
- Unit 1 Checklist, p. 5

Social Studies Skills Handbook
- Drawing Conclusions, p. 52

Technology

Guided Reading Audiotapes (English/Spanish),
Chapter 1, Section 2

Section Reading Support Transparencies,
Chapter 1, Section 2

World Geography Map and Photo Transparencies
- Tectonic Plates

Book on CD, Chapter 1

Social Studies Skills Tutor CD-ROM

Companion Web site, www.phschool.com
- Chapter 1 Activities

rocks, landforms, and other surface features make up the **lithosphere.** The **atmosphere** is the layer of air, water, and other substances above the surface. The **hydrosphere** consists of water in oceans, lakes, and rivers, and even under the ground. The **biosphere** is the world of plants, animals, and other living things that occupy the land and waters of the planet. Physical geography studies the ways that these spheres operate and interact with each other and with people.

Photographs of the earth taken from space show clearly that it is truly a "watery planet." More than 70 percent of the earth's surface is covered by water, mainly the salt water of oceans and seas. The large landmasses in the oceans are the **continents.** Although some of these landforms are not completely separated by ocean waters, geographers define seven separate continents. Asia is the largest, Australia the smallest.

Landforms are commonly classified according to differences in **relief**—the difference in elevation between the highest and lowest points. Another important characteristic is whether they rise gradually or steeply.

The major types of landforms are mountains, hills, plateaus, and plains. Mountains have high relief, rising at least 2,000 feet (610 m) above the surrounding terrain. Hills are lower, rounded, and generally less steep than mountains. The elevation of the surrounding land determines whether a landform is called a mountain or a hill. For example, a mountain in the British Isles might be considered a hill in western Canada.

Plateaus and plains are also landforms. A plateau is also a raised area, but its surface is generally level. Some plateaus, however, have deep gulleys or canyons, making the surface seem rough rather than flat. A plain is a flat or gently rolling area where there are few changes in elevation.

Other landforms include valleys, canyons, and basins, as well as rivers, peninsulas, and islands. Many of the earth's landforms are shown on the diagram on page 46.

Physical Processes

When geologists or geographers look at an area they often ask, "What forces shaped the landforms here?" Landforms are shaped first by internal forces that originate in the earth's interior. One of these forces is volcanism, which involves

The Earth's Layers

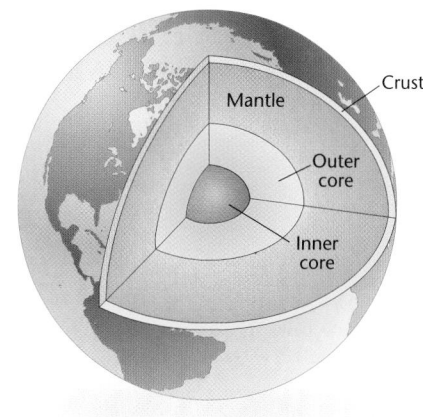

DIAGRAM SKILLS

● **Physical Characteristics** This diagram shows what geologists believe is the internal structure of the earth. Recent discoveries suggest that the inner core may be spinning at a different rate from the rest of the earth.
• *On what layer of the earth do people live?*

the movement of magma, or molten rock, inside the earth. Other major internal forces consist of movements that fold, lift, bend, or break the rock of the earth's crust.

Volcanoes Volcanoes form when magma breaks through the earth's crust. On the surface, the molten rock is called lava. When lava flows evenly, it produces a plateau-like shield volcano. Ash and cinders erupting from a break in the ground may produce another type of volcano: small cinder cones. Alternating sequences of explosive eruptions and smooth lava flows create distinctive cone-shaped mountains. One example of this type of volcano is Japan's Mount Fuji.

Movements in the Crust The movements that bend and break the earth's crust are varied and complex. When rock layers bend and buckle, the result is a fold. Other stresses on rocks cause faults, or breaks in the earth's crust. Whether rock layers fault or fold is determined by the hardness of the rock and the strength of

Tectonic This word is derived from the Latin word *tectonicus* and the Greek word *tektonikós,* which mean "pertaining to construction."

The Physical World

Earthquakes The magnitude (M) of earthquakes is measured on the Richter scale. Some major earthquakes in this century include San Francisco, California (1906) M7.8; Rat Island, Alaska (1965) M8.4; Tangshan, China (1976) M8.2; Mexico City, Mexico (1985) M8.1; Southern California (1991) M7.1; Manzanillo, Mexico (1995) M7.6; Kobe, Japan (1995) M6.9; Gujarat, India (2001) M7.7; El Salvador (2001) M7.6.

Daily Life

Earthquake Safety If you are indoors during an earthquake, the United States Geological Survey advises you to duck, cover, and hold: Duck under a table or another strong piece of furniture; cover your head; and hold on to the furniture, using it as a shield from falling debris.

the movement. Sometimes the rock on either side of a fault slips or moves suddenly. Rock on one side of a fault may move sideways, up, or down in relation to the rock on the other side of the fault. Slow movements along a fault will produce subtle, almost unnoticeable changes. A large, sudden movement along a fault can send out shock waves through the earth, causing an earthquake.

Understanding the Past

Most changes in the earth's surface take place so slowly that they are not immediately noticeable to the human eye. Geologists have reconstructed much of the earth's history from the record they read in the rocks. For many years scientists assumed that the oceans and continents had always stayed in the same positions. Today, however, most accept the idea that the earth's landmasses have broken apart, rejoined, and moved to other parts of the globe. This concept forms part of a theory that suggests answers to many puzzling questions about the earth's landforms.

Plate Tectonics According to this theory of **plate tectonics,** the earth's outer shell is not one solid sheet of rock. Instead, the lithosphere— the earth's crust and the brittle, upper layer of the mantle—is broken into a number of moving plates. The plates vary in size and thickness. The North American Plate stretches from the mid-Atlantic Ocean to the northern tip of Japan. The Cocos Plate covers a small area in the Pacific Ocean just west of Central America. These plates are not anchored in place, but slide over a hot and flexible layer of the mantle.

The earth's oceans and continents ride atop the plates as they move in different directions. The map on page 47 shows the boundaries of the different plates. It also shows the direction in which the plates are moving. The Pacific Plate and the Nazca Plate, for example, are moving apart. The Nazca Plate and the South American Plate, however, are moving toward each other. Most earthquakes, volcanoes, and other geologic events occur along plate boundaries.

Plate tectonic theory was built on earlier ideas and research. It began to be widely accepted in

Landforms and Water Bodies

DIAGRAM SKILLS

● **Physical Characteristics** The diagram shows many of the earth's most common landforms. Examine the landforms and their labels.
  • *How does a plateau differ from a plain?*

Answer to Diagram Skills

A plateau is at a higher elevation than a plain.

Tectonic Plate Boundaries

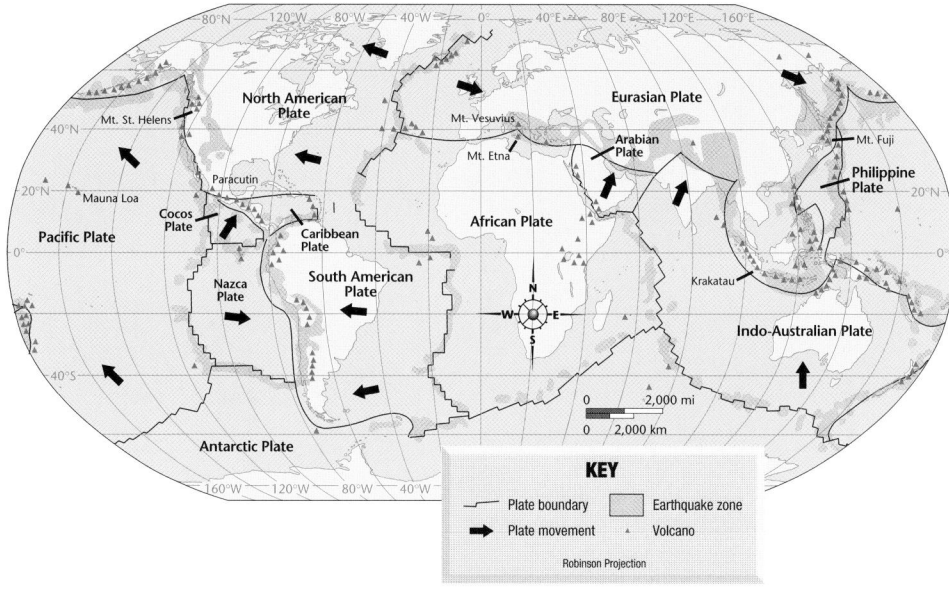

APPLYING THE GEOGRAPHIC THEMES

● **Movement** The world's continents and oceans ride atop moving tectonic plates.
- *In which directions are the Nazca and South American plates moving?*
- *What results would you expect from this movement?*

the 1960s, as scientists identified its connections with the theories of continental drift and seafloor spreading.

Continental Drift As early as the 1600s, people looking at maps noticed that several continents seemed to fit together like jigsaw puzzle pieces. Could they once have been joined as one gigantic landmass?

In the early 1900s a German explorer and scientist named Alfred Wegener suggested the **continental drift theory.** Wegener proposed that there was once a single "supercontinent." He called it Pangaea (pan JEE uh), from the Greek words *pan,* meaning "all," and *gaia,* personifying the earth. Wegener theorized that about 180 million years ago, Pangaea began to break up into separate continents.

To support his theory, Wegener found evidence that showed that fossils—the preserved remains of ancient animals and plants—from South America, Africa, India, and Australia were almost identical. The rocks containing the fossils were also much alike. Still, many scientists remained unconvinced by these arguments.

Seafloor Spreading The other theory supporting plate tectonics emerged from study of the ocean floor. Using sonar, scientists began to map the floor of the Atlantic Ocean and found that the ocean floor was not flat. The landforms under water closely resembled continental landforms, including rugged mountains, deep canyons, and wide plains. Scientists were surprised to find that rocks taken from the ocean floor were much younger than those found on the continents. The youngest rocks of all were those nearest the underwater ridge system—a series of underwater mountains that extend around the world, stretching more than 40,000 miles (64,000 km).

Articles From
NATIONAL GEOGRAPHIC

The following article may be used to extend the content in this section.

Stager, Curt, and Chris Johns, photographer. "Africa's Great Rift." *National Geographic,* Vol. 177, No. 5 (May 1990), pp. 2–41.

East Africa's Great Rift Valley illustrates the theory of plate tectonics.

Science Use the following experiment to help students understand the process of *convection,* or the circular movement created by heating a material.

Boil water in a clear, unbreakable container. Cover the container for a few minutes after the water comes to a boil. Then, using a potholder, lift the lid and have students observe how the liquid moves upward from the bottom. Point out that water vapor collects in the lid, cools, and forms droplets that fall back into the water. Instruct students to diagram the process in their notebooks—heated water rising, cooling at the top, and falling downward. Then point out that convection is constantly happening within the earth. Refer to the diagram of the earth's layers on page 45. Explain that the earth's core and parts of the mantle are very hot. Heat makes the mantle rock expand, melt, and push upward. The force is so strong that it moves the plates that make up the earth's crust.

Pangaea and the Drifting Continents

Pangaea 200 million years ago

135 million years ago

65 million years ago

The world today

Mollweide Projection

APPLYING THE GEOGRAPHIC THEMES

● **Place** Scientists theorize that the earth once supported a single "supercontinent," which they have named Pangaea.
• *Between which years did South America break away from Africa?*
• *What two giant landmasses do scientists believe existed 135 million years ago?*

The explanation first suggested in the 1960s is the theory of seafloor spreading. According to this theory, molten rock from the mantle rises beneath the underwater ridge and breaks through a split, called a rift valley, at the top of the ridge. The rock then spreads out in both directions from the ridge as if it were on two huge conveyor belts. As the seafloor moves away from the ridge, it carries older rocks away. Seafloor spreading, along with the older theory of continental drift, became part of the theory of plate tectonics.

Plate Movement One reason that people in the 1920s doubted the continental drift theory was the question of just *how* the continents moved. What force is powerful enough to send gigantic plates sliding around the earth?

Today, most scientists believe this force is a process called convection. Convection is a circular movement caused when a material is heated, expands and rises, then cools and falls. This process is thought to be occurring in the mantle rock beneath the plates. The heat energy that drives convection probably comes from the slow decay of materials under the crust.

When Plates Meet As mentioned earlier, the places where plates meet are some of the most restless parts of the earth. Plates can spread apart, crash into each other, or slide past each other.

When plates pull away from each other—a process known as spreading—they form a diverging plate boundary, or spreading zone. Such areas are likely to have a rift valley, earthquakes, and volcanic action.

Answers to Map Caption

between 135 million and 65 million years ago

Laurasia and Gondwana

What happens when plates meet depends on the densities of the colliding plates. Oceanic plates are denser than continental plates. When an oceanic plate meets a continental plate, it slides beneath the lighter plate down toward the mantle. This process is known as subduction. As it sinks, the oceanic rock melts. Much of this molten material will cool beneath the surface, but some will erupt back to the surface in the form of volcanoes. The Cascade Range of the northwestern United States and the Andes of western South America are examples of mountains formed in this way.

In a similar manner, when two oceanic plates collide, the denser plate will slide beneath the other, and an arc of volcanic islands may form along the plate boundary. But, when two continental plates collide, neither will sink. The collision, called convergence, will be slow but violent. The buckling, folding, and faulting of rocks pressed against each other will produce spectacular mountain ranges. The world's tallest range, the Himalayas, emerged when the Indo-Australian Plate began to slam into the Eurasian Plate. Even today, the Indo-Australian Plate continues to push against the Eurasian Plate at a rate of about 2 inches (5 cm) a year.

Finally, instead of pulling away from each other or colliding with each other, plates sometimes slip or grind past each other along faults. This process is known as faulting. The San Andreas Fault in California is a well-known example of faulting.

Explaining Volcanoes Plate tectonic theory attempts to explain many of the processes affecting the earth, such as volcanic eruptions. Most eruptions occur along plate boundaries. The **Ring of Fire** is a circle of volcanoes surrounding the Pacific Ocean. The ring includes the Cascades in North America, the islands of Japan and Indonesia, and the Andes in South America. Locate the Ring of Fire on the map on page 47.

Plate tectonic theory also attempts to explain how volcanic island arcs, or chains of islands, are

Plate Movement

Natural Hazards California's San Andreas Fault lies on the boundary of the North American Plate and the Pacific Plate (see the map on page 47). The fault, which is over 750 miles (1,210 km) long, frequently plagues California with earthquakes.

Movement *What types of movement take place at plate boundaries?*

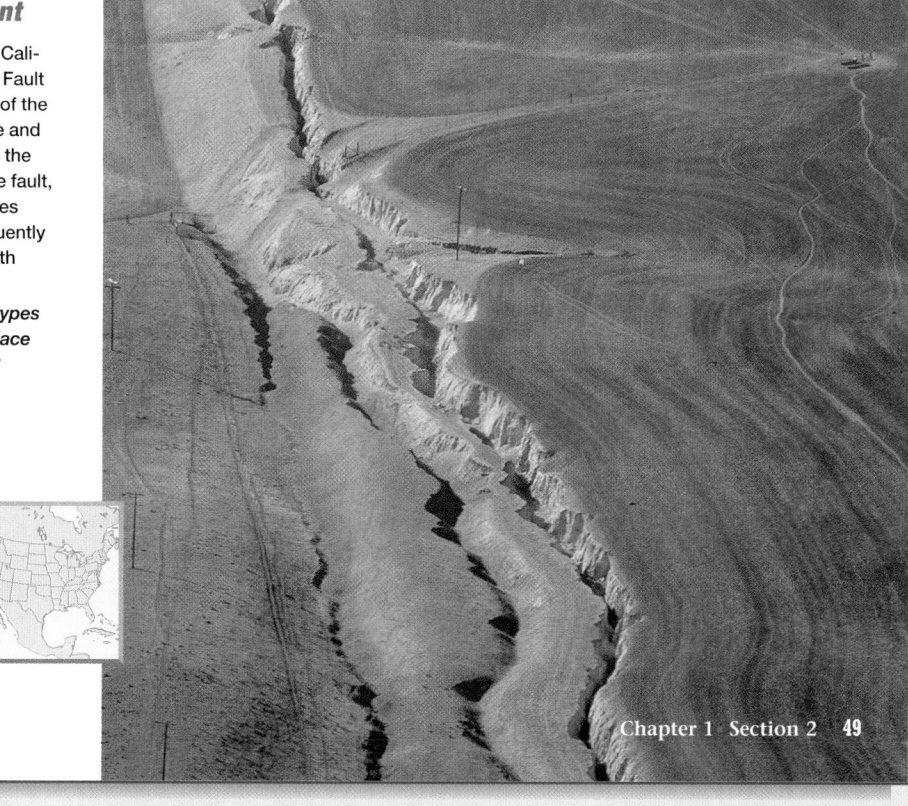

The Physical World

Mauna Loa The world's largest volcano—Mauna Loa—is located in Hawaii. It is about 56,000 feet (17 km) high. However, because its base is underwater, only about 13,000 feet (4 km) of the volcano are visible above sea level.

Geography on Video

The Creation of the Universe
(PBS Home Video, Northstar Productions, 1985) provides a context for the study of the earth by inquiring into the existence of the universe itself. Einstein's unified theory continues to inspire scientists to examine everything from the smallest subatomic particles in our bodies to galaxies billions of light-years away. Clues to the possible origins of the universe are presented in terms of modern physics and astronomy. A film that raises more questions than it answers, it also clearly presents an explanation of modern physics.

Alternative Assessment

Mid-Point Monitoring

Participating in a Classroom Discussion You may wish to monitor students' progress on preparing for the classroom discussion. Confer with students to see if they are taking notes to support their ideas about the interactions of people and the earth's forces.

Answer to Diagram Skills

a subduction zone

Major Types of Plate Movement

Subduction

Spreading

Converging

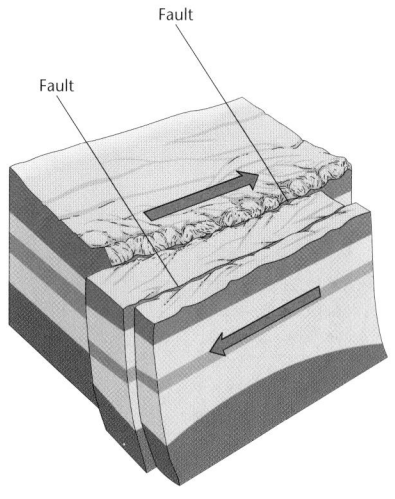

Faulting

DIAGRAM SKILLS

● **Physical Processes** In a subduction zone, one plate slides or dives under another. In a spreading zone, two plates move apart from each other, creating a rift in the earth's crust. In a converging zone, two plates collide and push slowly against each other. At a fault, plates grind or slide past each other, rather than collide.
  • ***Which type of plate boundary occurs when an oceanic plate meets a continental plate?***

RESOURCE DIRECTORY

Teaching Resources
Unit 1, Chapter 1
• Section 2 Quiz, p. 5
Spanish Resources
• Section 2 Quiz, p. 5

Geysers

Physical Characteristics Hot rocks heat springs deep within the earth. Steam pressure then forces the remaining water upward. Such violent eruptions of water and steam are called geysers. Old Faithful, in Yellowstone National Park, erupts at an average rate of once every 73 minutes.

Place *How are geysers similar to volcanoes?*

formed far away from plate boundaries. "Hot spots" are hot regions deep within the earth's mantle. Columns of magma rise from these regions toward the earth's surface. As the molten rock rises from a hot spot, the magma may heat underground water and produce hot springs or geysers. Some of the world's most famous geysers can be found in Iceland or in Yellowstone National Park in the United States. However, if molten rock flows out of a crack in the earth's surface, it may produce a volcanic island chain as the plate drifts over a stationary hot spot. The easterly island of Hawaii is part of an island arc that formed in the center of a plate. Hawaii, which is currently over a hot spot, is constantly erupting. Other islands to the west have remained dormant since the moving Pacific Plate shifted them away from the hot spot.

SECTION 2 ASSESSMENT

1. **Key Terms** Define **(a)** core, **(b)** mantle, **(c)** crust, **(d)** lithosphere, **(e)** atmosphere, **(f)** hydrosphere, **(g)** biosphere, **(h)** continent, **(i)** relief, **(j)** plate tectonics, **(k)** continental drift theory, **(l)** Ring of Fire.

2. **Physical Characteristics** Describe the internal and external structures of the earth.

3. **Physical Processes** How do forces inside the earth affect its surface?

4. **Understanding the Past** Explain how the theories of continental drift and seafloor spreading support the theory of plate tectonics.

5. **Critical Thinking Drawing Conclusions** Over time, how might forces within the earth affect the environment on the surface?

Activity
Creating a Model Study the map on page 47. Using cardboard for oceanic plates and aluminum foil for continental plates, create a three-dimensional model based on the map. Choose three plate boundaries and demonstrate the outcome of collisions between plates. Be sure that your demonstration shows both subduction and convergence.

CUSTOMIZE FOR...

Students Acquiring English/ESL

Picture Clues Have students create picture clues for each of the key terms listed in the Section Preview. Then have them work in teams to identify and define terms based on the clues.

Answers to Section 2 Assessment

1. **(a)** core, p. 44 **(b)** mantle, p. 44 **(c)** crust, p. 44 **(d)** lithosphere, p. 45 **(e)** atmosphere, p. 45 **(f)** hydrosphere, p. 45 **(g)** biosphere, p. 45 **(h)** continent, p. 45 **(i)** relief, p. 45 **(j)** plate tectonics, p. 46 **(k)** continental drift theory, p. 47 **(l)** Ring of Fire, p. 49

2. The inner core is solid hot metal, while the outer core is molten. Around the core is the mantle, a thick layer of rock. Surrounding this is the rocky surface layer called the crust.

3. Magma can cause volcanic eruptions, and stresses can fold, fault, or fracture rock.

4. Continental drift suggested that the plates had been arranged differently in the past, and seafloor spreading demonstrated how convection could move plates.

5. Possible answer: Island groups or mountain ranges may form where plates meet.

Activity Rubrics Share rubrics with students before they create their models.

Attempted Materials gathered but demonstration fails to show understanding of plate tectonics.

Minimal The model is complete but does not adequately show subduction and convergence.

Adequate The model is complete and shows student understanding of subduction and convergence.

Exemplary The model skillfully presents the concepts of plate tectonics and shows a complete understanding of subduction and convergence.

Answer to Photo Caption

In both cases the thermal energy within the earth forces liquid to burst through the surface of the earth.

Section 3 *pp. 52–57*

Objectives
Upon completion of Section 3, students should be able to:

◆ explain how mechanical and chemical weathering affect a place's physical landscape;

◆ describe how the physical process of erosion alters the landscape.

 National Geography Standards
The following National Geography Standards are highlighted in this section: 1, 4, 7, 15

 Bellringer
Display pictures or write descriptions on the chalkboard of the following examples of weathering: a cracked sidewalk, an old tombstone or statue, and an old barn or other wooden structure. Have students describe how these things might have looked when they were new. Ask: **What changed their appearance?** (effects of wind, rain, ice, pollution)

····························

LESSON PLAN

1. Focus Show students a photograph of the Grand Canyon and point out its location on a map. Ask: **What created the Grand Canyon?** (erosion by the Colorado River) Explain that Section 3 will describe how natural forces change the landscape.

2. Instruct Begin a chart on the board with the following column headings: *Mechanical Weathering, Chemical Weathering, Water Erosion, Wind Erosion, Glacial Erosion.* Under each heading, have students write a simple definition of the process and give an example of the results of the process.

3. Close/Reteach Challenge students to explain how landforms are created. Elicit that landforms are first created by internal processes and then changed and transformed by external processes of weathering and erosion. Students might work in small groups to illustrate the creation and transformation of a landform.

---

3 Changes on the Earth's Surface

Reading Focus
• **What are the lasting effects of the two kinds of weathering—mechanical and chemical—on the physical landscape of a place?**
• **How do the three most common causes of erosion—water, wind, and glaciers—alter the physical landscape of a place?**

Key Terms

weathering	sediment
mechanical weathering	loess
chemical weathering	glacier
acid rain	moraine
erosion	

Main Idea The surface forces of weathering and erosion affect the earth's appearance.

Physical Processes Weathering and erosion have sculpted portions of the earth.

Mixed in the soil of the Hawaiian Islands is a crumbly, gray clay that is older than the islands themselves. For years scientists wondered how this soil had formed. Now they think that the clay comes from a desert in far-off China. Blown across thousands of miles of ocean by the wind, the soil was deposited on the islands by centuries of rainstorms. This process is still going on today. World Watch Institute Chairman of the Board Lester Brown explains:

> ❝So much soil from the Asian mainland blows over the Pacific Ocean that scientists taking air samples at the Mauna Loa observatory in Hawaii can now tell when spring plowing starts in North China.❞

Wind is only one of several external agents that change the earth's surface. These forces, which can act over thousands or even millions of years, are usually grouped into two broad categories: weathering and erosion.

Weathering

Weathering is the breakdown of rock at or near the earth's surface into smaller and smaller pieces. Over millions of years, weathering can reduce a mountain to gravel. There are two kinds of weathering: mechanical and chemical.

Mechanical Weathering The process of **mechanical weathering** occurs when rock is actually broken or weakened physically. Mechanical weathering breaks large masses of rock into ever smaller pieces, producing boulders, stones, pebbles, sand, silt, and dust. Mechanical weathering is one of the primary processes involved in soil-building.

The most common type of mechanical weathering takes place when water freezes to ice in a crack in the rock. Because water expands when it freezes, the ice widens the crack and eventually splits the rock. This process is known as frost wedging.

Frost wedging is most likely to occur in areas where the freezing is both frequent and intense.

RESOURCE DIRECTORY

Teaching Resources
Unit 1, Chapter 1
• Section 3 Guided Reading and Review, p. 6
Guide to the Essentials (English/Spanish)
• Section Summary, Chapter 1, Section 3
Mental Mapping booklet
• Unit 1 Checklist, p. 5
Simulations, Games, and Lab Activities
• Exploring Local Geography, Environmental Problems, p. 4

Technology
Guided Reading Audiotapes (English/Spanish), Chapter 1, Section 3
Section Reading Support Transparencies, Chapter 1, Section 3
Book on CD, Chapter 1
Social Studies Skills Tutor CD-ROM
Companion Web site, www.phschool.com
• Chapter 1 Activities

Over time it can even cause huge parts of a mountainside to break and fall away.

Another kind of mechanical weathering occurs when seeds take root in cracks in rocks. In the same way as sidewalks crack when tree roots grow beneath them, a rock will split as plants or trees grow within a fracture.

Chemical Weathering While mechanical weathering can destroy rock, it changes only the physical structure, not the original crystals or minerals that make up the rock. It leaves the chemical structure unchanged. One important effect of mechanical weathering is to expose bedrock to the forces of **chemical weathering.** The process of chemical weathering alters a rock's chemical makeup by changing the minerals that form the rock or combining them with new chemical elements. Unlike mechanical weathering, chemical weathering can change one kind of rock into a completely different kind.

The most important factors in chemical weathering are water and carbon dioxide. Carbon dioxide from the air or soil combines with water to make a weak solution of carbonic acid. When the acidic water seeps into cracks in certain types of rock, such as limestone, it can dissolve the rock. Many caves were formed in this way.

Moisture is an important element in chemical weathering. In a damp or wet area, chemical weathering occurs quickly and is widespread. Chemical weathering is also more likely to occur under high temperature conditions than in cooler regions. In tropical rain forests, where the chemical properties of soil materials change rapidly, valuable minerals may be lost through a process called leaching, leaving the soils with very low fertility.

Another type of chemical weathering is **acid rain.** Chemicals in the polluted air combine with water vapor and fall back to earth as acid rain. Acid rain not only destroys forests and pollutes water, but also eats away the surfaces of stone buildings and natural rock formations. Industrial pollution, acid-producing agents from the ocean, and volcanic activity are among the known causes of acid rain.

Observing Weathering The effects of weathering can be seen on almost any old stone structure. Weathering blurs the lettering on old tombstones, softens the sharp features on carved

Chemical Weathering

Physical Processes Chemical weathering has contributed to the bedraggled look of this stone traveler.
Human-Environment Interaction *What impact has human activity had on acid rain?*

stone statues, and breaks down the mortar that holds together stone or brick walls.

Weathering changes natural landforms, too. Over millions of years, mountains can be worn from jagged peaks to rounded hills. In an area where temperature changes cause frost wedging, the south side of a mountain in the Northern Hemisphere is likely to be more rugged than the north slope. Because the south side receives

Vocabulary

Weathering and Erosion Refer to the Key Terms list on page 52. Have students look up the definitions of *weathering* and *erosion*. Ask: **How do these processes differ?** (Weathering splits or chemically changes rock; erosion grinds and moves it to other places.)

BACKGROUND

Word Origin

Erosion The term *erosion* comes from the Latin *rodere,* which means "to gnaw away." The word *rodent* has the same Latin origin.

BACKGROUND

Word Origin

Canyon The word *canyon* is from a Spanish word meaning "hollow tube." Canyons form some of the most beautiful scenery in the world.

TEST PREPARATION

Have students read the subsection Chemical Weathering on this page to answer the following question.
Which would show the least evidence of chemical weathering?
  A Mountain
  B Rain forest
  Ⓒ Beach
  D Cave

Answer to Photo Caption

Industrial pollution is one cause of acid rain.

ACTIVITY

Reteach

Water Erosion In a wash basin, mound a few handfuls of sand into a miniature hill. Then pour a steady stream of water down the slope. Ask students to describe the effects. (The water formed a gully in the sand; the sand built up into a mound at the bottom.) (Bodily/Kinesthetic)

BACKGROUND

The Global Economy

Niagara Falls About 12,000 years ago, melting ice caused Lake Erie to overflow and form the Niagara River. Over the centuries, the river cut through a high cliff and formed Niagara Falls. During the 1800s, many hotels were built on both sides of the falls, which are located on the border between the United States and Canada. This popular tourist attraction is now visited by about 12 million people every year.

Water Erosion

Natural Hazards Water can make dramatic changes to the earth's surface. Some changes, such as the creation of canyons, are made slowly over time. Other changes are more immediately felt. Water overflowing the Mississippi River can flood homes and farms located on the flood plain. **Movement** *What do river waters carry?*

more sunlight, water in the cracks of rocks thaws and freezes more often than on the cold north side. As a result, rocks on the southern slope are more likely to split and fall away, making the mountainside uneven.

Erosion

Erosion is the movement of weathered materials such as gravel, soil, and sand. The three most common causes of erosion are water, wind, and glaciers.

Erosion is an important part of the cycle that has made and kept the earth a place where living things can survive. Without this process, the earth's surface would be barren rock, with no soil where plants can grow. Erosion is actually a significant agent in mechanical weathering and soil-building. The erosive forces that caused the "weathering away" that created Niagara Falls and the Grand Canyon, for example, are all part of mechanical weathering.

Water The largest canyons and the deepest valleys on the earth were created in part by moving water. Moving water—rain, rivers, streams, and oceans—is the greatest cause of erosion. Over time, water can cut into even the hardest rock and wear it away.

It is not water alone that carves out valleys and canyons. Water moving swiftly down a streambed carries **sediment**—small particles of soil, sand, and gravel. Like sandpaper, the sediment helps grind away the surface of rocks along the stream's path.

The rocks and soil carried away by water are eventually deposited somewhere else. When the stream or river slows down, sediment settles out of the water and lands on the banks or streambed, creating new kinds of landforms. A broad flood plain, or alluvial plain, may form on either side of the river, or a delta may form. A delta is a flat, low-lying plain that is sometimes formed at the mouth of a river—the place where the river enters a lake, a larger river, or an ocean.

The Mississippi River, for example, carries an estimated 159 million tons (144 million metric tons) of sediment a year. The river deposits some of this rich sand, silt, gravel, and clay along its flood plain, which is as much as 80 miles (129 km) wide in some places. The rest of the sediment builds up in the delta where the river empties into the Gulf of Mexico.

Rivers and streams play the largest role in water erosion. But crashing ocean surf or the gentler waves along a lakeshore can also erode beach cliffs, carve steep bluffs, and pile up sand dunes. As bluffs are undercut by the force of water, rocks tumble down cliffs into the water. Continuing erosion wears rocks into sandy beaches, then carries the sand farther down the shoreline.

Ocean waves may move sand away from the shore. For example, the barrier islands off the coast of North Carolina, known as the Outer Banks, have been slowly eroding due to wave action. The Cape Hatteras Lighthouse, built in 1870 on the Outer Banks, once stood over 1,500 feet (457 m) from the ocean. Erosion brought the shore to within 100 feet (30 m) of the lighthouse. In 1999, the lighthouse was moved to a point 3,000 feet (914 m) from the shore.

Wind Wind is a second major cause of erosion, especially in areas with little water and few plants to hold the soil in place. In the 1930s wind erosion devastated the Great Plains in the central United States. As the population grew, farmers plowed under more farmland. More land was stripped of its plant life and was exposed to the wind. The upper layers of soil that are usually rich in minerals and nutrients were dry from a long drought. As a result, the wind picked up and carried away the soil in great dust storms. As their

farms' fertile soil blew away, several states became part of what was called a "dust bowl." Writer George Greenfield described it in this way:

> **❝** In this country there is now no life for miles upon miles; no human beings, no birds, no animals. Only a dull brown land with cracks showing. Hills furrowed with eroded gullies—you have seen pictures like that in ruins of lost civilizations. **❞**

On the other hand, the windblown deposits of mineral-rich dust and silt called **loess** (Lō es) have benefited farmers in China, the American Midwest, and other parts of the world. Loess is valued in part because it is extremely porous. This allows it to absorb and hold on to great amounts of water. Because its particles are so fine, loess may be blown thousands of miles.

Sandstorms, or windblown sand, are major causes of erosion, especially near deserts. Just as sandblasting cleans stone buildings, windblown sand carves or smoothes the surfaces of both rock formations and objects made by humans.

Sand and dust carried by the wind are eventually deposited when the wind dies down. The cumulative effects of windblown sand can be seen both in the desert and along ocean shores in the form of sand dunes, loose windblown sand heaped into a mound or a low hill. Winds

Wind Erosion

Environmental Change Strong winds have caused sands to drift like snow, nearly burying this Texas farm.

Human-Environment Interaction *How has human activity contributed to erosion?*

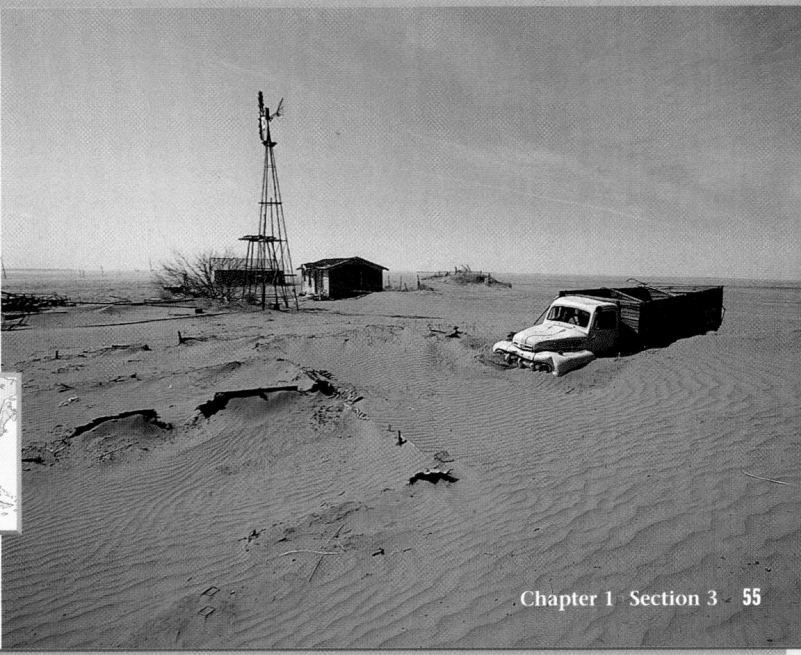

Chapter 1 Section 3 **55**

Glaciers and Erosion

Physical Processes Columbia Glacier in the Canadian Rocky Mountains is an example of an alpine glacier. Alpine glaciers form on mountainsides and move downhill by the force of gravity.

Place *How do glaciers alter the landscape?*

may move shifting dunes so far that they bury any vegetation or human settlements in their path. Grasses that take root in ocean dunes help prevent further wind erosion. Human development along the shoreline has contributed to beach erosion. When natural vegetation barriers are removed for construction, wind erosion occurs at a faster pace.

Glaciers Another major agent of erosion is **glaciers**—huge, slow-moving sheets of ice. They form over many years as layers of unmelted snow are pressed together, thaw slightly, and then turn to ice. As glaciers move, they carry dirt, rocks, and boulders. The terrain is worn away by the rock debris dragged along with the moving ice.

When the earth was cooler than it is today, much of the planet's water became locked up in immense glaciers that covered up to a third of the earth's surface. Over thousands of years the glaciers melted back, then grew again when the earth became colder. Long periods of these colder temperatures are known as Ice Ages. Geologists believe that there have been at least four Ice Ages in the past 600 million years, the last of which peaked about 18,000 years ago.

If you live in the northern part of the United States you might see the effects of Ice Age glaciers.

Like giant bulldozers, glaciers scooped out the basins of the Great Lakes, as well as thousands of smaller lakes elsewhere in the United States and Canada. When glaciers melted and receded in some places, they left behind ridgelike piles of rocks and debris called **moraines** (muh RAYNS). In some places, moraines acted like dams, blocking valleys and creating areas where water collected into lakes. In other cases glacial debris formed long ridges of land. Long Island in New York is one such example of a moraine.

The glaciers of the Ice Ages were mainly continental glaciers, or ice sheets. Today such broad, flat glaciers exist in only a few places in the world. They cover about 80 percent of Greenland and most of the continent of Antarctica. The Greenland glacier is estimated to be 9,900 feet (3,018 m) thick. The front of the glacier usually moves forward a few feet each winter and then recedes during the summer. Great chunks of continental glaciers frequently break off from the edges of the ice sheets to produce floating icebergs.

Valley or alpine glaciers, on the other hand, are found throughout the world in high mountain valleys where the climate is not warm enough for the ice to melt. In North America, valley glaciers snake through the Rocky and Cascade mountains, the Sierra Nevada, and the Alaskan ranges.

Although glaciers are sometimes described as "rivers of ice," they do not move and flow quickly like water. Glaciers slide forward because of their great weight. The entire mass does not move at once; rather it oozes outward down-valley from the top of an alpine glacier. Large valley glaciers in Europe may move nearly 600 feet (183 m) in a year. Glacial landscapes are distinctly different from landscapes formed by water. While rivers cut sharp-sided, V-shaped valleys, glaciers carve out valleys that are rounded and U-shaped. The amount of erosion that occurs when a glacier passes by varies. It depends partly on the size and speed of the glacier and partly on the terrain and texture of bedrock being covered. On flat land, glacial erosion is relatively minor, whereas in mountainous areas the erosion can be significant.

SECTION 3 ASSESSMENT

1. **Key Terms** Define (a) weathering,
   (b) mechanical weathering, (c) chemical
   weathering, (d) acid rain, (e) erosion,
   (f) sediment, (g) loess, (h) glacier, (i) moraine.

2. **Physical Characteristics** Demonstrate how
   the physical landscape can be changed by
   (a) mechanical weathering, (b) chemical
   weathering.

3. **Physical Processes** How can the physical
   processes of erosion—water, wind, and glaciers—
   affect the landscape?

4. **Critical Thinking** **Applying Information**
   How might erosion affect homes built along a
   seacoast?

Activity

Take It to the NET

Writing a Summary Visit the World Geography section of **www.phschool.com** to learn
more about recent developments involving glaciers. Choose one news story and write a one-
paragraph summary. Illustrate your summary
with a world map indicating the location of the
glacier you have chosen.

Articles From
NATIONAL GEOGRAPHIC

The following article may be used to extend
the content in this section.

> Carster, Peter, photographer. "Into the Heart
> of Glaciers." *National Geographic,* Vol. 189,
> No. 2 (Feb. 1996), pp. 70–81.

Glacial caves offer explorers a new experience
with each visit.

Creating a Chapter Summary

As a reteaching opportunity, pair a more able student with a less able student to complete this chapter summary.

Possible answers: Internal forces—
Volcanoes, Movements in the crust causing earthquakes and seafloor spreading **External forces—**
Weathering, Mechanical weathering, Chemical weathering, Erosion, Water, Wind, Glaciers.

Reviewing Key Terms

1–10. Students' sentences should demonstrate a clear understanding of the key terms.

Understanding Key Ideas

11. sonar, satellites, global positioning system, geographic information system

12. Physical characteristics include landforms, ecosystems, and climate. Human characteristics include type of economy, government, language, customs, and beliefs.

13. volcanoes and movements in the earth's crust

14. Several continents seem to fit together like jigsaw puzzle pieces. Also, some fossils from South America, Africa, India, and Australia have been found to be almost identical.

15. Mechanical weathering breaks apart rock; chemical weathering alters a rock's chemical makeup by changing the minerals that form the rock.

16. water, wind, and glaciers

Critical Thinking and Writing

17. Possible answer: Information about population patterns and urban growth would be useful in determining the best location for the road; information about elevation, terrain, and vegetation would be helpful in the actual construction of the road.

18. Possible answer: Texas is part of the United States, as well as its own political region governed by state laws. Some perceive it as a southern state, others as a western state. It is also generally thought of as part of the Sunbelt.

Creating a Chapter Summary

Copy this concept web on a piece of paper. Add supporting details about the internal and external forces that affect the earth's geology. Some entries have been filled in to serve as examples.

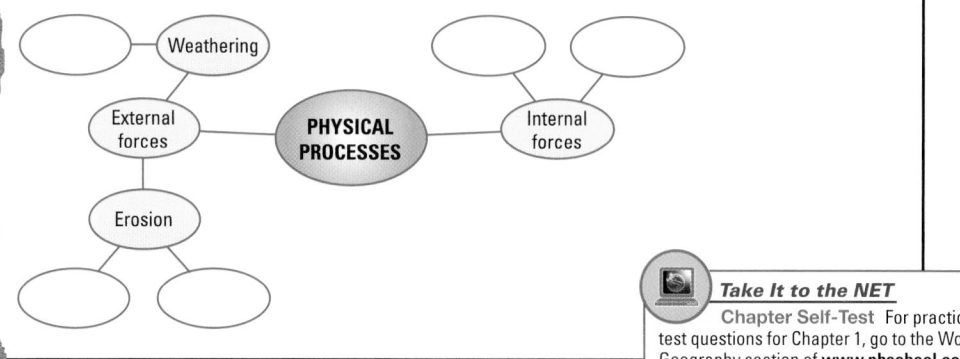

Take It to the NET
Chapter Self-Test For practice test questions for Chapter 1, go to the World Geography section of **www.phschool.com**.

Reviewing Key Terms

Write sentences using the key terms listed below, leaving blanks where the key terms would go. Exchange your sentences with those of another student and fill in the blanks in each other's sentences.

1. geography   **6.** atmosphere

2. hemisphere   **7.** continent

3. formal region   **8.** plate tectonics

4. core   **9.** erosion

5. lithosphere   **10.** glacier

Understanding Key Ideas

11. Science and Technology What recent technological advances have helped geographers study the earth?

12. Geographic Tools What kinds of physical and human characteristics do geographers use to describe a place?

13. Physical Processes What two internal forces shape the earth's landforms?

14. Understanding the Past What evidence suggests that there was once a single "supercontinent"?

15. Physical Processes How does chemical weathering differ in nature from mechanical weathering?

16. Physical Processes What are the three most common causes of erosion?

Critical Thinking and Writing

17. Making Decisions Suppose that you were planning to build a new road. What type of geographic information would you need, and how would you use it?

18. Identifying Relationships How can the state of Texas be considered to be part of more than one region?

19. Asking Geographic Questions When planning a trip, which do you think is more important, absolute location or relative location? Explain.

20. Recognizing Points of View In the 1930s, why did some people refer to the Great Plains as a "dust bowl"?

19. relative location, to determine how to get from one place to another

20. Plowing by farmers had destroyed the grasses that once held the soil in place. Exposed to the wind and dry conditions from a long drought, the upper layers of soil were blown away in great dust storms.

Applying Skills

Asking Questions Refer to the chart of questions on page 43 and to the photograph on page 53 to answer these questions:

21. When is it appropriate to ask a comprehension question?

22. How do analytical questions differ from questions that evaluate?

23. What is one prediction question you could ask about the photograph on page 53?

Reading a Diagram Study the diagram below, and answer the following questions:

24. How many layers of the earth are shown in this diagram?

25. Which layer contains continents and other landforms?

26. Would you expect the mantle to be hotter or cooler than the inner and outer cores? Explain your reasoning.

27. Would movement of the cores be considered an interior or exterior force?

The Earth's Layers

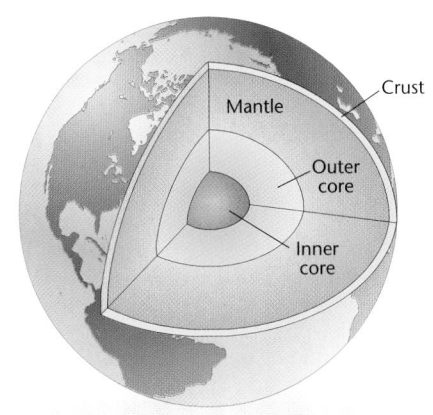

Crust
Mantle
Outer core
Inner core

Test Preparation

Read each question and choose the best answer.

28. Large land masses in the oceans are called —

A sediments

B continents

C loess

D glaciers

29. The Ring of Fire is a series of volcanoes surrounding the —

F Indo-Australian Plate

G Equator

H Pacific Ocean

J Mississippi River

Activities

MENTAL MAPPING

Review a world map that contains lines of longitude and latitude. On a separate piece of paper, create a sketch map of the world from memory. Draw and label the following places on your map:

- Equator
- Prime Meridian
- Northern Hemisphere
- Southern Hemisphere
- Tropic of Cancer
- Tropic of Capricorn

Take It to the NET

Making a Map Explore Web sites that focus on natural hazards such as earthquakes, tornadoes, and hurricanes. Create a map that identifies and locates the occurrences of these hazards in the United States over the past five years, and list safety precautions for each hazard. Visit the World Geography section of **www.phschool.com** for help in completing this activity.

Applying Skills

21. when one wishes to summarize or define basic information

22. Analytical questions involve higher-level critical thinking; evaluation questions involve making judgments and forming opinions.

23. Possible answer: If chemical weathering continues, what will become of this statue?

24. four

25. crust

26. cooler; the mantle gets its heat from the inner and outer cores.

27. interior

Test Preparation

28. B

29. H

Activities

Mental Mapping
Review students' maps and lines of latitude and longitude for accuracy.

Take It to the Net
Students' work should reflect sound research. Check students' work for accurate information about natural hazards and safety.

MENTAL MAPPING

Games for Review See pages 58–63 of the Simulations, Games, and Lab Activities booklet for games to review place names in preparation for the Chapter 1 Map Test.

Chapter Map Test Students should use their completed outline map and the Unit 1 Checklist in their Atlas Portfolios to prepare for the Chapter 1 Map Test. Point out to students that the test will cover Part I of the Unit 1 Checklist, Continents, Oceans, and Seas.

Alternative Assessment

Final Evaluation
Participating in a Classroom Discussion
Use the Classroom Discussion Evaluation Form on page 23 of the Alternative Assessment booklet in the Prentice Hall Assessment System to evaluate students' participation. Either teachers or students can complete the form to indicate which level of work was achieved for each of the criteria. The evaluation should include specific comments.

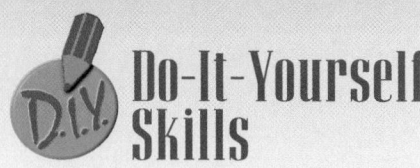

Objectives

Upon completion of this feature, students should be able to:

◆ explain what a table is and how it is used;

◆ organize data into tables.

National Geography Standards

The following National Geography Standards are highlighted in this feature: 1, 4

Bellringer

Ask students to look through the pages of this book to find examples of such graphic organizers as tables, diagrams, and graphs. Then have the class compare and contrast them, noting the type of data each one is used to display.

LESSON PLAN

1. Focus Tell students to examine the table on this page. Then ask them why tables are useful and how they might use tables in their own writing.

2. Instruct As students begin to create a chart showing earthquake data, have them draw two columns on the board. Label them *Include* and *Do Not Include.* Then ask students what information they would include or exclude from their tables, and why.

3. Close/Reteach When students finish creating their tables, ask them to brainstorm a list of other geographic data they can research on the Internet or in the library, such as hurricanes or floods. Ask them to identify pertinent column headings they would use to order their data.

Do-It-Yourself Skills

Organizing Data Into Tables

What Is a Table?

A table is a graphic organizer in which information is arranged in rows and columns according to logical categories. Tables help you to see information at a glance. They also make it easier to compare data and recognize patterns.

The Deadliest Volcanic Eruptions				
VOLCANO	**LOCATION**	**YEAR**	**DEATHS**	**MAJOR CAUSE OF DEATHS**
Tambora	Indonesia	1815	92,000	Starvation
Krakatau	Indonesia	1883	36,417	Tsunami
Mount Pelée	Martinique	1902	29,025	Ash flows
Ruiz	Colombia	1985	25,000	Mudflows
Unzen	Japan	1792	14,300	Volcanic collapse, tsunami
Laki	Iceland	1783	9,350	Starvation
Kelut	Indonesia	1919	5,110	Mudflows
Galunggung	Indonesia	1882	4,011	Mudflows
Vesuvius	Italy	1631	3,500	Mudflows, lava flows
Vesuvius	Italy	79	3,360	Ash flows and falls

Sources: *Volcano World;* University of North Dakota

How Can I Use This Skill?

It is important to know how to convert information from one form of communication into another. The ability to present data in a table will help you to create presentations and reports in both school and the workplace. When you organize data into tables, you are practicing important critical thinking skills, such as categorizing and sequencing.

Step by Step

Follow these steps to organize data into a table. As you proceed, use the table showing the deadliest volcanic eruptions (above) as a model.

1 Decide on a topic. Identify the information that you will convert into a table. This information may come from various sources, including textbooks, reference works, and Internet sites. For this lesson, use the information about earthquakes, on page 61, to make a table showing the deadliest earthquakes on record.

2 Study the information about earthquakes (right), and decide what data you will include in your table. You should only include data that are pertinent and available. For example, whether it was sunny or rainy when an earthquake occurred has little to do with the earthquake. The fact that an earthquake occurred on the San Andreas Fault is pertinent, but if you do not have information about faults for other earthquakes, you probably should not include this fact in your table.

3 Based on the data you chose in the step above, identify how many columns there will be and what the column headings will be. In the table on volcanoes, for example, the column headings are "Volcano," "Location," "Year," "Deaths," and "Major Cause of Deaths."

4 Decide the order in which you want data to appear. Do you want the first column to indicate where the earthquake happened, or when it happened, or something else? Generally, the first heading should be the piece of information that you think is most important for people to know.

5 Decide how many rows your table will have. For this lesson, include rows only for the eight deadliest earthquakes. This means that you are not going to include all the earthquakes for which you have information.

6 Decide the order in which you are going to list data in the rows. Are you going to list earthquakes in order of time, or in order of magnitude, or in some other order?

7 You now can construct the framework for your table. Give the table a title. Draw all the lines for your columns and rows. Write your column headings at the top of each column. Identify the source from which the data came.

8 Fill the table with data. Make sure the information goes into the correct boxes. This means that you should pay close attention to the column headings and the particular earthquake that you are describing.

9 Analyze your table. Do you see any patterns? In the table of earthquakes you have just created, what do you notice about the locations of the earthquakes?

The following information about the deadliest earthquakes on record is from the National Earthquake Information Center of the United States Geological Service (USGS):

- About 830,000 people died in China in 1556 as a result of an earthquake of unknown magnitude.
- In 1976, an earthquake measuring 7.5 on the Richter scale is estimated to have caused the deaths of more than 600,000 Chinese people.
- In Syria, in 1138, an earthquake killed 230,000 people.
- A 7.9-magnitude earthquake resulted in 200,000 Chinese deaths in 1927.
- In 856, an earthquake was responsible for 200,000 deaths in Iran.
- A 1920 earthquake of magnitude 8.6 caused the deaths of 200,000 people in China.
- Some 150,000 Iranians died as a result of a quake in 893.
- In 1923, in Japan, 143,000 people were killed by a quake measuring 7.9 on the Richter scale.
- As many as 70,000 people in Italy died as a result of a 7.2-magnitude earthquake in 1908.
- A quake of unknown magnitude killed 100,000 people in China in 1290.

TIP

Selecting Data

A table should present the most important information rather than all the information. The more complicated the table, the less effective it is.

APPLY YOUR SKILL

Look up information about major earthquakes around the world since 1980, using either the Internet or other research materials in your school library. Follow the steps above to organize the data into a table, and draw conclusions about which regions experience tectonic instability.

CUSTOMIZE FOR...

Less Proficient Readers

Find the Main Point Read the "Step by Step" as a class. Encourage students to find the main point of each paragraph. Remind students that writers frequently state the main point at the beginning of a paragraph. Help them see that in each step, the main idea appears in the first sentence.

ACTIVITY

Group Work

Activity: Creating tables to compare costs

Purpose: Explain to students that creating tables can help them comparison shop for items they need. Tell the groups that they are to look at advertisements in newspapers to compare the costs of such items as computers and CD players. Have them create a table that shows the costs of the items at two or three different stores.

Roles: Groups should include a group leader, table layout designer, and comparison shoppers.

Result: Groups should write a paragraph stating where they would buy the computer or CD player, and why.

Answers to Apply Your Skill

Check students' tables for evidence of careful research and logical organization.

Resource Manager

	CORE INSTRUCTION	READING/SKILLS

Chapter-Level Resources	📖 Teaching Resources
	📘 **Unit 1**/Ch. 2
	  • Reviewing Main Ideas, p. 21
	📙 **Mental Mapping booklet**
	  • Unit 1 Checklist, p. 5
	📙 **Simulations, Games, and Lab Activities**
	  • Place Location Review Games, pp. 58–63
	💿 **TeacherExpress™ CD-ROM**, Ch. 2
	💻 **Companion Web site,**
	www.phschool.com
	  • eTeach
		📖 Teaching Resources
		📘 **Unit 1**/Ch. 2
		  • Map/Graph Skills, p. 23
		💿 **Book on CD**, Ch. 2
		💿 **Social Studies Skills Tutor CD-ROM**

1 Weather and Climate
  1. Describe how weather and climate are affected by the relative positions of the earth and sun.
  2. Explain how wind and ocean currents redistribute the sun's heat.
  3. List the factors that influence the world's climate regions.
  4. Summarize why climatic change is a cause for concern.
	📖 Teaching Resources
	📘 **Unit 1**/Ch. 2
	  • Guided Reading and Review, p. 17
	📙 **Simulations, Games, and Lab Activities**
	  • Exploring Local Geography, Analyzing the Weather, p. 3
	💿 **Prentice Hall Presentation Pro CD-ROM**, Ch. 2, Sec. 1
		📖 Teaching Resources
		📙 **Guide to the Essentials (English/Spanish)**
		  • Section Summary, Ch. 2, Sec. 1
		📙 **Mental Mapping booklet**
		  • Outline Map, Ch. 2, p. 9
		📙 **Social Studies Skills Handbook**
		  • Map and Globe Skills, Reading an Ocean Currents Map, p. 37
		  • Map and Globe Skills, Reading a Wind Map, p. 38
		📼 **Guided Reading Audiotapes (English/Spanish)**, Ch. 2, Sec. 1
		📑 **Section Reading Support Transparencies**, Ch. 2, Sec. 1

2 Ecosystems
  1. Identify the conditions that affect life in an ecosystem.
  2. Explain why there are different types of forests.
  3. Locate grasslands globally.
  4. Explain how life survives in harsh deserts and tundras.
	📖 Teaching Resources
	📘 **Unit 1**/Ch. 2
	  • Guided Reading and Review, p. 19
	📙 **Creative Teaching Activities**
	  • Biomes and Vegetation Regions, p. 4
	💿 **Prentice Hall Presentation Pro CD-ROM**, Ch. 2, Sec. 2
		📖 Teaching Resources
		📙 **Guide to the Essentials (English/Spanish)**
		  • Section Summary, Ch. 2, Sec. 2
		📼 **Guided Reading Audiotapes (English/Spanish)**, Ch. 2, Sec. 2
		📑 **Section Reading Support Transparencies**, Ch. 2, Sec. 2

ENRICHMENT/HONORS/PREAP

Teaching Resources

📗 **Unit 1**/Ch. 2
- Critical Thinking, p. 22

📙 **Mental Mapping booklet**
- Atlas Activity, p. 10

📙 **Social Studies Skills Handbook**
- Study and Research Skills, pp. 94–108

📺 **World Geography Map and Photo Transparencies**
- World Climate Zones
- How the Earth Works, Unit 1

📹 **World Geography Videos**
- Climate Ecosystems: Ecosystems, Tape 1

💻 **Companion Web site, www.phschool.com**
- Chapter 2 Activities

📺 **World Geography Map and Photo Transparencies**
- Continents and Oceans

💻 **Companion Web site, www.phschool.com**
- Chapter 2 Activities

Teaching Resources

📙 **Social Studies Skills Handbook**
- Critical Thinking Skills, Recognizing Cause and Effect, p. 49

📺 **World Geography Map and Photo Transparencies**
- World Ecosystems

💻 **Companion Web site, www.phschool.com**
- Chapter 2 Activities

ASSESSMENT

PRENTICE HALL
ASSESSMENT SYSTEM

Core Assessment
📙 ExamView Test Bank booklet, Ch. 2
💿 ExamView Test Bank CD-ROM, Ch. 2

Standardized Test Preparation
Review and Reteach
📗 Review Book for World Geography, pp. 3–4

Practice and Assess
📙 Test-taking Strategies With Transparencies for High School

Test-taking Strategy Poster

📙 Alternative Assessment booklet

📙 Test Prep Book for World Geography

Teaching Resources

📗 **Unit 1**/Ch. 2
- Section Quizzes, pp. 18, 20
- Test Forms A and B, pp. 24–29

📙 **Guide to the Essentials (English/Spanish)**
- Chapter 2 Test

📙 **Spanish Resources,** Ch. 2
- Section Quizzes, pp. 7–8

📙 **Mental Mapping booklet**
- Chapter 2 Map Test, p. 11

💻 **Companion Web site, www.phschool.com**
- Chapter 2 Self-Test

CUSTOMIZE FOR INDIVIDUAL NEEDS

Honors/PreAP
- Teacher's Edition, Customize for . . . , p. 81

Less Proficient Readers
- Guide to the Essentials (English), Ch. 2, Section Summaries
- Social Studies Skills Handbook, p. 69
- Guided Reading Audiotapes (English), Ch. 2
- Section Reading Support Transparencies, Ch. 2
- Book on CD, Ch. 2
- Teacher's Edition, Reading Strategy, pp. 70, 80
- Teacher's Edition, Activity: Vocabulary, pp. 67, 79

Students Acquiring English/ESL
- Guide to the Essentials (English/Spanish), Ch. 2
- Guided Reading Audiotapes (English/Spanish), Ch. 2
- Section Reading Support Transparencies, Ch. 2
- Book on CD, Ch. 2
- Teacher's Edition, Customize for . . . , p. 71

Less Proficient Writers
- Social Studies Skills Handbook, p. 78
- Alternative Assessment, Writing Assignment Rubric, p. 6
- Teacher's Edition, Customize for . . . , p. 75

MENTAL MAPPING

Review the geographic theme of region with the students (a group of places with at least one common characteristic). Point out that climate and vegetation are characteristics that define formal regions. Refer students to the maps on pages 70–71 and 78–79. Have them identify the climate region and the ecosystem in which they live. Then ask them to speculate on the relationship between climates and ecosystems. (A region's climate helps determine its ecosystem.)

Mapping the Region Direct students to the map on this page. Point out the seven continents and the mountains, deserts, and peninsulas on each. Ask students to sketch a map like the one shown on this page, or distribute the Chapter 2 Outline Map on page 9 of the Mental Mapping booklet in the Teaching Resources. Ask students to lightly shade each continent a different color. Then ask them to shut their books and add labels for the mountains, deserts, and peninsulas that are listed in Part II of the Unit 1 Checklist.

eTeach

Be sure to check out this month's online forum with a Master Teacher to join in an exchange of teaching ideas. **www.phschool.com**

C H A P T E R
2

Climates and Ecosystems

SECTIONS

| 1 | Weather and Climate |
| 2 | Ecosystems |

The World: MOUNTAINS, DESERTS, AND PENINSULAS

Robinson Projection

Go Online
PHSchool.com

For: More geographic information about climates and ecosystems and access to the Take It to the Net activities
Visit: phschool.com
Web Code: mjk-0003

RESOURCE DIRECTORY

Teaching Resources
Unit 1, Chapter 2
• Section 1 Guided Reading and Review, p. 17
Guide to the Essentials (English/Spanish)
• Section Summary, Chapter 2, Section 1
Mental Mapping booklet
• Atlas Activity, p. 10
• Unit 1 Checklist, p. 5
• Outline Map 2, p. 9

Technology
Guided Reading Audiotapes (English/Spanish),
 Chapter 2, Section 1

Section Reading Support Transparencies,
 Chapter 2, Section 1
World Geography Map and Photo Transparencies
• World Climate Zones
Book on CD, Chapter 2
World Geography Videos
• Climates and Ecosystems: Ecosystems, Tape 1
TeacherExpress™ CD-ROM, Chapter 2
Prentice Hall Presentation Pro CD-ROM, Chapter 2
Social Studies Skills Tutor CD-ROM
Companion Web site, www.phschool.com
• Chapter 2 Activities

1 Weather and Climate

Reading Focus

- How are weather and climate affected by the relative positions of the earth and sun?
- How do wind and ocean currents redistribute the sun's heat?
- What factors influence the world's climate regions?
- Why is climatic change a cause for concern?

Key Terms

weather	solstice	continental climate
climate	equinox	
rotation	precipitation	
revolution	front	

Main Idea Climate is influenced by many factors, such as the relationship between the earth and sun, latitude, ocean currents, and elevation.

Natural Hazards Climate and weather can cause severe damage, as shown by this hurricane near Corpus Christi, Texas.

Everybody talks about the weather. No matter where you live or what language you speak, you probably know some folk sayings for predicting weather. In India, people sometimes say, "When the frog croaks in the meadow, there will be rain in three hours' time." In Britain and America, the advice is different: "Rain before seven, sun by eleven." Weather seems so important because it affects everyday life—planting, harvests, and sometimes survival.

Weather and Climate

What is "weather"? **Weather** is the condition of the bottom layer of the earth's atmosphere in one place over a short period of time. The atmosphere is a multilayered band of gases, water vapor, and dust above the earth. A description of the weather usually mentions temperature, moisture or precipitation, and wind. That is, a day might be "warm, dry, and calm" or "cold, snowy, and windy." Weather is in an almost constant state of change, sometimes shifting erratically from warm to cool and back again in a short period of time.

◄ Tornado (photo left)

The weather in one region may influence, or be influenced by, the weather in an area far away.

Climate is the term for the weather patterns that an area typically experiences over a long period of time. The climate of an area depends on a number of factors, including its elevation, latitude, and location in relation to nearby landforms and bodies of water. Climate can change, but these changes usually take place over a longer period of time.

The concepts of weather and climate, then, are related but are not synonymous. The distinction between the two is the difference between specifics and generalities. According to an old farmer's saying, "Climate is what you expect; weather is what you get."

The Sun and the Earth

The ultimate source of the earth's climates—and of life on earth—lies some 93 million miles (150 million km) away. The sun, an intensely hot star, gives off energy and light that are essential for the survival of plants and animals.

Chapter 2 ▪ Section 1 **63**

TEACHING TIP
From A Master Teacher

Climate and Vegetation Students can gain an understanding of climate and vegetation by starting with a description of the climate and vegetation with which they are familiar. As students study the chapter, have them identify the influences that create the conditions surrounding them and how human activity can affect some of these conditions. By knowing how the systems of the earth operate and change, students learn the basic principles that guide programs for environmental management.

Pacing Suggestions

For 60-minute Blocks

You will want to vary activities.

- Have students complete the Recognizing Cause and Effect activity on page 49 of the Social Studies Skills Handbook in the Teaching Resources. After they have finished the activity, tell students that a cause and effect relationship can also be seen between the rotation of the earth and the time of day. Explain how the earth's rotation on its axis (the cause) leads to a continual cycle of night and day (the effect). Encourage students to think of other cause-and-effect relationships in geography.

Section 1 pp. 63–73

Objectives
Upon completion of Section 1, students should be able to:

- ◆ describe how weather and climate are affected by the relative positions of the earth and sun;
- ◆ explain how wind and ocean currents redistribute the sun's heat;
- ◆ list the factors that influence the world's climate regions;
- ◆ summarize why climatic change is a cause for concern.

National Geography Standards

The following National Geography Standards are highlighted in this section: 1, 5, 7, 9, 14, 17, 18

Bellringer

Ask students: **In what ways has weather influenced your life this week?** (Possible answers include deciding what to wear and determining outdoor activities.)

LESSON PLAN

1. Focus Refer students to the first subsection on this page. Help them differentiate between *weather* and *climate*. Then ask them to describe their local climate.

2. Instruct Draw a chart on the board with the following headings: *Weather and Climate, Distributing the Sun's Heat, Influences on Climate,* and *Concerns About Climatic Changes.* As they read Section 1, have students fill in key concepts under the headings.

3. Close/Reteach Write the name of each climate type from the table on page 72 on a separate slip of paper. Have a student draw a slip and locate a place on the map on pages 70–71 that represents that climate region. Have another student describe average temperature and precipitation in that region.

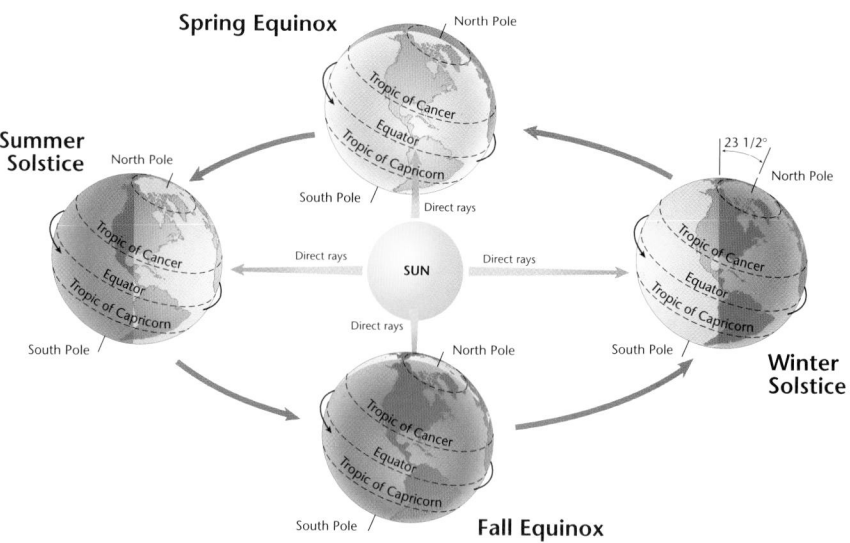

Spring Equinox — North Pole — Tropic of Cancer — Equator — Tropic of Capricorn — South Pole — Direct rays

Summer Solstice — North Pole — Tropic of Cancer — Equator — Tropic of Capricorn — South Pole

SUN — Direct rays — Direct rays — Direct rays

23 1/2° — North Pole — Tropic of Cancer — Equator — Tropic of Capricorn — South Pole — Winter Solstice

North Pole — Tropic of Cancer — Equator — Tropic of Capricorn — South Pole — Fall Equinox

DIAGRAM SKILLS

● **Physical Processes** Because of the earth's tilt and revolution around the sun, there is seasonal variation in the amount of energy received by different parts of the earth. This variation influences global climate patterns.

* *Why does the Northern Hemisphere experience winter at the same time that the Southern Hemisphere experiences summer?*

The Greenhouse Effect Only a small amount of solar radiation reaches the earth's atmosphere. Some of the radiation is reflected back into space by the atmosphere and by the earth's surface, but enough remains to warm the earth's land and water. The atmosphere also prevents heat from escaping back into space too quickly.

In this sense, the earth's atmosphere has been compared to the glass walls and roof of a greenhouse, which trap the sun's warmth for growing plants. Without this so-called "greenhouse effect," the earth would be too cold for most living things.

Not all places on the earth get the same amount of heat and light from the sun. Day and night, seasonal change, and differing climates are all largely determined by the relative positions of the sun and the earth.

Rotation and Revolution As the earth moves through space, it spins on its axis like a top.

This movement is known as **rotation.** The axis is an invisible line through the center of the earth from pole to pole. The earth completes one rotation in approximately twenty-four hours. On the side that faces the sun, it is daytime. On the side turned away, it is night. The earth spins from west to east, so the sun appears to rise in the east and set in the west.

The earth also revolves, or moves, around the sun in a nearly circular path called an orbit. A **revolution** is one complete orbit around the sun. The earth completes one revolution every 365¼ days—the length of a year. To account for the quarter day, every four years we make the year 366 days long by adding one day to the month of February. This is known as Leap Year.

As the earth revolves, its position relative to the sun is not straight up-and-down. Rather, the earth is tilted 23½° on its axis. Because of the earth's tilt, the Tropic of Cancer at 23½°N and the Tropic of Capricorn at 23½°S mark the boundaries of the places on the earth that receive the most direct sunlight.

Global Warming With no greenhouse effect the earth would be much colder, and few animals and plants could survive. However, some scientists believe that the greenhouse effect has been increasing in recent years. They claim that exhaust fumes from cars and industries are making the atmosphere denser. Consequently, the atmosphere is holding more heat, and the planet is warming up. This process is called global warming.

ACTIVITY

Reteach

Model Use a model to demonstrate how the earth's revolution around the sun affects the planet's climate. Take a foam ball three to six inches in diameter to represent the earth. Insert a pencil through the center to represent the earth's axis. Mark the pencil's ends as the North and South poles. Draw the Equator perpendicular to the axis. Place a light source, such as a lamp with the shade removed, in the center of a table to represent the sun. Then tilt the ball at a slight angle and move it around the light to mimic the earth's revolutions. Have students notice the point at which each pole is nearest the sun and identify what season it would be in each hemisphere. (Visual/Spatial)

 Alternative Assessment

Introduce the Activity

Creating a Map Ask students to choose a continent and to create a map showing climate regions and/or ecosystems for that continent. Students might refer to maps in this chapter and in the Atlas when preparing their maps. Distribute the Map Rubric found on page 14 of the Alternative Assessment booklet in the Prentice Hall Assessment System for students' reference.

Answer to Diagram Skills

because of the earth's tilt

RESOURCE DIRECTORY

Prentice Hall Assessment System
Alternative Assessment booklet
• Map Rubric, p. 14

Technology
World Geography Map and Photo Transparencies
• Continents and Oceans

The earth's tilt also means that sunlight strikes different parts of the planet more directly at certain times of the year. As the diagram on page 64 shows, when the North Pole is tilted toward the sun, the sun's rays fall more directly on the Northern Hemisphere, bringing longer, warmer days. This is summer in the Northern Hemisphere and winter in the Southern Hemisphere. As the earth moves halfway around the sun, the Southern Hemisphere tilts closer to the sun, and the situation is reversed. These changes in season are marked by the summer and winter **solstices,** on or about June 21 and December 21, the days when the sun appears directly overhead at the Tropics of Capricorn and Cancer.

The other markers for seasonal change occur on or about March 21 and September 23. These dates are known as the spring and fall **equinoxes.** On those days, the sun, at noon, appears directly overhead at the Equator. Around these dates, the lengths of day and night are nearly equal everywhere on the earth.

Latitude and Climate The angle of the sun's rays affects weather and climate in other ways. Because the earth is nearly round, the sun's rays always fall most directly at or near the Equator. As the diagram on page 64 shows, the rays grow less and less direct as they fall closer to the North and South poles. As a result, most places near the Equator have warm climates, while the areas farthest from the Equator are cold.

Geographers use latitude, or distance from the Equator, to divide the world into zones. The tropical zones are low-latitude zones reaching 23½° north and south of the Equator. Most places in the tropics are hot year-round. The earth's two temperate zones are in the middle latitudes. They extend from 23½°N to 66½°N and from 23½°S to 66½°S. The temperate zones are generally cooler than the tropics and have a wide range of temperatures. The polar zones are in the high latitudes, from 66½°N and 66½°S to the poles. Because sunlight strikes here very indirectly, the sun's rays are spread out over a wide area. Polar climates are always cool or bitterly cold. These zones are shown in the diagram on page 66.

Distributing the Sun's Heat

Heat from the sun does not all stay where it falls. If it did, the tropics would grow hotter each year and the polar regions colder. Instead,

A Study in Contrasts

Climates Reindeer fur and hide offer people protection from the cold in Siberia, located in the far northern latitudes (left). Near the Equator, people in Java (top) enjoy a tropical lifestyle.

Location *How does location affect climate?*

Chapter 2 ▪ Section 1 **65**

Articles From ....
NATIONAL GEOGRAPHIC

The following article may be used to extend the content in this section.

Suplee, Curt, and Joanna B. Pinneo, photographer. "Unlocking the Climate Puzzle." *National Geographic,* Vol. 193, No. 5 (May 1998), pp. 38–71.

This article looks at global warming and the human activities that may be encouraging it.

GLOBAL CONNECTIONS

Climates
Around the world, rain falls in varying amounts. The world's rainfall record is held by Mt. Waialeale, Hawaii, with an average of about 450 inches per year. During one year, it even received 642 inches, an average of almost 2 inches per day. In contrast, Iquique, Chile, received no rain for 14 years.

heat is distributed by a process called convection—the transfer of heat from one place to another.

Convection occurs because warm gases and liquids are lighter or less dense than cool gases and liquids. Therefore, warm gases and liquids tend to rise, while cooler, heavier gases and liquids sink and displace the lighter materials.

This process takes place in both air and water. Movements of air are called winds; movements of water are called currents. Warm air and warm water both flow from the Equator toward the poles. Cold air and cold water tend to move from the poles toward the Equator. Within these broad movements are complex smaller patterns.

Wind Atmospheric pressure is the weight of the atmosphere overhead. Rising warm air creates areas of low pressure; falling cool air causes areas of high pressure. Winds move from areas of high pressure into areas of low pressure. The movement of winds worldwide redistributes the sun's heat over the earth's surface.

The pattern of winds begins when light, warm air rises from the Equator and flows northward and southward toward the poles. At the same time, air from the cooler regions sinks down and moves toward the Equator.

If the world were standing still, these winds would blow in a straight line. But the earth is rotating, and its movement deflects, or bends, them. This deflection is called the Coriolis effect. In the Northern Hemisphere the path of the winds curves to the right, while in the Southern Hemisphere it curves left. The diagram below shows these patterns.

Wind Patterns In each latitude zone, temperature and pressure combine to create a pattern

Zones of Latitude and Prevailing Winds

KEY

Low latitudes
Middle latitudes
High latitudes
Prevailing winds

Robinson Projection

APPLYING THE GEOGRAPHIC THEMES

● **Regions** Because of the Coriolis effect, winds are deflected from their straight path toward the poles.
• *Which prevailing winds arise in the polar zones?*

of prevailing, or dominant, winds. At the Equator, the rising warm air causes calm weather or very light, variable breezes. Thus, the region called the "doldrums" at the Equator has light winds.

Two other regions of light and unpredictable winds are at about 30° North and South latitudes, where cool air sinks toward earth. Sailing ships had trouble getting enough wind to travel in these "horse latitudes." Supposedly, this name arose when Spaniards sailing to the Americas threw their horses overboard in order to lighten their ships and move faster.

Between the horse latitudes and the Equator, the "trade winds" blow steadily toward the Equator from the northeast and southeast. These winds got their name because merchant trading ships depended on them to push the ships laden with goods across the ocean.

Currents The waters of the oceans also help to distribute heat. Following convection patterns similar to those of winds, ocean currents, both near the ocean's surface and far below it, carry warm water from the tropics to the poles. Other currents return cold water to the Equator. Wind and the Coriolis effect influence the circular patterns of currents in the oceans. The map below shows the major warm and cold ocean currents.

Precipitation

Humidity is the amount of water vapor contained in the atmosphere. **Precipitation,** on the other hand, is all forms of water that fall from the atmosphere onto the earth's surface. Timing and volume of precipitation are important aspects of climate.

Precipitation forms as air temperature changes. Warm, less-dense air absorbs more moisture than cool air. When this air cools, it cannot retain all of its water vapor, so excess water vapor condenses into a liquid. Tiny droplets of water gather together to form clouds. Precipitation occurs when more water collects in clouds than they

Ocean Currents

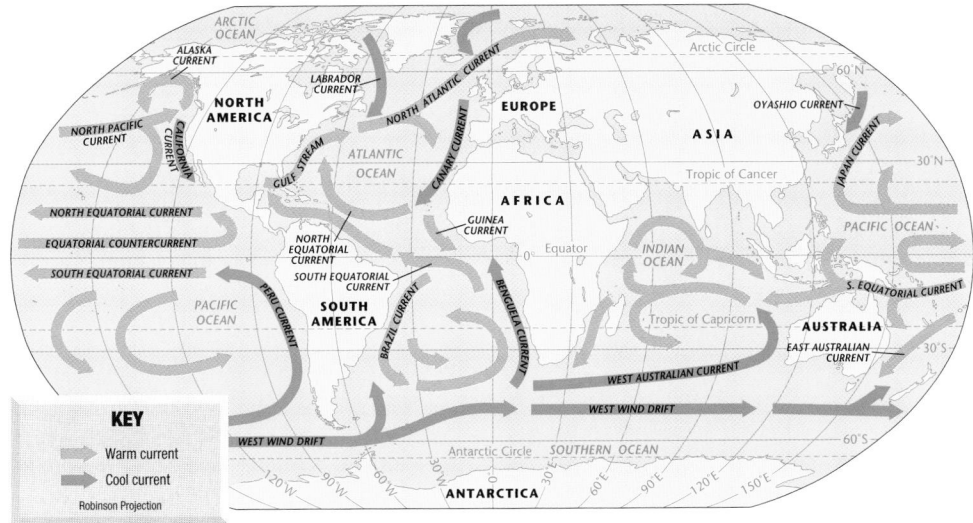

KEY
- Warm current
- Cool current

Robinson Projection

APPLYING THE GEOGRAPHIC THEMES

● **Movement** Warm and cold ocean currents, like the winds, help redistribute heat from the regions near the Equator to the polar regions.
- *Which ocean current moves north along Africa's west coast?*

GLOBAL CONNECTIONS

Environmental Change

Ocean Pollution The ability of ocean currents to move pollution to all parts of the planet is significant. An oil spill, a discharge of industrial waste, or runoff from agriculture and urban areas can threaten marine life and coastal areas hundreds of miles away. Such was the case when the *Exxon Valdez* oil tanker spilled almost 11 million gallons of crude oil off the coast of Alaska on March 24, 1989. The spill left 1,500 miles (2,400 km) of beaches black with an oily residue. The oil covered the ocean surface for over 500 miles (800 km), killing or injuring hundreds of thousands of birds, sea otters, seals, and other animals.

ACTIVITY

Vocabulary

Precipitation Point out the Key Terms list on page 63. Have students look up *precipitation* in the Glossary and paraphrase the definition. Then have them identify the kinds of precipitation in their area.

TEST PREPARATION

Have students read the subsection Wind Patterns that begins on the previous page to answer the following question.

At the Equator, rising warm air causes calm weather and light, variable breezes called —

- **(A)** doldrums
- **B** trade winds
- **C** precipitation
- **D** horse latitudes

Answer to Map Caption

the Benguela Current

DIAGRAM SKILLS

● **Physical Processes** The movement of all of the water on the earth's surface is called the water cycle. About 97 percent of the earth's water is in the oceans. More than 2 percent is frozen in glaciers and ice sheets. Less than 1 percent is in streams and lakes, or underground.

• *How is the water on earth recycled?*

can hold. Snow, rain, sleet, or hail may fall, depending on air temperature and wind conditions. The water cycle, shown in the diagram above, illustrates the movement of all of the water in the ground and in the air.

Geographers divide precipitation into three types: convectional, orographic, and frontal. These types, shown in the diagram on page 69, are described below.

Convectional Precipitation Convectional precipitation occurs when hot, humid air rises from the earth's surface and cools, thereby losing its ability to hold much water. Convectional precipitation is common near the Equator and in the tropics, where generally hot, humid surface air exists. Convectional precipitation produces nourishing rainfalls that feed lush, tropical forests.

Orographic Precipitation Sometimes warm, moist air is forced upward when passing over high landforms, causing precipitation. This effect—called orographic precipitation—is common on seacoasts where moist, ocean winds blow toward coastal mountains. The warm winds cool as they rise up over the mountains. Clouds form and rain or snow falls. The air is cool and dry by the time it reaches the other side of the mountains. For example, winds from

the Pacific Ocean deposit moisture on the windward, or wind-facing, slopes of the Cascade Range on the west coast of the United States. This thickly forested area is often foggy and rainy.

The land on the leeward side of the mountains—away from the wind—lies in what is called a rain shadow. After losing its moisture crossing the mountains, the air warms up again as elevation drops. This dry, hot air often creates dry climates behind coastal mountains. For example, California's Mohave Desert lies inland behind the Sierra Nevada.

Frontal Precipitation Frontal precipitation, the most common kind of precipitation, occurs when two **fronts,** or air masses, of different temperatures meet. The warm air is forced upward by the heavier, cool air. The rising warm air cools, and frontal precipitation forms.

Other Influences on Climate

Temperature and precipitation are the major factors affecting weather and climate. Other influences on specific areas include nearby bodies of water, elevation, and location in relation to nearby landforms.

Nearby Bodies of Water Land and water absorb and store heat at very different rates. Within a few hours, land temperatures can change many degrees. Across seasons, the change is even more dramatic. In parts of Siberia on the Asian mainland,

land temperatures can vary by as much as 140°F (60°C) from summer to winter. By contrast, water temperatures change much more slowly. Average temperatures on ocean surfaces, for example, vary less than 10°F (6°C) throughout the year.

Because of this difference, large bodies of water—oceans or large lakes—affect the surrounding climates. Winds that blow over water take on the water's temperature. These winds moderate land temperatures as they blow onshore. Such areas often have milder climates than other areas that are at the same latitude but far from a large body of water.

Coastal areas have specific climate types. Some mid-latitude areas on continental west coasts have mild, humid, marine climates. Prevailing westerlies supply warm, moist ocean air. Marine climates are found on the Pacific coast of North America and in southern Chile.

The British Isles and the countries of Western Europe also have a marine climate. Although these countries are located relatively far north, the winds that blow onshore from the Atlantic have been warmed by the North Atlantic Current, a branch of the warm-water Gulf Stream.

Away from the moderating influence of the oceans, the great central areas of continents in the Northern Hemisphere have what are known as **continental climates.** Most areas with continental climates have cold, snowy winters and warm or hot summers. Humidity and precipitation vary, and temperatures often reach extremes of hot and cold. Regions with this climate are the transition zones between mild and polar climates. Central Europe, Northern Eurasia, parts of China, and much of North America have continental climates.

Elevation Although it is located almost on the Equator in Tanzania, Africa, Mount Kilimanjaro is capped with snow year-round. The mountain's elevation of 19,341 feet (5,895 m) above

DIAGRAM SKILLS

● **Physical Processes** Precipitation occurs when rising warm air cools to form water droplets, which are then released by clouds.
  • *In the center illustration of orographic precipitation, why has a desert formed on the leeward side of the mountains?*

Types of Precipitation

CONVECTIONAL PRECIPITATION

Warm air

OROGRAPHIC PRECIPITATION
Windward side
Leeward side
Rain
Warming dry air
Inland desert
Ocean coast
Snow
Rainshadow
Cooling moist air

FRONTAL PRECIPITATION
Warm air
Front
Cool air

▶▶▶ *Career Prep*

Careers in Geography

Meteorologist A meteorologist is a scientist who studies the atmosphere and earth's weather patterns. Often, meteorologists are employed by government agencies or research stations to study and help better predict weather phenomena.

ACTIVITY

Group Work

Activity: Studying weather forecasting

Purpose: Have groups of students collect weather maps and predictions from local newspapers for five consecutive days. After studying these materials, have each group list questions about its local climate as well as about weather and climate in general. Then have a spokesperson from each group share its questions with the entire class to create a class list of questions. Invite a weather forecaster from a local television or radio station to visit the class and answer the questions.

Roles: Each group should have a scribe and a spokesperson. Appoint class spokespersons to read questions during the forecaster's visit.

Result: The class spokespersons should ask as many questions as time permits.

Answer to Diagram Skills

The rising moist air on the windward side of the mountains produced rain at high elevations. The air mass, now descending and warming, is dry.

Visualizing

Remind students that visualizing information will help them to internalize what they read. Before you begin reading the subsection World Climate Regions, point out the Climate Regions map and its key. Explain that the map is a visual representation of some of the information in the text. Direct students to follow along silently in their texts as you read the subsection aloud. When you reach the listings of the six broad types of climate regions, pause and ask students to locate each of the regions on the map. Instruct students to visualize the climates of some of the places they've located on the map. (For example, students may be able to "see" the Arctic as cold and snow-covered, and the Southwest region of the United States as dry and hot.)

Daily Life

Microclimates A microclimate is the climate of a small, discrete area. Contrasts between nearby microclimates may be extreme. For example, in Los Angeles tourists can ski on nearby mountains one day and spend the next sunbathing on hot beaches. Likewise, farmers who irrigate their land alter the microclimate of the fields. The adjacent land that is not irrigated remains dry and barren while crops thrive in the watered fields.

sea level affects its climate much more than does its location in the tropics. Elevation has a dramatic effect on climate in highland areas worldwide.

Air temperature decreases at a rate of about 3.5°F (2°C) for every 1,000 feet (305 m) in elevation. For this reason, hikers must use caution when planning a climb. They can leave the base of a mountain in hot weather yet face a snowstorm at the peak.

Nearby Landforms Variations in climate occur naturally. Indeed, no climate is ever completely uniform. Coastal mountains are one of the landforms that affect climate. Inland mountains, large desert areas, lakes, forests, and other natural features can influence climate, too. Even a concentration of tall buildings can influence climate in the surrounding area. The pavement and concrete of large cities absorb vast amounts of solar energy. This causes the average temperature of the city proper to be greater than that of the more open areas surrounding the city. Such small variations within a region are called microclimates.

The World: CLIMATE REGIONS

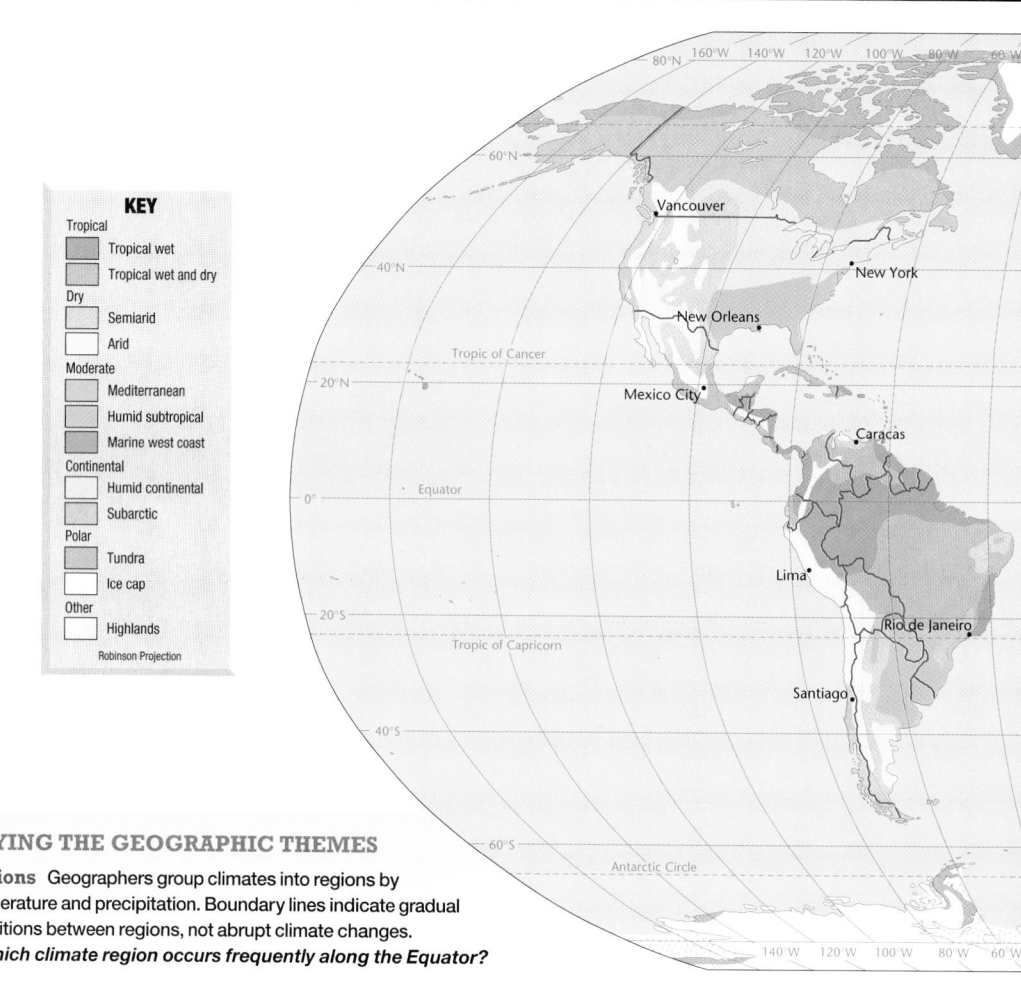

APPLYING THE GEOGRAPHIC THEMES

● **Regions** Geographers group climates into regions by temperature and precipitation. Boundary lines indicate gradual transitions between regions, not abrupt climate changes.
  • *Which climate region occurs frequently along the Equator?*

Answer to Map Caption

tropical wet

World Climate Regions

Geographers and climatologists have developed many different classification systems to define the world's major climate regions. Defining these climate regions is difficult because of changing climate conditions and the lack of accurate weather data in many parts of the world. Most efforts to classify climate regions rely on two factors: temperature and precipitation.

Generally, climates are classified using variations of a system developed in the early 1900s by Wladimir Köppen (VLAD uh meer KEPP pen), a German scientist. These systems identify five broad types of climate regions—tropical, dry, moderate, continental, and polar. Highland climates, found in major mountain systems, are similar to the climates of polar regions. Most of the climate groups have specific subdivisions.

The table on page 72 describes the climate classification system used in this book. The map on these pages shows climate regions using this system. Regional divisions on the map do not mean that climate changes abruptly. Instead,

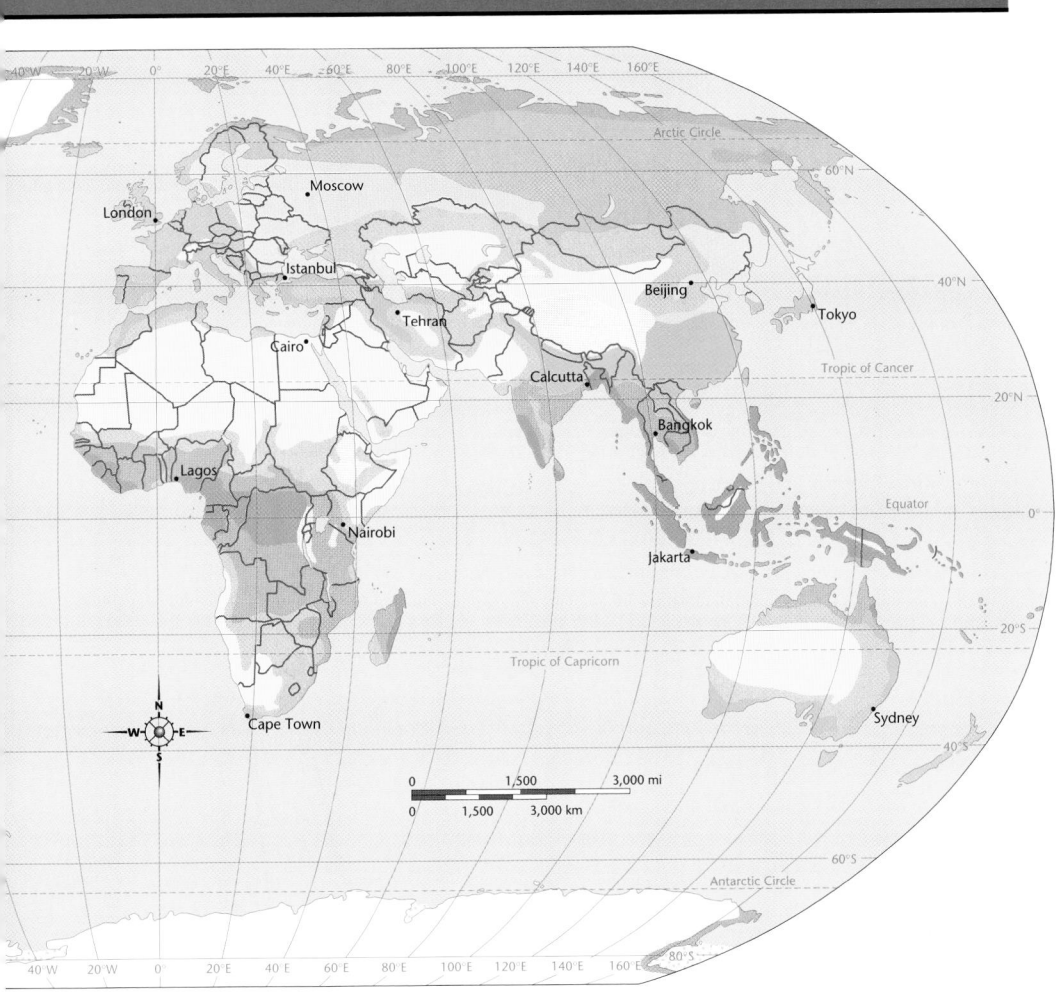

Group Work

Activity: Map reading

Purpose: Have groups of students focus on a different area and climate of the map on pages 70–71. Each group should make lists of what types of weather they think might occur in that region, plants that might grow in such a climate, and how people living in that region may have acclimated.

Roles: Each group should have a spokesperson and three scribes to jot down the group's ideas—one for each of the three categories: weather, plants, and people. Every member should provide at least one reasoned example.

Result: Each spokesperson should share the group's ideas and reasons with the class.

CUSTOMIZE FOR...

Students Acquiring English/ESL
Creating Posters Pair fluent speakers with students acquiring English to create posters illustrating the answer to one of the following questions: (1) What main factors influence climate? (2) How does the earth's movement around the sun affect climate? (3) How does convection distribute the sun's heat around the world? Have students display their completed posters and explain what they included in their illustrations and why.

Group Work

Activity: Illustrating climate types

Purpose: Assign each group a different climate type from the chart on this page. Instruct each group to write the name of its climate type as a heading on a large piece of paper and then to divide the paper in half. Direct students to label one half "Summer" and the other half "Winter." Groups should use information from the chart to imagine what summer and winter in a rural area in their climate type would look like, illustrating it on each half of their papers. Students may also list the statistics from the chart on this page in the margins of their two illustrations.

Roles: Designers, illustrators

Result: Display the illustrations and use them for reference as you compare climate types and review for the Chapter 2 Test. For example, you may wish to allow volunteers to group climate types by humidity, temperature, or other similarities.

Alternative Assessment

Mid-Point Monitoring

Creating a Map You may wish to monitor students' progress on creating their maps. Confer with students to see if they have drawn a map of their continent and if they will soon complete the shading and labeling to indicate climate and/or ecosystem.

World Climate Regions

CLIMATE TYPE	TEMPERATURE	PRECIPITATION
Tropical		
Tropical Wet	Hot all year (avg.) 79°F (26°C)	*Yearly:* 100 in. (254.0 cm) *Monthly* (avg.): 8.3 in. (21.1 cm)
Tropical Wet and Dry	Hot all year 79°F (26°C)	*Yearly:* 50 in. (127.0 cm) Summer: 10.2 in. (25.9 cm) Winter: 0.5 in. (1.3 cm)
Dry		
Semiarid	Hot summers, mild-to-cold winters Summer (avg.): 78°F (26°C) Winter (avg.): 51°F (11°C)	*Yearly:* 18 in. (45.7 cm) *Monthly* (avg.): Summer: 3.4 in. (8.6 cm) Winter: 0.2 in. (0.5 cm)
Arid	Hot days, cold nights Summer (avg.): 81°F (27°C) Winter (avg.): 55°F (13°C)	*Yearly:* 5 in. (12.7 cm) *Monthly* (avg.): Summer: 0.6 in. (1.5 cm) Winter: 0.1 in. (0.3 cm)
Moderate		
Mediterranean	Hot summers, cool winters Summer (avg.): 72°F (22°C) Winter (avg.): 52°F (11°C)	*Yearly:* 23 in. (58.4 cm) *Monthly* (avg.): Summer: 0.4 in. (1.0 cm) Winter: 3.8 in. (9.7 cm)
Humid Subtropical	Hot summers, cool winters Summer (avg.): 77°F (25°C) Winter (avg.): 47°F (8°C)	*Yearly:* 50 in. (127.0 cm) *Monthly* (avg.): Summer: 6.2 in. (15.7 cm) Winter: 2.8 in. (7.1 cm)
Marine West Coast	Warm summers, cool winters Summer (avg.): 60°F (16°C) Winter (avg.): 42°F (6°C)	*Yearly:* 45 in. (114.3 cm) *Monthly* (avg.): Summer: 2.5 in. (6.4 cm) Winter: 5.5 in. (14.0 cm)
Continental		
Humid Continental	Warm summers, cold winters Summer (avg.): 66°F (19°C) Winter (avg.): 21°F (-6°C)	*Yearly:* 27 in. (68.6 cm) *Monthly* (avg.): Summer: 3.2 in. (8.1 cm) Winter: 1.6 in. (4.1 cm)
Subarctic	Cool summers, very cold winters Summer (avg.): 56°F (13°C) Winter (avg.): -8°F (-22°C)	*Yearly:* 17 in. (43.2 cm) *Monthly* (avg.): Summer: 1.8 in. (4.6 cm) Winter: 1.2 in. (3.0 cm)
Polar		
Tundra	Cold summers, very cold winters Summer (avg.): 40°F (4°C) Winter (avg.): 0°F (-18°C)	*Yearly:* 16 in. (40.6 cm) *Monthly* (avg.): Summer: 1.9 in. (4.8 cm) Winter: 1.2 in. (3.0 cm)
Ice Cap	Cold all year Summer (avg.): 32°F (0°C) Winter (avg.): -14°F (-26°C)	*Yearly:* 8 in. (20.3 cm) *Monthly* (avg.): Summer: 1.0 in. (2.5 cm) Winter: 0.4 in. (1.0 cm)
Highlands		
	Varies, depending on elevation	*Yearly:* Ranges from 3 in. (7.6 cm) to 123 in. (312.4 cm)

Source: *Goode's World Atlas*, Rand McNally

RESOURCE DIRECTORY

Teaching Resources

Unit 1, Chapter 2
• Section 1 Quiz, p. 18

Spanish Resources
• Section 1 Quiz, p. 7

Simulations, Games, and Lab Activities
• Exploring Local Geography, Analyzing the Weather, p. 3

these boundary lines usually indicate areas of transition where one climate region merges with another. Although climate is generally constant in a region, temporary variations can and do take place.

Changing Climates

Many climate changes result from changes in nature, but more may now be caused by human action. Increasing amounts of carbon dioxide and other substances in the earth's atmosphere may lead to what scientists call "global warming"— a rise in the earth's temperature. Global warming could partially melt polar ice caps, causing a rise in the level of the oceans and flooding of densely populated low-lying areas. Other possible effects of global warming include an increase in precipitation in some areas and a decline in others. Areas that now support agriculture could become deserts.

A few scientists theorize that global warming may be largely due to natural cyclical changes. For example, historians believe that ancient Scandinavian explorers called Vikings first settled on the shores of Greenland and Iceland in the

Global Warming

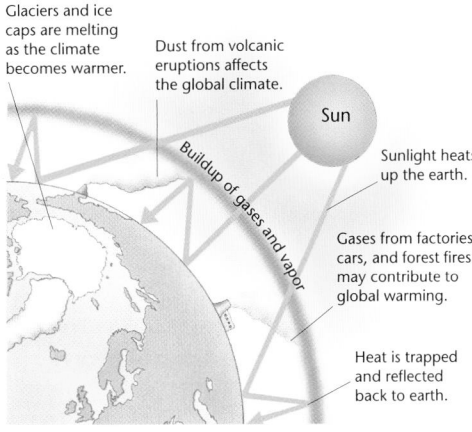

Glaciers and ice caps are melting as the climate becomes warmer.

Dust from volcanic eruptions affects the global climate.

Sun

Sunlight heats up the earth.

Buildup of gases and vapor

Gases from factories, cars, and forest fires may contribute to global warming.

Heat is trapped and reflected back to earth.

DIAGRAM SKILLS

● **Environmental Change** The earth's atmosphere traps heat from the sun and reflects it back to earth. As gases build up in the atmosphere, more and more heat is trapped and global temperatures rise.
  • *What human activities may contribute to global warming?*

tenth century when those regions were somewhat warmer. But in the mid-1500s, North Atlantic climates cooled. Lower temperatures made agriculture difficult, resulting in lower population levels. As the Greenland ice sheet expanded, the Greenland settlements were finally abandoned.

SECTION 1 ASSESSMENT

1. **Key Terms** Define **(a)** weather, **(b)** climate, **(c)** rotation, **(d)** revolution, **(e)** solstice, **(f)** equinox, **(g)** precipitation, **(h)** front, **(i)** continental climate.

2. **Physical Processes** How does the earth's position in relationship to the sun affect weather and climate?

3. **Physical Processes** How do winds and currents affect the distribution of solar warmth around the earth?

4. **Climates (a)** Why does California's Mohave region have an arid climate? **(b)** What are some possible effects of global warming?

5. **Critical Thinking Developing a Hypothesis** In the future, how might global warming influence migration patterns? Explain.

Activity

Take It to the NET

Making and Analyzing a Table Choose four cities in different climate regions. On the Internet, find precipitation and temperature data for each city. Display the data in a table. Analyze the data and write a report on the climatic conditions for each city. Visit the World Geography section of **www.phschool.com** for help in completing this activity.

---

1. (a) weather, p. 63 **(b)** climate, p. 63 **(c)** rotation, p. 64 **(d)** revolution, p. 64 **(e)** solstice, p. 65 **(f)** equinox, p. 65 **(g)** precipitation, p. 67 **(h)** front, p. 68 **(i)** continental climate, p. 69

2. The earth's tilt and revolution around the sun affect the angle of the sun's rays on different parts of the earth.

3. They distribute the sun's heat over the earth's surface.

4. (a) because it lies inland, on the leeward side of the Sierra Nevada **(b)** Global warming could partially melt polar ice caps, causing rising ocean levels and flooding.

5. Possible answer: Population might move inland because low-lying coastal areas are subject to flooding.

Activity Rubrics Share rubrics with students before they begin their tables.

Attempted The table is incomplete and is messy or difficult to read.

Minimal The table contains data for four cities in different climate regions.

Adequate The table is complete and easily readable.

Exemplary The table is complete, easy to read, and visually attractive.

Answer to Chart Skills

tropical wet or highlands

Answer to Diagram Skills

Possible answers: transportation, industry

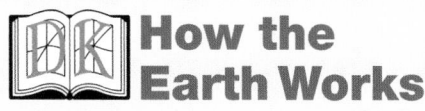

How the Earth Works

pp. 74–75

Objectives

Upon completion of this feature, students should be able to:

◆ name the layers of the earth's atmosphere and the gases it contains;

◆ describe how the atmosphere supports human and plant life on the earth;

◆ explain how the atmosphere was formed and how the ozone layer is in danger of being destroyed.

National Geography Standards

The following National Geography Standards are highlighted in this feature: 7, 14, 15

Bellringer

Ask students what images come to mind when they think of the earth's atmosphere. Ask: **Do you usually think about the atmosphere as just containing the bottom layer where weather occurs? Do you know what that layer is called? Do you know how many other layers there are?**

....

LESSON PLAN

1. Focus After students read the paragraph labeled Earth's Atmosphere, tell them that the *troposphere* includes the air they breathe. Have students brainstorm to create a list of gases that exist in the troposphere.

2. Instruct Discuss the role of oxygen and carbon dioxide in the earth's atmosphere. Then have volunteers draw a cause-and-effect chart on the board to show the cycle of how gases are created and used by humans and plants.

3. Close/Reteach Have students examine the hole in the ozone layer shown on the next page. Have students predict some of the problems South America might be experiencing because of the hole.

How the Earth Works

Earth's Atmosphere

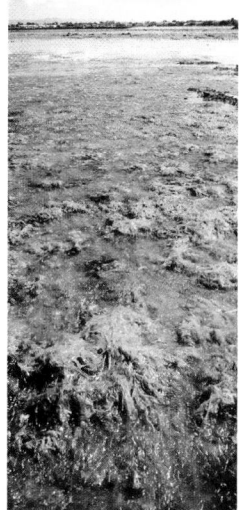

The outermost part of the earth is the atmosphere, a multilayered mixture of gases, water vapor, and tiny solid particles. It extends at least 600 miles (1,000 km) above the solid surface of the earth, but about half the mass of these gases is in the lowest 3.8 miles (6.2 km). The atmosphere's gases support plant and animal life. They also protect the earth from the sun's harmful rays. The layer of the atmosphere closest to land is the **troposphere.** It contains the air that we breathe. Here, temperature and humidity change rapidly, and the air is turbulent, creating weather patterns.

OXYGEN FROM PHOTOSYNTHESIS
Oxygen is a relative newcomer in the earth's atmosphere. It has come from plants that, during **photosynthesis,** use carbon dioxide to make their food, while giving out oxygen. The earliest photosynthesizing plants, which probably looked like these algae, evolved about 3,000 million years ago.

THE ATMOSPHERE FROM SPACE
Viewed from space, the earth looks totally unlike other planets of our solar system. It is partly shrouded in white clouds, which swirl in patterns, making weather. **Clouds** are masses of tiny particles of water and dust floating in the atmosphere. A very low cloud is called fog.

OXYGEN CYCLE
A vast store of oxygen exists in oceans, rocks, and the atmosphere. Oxygen created by plant photosynthesis balances oxygen used by people and animals.

A large amount of oxygen is stored in the atmosphere

Oxygen given off by marine plants

Oxygen used in burning fossil fuels

Oxygen used by marine animals

Oxygen used by animals and humans

Oxygen given off by plants

FERTILE LAND
The atmosphere helps life to flourish on the earth. It offers protection from harmful radiations and provides nourishment for both plants and animals. Winds in the troposphere moderate daily and seasonal temperatures by distributing heat around the world.

RESOURCE DIRECTORY

Technology
World Geography Map and Photo Transparencies
• How the Earth Works, Unit 1
Companion Web Site, www.phschool.com
• Chapter 2 Activities

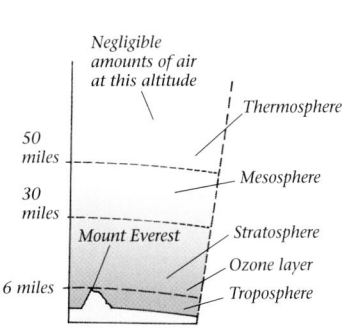

LAYERS OF ATMOSPHERE
The earth's atmosphere has several layers. The heights of these layers vary with season and latitude. Weather is confined to the troposphere, and almost all clouds are below this level. In the stratosphere lies the important ozone layer that filters the sun's rays.

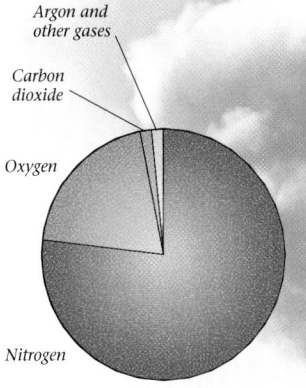

GASES IN THE ATMOSPHERE
The most abundant gas in the lower atmosphere is nitrogen, which makes up about 78 percent of air. Oxygen, about 21 percent of air, is essential for supporting animal life. Carbon dioxide is just a tiny fraction of the atmosphere, but it is vital in sustaining plant life.

OZONE HOLE
Within the stratosphere is the **ozone layer**, a band of ozone gas that absorbs the sun's harmful ultraviolet rays. In recent years, the ozone layer has been getting thinner. Certain pollutant gases, such as chlorofluorocarbons, cause ozone molecules to break down. Some scientists suggest that ozone depletion also may be caused by natural phenomena. Holes in the ozone layer were first detected over Antarctica and the Arctic. At times, the southern hole has expanded over populated areas of South America, as shown by the dark blue color in this NASA satellite photograph.

VOLCANIC GASES
About 4 billion years ago, the earth had no atmosphere and its surface was covered with erupting volcanoes. The earth's atmosphere was formed mostly from gases spewed out by volcanoes since the earth began, although some gases, like oxygen, are a later contribution.

ASSESSMENT

1. **Key Terms** Define **(a)** troposphere, **(b)** photosynthesis, **(c)** cloud, **(d)** ozone layer.

2. **Physical Processes** How was the earth's atmosphere formed?

3. **Natural Resources** How does carbon dioxide support life?

4. **Geographic Tools** How does the NASA satellite photograph display the growing problem of ozone holes?

5. **Critical Thinking Analyzing Processes** Study the diagram showing the oxygen cycle. **(a)** How would extensive deforestation affect the oxygen cycle? **(b)** Which part of the cycle can damage the ozone layer?

BACKGROUND

The Physical World

Mountain Climbing and Oxygen
Although the entire troposphere contains oxygen, the amount of oxygen varies at different altitudes. The summit of Mount Everest is the highest point on earth, measuring 29,035 feet, or approximately 5.5 miles. At that level, oxygen levels are extremely low, which makes climbing Everest very dangerous. If climbers do not get enough oxygen, they become dizzy and disoriented. Today, climbing teams carry tanks of oxygen with them in their efforts to reach the summit.

ACTIVITY

Vocabulary

Stratosphere and Troposphere
Have students explain how the *stratosphere* differs from the *troposphere*. Then have them use the words to write sentences.

Answers to Assessment

1. (a) troposphere, p. 74 **(b)** photosynthesis, p. 74 **(c)** cloud, p. 74 **(d)** ozone layer, p. 75

2. It was formed mainly from gases spewed out by volcanoes. Some gases, like oxygen, formed later.

3. Plants use carbon dioxide to complete the process of photosynthesis.

4. It uses color to show how the ozone hole over Antarctica has spread.

5. (a) It would reduce the number of oxygen-producing plants. **(b)** burning fossil fuels

CUSTOMIZE FOR...

Less Proficient Writers
Visual Representations Encourage students to use the pictures on these pages as a guide for taking notes. Have them study each picture and write down from memory the topic it illustrates. Then have them scan the text for more facts to add to their notes.

Teaching the Skill

Review the use of thematic maps with students. Ask: **What kinds of information could be shown using a thematic map?** (Possible answers: weather, time zones, vegetation, climate, economic activity, population, temperature, natural resources) Create a seating chart for your classroom on the chalkboard. Instruct the students to copy this "physical map" and use it as the basis for their own thematic maps. You may use a class theme or allow students to choose individual themes. Some simple themes (gender, hair color, or clothing) would involve limited symbols and colors. More complex themes (favorite ice cream flavor or favorite type of music) would involve polling and more complex markings. Discuss how thematic maps can show spatial relationships that listed data cannot.

Answers to Learn the Skill

1. (a) the northern interior
(b) Minneapolis, Denver
2. (a) Answers include Washington, New York, Pennsylvania, West Virginia, Virginia, North Carolina, and Oregon **(b)** the north central region
3. (a) cooler temperatures **(b)** no
4. Possible answer: clothing suited for the cooler temperatures and rain

Answer to Practice the Skill

Students should make reasonable predictions about weather conditions and sound recommendations based on their predictions.

Interpreting a Thematic Map

A thematic map is a specialized map that uses symbols and colors to provide information on a specific subject. The map below uses symbols and colors to show the weather patterns and temperatures on one day. By learning to decode thematic maps, you can unlock the information they provide.

Learn the Skill Use the following steps to learn how to understand and analyze thematic maps.

1 *Determine what the colors on the map represent.* Thematic maps use color to show areas with specific characteristics. For example, the map below uses colors to show temperature ranges. **(a)** *What region of the country is the coldest?* **(b)** *Which cities are the coldest?*

2 *Identify the meaning of each symbol.* Depending on the topic of the map, symbols will have different meanings. On the weather map, the slanted lines show rain. **(a)** *Name two states that are experiencing rain.* **(b)** *What area is experiencing snow?*

3 *Use the symbols to interpret the map.* Some symbols are specific to particular kinds of maps. The blue arrows and red half circles on this map indicate the direction in which fronts and air masses are moving. A weather front is the boundary between two air masses of different temperature and humidity. Fronts often signal sudden weather changes. **(a)** *What change in*

weather can Miami expect? **(b)** *Will El Paso be affected by a cold front?*

4 *Make predictions and recommendations.* Suppose that a weather map shows a large cold front with temperatures in the 20s moving toward Florida. A reasonable prediction would be that Florida can expect below-freezing temperatures. In response, farmers should take steps to protect their crops from frost. *Based on the map below, what items would you pack if you were traveling from Miami to Washington, D.C.? Explain.*

Practice the Skill Find a weather map in your local newspaper or on an Internet weather site. Analyze the map and make some predictions about what the weather will be like in your region during the next few days. Identify some kind of business that would be affected by that weather, and make recommendations for what the owners of such a business might do to benefit from the weather or avoid harm.

Apply the Skill See Chapter 2 Review and Assessment.

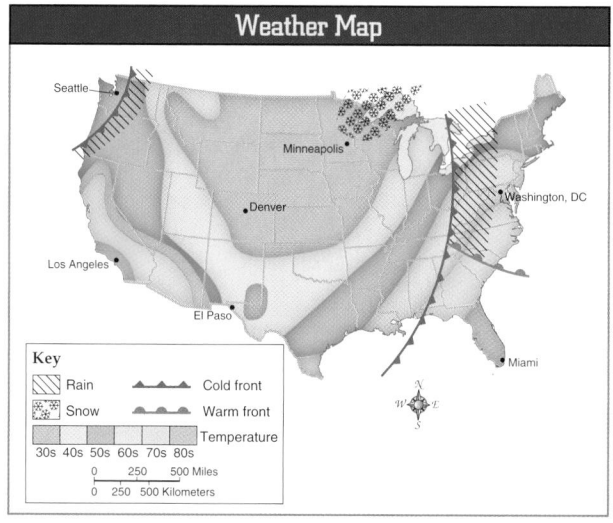

Weather Map

RESOURCE DIRECTORY

Teaching Resources
Creative Teaching Activity, Biomes and Vegetation Regions, p. 4
Unit 1, Chapter 2
• Section 2 Guided Reading and Review, p. 19
Guide to the Essentials (English/Spanish)
• Section Summary, Chapter 2, Section 2
Mental Mapping booklet
• Unit 1 Checklist, p. 5

Technology
Guided Reading Audiotapes (English/Spanish), Chapter 2, Section 2

Section Reading Support Transparencies, Chapter 2, Section 2
World Geography Map and Photo Transparencies
• World Ecosystems
Book on CD, Chapter 2
World Geography Videos
• Climates and Ecosystems: Ecosystems, Tape 1
Social Studies Skills Tutor CD-ROM
Companion Web site, www.phschool.com
• Chapter 2 Activities

2 Ecosystems

Reading Focus

- **What conditions affect life in an ecosystem?**
- **Why are there different types of forests?**
- **Where are grasslands located?**
- **How does life survive in harsh deserts and tundras?**

Key Terms

ecosystem	chaparral	prairie
biome	savanna	tundra
deciduous	herbivore	permafrost
coniferous	carnivore	

Main Idea The interaction of plant life, animal life, and the physical environment forms the earth's many ecosystems.

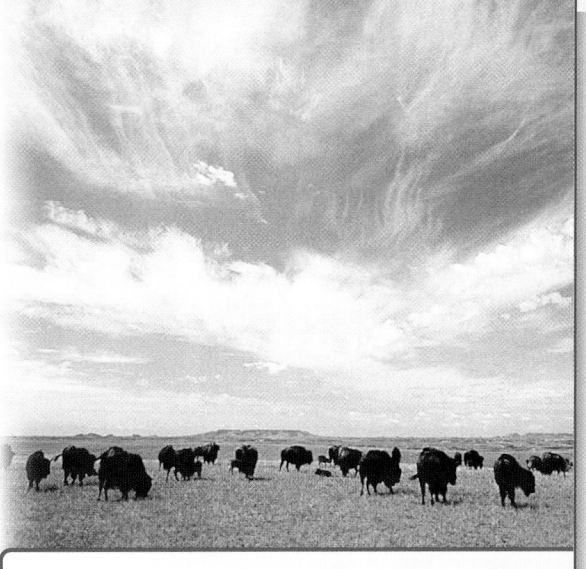

Ecosystems Huge herds of buffalo once grazed on the plains of North America.

Even in harsh polar regions and arid deserts, plants and animals grow in response to their environments. Vegetation ranges in size from microscopic, one-celled plants to gigantic redwood trees; and animals may range in size from tiny mites to large elephants or whales. Plants and animals are important to people because they supply food and other materials on which people depend.

Ecosystems

Groups of plants and animals tend to be interdependent. They depend on one another for things such as shade, support, and nourishment. An **ecosystem** is formed by the interaction of plant life, animal life, and the physical environment in which they live.

Various physical conditions affect the survival and growth of life in an ecosystem. These factors include climate, sunlight, temperature, precipitation, elevation, soil, and landforms. Environments with similar conditions tend to support similar communities of plants and animals.

Environmental Change Because of interaction, change in one aspect of an ecosystem

leads to other changes. In a forest, for example, the loss of oak trees will endanger squirrels and other animals that rely on acorns for food. As human populations have grown, ecosystems have changed dramatically. Areas that were once grasslands are now farmland. The loss of natural habitat usually leads to severe declines in animal and plant populations. However, some species have thrived in spite of or because of human changes to the environment. In suburban neighborhoods across the United States, deer munch on grass and shrubs, while raccoons and other animals forage in trash cans.

Biomes Geographers classify ecosystems by their natural plant and animal life. The term **biome** (BY ōm) is used to describe major types of ecosystems that can be found in various regions throughout the world. A deciduous forest is one example of a biome. Whether in North America, Europe, or Asia, a mid-latitude deciduous forest is likely to have moderate climate conditions,

GEOFacts

Biosphere 2 is an enclosed, living laboratory in the Arizona desert. By adjusting rainfall, temperature, light, carbon dioxide, and other qualities of the air and soil, scientists study the effects of environmental change on plants and animals within an ecosystem.

TEST PREPARATION

Have students read the section Ecosystems on this page to answer the question below. Which of the following scenarios does *not* affect the survival and growth of life in an ecosystem?

- **A** Humans plant trees in a barren area.
- **B** A volcano erupts violently on a populated island.
- **C** A bear catches fish in a stream.
- **D** An irrigation system provides water to a field.

Objectives

Upon completion of Section 2, students should be able to:

- ◆ identify the conditions that affect life in an ecosystem;
- ◆ explain why there are different types of forests;
- ◆ locate grasslands globally;
- ◆ explain how life survives in harsh deserts and tundras.

National Geography Standards

The following National Geography Standards are highlighted in this section: 1, 3, 5, 7, 8, 14

Bellringer

Ask students: **What do houseplants need to stay healthy?** (Possible answers: water, fertilizer, sunlight, proper temperatures) Then ask: **In the wild, plants survive without help from humans. Why would they need help when they are in a home?** (Possible answer: Houseplants live in an artificial environment.)

LESSON PLAN

1. Focus Show students photographs of three very different regions (for example, grasslands, tundra, and rain forest). Then ask: **Why do certain plants grow only in some regions and not in others?** Tell students to look for the answer as they read Section 2.

2. Instruct Draw three columns labeled *Regions, Climate,* and *Plant Life* on the board. Have students identify the eight specific regions discussed in Section 2 and list them in the first column. Ask volunteers to write in the climates and types of plants associated with each region.

3. Close/Reteach For review, show students photographs of the following: rain forest, coniferous forest, grassland, desert, and tundra. For each photograph, have students write a caption that includes the name of the region, its typical climate, and its native plants.

BACKGROUND

United States and the World

Natural Vegetation Few other countries have the variety of natural vegetation that grows in the United States. It ranges from tundra to desert scrub and from coniferous forest to tropical rain forest.

BACKGROUND

Connecting With . . .

Science Open areas, such as a vacant lot, fire-scarred woods, or an unused field, are first inhabited by plants that like sunlight and grow quickly. As the first plants grow taller, they provide shade. Eventually, shade-loving plants take hold and crowd out earlier groups of plants. This is called "plant succession."

oak or maple trees, and animals such as deer, squirrels, cardinals, and owls.

Forest Regions

The word *forest* probably makes you think of whatever kind of forest is most familiar to you—towering groves of redwoods, thick clumps of oaks and maples, clusters of hickories or beeches, hillsides covered with fragrant pines. All these forests exist in North America. In other parts of the world there are different types of forest regions.

Forest vegetation of one kind or another grows on every continent except Antarctica.

Tropical Rain Forest In areas near the Equator, where the temperature is warm and great amounts of rain fall, thick, tropical rain forests grow. The largest are in the Amazon River basin in South America and the Congo River basin in central Africa. Within the rain forest, tall trees form a dense canopy of leaves that blocks much of the sun from the forest floor. Because of varying environmental conditions, each layer of

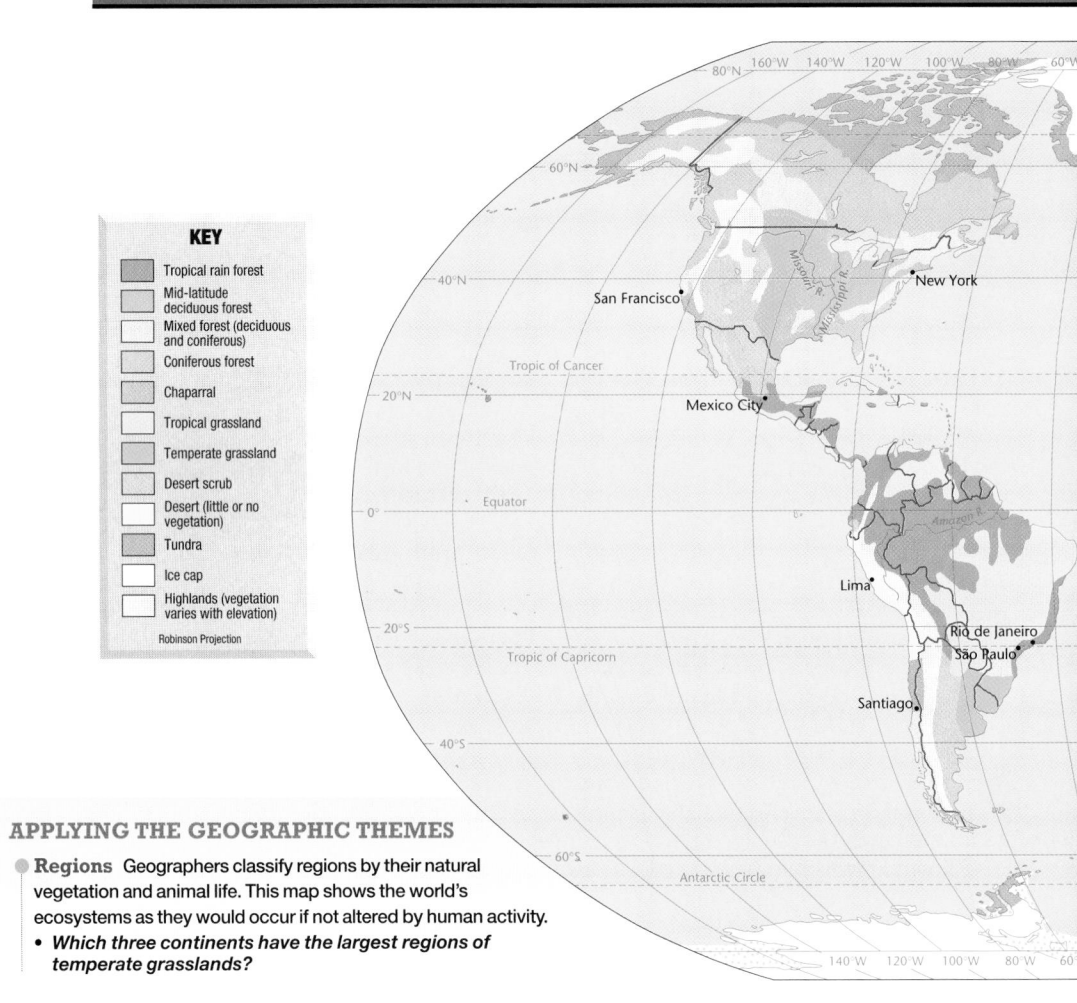

The World: ECOSYSTEMS

KEY

- Tropical rain forest
- Mid-latitude deciduous forest
- Mixed forest (deciduous and coniferous)
- Coniferous forest
- Chaparral
- Tropical grassland
- Temperate grassland
- Desert scrub
- Desert (little or no vegetation)
- Tundra
- Ice cap
- Highlands (vegetation varies with elevation)

Robinson Projection

APPLYING THE GEOGRAPHIC THEMES

● **Regions** Geographers classify regions by their natural vegetation and animal life. This map shows the world's ecosystems as they would occur if not altered by human activity.

• *Which three continents have the largest regions of temperate grasslands?*

RESOURCE DIRECTORY

Technology
World Geography Map and Photo Transparencies
• World Ecosystems

Answer to Map Caption
North America, Asia, Australia

78 Chapter 2

the forest supports a different community of plants and animals. Rain forests cover only about 6 percent of the earth's surface, but contain more than half of the earth's plant and animal species.

Mid-Latitude Forest The trees in the tropical rain forest are broadleaf evergreens, which keep their leaves year-round. By contrast, the dominant trees in the forests of the middle latitudes are **deciduous**. That is, they shed their leaves during one season, usually autumn. These forests look dramatically different, depending on the season—stark and bare in the winter and lush and green in the summer. In some parts of the world, the broad leaves of these trees—such as oaks, birches, and maples—turn brilliant colors before they fall. The New England states are famous for their vibrant fall foliage.

Broadleaf deciduous forests once covered much of Europe, eastern North America, and eastern Asia. Except in relatively hilly areas, a large part of this type of forest was cleared over the centuries for agriculture and other human uses. Very little of the original natural vegetation

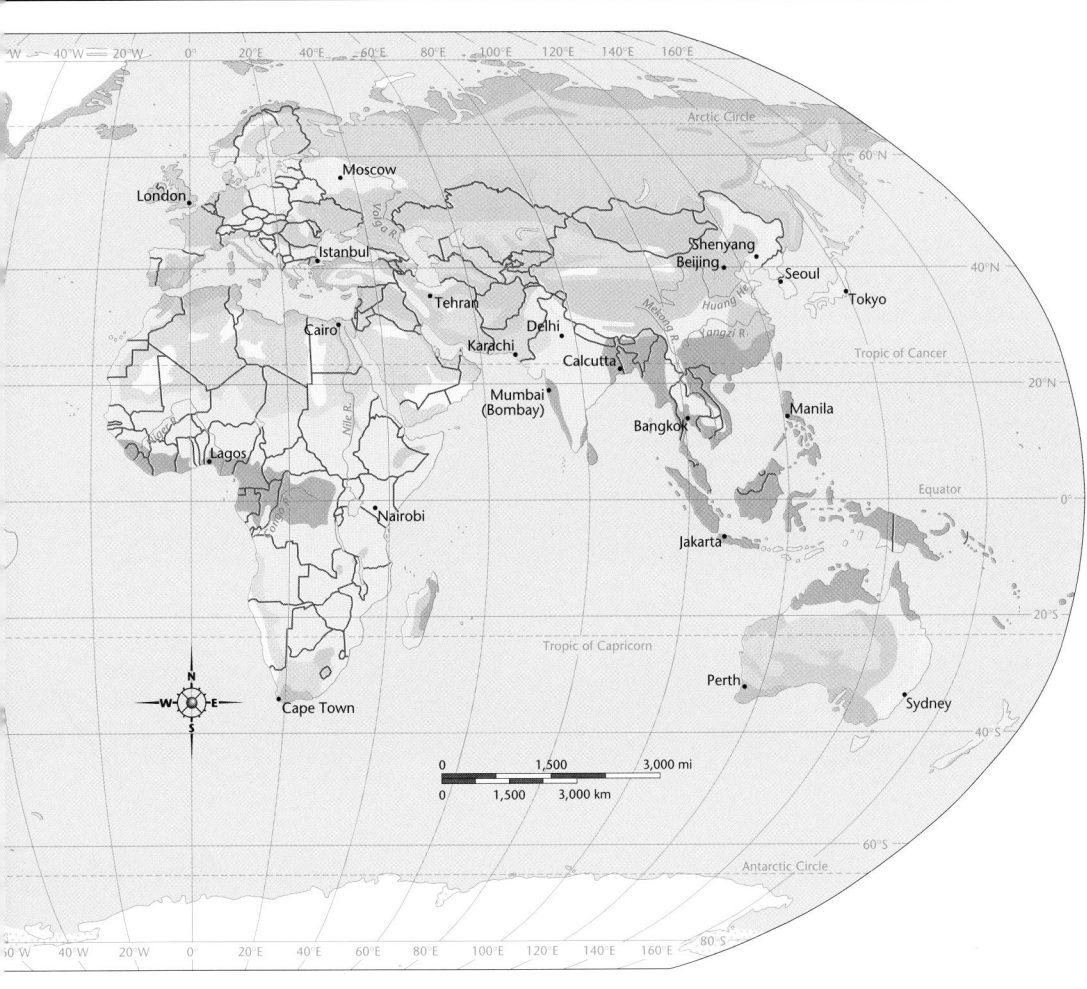

Vocabulary

Deciduous Point out the Key Terms list on page 77. Have a volunteer find the definition of *deciduous* in the glossary and read it aloud to the class. Instruct students to look at the map on pages 78–79. Then ask: **Besides the United States, where can we find mid-latitude deciduous forests?** (Answers include: Great Britain, France, and parts of Spain, Russia, and China)

Critical Thinking

Human Interaction Discuss the following question with students as a group: **How do human activities affect plant communities?** (A possible answer could be that when people clear the land for building, farming, logging, etc., they destroy or permanently damage whole plant communities.)

Articles From
NATIONAL GEOGRAPHIC

The following article may be used to extend the content in this section.

Parfit, Michael, and Peter Essick, photographer. "California Desert Lands: A Tribute to Desolation." *National Geographic,* Vol. 189, No. 5 (May 1996), pp. 54–79.

Over 9 million acres of desert, once considered useless, are a thriving ecosystem protected by the government.

Ask students to think about the type of information they read under the heading Forest Regions. (The location, climate, and vegetation of the types of forests listed.) Tell students to look at the headings of the Grasslands section. Then, ask students: **Based on the structure of the Forest Regions section, what do you expect will be discussed in the Grasslands section?** (The students should expect the Grasslands section to include the same types of information discussed in the Forest Regions section. They should also predict that this section will present information about tropical grasslands and temperate grasslands.)

remains. In some places, fields have been abandoned and the natural vegetation is reclaiming the land. These lands in the middle latitudes have a temperate climate with adequate rainfall, warm summers, and cool or cold winters.

Coniferous Forest In the colder parts of the middle latitudes grow several kinds of trees that can survive long, cold winters. Pines, spruces, firs, and their relatives have long, thin "needles" rather than broad, flat leaves. Needles expose only a small surface to the cold and so can remain on the tree in winter without freezing.

The northern forests are named **coniferous** after the cones that protect their seeds. Coniferous forests stretch across northern North America, Europe, and Asia. Some large mammals, like moose and bears, live in these forests, but most animals are smaller and are well adapted to the harsh conditions that exist much of the year.

Other Forest Types Some small areas of the world have unique forest vegetation. In most places, however, forest regions overlap. A mixed region has coniferous and broadleaf deciduous trees growing together in the same area. Clusters

of such forests are common in many places, including the northern United States. They grow in cool parts of the middle latitudes or at high elevations where winters are mild or very cold.

Another distinctive forest type is **chaparral,** which includes small evergreen trees and low bushes, or scrub. *Chaparral* is a Spanish word for "an area of underbrush and small trees." This vegetation is uniquely adapted to a Mediterranean climate, where most of the precipitation falls during the winter and where summers are hot and dry. Many chaparral plants have leathery leaves to hold moisture over the dry summer. Regions of chaparral are found on the coasts of the Mediterranean Sea, southern California, Chile, South Africa, and Australia, as well as in a few inland areas of the American Southwest.

Grasslands

The central regions of several continents are covered by grasslands. At the edges, grasslands and forest often mix. In addition, scattered clumps of trees often grow on grasslands where there is enough water. Like forests, the characteristics of grasslands vary depending on their latitudes.

Australian Chaparral

Ecosystems Chaparrals receive most of their precipitation during the winter. In this chaparral in western Australia, the wet winter months are June through August.

Regions *How are plants in chaparral regions able to survive the long dry summers?*

RESOURCE DIRECTORY

Teaching Resources
Social Studies Skills Handbook
• Critical Thinking Skills, Recognizing Cause and Effect, p. 49

Answer to Photo Caption

They have leathery leaves to hold moisture over the dry summer.

Death Valley

Ecosystems Despite its name, Death Valley does support some life, as evidenced by this tarantula and desert plant.

Regions *What might be the biggest challenge for plants and animals in this desert?*

Daily Life

Desert Farming The Jacob Blaustein Institute for Desert Research is located in Israel's Negev Desert. On the Institute's experimental farms, researchers use special greenhouses to reduce evaporation. Some of the methods used to collect rainwater are 2,000 years old! Growing food in the desert is a way to maximize limited water resources and to create a more self-reliant economy for the people of the desert.

ACTIVITY

Connecting With . . .

Science Draw two columns on the board; label one *Environment* and the other *Plants*. In the first column, list some features of your local environment. In congested urban areas, for example, students might include such features as noise, pollution, and construction. In the other column, direct students to list local outdoor plants, including those growing in parks. Point out that some plants on this list are surviving because they have adapted successfully to their particular environmental conditions while others are surviving because people have modified the plants' environments using irrigation, fertilization, or other means.

Tropical Grasslands Huge tropical grasslands, or **savannas,** grow in warm lands near the Equator. Scattered trees and other plants that can survive dry periods dot the savanna. Savannas have three seasons. During the wet season, the grasses grow tall and green. This is followed by a dry season, when the grasses turn brown and die above ground. The third season is a time of naturally occurring wildfires. These fires help maintain the savanna by encouraging new grasses to grow. A rich array of animals are found in savannas. **Herbivores,** or plant-eating animals, include gazelles and zebras. **Carnivores,** such as lions and hyenas, are meat-eating animals whose survival depends on thriving herbivore populations.

Temperate Grasslands The grasslands in cooler parts of the world are known by several names. They differ in the length and kinds of grasses, which in turn vary with the amount of rainfall and soil types.

The temperate grasslands of North America are called **prairies.** Rainfall amounts vary across the prairies and give rise to several types of grasses. In the east, which gets as much as 40 inches (102 cm) of rain a year, "tallgrass" prairie once grew. This true prairie is typified by tall grasses dotted with colorful wildflowers. Grasses are shorter as you move west toward the central prairies and the dry Great Plains.

In most parts of the prairies, trees and shrubs grow along the banks of rivers and streams. Grass fires are fairly common in the summer season. Though prairie grasses once covered the American Midwest, little of the natural prairie vegetation is now left. Much of the grassland region was plowed under to provide fertile farmland for growing grain.

The cool, dry, temperate grasslands of Northern Eurasia and Central Asia—called the steppes—are similar to the Great Plains. The word *steppe* comes from a Russian word meaning "treeless plain." Other well-known and productive grasslands are the pampas of Argentina and the veld of South Africa.

Deserts

Desert regions are not just barren expanses of sand. Many plants and animals have adapted to survive with almost no water. Cactus plants, for example, store water in thick stems. The saguaro cactus expands like a sponge to make room for water in its trunks and branches. It can store hundreds of gallons of water.

Cactus leaves are prickly needles, which protect them and their water supply from animals. Other desert plants have small leaves, which lose little moisture into the air through evaporation. Still others have seeds that can survive for many

CUSTOMIZE FOR...

Honors/PreAP

Newscasts Using news articles and information from state and local officials and environmental groups, have students find out how human activities are affecting plants and wildlife in your area. For example, have building sites eliminated fields or forests? Is industrial pollution affecting plants and fish in local rivers and streams? Have students present their information in a short "newscast" for the class.

Answer to Photo Caption

finding adequate moisture

Arctic Tundra

Ecosystems Arctic tundra is found in the extreme northern latitudes, such as here in Denali National Park, Alaska. It supports many kinds of wildlife, such as foxes, wolves, polar bears, moose, caribou, and more than eighty species of birds.
Regions What kinds of vegetation are found in this region?

years until there is enough water for them to sprout. These plants have a short life cycle. After a rain they will sprout, grow, flower, produce new seeds, and die in a short period—all to ensure that their seeds will be ready for the next rainfall.

Like plants, animals in the desert are adapted to extreme temperatures and scarcity of water. Many desert animals do not need to drink at all. They get moisture from the seeds, plants, or other animals that they eat. Camels can survive for many days without food or water by drawing on the fat stored in their humps. Insects are abundant in the desert, providing a source of food for birds, bats, and lizards.

Tundras

In **tundra** regions, where temperatures are always cool or cold, only specialized plants can grow. One type of tundra—alpine tundra—exists in high mountains. No trees grow at these high elevations. Small plants and wildflowers grow in sheltered spots. Tiny, brightly colored plants called lichens (LYE kenz) make patterns on the rocks.

In another type of tundra, the arctic tundra, plants must also be able to live in cold temperatures and short growing seasons. In addition, they must go without sunlight for most of the winter. Arctic landscapes are treeless, covered with grasses, mosses, lichens, and some flowering plants. Some species have developed extremely large leaves that tilt toward the sun. This allows them to catch as much light as possible. In parts of the tundra, a layer of soil just below the surface, known as **permafrost,** stays permanently frozen. The soil above this layer of permafrost is soggy and waterlogged in summer.

Although the tundra sounds like a bleak place, many people find it beautiful. One naturalist wrote this description of the Alaskan tundra in late June:

66When we climbed the higher, drier [river] banks we looked over an eternal expanse of green and brown. . . . It was a glorious garden of arctic plants, this summer tundra-delta, and stiff with northern birds, so that never for a moment were we out of sight or hearing of crane, goose, duck, or wader.99

Although plants and animals may be rare in some regions of the world where climates are especially severe, scientists have found that life-forms may still exist. Recent discoveries have identified specially adapted plants and animals in environments as harsh—and diverse—as the scorching heat of thermal vents deep beneath the ocean and the frigid ice sheets of Greenland and Antarctica. As scientists explore more and more of the earth's extreme climate regions, they are finding that there are really very few places on earth with no plants growing at all. These discoveries lead geographers and other scientists to continually examine the complex ways in which people, plants, and animals interact in the earth's changing environments.

SECTION 2 ASSESSMENT

1. **Key Terms** Define **(a)** ecosystem, **(b)** biome, **(c)** deciduous, **(d)** coniferous, **(e)** chaparral, **(f)** savanna, **(g)** herbivore, **(h)** carnivore, **(i)** prairie, **(j)** tundra, **(k)** permafrost.

2. **Ecosystems** What aspects of the environment affect plants and animals in an ecosystem?

3. **Physical Characteristics** How do the characteristics of forests vary depending on latitude?

4. **Climates** How do climate conditions affect the prairies of the United States?

5. **Ecosystems** Why is it so difficult for plants and animals to survive in deserts and tundras?

6. **Critical Thinking** **Asking Geographic Questions** What questions would you have to ask in order to define an ecosystem?

Activity

Creating a Field Guide Choose an ecosystem described in this section. Then, create a brief field guide to some of the plants and animals typically found there. Include information on how plants and animals are adapted to the physical environment. Illustrate your guide with your own drawings or pictures from magazines or Internet sources.

Creating a Chapter Summary

As a reteaching opportunity, pair a more able student with a less able student to complete this chapter summary.

Additional entries might include the following: **Weather and Climate:** Latitude, Wind patterns, Ocean currents **Ecosystems:** Mid-latitude forest, Grasslands, Tundra

Reviewing Key Terms

1–10. Students' sentences should show a clear understanding of each term.

Understanding Key Ideas

11. When the Southern Hemisphere is tilted toward the sun, the Northern Hemisphere is tilted away from it.
12. Warm, moist air is forced upward when passing over the mountains, causing precipitation on the windward side. The air is cool and dry by the time it reaches the other side.
13. because the plants, animals, and the physical environment are interdependent
14. Deciduous trees have broad, flat leaves that are shed during one season, while coniferous trees have long, thin "needles" that stay on the tree all year long.
15. warm climates with wet and dry seasons
16. by adjusting the rainfall, temperature, light, carbon dioxide, and other factors in the closed environment and examining the effects on the ecosystem

Critical Thinking and Writing

17. Prevailing winds and ocean currents carry warm air and water from the western coast of Africa to the eastern coast of North America.
18. Answers will vary. Students should explain the changes they observe in terms of the earth's revolution around the sun and the tilt of the earth on its axis.
19. (a) humid continental
(b) tropical wet

(Continued on next page.)

Creating a Chapter Summary

Copy this concept web on a piece of paper. Using information from Chapter 2, fill in information about the earth's ecosystems. Add circles as needed. Some information has been filled in to help you get started.

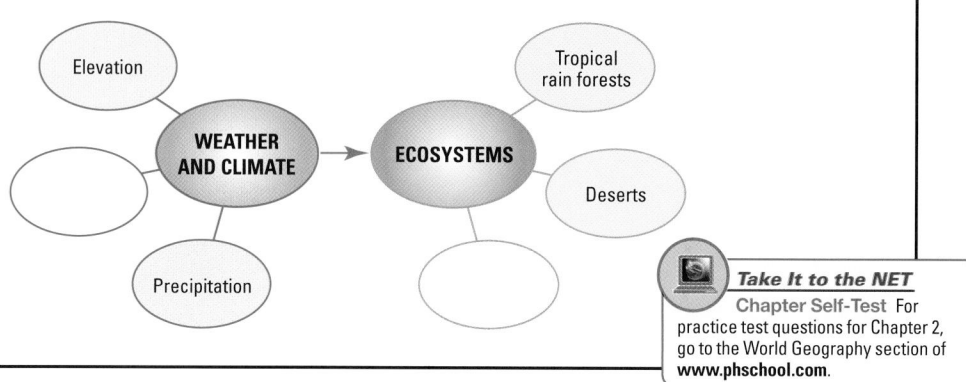

Take It to the NET
Chapter Self-Test For practice test questions for Chapter 2, go to the World Geography section of **www.phschool.com**.

Reviewing Key Terms

Review the meaning of the following terms. Use each term in a sentence that shows its meaning.

1. climate
2. rotation
3. solstice
4. precipitation
5. ecosystem

6. deciduous
7. chaparral
8. savanna
9. tundra
10. permafrost

Understanding Key Ideas

11. **Physical Processes** Why does summer occur in Australia at the same time that winter occurs in North America?
12. **Physical Characteristics** Why does one side of a mountain range sometimes have significantly less precipitation than the other side?
13. **Environmental Change** Why does one change in an ecosystem often lead to other changes in the ecosystem?

14. **Ecosystems** What distinguishes a deciduous forest from a coniferous forest?
15. **Climates** What type of climate gives rise to a tropical grassland?
16. **Geographic Tools** How are geographers using Biosphere 2 to learn about ecosystems and environmental change?

Critical Thinking and Writing

17. **Analyzing Causes and Effects** Explain how weather on the western coast of Africa might affect the weather on the eastern coast of North America.
18. **Analyzing Information** Check your local newspaper to find the times for sunrise and sunset for each day of the week. Are the days growing shorter or longer? What physical process causes this change? Explain.
19. **Recognizing Patterns** Study the maps on pages 70–71 and 78–79. **(a)** What kind of climate often supports deciduous forests? **(b)** What kind of climate supports tropical rain forests?

20. Analyzing Change What is the natural ecosystem in the region in which you live? How have human activities changed the environment?

Applying Skills

Interpreting a Thematic Map Refer to the thematic map on page 76 to answer these questions:

21. Which two regions of the United States are the warmest?

22. What is the temperature range in Denver?

23. Based on the map, what do you think would be the forecast for Washington, D.C.?

Reading a Diagram Study the diagram below, and answer the following questions:

24. What role does vegetation play in the water cycle?

25. What happens after water evaporates from lakes, streams, and oceans?

26. Why does surface runoff flow toward the ocean?

27. What are the main forms of precipitation in the water cycle?

The Water Cycle

Test Preparation

Read each question and choose the best answer.

28. Naturally occurring wildfires encourage new grasses to grow in the—

A tundra

B savanna

C desert

D marshland

29. Which of the following ecosystems would you NOT find near the Equator?

A tundra

B rain forest

C tropical grassland

D highland

Activities

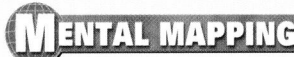

Review the ecosystems map in this chapter. On a separate piece of paper, draw a map of South America from memory. Label the following ecosystems on your map:

- Tropical rain forest
- Tropical grassland
- Mixed forest
- Desert scrub
- Chaparral
- Desert
- Temperate grassland
- Highland

 Take It to the NET

Research on the Internet to find the maximum and minimum temperatures and rainfall recorded for your state. Also, search to discover what extreme weather warnings were issued by the National Weather Service for your area last year. Visit the World Geography section of **www.phschool.com** for help in completing this activity.

Critical Thinking and Writing (cont.)

20. Answers will vary.

Applying Skills
21. Southeast and Southwest
22. 30s
23. rain
24. Moisture from plants is released into the atmosphere.
25. It collects in clouds.
26. It flows into rivers that empty into the ocean.
27. rain, snow, sleet, hail

Test Preparation
28. B
29. A

Activities

Mental Mapping
Review students' maps for relative and absolute location. Refer to the Ecosystems map on pages 78–79.

Take It to the Net
Students' work should reflect sound research on temperature, rainfall, and other weather conditions in your state.

MENTAL MAPPING

Games for Review See pages 58–63 of the Simulations, Games, and Lab Activities booklet for games to review place names in preparation for the Chapter 2 Map Test.

Chapter Map Test Students should use their completed outline map and the Unit 1 Checklist in their Atlas Portfolios to prepare for the Chapter 2 Map Test. Point out to students that the test will cover only Part II of the Unit 1 Checklist, Mountains, Deserts, and Peninsulas.

Alternative Assessment

Final Evaluation

Creating a Map Use the Map Evaluation Form on page 15 of the Alternative Assessment booklet in the Prentice Hall Assessment System to evaluate students' maps. Either teachers or students can complete the form to indicate which level of work was achieved for each of the criteria. The person evaluating the map should use the space on the form to provide specific examples and comments.

Chapter 3 Planning Guide

Resource Manager

	CORE INSTRUCTION	READING/SKILLS
Chapter-Level Resources	📓 Teaching Resources 📗 **Unit 1**/Ch. 3 • Reviewing Main Ideas, p. 34 📘 **Mental Mapping booklet** • Unit 1 Checklist, p. 5 📘 **Simulations, Games, and Lab Activities** • Place Location Review Games, pp. 58–63 📘 **Creative Teaching Activities** • Culture Hearths, p. 5 💿 **TeacherExpress™ CD-ROM**, Ch. 3 💻 **Companion Web site,** **www.phschool.com** • eTeach	📓 Teaching Resources 📗 **Unit 1**/Ch. 3 • Map/Graph Skills, p. 36 📘 **Social Studies Skills Handbook** • Mean, Median, and Mode, p. 63 • Analyzing Statistics, p. 64 💿 **Book on CD**, Ch. 3 💿 **Social Studies Skills Tutor CD-ROM**
1 **The Study of Human Geography** 1. Explain why population density is distributed unevenly around the world. 2. Identify some possible effects of population growth. 3. List some of the elements of culture. 4. Describe how cultures change.	📓 Teaching Resources 📗 **Unit 1**/Ch. 3 • Guided Reading and Review, p. 30 📘 **Simulations, Games, and Lab Activities** • Exploring Local Geography, The Shape of Your Community, p. 9 💿 **Prentice Hall Presentation Pro CD-ROM**, Ch. 3, Sec. 1	📓 Teaching Resources 📘 **Guide to the Essentials (English/Spanish)** • Section Summary, Ch. 3, Sec. 1 📘 **Mental Mapping booklet** • Outline Map 3, p. 12 📘 **Social Studies Skills Handbook** • Reading a Line Graph, p. 54 • Reading a Circle Graph, p. 55 📼 **Guided Reading Audiotapes (English/Spanish)**, Ch. 3, Sec. 1 📖 **Section Reading Support Transparencies**, Ch. 3, Sec. 1
2 **Political and Economic Systems** 1. List four characteristics shared by all countries. 2. Describe how various types of government differ from one another. 3. Explain how various types of economic systems differ from one another.	📓 Teaching Resources 📗 **Unit 1**/Ch. 3 • Guided Reading and Review, p. 32 💿 **Prentice Hall Presentation Pro CD-ROM**, Ch. 3, Sec. 2	📓 Teaching Resources 📘 **Guide to the Essentials (English/Spanish)** • Section Summary, Ch. 3, Sec. 2 📼 **Guided Reading Audiotapes (English/Spanish)**, Ch. 3, Sec. 2 📖 **Section Reading Support Transparencies**, Ch. 3, Sec. 2

ENRICHMENT/HONORS/PREAP

Teaching Resources

Unit 1/Ch. 3
- Critical Thinking, p. 35

Mental Mapping booklet
- Atlas Activity, p. 13

Social Studies Skills Handbook
- Study and Research Skills, pp. 94–108

World Geography Map and Photo Transparencies
- World: Political
- World: Population Growth
- World: Population Cartogram
- Per Capita GDP

World Geography Videos
- Population and Culture: Economic Systems, Tape 1

Companion Web site,
www.phschool.com
- Chapter 3 Activities

Teaching Resources

Simulations, Games, and Lab Activities
- Simulation: Population Strains City Services, p. 16

Companion Web site,
www.phschool.com
- Chapter 3 Activities

Teaching Resources

Simulations, Games, and Lab Activities
- Simulation: How Is the Wealth of the World Distributed?, p. 13

Companion Web site,
www.phschool.com
- Chapter 3 Activities

ASSESSMENT

PRENTICE HALL
ASSESSMENT SYSTEM

Core Assessment
- ExamView Test Bank booklet, Ch. 3
- ExamView Test Bank CD-ROM, Ch. 3

Standardized Test Preparation

Review and Reteach
- Review Book for World Geography, pp. 3–4

Practice and Assess
- Test-taking Strategies With Transparencies for High School
- Test-taking Strategy Poster
- Alternative Assessment booklet
- Test Prep Book for World Geography

Teaching Resources

Unit 1/Ch. 3
- Section Quizzes, pp. 31, 33
- Test Forms A and B, pp. 37–42

Guide to the Essentials (English/Spanish)
- Chapter 3 Test

Spanish Resources, Ch. 3
- Section Quizzes, pp. 9–10

Mental Mapping booklet
- Chapter 3 Map Test, p. 14

Companion Web site, www.phschool.com
- Chapter 3 Self-Test

CUSTOMIZE FOR INDIVIDUAL NEEDS

Less Proficient Readers
- Guide to the Essentials (English), Ch. 3, Section Summaries
- Social Studies Skills Handbook, p. 70
- Guided Reading Audiotapes (English), Ch. 3
- Section Reading Support Transparencies, Ch. 3
- Book on CD, Ch. 3
- Teacher's Edition, Reading Strategy, pp. 97, 103
- Teacher's Edition, Activity: Vocabulary, p. 89
- Teacher's Edition, Customize for . . . , p. 91

Students Acquiring English/ESL
- Guide to the Essentials (English/Spanish), Ch. 3
- Guided Reading Audiotapes (English/Spanish), Ch. 3
- Section Reading Support Transparencies, Ch. 3
- Book on CD, Ch. 3
- Teacher's Edition, Customize for . . . , p. 103

Less Proficient Writers
- Social Studies Skills Handbook, p. 79
- Alternative Assessment, Writing Assignment Rubric, p. 6

Introducing
CHAPTER
3
pp. 86–107

MENTAL MAPPING

Ask students to study the map on this page and identify the countries in which each city is located. Then have students discuss what they know about cities and the reasons people move to or live in cities. Ask them to list the advantages and disadvantages of living in a city. Then have them discuss the factors that lead people to live where they do.

Mapping the World Ask students to study the map on this page. Then have them sketch their own outline maps of the world, or distribute the Chapter 3 Outline Map on page 12 of the Mental Mapping booklet in the Teaching Resources. Ask students to lightly shade each continent a different color. Then have them add labels for each of the cities listed under Part III of the Unit 1 Checklist. Students should keep their maps in their Atlas Portfolios in order to prepare for the Chapter 3 Map Test.

eTeach

Be sure to check out this month's online forum with a Master Teacher to join in an exchange of teaching ideas. **www.phschool.com**

Population and Culture

SECTIONS

1 The Study of Human Geography

2 Political and Economic Systems

Cities of the World

Robinson Projection

Go Online
PHSchool.com

For: More geographic information about population and culture and access to the Take It to the Net activities
Visit: phschool.com
Web Code: mjk-0004

RESOURCE DIRECTORY

Teaching Resources
Unit 1, Chapter 3
• Section 1 Guided Reading and Review, p. 30
Guide to the Essentials (English/Spanish)
• Section Summary, Chapter 3, Section 1
Mental Mapping booklet
• Atlas Activity, p. 13
• Unit 1 Checklist, p. 5

Technology
Guided Reading Audiotapes (English/Spanish), Chapter 3, Section 1
Section Reading Support Transparencies, Chapter 3, Section 1

World Geography Map and Photo Transparencies
• World: Political
Book on CD, Population and Culture: Economic Systems, Tape 1
World Geography Videos
• Population and Culture: Economic Systems, Tape 1
TeacherExpress™ CD-ROM, Chapter 3
Prentice Hall Presentation Pro CD-ROM, Chapter 3
Social Studies Skills Tutor CD-ROM
Companion Web site, www.phschool.com
• Chapter 3 Activities

1 The Study of Human Geography

Reading Focus

- **Why is population density distributed unevenly around the world?**
- **What are some possible effects of population growth?**
- **What are some of the elements of culture?**
- **How do cultures change?**

Key Terms

culture	rural
population density	culture hearth
birthrate	cultural convergence
immigrant	diffusion
emigrant	cultural divergence
urbanization	

Main Idea The study of human geography focuses on a number of population topics, as well as many cultural topics.

Population Growth This crowded beach in Tel Aviv, Israel, is a dramatic indicator of the impact of population growth.

 Geographers are interested in people as well as the physical environment. Human geography includes a wide range of topics, such as the study of languages, religions, customs, and economic and political systems.

A particular focus of human geography is demography—the study of populations—including such topics as birth, marriage, migration, and death. Human geographers also study **culture**—the beliefs and actions that define a group of people's way of life.

Where People Live

More than 6 billion people now live on the earth. It is difficult to imagine how vast the numbers 1 million or 1 billion are. For instance, you had lived a million seconds when you were 11.6 days old. You won't have lived a billion seconds until you are 31.7 years old. In some areas, the **population density**—the average number of people in a square mile or a square kilometer—is very high. Other areas have few or no inhabitants.

What factors lead people to live where they do? Natural obstacles greatly restrict where people can comfortably live. More than two thirds of the earth is covered by water, and about half of the land area is almost unlivable because of harsh deserts, rugged mountains, or bitterly cold climates. As a result, almost all people live on a relatively small share of the earth's surface—areas where the soil is fertile enough, water is plentiful enough, and the climate is mild enough to grow crops.

People and Environments People have always adapted their way of life in response to the surrounding environment. For example, in colder areas they wear heavier clothes. These adaptations have allowed people to survive in areas that might appear hostile to human life.

At the same time, human activity has dramatically altered the earth's physical landscape. By cutting trees, grazing their animals on wild grasses, plowing soils, and damming rivers, people have modified the earth. Some of these modifications

◀ **Hand-carved stone sculptures, Kyoto, Japan** *(photo left)*

Chapter 3 ▪ Section 1 **87**

Objectives

Upon completion of Section 1, students should be able to:

- ◆ explain why population density is distributed unevenly around the world;
- ◆ identify some possible effects of population growth;
- ◆ list some of the elements of culture;
- ◆ describe how cultures change.

National Geography Standards

The following National Geography Standards are highlighted in this section: 1, 2, 3, 4, 5, 9, 10, 12, 18

Bellringer

List the following items on the board and challenge students to identify the culture from which we borrowed or adapted each one: hamburgers and hot dogs (German); chocolate (Aztec); democratic government (Greek); Halloween (Celtic); number system (Hindu-Arab); hockey (Canadian); paper money (Chinese).

LESSON PLAN

1. Focus Ask students to define the term *culture*. Tell them to view their school as a culture. Then ask them to list traits that are part of the school's culture. These include foods and eating customs, language, school traditions, accepted behaviors, and fashion.

2. Instruct Draw a simple map of an island on the board, including two freshwater springs, a dense inland forest, a rocky coast, and a small grassy clearing near one spring. Ask students to imagine that they have been stranded on this island with 100 other people. Have them indicate on the map where they would settle. Point out how resources influence population density.

3. Close/Reteach Remind students that one of the most important questions geographers ask is "Where do people live and why?" Have students identify at least three geographic factors that have contributed to the growth of their town or city.

Chapter 3 ▪ Section 1 **87**

Pacing Suggestions

For 60-minute Blocks

You will want to vary activities.

- Adapt the Creative Teaching Activity on page 5 of the Creative Teaching Activities booklet by having the class concentrate on one ancient culture hearth. Ask one group to prepare a map showing the culture's location, and instruct other groups to research inventions or discoveries in specific areas, such as agriculture, languages and literature, government, or the sciences. Then, have the class complete the chart, organizing students' data.

Critical Thinking

Population Density Ask volunteers to locate the following in an almanac or encyclopedia: population of your community or state and total land area of your community or state. Use the simple method mentioned in the text to calculate population density. Then help students assess their results by asking: **Does this figure reflect our population density accurately?** (Answers will vary.) **Are there areas in our community or state where the population density is greater or lesser?** (Answers will vary but should take into account varied uses of land and physical features, such as farming, city dwelling, deserts, or mountains.)

Connecting With . . .

Math/Science A census is an official counting of the population. Governments employ demographers (geographers who specialize in the study of the size, density, and distribution of human populations) to design and conduct censuses in a precise and scientific manner. Local and national governments use the information for economic planning and distribution of services. In addition to population, a census may also attempt to gather economic and cultural data about the population. In addition to census data, demographers use vital statistics, or records of births, deaths, marriages, and divorces.

have been mild with minimal impact, while others have been drastic.

Population Density The simple way to calculate population density is to divide the total population of a region by the region's land area. The results can be misleading, however. In Egypt, for example, more than 90 percent of the land is desert, and nearly all Egyptians live along a narrow strip beside the Nile River.

Some geographers thus prefer to figure a country's population density in terms of its arable land—land that can be farmed—rather than its total land area. Egypt had an overall population density in 2000 of about 177 people per square mile (68 per sq km). Measured in terms of arable land, the density was about 8,839 people per square mile (3,413 per sq km)!

Population Growth

The world's population has increased dramatically in recent centuries. Several factors have contributed to this growth. Modern technology has helped food production to increase. Improved medical care, meanwhile, has enabled people to live much longer. The overwhelming growth rate poses a special problem for poorer countries and poses a difficult challenge for the world as a whole.

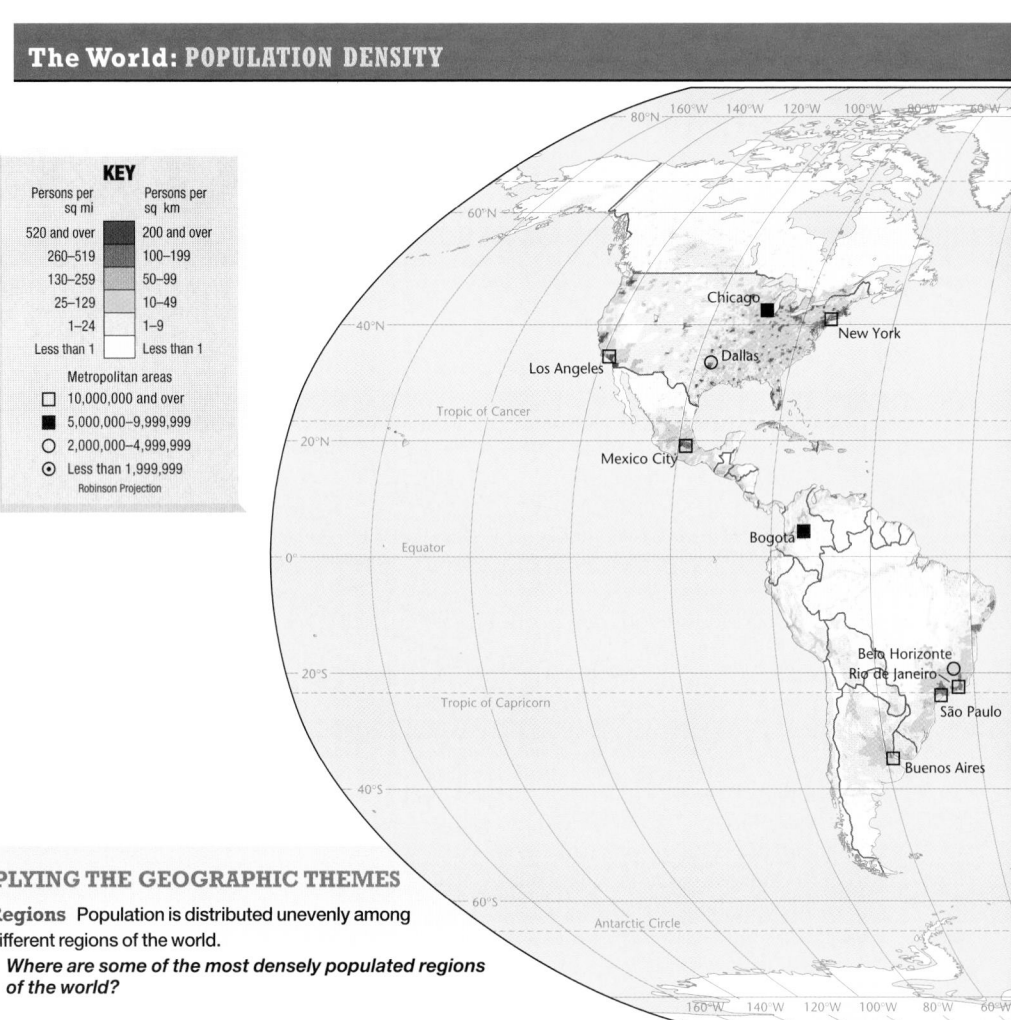

The World: POPULATION DENSITY

APPLYING THE GEOGRAPHIC THEMES

● **Regions** Population is distributed unevenly among different regions of the world.
  • *Where are some of the most densely populated regions of the world?*

Teaching Resources
Mental Mapping booklet
• Outline Map 3, p. 12

Prentice Hall Assessment System
Alternative Assessment booklet
• Writing Assignment Rubric, p. 6

Technology
World Geography Map and Photo Transparencies
• World Population Growth
• World Population Cartogram

Answer to Map Caption

Northeast United States, Western Europe, India, East Asia

The Effects of Growth What will the effects of rapid population growth be? This question has been debated for centuries. Some demographers predict increases in famine, disease, and natural resource depletion. Others are optimistic about the future and predict that as the number of humans increases, levels of technology and creativity will also increase.

Comparing Growth Rates World population growth is very uneven. Different countries have different balances between the **birthrate**—the number of live births each year per 1,000 people—and the death rate—the number of deaths each year per 1,000 people. A country's total population is also affected by differences in the number of **immigrants** (people who move into the country) and **emigrants** (people who leave the country to live in other places).

When the combined birthrate and immigration rate equals the combined death rate and emigration rate, a country is said to have reached "zero population growth." This is the case in some highly industrialized countries today. In many developing countries, however, birthrates are still high, while death rates have fallen because of improved health.

Articles From

NATIONAL GEOGRAPHIC

The following article may be used to extend the content in this section.

Reid, T. R., and Robb Kendrick, photographer. "Feeding the Planet." *National Geographic*, Vol. 194, No. 4 (Oct. 1998), pp. 56–75.

Producing and distributing food to a rapidly growing world population presents a variety of challenges.

Urbanization Help students analyze the effects of urbanization by discussing the following questions: **Why are the densest concentrations of people in urban areas?** (availability of jobs and services) **Why is urbanization a problem in many countries?** (overcrowding; lack of jobs leads to poverty and homelessness.)

Connecting With . . .

Math According to a United Nations report, there were 6 billion people living on earth in the year 2000. Approximately 4 children are born per second. Nearly 220,000 people are added to the earth's population daily, which results in about 80 million people annually. Figures collected in 1997 suggest that about 80 percent of the world population lives in underdeveloped and developing countries. Annual population growth in underdeveloped and developing countries is 10 times the rate in industrialized nations.

Change Over Time

Urban Change

Urbanization Urban populations are increasing throughout the world. This trend is expected to continue.

Location *By 2015, how many urban areas will have more than 14 million inhabitants? Locate those areas on the map on pages 88–89.*

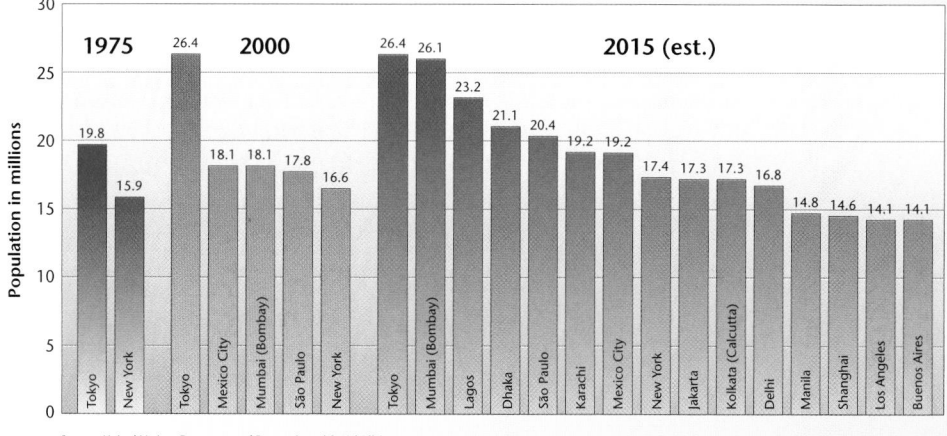

Source: United Nations Department of Economic and Social Affairs

Patterns of Settlement The map on pages 88–89 illustrates the uneven distribution of the world population. The densest concentrations of people are in four regions: East Asia, South Asia, Europe, and eastern North America.

Many of the people in these population clusters live in metropolitan areas—central cities surrounded by suburbs. Today, most Europeans and North Americans live in cities, and **urbanization**—the growth of city populations—is going on throughout the world. In many countries, urban populations are growing twice as fast as **rural**—countryside—populations.

The Nature of Culture

Differences in population patterns are, in part, reflections of differences in culture. As children grow up in a given culture, they learn skills, language, eating customs, and many other cultural traits. Later, they pass these traits on to their own children. Over time, cultures change but usually very slowly.

Culture is reflected in both objects and ideas—that is, in material and nonmaterial ways. Material

culture includes things that people make, such as food, clothing, architecture, arts, crafts, and technology. Nonmaterial culture includes religion, language, spiritual beliefs, and patterns of behavior. It also includes government systems, education systems, and attitudes toward the roles of women and men. Some cultures, for example, value cooperation and group activities, whereas others place greater value on individual achievement.

Cultural patterns vary from country to country and from region to region. Furthermore, within each society there is often a variety of cultural groups and patterns. The result is a complex mosaic of peoples and cultures.

Culture Hearths A **culture hearth** refers to a place where important ideas begin and from which they spread to surrounding cultures. The term is usually used for areas where, in ancient times, major traits of human culture first developed. In Southwest Asia, for example, people first learned to tame and herd animals and to grow crops from wild grasses. Writing and mathematics also originated in this culture hearth.

Fifteen urban areas. Check that students can locate the cities on the map.

Teaching Resources
Creative Teaching Activities, Culture Hearths, p. 5
Unit 1, Chapter 3
• Critical Thinking, p. 35
Mental Mapping booklet
• Chapter 3 Atlas Activity, p. 13
Social Studies Skills Handbook
• Reading a Line Graph, p. 54
Simulations, Games, and Lab Activities
• Exploring Local Geography, The Shape of Your Community, p. 9
• Simulation, Population Strains City Services, p. 16

The culture hearth for most of East Asia was ancient China. Its language, arts, technology, and government influenced neighboring lands and peoples. The cultures of the Olmec, the Teotihuacán (tay uh tee wah KAHN), and the Maya in Mexico and Central America formed early culture hearths in the Americas.

Language Language is the cornerstone of culture. Without language, people would not be able to communicate. They could not pass on what they know or believe to a new generation. All cultures have language, although not all have written languages.

Language reflects a culture's identity. People who speak the same language often share other customs. Many societies, however, include large groups of people who speak different languages. India, for example, has more than 700 languages. The map on pages 92–93 shows the major language families around the world.

Religion Religion is another important aspect of culture. Religion helps people answer basic questions about the meaning and purpose of life. It supports the values that a group of people consider important.

Religious beliefs vary around the world. The worship of one god is called monotheism. The worship of more than one god is called polytheism. Religious practices such as prayers and rituals also vary from one culture to another. The map on pages 94–95 shows the major religions of the world.

Struggles over religious differences are a problem in many countries. These troubles often find their roots in the past. Religious differences are usually not the only cause of fighting, however. Lack of political power or economic opportunity often fuels rivalries.

Cultural Landscapes Technology is an important part of culture. As human beings use natural resources or alter the surface of the earth, they produce unique cultural landscapes that reflect specific cultures. Compare the landscapes of the Great Plains of the United States with rural landscapes in parts of China, for example. In the

(Text continues on page 96)

World Population Growth: 1200 to 2050

Source: United Nations Population Division
*Estimate

CHART SKILLS

● **Population Growth** Rapid population growth is a recent phenomenon.
- *Approximately when did the world's population reach 2 billion?*
- *By what year might world population reach 10 billion? Explain.*

CUSTOMIZE FOR...

Less Proficient Readers

Personal Glossary As students read this page, encourage them to create a personal glossary in which they list unfamiliar words. One example of a word they might add to their lists is *cornerstone*. Explain that one meaning of cornerstone is a stone that is laid at the corner of two walls. Let them know that on this page, it is used to refer to the foundation or basis of something.

ACTIVITY

Connecting With . . .

Music Have students research the development of jazz and its spread from New Orleans to the rest of the country. Reports might show how jazz combined several cultural traditions and influenced American music.

BACKGROUND

History

Two Irelands The conflict between Catholics and Protestants in Northern Ireland is a good example of a conflict that seems religious at first glance but is primarily political. The Irish high king recognized King Henry II of England as lord of Ireland in 1175, but English settlement did not become widespread for centuries. In the 1600s, under King James I, Irish lands were turned over to English and Scots landlords, tenents, and laborers. For hundreds of years, many Irish have resented British rule. In 1921, Britain granted independence to four southern provinces of Ireland. The northern province remained under British government. Today, many Catholics in Northern Ireland believe that their province should be reunited with the Republic of Ireland to the south. Meanwhile, many Protestants believe that Northern Ireland should remain under British rule.

Answers to Chart Skills

roughly 1930

Based on a steady rate of increase, population could reach 10 billion by the year 2100.

Group Work

Activity: Making collages

Purpose: Assign each group one of the following concepts: population distribution, urbanization, or language distribution. Each group may use pictures, sketches, cartoons, words, poems, or objects to make a collage illustrating its concept.

Roles: Assign a group leader who will be responsible for making sure each member contributes to the collage.

Result: Display completed collages. Have group members explain why particular items were included.

The World: MAJOR LANGUAGE FAMILIES

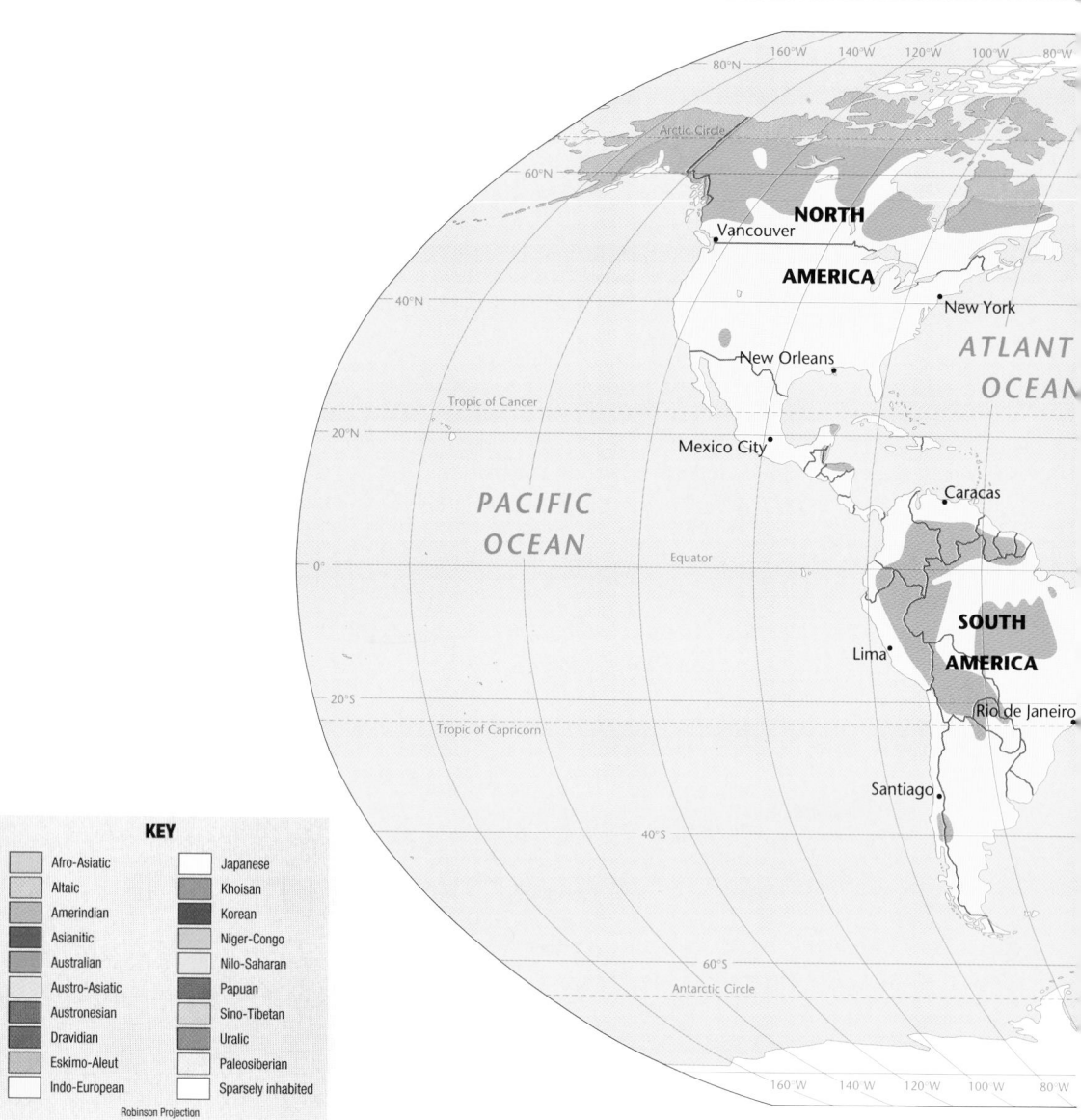

KEY

	Afro-Asiatic		Japanese
	Altaic		Khoisan
	Amerindian		Korean
	Asianitic		Niger-Congo
	Australian		Nilo-Saharan
	Austro-Asiatic		Papuan
	Austronesian		Sino-Tibetan
	Dravidian		Uralic
	Eskimo-Aleut		Paleosiberian
	Indo-European		Sparsely inhabited

Robinson Projection

APPLYING THE GEOGRAPHIC THEMES

● **Regions** Around 3,000 languages are spoken in the world today. Based on their similarities and ancestry, languages can be grouped into a few major categories called language families.
  • *What is the major language family in North America?*

RESOURCE DIRECTORY

Technology
World Geography Map and Photo Transparencies
• World: Political

Answer to Map Caption

Indo-European

Arctic Circle

60°N

40°N

Tropic of Cancer

20°N

Equator 0°

20°S

Tropic of Capricorn

40°S

60°S

Antarctic Circle

80°S

ARCTIC OCEAN

EUROPE

London

Moscow

Istanbul

Tehran

Cairo

ASIA

Beijing

Tokyo

Calcutta

Bangkok

PACIFIC OCEAN

Lagos

AFRICA

Nairobi

INDIAN OCEAN

Jakarta

ATLANTIC OCEAN

Cape Town

AUSTRALIA

Sydney

ANTARCTICA

0   1,500   3,000 mi
0   1,500   3,000 km

N
W   E
S

ACTIVITY

Connecting With . . .

Language Arts Help students brainstorm a list of stories, myths, fables, and books they have read that come from different countries around the world. Have them do research to find out what language those texts were originally written in. Make a copy of the map on these pages and have students create labels to show where the stories were written and in what language they were originally composed.

ACTIVITY

Group Work

Activity: Researching world religions

Purpose: Assign each group a country from the map on these pages. Have each group research the major religion and at least one other religion in the assigned area. Encourage groups to pay special attention to the main beliefs of each religion, where worship takes place, central rituals or practices, and important holy days.

Roles: Assign a group leader to direct research efforts.

Result: Have groups create posters showing the results of their research. Encourage students to include locator maps, illustrations, photos, word collages, and text.

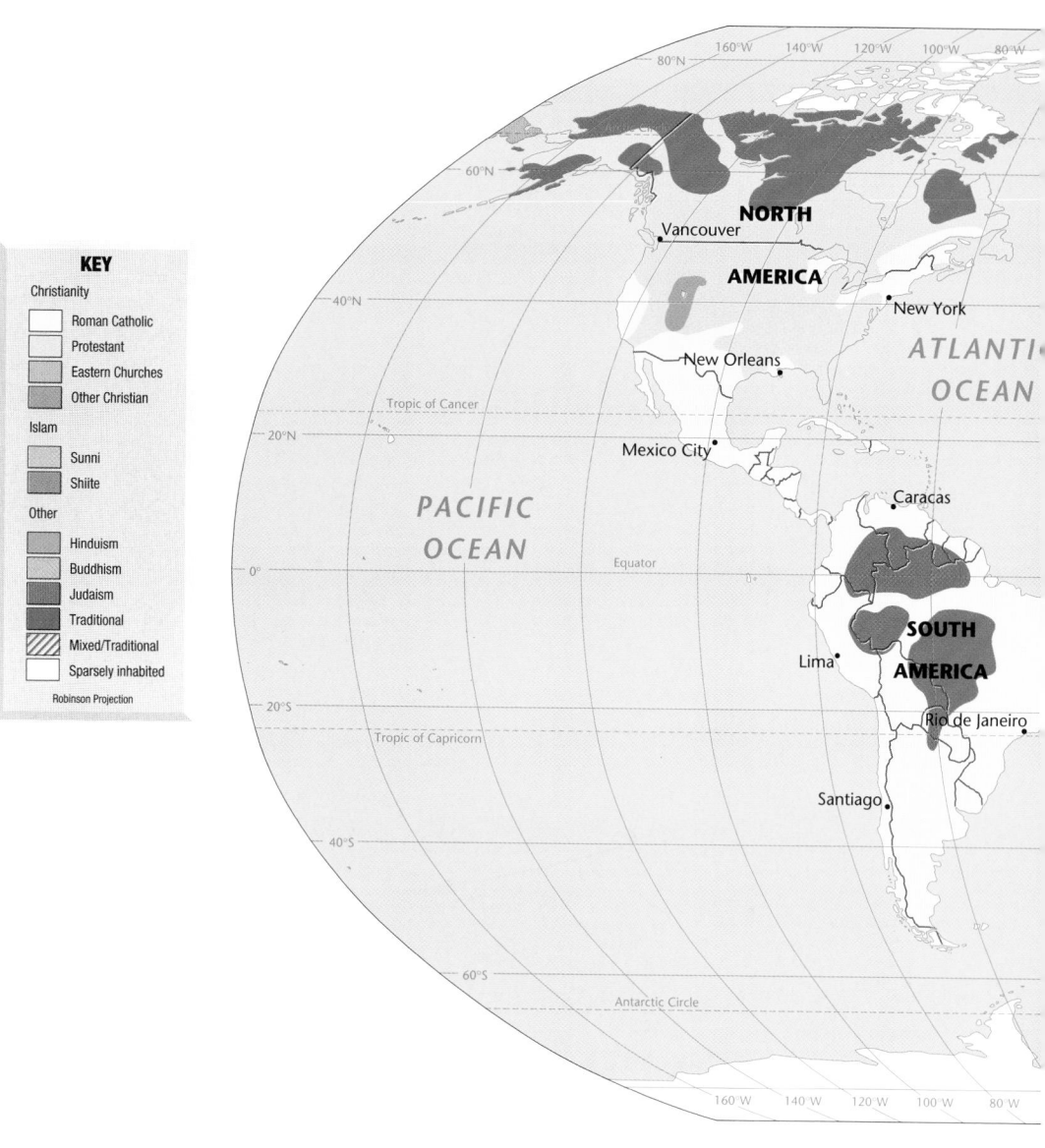

KEY

Christianity
- Roman Catholic
- Protestant
- Eastern Churches
- Other Christian

Islam
- Sunni
- Shiite

Other
- Hinduism
- Buddhism
- Judaism
- Traditional
- Mixed/Traditional
- Sparsely inhabited

Robinson Projection

APPLYING THE GEOGRAPHIC THEMES

Regions Religious beliefs and practices vary around the world. This map shows the general distribution of the major world religions, with the largest religious group shown for each region.
- *In what regions of the world is Islam the predominant religion?*

Answer to Map Caption

North Africa, East Africa, Southwest Asia, Central Asia, and parts of Southeast Asia

RESOURCE DIRECTORY

Teaching Resources

Unit 1, Chapter 3
- Map/Graph Skills, p. 36

Social Studies Skills Handbook
- Reading a Circle Graph, p. 55

Technology

World Geography Map and Photo Transparencies
- World: Political

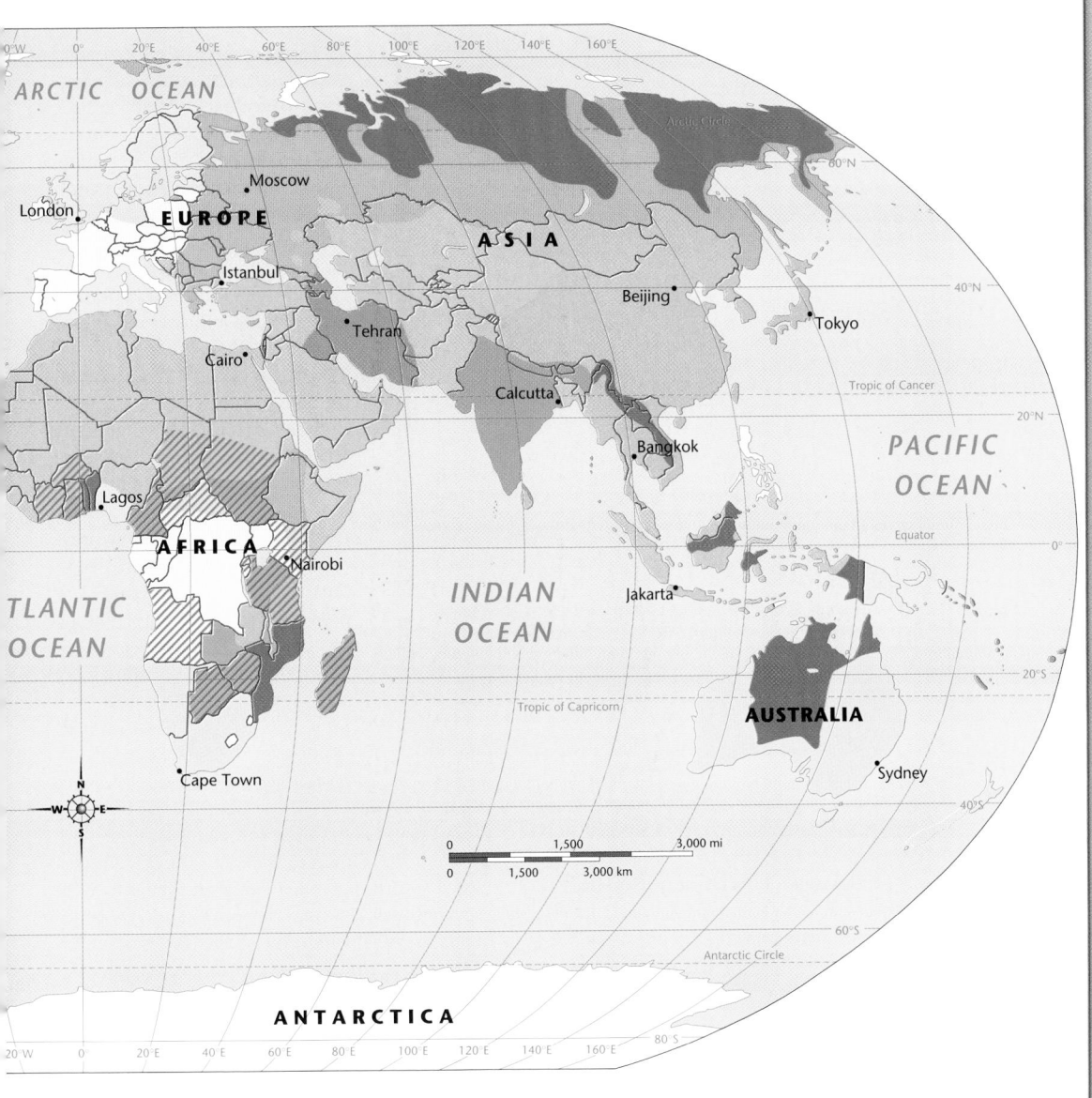

ARCTIC OCEAN

London
EUROPE
Moscow
ASIA
Istanbul
Tehran
Beijing
Tokyo
Cairo
Calcutta
Bangkok
PACIFIC OCEAN
Tropic of Cancer
AFRICA
Lagos
Nairobi
INDIAN OCEAN
Jakarta
Equator
ATLANTIC OCEAN
AUSTRALIA
Tropic of Capricorn
Cape Town
Sydney

ANTARCTICA

0   1,500   3,000 mi
0   1,500   3,000 km

Reteach

Summarizing Make a chart on the board with the headings *Where People Live, Population Growth,* and *The Nature of Culture.* Have students copy the headings and summarize the main ideas of each subsection on their own charts. Ask volunteers to write their summaries on the board. (Visual/Spatial; Bodily/Kinesthetic)

Daily Life

Social Roles The social structure of a culture is based on the social roles of its members. Social roles are the relationships people have within society. For example, a woman may be a daughter, a wife, a mother, and a doctor. Social roles are learned from a culture; they are not instinctive. In most cultures, children learn social roles from their parents and other important people in their lives. Social roles vary widely from culture to culture.

Connecting With . . .

History At different points in U.S. history, people have tried to pass laws to protect minorities from discrimination. For instance, from 1923 to 1982, women's rights advocates attempted to gain support for the Equal Rights Amendment (ERA), which proposed that women and men should be treated equally under the law. The amendment passed both houses of Congress in 1972, but it was not ratified by enough states to make it a constitutional amendment. Regardless, the effort to pass the ERA raised new consciousness about women's rights. As a result, today a number of states guarantee equal rights to women under the law.

CULTURAL CHANGE

Meaning	Outline character about 3000 B.C.	Sumerian about 2000 B.C.	Babylonian about 500 B.C.
Sun			
God or heaven			
Mountain			
Ox			
Fish			

CHART SKILLS

● **Cultures** Ancient Sumerians developed a form of writing known as cuneiform. Later, other peoples adapted cuneiform to their own languages.

• *How does this chart illustrate cultural change as a result of diffusion?*

Great Plains, farmhouses and big sheds storing large farm machines are sparsely scattered among large, open wheat fields. In contrast, people in many parts of rural China use only hand-held tools to grow rice on small, flooded paddies that stand amid rows of many small houses.

Not all landscapes are so different, however. Business executives who travel to cities on different continents sometimes complain that those cities start to look alike. The tall office towers, the bright signs, the rushing traffic, and modern airports all help to create similar urban cultural landscapes.

Social Organization Every culture creates a social structure by organizing its members into smaller units. This social organization is meant to help the people of a culture work together to meet their basic needs. In all cultures, the family is the most important unit of social organization, although family structure varies among cultures.

Most cultures have social classes that rank people in order of status. Social class may be based on money, occupation, education, ancestry, or any other factor that a culture values highly. In the past, a person was usually born into a class and stayed there for life. Today, people in many cultures have at least some degree of social mobility. They have the opportunity to rise in society through education, economic achievement, and political action.

Women and Minorities In many cultures, however, social mobility is restricted. When there are limits, they are often imposed on women, ethnic minorities, and religious minorities. Some cultures, for example, discourage women from assuming leading roles in business and government. They believe that a woman's role should be that of wife and mother.

In some societies, women are encouraged to disfigure their bodies. Centuries ago, for example, Chinese women were expected to have their feet tightly bound with cloth in order to stunt the growth of their feet by about half. Footbinding was painful and made it difficult for women to walk, but the custom persisted because parents feared that a daughter with large feet would be unable to find a good husband. The custom also reinforced the traditional Chinese belief that women were "inside people" who should not do any outside work.

Around the world, there is a long history of discrimination and violence against ethnic and religious minorities. At various times and in various places, Jews, Christians, Muslims, and other religious groups have all suffered as minorities. Majority groups frequently use economic measures to discriminate against the minority. People may be denied high-paying jobs or the best agricultural lands. Their property may be seized by the government or they may be forced to live within a restricted area.

Answer to Chart Skills

Possible answer: Over the course of time, the characters changed in terms of style, but the basic form and meaning remained the same; so each culture adopted the writing with only minor changes.

Cultural Change

Cultures are changed by both internal and external influences. Within a culture, new discoveries and ideas can bring change. Technology is another important part of cultural change. Many of the cultural changes in a society result from the invention of new items or new ways of doing things. For the earliest humans, the use of fire for heating and cooking was a significant advance. Other early technological achievements were the use of tools and the development of language.

Cultural Convergence Today, modern transportation and communication intensifies the speed and frequency of cultural change. **Cultural convergence** occurs when the skills, arts, ideas, habits, and institutions of one culture come in contact with those of another culture. For example, a hit music video in the United States can quickly become a hit around the world as it is transmitted by cable and satellite. The popularity of Mexican food in the United States is another example of cultural convergence.

Diffusion is the process by which a cultural element is transmitted across some distance from one group or individual to another. Diffusion often occurs through the migration of people who take their cultural traits with them to new locations. One example of this kind of relocation diffusion was the introduction of new religions to the Americas when Europeans and Africans arrived in this hemisphere starting more than 500 years ago. This process of adapting some traits from other cultures is called acculturation.

Cultural traits and practices also can diffuse when different groups of people come in contact with one another and exchange goods and ideas. This kind of expansion diffusion was evident when people from the Eastern and Western hemispheres began frequent contact in the early 1500s. Products that Native Americans had grown, such as

Cultural Landscape in China

Cultures Farmers in this region of China grow rice and other crops on terraces that they have carved into the hillsides.

Human-Environment Interaction *How does this cultural landscape differ from that of the Great Plains region of the United States? Why?*

Chapter 3 Section 1 97

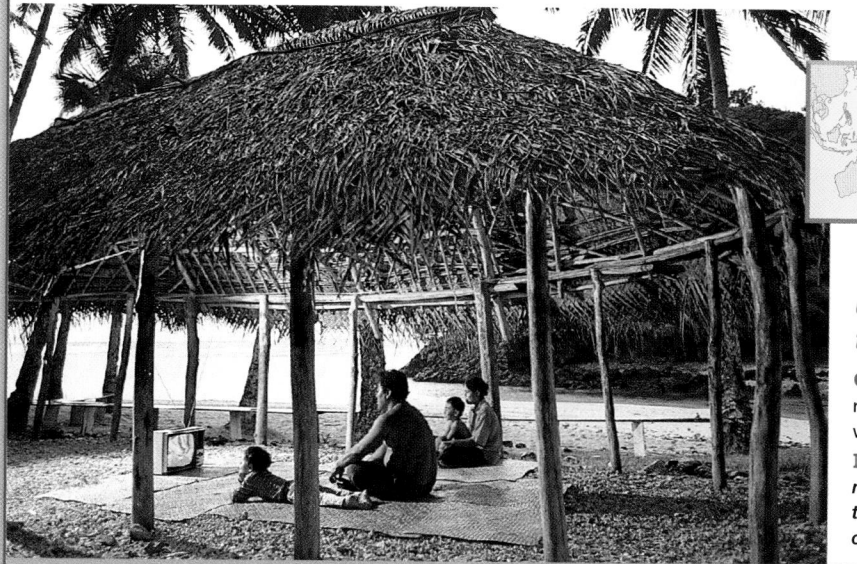

Cultural Change in the South Pacific

Cultures Under a thatched roof, a Pacific Island family watches television together.

Movement *How does modern technology quicken the speed and extent of cultural change?*

potatoes, corn, and beans, were taken back to Europe, where they quickly became major sources of food for people and livestock.

Cultural Divergence In order to limit cultural contact and the spread of ideas, repressive governments seek to control transportation and communication. They restrict free movement into and out of their countries. They also limit free access to newspapers, Internet links, and radio and television transmissions. In this way, repressive leaders enforce **cultural divergence**, which is the restriction of a culture from outside cultural influences.

Some historians suggest that a major cause of the fall of Communist governments during the late 1980s and early 1990s was that Communist leaders were unable to prevent ideas about rights and freedoms from entering their countries. Then, as change started to occur, rapid communication quickly spread the news. As a result, stories of the success of one nation in shedding Communist control quickly spread to other nations, further fanning the flames of revolution.

SECTION 1 ASSESSMENT

1. **Key Terms** Define **(a)** culture, **(b)** population density, **(c)** birthrate, **(d)** immigrant, **(e)** emigrant, **(f)** urbanization, **(g)** rural, **(h)** culture hearth, **(i)** cultural convergence, **(j)** diffusion, **(k)** cultural divergence.

2. **Patterns of Settlement** Which four regions of the world have the densest concentration of people?

3. **Population Growth** **(a)** Why has population growth dramatically increased over the past few centuries? **(b)** What are some possible effects of population growth?

4. **Cultures** Describe several ways in which cultures can differ from one another.

5. **Cultures** Describe two distinct ways in which cultures can change.

6. **Critical Thinking** **Recognizing Bias** Why might some people want to limit cultural contact and the spread of ideas?

Activity

Take It to the NET

Gathering Information Search the Internet for information about economic opportunities for women and religious minorities in different countries. Arrange the information in a table. Visit the World Geography section of **www.phschool.com** for help in completing this activity.

Analyzing Statistical Data

Information is often presented to us in the form of statistical data. You can use data to make comparisons, draw conclusions, plan for the future, and do other critical thinking activities. You use this skill already, such as when you make sense out of sports statistics or when you understand tomorrow's weather based on a forecast.

Learn the Skill Use the table below and the following steps to learn how to analyze statistical data.

1 *Identify the topic of the data.* Read the table title to find out the subject of the table. Check the headings to identify more specific information. **(a)** *What is the subject of this table?* **(b)** *What kinds of statistics are represented in the table?* **(c)** *How many countries are shown?*

2 *Interpret the statistics.* Make sure you understand the meaning of the data. If necessary, look up unfamiliar terms in a dictionary. Sometimes, data are presented with explanations and definitions. **(a)** *What is meant by life expectancy?* **(b)** *What is meant by infant mortality rate?*

3 *Find relationships among the figures.* Determine the kind of thinking that will enable you to develop ideas based on the data. You might want to compare, look for patterns or trends, or identify causes and effects. **(a)** *In which country is population growing at the fastest rate?* **(b)** *In which country does a newborn baby have the least chance of survival?* **(c)** *Is there a relationship*

between fertility rates and population growth rates? Explain.

4 *Read the statistics with a critical attitude.* Statistics usually provide limited information. Avoid drawing conclusions that cannot be supported by the data. **(a)** *Can you use the data below to estimate the population of China in the years ahead? Explain.* **(b)** *Can you use the data to determine why life expectancy in China is 72 years? Explain.*

5 *Draw conclusions.* Use the data to form some conclusions. For example, the data in the table indicate that it is probable that India will one day have a greater population than China. *How does the data support the hypothesis that India's population will one day be greater than China's population?*

 ## Do It Yourself

Practice the Skill Use library or Internet resources to find population data for your state or community. Follow the steps above to analyze the data. Then, write a short summary in which you identify and explain your conclusions.

Apply the Skill See Chapter 3 Review and Assessment.

The World's Most Populous Countries

Country	Total Population (in millions)	Population Growth Rate (percent)	Total Life Expectancy (years)	Infant Mortality Rate*	Total Fertility Rate†
China	1,284	0.87	72	27	1.8
India	1,046	1.51	63	61	2.9
United States	280	0.89	77	6	2.0
Indonesia	231	1.54	68	39	2.5
Brazil	176	0.87	63	36	2.0
Russia	145	−0.33	67	20	1.3
Pakistan	148	2.06	62	78	4.2
Bangladesh	133	1.59	61	68	2.7
Japan	126	0.15	81	4	1.4
Nigeria	130	2.54	51	72	5.4

Source: *The World Factbook*
*Infant deaths per 1,000 live births. †Average number of children born to a woman during her lifetime.

Teaching the Skill
Encourage students to examine the chart on this page slowly and carefully. As you read the title and headings together, be sure to point out the subheads that explain the units of measure (millions, percent, years). Also remind them to find and pay attention to the information signaled by asterisks or other marks. Point out that Infant Mortality Rate may be measured differently depending on the subject matter, so it is important for readers to be aware of the unit of measure for the chart they are reading.

Answers to Learn the Skill
1. (a) the world's most populous countries **(b)** total population, population growth rate, life expectancy, infant mortality rate, fertility rate **(c)** 10
2. (a) the average life span **(b)** the number of infant deaths per 1,000 live births
3. (a) Nigeria **(b)** Pakistan **(c)** Yes. Countries with greater population growth rates have higher fertility rates.
4. (a) Yes, by using the population growth rate. **(b)** No. The table gives figures for life expectancy but does not indicate the reasons for those figures.
5. India's population is growing at a faster rate than China's.

Answer to Practice the Skill
Students' work should reflect sound research. Check that students have drawn valid conclusions and explained them clearly in their summaries.

 ## ▶▶▶ *Career Prep*

Careers in Geography
Demographer Some geographers specialize in demography, the study of the size, density, and distribution of human populations. Private agencies and governments hire demographers to help them predict how populations will grow over time and to analyze the problems that might be encountered with population growth or change.

Objectives

Upon completion of Section 2, students should be able to:

◆ list four characteristics shared by all countries;

◆ describe how various types of government differ from one another;

◆ explain how various types of economic systems differ from one another.

National Geography Standards

The following National Geography Standards are highlighted in this section: 2, 4, 5, 11, 13, 17

Bellringer

Ask students to list some ways in which government affects their daily lives. (protects their rights, guarantees freedoms, makes laws, punishes lawbreakers, provides services)

LESSON PLAN

1. Focus Tell students to imagine that they have traveled to another planet with a group of people to set up a new society. Discuss the following questions: What kind of government would their society have? How would they choose leaders? How would they settle disputes? Tell students to compare their plans with the governments described in Section 2.

2. Instruct Draw the following diagram on the board: one large circle above several smaller circles with arrows pointing from the large circle to the small circles. Explain that this represents a unitary system because the central government makes all laws. Have students draw similar diagrams to illustrate a federation and a confederation.

3. Close/Reteach Write the following pairs of concepts on the board: *unitary system and federation; federation and confederation; dictatorship and democracy; dictatorship and monarchy; totalitarianism and dictatorship; traditional economy and market economy; market economy and command economy.* Have students compare each pair of concepts.

2 Political and Economic Systems

Reading Focus

• **What are four characteristics shared by all countries?**

• **How do various types of government differ from one another?**

• **How do various types of economic systems differ from one another?**

Key Terms

sovereignty	authoritarian	democracy
unitary system	dictatorship	traditional economy
federation	totalitarianism	market economy
confederation	monarchy	command economy

Main Idea The world's countries have a variety of government and economic systems based on differing philosophies.

Government and Citizenship At the Women['s] World Cup, flags represent countries from around the wor[ld]

Two important traits of any culture are its political and economic systems. Governments usually reflect beliefs about authority, independence, and human rights. Economic systems reflect people's ideas about the use of resources and the distribution of wealth.

The World's Countries

Nearly 200 independent countries exist in the world today. They vary greatly in size, military power, natural resources, economic importance, and many other ways. Each one, however, has four specific characteristics that define it as a country. These are (1) clearly defined territory, (2) population, (3) sovereignty, and (4) a government.

Territory A country's territory includes the land, water, and natural resources within its boundaries. Modern countries range in size from Russia, with more than 6.5 million square miles (16.8 million sq km), to Vatican City, with 0.17 square mile (0.44 sq km). The total area of the United States is 3.7 million square miles (9.5 million sq km).

A country's resources may be even more important than its size. For example, several small countries in the Persian Gulf region are extremely wealthy because of their huge reserves of oil. The earth's natural resources are not evenly distributed around the world. This unequal distribution has led to conflict between nations. Throughout history, disputes over territory—land and resources—have been a common cause of war.

Several factors play an important role in how a nation defines the boundaries that separate it from other nations. Natural divisions, such as rivers and mountains, often serve as boundaries. A nation's boundaries can shrink or expand as a result of wars and conquests. National borders can also change through negotiations that result in international treaties or agreements.

Geographic factors often influence a nation's power to control territory. For example, one reason Great Britain was able to spread its power around the world was that it was an island nation with easy access to ocean travel and trade. It also had large supplies of coal and iron, which helped it become an industrial and military power.

RESOURCE DIRECTORY

Teaching Resources

Unit 1, Chapter 3
• Section 2 Guided Reading and Review, p. 32

Guide to the Essentials (English/Spanish)
• Section Summary, Chapter 3, Section 2

Mental Mapping booklet
• Unit 1 Checklist, p. 5

Technology

Guided Reading Audiotapes (English/Spanish), Chapter 3, Section 2

Section Reading Support Transparencies, Chapter 3, Section 2

World Geography Map and Photo Transparencies
• Per Capita GDP

Book on CD, Chapter 3

Social Studies Skills Tutor CD-ROM

Companion Web site, www.phschool.com
• Chapter 3 Activities

Population The size of the population does not determine the existence of a country. Countries vary widely in both the size and the makeup of their populations. Some countries, such as Canada and Australia, have vast land areas that are largely unpopulated. Other countries, such as Japan and the Netherlands, are small in terms of land area, but extremely densely populated. Some countries, such as India and the United States, contain a wide diversity of people and cultures. In others, such as Sweden or Greece, most people share a similar background, language, and culture.

As citizens of a nation, people are usually assured of protection by their government. In return, citizens usually must pay taxes, serve in the military, or carry out other obligations to the government.

Sovereignty A nation's freedom from outside control is called **sovereignty.** A sovereign country is one that can rule itself by establishing its own policies and determining its own course of action. A country's sovereignty entitles it to act independently, deal equally with other sovereign countries, and protect its territory and citizens.

Geographic factors can help a nation defend and maintain its sovereignty. The United Kingdom, for example, has benefited by being separated from the rest of Europe by the English Channel and the North Sea. Switzerland stands in the very middle of Europe, but its high mountains have made entry more difficult, a fact that has helped the Swiss to stay out of many of the wars waged by the nations that surround it.

On the other hand, geographic conditions can weaken a country's ability to maintain its sovereignty. Both Belgium and Poland, for example, stand on a plain that invading armies have easily passed over numerous times. The same European plain has also contributed to Russia being a frequent victim of invasion. However, the vastness of Russia and its harsh winters have often worked against the invaders, enabling the Russians to maintain their independence.

Types of Government

Government is the institution through which a society makes and enforces its public policies and provides for its common needs. These needs include

Vatican City

Government and Citizenship The countries of the world vary greatly in size. One of the tiniest is Vatican City, which is located within Rome, Italy, and covers only about 109 acres (44 hectares).

Place *What specific characteristics make Vatican City a country?*

Articles From ·········
NATIONAL GEOGRAPHIC

The following article may be used to extend the content in this section.

Connif, Richard, and Jodi Cobb, photographer. "Monaco." *National Geographic*, Vol. 189, No. 5 (May 1996), pp. 80–95.

The tiny Mediterranean country of Monaco is home to a centuries-old monarchy and a thriving economy.

Authoritarian Government in China

Cooperation and Conflict In 1989, the Chinese government used brutal force to crack down on students protesting against authoritarian dictatorship. Here, burned vehicles remain on the streets of Beijing the morning after the crackdown.

Place Do you think the people in this photograph felt that political change was likely to occur soon in China? Explain.

keeping order within a society, protecting the society from outside threats, and providing some services to its people.

Though there are many countries in the world, there are only a few kinds of political systems. Each system can be classified according to its structure and its basis of authority.

Government Structure Nearly every country contains smaller units. These may be called states, provinces, or republics. One way of classifying governments is based on the relationship between these smaller units and the central government.

If one central government runs the nation, the system is said to be a **unitary system.** The central government makes laws for the entire nation; local governments have only those powers that the central government gives to them. Great Britain and Japan are among the countries with unitary governments.

In a **federation,** some powers are given to the national government and other powers are reserved for more local governments. The United States is a federation. Many of the articles in the United States Constitution outline the powers held by the federal government and the powers held by the 50 state governments.

The third type of government structure is a **confederation.** In this system, smaller political units keep their sovereignty and give the central government only very limited powers, typically in such fields as defense and foreign commerce. A confederate system makes it possible for the several states to cooperate in common concerns and still retain their separate identities. During the 1860s, southern states separated from the United States of America and formed a confederation— the Confederate States of America.

Government Authority Another way of defining a government is according to the source

Answer to Photo Caption

Possible answer: no, because most of the people look like they're going about their business as if nothing had happened of its authority. Until fairly modern times, most countries had **authoritarian** governments. The leaders held all, or nearly all, political power.

Authoritarian governments take different forms. Today, the most common form of authoritarian government is **dictatorship**, in which power is concentrated in a small group or even a single person. Most dictators use military force or political terror to gain and exercise power. People are not free to express their own opinions.

The most extreme form of dictatorship is **totalitarianism.** In countries under totalitarian rule, the government tries to control every part of society—politics, the economy, and people's personal lives. Nazi Germany under Hitler and the Soviet Union under Stalin are examples of totalitarian rule.

Throughout much of history, the most common kind of authoritarian government has been a **monarchy.** Monarchs—kings, queens, pharaohs, shahs, sultans—inherit their positions by being born into the ruling family.

In the past, monarchs often ruled with dictatorial power. Today, however, nearly all remaining monarchies—including the British monarchy, which is perhaps the best known—are constitutional monarchies. Real power rests with an elected lawmaking body, such as a legislature or parliament. The monarch serves primarily as a symbol of national unity.

Any country in which the people choose their leaders and have the power to set government policy is a **democracy.** (A constitutional monarchy can also be a democracy.) Today, democratic countries have representative democracies. All of the nation's eligible adult citizens have the right to choose the representatives making the country's laws. In most representative democracies the elected legislature makes and carries out the laws. One of the world's most populous democratic nations is the United States.

Over the last few decades, many other nations have set aside more authoritarian governments and established democracies. Germany and Japan after World War II and Russia and other Communist nations starting in the late 1980s have turned to democratic forms of governance.

Types of Economic Systems

Any economic system must answer three basic questions: What (and how many) goods and services will be produced? How will these products be produced? How will the products and the wealth gained from their sale be distributed?

Traditional Economy In many parts of the world, especially in rural parts of less developed nations, nearly all goods and services produced by people are consumed in their own family or village. There is little left over for trade with other communities. These **traditional economies** also are known as subsistence economies, because little

The Global Economy

Developing Economies About three fourths of the world's people live in underdeveloped and developing countries in Africa, Asia, and Latin America. Such countries are characterized by poverty, overpopulation, and few resources. Aid from the United States and European nations has helped some underdeveloped and developing countries build industries and train workers. Other developing countries, such as Brazil, South Korea, and Singapore, have the world's most rapidly growing economies.

Critical Thinking

Supply and Demand Encourage students to use their own experience to figure out how supply and demand affects prices. Offer them the following scenario: An unexpectedly harsh winter kills orange groves in Florida. Then ask: **What will happen to the supply of oranges?** (It will decrease.) **If the demand for orange juice exceeds the supply, what will happen to the price of orange juice?** (It will rise.) When students finish answering these questions, encourage them to explain why prices drop when supply exceeds demand. (Vendors lower prices so people will buy their goods.)

Answers to Diagram Skills

command economy

Responses will vary, but they should reflect consideration of the availability of basic services and the freedom of a market economy.

104 Chapter 3

World Economic Systems

Market Economy

Command Economy

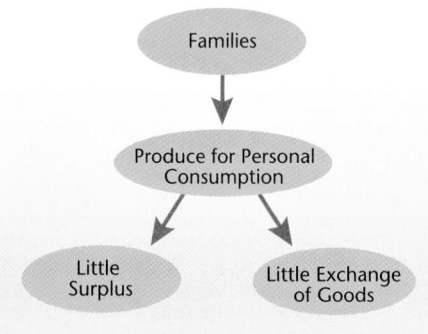

Traditional Economy

DIAGRAM SKILLS

● **Economic Systems** These three economic systems provide different ways of producing and distributing goods and services.
- *In which economic system is the government the most involved in making key economic decisions?*
- *What are the advantages and disadvantages of each economic system?*

---

surplus is produced, and there is relatively little need for markets where people can buy or sell excess goods.

Market Economy An economic system that gives great freedom to individuals and groups is called a **market economy,** or free enterprise system. The primary form of a market economy in the world today is capitalism.

In a capitalist market economy, private individuals and groups decide what will be produced, how much will be produced, and the prices that will be charged for goods and services. Their decisions are strongly influenced by the "laws of supply and demand." The major motivating force in a market economy is the drive of each individual or group participating in the market to increase their economic well-being.

Under a system of "pure" capitalism, government would take no part in the economy. In fact, in the United States and in other capitalist countries, governments do provide some goods and services such as a postal service, highways, and public education. To protect the public, governments also play a limited role in regulating private business. Government regulations affect such areas as worker health and safety and environmental pollution.

Command Economy When an economic system is controlled by a single, central government, it is called a **command economy.** Nearly all economic decisions are made by government leaders exerting authoritarian control. The government decides what and how much to produce, where economic activities will be located, and what prices will be charged for goods and services.

In a command economy, decisions are often made to achieve social or political goals. For example, it may cost $1 to produce a quart of orange juice, but the price may be set at only 25 cents to make sure that all consumers are able to afford adequate supplies of juice.

One example of a command economy is communism. Under a Communist economy, the state owns and operates all the major farms, factories, utilities, and stores. Government planners decide what products will be made, how much workers will be paid, and how much things will cost. Because of their centralized economic planning, Communist systems also are called planned economies.

New York Stock Exchange

Economic Activities
On the trading floor of the stock exchange, excited traders buy and sell stock. In a capitalist economy, most economic decisions take place without government involvement.

Place *How are prices determined in the market economy of the United States?*

Mixed Economy The economic systems of some nations include a mix of traditional, command, and market economies. Socialism can be an example of a mixed economy. The basic philosophy of socialism is that the state should own and run some basic industries, such as transportation, communications, banking, coal mining, and the steel industry, while private enterprise operates in most other parts of the economy.

Socialists believe that wealth should be distributed more equally and that everyone is entitled to certain goods and services. Socialist countries are sometimes known as "welfare states" because they provide many social services such as housing, health care, child care, and pensions for retired workers. To pay for these services, governments of socialist countries usually impose high tax rates on their citizens.

SECTION 2 ASSESSMENT

1. **Key Terms** Define **(a)** sovereignty, **(b)** unitary system, **(c)** federation, **(d)** confederation, **(e)** authoritarian, **(f)** dictatorship, **(g)** totalitarianism, **(h)** monarchy, **(i)** democracy, **(j)** traditional economy, **(k)** market economy, **(l)** command economy.

2. **Government and Citizenship** What characteristics do all countries have in common?

3. **Government and Citizenship (a)** In which type of government structure do local states have the greatest power? Explain. **(b)** Is totalitarianism an authoritarian or democratic system of government? Explain.

4. **Economic Systems** How does a market economy differ from a command economy?

5. **Critical Thinking Analyzing Processes** How would you expect the decision-making process in a culture that values authoritarianism to differ from the decision-making process in a culture that values democracy?

Activity

Making a Map Make a map using colors and a key to indicate the boundaries of each territory that became a part of the United States between 1789 and today. Use library or Internet resources to gather the information that you need. For a greater challenge, write a brief explanation of how the United States gained each territory.

Answers to Section 2 Assessment

1. **(a)** sovereignty, p. 101 **(b)** unitary system, p. 102 **(c)** federation, p. 102 **(d)** confederation, p. 102 **(e)** authoritarian, p. 103 **(f)** dictatorship, p. 103 **(g)** totalitarianism, p. 103 **(h)** monarchy, p. 103 **(i)** democracy, p. 103 **(j)** traditional economy, p. 103 **(k)** market economy, p. 104 **(l)** command economy, p. 104

2. They all have clearly defined territories, populations, sovereignty, and government.

3. **(a)** confederations; The smaller political units keep their sovereignty and give the central government very limited powers. **(b)** authoritarian; A totalitarian government tries to control every part of society, including politics, the economy, and people's personal lives.

4. A market economy gives freedom to individuals and groups, while a command economy is controlled by the central government.

5. A culture that values authoritarianism will allow all decisions to be made by the central government, while one that values democracy will take the decisions to the people so they can vote.

Activity Rubrics Share rubrics with students before they create their maps.
Attempted Map is incomplete and reflects insufficient research.
Minimal Map includes the required information, but the labeling is messy and difficult to read.
Adequate Map is complete, accurate, and legible.
Exemplary Map is accurately and neatly labeled, color is used to depict the different territories, and it includes a complete explanation of how the United States gained each territory.

TEST PREPARATION

Have students read the subsection Mixed Economy on this page to answer the following question.
Which of the following is *not* a feature of a socialist society?

(A) Low taxes
B Health care for everyone
C State-run industries
D Pensions for retired workers

Answer to Photo Caption

by the laws of supply and demand

Creating a Chapter Summary
As a reteaching opportunity, pair a more able student with a less able student to complete this chapter summary.

Additional entries students might make include the following: Political systems, Religion, Social organization, Patterns of settlement.

Reviewing Key Terms
1–10. Students should correctly match all 10 key terms with their definitions.

Understanding Key Ideas
11. Many people choose to live where the soil is fertile, water is plentiful, and the climate is mild enough to grow crops.
12. increase in famine and disease, natural resource depletion, and increases in levels of technology and creativity
13. They help people of a certain area or region define who they are as a people; without language, people could not communicate, religion helps people to answer questions about the meaning and purpose of life, and other patterns of culture make a specific people unique.
14. Some people feel that women and minorities should not have the power that comes with economic independence. There are some cultures that believe women and minorities can fulfill only certain roles in society and not others.
15. It was an island nation with easy access to travel and trade. It also had large supplies of coal and iron.
16. in rural and less-developed nations; people only produce what they can consume with their family or village—there is little left over to trade with other communities.

Critical Thinking and Writing
17. They are growing.
18. (a) It now takes years instead of centuries to double the population. **(b)** Possible answers: advances in agricultural technology, medical breakthroughs
19. Possible answers: The community is rustic. Modern technology does not appear to be available in the region.

(Continued on next page.)

Chapter Summary

Copy this concept web on a piece of paper. Add supporting details about what human geographers study. Some entries have been completed to serve as a sample.

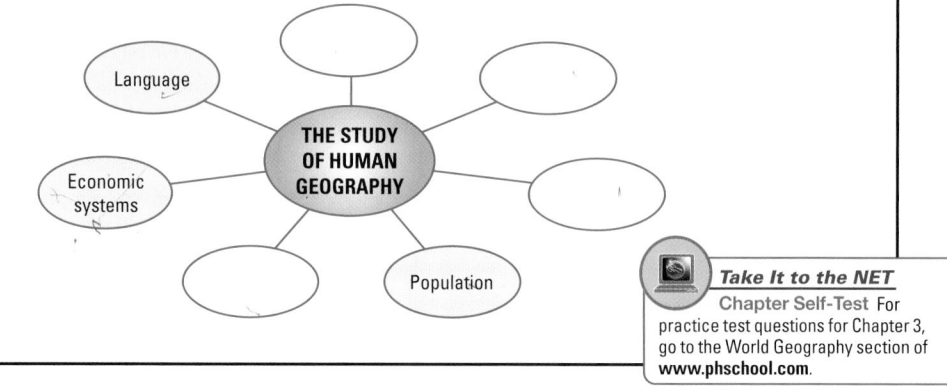

Take It to the NET
Chapter Self-Test For practice test questions for Chapter 3, go to the World Geography section of **www.phschool.com**.

Reviewing Key Terms

Use the key terms listed below to create a matching game. Write one column of terms in any order. Then, write the terms' definitions in a second column, also in any order. Exchange games with those of a classmate. Match the terms, and then check each other's answers.

1. population density
2. immigrant
3. rural
4. diffusion
5. cultural divergence

6. federation
7. authoritarian
8. totalitarianism
9. monarchy
10. democracy

Understanding Key Ideas

11. Patterns of Settlement Why does population density vary a great deal across the world?

12. Population Growth What are some possible effects of world population growth?

13. Cultures Explain how language, religion, and other patterns of culture make specific regions of the world distinctive.

14. Economic Activities Why do economic opportunities for women and minorities vary in different regions of the world?

15. Government and Citizenship How did geographic factors help Great Britain to control territory around the world?

16. Economic Systems In what kind of a country are you most likely to find a traditional economy? Explain.

Critical Thinking and Writing

17. Making Generalizations Review the graph on page 90. Based on the graph, what general trends can you identify about cities in the world today?

18. Analyzing Data Study the graph on page 91. **(a)** How has the time that it takes for world population to double changed over the years? **(b)** What are some reasons for this change?

19. Analyzing Photographs Study the photograph of a rural Chinese community on page 97. What does the photograph reveal about rural Chinese culture in the region?

20. Distinguishing Fact From Opinion
Consider the following statement: A federal system of government is better than a government that is a confederation. Is this statement a fact or an opinion? Explain.

Applying Skills

Analyzing Statistical Data Refer to the table on page 99 to answer these questions:

21. In which country is population growing at the slowest rate?

22. What do the data indicate about the reasons for India's high fertility rate? Explain.

23. Which countries probably have poor nutrition and medical care, compared to other countries in the table? Explain.

Analyzing Photographs Study the photograph below, and answer the following questions:

24. (a) In what kind of a climate zone do these people probably live? **(b)** How does the photographic evidence support your hypothesis?

25. How did these people use natural resources to build their shelter?

26. Do you expect that people in this community will experience cultural change in the future? Explain.

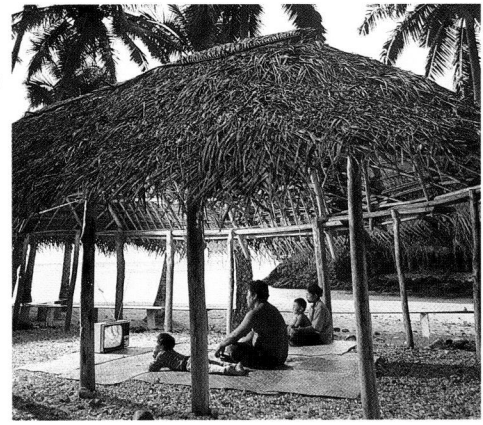

Test Preparation

Read each question and choose the best answer.

27. Which of the following is the best example of diffusion of culture?

  A The invention of the airplane

  B The spread of baseball to Japan

  C Isolation of one culture from another

  D The growth of population

28. In which kind of economic system is trade with countries around the world least important?

  F Traditional economy

  G Market economy

  H Command economy

  J Mixed economy

Activities

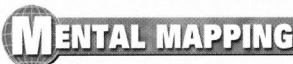 **MENTAL MAPPING**

Review the population density map on pages 88–89. On a separate piece of paper, draw a sketch map of the world from memory. Label the following cities on your map:

- Tokyo
- Mumbai
- Lagos
- São Paulo
- Mexico City
- New York
- Jakarta
- Calcutta
- Manila
- Shanghai

 Take It to the NET

Analyzing Current Events Use the search engines of online newsproviders to find news articles about the formation of political boundaries or disputes about political boundaries. Select one of the articles and read it. Summarize the main ideas of the article. Is the boundary issue being settled through cooperation, conflict, or a combination of the two? Explain.

Chapter 3 ▪ Review and Assessment **107**

Critical Thinking and Writing (cont.)

20. This is an opinion. Governments usually reflect beliefs about authority, independence, and human rights. Because people have different views about these things, their views about government may also differ.

Applying Skills
21. Japan
22. The data do not indicate anything about the reasons for India's high fertility rate.
23. Possible answers: Nigeria, Bangladesh, Pakistan. They have the lowest life expectancies and the highest infant mortality rates of the countries listed.
24. (a) tropical **(b)** Possible answers: There are palm trees; the walls of the building are open to let in the air; the people are not dressed warmly; the building is on a beach.
25. Possible answer: They used pieces of palm trees to build their shelter and weave their mats.
26. Possible answer: Yes. There is a television, which allows the people to see other cultures. As people have access to other cultures, they are more likely to be affected by cultural convergence or diffusion.

Test Preparation
27. B
28. F

Activities

Mental Mapping
Review students' maps for relative and absolute location.

Take It to the Net
Students' work should reflect sound research. Check summaries for accurate coverage of political issues and boundary disputes.

 MENTAL MAPPING

Games for Review See pages 58–63 of the Simulations, Games, and Lab Activities booklet for games to review place names in preparation for the Chapter 3 Map Test.

Chapter Map Test Students should use the completed Chapter 3 outline maps and the Unit 1 Checklist in their Atlas Portfolios to prepare for the Chapter 3 Map Test. Point out to students that the test will cover only Part III of the Unit 1 Checklist, Cities of the World.

Alternative Assessment

Final Evaluation
Writing a Report Use the Writing Assignment Evaluation Form on page 7 of the Alternative Assessment booklet in the Prentice Hall Assessment System to evaluate students' reports. Either teachers or students can complete the forms to indicate which level of work was achieved for each of the criteria. The evaluation should include specific examples and comments.

Chapter 3 **107**

Resource Manager

Chapter-Level Resources	CORE INSTRUCTION	READING/SKILLS
	Teaching Resources	**Teaching Resources**
	Unit 1/Ch. 4	**Unit 1**/Ch. 4
	• Reviewing Main Ideas, p. 47	• Map/Graph Skills, p. 49
	Mental Mapping booklet	**Book on CD,** Ch. 4
	• Unit 1 Checklist, p. 5	**Social Studies Skills Tutor CD-ROM**
	Simulations, Games, and Lab Activities	
	• Place Location Review Games, pp. 58–63	
	TeacherExpress™ CD-ROM, Ch. 4	
	Companion Web site, www.phschool.com	
	• eTeach	

1 World Resources

1. Differentiate between renewable and nonrenewable resources.
2. List energy sources available to nations and individuals.

	CORE INSTRUCTION	READING/SKILLS
	Teaching Resources	**Teaching Resources**
	Unit 1/Ch. 4	**Guide to the Essentials (English/Spanish)**
	• Guided Reading and Review, p. 43	• Section Summary, Ch. 4, Sec. 1
	Simulations, Games, and Lab Activities	**Mental Mapping booklet**
	• Exploring Local Geography, Land Use Disputes, p. 5	• Outline Map, Ch. 4, p. 15
	Prentice Hall Presentation Pro CD-ROM, Ch. 4, Sec. 1	**Guided Reading Audiotapes (English/Spanish),** Ch. 4, Sec. 1
		Section Reading Support Transparencies, Ch. 4, Sec. 1

2 World Economic Activity

1. Distinguish four different categories of economic activities.
2. Explain why global trade patterns are changing today.
3. Evaluate data as an indicator of a country's level of development.

	CORE INSTRUCTION	READING/SKILLS
	Teaching Resources	**Teaching Resources**
	Unit 1/Ch. 4	**Guide to the Essentials (English/Spanish)**
	• Guided Reading and Review, p. 45	• Section Summary, Ch. 4, Sec. 2
	Creative Teaching Activities	**Social Studies Skills Handbook**
	• Negotiating Trade Agreements, p. 6	• Reading an Economic Activity Map, p. 27
	Prentice Hall Presentation Pro CD-ROM, Ch. 4, Sec. 2	**Guided Reading Audiotapes (English/Spanish),** Ch. 4, Sec. 2
		Section Reading Support Transparencies, Ch. 4, Sec. 2

ENRICHMENT/HONORS/PREAP

Teaching Resources

Unit 1/Ch. 4
- Critical Thinking, p. 48

Mental Mapping booklet
- Atlas Activity, p. 16

People and Geography
- Water, pp. 2–7

Social Studies Skills Handbook
- Study and Research Skills, pp. 94–108

World Geography Map and Photo Transparencies
- Per Capita GDP
- World Trade Cartogram
- World Climate Zones: Annual Precipitation

World Geography Videos
- Resources and Land Use: Economic Activities, Tape 1

Companion Web site, www.phschool.com
- Chapter 4 Activities

World Geography Map and Photo Transparencies
- Energy Production

Companion Web site, www.phschool.com
- Chapter 4 Activities

Companion Web site, www.phschool.com
- Chapter 4 Activities

ASSESSMENT

PRENTICE HALL ASSESSMENT SYSTEM

Core Assessment
- ExamView Test Bank booklet, Ch. 4
- ExamView Test Bank CD-ROM, Ch. 4
- ExamView Test Bank CD-ROM, Unit 1

Standardized Test Preparation

Review and Reteach
- Review Book for World Geography, pp. 3–4

Practice and Assess
- Test-taking Strategies With Transparencies for High School
  Test-taking Strategy Poster
- Alternative Assessment booklet
- Test Prep Book for World Geography

Teaching Resources

Unit 1/Ch. 4
- Section Quizzes, pp. 44, 46
- Test Forms A and B, pp. 50–55

Guide to the Essentials (English/Spanish)
- Chapter 4 Test

Spanish Resources, Ch. 4
- Section Quizzes, pp. 11–12

Mental Mapping booklet
- Chapter 4 Map Test, p. 17
- Unit 1 Map Test, p. 18

Companion Web site, www.phschool.com
- Chapter 4 Self-Test

CUSTOMIZE FOR INDIVIDUAL NEEDS

Less Proficient Readers
- Guide to the Essentials (English), Ch. 4, Section Summaries
- Social Studies Skills Handbook, p. 71
- Guided Reading Audiotapes (English), Ch. 4
- Section Reading Support Transparencies, Ch. 4
- Book on CD, Ch. 4
- Teacher's Edition, Reading Strategy, pp. 110, 117
- Teacher's Edition, Activity: Vocabulary, p. 116
- Teacher's Edition, Customize for . . . , pp. 113, 115

Students Acquiring English/ESL
- Guide to the Essentials (English/Spanish), Ch. 4
- Guided Reading Audiotapes (English/Spanish), Ch. 4
- Section Reading Support Transparencies, Ch. 4
- Book on CD, Ch. 4
- Teacher's Edition, Customize for . . . , p. 111

Less Proficient Writers
- Social Studies Skills Handbook, p. 80
- Alternative Assessment, Writing Assignment Rubric, p. 6

MENTAL MAPPING

Write the term *natural resources* on the board and ask students to give examples. List responses on the board (forests, soil, coal, oil, gold, iron, copper, etc.). Point out that not all countries have the resources they need. Explain that people around the world use resources differently, and that nations are at various stages of development.

Mapping the World Tell the students to create a map like the one on this page, lightly shading each continent a different color. Then have them label on their maps the rivers and lakes listed under Part IV of the Unit 1 Checklist. Students can either sketch their own outline maps or use the Chapter 4 Outline Map on page 15 of the Mental Mapping booklet in the Teaching Resources. Remind students to keep their maps in their Atlas Portfolios to prepare for the Chapter Map Test.

eTeach

Be sure to check out this month's online forum with a Master Teacher to join in an exchange of teaching ideas. **www.phschool.com**

C H A P T E R

4

Resources and Land Use

SECTIONS

1 World Resources

2 World Economic Activity

The World: RIVERS AND LAKES

Miller Projection

Go Online
PHSchool.com

For: More information about resources and land use and access to the Take It to the Net activities
Visit: phschool.com
Web Code: mjk-0005

RESOURCE DIRECTORY

Teaching Resources
Unit 1, Chapter 4
• Section 1 Guided Reading and Review, p. 43
Guide to the Essentials (English/Spanish)
• Section Summary, Chapter 4, Section 1
Mental Mapping booklet
• Outline Map 4, p. 15
• Atlas Activity, p. 16
• Unit 1 Checklist, p. 5

Technology
Guided Reading Audiotapes (English/Spanish),
Chapter 4, Section 1

Section Reading Support Transparencies,
Chapter 4, Section 1
World Geography Map and Photo Transparencies
• Energy Production
Book on CD, Chapter 4
World Geography Videos
• Resources and Land Use: Economic Activities, Tape 1
TeacherExpress™ CD-ROM, Chapter 4
Prentice Hall Presentation Pro CD-ROM, Chapter 4
Social Studies Skills Tutor CD-ROM
Companion Web site, www.phschool.com
• Chapter 4 Activities

1 World Resources

Reading Focus
- **How do renewable resources and nonrenewable resources differ?**
- **What energy sources are available to individuals and nations?**

Key Terms
natural resource
renewable resource
nonrenewable resource
fossil fuel
nuclear energy
water power
geothermal energy
solar energy

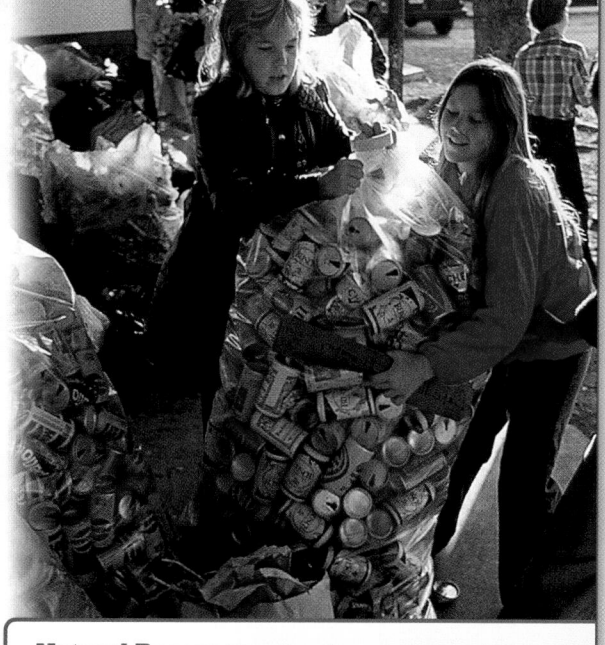

Natural Resources Recycling programs can help people conserve resources and protect the environment.

> **Main Idea** Natural resources, such as fossil fuels and other energy sources, are unevenly distributed throughout the world.

People have always depended on soil, water, plants, animals, minerals, and other resources for their survival. A resource is something of value. The exact value can vary, depending on human needs and technology. The value of petroleum, for example, increased greatly after the invention of automobiles. Likewise, uranium's worth rose suddenly with the development of nuclear energy. The ways that people use world resources, where resources are located, how resources are distributed, and how the use of resources affects the earth are all subjects that geographers study.

Natural Resources

Resources come in different kinds. Capital resources are the money and machines used to produce goods or services. Human resources are the people who perform various tasks. **Natural resources** are materials in the natural environment that people value and use to satisfy their needs.

Renewable Resources Some natural resources, called **renewable resources,** are constantly being regenerated or replaced by the environment. Soil, for example, is always being created by the weathering of rocks and by decomposing plant and animal material. The water cycle is an ongoing process that returns new supplies of fresh water to the land as rain or snow. Our most important energy resource, the sun, although not renewable, will probably keep the earth warm for 5 billion years or more.

Natural growth takes time, however, and human activities can interfere with the process of renewal. An oil spill, for example, might affect the wildlife in a bay for many years.

Nonrenewable Resources As their name suggests, **nonrenewable resources** cannot be replaced once they have been used. Nonrenewable resources are minerals formed in the earth's crust over millions of years. The earth has only a limited supply of them, and it would take millions of years to replace them.

Among the most important nonrenewable mineral resources are **fossil fuels.** These fuels are coal, oil, and natural gas, which formed from the remains of ancient plants and animals. Other

 Logging in the Tongass National Forest, Alaska *(photo left)*

Chapter 4 ▪ Section 1 **109**

Objectives
Upon completion of Section 1, students should be able to:
- ◆ differentiate between renewable and nonrenewable resources;
- ◆ list energy sources available to nations and individuals.

National Geography Standards
The following National Geography Standards are highlighted in this section: 1, 14, 16, 18

Bellringer
Give students five minutes to list as many uses of forest products as they can think of. Lists should include uses of wood, fiber, chemical and fuel products, and food products that come from trees.

LESSON PLAN

1. Focus Have students identify the energy resources they use. Then discuss what adjustments they would have to make if those resources were not available.

2. Instruct Work with students to make lists of renewable and nonrenewable resources. For each renewable resource, have students suggest ways to conserve it. For each nonrenewable resource, have students suggest alternative resources.

3. Close/Reteach Using the World outline map on page 15 of the Mental Mapping booklet in the Teaching Resources, have students label where major deposits of minerals are found. Have each student choose one mineral to map. They may use world atlases or the *Nystrom Desk Atlas* to locate the information.

TEACHING TIP
From A Master Teacher

Resources and Trade The uneven distribution of resources around the world creates the need for trade. Trade creates a need for global economic, transportation, and communication systems to exchange raw materials, manufactured goods, investments, and services. Global interdependence affects human migration, patterns of trade, and cultural and political alliances. To illustrate these ideas, you might want students to consider the consequences if all the oil in the Middle East had been in Canada instead.

Pacing Suggestions

For 90-minute Blocks

You will want to vary activities.
- Complete the Creative Teaching Activity for Chapter 4. Explain that trade is often affected by many factors. Repeat the activity, but add the following complications: The herder and the farmer are having a land dispute and the hunter refuses to make deals with the gatherer because of an old grudge. In a class discussion, compare these results to the original results.

Chapter 4 ▪ Section 1 **109**

READING STRATEGY

Asking Questions

Have students write at least five questions as they read the subsection Energy Sources. After students have completed their questions, organize students into pairs. Have each member of the pair answer the other's questions.

GLOBAL CONNECTIONS

Economic Activities

Recycling In the United States, recycling provides economic as well as environmental gains. In 2000, more than 28,000 people were working in the recycling industry in New York alone. Some nations may suffer economic repercussions from recycling, however. For example, the economies of Australia, Jamaica, and Guinea—countries that produce bauxite, an ore from which aluminum is obtained—may suffer because of increased recycling of aluminum cans.

Alternative Assessment

Introduce the Activity

Writing a Position Paper Present the following arguments for students to consider: (1) Industrialized nations have a responsibility to help developing nations through economic aid and technological assistance. (2) Foreign aid supports ineffective governments and discourages economic growth. Have students choose one of the arguments and write a two-page position paper defending it. Positions must be supported by research. Distribute the Position Paper Rubric found on page 8 of the Alternative Assessment booklet in the Teaching Resources for students' reference.

While advanced technologies may help us find new mineral deposits in the future, recycling is a way to increase nonrenewable resource supplies right now. For example, Americans recycle about 1,500 aluminum cans every second. Some experts believe half of all trash currently thrown away could be recycled. The other way to stretch the limited supply of nonrenewable resources is to reduce the overall consumption level.

Energy Sources

Modern industrial countries use energy to light cities, power cars and airplanes, and run computers and other machines. The main energy source is nonrenewable fossil fuels. Today, nations are searching for new energy sources and competing for those that already exist.

Depending on Fossil Fuels Nearly all modern industrialized countries, including the United States, depend heavily on fossil fuels. Few of these nations have sufficient supplies to meet their own needs. Thus, they must import much of what they use.

Oil and natural gas reserves are unevenly spread around the world. Over half of the world's known oil supply is located in just a few countries in

Coal deposits are larger and more widely distributed than oil reserves. The United States, China, and Russia have rich deposits. Industrial areas in Europe also arose near coal supplies. The world's reserves of coal are thought to be enough

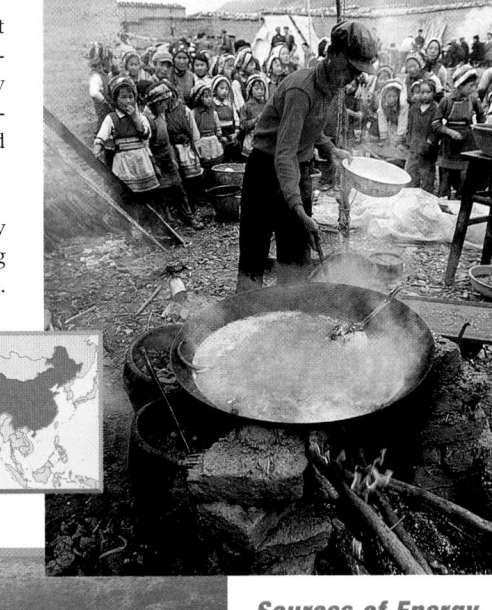

Sources of Energy

Natural Resources This vast Canadian oil refinery (left) is a reminder of how much industrialized nations depend on fossil fuels. In less developed areas of the world, such as rural China (above), people rely on other fuels.

Human-Environment Interaction How do the two activities shown here affect the environment?

110

Answers to Photo Caption

Possible answers: Trees are cut down to provide fuel for wood fires. Oil refineries can release pollutants.

110 Chapter 4

RESOURCE DIRECTORY

Teaching Resources

Unit 1, Chapter 4
• Section 1 Quiz, p. 44

Spanish Resources
• Section 1 Quiz, p. 11

Simulations, Games, and Lab Activities
• Exploring Local Geography, Land-Use Disputes, p. 5

Prentice Hall Assessment System

Alternative Assessment booklet
• Position Paper Rubric, p. 8

world's reserves of coal are thought to be enough for at least two hundred years. Coal, however, has its drawbacks. Burning coal can create air pollution and cause acid rain.

Nuclear Energy Many countries now supply part of their energy through electricity that is created by nuclear power. **Nuclear energy** today is produced by fission—the splitting of uranium atoms in a nuclear reactor to release their stored energy.

Many questions and concerns surround the use of nuclear power. Opponents of nuclear power warn of leaks, explosions, and the disposal of radioactive wastes, which can remain toxic for thousands of years. Nuclear fission also uses uranium, a limited and nonrenewable resource. Although nuclear fission does not contribute to global warming, the process of refining uranium does. Scientists hope to find a way to generate energy through fusion, a type of nuclear reaction for which the fuel is plentiful.

Other Energy Sources Many experts think that nations must begin to replace their dependence on fossil fuels with renewable energy sources. These sources are in limited use today around the world.

One ancient source of energy, **water power,** uses the energy of falling water to move machinery or generate electricity. Although new dams must be built from time to time, water power is a renewable energy source. Ocean tides and wind are other sources of power.

In areas with volcanic activity, a potential energy source is **geothermal energy,** which is energy that comes from the earth's internal heat. Magma heats underground water, producing steam that can be used to heat homes or make electricity. Iceland, Italy, Japan, and New Zealand all make use of geothermal energy.

Solar energy is energy produced by the sun. Systems to collect and store the sun's energy have been used for years to heat water and homes. Generating electricity from solar energy has been more difficult. Nevertheless, solar radiation is potentially the greatest renewable energy source.

Distribution of Resources The earth's natural resources are not evenly distributed around the world. This uneven distribution affects where people live, what sorts of economic activities they pursue, and the trade networks that they develop. Population centers often develop near resources or near easy means of transporting resources. When resources are not accessible, people often migrate to areas where the resources are available. Another alternative is to buy the needed materials from people in other regions. In this way, as you will learn in the next section, a trade network develops.

GE Facts

In California, wind power generates enough electricity to reduce the state's reliance on oil by 5 million barrels per year and lowers annual greenhouse gas emissions by 2.6 billion pounds.

SECTION 1 ASSESSMENT

1. **Key Terms** Define **(a)** natural resource, **(b)** renewable resource, **(c)** nonrenewable resource, **(d)** fossil fuel, **(e)** nuclear energy, **(f)** water power, **(g)** geothermal energy, **(h)** solar energy.

2. **Natural Resources** Why does the value of certain natural resources vary?

3. **Planning for the Future** Why do some people and nations encourage the development of energy sources other than fossil fuels?

4. **Critical Thinking** **Analyzing Information** How does the distribution of resources around the world affect patterns of settlement and migration?

Activity

Organizing Information Create a table that lists the advantages and disadvantages of the following energy sources: coal, nuclear power, water power, geothermal energy, solar energy. Compare your table with those created by other students, and add any information you may have overlooked.

Answers to Section 1 Assessment

1. **(a)** natural resource, p. 109 **(b)** renewable resource, p. 109 **(c)** nonrenewable resource, p. 109 **(d)** fossil fuel, p. 109 **(e)** nuclear energy, p. 111 **(f)** water power, p. 111 **(g)** geothermal energy, p. 111 **(h)** solar energy, p. 111

2. Possible answers: Different cultures value different resources. The value depends on human need as well as on the availability of technology to use a resource.

3. Fossil fuels are nonrenewable. Their use can also cause pollution.

4. People tend to settle where resources are available or near the means of transporting them. Migration patterns may also be determined by access to resources.

Activity Rubrics Share rubrics with students before they begin their tables.
Attempted The table is incomplete or contains erroneous information.
Minimal The table shows some understanding of the advantages and disadvantages of various energy sources.
Adequate The table accurately summarizes the advantages and disadvantages of each energy source listed.
Exemplary The table is detailed and reflects a thorough understanding of the advantages and disadvantages of various energy sources.

CUSTOMIZE FOR...

Students Acquiring English/ESL
Outline Help students develop an outline of Section 1, using the main subsections as headings and details as subheadings. Remind them to use their outlines as a study aid.

TEST PREPARATION

Have students read the paragraphs about energy on this page to answer the following question.
Which of the following items uses a renewable fuel source?
  A A diesel truck
  B A steam engine that burns coal
  C A solar–powered calculator
  D A gas–powered clothes dryer

People and Geography

pp. 112–113

Objectives

Upon completion of this feature, students should be able to:

◆ describe how drought contributes to water scarcity, particularly in Africa;

◆ discuss the strain that booming populations place on water supplies, particularly in China;

◆ explain the effects of water pollution, particularly in Europe.

National Geography Standards

The following National Geography Standards are highlighted in this feature: 4, 7, 8, 9, 14, 15, 16, 17, 18

Bellringer

Have students make a list of their daily activities that involve using water. Ask them if they have ever been without enough water for drinking or bathing. Ask if they recall a time when water restrictions were imposed. Ask: **How did the restrictions affect their lives?**

LESSON PLAN

1. Focus Discuss how life in a water-rich area differs from life in a water-scarce area. For example, you could ask: **How might farming practices differ? How might people's bathing routines be different? How might recreational activities differ?**

2. Instruct Draw a two-column chart on the board and label the columns *Causes of Water Scarcity* and *Effects of Water Scarcity*. Then have students reread these pages to describe water scarcity in Africa, China, and Europe.

Answer to Map Caption

North Africa, South Asia, China, and other smaller regions of the world

Answer to Photo Caption

Drought prevents farmers from growing enough food.

112   Chapter 4

People and Geography
Water Scarcity

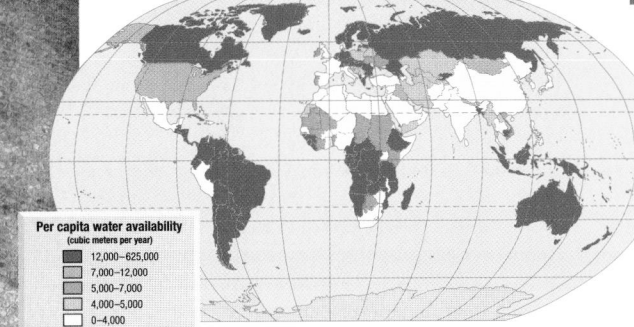

Per capita water availability
(cubic meters per year)
- 12,000–625,000
- 7,000–12,000
- 5,000–7,000
- 4,000–5,000
- 0–4,000
- No data

Source: The National Geographic Desk Reference

Global Water Supplies
What regions of the world are the most water-stressed?

The Issue

Water is a renewable but limited resource. Therefore, as population increases, the water supply per person decreases. Drought and pollution also contribute to water scarcity. Currently about 460 million people live in water-stressed countries where the supply of clean, fresh water per person is not enough to meet all human needs. Some experts fear that this number will jump to about 3 billion over the next 30 years.

Africa

A drought is a long period without normal levels of rainfall. Droughts can affect many parts of the world, but they are especially damaging in regions of Africa that are located near desert. As a result of farming and grazing, these arid lands are often cleared of trees and other natural vegetation. Afterward, these lands cannot hold rainwater as well as they did before. Drought causes crops to fail and livestock to die. Often, the results are famine, disease, and loss of life. Many African countries lack the economic means to deal with the effects of drought. Efforts are focused on predicting drought and teaching farmers to use methods that help the land retain water.

Coping With Drought
Why do you think drought-stricken countries often need food aid?

U.S. Response to Drought		
Country	Population at Risk	U.S. Food Aid
Djibouti	150,000	$4.6 million
Eritrea	1,504,000	$37.4 million
Ethiopia	10,812,940	$330.4 million
Kenya	3,476,636	$56.5 million
Somalia	1,200,000	$15.2 million
Sudan	2,946,430	$74.1 million
Uganda	571,500	$14.4 million
TOTAL	20,661,506	$532.6 million

Source: U.S. Agency for International Development

RESOURCE DIRECTORY

Teaching Resources
People and Geography
• Water, pp. 4–9

Technology
World Geography Map and Photo Transparencies
• World Climate Zones: Annual Precipitation

Asia

Irrigation is the biggest consumer of water in the world. Providing water to farmlands is essential for feeding the world's population. This is especially true in China, where more than 1 billion people live. Water supplies in the area are increasingly inadequate. For example, the Huang He, or Yellow River, often runs dry before it reaches the Pacific Ocean. Water shortages in northern China are so severe that the government relocates thousands of people out of areas where farming has become impossible. To combat the problem, the Chinese government has planned a canal to bring Yangtze River water to northern China. The government also tries to limit population growth.

Irrigation of Farmland
How does population growth cause water usage for agriculture to increase?

Water Pollution
What can be done to reduce the pollution that fouls the Danube River and killed these fish?

Europe

All too often, adequate water supplies are fouled by pollution. The Danube River flows approximately 1,770 miles (2,848 km) through nine European countries. As it flows to the Black Sea, the river collects raw sewage, agricultural chemicals, and factory waste. Pollution of the Danube has made the water unfit for drinking and for most irrigation. Pollution has also damaged fishing grounds, tourism, and ecosystems. Water pollutants encourage the growth of algae, which, in turn, can choke marine life. The international Danube River Protection Convention is working on programs to clean up the river, but progress is slow.

ASSESSMENT: Solving Problems

1. **Identify the Problem** Why is water scarcity a problem around the world?

2. **Gather Information** (a) What are some causes of this problem? (b) What are some effects?

3. **Identify Options** (a) What can governments do to help solve the problem? (b) What can engineers and scientists do? (c) How can citizens help?

4. **Choose a Solution** Which option or combination of options for solving the problem seems most likely to succeed? Explain.

5. **Plan for the Future** Do research to learn about the measures that are being taken in your state or local community to ensure adequate supplies of unpolluted water for the future.

CUSTOMIZE FOR...

Less Proficient Readers

Organizing Information Tell students that the three text sections on these pages are organized in the same way. They begin by explaining the cause of water scarcity. Then they discuss the effects of water scarcity and steps being taken to deal with it in certain countries and regions. Have students use this information to help them outline the three sections.

ACTIVITY

Group Work

Activity: Creating a water conservation collage

Purpose: Have students research a part of the United States where water is scarce. Encourage them to find out what steps people take to conserve water in those areas. Have each group create a collage out of pictures, drawings, and words that depicts what they have learned.

Roles: Researchers, a collage designer, and a reporter

Result: Reporters present the collages and explain how they illustrate people's efforts to conserve water.

Answers to Assessment

1. There are many countries around the world where there is not enough water to meet all human needs.

2. **(a)** causes: drought, pollution, population increases **(b)** effects: crops fail, livestock and people may die, famine, disease, fishing waters are damaged, limited supplies of fresh drinking water available, vacation spots are ruined

3. **(a)** Possible answer: mandate water conservation, take steps to clean pollution, and build canals to bring water to dry areas **(b)** Possible answer: develop new technologies to retain water in drought-stricken regions **(c)** Possible answer: be careful of their water use and help support efforts to reduce water pollution

4. Answers will vary. Students should provide reasons for their answers.

5. Check students' research for accuracy.

Answers to Photo Captions

A larger population requires more agricultural products, which in turn require more water for irrigation.

Possible answers: The government can prohibit industries from dumping chemicals into the river. Agricultural programs can encourage the use of natural fertilizers.

Teaching the Skill

Make sure students understand the different economic activities shown on the map. Ask volunteers for definitions of nomadic herding, commercial farming, and subsistence farming. (Nomadic herding is moving cattle or other herds from one area to another to provide them with water and food. Commercial farming is raising crops to sell. Subsistence farming is raising crops for a family or small group to eat.) Then ask questions to help students think about the relationship between geography and economic activity. **Which activities would you expect to take place in cities?** (trade and manufacturing) **In the country?** (commercial and subsistence farming) **Along a coastline?** (commercial fishing) **In the desert?** (nomadic herding) Have students check the map to see if their predictions are correct. Then encourage them to explain how resources or a lack of resources makes a place well suited for certain kinds of economic activity. (Cities have a ready supply of workers for mills and factories. The country has undeveloped land needed for farming. Coastlines have the water needed for fishing. Water is sparse in the desert, so nomads must drive their cattle from one oasis to another.)

Answers to Learn the Skill

1. (a) yes **(b)** no **(c)** northwest
2. (a) near coasts and island regions **(b)** northern Canada and northern Asia **(c)** Food and other natural resources are scarce.
3. (a) commercial farming **(b)** Products from the commercial farms are shipped to the people who live and work in the manufacturing centers. Raw materials from the farms may be needed in manufacturing.

Answer to Practice the Skill

Answers will vary depending on your state. In general, population tends to be concentrated near major cities and the highways that provide access to them.

Recognizing Patterns in Maps

A pattern is a predictable arrangement of certain features or elements. If you look at the maps on pages 66 and 67, you will see that winds and ocean currents follow patterns. Human economic activity as shown on the map below also follows patterns. Some of these activities are affected by patterns in nature. Recognizing patterns helps you understand the world around you.

Learn the Skill Use the following steps to learn how to recognize patterns on a map.

1 *Read the map below, using the map key as a guide.* Match the colors on the key and the activities they represent with the same colors on the map. **(a)** *Is livestock raising a major economic activity in Australia?* **(b)** *Is nomadic herding a major economic activity in South America?* **(c)** *In what part of North America does forestry occur?*

2 *Look for patterns on the map.* After you have identified the various economic activities and where they are located, look for patterns. Where are the places that certain activities appear time and time again? **(a)** *Generally, where is commercial fishing located?* **(b)** *Where are the greatest areas of hunting and gathering?* **(c)** *How might you explain those locations?*

3 *Look for relationships between patterns.* Some patterns have relationships between them. If you compare a map with cities located on it with a population density map, you will see a relationship. Cities have dense populations. As you learn more about geography, you will be able to explain some of the relationships visible on this map. **(a)** *What economic activity is located near areas of manufacturing and trade in North America and Europe?* **(b)** *Based on what you know, how might you explain this apparent relationship?*

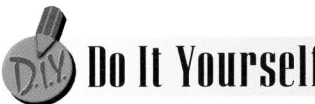

Practice the Skill Look at a highway map of your state. Locate the largest cities in your state. How does the pattern of the layout of major highways relate to the location of major cities? How would you expect the pattern of population distribution to relate to the distribution of cities and highways?

Apply the Skill See Chapter 4 Review and Assessment.

The World: Economic Activities

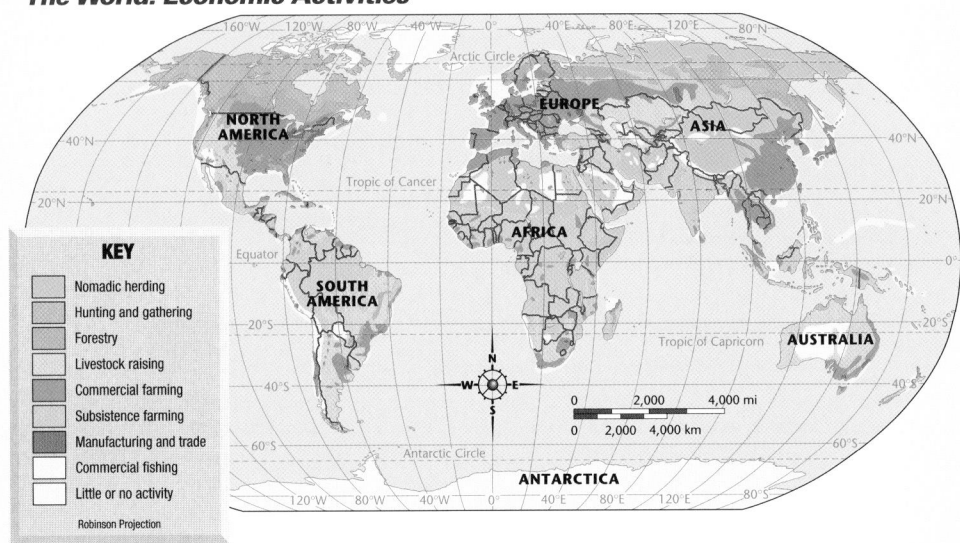

KEY
- Nomadic herding
- Hunting and gathering
- Forestry
- Livestock raising
- Commercial farming
- Subsistence farming
- Manufacturing and trade
- Commercial fishing
- Little or no activity

Robinson Projection

RESOURCE DIRECTORY

Teaching Resources

Unit 1, Chapter 4
- Section 2 Guided Reading and Review, p. 45

Guide to the Essentials (English/Spanish)
- Section Summary, Chapter 4, Section 2

Social Studies Skills Handbook
- Reading an Economic Activity Map, p. 27

Technology

Guided Reading Audiotapes (English/Spanish), Chapter 4, Section 2

Section Reading Support Transparencies, Chapter 4, Section 2

World Geography Map and Photo Transparencies
- Per Capita GDP
- World Trade Cartogram

Book on CD, Chapter 4

World Geography Videos
- Chapter 4 Video

Social Studies Skills Tutor CD-ROM, Analyzing and Interpreting Special Purpose Maps

Companion Web site, www.phschool.com
- Chapter 4 Activities

2 World Economic Activity

Reading Focus

- **What are four different categories of economic activities?**
- **Why are global trade patterns changing today?**
- **What kinds of data indicate a country's level of development?**

Key Terms

primary economic activity

subsistence farming

commercial farming

secondary economic activity

cottage industry

commercial industry

tertiary economic activity

quaternary economic activity

export

import

Main Idea Technology and resource distribution affect economic activities and trade patterns, which, in turn, affect level of development.

Economic Activities Draining latex from a tree is a primary economic activity in the Amazon region of South America.

E very morning in the cities of Asia, Africa, Europe, and the Americas, millions of people ride trains, cars, buses, or bicycles so that they can work in stores, factories, and offices. Every night they go home. To them, this seems to be a natural way to live and work.

To millions of other people, this way of living would seem strange. For these people, working means farming the land where they live, traveling with herds of animals, or catching fish far out at sea.

Economic Activities

People acquire the things that they need to survive and the luxuries that they desire by engaging in many different activities. Geographers and economists classify these economic activities into four categories.

Primary Activities Those economic activities that rely directly upon natural resources are classified as **primary economic activities.** When people are fishing or engaged in forestry

or mining, they directly take or use natural resources. When they are farming, people are using natural resources like soils and water to produce crops or raise animals. Primary economic activities are located near the natural resources that are being exploited. For example, a tin mine is located at the site of a tin deposit.

Hunting, gathering, and herding are the most ancient primary activities. People who pursue these activities tend to live in small groups in remote areas. Some people, such as the San of southern Africa and the Mountain Lapps of northern Scandinavia, still practice these activities.

The way of life of hunters, gatherers, and herders is based on environmental knowledge that has been passed down from generation to generation. Herders often follow large herds of animals over huge expanses of grazing land, traveling from place to place in different seasons. One group of people who follow this nomadic lifestyle are the Lapps of northern Scandinavia. They keep their reindeer on high alpine meadows to graze during summer, but move them to more protected valleys during winter.

Chapter 4 ▪ Section 2 **115**

Objectives

Upon completion of Section 2, students should be able to:

- ◆ distinguish four different categories of economic activities;
- ◆ explain why global trade patterns are changing today;
- ◆ evaluate data as an indicator of a country's level of development.

National Geography Standards

The following National Geography Standards are highlighted in this section: 1, 2, 3, 12, 14, 16

Bellringer

Ask students to make a list of ways in which people earn money. Point out that these are economic activities. Ask students how they think their economic activities will change in the next five years.

LESSON PLAN

1. Focus Discuss the economic activities in your community and make a list of occupations. Discuss whether these occupations are related to nearby resources.

2. Instruct Have students identify the characteristics of developed countries and less developed countries. Refer to the map of economic activity on page 114. Ask: **In what hemisphere are most of the world's developed countries located?** (Northern) **How can you tell?** (Areas with manufacturing and trade are located there.)

3. Close/Reteach Instruct students to find pictures of farming in different parts of the world. Arrange these around a world map and indicate where each kind of farming is done. Discuss how farming is related to economic development.

CUSTOMIZE FOR...

Less Proficient Readers
Writing Questions Have students write two questions from each of the three main subsections of Section 2. Have them exchange their questions and write the answers.

Subsistence farming Have students find the definition of *subsistence farming* in the Glossary. Then ask them to restate the definition in their own words.

Alternative Assessment

Mid-Point Monitoring

Writing a Position Paper You may wish to monitor students' progress on writing their position papers. Confer with students to see if they are finding references to support their arguments and if they have started a first draft of their papers.

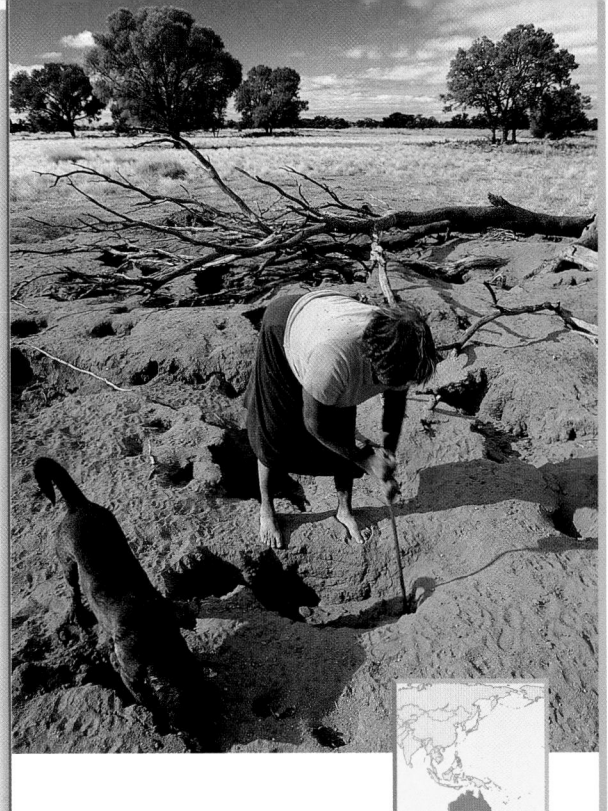

Gathering

Economic Activities Before the development of agriculture, hunting and gathering was the basis of human economic activity. This Aboriginal woman is digging for tubers in the Australian outback.

Human-Environment Interaction *Do you think this woman is performing a subsistence activity or a commercial activity? Explain.*

The most important primary economic activity around the world is farming. In nations with developing economies, roughly one half of all people are engaged in agriculture of some kind. In nations with more advanced economies, such as the United States, that figure is often less than 10 percent.

People around the world use a variety of agricultural methods. Much of the agriculture in developing countries is **subsistence farming.** People grow only enough food for their own family's or village's needs. If they are lucky enough to have a very good crop or an extra animal, they may sell or trade it, but they grow food to eat, not to sell.

Tools and techniques used in subsistence agriculture usually are very basic and time consuming. Farm animals and family members provide the main source of labor in subsistence farming. Family sizes often are large. Extra children may be extra mouths to feed, but they also provide additional workers.

In countries with more advanced economies, nearly all farmers raise crops and livestock to sell in the market. The production of food and other agricultural products for sale in markets is **commercial farming.** Modern techniques and equipment make this type of farming more productive. As a result, only a small part of a country's labor force is needed to produce enough food to feed the entire population. In Japan, for example, less than 7 percent of workers are involved in farming or fishing.

Some commercial farming also takes place in developing countries. Large plantations in tropical regions produce bananas, coffee, sugar, rubber, and other crops. Until recently, most plantations in developing countries were owned by foreign investors.

Geographic and economic factors affect the location of different types of commercial farms. For example, land near cities is usually very expensive. As a result, dairy farms and some kinds of fruit and vegetable farms may be found near urban areas. That is because these activities can yield high profits from small amounts of land. Ranches and large-scale grain farms, on the other hand, are usually located far from cities, where land prices are cheaper.

Secondary Activities When people use raw materials to produce or manufacture new products of greater value, they are engaging in a **secondary economic activity.** Examples of secondary activities include processing wheat into flour, milling lumber into plywood, and producing electrical power.

In a subsistence economy, secondary activities are generally small in size and use relatively little advanced technology. Because they traditionally take place in or near people's homes, they are known as **cottage industries.** A cottage industry usually involves the production of something by hand.

In more advanced market economies, the scale and sophistication of manufacturing are usually

Answer to Photo Caption

Subsistence. She is using her hands, not machinery, to pull food from the ground, most likely for her family's consumption.

much greater. Hundreds or thousands of people work in large factories located in and near major cities. These **commercial industries** turn out large quantities of manufactured goods, such as clothing, automobiles, household appliances, and heavy machinery. The finished goods are often shipped to other regions of the world.

A number of considerations affect the location of secondary activities. Factories are usually built near needed raw materials or near markets where the goods will be sold. The decision on the location of a factory depends on whether the raw materials or the finished goods will cost more to ship. The ideal region in which to build a factory is one with skilled workers, low labor costs, low energy costs, and access to easy transportation.

Tertiary Activities Service industries are considered to be **tertiary economic activities.** People engaged in this type of work do not directly gather or process raw materials. Instead, they pursue activities that serve others. Lawyers, doctors, and salespersons all engage in this kind of work. So do truck drivers, firefighters, and police officers. Tertiary activities are located where services are required. You will, therefore, find them wherever people live and work.

Quaternary Activities In modern economies like that of the United States, many people work at jobs that focus on the acquisition, processing, and sharing of information. Examples of such **quaternary economic activities** include education, government, information processing, and research.

Quaternary economic activities do not need to be located near resources or a market. Because of advanced communication technology, they can be located almost anywhere. However, information activities do tend to be clustered in regions that have high concentrations of highly educated workers and excellent communication networks. The rapid growth of the Internet has highlighted the increasingly important role of information in modern, market economies.

Global Trade Patterns

Each country in the world possesses different types and quantities of resources. In addition, individuals and countries may specialize in producing certain goods and services, rather than all the items that they need or desire. American farmers, for example, grow wheat, corn, and other crops that are suited to the soils and climatic conditions in the United States.

When nations do not have all the resources and goods that they want, they usually establish a trading network. Items that they have in abundance are sold to people in other countries. Items that are in short supply are bought from people in other countries. The goods that are sent out of the country are called **exports.** The goods that are brought into the country are called **imports.**

Commercial Farming

Economic Activities
Commercial farms in the United States yield vast amounts of grain. Much of the grain is turned into flour, which is then used to make breads, breakfast cereals, and other products.

Human-Environment Interaction *When workers use flour to make breakfast cereals, are they engaging in a primary or secondary economic activity? Explain.*

Articles From
NATIONAL GEOGRAPHIC

The following article may be used to extend the content in this section.

White, Peter T., and Charles O'Rear, photographer. "The Power of Money." *National Geographic*, Vol. 183, No. 1 (Jan. 1993), pp. 80–108.

From chickens to checking accounts, some form of currency is used in every corner of the world.

BACKGROUND

Connecting With . . .

History Point out that economic activities change over time. Regions that now have manufacturing centers, such as the Great Plains in the United States, once had nomadic herding, hunting, and gathering as their economic activities.

ACTIVITY

Group Work

Activity: Making a chart
Purpose: Divide the class into small groups. Direct each group to make a chart listing specific primary, secondary, tertiary, and quaternary economic activities.
Roles: Illustrator and writer
Result: Display charts in the classroom. Have students identify the types of economic activities that are most common in your community.

READING STRATEGY

Visualizing

Have students work in small groups to illustrate subsistence and commercial farming or cottage and commercial industries.

Answer to Photo Caption
Secondary. They are producing new products of greater value.

Group Work

Activity: Creating a skit

Purpose: Have students research developments in technology that have made it possible to export goods to foreign markets in the last 100 years. Direct groups to write and perform two-part skits to showcase the information they find. The first half of each skit should show the difficulties of exporting goods before the developments in technology; the second should show how exportation is now possible with the developments.

Roles: Writers, actors

Result: Have the groups perform their skits for the rest of the class.

At the Supermarket

Global Trade Patterns These shoppers browse a supermarket produce aisle. They can buy fruits and vegetables that were grown in different regions of the United States and the world.

Movement *Why is it necessary for people to import products from other parts of the world?*

Trade Balance Governments seek a favorable balance between imports and exports. Excessive imports can be damaging to a nation's economy. If people buy too many foreign goods, domestic businesses may lose profits and fail. Unemployment can then rise. Another negative effect of excessive imports is that a nation's debt to other countries increases. For these reasons, governments often try to limit imports. One way of doing this is to impose taxes on foreign goods.

Trade Routes Trade routes are determined by geography, transportation technology, and international relations. These factors all played a part, for example, in the global spice trade of the 1500s. During that time, European merchants sailed around Africa to trade for spices in East Asia. Innovations in navigation equipment and ship design made the ocean journeys possible. Overland routes were avoided because of deserts, mountains, and other geographic obstacles. Another reason for avoiding the land routes was that they went through states that were unfriendly toward the Europeans.

Today, modern technology is changing the nature of global trade. Developments in communication and computer science make electronic trading possible. Goods are still transported between nations, but business deals and payment transactions are often made via computer and satellite networks.

Level of Development

Economic activities and trade patterns influence a country's level of development. Modern industrial societies, such as France, the United States, and Japan, are said to be developed countries. Countries with lower levels of prosperity are considered underdeveloped. They lack adequate industries and modern technology and depend on developed countries for many of their manufactured goods. Nations showing evidence of political, economic, and social progress are called developing countries.

A number of statistics are used to measure a country's level of development. One way to compare the wealth of countries is to look at the per capita gross domestic product (GDP), the total value of goods and services produced in a country in a year divided by the total population. The average per capita GDP is vastly greater in developed countries than in developing or underdeveloped countries.

Developed countries enjoy a high standard of living. Compared to less developed countries, they have higher levels of education and health care. They also have more transportation and communication facilities per person. Airports, highways, and automobiles are more plentiful in developed countries than underdeveloped ones, as are telephones, newspapers, televisions, and computers. People in developed countries generally consume more food and live longer than people in poorer nations.

Answer to Photo Caption

The region they live in may not produce all the goods and services they require.

San Antonio River Walk

Economic Systems
Highly developed economies provide people with enough income and free time to pursue leisure activities. In Texas, the San Antonio River Walk is a favorite destination for local residents and tourists from around the world.

Place *How does this photo indicate that San Antonio has a high standard of living?*

The large differences in levels of economic development worry some people. Although many people want to see standards of living raised in developing nations, there is great disagreement about how to achieve this.

Global trade patterns have a significant impact on economic development. Wealthy nations invest money in less developed nations, which enables poorer countries to build their economies. In addition to goods and services, ideas and information are exchanged between developed and underdeveloped countries. This exchange can help promote political, economic, and social change.

SECTION 2 ASSESSMENT

1. **Key Terms** Define **(a)** primary economic activity, **(b)** subsistence farming, **(c)** commercial farming, **(d)** secondary economic activity, **(e)** cottage industry, **(f)** commercial industry, **(g)** tertiary economic activity, **(h)** quaternary economic activity, **(i)** export, **(j)** import.

2. **Economic Activities** What factors affect the location of different types of economic activities?

3. **Global Trade Patterns** How does the distribution of resources affect global trade patterns?

4. **Economic Systems** How do GDP and standard of living vary between developed and developing nations?

5. **Critical Thinking** **Making Comparisons** Why are global trade patterns today significantly different from global trade patterns of the 1500s?

Activity

Take It to the NET

Creating a Brochure Search the Internet to find information about how the U.S. government works to protect the balance of trade. Create a poster that can help business owners understand what types of assistance the government provides. Visit the World Geography section of **www.phschool.com** for help in completing this activity.

Answers to Section 2 Assessment

1. (a) primary economic activity, p. 115 **(b)** subsistence farming, p. 116 **(c)** commercial farming, p. 116 **(d)** secondary economic activity, p. 116 **(e)** cottage industry, p. 116 **(f)** commercial industry, p. 117 **(g)** tertiary economic activity, p. 117 **(h)** quaternary economic activity, p. 117 **(i)** export, p. 117 **(j)** import, p. 117

2. Primary economic activities are located near the necessary natural resources. Secondary activities are located near needed materials or markets. Their locations also depend on labor availability, energy costs, and transportation. Tertiary activities are located where services are required. Quaternary activities tend to be located in regions with high concentrations of educated workers and excellent communication networks.

3. Nations establish trading networks to export their surplus resources and goods and import what they need.

4. Developed countries have higher GDPs and a higher standard of living than developing countries.

5. Possible answer: Because of modern transportation and communication technologies, trade is quicker and can be conducted almost anywhere in the world.

Activity Rubrics Share rubrics with students before they begin their brochures.

Attempted The brochure is incomplete or inaccurate.

Minimal The brochure provides some information on government assistance available to business owners.

Adequate The brochure reflects ample research and is accurate, neat, and readable.

Exemplary The brochure reflects extensive research and is highly informative, well written and organized, and visually attractive.

TEST PREPARATION

Have students read the subsection Level of Development on the opposite page to answer the following question.

Which of the following is *not* a feature of a developed country?

   A High levels of education
   B Low per capita gross domestic product
   C Numerous airports
   D Advanced technology

Answer to Photo Caption

Possible answer: People have ample income and leisure time to enjoy the amusements along the River Walk.

Creating a Chapter Summary

As a reteaching opportunity, pair a more able student with a less able student to complete this chapter summary.

Possible entries: **Secondary:** Use raw materials to produce new products of greater value; Located near raw materials or markets **Tertiary:** Pursue activities that serve others; Located wherever people live and work **Quaternary:** Focus on the acquisition, processing, and sharing of information

Reviewing Key Terms

1–10. Students' sentences should show a clear understanding of each term.

Understanding Key Ideas

11. The resources can be depleted.
12. by recycling and conserving
13. People live and work near resources or easy access to them.
14. (a) farming **(b)** In developing economies, most farming is subsistence. In more advanced economies, farming is mainly commercial.
15. Commercial industries; the scale and sophistication of manufacturing is greater.
16. Wealthy nations invest in less developed nations. The exchange of goods, services, and information can help promote economic change.

Critical Thinking and Writing

17. A drought will reduce the amount of water in the region and negatively impact activities such as farming that depend on that water.
18. (a) Possible answer: by funding efforts to develop alternative energy sources. For example, they might provide subsidies to automotive makers to produce electric cars. **(b)** Citizens can lobby the government and elect candidates who support such policies.
19. Labor, raw materials, markets, and transportation are available there.
20. Possible answers: The main activity—the acquisition and sharing of information—is a quaternary economic activity. Students may classify additional school activities in other categories. Food service and maintenance, for example, would be tertiary activities.

(Continued on next page.)

Creating a Chapter Summary

On a sheet of paper, draw a graphic organizer like the one below. Fill in information about different types of economic activities. Some information has already been filled in to help you get started.

ECONOMIC ACTIVITIES

Primary
• Use natural resources directly
• Located at site of natural resource being developed

Quaternary
• Can be located anywhere

Take It to the NET
Chapter Self-Test For practice test questions for Chapter 4, go to the World Geography section of **www.phschool.com**.

Reviewing Key Terms

Write sentences, using the key terms listed below, leaving blanks where the key terms would go. Exchange your sentences with those of another student and fill in the blanks in each other's sentences.

1. natural resource
2. renewable resource
3. fossil fuel
4. nuclear energy
5. geothermal energy
6. subsistence farming
7. commercial farming
8. cottage industry
9. export
10. import

Understanding Key Ideas

11. **Natural Resources** What challenge can result from overuse of renewable resources?
12. **Planning for the Future** How can people extend the supply of nonrenewable resources?
13. **Patterns of Settlement** How does the distribution of resources influence people's choices about where to live and work?
14. **Economic Activities** (a) What is the most widespread primary economic activity today?

(b) How does this activity vary between developing economies and advanced economies?
15. **Economic Systems** Is an advanced market economy more likely to depend the most on commercial industries or cottage industries? Explain.
16. **Global Trade Patterns** How can global trade patterns affect economic development?

Critical Thinking and Writing

17. **Predicting Consequences** How might a prolonged drought in a region affect renewable water resources and the economic activities that depend on those resources?
18. **Identifying Alternatives** (a) How can governments encourage the development of new energy sources? (b) What effect can citizens have on such policies?
19. **Identifying Relationships** Why are many factories located in or near major cities?
20. **Analyzing Information** How might a geographer classify economic activities that take place at your school? Explain.

21. Analyzing Causes and Effects How can excessive reliance on imports affect a nation's economy?

22. Defending a Position Should a government tax imports in order to limit the amount of goods coming into a country? Provide arguments to defend your position.

Applying Skills

Refer to the map and skill lesson on page 114 to answer these questions:

23. What type of economic activity is predominant in the deserts of North Africa and Southwest Asia?

24. (a) Where is there little or no economic activity? **(b)** Why is there little activity in those regions?

Analyzing a Photograph Study the photograph below, and answer the following questions:

25. What natural resource is being recycled by these school children?

26. How does this activity help to protect the environment?

27. How does the activity benefit the economy?

28. How can government encourage people to recycle natural resources?

29. Do you think government should encourage conservation of natural resources? Why or why not?

Test Preparation

Read each question and choose the best answer.

30. Which of the following energy sources causes concern about radioactive waste?

A fossil fuels

B geothermal energy

C solar energy

D nuclear energy

31. How are excessive imports likely to affect employment rates in a country?

A Unemployment may increase as foreign goods outsell domestic goods.

B Unemployment may increase as people spend all of their money on foreign goods.

C Unemployment may decrease because people will find jobs in the import sector.

D Unemployment may decrease because people will find jobs in other countries.

Activities

 MENTAL MAPPING

Review a map of the world's rivers and lakes. On a separate piece of paper, draw a map of the world from memory. Label the following places on your map:

- Amazon River
- Congo River
- Volga River
- Yangzi River
- Nile River
- Mississippi River
- Mekong River
- Lake Baikal
- Great Lakes
- Lake Victoria

Take It to the NET

Writing a Proposal Search the Internet for recommendations about how schools can decrease their reliance on fossil fuels. Identify three energy-use goals your school might adopt, and write a proposal to your school board identifying the benefits of adopting the goals. Visit the World Geography section of **www.phschool.com** for help in completing this activity.

21. Possible answer: Domestic businesses may lose money and have to fire their workers.

22. Students should provide reasons to support their position.

Applying Skills

23. nomadic herding

24. (a) Antarctica, parts of northern Canada and Greenland, parts of Asia, the deserts of Southwest Asia and North Africa, western Australia, western coast of South America **(b)** because of extreme climate and physical conditions

25. aluminum cans

26. The aluminum can be reused instead of becoming trash.

27. Many people are employed in the recycling industry.

28. institute incentives to recycle and penalties for not recycling

29. Answers will vary, but students should provide reasons to support their points of view.

Test Preparation

30. D

31. A

Activities

Mental Mapping
Review students' maps and labels for accuracy.

Take It to the Net
Students' work should reflect sound research. Check that students' proposals are reasonable and that they have accurately described the benefits of adopting their goals.

 MENTAL MAPPING

Games for Review See pages 58–63 of the Simulations, Games, and Lab Activities booklet for games to review place names.

Chapter Map Test Students should use the completed outline maps and the Unit 1 Checklist in their Atlas Portfolios to prepare for the Chapter 4 Map Test.

Unit Map Test To prepare for the Unit 1 Map Test, students will need to study the location of all the place names on the Unit 1 Checklist.

Alternative Assessment

Final Evaluation

Writing a Position Paper Use the Position Paper Evaluation Form on page 9 of the Alternative Assessment booklet in the Teaching Resources to evaluate students' papers. Either teachers or students can complete the forms to indicate which level of work was achieved for each of the criteria. The person evaluating the paper should use the space on the form to provide specific examples and comments.

TEST PREPARATION

Use this sample exam to help your students prepare for standardized tests.

You might want to remind your students of the following:

Tips for Test Taking

1. Read the directions carefully.

2. Read each question carefully.

3. For multiple choice questions, try to answer the question before you look at the choices. Read all the choices. Then, eliminate those that are absolutely incorrect.

4. For short answer questions, be sure to answer the question completely if there is more than one part.

5. Answer the easy questions first. Then, go back to the ones that will take more time.

6. Pace yourself. Be sure to set aside enough time for the writing questions.

Write answers on a separate sheet of paper.

Multiple Choice

1 What kind of ecosystem found near the Equator is characterized by a heavy undergrowth of vines, broadleaf evergreen trees, and abundant rain?

   A Mid-latitude coniferous forest

   B Mid-latitude deciduous forest

   C Chaparral

   D Tropical rain forest

2 Natural gas, copper, iron, and oil are all classified as —

   A renewable resources

   B nonrenewable resources

   C fossil fuels

   D alternative energy sources

3 Which activity would be most appropriate for a site located at a latitude of 70°S?

   A A tropical vacation

   B Cattle herding

   C Polar exploration

   D Coal mining

4 When sediment accumulates on either side of a river, what kind of landform often results?

   A Alluvial plain

   B Glacier

   C Mantle

   D Savanna

5 The metropolitan region of Denver, Colorado, consists of the city of Denver plus its surrounding suburbs. Many people in the suburbs travel each day to work in Denver. These statements describe which kind of region?

   A Perceptual region

   B Formal region

   C Functional region

   D Absolute region

6 Which of the following are significant causes of water scarcity for people in the world today?

   A The increasing development of nuclear energy and solar energy

   B Migration and urbanization

   C Mechanical weathering and chemical weathering

   D Pollution and irrigation

7 A scientist mentioning "the breakup of Pangaea" probably would be discussing which of the following geographic topics?

   A Chemical and mechanical weathering

   B Autonomous regions

   C Land redistribution

   D The continental drift theory

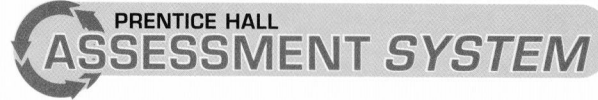

PRENTICE HALL
ASSESSMENT *SYSTEM*

Diagnose and Prescribe
 • Profile student skills with Diagnostic Tests A&B.
 • Address student needs with program materials identified in the test.

Review and Reteach
 • Provide cumulative content review with the Review Book.

Practice and Assess
 • Build test-taking skills with Test-Taking Strategies on Transparencies.

Use the chart **and** your knowledge of social studies to answer the following question.

untry	Wheat Production, 1990 (metric tons)	Wheat Production, 1994 (metric tons)	Corn Production, 1990 (metric tons)	Corn Production, 1994 (metric tons)
	3,094,000	2,276,000	21,348,000	32,305,000
	49,850,000	59,131,000	8,962,000	10,500,000
khstan	16,197,000	9,052,000	442,000	233,000
tan	14,316,000	15,114,000	1,185,000	1,288,000
Africa	1,730,000	1,850,000	8,709,000	11,811,000
ne	30,374,000	13,857,000	4,737,000	1,539,000

: Statistical Abstract of the United States

8 In which country did wheat production decline by more than 50 percent between 1990 and 1994?

A Brazil

B Ukraine

C Pakistan

D South Africa

9 Which of the following statements best explains the abundance of oxygen in the earth's atmosphere?

A Plants create oxygen as a byproduct of photosynthesis.

B The sun's radiation produces oxygen, which travels rapidly through space and enters the atmosphere.

C Industrial emissions from factories add large amounts of oxygen and nitrogen to the earth's atmosphere.

D The ozone layer of the stratosphere produces oxygen during the summer when temperatures are warmest.

10 When people move to cities in search of better jobs, which concepts of human geography are they exhibiting?

A Push factors and culture hearths

B Traditional economy and the population pyramid

C Urbanization and migration

D Natural hazards and population density

Writing Practice

11 How does erosion change the surface of the earth? Describe two different ways in which erosion can occur.

12 Briefly discuss a primary economic activity, a secondary economic activity, and a tertiary economic activity that you think could develop in a newly settled seacoast area.

13 Based on world population trends over the past hundred years, do you expect world population to increase, decrease, or remain about the same over the next ten years? Explain the reasons for your hypothesis.

Test Preparation Answers

Multiple Choice

1 D

2 B

3 C

4 A

5 C

6 D

7 D

8 B

9 A

10 C

Writing Practice

11 Water, wind, and glaciers move such weathered material as gravel, soil, and sand, causing great changes on the surface of the earth. An example of water erosion is the formation of large canyons caused by the movement of rivers. Strong winds can cause soil erosion. The movement of large glaciers has resulted in the formation of large lakes and islands.

12 Students' responses should demonstrate an understanding of the three terms. In the area described, for example, fishing might be a reasonable primary economic activity, for it would take directly from the natural resource of the ocean. A secondary economic activity might be a food-processing plant in which the catch is prepared as frozen fish products for sale. Driving a refrigerated truck to its deliveries at supermarkets might be a tertiary economic activity.

13 Possible answer: World population is likely to increase due to factors such as increased access to better medical care. Better medical care allows people to live longer. In developing nations, the birthrate will probably remain high.

Introducing
UNIT
2
pp. 124–201

The United States and Canada

Activating Prior Knowledge

Canvass the class to find out what students think of or visualize when they hear or see the word *Canada*. How much do they know about our northern neighbor? Ask them to describe what kind of people they think live there. Find out if they can name what lies to the east (Greenland and the North Atlantic Ocean), west (the North Pacific Ocean and Alaska), and north of Canada (the North Pole). Have them visualize a globe and what lies opposite Canada in the Northern Hemisphere. (Russia, mostly Siberia) Finally, ask the class to consider their own region and where it is relative to Canada.

Photo Study

Banff National Park

Banff National Park boasts some of Canada's most beautiful scenery. Among the attractions is Lake Louise, which is set among the high mountain peaks. Banff is located about 80 miles (128 km) west of Calgary and 150 miles (240 km) north of the United States border. **Drawing Conclusions** Ask students to use the map on page 182 to determine which mountains provide the dramatic scenery at Banff. (the Rocky Mountains)

eTeach

Be sure to check out this month's online forum with a Master Teacher to join in an exchange of teaching ideas. **www.phschool.com**

124 Unit 2

UNIT two

The United States and Canada

A Global Perspective

The United States and Canada occupy most of the sprawling continent of North America. The northwestern tip of North America almost reaches the northeastern tip of Asia. The southern part of North America, which borders the United States, is a land link to another continent—South America. Seen from this perspective, the United States and Canada are right in the center of today's busy world.

Robinson Projection

124

RESOURCE DIRECTORY

Teaching Resources

Unit 2
- Geography and World Literature, House Made of Dawn, p. 56

Mental Mapping booklet
- Unit 2 Checklist, p. 19
- Unit 2 Map Test, p. 33

Simulations, Games, and Lab Activities
- Where on Earth? Games, pp. 66–67

Global Environmental Posters

Technology

TeacherExpress™ CD-ROM
World Geography: Building a Global Perspective Teaching Resources on CD-ROM offers lesson planning flexibility, test-generation capability, and resource manageability.

Prentice Hall Presentation Pro CD-ROM
This CD-ROM allows you to create custom lessons for instruction or review for every chapter.

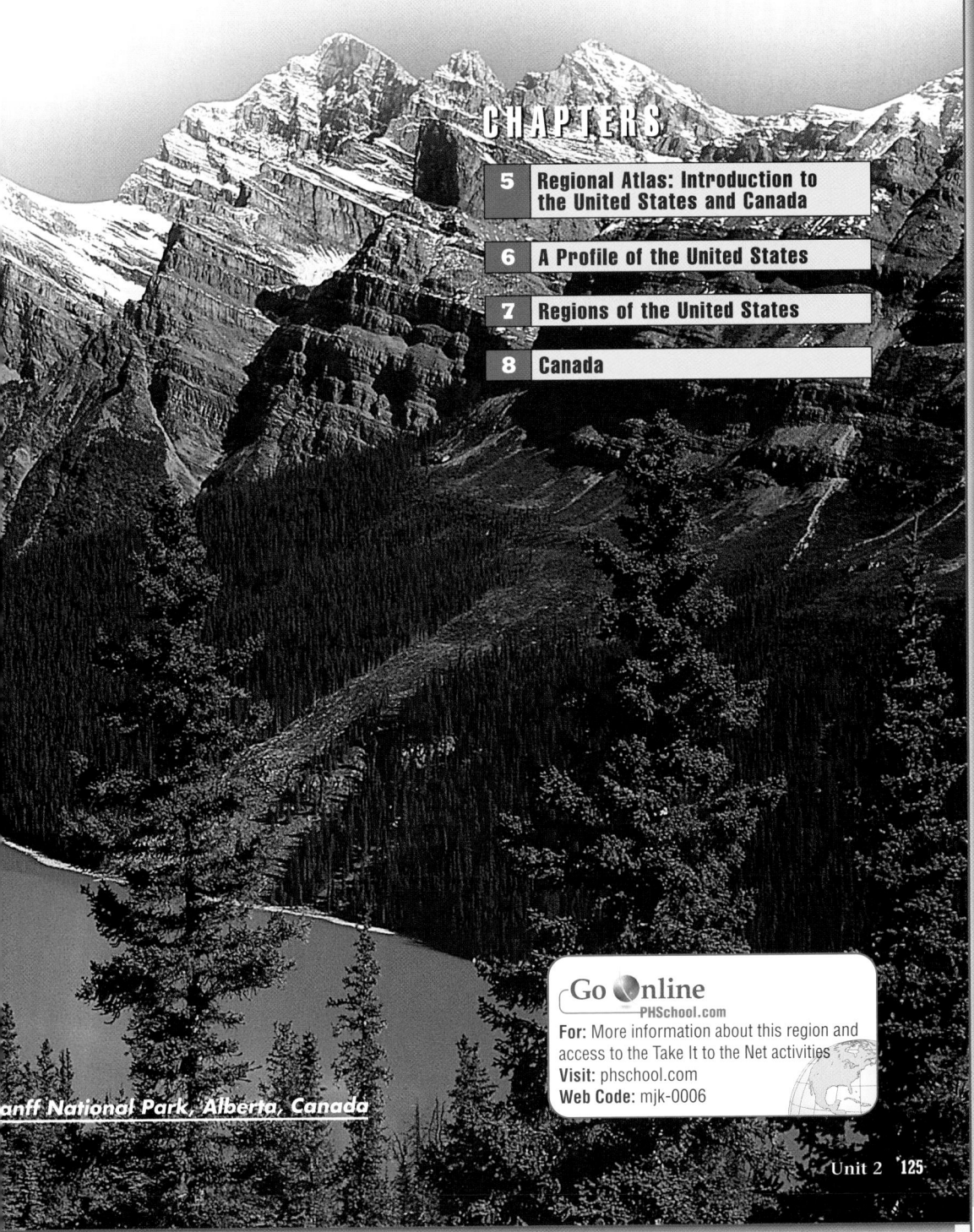

CHAPTERS

anff National Park, Alberta, Canada

Go Online
PHSchool.com
For: More information about this region and access to the Take It to the Net activities
Visit: phschool.com
Web Code: mjk-0006

Unit 2 **125**

Promoting Geographic Understanding

Introduce the unit by using the themes below.

1. Location Direct students' attention to the Robinson projection map on page 124 and ask them to locate the United States and Canada. (Refer students to the area highlighted on the map.)

2. Place Ask students to use their prior knowledge to state one fact relating to the physical aspects of this place (the United States and Canada) and one fact relating to the cultural aspects of this place.

3. Region Point out that in Chapter 5, students will see that the United States and Canada share the same landmass and many of the same landforms.

Resource Manager

	CORE INSTRUCTION	READING/SKILLS
Chapter-Level Resources	**Teaching Resources** ■ **Unit 2**/Ch. 5 • Regional Atlas Study Guide, p. 2 ■ **Mental Mapping booklet** • Unit 2 Checklist, p. 19 ■ **Simulations, Games, and Lab Activities** • Place Location Review Games, pp. 58–63 ⊙ **TeacherExpress™ CD-ROM**, Ch. 5 ▣ **Companion Web site, www.phschool.com** • eTeach	**Teaching Resources** ■ **Unit 2**/Ch. 5 • Regional Atlas Review, p. 3 ■ **Guide to the Essentials (English/Spanish)** • Chapter 5 Summary ■ **Spanish Resources** • Regional Atlas Review, p. 13 ▦ **Guided Reading Audiotapes (English/Spanish)**, Ch. 5 ▤ **Section Reading Support Transparencies**, Ch. 5 ⊙ **Book on CD**, Ch. 5 ⊙ **Social Studies Skills Tutor CD-ROM**
Historical Overview Describe significant events and developments in the history of the United States and Canada.	**Teaching Resources** ■ **Mental Mapping booklet** • Outline Map 5A, p. 20 ⊙ **Prentice Hall Presentation Pro CD-ROM**, Ch. 5	**Teaching Resources** ■ **Social Studies Skills Handbook** • Reading a Political Map, p. 19
Physical Characteristics Identify major physical characteristics of the United States and Canada.	**Teaching Resources** ■ **Mental Mapping booklet** • Outline Map 5B, p. 21 ⊙ **Prentice Hall Presentation Pro CD-ROM**, Ch. 5	**Teaching Resources** ■ **Social Studies Skills Handbook** • Using Political and Physical Maps, pp. 20–23
Climates Compare climate regions in the United States and Canada.	⊙ **Prentice Hall Presentation Pro CD-ROM**, Ch. 5	**Teaching Resources** ■ **Social Studies Skills Handbook** • Reading a Climate Map, p. 26
Ecosystems Describe characteristics of major ecosystems in the United States and Canada.	⊙ **Prentice Hall Presentation Pro CD-ROM**, Ch. 5	**Teaching Resources** ■ **Social Studies Skills Handbook** • Reading a Natural Vegetation Map, p. 25
People and Cultures Discuss elements of culture in the United States and Canada.	**Teaching Resources** ■ **Creative Teaching Activities** • Native American Art and Culture, p. 7 ■ **Simulations, Games, and Lab Activities** • Exploring Local Geography, Local Immigration Patterns, p. 11 ⊙ **Prentice Hall Presentation Pro CD-ROM**, Ch. 5	**Teaching Resources** ■ **Social Studies Skills Handbook** • Reading a Population Distribution Map, p. 33 • Analyzing a Political Cartoon, p. 60
Economics, Technology, and Environment Identify how the economy, technology, and the environment interact in the United States and Canada.	⊙ **Prentice Hall Presentation Pro CD-ROM**, Ch. 5	**Teaching Resources** ■ **Social Studies Skills Handbook** • Reading an Economic Activity Map, p. 27 • Reading a Natural Resources Map, p. 34
Database • Explain the difference between nonrenewable and renewable resources of energy. • Identify several types of nonrenewable and renewable resources. • Compare energy production and use in Canada to energy production and use in the United States.	**Teaching Resources** ■ **Unit 2**/Ch. 5 • Regional Atlas Database Skills, p. 4 ⊙ **Prentice Hall Presentation Pro CD-ROM**, Ch. 5	**Teaching Resources** ■ **Unit 2**/Ch. 5 • Regional Atlas Database Skills, p. 4 ■ **Social Studies Skills Handbook** • Reading a Table, p. 62

ENRICHMENT/HONORS/PREAP

📖 **Teaching Resources**

📘 **Mental Mapping booklet**
- Atlas Activity, p. 22

📘 **Social Studies Skills Handbook**
- Study and Research Skills, pp. 94–108

🗺️ **World Geography Map and Photo Transparencies**
- The United States and Canada: Maps and Photos

📺 **World Geography Videos**
- Regional Atlas: The United States and Canada, Tape 1

💻 **Companion Web site, www.phschool.com**
- Chapter 5 Activities

🗺️ **World Geography Map and Photo Transparencies**
- The United States and Canada: Political

🗺️ **World Geography Map and Photo Transparencies**
- The United States and Canada: Physical

🗺️ **World Geography Map and Photo Transparencies**
- World Climate Zones

🗺️ **World Geography Map and Photo Transparencies**
- The United States and Canada: Natural Hazards

🗺️ **World Geography Map and Photo Transparencies**
- The United States and Canada: Population Density

📖 **Teaching Resources**

📘 **Simulations, Games, and Lab Activities**
- Simulation: Disposing of Toxic Wastes, p. 15

🗺️ **World Geography Map and Photo Transparencies**
- The United States and Canada: Economic Activities

🗺️ **World Geography Map and Photo Transparencies**
- The United States and Canada: Natural Resources

ASSESSMENT

PRENTICE HALL ASSESSMENT SYSTEM

Core Assessment

📘 ExamView Test Bank booklet, Ch. 5

💿 ExamView Test Bank CD-ROM, Ch. 5

Standardized Test Preparation

Diagnose and Prescribe

📘 **Diagnostic Tests for High School Social Studies Skills**

Review and Reteach

📘 **Review Book for World Geography,** pp. 5–6

Practice and Assess

📘 **Test-taking Strategies With Transparencies for High School**

Test-taking Strategy Poster

📘 **Alternative Assessment booklet**

📘 **Test Prep Book for World Geography**

📖 **Teaching Resources**

📘 **Unit 2**/Ch. 5
- Test Forms A and B, pp. 5–10

📘 **Guide to the Essentials (English/Spanish)**
- Chapter 5 Test

📘 **Mental Mapping booklet**
- Chapter 5 Map Test, p. 23

💻 **Companion Web site, www.phschool.com**
- Chapter 5 Self-Test

CUSTOMIZE FOR INDIVIDUAL NEEDS

Less Proficient Readers
- Guide to the Essentials (English), Ch. 5
- Social Studies Skills Handbook, p. 72
- Guided Reading Audiotapes (English), Ch. 5
- Section Reading Support Transparencies, Ch. 5
- Book on CD, Ch. 5

Students Acquiring English/ESL
- Guide to the Essentials (English/Spanish), Ch. 5
- Guided Reading Audiotapes (English/Spanish), Ch. 5
- Section Reading Support Transparencies, Ch. 5
- Book on CD, Ch. 5
- Teacher's Edition, Customize for . . . , pp. 129, 141

Less Proficient Writers
- Social Studies Skills Handbook, p. 81
- Alternative Assessment, Writing Assignment Rubric, p. 6

Introducing
C H A P T E R
5
pp. 126–141

Objectives
Upon completion of the Regional Atlas, students should be able to:

- describe significant events and developments in the history of the United States and Canada;

- identify major physical characteristics of the United States and Canada;

- compare climate regions in the United States and Canada;

- describe characteristics of major ecosystems in the United States and Canada;

- discuss elements of culture in the United States and Canada;

- identify how the economy, technology, and the environment interact in the United States and Canada.

 National Geography Standards
The following National Geography Standards are highlighted in this section: 1, 2, 3, 4, 5, 8, 9, 10, 11, 16, 17

Bellringer
Ask students to review the photographs, maps, and charts in the Regional Atlas. Tell them to close their books and brainstorm words that describe the physical features, climate, ecosystems, and population of your region.

Answers to Assessment

1. (a) colony, p. 126 **(b)** annex, p. 126 **(c)** cede, p. 126 **(d)** civil war, p. 126 **(e)** Industrial Revolution, p. 126

2. Answers include Miami, Houston, San Antonio, Dallas, and Phoenix.

3. Similarities include: both Canada and the United States were colonized by other nations; both expanded westward to the Pacific. Differences include: Canada remained tied to Great Britain for a longer period of time; the United States experienced a civil war over slavery in the 1860s.

126 Chapter 5

CHAPTER 5
Introduction to THE UNITED STATES AND CANADA

Historical Overview

Scientists believe that thousands of years ago, people migrated to North America from Asia. Known today as Native Americans, these people formed diverse cultures. By the 1500s, Europeans and Africans had begun to arrive.

Colonial Heritage The Spanish settled in Florida, Texas, and the present-day southwestern United States. The French, meanwhile, founded the colony of Quebec in present-day Canada. A **colony** is any territory separated from but subject to a ruling power. English settlers established 13 colonies on the Atlantic coast. After a revolution, these 13 colonies broke free and formed the United States of America. English traditions of individual rights and representative government provided the new nation with a strong foundation on which to build democratic government.

To the north, Canada remained closely tied to Great Britain for a longer period of time, but it, too, shared in the traditions that eventually gave rise to democracy. After several wars in the 1700s, French Quebec had come under British rule. Today, the majority of people in the province of Quebec remain French-speaking.

Growth and Conflict Both Canada and the United States expanded westward to the Pacific. In 1803, American territory reached the Rocky Mountains as a result of the Louisiana Purchase from France. In 1845, Texas was **annexed,** or incorporated, into the United States. War with Mexico resulted. After being defeated, Mexico

ceded, or transferred, California and a large area of the Southwest to the United States. Also in the 1840s, the United States negotiated with Britain to acquire the Oregon Territory. Other lands were gained by wars and treaties with the Native Americans.

In the 1860s, the United States experienced a terrible conflict. The northern states and southern states fought each other in a **civil war,** a conflict between opposing groups of citizens of the same country. Regional differences and disagreements over slavery caused the war. After the North's victory, the South faced a difficult period of recovery.

New Technology Throughout the 1800s, new technology fueled economic growth in Canada and the United States. The **Industrial Revolution** introduced power-driven machinery, enabling factories to produce great quantities of goods. Attracted by jobs, workers migrated to the growing cities. Railroads and steamships eased the movement of people and products. With new agricultural machinery, farmers cultivated more land and harvested more crops.

Global Powers In the 1900s, the United States and Canada assumed leading roles in the world. Both nations fought as allies in two world wars. As a result, their ties to one another grew stronger. Recently, both countries have continued to oppose oppression in various parts of the world. Their economies remain vibrant today, driven by abundant resources and technology.

ASSESSMENT

1. **Key Terms** Define **(a)** colony, **(b)** annex, **(c)** cede, **(d)** civil war, **(e)** Industrial Revolution.

2. **Map Skills Regions** Which cities shown on the map are located in areas that were once under Spanish rule?

3. **Critical Thinking Making Comparisons** How are the histories of Canada and the United States similar and different?

126   Chapter 5 ▪ Regional Atlas: The United States and Canada

RESOURCE DIRECTORY

Teaching Resources
Unit 2, Chapter 5
- Regional Atlas Study Guide, p. 2

Guide to the Essentials (English/Spanish)
- Chapter 5 Summary

Mental Mapping booklet
- Unit 2 Checklist, p. 19
- Outline Map 5A, p. 20

Social Studies Skills Handbook
- Reading a Political Map, p. 19

Technology
Guided Reading Audiotapes (English/Spanish), Chapter 5

Section Reading Support Transparencies, Chapter 5

World Geography Map and Photo Transparencies
- The United States and Canada: Maps and Photos

World Geography Videos
- Regional Atlas: The United States and Canada, Tape 1

Book on CD, Chapter 5

REGIONAL ATLAS

The United States and Canada: POLITICAL

KEY
- ⊗ National capital
- ◉ State/Provincial capital
- • Other city

Lambert Azimuthal Equal-Area Projection

Map labels:
Bering Sea
ARCTIC OCEAN
ALASKA (U.S.)
Baffin Bay
Arctic Circle
Labrador Sea
Hudson Bay
CANADA
Edmonton
Calgary
Saskatoon
Vancouver
Seattle
Winnipeg
Quebec
Ottawa
Montreal
Minneapolis
St. Paul
Toronto
Buffalo
Boston
Detroit
Cleveland
New York City
Chicago
Baltimore
Philadelphia
UNITED STATES
San Francisco
Denver
Indianapolis
Washington, D.C.
St. Louis
Los Angeles
Phoenix
Atlanta
Dallas
Houston
New Orleans
San Antonio
Miami
Gulf of Mexico
Tropic of Cancer
MEXICO
ATLANTIC OCEAN
PACIFIC OCEAN
Great Lakes
Caribbean Sea

PACIFIC OCEAN
HAWAII (U.S.)
Honolulu
0   200 mi
0   200 km

0   500   1,000 mi
0   500   1,000 km

MENTAL MAPPING

Making a Political Map Study this political map, and then draw your own sketch map of the United States and Canada. Label the countries and major cities of the region. Use various colors to outline and shade each country.

LESSON PLAN

1. Focus Draw two interlocking circles on the board. Label one "Canada" and the other "United States." In the space where the circles overlap, have students write words that suggest ways in which Canada and the United States are alike. In the other sections, have them write words suggesting the differences.

2. Instruct Have students complete the Mental Mapping activities and the questions in the Regional Atlas. Review answers as a class.

3. Close/Reteach Ask students to imagine that the border between Canada and the United States runs north and south along the 100th meridian instead of east and west along the 49th parallel. Ask each student to list three ways this division would make Canada and the United States more similar than they are now.

MENTAL MAPPING

Unit Checklist Distribute the Unit 2 Checklist on page 19 of the Mental Mapping booklet in the Teaching Resources. This list includes all of the place names students should learn in this unit.

Making a Political Map Students can complete the mapping activity on this page either by sketching their own maps or by coloring and labeling the Chapter 5A Outline Map in the Mental Mapping booklet. Ask students to label all of the countries and major cities listed under Part I of the Unit 2 Checklist.

Alternative Assessment

Introduce the Activity

Creating a Map You may wish to distribute the Map Rubric found on page 14 of the Alternative Assessment booklet in the Prentice Hall Assessment System.

TEACHING TIP
From A Master Teacher

North America's Environment As students study North America, have them identify how its wide range of environments and rich array of resources have contributed to its economic welfare. Ask students to explain how people have modified the environments in dramatic ways over the years. Have students discuss how the introduction of new species, replacement of natural vegetation with agriculture and cities, and alteration of the course of its waterways could affect the continent's environments.

Map Study Extension

Use the questions below to develop additional geographic themes.

1. Location Look at the map on page 129. Ask: **Which country extends farther to the east—Canada or the United States?** (Canada) **Name the area that is farthest to the east.** (Newfoundland)

2. Location Look at the map on page 129. Ask: **What major landforms lie between the Sierra Nevada and the Rocky Mountains?** (the Grand Canyon and the Great Basin)

3. Movement Look at the map on page 129. Ask: **If you wanted to travel by plane from the Rio Grande to the northern shore of the Hudson Bay, about how many miles would your journey be?** (about 2,500 miles, or 4,023 kilometers) **About how many miles are there between New York City and Vancouver Island?** (about 2,500)

B A C K G R O U N D

The Physical World

Glaciers One of the largest freshwater lakes in the world is located in North America. Lake Superior, one of the five Great Lakes, was created by the action of glaciers during the Ice Age. Moving glaciers also scooped out the riverbeds of the Mississippi River.

Answers to Assessment

1. (a) continental divide, p. 128 **(b)** drainage basin, p. 128 **(c)** tributary, p. 128 **(d)** striation, p. 128

2. Answers include the Missouri, Ohio, and Arkansas rivers.

3. Possible answer: The Appalachians. Their once-sharp peaks have been worn down by erosion.

Answers to Photo Captions

Great Lakes The striated rocks are evidence of glaciation.

Monument Valley The soil is very dry, and there is little vegetation to anchor it. It could be washed away in a heavy thunderstorm.

Cross Section the Rocky Mountains

128 Chapter 5

Physical Characteristics

The United States and Canada share a number of physical features. Both nations have high mountain chains in the west, plains in the central area, and lower mountains in the east. The Rocky Mountains form the **continental divide,** a boundary that separates rivers flowing toward opposite sides of a continent. It also separates **drainage basins,** areas of land that are drained by major rivers and their **tributaries**—rivers and streams that carry water to a major river.

Great Lakes

The five Great Lakes, which lie along the border of the United States and Canada, were formed by glaciers more than 10,000 years ago. Glaciated areas are characterized by polished rocks and scratch marks called **striations. PHYSICAL PROCESSES** *How does this photograph suggest glaciation?*

Monument Valley

Wind erosion sculpts the dramatic towers of Monument Valley, in Arizona and Utah. Erosion shapes landforms across the continent. In the eastern United States, the once-sharp peaks of the Appalachian Mountains have been worn down by rain, ice, and wind. **ENVIRONMENTAL CHANGE** *How could heavy thunderstorms cause erosion in Monument Valley?*

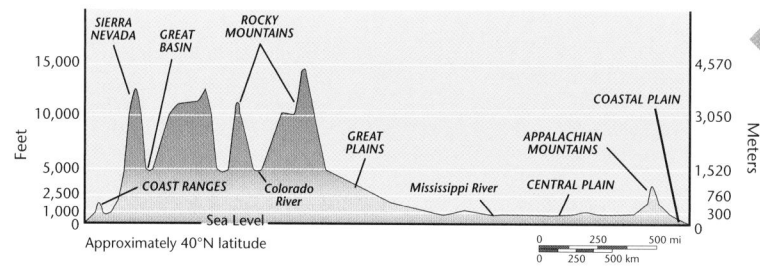

Cross Section

This cross section illustrates the differences in elevation across North America. **PHYSICAL CHARACTERISTICS** *In what mountain range does the Colorado River begin?*

ASSESSMENT

1. **Key Terms** Define **(a)** continental divide, **(b)** drainage basin, **(c)** tributary, **(d)** striation.

2. **Map Skills** **Regions** In the central United States, which rivers are tributaries of the Mississippi River?

3. **Critical Thinking** **Drawing Conclusions** Has erosion had a greater effect on the Rocky Mountains or on the Appalachians? Explain.

RESOURCE DIRECTORY

Teaching Resources
Mental Mapping booklet
• Outline Map 5B, p. 21
• Unit 2 Checklist, p. 19
Social Studies Skills Handbook
• Using Political and Physical Maps, pp. 20–23

Technology
World Geography Map and Photo Transparencies
• The United States and Canada: Maps and Photos
TeacherExpress™ CD-ROM, Chapter 5
Prentice Hall Presentation Pro CD-ROM, Chapter 5
Social Studies Skills Tutor CD-ROM
Companion Web site, www.phschool.com
• Chapter 5 Activities

REGIONAL ATLAS

The United States and Canada: PHYSICAL

KEY

Elevation

Feet		Meters
14,000		4,270
7,000		2,135
1,500		457
700		213
(sea level) 0		0 (sea level)

• Major city
▲ Mountain
△ Volcano

Lambert Azimuthal Equal-Area Projection

HAWAII
(U.S.)

0   200 mi
0   200 km

MENTAL MAPPING

Making a Physical Map Students can complete the mapping activity on this page either by adding labels to the political maps they have completed, or by coloring and labeling the Chapter 5B Outline Map on page 21 of the Mental Mapping booklet in the Teaching Resources. Ask students to label all of the bodies of water and landforms listed under Part II of the Unit 2 Checklist at this time.

ACTIVITY

Enrichment

Comparing Have students find two pictures of landforms that can be found in both Canada and the United States and one picture for each country showing a feature unique to it. Students may use their textbooks and books in the school library. Compare the photos as a class. (Visual/Spatial)

MENTAL MAPPING

Making a Physical Map Study this physical map and then draw your own sketch map of the United States and Canada. Label the major physical features, including rivers and other bodies of water.

CUSTOMIZE FOR...

Students Acquiring English/ESL

Creating an Illustration One way to visualize the Canadian Shield is to imagine an old parking lot that has been pounded and scraped of all debris by heavy equipment. The slabs of concrete are broken up in large chunks and tilted in various directions. Numerous potholes contain stagnant water filled with vegetation. Here and there, some vegetation grows in the thin soil that has collected between the cracks, but in general the lot is fairly desolate and almost impassable. After reading students the description above, have them sketch a drawing of the Canadian Shield.

Map Study Extension

Use the questions below to develop additional geographic themes.

1. Location Have students find the subarctic region, and note that it stretches east and west all the way across the continent. Ask: **How does location affect this region's climate?** (It is located in the polar zone, a region that receives indirect sunlight.)

2. Place Focus student attention on the large variety of climate regions in the contiguous states of the United States. Ask: **What are the three largest climate regions?** (humid continental, humid subtropical, and semiarid)

Answers to Assessment

1. rain shadow, p. 130

2. Dallas, St. Louis, Washington, D.C.

3. (a) Canada is farther north.
(b) Possible answer: More money must be spent heating homes and businesses.

Climates

Latitude, elevation, and distance from oceans affect the climates of the United States and Canada. Canada lies farther north than most of the United States except for Alaska, and generally has a colder climate. Both nations have climate differences between east and west, partly because the Rocky Mountains block moisture-laden winds from the Pacific Ocean. The eastern slopes of the Rockies and the plains lie in a **rain shadow,** an area of reduced rainfall on the leeward side of high mountains.

Arid Climate

Big Bend National Park, which marks part of Texas's border with Mexico, has little rainfall for most of the year. Winter rains, however, can lead to spectacular wildflower displays in the spring. **PHYSICAL PROCESSES** *Do you think this landscape looks the same all year? Explain.*

Humid Continental Climate

Warm summers and cold winters are a hallmark of humid continental climate regions. The colorful trees on this Vermont farm indicate the arrival of cool autumn temperatures. **CLIMATES** *What regions of the United States and Canada have the same climate as Vermont?*

Climatic Differences

The data for these five cities show the variety of climate zones throughout the United States. Temperature, rainfall, and snowfall are all indicators of climate. **CLIMATES** *Which city in the table has the highest average July temperature?*

Climate Conditions of Selected U.S. Cities

City	Average Monthly Temperature (°F)		Average Annual Precipitation (in.)	Average Annual Precipitation (days)	Average Annual Snowfall (in.)
	January	July			
Chicago, IL	21	73	33.3	127	40.3
Dallas–Ft. Worth, TX	44	86	29.5	78	3.1
Miami, FL	67	83	57.6	129	0.0
New York, NY	32	76	42.8	119	26.1
Seattle, WA	39	65	38.6	158	12.8

Source: National Oceanic and Atmospheric Administration

ASSESSMENT

1. **Key Term** Define rain shadow.

2. **Map Skills** **Regions** Which cities on the map are located in the humid subtropical climate zone?

3. **Critical Thinking** **Analyzing Causes and Effects** **(a)** Why is Canada's climate generally colder than that of the United States? **(b)** How can a colder climate have economic effects for both individuals and businesses?

Answers to Photo Captions

Arid Climate Possible answer: No. Little plant life is probably evident the rest of the year, when rainfall is scarce.

Humid Continental Climate the southeastern portion of Canada and the northeastern and north central portion of the United States

Climatic Differences Dallas–Fort Worth

RESOURCE DIRECTORY

Teaching Resources
Social Studies Skills Handbook
• Reading a Climate Map, p. 26

Technology
World Geography Map and Photo Transparencies
• The United States and Canada: Maps and Photos

REGIONAL ATLAS

Critical Thinking

Conducting Interviews Arrange students in pairs. Assign each pair one of the climate regions shown on the map on this page. Explain that each pair will conduct an interview for a radio show. One member will act as the interviewer, the other as a resident of the assigned climate region. Have students conduct the interview without telling the class which climate they will be discussing. The class must figure out which climate the pair has been assigned. Ask students to prepare for the interview by researching their region using library resources or the Internet.

The United States and Canada: CLIMATE REGIONS

KEY

- Tropical wet
- Tropical wet and dry
- Semiarid
- Arid
- Mediterranean
- Humid subtropical
- Marine west coast
- Humid continental
- Subarctic
- Tundra
- Highlands

Lambert Azimuthal Equal-Area Projection

Take It to the NET
Enrichment To learn more about climate regions around the world, visit the World Geography section of **www.phschool.com**.

Chapter 5 ▪ Regional Atlas: The United States and Canada   **131**

TEST PREPARATION

Have students use the climate table on the opposite page to answer the following question.

Which one of the following cities has the highest average number of days of rainfall per year?

- **A** Seattle
- **B** Miami
- **C** New York
- **D** Chicago

Map Study Extension

Use the questions below to develop additional geographic themes.

1. Location Ask: **Where in the United States would you go to find tropical rain forest?** (Hawaii)

2. Region Ask: **Which region of the United States is in the tundra?** (northern Alaska)

Answers to Assessment

1. coniferous forest, temperate grassland, mid-latitude deciduous forest, mixed forest

2. It preserves the natural ecosystems by setting aside the land and limiting development.

Ecosystems

The variety of ecosystems found in the United States and Canada includes arctic tundra, several types of forests, grasslands, and desert scrub. In a few areas, such as Hawaii, northern Canada, and Alaska, much of the natural vegetation remains. In many other places, however, people have changed the environment dramatically, limiting the range of native plant and animal life.

Florida Everglades

The grassy waters of the Everglades, covering much of southern Florida, provide a home for a wide variety of plants and animals. Alligators, Florida panthers, cypress trees, and palms are among the residents of this ecosystem. **ENVIRONMENTAL CHANGE** *How might increased agricultural development affect an ecosystem like the Everglades?*

Forest Ecosystems

There are several different kinds of forests in North America. Coniferous forests contain trees with cones that carry and protect their seeds. Deciduous forests are made up of trees that shed their leaves when winter approaches. **ECOSYSTEMS** *Compare this map with the map on page 131. In what climate regions are coniferous forests most common?*

Grasslands and Highlands

The dry interior plains of Canada and the United States are temperate grasslands. These grasslands are found in mid-latitude zones. In the Rockies, vegetation and animal life vary with altitude. **ECOSYSTEMS** *How are buffalo well suited to the environment in which they live?*

ASSESSMENT

1. **Map Skills** **Regions** Which ecosystems span the border of the United States and Canada?

2. **Critical Thinking** **Predicting Consequences** How do you think the United States national park system affects natural ecosystems? Explain.

132   Chapter 5 ▪ Regional Atlas: The United States and Canada

Answers to Photo Captions

Florida Everglades Possible answer: Habitat for plants and animals would disappear. Pesticides or fertilizers might affect water quality.

Forest Ecosystems subarctic

Grasslands and Highlands Possible answer: They graze on the grasses of the plains. Their coats protect them from the elements.

REGIONAL ATLAS

The United States and Canada: ECOSYSTEMS

KEY

- Tropical rain forest
- Mid-latitude deciduous forest
- Mixed forest (deciduous and coniferous)
- Coniferous forest
- Chaparral
- Tropical grassland
- Temperate grassland
- Desert scrub
- Tundra
- Ice cap
- Highlands (vegetation varies with elevation)

Lambert Azimuthal Equal-Area Projection

Take It to the NET
Enrichment To learn more about ecosystems around the world, visit the World Geography section of **www.phschool.com**.

Reteach

Creating Ecosystem Maps
Distribute Chapter 5 outline maps from the Mental Mapping booklet or have students sketch their own outline maps of the United States and Canada. Have students refer to the ecosystems map and key on this page. Ask each student to create a new ecosystems map key by choosing an appropriate symbol to represent each ecosystem shown. Instruct them to place their symbols correctly on their outline maps, repeating the same symbol several times as needed for large areas. Have students share completed maps in class. (Visual/Spatial)

BACKGROUND

Connecting With . . .

History and Science When Europeans arrived in the Americas, they noted that the western end of the humid continental climate zone—in the area of present-day Iowa and Illinois—was covered with tall, dense prairie grasses. Their accounts have puzzled modern scientists. Given the ample precipitation of this region, scientists would normally expect forests rather than grasslands to have grown here. To explain this mystery, some scientists have suggested that prehistoric Native Americans burned the forests so often that fire-resistant grasses eventually replaced the trees.

Map Study Extension
Use the questions below to develop additional geographic themes.

1. Location Look at the population density map on page 135. Ask: **What large city is located at about 61°N, 150°W?** (Anchorage, Alaska)

2. Movement The United States and Canada are very similar in that both are multiethnic nations. Many of the countries' inhabitants arrived by water on the two coasts. Ask: **What continents did people who arrived on the Atlantic Coast come from?** (Europe and Africa) **What continent did people who arrived on the Pacific Coast come from?** (Asia) Look at the pie graph on this page. Ask: **What percentage of immigrants come from Europe?** (15 percent)

The populations of the United States and Canada differ greatly in number. The United States has over 275 million people, whereas Canada has approximately 31 million people. In other ways, however, the populations of the two countries are similar. At least three fourths of people in both countries live in urban areas, and both nations have long life expectancies. Extensive education systems contribute to high rates of **literacy,** or the ability to read and write.

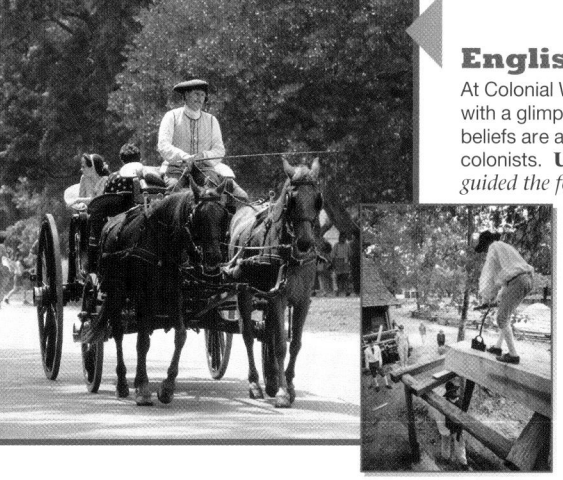

English Colonial Heritage
At Colonial Williamsburg, costumed guides provide modern-day visitors with a glimpse at America's past. Language, legal system, and political beliefs are among the cultural legacies handed down from English colonists. **UNDERSTANDING THE PAST** *What political beliefs guided the founders of the United States?*

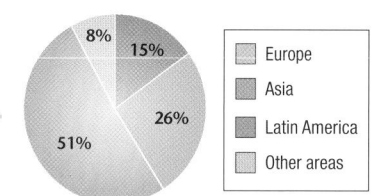

- 8%
- 15%
- 26%
- 51%

Legend:
- Europe
- Asia
- Latin America
- Other areas

Immigration
Immigration has shaped the populations of both nations. At the beginning of the twenty-first century, more than 28 million people in the United States had been born in other countries around the world. **CULTURES** *What region of origin does this graph show for most foreign-born people in the United States?*

Suburban Growth
Affordable housing draws many people to **suburbs,** or residential areas outside a central city. Some argue that suburban growth may harm the environment. **ENVIRONMENTAL CHANGE** *How does suburban growth change the environment?*

ASSESSMENT

1. **Key Terms** Define **(a)** literacy, **(b)** suburb.

2. **Map Skills Regions** Which region of the United States has the largest area of dense population?

3. **Critical Thinking Recognizing Patterns** Study this map and the maps on pages 131 and 133. Why do you think most Canadians live near their nation's southern border?

Answers to Assessment
1. (a) literacy, p. 134 **(b)** suburb, p. 134

2. the Northeast

3. Possible answer: The climate is likely to be less cold there than it would be farther north.

Answers to Photo Captions
English Colonial Heritage Possible answers: individual rights, representative government

Immigration Latin America

Suburban Growth Roads and houses replace open lands.

RESOURCE DIRECTORY

Teaching Resources
Creative Teaching Activities, Native American Art and Culture, p. 7
Social Studies Skills Handbook
- Reading a Population Distribution Map, p. 33
- Analyzing a Political Cartoon, p. 60
Simulations, Games, and Lab Activities
- Exploring Local Geography, Local Immigration Patterns, p. 11

Technology
World Geography Map and Photo Transparencies
- The United States and Canada: Maps and Photos

REGIONAL ATLAS

The United States and Canada: POPULATION DENSITY

KEY

Persons per sq mi	Persons per sq km
520 and over	200 and over
260–519	100–199
130–259	50–99
25–129	10–49
1–24	1–9
Less than 1	Less than 1

Metropolitan areas

▢ 10,000,000 and over
◼ 5,000,000–9,999,999
◯ 2,000,000–4,999,999
◉ 1,000,000–1,999,999
● 250,000–999,999

Lambert Azimuthal Equal-Area Projection

GET THE FACTS . . .
Go to the **Table of Countries** at the back of this book for additional population data.

Group Work

Activity: Celebrating U.S.–Canadian Friendship Day

Purpose: Tell each group to imagine that they have been chosen as an entertainment committee for a U.S.–Canadian Friendship Day. They need to produce a speech, song, or skit that highlights the physical and cultural ties between the two countries. Their piece should also note some of the ways in which each nation is unique.

Roles: Assign a group leader.

Result: Have groups present their work to the class.

BACKGROUND

United States and the World

Diversity In the United States, there are many diverse groups with distinct identities. For many years, Americans considered their country a "melting pot" in which diverse groups were melted down into a single, consistent group that combined the differing identities. Today, some people feel that the United States is more of a "tossed salad" in which groups retain their individuality but are thrown together and mixed in a single bowl.

ACTIVITY

Area Comparison

Using the Table of Countries Ask students to use the Table of Countries beginning on page 742 of their textbooks to compare the land areas and populations of the United States and Canada. **Connections: Math** Which country has the greater population density? (The United States; while their land areas are very similar, the population of the United States is about nine times greater than that of Canada.)

Articles From
NATIONAL GEOGRAPHIC

The following article may be used to extend the content in this section.

Ortiz, Alfonso, and Felipe Davalos, illustrator. "1491: America Before Columbus." *National Geographic,* Vol. 180, No. 4 (Oct. 1991), pp. 4–99.

This article presents five portraits of America before the arrival of Columbus.

Map Study Extension

Use the questions below to develop additional geographic themes.

1. Region Ask: **Where are petroleum resources concentrated?** (southern United States)

2. Region Locate the area in the southwestern United States that shows little or no economic activity. Ask: **Why do you think there is little economic activity in this area?** (Desert climate makes farming and other activity very difficult.)

ACTIVITY

Connecting With . . .

Government Canada and the United States are so close geographically and share so much economically that the two governments are faced with some important issues that must be solved together. Two of these issues are acid rain related to industry in the northeastern United States and the Great Lakes region, and trade restrictions. Have students choose one of these issues and write a report on how the two governments have worked to address these issues during the 1990s and the beginning of the twenty-first century.

Answers to Assessment

1. standard of living, p. 136

2. (a) silver, coal, hydroelectric power, lead, phosphates **(b)** They have few resources and people.

3. Possible answer: The manufacturing activity around the southern Great Lakes could be a source of water pollution.

Answers to Photo Captions

Advanced Technology Possible answers: money, educated people, space

Electricity Needs Possible answers: nuclear generators, solar panels, hydroelectricity

Recycling Possible answers: The mounting garbage is unsightly and may produce odors; contaminants may leach out from the garbage into the groundwater.

Economics, Technology, and Environment

Both the United States and Canada have a wide variety of resources and economic activities. The people of both nations have a high **standard of living**, a measurement based on available education, housing, health care, and nutrition. Some assert, however, that economic success is not permanent and that countries like the United States and Canada should seek new ways to avoid overuse of resources.

Advanced Technology

Computer companies must create "clean rooms," or dust-free environments, in which components are made. Technological development has made high-tech industries an influential part of the United States and Canadian economies. **ECONOMIC ACTIVITIES** *What resources would be required to set up the type of facility shown here?*

Electricity Needs

These windmills in California produce electricity. In the early 2000s, power shortages in California led to rolling blackouts, or electricity shutdowns, across the state. **SCIENCE AND TECHNOLOGY** *What other technology can be used to generate electricity?*

Recycling

Although this landfill in Staten Island, New York, closed in 2001, waste disposal continues to be a common problem for many cities in the United States and Canada. Many people encourage recycling, or the reuse of materials, to reduce waste materials and resource use. **ENVIRONMENTAL CHANGE** *Why might people object to landfills such as the one shown here?*

ASSESSMENT

1. **Key Term** Define standard of living.

2. **Map Skills** **Regions** **(a)** What natural resources exist along the Atlantic coast? **(b)** Why is there little economic activity in parts of Canada and the United States?

3. **Critical Thinking** **Drawing Conclusions** How do you think the Great Lakes might be affected by economic activity in the regions around them?

REGIONAL ATLAS

The United States and Canada: ECONOMIC ACTIVITIES AND RESOURCES

KEY

- Hunting and gathering
- Forestry
- Livestock raising
- Commercial farming
- Manufacturing and trade
- Commercial fishing
- Little or no activity
- Coal
- Petroleum

- Hydroelectric power
- Iron
- Copper
- Bauxite
- Gold
- Silver
- Phosphates
- Uranium
- Lead
- Nickel
- Tungsten

Lambert Azimuthal Equal-Area Projection

HAWAII (U.S.)

0   200 mi
0   200 km

Take It to the NET

Enrichment To learn more about the economic activities and resources of this region, visit the World Geography section of **www.phschool.com**

Chapter 5 ▪ Regional Atlas: The United States and Canada   **137**

Science and Technology

Resource in the Sky People throughout the world are concerned with finding reliable sources of power. In African countries that receive abundant sunshine, people are harvesting energy from the sun. Solar-powered generators supply electricity to locations where resources are limited and where gas and electric lines are not available. Such machines power surgery lights and other necessities at remote medical clinics. Sunlight is also collected to run community water pumps. Some African women use aluminum foil to build solar ovens for cooking, reducing their need for firewood.

Database:
Comparing Energy Resources

pp. 138–139

Objectives

Upon completion of this lesson, students should be able to:

◆ explain the difference between nonrenewable and renewable resources of energy;

◆ identify several types of nonrenewable and renewable resources;

◆ compare energy production and use in Canada to energy production and use in the United States.

 National Geography Standards

The following National Geography Standards are highlighted in this feature: 9, 11, 15, 16, 18

 Bellringer

Write the following on the board: *Energy resources are important to me because . . .* Ask students to jot down two or three different endings to the sentence.

LESSON PLAN

1. Focus Call on volunteers to share their sentence endings. Use their responses to arrive at two or three generalizations about how people of the United States depend on energy. Write the generalizations on the chalkboard.

2. Instruct Ask: **Would you expect Canadians to create similar sentence endings and generalizations?** Point to the per capita consumption of electricity to guide the class to an affirmative answer. As a group, read pages 138 and 139 of the text and discuss the Assessment questions.

3. Close/Reteach Have students write three or four statements comparing and contrasting energy resources and use under the headings "Canada" and "United States." Share responses in class, striving for variety.

Database: Comparing Energy Resources

Start a car, turn on the computer, or set your home's thermostat, and you use energy. Most people in the United States and Canada have easy access to energy. In fact, the United States and Canada are two of the world's largest energy producers and energy consumers. By comparing the data below, you will see that there are similarities as well as differences in how energy is produced and used in the two countries.

Source: *Encarta World Atlas*

Key Term: **per capita**

GET THE FACTS . . .

Go to the Table of Countries at the back of this book to view additional data for the United States and Canada.

 Take It to the NET
Data Update For the most recent update of this database, visit the World Geography section of **www.phschool.com**.

United States

Electricity Consumption	3,279 billion kilowatt-hours
Electricity Consumption per Capita	12,235 kilowatt-hours
Total Electricity Generation	3,674.1 billion kilowatt-hours
Electricity Production by Source	Fossil fuel: 70.34%
	Hydro: 8.96%
	Nuclear: 18.61%
	Other: 2.09%
Electricity Imports	48 billion kilowatt-hours
Electricity Exports	16 billion kilowatt-hours
Crude Petroleum Production	2.4 billion barrels per year
Total Petroleum Consumption	6.8 billion barrels per year
Petroleum Imports	2.7 billion barrels per year
Petroleum Exports	40.1 million barrels per year
Coal Consumption	933.7 million metric tons
Fuel Imports as a Share of Total Imports	9.4%
Fuel Exports as a Share of Total Exports	2%

Fossil fuels are the primary sources of energy in the United States. Coal, oil, and natural gas—all fossil fuels—are nonrenewable resources of energy, meaning they cannot be replaced once they are used. For this reason, the U.S. government has developed policies that call for careful management of these energy resources. The United States also makes use of renewable resources, which the environment continues to supply or replace. These include hydroelectricity, solar power, and wind power. Nuclear energy produces more than 18 percent of the electricity in the United States.

The United States has large reserves of coal, natural gas, and oil. About 25 percent of all the known coal in the world is found in the United States. Natural gas and oil are also present in large amounts. Not all of these reserves are easy to reach, however. At the same time, the United States consumes the greatest amount of energy in the world. Despite an abundance of fossil fuels, the United States must import a great deal of energy to meet its needs.

RESOURCE DIRECTORY

Teaching Resources

Unit 2, Chapter 5
• Regional Atlas Review, p. 3
• Regional Atlas Database Skills, p. 4
• Test Forms A and B, pp. 5–10
Spanish Resources
• Regional Atlas Review, p. 13
Guide to the Essentials (English/Spanish)
• Chapter 5 Test
Mental Mapping booklet
• Chapter 5 Map Test, p. 23
Simulations, Games, and Lab Activities
• Place Location Review Games, pp. 58–63

Social Studies Skills Handbook
• Study and Research Skills, pp. 94–108

Prentice Hall Assessment System
Alternative Assessment booklet, Map Evaluation Form, p. 15

Technology
ExamView Test Bank CD-ROM, Chapter 5 Test
Companion Web site, www.phschool.com
• Chapter 5 Self-Test

REGIONAL ATLAS

Canada

Electricity Consumption	475.1 billion kilowatt-hours
Electricity Consumption per Capita	15,661 kilowatt-hours
Total Electricity Generation	547.2 billion kilowatt-hours
Electricity Production by Source	Fossil fuel: 27.18% Hydro: 59.77% Nuclear: 12.25% Other: 0.8%
Electricity Imports	14 billion kilowatt-hours
Electricity Exports	48 billion kilowatt-hours
Crude Petroleum Production	702.1 million barrels per year
Total Petroleum Consumption	678.3 million barrels per year
Petroleum Imports	255.7 million barrels per year
Petroleum Exports	361.8 million barrels per year
Total Coal Consumption	56.0 million metric tons
Fuel Imports as a Share of Total Imports	4.4%
Fuel Exports as a Share of Total Exports	10.3%

Canada is a world leader in energy production and is one of the few countries to be self-sufficient in its energy needs. Energy production in Canada plays a vital economic role in terms of investment, trade, and employment.

A significant portion of Canada's energy comes from fossil fuels, but much is derived from hydroelectricity. Canada is the world's leading producer of hydroelectricity. Smaller amounts of Canada's energy come from nuclear power and other sources such as solar and wind power.

Although total electricity consumption is higher in the United States, Canada uses more electricity **per capita,** or per person. Canada has great seasonal changes and large regional variations in temperature. Distances between population centers also contribute to this difference.

Since 1969, Canada has exported more energy than it has imported. The United States is Canada's largest energy customer, purchasing more than 90 percent of the energy Canada sells.

ASSESSMENT

1. **Key Term** Define per capita.

2. **Science and Technology** **(a)** What energy source is used to produce the largest percentage of the electricity in Canada? **(b)** What energy source is used to produce the largest percentage of the electricity in the United States?

3. **Global Trade Patterns** **(a)** Which of the two nations consumes more petroleum than it produces? **(b)** How does this nation make up the difference?

4. **Natural Resources** **(a)** Which of the two nations consumes more electricity per person? **(b)** Which relies more heavily on non-renewable sources of energy?

5. **Government and Citizenship** Why would governments adopt policies that promote the wise use of energy resources?

6. **Critical Thinking** **Drawing Conclusions** How might climate and great distances between population centers contribute to higher energy use per capita in Canada?

Chapter 5 ▪ Regional Atlas: The United States and Canada **139**

MENTAL MAPPING

Games for Review See pages 58–63 of the Simulations, Games, and Lab Activities booklet in the Teaching Resources for games to review place names in preparation for the Chapter 5 Map Test.

Chapter Map Test Students should use the completed Chapter 5 outline maps and the Unit 2 Checklist to prepare for the Chapter 5 Map Test. Point out to students that the test will cover only Parts I and II of the Unit 2 Checklist, Countries and Cities, and Physical Features.

Alternative Assessment

Final Evaluation

Creating Maps Use the Map Evaluation Form on page 15 of the Alternative Assessment booklet in the Prentice Hall Assessment System to evaluate students' maps.

Answers to Assessment

1. per capita, p. 139

2. (a) hydroelectricity **(b)** fossil fuels

3. (a) United States **(b)** by importing petroleum

4. (a) Canada **(b)** United States

5. to ensure that there are adequate supplies for their citizens

6. Canada's colder climate means that more energy is needed to heat homes and businesses. More fuel is required to travel between population centers because of the distances between them.

Do-It-Yourself Skills

pp. 140–141

Objectives

Upon completion of this feature, students should be able to:

- understand the uses of a political map;
- analyze a political map and draw conclusions;
- create a political map.

National Geography Standards

The following National Geography Standards are highlighted in this feature: 1, 2, 3, 9, 12, 17

Bellringer

Ask students to define the words *border* and *boundary.* Explain that although both words denote a line or area separating one piece of territory from another, they have different connotations. For example, a boundary is often referred to as just a limiting line, whereas a border is a line that separates political entities.

LESSON PLAN

1. Focus Discuss with students why it is useful to present political data in the form of a map. Ask students where they have seen political maps.

2. Instruct Have students look at a population density map for the United States in the regional atlas or use library resources or the Internet to find a population density map for Florida. Ask students to describe the trends they see when they compare population density and election results.

3. Close/Reteach Have students compare the map of Florida election results to the map they made for Maryland. Help students make generalizations about the election results from each state.

Do-It-Yourself Skills

Making and Analyzing Political Maps

What Is a Political Map?

A political map shows political boundaries or distribution of political power. It can show the borders of political entities such as states, counties, cities, and towns. It may also be a thematic map that uses colors and symbols to communicate information about the spatial distribution of political power. One example of this type of map is an election results map, such as the Florida map below.

How Can I Use This Skill?

Political maps often appear in print and broadcast news reports. They are used to analyze historical or current events and trends. This map illustrates the Florida results for the 2000 United States presidential election. Counties in which a majority voted for the Democratic candidate Al Gore are colored blue. The red counties are those in which the majority voted for the Republican candidate George W. Bush. By studying the map, you can recognize patterns. You can then draw conclusions by comparing the patterns with other data and thematic maps, available from the U.S. Census Bureau Web site. For example, you might find that heavily rural counties in Florida voted for Bush, whereas heavily urban counties voted for Gore.

Step by Step

Follow these steps to make and analyze a political map showing election results. As you proceed, use the 2000 presidential election results map for Florida (right) as a model.

1. Select an election and political units. You can map election results for regions, states, counties, and districts. For this lesson, you will map the 2000 presidential election results for each county in Maryland.

2. Find the data. Statistics for Maryland came from the Web site of the Maryland State Board of Elections. Other states have similar Web sites.

2000 Presidential Election in Florida

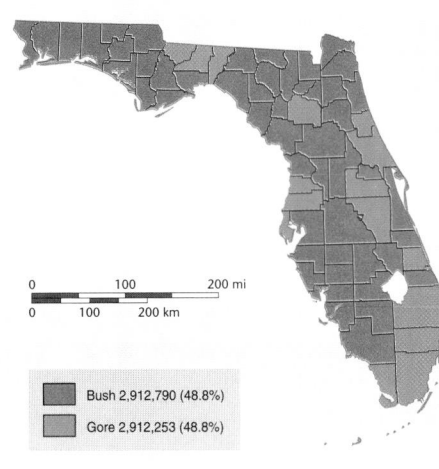

Bush 2,912,790 (48.8%)

Gore 2,912,253 (48.8%)

RESOURCE DIRECTORY

Teaching Resources
Social Studies Skills Handbook
- Reading a Political Map, p. 19

Technology
Social Studies Skills Tutor CD-ROM, Analyzing and Interpreting Special Purpose Maps

Organize the data. In the table (right), notice that a red check mark appears next to counties that the Republican, Bush, won. Counties won by the Democrat, Gore, are checked in blue.

Make an outline map. On a separate piece of paper, make a map of Maryland like the one below right. Due to space limitations, each county is labeled with a letter rather than the county name. You can use the data chart to determine the name of each county. For example, the letter E represents Calvert County. You can find county maps for other states in various atlases. State government Web sites also provide maps.

Make a key and color the map to represent the election results. Following the method used for Florida, you could use red for Maryland counties that Bush won and blue for counties that Gore won.

Analyze the map by finding patterns and comparing them with other demographic data. For example, by comparing your election map with a population density map of Maryland, you would learn that densely populated counties were won by Gore, indicating his appeal to people in urban communities.

TIP

Comparing Data

Political analysts often draw conclusions by comparing election results with other data, such as per capita income, level of education, and ethnicity.

2000 Presidential Election in Maryland

COUNTIES (and Baltimore City)	AL GORE (Democratic)	GEORGE W. BUSH (Republican)
(A) Allegany	10,894	14,656 √
(B) Anne Arundel	89,624	104,209 √
(C) Baltimore City	158,765 √	27,150
(D) Baltimore	160,635 √	133,033
(E) Calvert	12,986	16,004 √
(F) Caroline	3,396	5,300 √
(G) Carroll	20,146	41,742 √
(H) Cecil	12,327	15,494 √
(I) Charles	21,873 √	21,768
(J) Dorchester	5,232	5,847 √
(K) Frederick	30,725	45,350 √
(L) Garrett	2,872	7,514 √
(M) Harford	35,665	52,862 √
(N) Howard	58,556 √	49,809
(O) Kent	3,627	4,155 √
(P) Montgomery	232,453 √	124,580
(Q) Prince George's	216,119 √	49,987
(R) Queen Anne's	6,257	9,970 √
(S) Somerset	3,785 √	3,609
(T) St. Mary's	11,912	16,856 √
(U) Talbot	5,854	8,874 √
(V) Washington	18,221	27,948 √
(W) Wicomico	14,469	16,338 √
(X) Worcester	9,389	10,742 √
Total	**1,145,782**	**813,797**
Total %	**57%**	**40%**

Maryland Counties

APPLY YOUR SKILL

Make another election results map for an election and geographic entity of your choice. You might map the 2000 presidential election results in another state. Or you could map the results of a recent congressional election in your own state. Compare your map with thematic data and maps available from the U.S. Census Bureau Web site. Then, draw conclusions.

ACTIVITY

Enrichment

Researching The political map on the opposite page shows election results for George W. Bush and Al Gore only. Encourage students to find information about the percentage of votes originally reported for these and other candidates in various counties. Have them use that information to create maps of counties where the race was particularly close. (Verbal/ Linguistic)

BACKGROUND

History

Election 2000 In the 2000 U.S. presidential election, results in Florida were so close that the ballots were recounted. After the recount, George W. Bush was declared the winner of the popular vote in Florida and was awarded its electoral college votes. This gave him more electoral votes than Al Gore, who had won the popular vote nationally. Since the president is officially elected by the electoral vote rather than the popular vote, George W. Bush was named 43rd President of the United States.

Answers to Apply Your Skill

Check students' maps for accuracy. Conclusions will vary depending on which state and election students choose.

CUSTOMIZE FOR...

Students Acquiring English/ESL

Roots and Meaning Write the term *spatial distribution* on the board. Show students that each word has root words (*spatial* has the root *space*, and *distribution* has the prefix *dis-* and the root *tribute*). Explain that finding the roots of words can help them to understand what words mean. Have students look up *space*, *dis-*, and *tribute* and offer possible definitions for the term *spatial distribution*.

Resource Manager

	CORE INSTRUCTION	READING/SKILLS
Chapter-Level Resources	**Teaching Resources** **Unit 2**/Ch. 6 • Reviewing Main Ideas, p. 15 **Mental Mapping booklet** • Unit 2 Checklist, p. 19 **Simulations, Games, and Lab Activities** • Exploring Local Geography: Local Attitudes Toward Land, p. 6; Street Patterns, p. 7; The Shape of Your Community, p. 9 • Place Location Review Games, pp. 58–63 **Creative Teaching Activities** • Music as Literature, p. 8 **TeacherExpress™ CD-ROM**, Ch. 6 **Companion Web site,** **www.phschool.com** • eTeach	**Teaching Resources** **Unit 2**/Ch. 6 • Map/Graph Skills, p. 17 **Book on CD**, Ch. 6 **Social Studies Skills Tutor CD-ROM**
1 A Resource-Rich Nation 1. Describe how natural resources promote the economic success of the United States. 2. Explain why transportation and communication are the keys to economic development. 3. Discuss how respect for individual freedoms encourages economic growth.	**Teaching Resources** **Unit 2**/Ch. 6 • Guided Reading and Review, p. 11 **Prentice Hall Presentation Pro CD-ROM**, Ch. 6, Sec. 1	**Teaching Resources** **Guide to the Essentials (English/Spanish)** • Section Summary, Ch. 6, Sec. 1 **Mental Mapping booklet** • Outline Map 6, p. 24 **Social Studies Skills Handbook** • Reading a Natural Resources Map, p. 34 **Guided Reading Audiotapes (English/Spanish)**, Ch. 6, Sec. 1 **Section Reading Support Transparencies**, Ch. 6, Sec. 1
2 A Nation of Cities 1. Identify the ways in which metropolitan areas in the United States have been affected by changes in transportation technology. 2. Explain why many Americans migrated to the South and West. 3. Describe how cities interconnect with smaller towns.	**Teaching Resources** **Unit 2**/Ch. 6 • Guided Reading and Review, p. 13 **Prentice Hall Presentation Pro CD-ROM**, Ch. 6, Sec. 2	**Teaching Resources** **Guide to the Essentials (English/Spanish)** • Section Summary, Ch. 6, Sec. 2 **Social Studies Skills Handbook** • Analyzing Art, p. 59 **Guided Reading Audiotapes (English/Spanish)**, Ch. 6, Sec. 2 **Section Reading Support Transparencies**, Ch. 6, Sec. 2

ENRICHMENT/HONORS/PREAP

Teaching Resources

Unit 2/Ch. 6
- Critical Thinking, p. 16

Simulations, Games, and Lab Activities
- Simulation: Resolving a Land Dispute, pp. 49–57

Mental Mapping booklet
- Atlas Activity, p. 25

Social Studies Skills Handbook
- Study and Research Skills, pp. 94–108

World Geography Map and Photo Transparencies
- The United States and Canada: Maps and Photos

World Geography Videos
- Migration: A Profile of the United States, Tape 1

Companion Web site, www.phschool.com
- Chapter 6 Activities

Teaching Resources

Unit 2/Ch. 6
- Geography and World Literature, p. 56

Companion Web site, www.phschool.com
- Chapter 6 Activities

Companion Web site, www.phschool.com
- Chapter 6 Activities

ASSESSMENT

PRENTICE HALL ASSESSMENT SYSTEM

Core Assessment
- ExamView Test Bank booklet, Ch. 6
- ExamView Test Bank CD-ROM, Ch. 6

Standardized Test Preparation

Review and Reteach
- Review Book for World Geography, pp. 5–6

Practice and Assess
- Test-taking Strategies With Transparencies for High School
- Test-taking Strategy Poster
- Alternative Assessment booklet
- Test Prep Book for World Geography

Teaching Resources

Unit 2/Ch. 6
- Section Quizzes, pp. 12, 14
- Test Forms A and B, pp. 18–23

Guide to the Essentials (English/Spanish)
- Chapter 6 Test

Spanish Resources, Ch. 6
- Section Quizzes, pp. 14–15

Mental Mapping booklet
- Chapter 6 Map Test, p. 26

Companion Web site, www.phschool.com
- Chapter 6 Self-Test

CUSTOMIZE FOR INDIVIDUAL NEEDS

Less Proficient Readers
- Guide to the Essentials (English), Ch. 6, Section Summaries
- Social Studies Skills Handbook, p. 73
- Guided Reading Audiotapes (English), Ch. 6
- Section Reading Support Transparencies, Ch. 6
- Book on CD, Ch. 6
- Teacher's Edition, Reading Strategy, pp. 147, 152
- Teacher's Edition, Activity: Vocabulary, p. 144
- Teacher's Edition, Customize for . . . , p. 149

Students Acquiring English/ESL
- Guide to the Essentials (English/Spanish), Ch. 6
- Guided Reading Audiotapes (English/Spanish), Ch. 6
- Section Reading Support Transparencies, Ch. 6
- Book on CD, Ch. 6
- Teacher's Edition, Customize for . . . , p. 145

Less Proficient Writers
- Social Studies Skills Handbook, p. 82
- Alternative Assessment, Writing Assignment Rubric, p. 6

MENTAL MAPPING

Ask students to look at the map on this page, and point out that most of the United States lies south of Canada and north of Mexico. However, the state of Alaska is located north and west of Canada, and Hawaii is 2,090 miles, or 3,363 kilometers, to the southwest in the Pacific Ocean.

Mapping the Region Ask students to sketch their own outline maps of the United States, or distribute the Chapter 6 Outline Map on page 24 of the Mental Mapping booklet in the Teaching Resources. Have students lightly shade or outline each state in a different color. Next, direct them to label the states listed in Part III of the Unit 2 Checklist. Finally, ask them to label the bodies of water that are shown on the map on this page. Students should keep their maps in their Atlas Portfolios in order to prepare for the Chapter 6 Map Test.

eTeach

Be sure to check out this month's online forum with a Master Teacher to join in an exchange of teaching ideas. www.phschool.com

---

C H A P T E R
6

A Profile of the United States

SECTIONS

1 A Resource-Rich Nation

2 A Nation of Cities

The United States: POLITICAL

[Map of the United States showing states, Canada, Mexico, Pacific Ocean, Atlantic Ocean, Gulf of Mexico, with inset maps of Alaska and Hawaii]

Go Online
PHSchool.com

For: More information about the United States and access to the Take It to the Net activities
Visit: phschool.com
Web Code: mjk-0007

RESOURCE DIRECTORY

Teaching Resources

Unit 2, Chapter 6
- Section 1 Guided Reading and Review, p. 11
- Map/Graph Skills, p. 17

Guide to the Essentials (English/Spanish)
- Section Summary, Chapter 6, Section 1

Mental Mapping booklet
- Unit 2 Checklist, p. 19
- Outline Map 6, p. 24

Technology

Guided Reading Audiotapes (English/Spanish), Chapter 6, Section 1

Section Reading Support Transparencies, Chapter 6, Section 1

World Geography Map and Photo Transparencies
- The United States and Canada: Maps and Photos

Book on CD, Chapter 6

World Geography Videos
- Migration: A Profile of the United States, Tape 1

TeacherExpress™ CD-ROM, Chapter 6

Prentice Hall Presentation Pro CD-ROM, Chapter 6

Social Studies Skills Tutor CD-ROM

Companion Web site, www.phschool.com
- Chapter 6 Activities

1 A Resource-Rich Nation

Reading Focus

- How do natural resources promote the economic success of the United States?
- Why are transportation and communication the keys to economic development?
- How does respect for individual freedoms encourage economic growth?

Key Terms

gross national product
canal
telecommunication
free enterprise

Main Idea Natural resources, technology, and respect for individual freedoms encourage economic growth in the United States.

Economic Activities For some American families, farming remains a way of life.

Objectives

Upon completion of Section 1, students should be able to:

◆ describe how natural resources promote the economic success of the United States;

◆ explain why transportation and communication are the keys to economic development;

◆ discuss how respect for individual freedoms encourages economic growth.

 National Geography Standards

The following National Geography Standards are highlighted in this section: 4, 11, 14, 15, 16

 Bellringer

Explain that the United States is one of the richest countries in the world. Ask students to brainstorm the factors that have helped to produce this wealth.

LESSON PLAN

1. Focus Write the term *rugged individualism* on the board. Have students discuss its meaning and give examples of specific people who exhibit this quality.

2. Instruct Make a two-column chart on the board with the headings *U.S. Successes* and *Contributing Factors*. Label the first row *Political*, and the second row *Economic*. Work with the students to fill in the chart.

3. Close/Reteach Have students discuss the following questions: **Until the mid-1800s, where did most cities develop? Why?** (Most developed along waterways because trade by water was faster or easier than by land.) **How did the telegraph and telephone help U.S. trade?** (They increased the pace and volume of trade.)

Compared with most countries of the world, the United States is enormous. It is the world's fourth-largest country in area and is the third most populous. The United States is also wealthy. The nation's **gross national product** (GNP) is the highest in the world. The GNP is the total value of a nation's output of goods and services, including the output of domestic firms in foreign countries and excluding the domestic output of foreign firms.

How did the United States become such a wealthy country? At least four factors help answer this question: the nation's abundance of natural resources, innovations in transportation, innovations in communication, and respect for individual freedoms.

An Abundance of Natural Resources

"I think in all the world the like abundance is not to be found." These were the words of Arthur Barlowe, an English sea captain, shortly after his arrival in North America in 1584. The continent seemed to offer the newcomer an unbelievable degree of plenty and the promise of wealth.

Farming the Land One of the most abundant natural resources in the United States is the land itself. From earliest times, Americans have benefited from the land. Many Native American groups, such as the Cayuga, Creek, Natchez, and Cherokee, lived in permanent or semipermanent villages. There they grew crops such as maize, squash, beans, cotton, and tobacco.

After the United States was established, people could gain parcels of land from the government by promising to live on the land for at least five years. Much of that land was used for farming. When the nation's first census was taken in 1790, more than three fourths of the nation's people lived on farms.

As settlers expanded westward in the 1800s, they did not at first realize the potential for farming in the Great Plains. In one explorer's opinion, the region was "uninhabitable by people depending on agriculture for their subsistence." In 1862, though, the government encouraged development of this land with the passage of the Homestead Act. It granted 160 acres of land to settlers who agreed to farm. The United States Department of Agriculture was created that same year to promote farming. As agriculture thrived

 Chicago, Illinois *(photo left)*

Chapter 6 ▪ Section 1   **143**

Pacing Suggestions

For 90-minute Blocks

You will want to vary activities.

- Arrange students in four groups. Assign each group one of the following subsections of Chapter 6: Farming the Land; Finding Wealth Underground; Communication Technology; Respecting Individual Freedoms. Ask each group to find newspaper or magazine articles that relate to the subject of its subsection. Have each group write a brief summary of each news story. Then ask each group to write a paragraph explaining how each news story relates to geography.

Vocabulary

Gross national product Have students look up *gross national product* in the Glossary and paraphrase the definition. Ask: **Why is gross national product a useful economic measure?** (It allows economists to compare activity between countries, or to compare the activity of a given country over a period of time.)

Connecting With . . .

History With the Louisiana Purchase of 1803, the United States acquired an immense, relatively unknown territory that was to become a focus of settlement from the east and from Europe during the 1800s. Initially, the interior plains were viewed as uninhabitable and labeled as the "Great American Desert" on early maps.

Daily Life

Family Farms The government's nineteenth-century land-grant policies established the pattern of the family farm—one large enough to support a family and small enough that one family could operate it. Today, most farms in the United States are still family farms. One family member acts as manager while other family members pitch in with the work. Today's farm, however, is much larger than in the past: The average size is 432 acres. It is worked with expensive modern machinery and the extensive use of fertilizer.

Answers to Graph Skills

petroleum

Supplies might become scarce as consumption rises, causing prices to increase.

U.S. Energy Consumption

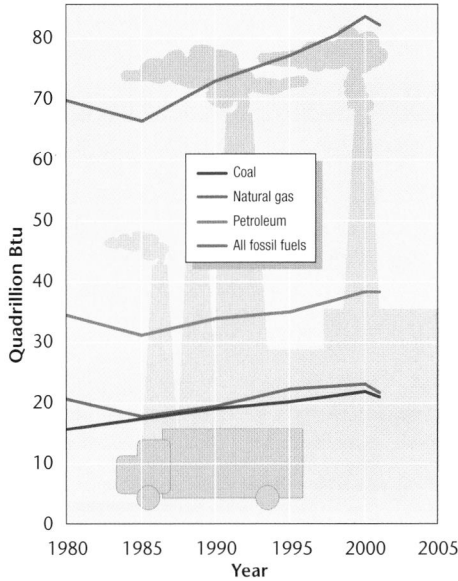

Source: *The World Almanac and Book of Facts*

GRAPH SKILLS

● **Natural Resources** The United States is the world's largest energy consumer. It mainly uses fossil fuels such as coal, natural gas, and petroleum. British Thermal Units, or Btu, are used to measure energy consumption.

- *Which fossil fuel does the United States rely on most?*
- *Because fossil fuels are nonrenewable, what problem might develop as consumption rises? Explain.*

on the Great Plains, settlers gradually perceived that this region was not a wasteland but was the nation's breadbasket.

Today, fewer than one quarter of Americans live in rural areas. Still, farm exports bring in about $50 billion annually. Other than Alaska, nearly half the land in the United States is used for raising crops or animals. In Nebraska, farmland makes up more than 90 percent of the state's total acreage—the highest percentage of farmland in the nation.

Clearing the Forests Forests are another of the United States' rich resources. They provide material for a startling array of products,

including lumber for housing and furniture construction, paper, rayon, photographic film, artificial sponges, charcoal, methanol, medicinal chemicals, maple sugar, and even plastics.

The United States' lumber industry, which sawed timber for barrel staves and board lumber and harvested trees to make ships' masts, began in colonial New England. After American independence, logging activity shifted to the South. Because of the South's mild climate, loggers could use rivers year-round to transport logs to the sawmills. Logging in the midwest was limited by the seasonal variations of the climate, yet the forests were quickly logged over in the late 1800s, and much of the land was converted to farmland.

By 1930, the forests of the east were depleted or converted to farmland, so the lumber industry moved west. Nearly half of the nation's lumber is now obtained west of the Rocky Mountains, primarily in California, Oregon, Washington, and Idaho.

Forests are a renewable resource, if managed carefully. A better understanding of forest ecosystems is leading to better management of the nation's timber. Grazing laws, harvesting regulations, better logging practices, and reforestation programs are helping to conserve the nation's forests. Thousands of acres of forest have been set aside as national parks, protecting not only the trees themselves but also the valuable watersheds and fish and wildlife habitats they support. Even so, only 5 percent of the nation's virgin forest remains.

Finding Wealth Underground Beneath the lush forests and rich soils of the United States lies an abundance of mineral resources. One of the country's most abundant minerals is coal, a solid fossil fuel that is used as a source of energy for industry, transportation, and homes. The United States produces about one fifth of the world's supply of coal.

Oil and natural gas are other fossil fuels found in the United States. They lie beneath the central and western plains, as well as in Alaska. In recent years, Americans have become concerned over the fact that these fuels, as well as coal, are nonrenewable. Because oil, natural gas, and coal are all extremely vital to the United States energy supply and economy, they require careful management.

The graph on page 144 shows the United States consumption of fossil fuels.

The United States produces very significant amounts of copper, gold, lead, titanium, uranium, zinc, and other non-fuel minerals. A nation's supply of minerals is important not only for trade, but for development of its industries as well. Copper, for example, is used in building construction, electrical and electronic equipment, transportation, and consumer products.

Moving Resources, Goods, and People

The United States could not have turned its resources into wealth without the development of new technologies for transportation. Improved transportation provided more and faster links that allowed producers to move raw materials to factories and finished goods from factories to consumers.

Travel Over Water In the 1800s, transportation was faster on water than on land. But river travel was still a cumbersome process. A keelboat could take as long as six weeks to float down the Mississippi and four months to make the return trip. But the successful development of the steam engine changed all that. Steam provided boats with the power to travel against both wind and current. By the 1850s, steamboats were a common sight on rivers, steaming their way across a watery transportation network. Steamboats also turned the Great Lakes into important transportation routes.

In the early 1800s, the United States also began building **canals,** or artificial waterways, to make even more places accessible by water. The combination of canals and the steamboat made transportation of people and goods over water both speedy and cheap.

Movement Over Land Steam-powered railroads later replaced steamboats as the most efficient means of transporting goods. A transcontinental railroad linking the east and west coasts of the country was completed in 1869. By 1900, people and goods in nearly every settled part of the country were within reach of a railroad. The network of railroads spurred economic growth.

Railroad Freight Yard

Science and Technology This freight yard is in Kansas City, Missouri, the second busiest rail hub in the country.
Movement *How does transportation technology contribute to economic prosperity?*

The invention of the automobile in the 1890s heralded the next revolution in transportation. Meanwhile, the powerful new diesel engine was used to drive heavy-duty modes of transport, such as ships, trains, trucks, and tractors. Individuals

Chapter 6 ▪ Section 1 **145**

Articles From
NATIONAL GEOGRAPHIC

The following article may be used to extend the content in this section.

Swerdlow, Joel L., and Bob Sacha, photographer. "Erie Canal: Living Link to Our Past." *National Geographic,* Vol. 178, No. 5 (Nov. 1990), pp. 38–65.

The author journeys the length of the Erie Canal, examining the canal's effect on local and national life, both past and present.

Group Work

Activity: Designing a magazine

Purpose: Assign each group one of the following industries: farming, mining, lumbering, transportation, or communications. Each group must work together to design a magazine showing the public how its industry has contributed to the economic growth of the United States. Each group will write a table of contents listing the magazine's articles and a "Message from the Publisher" summarizing the magazine's main point. The cover design should highlight the important themes of the magazine.

Roles: Assign an editor in chief responsible for the table of contents, a publisher responsible for the message, and a head designer responsible for the cover.

Result: Display the students' work in the classroom.

Reteach

Creating Posters Write the four main headings of Section 1 on the board. Have students choose one of the headings, reread that subsection, and draw a poster that illustrates the key points in the subsection. (Bodily/Kinesthetic, Visual/Spatial)

Answer to Photo Caption

People all over the world can communicate with each other by means of the telephone and the Internet.

146 Chapter 6

GLOBAL CONNECTIONS

Science and Technology
In 1866, the first successful transatlantic cable was laid to speed telegraph communication. It extended from Newfoundland to Ireland.

enjoyed the benefits of greater freedom of movement. By the 1950s, as more and more people owned cars, the nation began building an interstate highway system—a network of roads that link major cities across the nation.

Communication Technology

The industrial and economic growth of the United States was also closely tied to improved communications. In the early 1800s, communication required the transportation of people or paper, until Samuel F.B. Morse found a way to send messages by an electric current. In 1837, Morse demonstrated the first successful telegraph. A telegraph was capable of sending a coded message. Patterns of long and short sounds—or printed dots and dashes—were converted by the receiving telegraph operator into corresponding letters of the alphabet.

Telegraph lines were commonly strung along railroad rights of way. In exchange, telegraph

offices provided free service to railroad companies. With access to speedy communication, railroads were able to coordinate train schedules, locate trains, and establish standardized time.

By the 1860s, there were telegraph offices in every important city. Newspapers talked about the "mystic band" that now held the nation together. Telegraphs allowed Americans to transfer information in minutes instead of days. American businesses could now communicate more efficiently with the people who supplied raw materials and parts for their machines, as well as with their customers.

New forms of communication were the center of attention at the nation's centennial exposition in Philadelphia in 1876. The star of the show was a small device invented that year by Alexander Graham Bell—the telephone. By 1915, telephone wires connected people from coast to coast. Well over 90 percent of United States households now have telephones. Today, fiber optics, the conversion of electronic signals into light waves, is replacing the use of telephone wires. People can now communicate at the speed of light.

Many people and businesses today are also communicating and exchanging information via an elaborate web of computer networks. The Internet, telephone, satellite, and other forms of **telecommunication,** or communication by

Telecommunications Network

Science and Technology Complicated networks support the billions of telephone calls and electronic communications that Americans make every working day.

Regions *How has technology brought distant regions of the world closer together?*

RESOURCE DIRECTORY

Teaching Resources
Unit 2, Chapter 6
• Section 1 Quiz, p. 12
Spanish Resources
• Section 1 Quiz, p. 14
Creative Teaching Activities, Music as Literature, p. 8

electronic means, are becoming increasingly important to doing business.

Respecting Individual Freedoms

The interaction between production, transportation, and communication has been vital to the economic success of the country. So, too, has the political system of the United States. The government that was established by the people in 1789 reflected one of the most important shared values in the United States—the belief in individual equality, opportunity, and freedom. Important, too, was the belief that individuals acting in their own interest may also serve the interests of others. These ideals are supported by an economic system based on capitalism, or **free enterprise.** The system of free enterprise allows individuals to own, operate, and profit from their own businesses in an open, competitive market.

One of the notions behind free enterprise is that any hardworking individual—regardless of his or her wealth, cultural background, or religion—can find opportunity and success in the United States. It was this belief that drew, and continues to draw, many immigrants to the country. The people of the United States have long praised the quality of rugged individualism—the willingness of individuals to stand alone and struggle long and hard to survive and prosper, relying on their own personal resources, opinions, and beliefs.

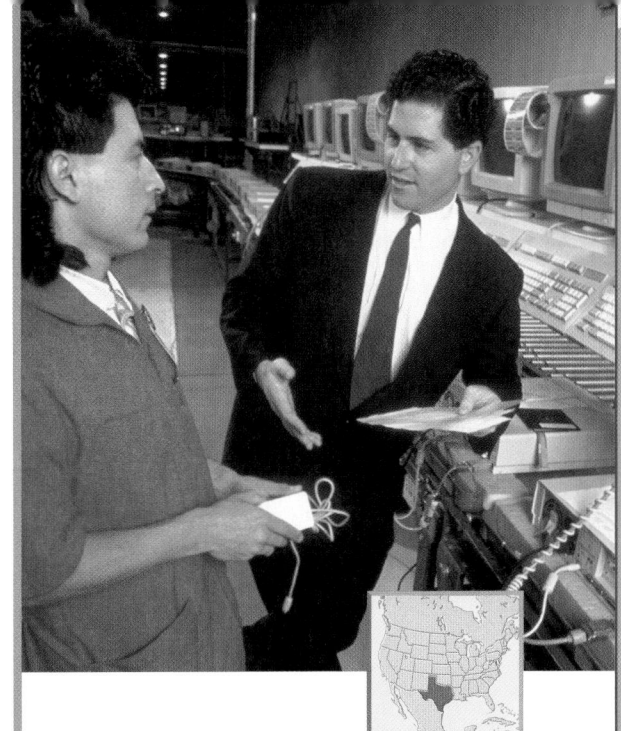

Opportunity and Success

Economic Activities In 1984, a 19-year-old University of Texas freshman, Michael Dell (right), began to pursue a simple idea. Why not sell made-to-order computers directly to customers? By the early 2000s, the Dell Computer Corporation was bringing in $18 billion a year and employing 25,000 people.

Place *In the United States, how does education influence one's chances for economic success?*

SECTION 1 ASSESSMENT

1. **Key Terms** Define **(a)** gross national product, **(b)** canal, **(c)** telecommunication, **(d)** free enterprise.

2. **Natural Resources** What natural resources have been important to the economic success of the United States?

3. **Science and Technology** Describe three ways in which transportation and communication strengthened the nation's economy.

4. **Economic Systems** How does a system of free enterprise encourage economic growth?

5. **Critical Thinking** **Recognizing Points of View** Some Americans favor the expansion of

laws that protect forests and other ecosystems from economic development. Other Americans think such laws should be limited in scope. Why do you think people have different points of view on this topic?

Activity

USING THE REGIONAL ATLAS

Review the Regional Atlas for the United States and Canada and this section. Make a list of the states that are leading producers of fossil fuels in the United States. Which of these states probably has the most difficulty transporting its fuels to other states of the nation? Explain.

TEST PREPARATION

Have students read the subsection Respecting Individual Freedoms on this page to complete the sentence below.

The idea that any individual can find opportunity and success in the United States helps drive the system of —

- **A** free enterprise
- **B** renewable resource
- **C** communication
- **D** energy consumption

Objectives

Upon completion of Section 2, students should be able to:

◆ identify the ways in which metropolitan areas in the United States have been affected by changes in transportation technology;

◆ explain why many Americans migrated to the South and West;

◆ describe how cities interconnect with smaller towns.

 National Geography Standards

The following National Geography Standards are highlighted in this section: 1, 3, 5, 9, 11, 12, 17, 18

 Bellringer

Ask students to identify the city nearest to them. What experiences have they had there? What functions does the city serve? (jobs, entertainment, shopping, cultural activities) Why did it grow to be a city? (location, transportation, economy, personal preferences)

LESSON PLAN

1. Focus Tell students to imagine that they have decided to move to a new city or town. Ask: **What might determine where you move? Climate? Employment? Good schools? More recreational activities?** Point out that this kind of decision making has determined the pattern of urban growth in the United States.

2. Instruct Write the names of two cities on the board—the nearest city and another listed on the map on page 127. Then make four columns with the headings *Location, Transportation, Economy,* and *Personal Preferences.* Work with the students to fill columns with the effect each has had on the growth of these cities.

3. Close/Reteach On the board, write the title *Urban Hierarchy* and draw four columns below with these headings: *Urban Area, Size, Activities,* and *Examples.* Work with the class to complete this chart for villages, towns, small cities, regional metropolises, and world metropolises.

2 A Nation of Cities

Reading Focus

- How have metropolitan areas in the United States been affected by changes in transportation technology?
- Why have many Americans migrated to the South and West?
- How do cities interconnect with smaller towns based on function and size?

Key Terms

metropolitan area

hierarchy

hinterland

Main Idea The growth of cities is influenced by available transportation, economic opportunities, and people's needs and wants.

Urbanization Chicago, Illinois, is an important center of commerce in the Midwest.

A s the economy of the United States grew, it also changed. It began as an economy based primarily on local agriculture. As the nation began to develop its other resources and make improvements in transportation and communication, its economic base shifted to industry and manufacturing.

Most recently, service industries have begun to make up a larger share of the nation's economy. Service industries are businesses that are not directly related to manufacturing or gathering raw materials. Health care, education, entertainment, banking, transportation, and government are all service industries. See the graph on page 151 for a description of how most Americans earn a living.

As these changes in the economy took place, life for men, women, and children in American villages and towns was transformed. In fact, by 1890 some rural places were all but abandoned by people who had left for new jobs and homes in the country's growing cities. Cities became the centers of transportation and production in the new industrial economy.

Metropolitan Areas and Location

The United States, today, is largely a nation of city dwellers. The country has more than 250 metropolitan areas. A **metropolitan area** comprises a major city and its surrounding suburbs. In some cases, a metropolitan area might also include nearby smaller communities. For example, at one time Denver and Boulder, Colorado, were separated by open lands. Today, smaller communities have grown up between them, making Boulder now part of Denver's metropolitan area. Why have some areas grown faster than others? To quote an old saying, the value of a parcel of land is determined by three factors: location, location, and location.

The value of a city's location, in turn, is affected by changes in transportation, changes in economic activities, and changes in popular preferences. As the technology, economy, and culture of the United States changed, so did the circumstances of each village, town, and city within the nation.

RESOURCE DIRECTORY

Teaching Resources

Unit 2, Chapter 6
- Section 2 Guided Reading and Review, p. 13

Guide to the Essentials (English/Spanish)
- Section Summary, Chapter 6, Section 2

Mental Mapping booklet
- Unit 2 Checklist, p. 19

Technology

Guided Reading Audiotapes (English/Spanish), Chapter 6, Section 2

Section Reading Support Transparencies, Chapter 6, Section 2

World Geography Map and Photo Transparencies
- The United States and Canada: Maps and Photos

Book on CD, Chapter 6

World Geography Videos
- Migration: A Profile of the United States, Tape 1

Social Studies Skills Tutor CD-ROM

Companion Web site, www.phschool.com
- Chapter 6 Activities

Transportation Affects Patterns of Settlement

For the first fifty years or so following American independence, sailing ships were the fastest and cheapest form of transportation. Cities functioned largely as places to carry on trade between the United States and Europe. All the major cities were busy Atlantic ports; some of the largest were Baltimore, Boston, New York, and Philadelphia.

Canals As the interior of the continent was developed, settlers came to rely on the country's abundant rivers to transport their crops. Many of the rivers the farmers used were tributaries of the Mississippi. New Orleans, at the mouth of the Mississippi, flourished as a steady flow of trade goods from the Midwest filled its harbor and moved out into the world.

The people of many eastern cities realized that they, too, could benefit from more direct ties to the West. In the early 1800s, the governor of New York, DeWitt Clinton, came up with a daring plan to dig a 363-mile (584-km) canal from Lake Erie to the Hudson River. Western crops could be floated east through the Great Lakes into the canal and down the Hudson River to New York City. The Erie Canal provided the best connection between the east coast and settlements near the Great Lakes.

New cities were established on the shores of the Great Lakes and also along the Ohio, Mississippi, and Missouri rivers. Buffalo, Cleveland, Detroit, and Chicago soon rivaled the older cities of the East. The success of the Erie Canal sparked a canal-building boom. Before the end of the 1800s, a vast canal system, stretching for more than 4,000 miles (6,436 km), linked the cities of the North and West.

Railroads The same benefits from trade that motivated the building of canals also motivated the construction of railroads. The first successful railroads were built in the United States in 1830. By 1840, there were more than 1,000 miles (1,609 km) of railroad tracks. The great wave of railroad building over the next fifty years united the nation.

Early railroad tracks, however, were laid out in short, unconnected lines, and most of them existed in the East. Goods and passengers had to be moved to different cars on different lines, resulting in costly delays and inconvenience. In 1862, Congress initiated a plan to build a single rail line connecting the East to the West.

The nation's first transcontinental rail line was laid out on approximately the 42nd parallel, from Omaha to Sacramento. Building such a line proved to be a geographical challenge. Train tracks need to be level and relatively straight, rather than curved.

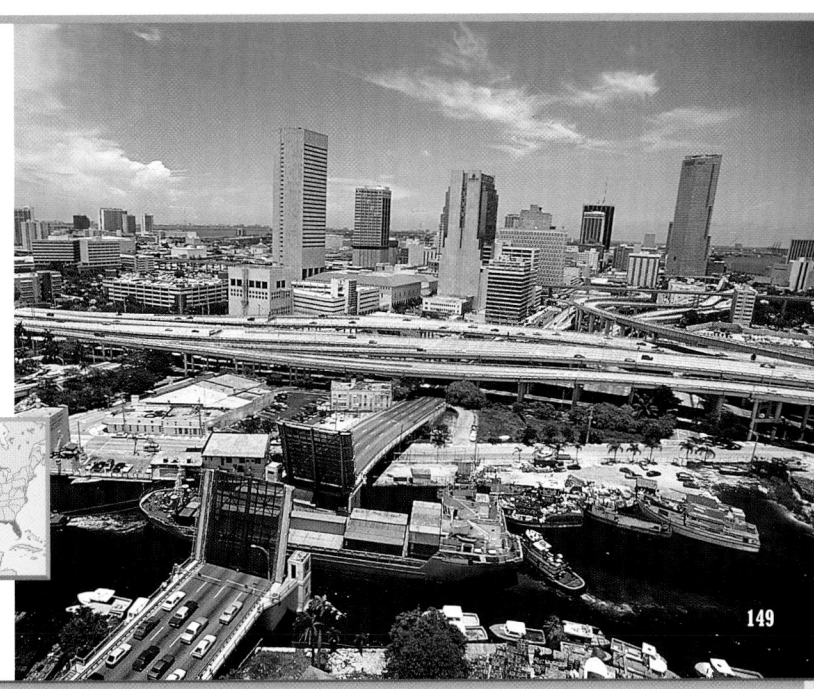

Miami on the Move

Global Trade Patterns
Miami is the second largest city in Florida. Its international airport is one of the busiest in the nation, its port serves both passenger and cargo ships from many countries, and its first railroad track was laid down more than 100 years ago.

Movement *Why is it so important for a city to have many forms of transportation?*

Answer to Photo Caption

Cities must have many means to transport people, resources, and goods efficiently. While people are able to travel by buses or subways, goods and resources may need to travel by trucks or by trains with boxcars.

Critical Thinking

Urban Growth Use the following questions to help students see the relationship among geography, transportation, and urban growth. **Why does location have so much impact on the growth of cities?** (Location affects climate and transportation.) **What changes in transportation occurred between 1800 and 1865, and how did these changes affect the growth of cities?** (Port cities like New Orleans developed along rivers; due to canals, new cities emerged along the Great Lakes and the Mississippi, Ohio, and Missouri rivers; and cities developed along railroad routes.) **Why are personal preferences more important in the growth of cities today?** (Cars allow people the freedom to choose their location according to preferences instead of depending on access to rail or shipping lines.)

The Global Economy

Oil Supply Point out that the automobile has allowed people to live in cities and suburbs many miles from where they work. Many people spend hours each day getting to work, school, or other activities. To continue this style of life, Americans must have an abundant supply of fuel. In the early 1970s, a national fuel shortage was created when foreign oil producers withheld supplies. This caused people to buy cars that were more fuel-efficient and to practice fuel conservation. Today, the United States is still dependent on foreign oil supplies.

Answer to Photo Caption

Possible answers: automobiles, airplanes

The Daily Commute

Patterns of Settlement Commuters wait for their train in Newark, New Jersey. Commuter trains enable people to work in major industrial centers and still make their homes away from the bustle of the city.

Movement *What other form of transportation has allowed individuals greater mobility?*

Yet, as you can see from the physical map of the United States on page 129, the Rocky Mountains and the Sierra Nevada formed huge geographical barriers. Thousands of Chinese and European immigrant workers performed the dangerous and difficult work of laying the tracks. By 1869, the continent's first transcontinental railroad was complete.

After the end of the Civil War in 1865, railroads became the country's most important form of transportation. Cities along the railroads grew rapidly. Chicago, located centrally between the coasts, had the best location on the railroad network, so it became the largest city in the Midwest. New York City acquired so many people, businesses, and activities that it developed into the foremost metropolitan area in the United States.

GEOFacts

Researchers are looking at fuel cells as a replacement for gasoline to power cars. Instead of spewing dangerous carbon monoxide into the air, cars running on fuel cells will release only water and heat into the environment.

Automobiles Until the invention of the automobile, efficient travel was limited to waterways and railroads. The automobile gave Americans a new freedom; they could go anyplace where there were roads at any time they wished. To meet the increasing demand for automobiles, auto manufacturers produced as many as 8 million new cars each year during the 1950s. The Federal-Aid Highway Act of 1956 provided $26 billion to build an interstate highway system more than 4,000 miles (6,436 km) long.

The increased availability of automobiles and public transportation, such as trolleys and subways, made it possible for people to travel longer distances to work. After World War II, many businesses and people moved from the cities to the suburbs—the mostly residential areas on the outer edges of a city. Suburbs grew at the end of rail lines because land there was available and less expensive. A 1952 advertisement for Park Forest, a town about 40 miles (64 km) outside of Chicago, attracted newcomers with these words: "Come out to Park Forest where small-town friendships grow—and you can still live so close to a big city." The scope of cities widened as suburbs grew.

The Impact of Migration on the Nation

All of these advances in transportation allowed people more freedom to select where their businesses would operate and where they would

United States Occupational Groups

Economic Activities
In the early 1900s, about 40 percent of the population was engaged in farming. This pie graph shows a much different situation in the early 2000s.

- *What three categories make up about 50 percent of the workforce today?*

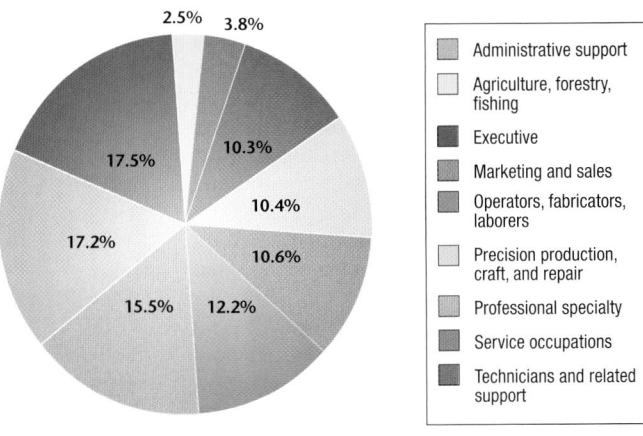

Legend:
- Administrative support
- Agriculture, forestry, fishing
- Executive
- Marketing and sales
- Operators, fabricators, laborers
- Precision production, craft, and repair
- Professional specialty
- Service occupations
- Technicians and related support

2.5% 3.8% 10.3% 10.4% 10.6% 12.2% 15.5% 17.2% 17.5%

Source: *The World Almanac and Book of Facts*

live. Today, many people choose locations that they feel offer the best possible surroundings. As a result, cities in the South and West, where winters are less severe than in the Northeast, have flourished. Because of new industries along the Gulf coast as well as its cultural attractions, New Orleans has regained the importance it had lost when railroads replaced steamboat traffic. At the same time, New York, Chicago, and other large centers have maintained their positions because they offer many jobs and varied activities.

Cities and Towns

Although today nearly 80 percent of all people in the United States live in metropolitan areas teeming with business and industry, about 20 percent continue to live in small towns and villages. Regardless of how small or large each of these places is, they all play a specific role in the nation's economy.

Interconnections The next time you are in a grocery store, find a can of peas or corn. Your can of vegetables may list the name of a major city. Obviously, the vegetables were not grown in that city, but the company that distributes the vegetables probably has its headquarters there.

The whole process of getting the food from the farm to your table involves different levels of economic activity. The primary economic activity is growing the vegetables on a farm. The crop is then transported to a processing plant where it is canned—a secondary economic activity. Transporting the cans from the processing plant to a warehouse is part of a tertiary activity. Managers at the distribution center are involved in a quaternary economic activity when they decide how many cans will be stored in their warehouse.

One hundred years ago, vegetables probably would not have gone farther than the dinner table on the farm where they were grown. Technological advances, however, allow consumers to find canned and fresh vegetables in cities many miles from the nearest fields.

Function and Size Geographers often talk about the nation's urban places in terms of a **hierarchy,** or rank, according to their function. Smaller places serve a limited area in limited ways, while larger cities provide other, wider-ranging functions.

Different terms describe urban places in each size category. Large cities are called metropolises, and their **hinterlands,** or areas that they influence, are quite large. For some activities, the hinterland may be the entire United States and much of the rest of the world. For example, New York is the most important financial center in the Western Hemisphere. Chicago is the nation's

Chapter 6 ▪ Section 2 151

Help students change each subheading of Section 2 into a question. Then review the section to find answers to these questions. Tell students to use the answers to write a paragraph summarizing Section 2. Remind them to use their paragraphs as a section review.

Answers to Section 2 Assessment

1. (a) metropolitan area, p. 148 **(b)** hierarchy, p. 151 **(c)** hinterland, p. 151

2. Advances in transportation have allowed people more flexibility in selecting where to live and operate businesses. Cities no longer need to be located in proximity to waterways and railroads.

3. Possible answers: milder climates, new industries, cultural attractions

4. Possible answer: Vegetables are grown in rural areas. Through secondary and tertiary economic activities, they are canned in processing plants and transported to grocery stores. The distribution company—and quaternary economic activities—is likely to be headquartered in a city.

5. Possible answer: There might be more development in the region, due to the increased access to the hinterlands.

Activity Rubrics Share rubrics with students before they write their proposals.

Attempted Proposal and map are attempted but are incomplete.

Minimal Proposal and map reflect limited understanding of how the Erie Canal affected economic development in New York.

Adequate Proposal reflects an understanding of the economic benefits of the canal. The map shows an understanding of location.

Exemplary Proposal reflects a thorough understanding of the reasoning behind location of the canal and the economic benefits it brought. The map is accurate and neatly drawn.

Answers to Diagram Skills

farm

Possible answers: financial centers, medical centers, museums, professional sports teams, large wholesale and retail shopping centers

152 Chapter 6

---

leading agricultural market, where orders for millions of farm animals and billions of bushels of grain are made. Los Angeles, California, is the world's leading film-production center.

Cities like Atlanta, Denver, Minneapolis–St. Paul, and San Antonio are regional metropolises and have much smaller hinterlands. But, like larger metropolises, they have advanced medical facilities, art galleries, major-league sports teams, and stores that sell expensive clothing and accessories. People from both surrounding suburbs and cities often travel to metropolises to enjoy the many cultural and economic services that the metropolises provide.

Smaller cities like Des Moines, Nashville, and Lubbock have a more limited range of activities and smaller hinterlands. These are places that usually have large shopping centers, daily newspapers, and computer software stores.

Some towns are small, and their service areas are quite limited. Few people outside the immediate area are familiar with these places. Such towns are home to automobile dealers, fast-food restaurants, and medium-sized supermarkets. Villages often have only small grocery stores. Post offices and video-rental stores may be present in some villages, but a general store often is the only business in the smallest hamlets.

Cities of similar size are not alike in all parts of the United States. They have distinct characteristics based in part on regional differences. In the next chapter, you will read about the nation's four distinct regions.

Urban Hierarchy

Largest city in a region

Metropolis
Offers special goods and services

City
Visited weekly for goods and services

Large Town
Visited daily for goods and services

Village

Farm
Dispersed farms and houses

DIAGRAM SKILLS

● **Economic Activities** The metropolis tops the urban hierarchy pyramid because it offers the most services and serves an extensive area.

• *Which place serves the most limited area?*
• *Which services does a large metropolis provide that cannot be found in a town?*

SECTION 2 ASSESSMENT

1. Key Terms Define **(a)** metropolitan area, **(b)** hierarchy, **(c)** hinterland.

2. Urbanization How have changes in transportation affected where cities have developed?

3. Migration What factors have encouraged people to move to the South and the West?

4. Economic Activities How do economic activities interconnect rural areas and cities?

5. Critical Thinking **Predicting Consequences** How might the construction of a major highway between two cities affect the region between them?

Activity

Take It to the NET

Writing a Proposal The Erie Canal in New York was one of the most important transportation projects of the early 1800s. Suppose that it was your idea to build the canal. Write a proposal explaining why the waterway should be built. Your proposal should include a hand-drawn map showing the canal route, your reasons for choosing that route, and a description of the economic benefits that the canal will bring. Visit the World Geography section of **www.phschool.com** for help in learning about the Erie Canal.

RESOURCE DIRECTORY

Teaching Resources

Unit 2, Chapter 6
• Section 2 Quiz, p. 14
• Reviewing Main Ideas, p. 15
• Test Forms A and B, pp. 18–23

Spanish Resources
Section 2 Quiz, p. 15

Guide to the Essentials (English/Spanish)
• Chapter 6 Test

Mental Mapping booklet
• Chapter 6 Map Test, p. 26

Simulations, Games, and Lab Activities
• Simulation: Resolving a Land Dispute, pp. 49–57

• Exploring Local Geography: Local Attitudes Toward Land; Street Patterns; The Shape of Your Community, pp. 6, 7, 9
• Place Location Review Games, pp. 58–63

Social Studies Skills Handbook
• Study and Research Skills, pp. 94–108

Technology

ExamView Test Bank CD-ROM
• Chapter 6 Test

Companion Web site, www.phschool.com
• Chapter 6 Self-Test

Comparing Geographic Models

The urban models below represent two views on the spatial organization of cities. By comparing them, you can analyze how people and economic activities may be distributed in an urban area. Government officials use models to create school districts and to decide on other public policies.

Learn the Skill Use the following steps to learn how to compare geographic models.

1 *Study the key to understand symbols.* The models below use numbers, lines, and colors to identify social and economic patterns in urban geography. *Which symbols represent middle-income housing?*

2 *Find similarities between the models.* If two models are on the same topic, there should be some common points on which they agree. **(a)** *In both models, where is the central business district located?* **(b)** *What is another similarity?*

3 *Find differences between the models.* By identifying the differences in the models, you are identifying the different views of the people who designed the models. **(a)** *According to Burgess, where is low-income housing located?* **(b)** *How does Hoyt's model differ on this point?*

4 *Analyze the models.* Now that you have identified the basic similarities and differences between the models, you are ready to summarize their main points. **(a)** *Why is Burgess's model called a concentric zone model?* **(b)** *Why is Hoyt's model called a sector model?*

5 *Do additional research.* If models differ, as these do, it may be necessary to find additional evidence or perspectives. *How would you find other models on this topic?*

6 *Draw conclusions and make recommendations.* One benefit of an accurate model is that it can help you to make informed decisions and recommendations. *In these models, which zones probably do not need a large number of schools to be built? Explain.*

Do It Yourself

Practice the Skill Create a geographic model of your city or community. Start by studying detailed maps or reports to gather the data you need. Then, identify and locate the kinds of zones that comprise your community. Compare your work with models made by your classmates, and see if you can make any recommendations.

Apply the Skill See Chapter 6 Review and Assessment.

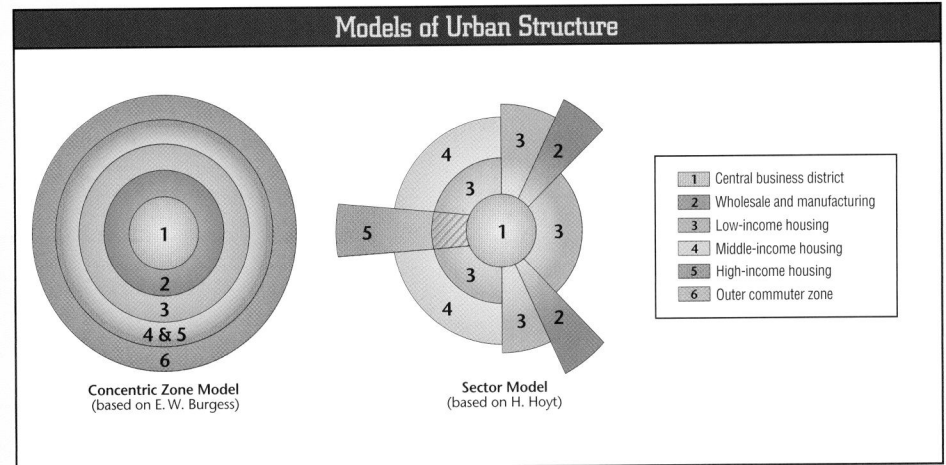

Models of Urban Structure

Concentric Zone Model
(based on E. W. Burgess)

Sector Model
(based on H. Hoyt)

1	Central business district
2	Wholesale and manufacturing
3	Low-income housing
4	Middle-income housing
5	High-income housing
6	Outer commuter zone

Teaching the Skill
Review the term "spatial organization," meaning the arrangement of items within a given area. Ask students: **How does an urban model differ from most city maps?** (Maps usually show streets and locations; models show land use.) Note that most cities grow up without a plan, yet they tend to follow many of the same land use patterns, which can be shown in several types of models. Then work through the six steps with the students.

Answers to Learn the Skill
1. the number four and the color yellow
2. (a) in the center **(b)** Possible answer: A wholesale and manufacturing zone is adjacent to the central business district.
3. (a) in a ring around the wholesale and manufacturing zone **(b)** Low-income housing does not form a ring and juts out from the central business district.
4. (a) The zones are arranged in concentric circles around the central business district. **(b)** The zones form sectors, more like the sections of a pie.
5. Possible answer: consulting reference works on geography and urban studies in the library or on the Internet
6. A large number of schools probably would not be needed in zones 1 and 2, the central business district and wholesale and manufacturing, where there are few residents.

Answer to Practice the Skill
Students' models should accurately convey the zones in your city or community.

▶▶▶ Career Prep

Urban Planner Urban planners are hired by cities to make sure that growth takes place efficiently and attractively. They study traffic flow and residential and commercial neighborhoods and make judgments about the best locations for parks, schools, businesses, and services.

Creating a Chapter Summary

As a reteaching opportunity, pair a more able student with a less able student to complete this chapter summary.

Reasons for Economic Prosperity **Natural Resources:** Rich soils, Forests, Mineral resources **Transportation:** Canals, Transcontinental railroad, Automobiles **Communication Technology:** Telegraph, Telephone, Telecommunication **Individual Freedoms:** Equality, Opportunity, Freedom

Reviewing Key Terms

1–6. Students' puzzle clues should show an understanding of each term.

Understanding Key Ideas

7. (a) Unlike renewable resources, nonrenewable resources cannot be replaced once they are used. **(b)** If managed carefully, forests are a renewable resource. However, if they are not managed well, they can be used up completely.
8. (a) steamboats and canals **(b)** railroads, automobiles
9. The belief that any individual can find opportunity and success in the United States has drawn many immigrants to this country.
10. transportation, economic activities, and popular preferences
11. Many people moved to communities outside the cities and commuted to work by car.

Critical Thinking and Writing

12. Possible answer: Americans have become more conscious of the need to conserve the nation's forests and protect the watersheds and wildlife habitats they support.
13. (a) Fossil fuels are nonrenewable resources. **(b)** conserving energy, managing existing supplies carefully, and searching for alternative sources
14. (a) Answers will vary depending on what product students decide to ship. **(b)** Students should give reasons to support their choice.
15. Answers will vary, depending on your community. Students should explain their choices.

Creating a Chapter Summary

On a sheet of paper, draw a graphic organizer like the one below. Fill in the reasons for the economic prosperity of the United States. Some information has been provided to help you get started.

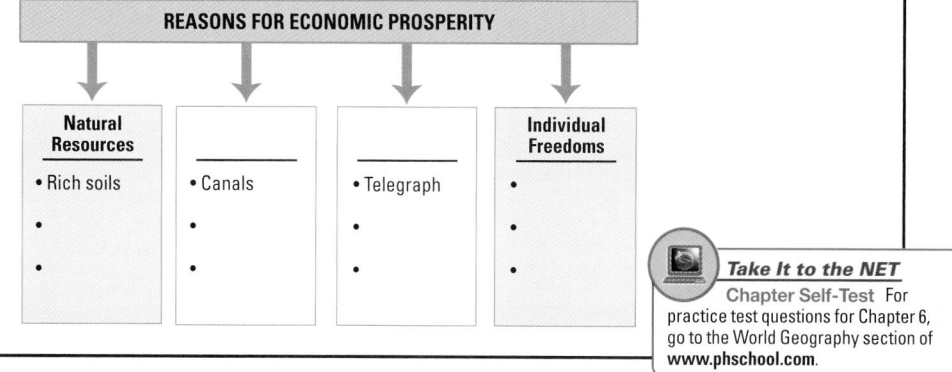

REASONS FOR ECONOMIC PROSPERITY

Natural Resources	___	___	Individual Freedoms
• Rich soils	• Canals	• Telegraph	•
•	•	•	•
•	•	•	•

Take It to the NET
Chapter Self-Test For practice test questions for Chapter 6, go to the World Geography section of **www.phschool.com**.

Reviewing Key Terms

Use the key terms below to create a crossword puzzle. Exchange puzzles with a classmate, complete the puzzles, and then check each other's answers.

1. canal
2. telecommunication
3. free enterprise
4. metropolitan area
5. hierarchy
6. hinterland

Understanding Key Ideas

7. **Natural Resources** (a) What is the difference between a renewable and nonrenewable natural resource? (b) Is a forest a renewable or nonrenewable resource? Explain.

8. **Science and Technology** (a) What technological developments simplified travel over water? (b) What technological developments simplified travel over land?

9. **Economic Systems** How has free enterprise affected immigration to the United States?

10. **Urbanization** What factors affect the value of a city's location?

11. **Patterns of Settlement** How did the automobile and the development of the interstate highway system affect the growth of towns?

Critical Thinking and Writing

12. **Analyzing Change** How have Americans' attitudes toward the clearing of forests changed over the centuries?

13. **Solving Problems** (a) Why are many Americans concerned about reliance on fossil fuels as an energy source? (b) What can be done to ease these concerns?

14. **Making Comparisons** Suppose that you work for a company that needs to ship products across the United States. (a) Would you be most likely to recommend transportation by canal, railroad, or automobile? (b) Identify the advantages and disadvantages of each in a brief letter to the company president, concluding with your recommendation.

15. **Drawing Conclusions** Where does your community fit into the urban hierarchy described on pages 151 and 152? Explain.

Applying Skills

Comparing Geographic Models Refer to the urban models on page 153 to answer these questions:

16. What are the significant differences between the concentric zone model and the sector model?

17. (a) What are the advantages of having one business district in the center of a city? **(b)** What are the disadvantages?

Reading a Graph Study the graph below, and answer the following questions:

18. Through the 1990s, which two fossil fuels were consumed at a fairly equal level?

19. If the cost of fossil fuels were to rise steeply, would you expect the lines on the graph to rise or fall? Explain.

U.S. Energy Consumption

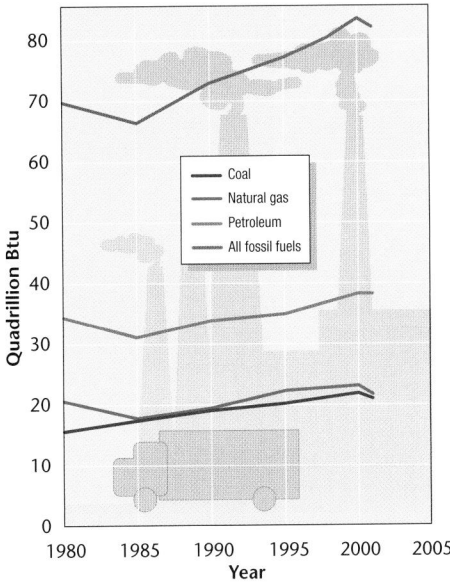

Source: *The World Almanac and Book of Facts*

Test Preparation

Read the question and choose the best answer.

20. Which factor has encouraged people to migrate to the South and West?

A The cities of the South and West are older than those of the Northeast.

B The South and West have milder winters than the Northeast.

C The South and West have fewer railroads than the Northeast.

D The ecosystems of the South and West are much more developed.

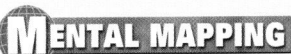

Activities

USING THE REGIONAL ATLAS

Using the population density map on page 135 as a model, make a map of your home state on which you identify the ten most populous cities in the state. Create symbols and a key to indicate the total population of each city.

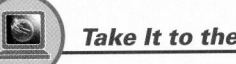

MENTAL MAPPING

Study a map of the United States. On a separate piece of paper, draw a sketch map of the United States from memory. Label the following places on your map:

- Atlantic Ocean
- Pacific Ocean
- Gulf of Mexico
- Your home state
- Neighboring states
- As many additional states as possible

Take It to the NET

Analyzing Data Explore government Web sites to find data about agriculture in the United States today. Analyze the data to determine some general trends regarding the number, distribution, and size of farms. Visit the World Geography section of **www.phschool.com** for help in completing this activity.

Chapter 6 ▪ Review and Assessment **155**

Applying Skills
16. Zones in the concentric zone model are organized in circles around the central business district. In the sector model, zones extend outward from the central business district.
17. (a) centralized services and activities **(b)** traffic, congestion
18. coal and natural gas
19. Possible answer: Fall. If fossil fuels became very expensive, people might tend to use less of them.

Test Preparation
20. B

Activities

Using the Regional Atlas
Check students' maps for accuracy. Check that students have correctly identified the location of the ten most populous cities.

Mental Mapping
Review students' maps for relative and absolute location.

Take It to the Net
Students' work should reflect sound research. Check students' work for accurate data about agriculture in the United States.

MENTAL MAPPING

Games for Review See pages 58–63 of the Simulations, Games, and Lab Activities booklet for games to review place names in preparation for the Chapter 6 Map Test.

Chapter Map Test Students should use the completed Chapter 6 outline map and the Unit 2 Checklist in their Atlas Portfolios to prepare for the Chapter 6 Map Test. Point out to students that the test will cover only Part III of the Unit 2 Checklist, States.

Alternative Assessment

Final Evaluation

Preparing a Time Line Use the Time Line Evaluation Form on page 12 of the Alternative Assessment booklet in the Prentice Hall Assessment System to evaluate students' time lines. Either teachers or students can complete the forms to indicate which level of work was achieved for each of the criteria. The evaluation should include specific comments.

Resource Manager

	CORE INSTRUCTION	READING/SKILLS
Chapter-Level Resources	**Teaching Resources** ■ **Unit 2**/Ch. 7 • Reviewing Main Ideas, p. 32 ■ **Mental Mapping booklet** • Unit 2 Checklist, p. 19 ■ **Simulations, Games, and Lab Activities** • Place Location Review Games, pp. 58–63 ■ **Creative Teaching Activities** • Regions of the United States, p. 9 ● **TeacherExpress™ CD-ROM,** Ch. 7 ■ **Companion Web site,** **www.phschool.com** • eTeach	**Teaching Resources** ■ **Unit 2**/Ch. 7 • Map/Graph Skills, p. 34 ● **Book on CD,** Ch. 7 ● **Social Studies Skills Tutor CD-ROM**
1 The Northeast 1. Discuss the effects of the Northeast's physical characteristics and resources on its economy. 2. Describe the development of industry in the Northeast. 3. Explain why the Northeast has become a megalopolis.	**Teaching Resources** ■ **Unit 2**/Ch. 7 • Guided Reading and Review, p. 24 ● **Prentice Hall Presentation Pro CD-ROM,** Ch. 7, Sec. 1	**Teaching Resources** ■ **Guide to the Essentials (English/Spanish)** • Section Summary, Ch. 7, Sec. 1 ■ **Mental Mapping booklet** • Outline Map 7, p. 27 ▦ **Guided Reading Audiotapes (English/Spanish),** Ch. 7, Sec. 1 ▨ **Section Reading Support Transparencies,** Ch. 7, Sec. 1
2 The South 1. Explain how warm climates and rich soils have affected vegetation in the South. 2. Identify the key natural resources that have influenced industrial development in the South. 3. Discuss how changes in the South have led to the growth of cities.	**Teaching Resources** ■ **Unit 2**/Ch. 7 • Guided Reading and Review, p. 26 ■ **Simulations, Games, and Lab Activities** • Exploring Local Geography: The Telephone Directory, p. 10 ● **Prentice Hall Presentation Pro CD-ROM,** Ch. 7, Sec. 2	**Teaching Resources** ■ **Guide to the Essentials (English/Spanish)** • Section Summary, Ch. 7, Sec. 2 ■ **Mental Mapping booklet** • Outline Map 7, p. 27 ▦ **Guided Reading Audiotapes (English/Spanish),** Ch. 7, Sec. 2 ▨ **Section Reading Support Transparencies,** Ch. 7, Sec. 2
3 The Midwest 1. Describe how climate supports the Midwest's agriculture. 2. Identify the reasons farming has become big business. 3. Explain how resources and transportation have promoted industry in the Midwest.	**Teaching Resources** ■ **Unit 2**/Ch. 7 • Guided Reading and Review, p. 28 ● **Prentice Hall Presentation Pro CD-ROM,** Ch. 7, Sec. 3	**Teaching Resources** ■ **Guide to the Essentials (English/Spanish)** • Section Summary, Ch. 7, Sec. 3 ■ **Mental Mapping booklet** • Outline Map, 7, p. 27 ▦ **Guided Reading Audiotapes (English/Spanish),** Ch. 7, Sec. 3 ▨ **Section Reading Support Transparencies,** Ch. 7, Sec. 3
4 The West 1. Explain how the abundance or scarcity of water resources affects natural vegetation in the West. 2. List the major natural resources that have influenced the economy in the Western United States. 3. Describe how geography and distance have affected where people live and work in the West.	**Teaching Resources** ■ **Unit 2**/Ch. 7 • Guided Reading and Review, p. 30 ● **Prentice Hall Presentation Pro CD-ROM,** Ch. 7, Sec. 4	**Teaching Resources** ■ **Guide to the Essentials (English/Spanish)** • Section Summary, Ch. 7, Sec. 4 ▦ **Guided Reading Audiotapes (English/Spanish),** Ch. 7, Sec. 4 ▨ **Section Reading Support Transparencies,** Ch. 7, Sec. 4

ENRICHMENT/HONORS/PREAP

Teaching Resources
- **Unit 2**/Ch. 7
  - Critical Thinking, p. 33
- **Mental Mapping booklet**
  - Atlas Activity, p. 28
- **Social Studies Skills Handbook**
  - Study and Research Skills, pp. 94–108
- **People and Geography**
  - Global Independence, pp. 8–13
- **World Geography Map and Photo Transparencies**
  - The United States and Canada: Maps and Photos
- **World Geography Videos**
  - Regions: Regions of the United States, Tape 1
- **Companion Web site, www.phschool.com**
  - Chapter 7 Activities

Companion Web site, www.phschool.com
- Chapter 7 Activities

Companion Web site, www.phschool.com
- Chapter 7 Activities

Companion Web site, www.phschool.com
- Chapter 7 Activities

Teaching Resources
- **Social Studies Skills Handbook**
  - Checking Consistency of Ideas, p. 44
- **Companion Web site, www.phschool.com**
  - Chapter 7 Activities

ASSESSMENT

PRENTICE HALL
ASSESSMENT SYSTEM

Core Assessment
- ExamView Test Bank booklet, Ch. 7
- ExamView Test Bank CD-ROM, Ch. 7

Standardized Test Preparation

Review and Reteach
- Review Book for World Geography, pp. 5–6

Practice and Assess
- Test-taking Strategies With Transparencies for High School
- Test-taking Strategy Poster
- Alternative Assessment booklet
- Test Prep Book for World Geography

Teaching Resources
- **Unit 2**/Ch. 7
  - Section Quizzes, pp. 25, 27, 29, 31
  - Test Forms A and B, pp. 35–40
- **Guide to the Essentials (English/Spanish)**
  - Chapter 7 Test
- **Spanish Resources**, Ch. 7
  - Section Quizzes, pp. 16–19
- **Mental Mapping booklet**
  - Chapter 7 Map Test, p. 29
- **Companion Web site, www.phschool.com**
  - Chapter 7 Self-Test

CUSTOMIZE FOR INDIVIDUAL NEEDS

Gifted and Talented
- Teacher's Edition, Customize for . . . , pp. 165, 171, 179

Honors/PreAP
- Teacher's Edition, Customize for . . . , pp. 159, 175

Less Proficient Readers
- Guide to the Essentials (English), Ch. 7, Section Summaries
- Social Studies Skills Handbook, p. 74
- Guided Reading Audiotapes (English), Ch. 7
- Section Reading Support Transparencies, Ch. 7
- Book on CD, Ch. 7
- Teacher's Edition, Reading Strategy, pp. 159, 163, 168, 173
- Teacher's Edition, Activity: Vocabulary, pp. 164, 168, 174

Students Acquiring English/ESL
- Guide to the Essentials (English/Spanish), Ch. 7
- Guided Reading Audiotapes (English/Spanish), Ch. 7
- Section Reading Support Transparencies, Ch. 7
- Book on CD, Ch. 7
- Teacher's Edition, Customize for . . . , p. 169

Less Proficient Writers
- Social Studies Skills Handbook, p. 83
- Alternative Assessment, Writing Assignment Rubric, p. 6

MENTAL MAPPING

Referring to the map on this page, point out that the United States lies within the Northern Hemisphere, north of Mexico and south of Canada. Hawaii is far enough south to be within tropical latitudes, while northern Alaska is within the Arctic Circle.

Mapping the Region Ask the students to create a map like the one shown on this page. Have students draw their own sketch maps, or distribute the Chapter 7 Outline Map on page 27 of the Mental Mapping booklet in the Teaching Resources. Ask students to lightly shade each region a different color. Then have students label the U.S. cities listed under Part I of the Unit 2 Checklist as well as the states under Part III. Students should keep their maps in their Atlas Portfolios in order to prepare for the Chapter 7 Map Test.

eTeach

Be sure to check out this month's online forum with a Master Teacher to join in an exchange of teaching ideas. **www.phschool.com**

CHAPTER
7

Regions of the United States

SECTIONS

1	The Northeast
2	The South
3	The Midwest
4	The West

The United States: REGIONS

Seattle
Minneapolis
Sacramento
San Francisco
WEST
MIDWEST   Chicago
St. Louis
Los Angeles
Phoenix
Dallas
Austin
Houston
NORTHEAST
New York
Boston
Washington, D.C.
ATLANTIC OCEAN
Atlanta
SOUTH
Miami
Gulf of Mexico
PACIFIC OCEAN

Arctic Circle
WEST
Anchorage
PACIFIC OCEAN
Gulf of Alaska
0   400 mi
0   400 km

WEST
Honolulu
0   100   200 mi
0   100 200 km

KEY
• City
○ State capital
⊛ National capital
Lambert Azimuthal Equal-Area Projection

Go Online
PHSchool.com
For: More information about the United States and access to the Take It to the Net activities
Visit: phschool.com
Web Code: mjk-0008

RESOURCE DIRECTORY

Teaching Resources

Unit 2, Chapter 7
• Section 1 Guided Reading and Review, p. 24

Guide to the Essentials (English/Spanish)
• Section Summary, Chapter 7, Section 1

Mental Mapping booklet
• Atlas Activity, p. 28
• Unit 2 Checklist, p. 19

Technology

Guided Reading Audiotapes (English/Spanish), Chapter 7, Section 1

Section Reading Support Transparencies, Chapter 7, Section 1

World Geography Map and Photo Transparencies
• The United States and Canada: Maps and Photos

Book on CD, Chapter 7

World Geography Videos
• Regions: Regions of the United States, Tape 1

TeacherExpress™ CD-ROM, Chapter 7

Prentice Hall Presentation Pro CD-ROM, Chapter 7

Social Studies Skills Tutor CD-ROM

Companion Web site, www.phschool.com
• Chapter 7 Activities

1 The Northeast

Reading Focus
- How have the physical characteristics and resources of the Northeast affected its economy?
- How did the Northeast become an early leader of industry?
- Why has the Northeast coastal region become a megalopolis?

Key Term
megalopolis

Main Idea Over time, the Northeast has developed into a major commercial center of the world.

Economic Activities A Maine lobsterman tends his traps in a coastal New England village.

People define regions in order to identify places that have similar characteristics or close connections. As you read in Chapter 1, there are many ways to define the regions of the United States: historically; by the ways people live, work, and play in them; or by their political orientation. As the maps in Chapter 5 show, landforms, climate, and vegetation all suggest different boundaries for North America's physical regions. The economic activity and population density maps suggest other divisions, based on human characteristics.

In this textbook, we look to the United States government for regional classifications. The government, for the purpose of collecting statistics, divides the country into four major regions: the Northeast, South, Midwest, and West. Look at the map on page 156 to identify these regions. The government's definition of these regions is based on a combination of physical, economic, cultural, and historical factors, many of which you will read about in this chapter.

Physical Characteristics of the Northeast

The New England region includes six states that are located in the northeastern part of the United States. The region is known for its beautiful landscape. Ogden Tanner, a writer whose ancestors settled in New England, once wrote:

66 I think if I had to show someone New England only at one instant, in one time and place, it would have to be this: from a canoe suspended on a silver river, surrounded by the great, silent autumnal explosion of the trees. On the hills the evergreens stand unchanging. . . . Scattered in abstract patterns through their ranks, the deciduous trees . . . produce the glorious golds, oranges, reds, and purples. 99

This brilliance is a result of the geography and climate of the region. The unique combination of precipitation, type of soil, and varieties of trees that thrive in the region give New England its breathtaking fall colors. But, the Northeast has far more to offer than magnificent forests.

A visitor wanting a broad view of the Northeast might head for the craggy coast of Maine, New York's spectacular Niagara Falls, or the rolling farmlands of Pennsylvania. Every year millions of tourists flock to the Northeast just to explore its world-famous cities. New York is considered by many to be the cultural center of the nation, whereas Boston and Philadelphia offer visitors a view into the nation's history.

◀ Autumn in New England (photo left)

Objectives
Upon completion of Section 1, students should be able to:
- ◆ discuss the effects of the Northeast's physical characteristics and resources on its economy;
- ◆ describe the development of industry in the Northeast;
- ◆ explain why the Northeast has become a megalopolis.

 National Geography Standards
The following National Geography Standards are highlighted in this section: 1, 2, 3, 4, 5, 11, 12, 14, 16, 17, 18

 Bellringer
Have students divide a sheet of paper into four equal sections, and then have them label the sections Northeast, South, Midwest, and West. Then have students divide a second sheet into four areas that they think are equal to the relative geographic size of each area. Compare students' estimates against the map on page 156.

LESSON PLAN

1. Focus Ask students to imagine that they are taking a vacation in the Northeast. Have them make a "wish list" of places to visit. Use the list to highlight some of the region's physical characteristics, industrial centers, and cities.

2. Instruct Draw a two-column chart on the board with the headings *Benefits* and *Challenges*. Discuss the growth of cities and the high population density in the Northeast. Fill in the chart with benefits and challenges associated with urban growth and high population density.

3. Close/Reteach Draw a cause-and-effect chart on the board with the following headings: *Physical Characteristics and Resources, Industrial Leadership,* and *Megalopolis*. Have students explain the links among these items. For example, the region's physical characteristics and resources helped make it an industrial leader.

TEACHING TIP
From A Master Teacher

Economics Have students identify how patterns of economic activities change over time in response to changes in technology, natural resources, transportation, supplies of workers, the availability of capital, and demand for goods nand services. Today, in developed economies, manufacturing is being replaced by services. This affects the locations of economic activities and the rise and decline of cities and regions. Older economic areas have been replaced in importance by new areas of economic growth.

Pacing Suggestions

 For 90-minute Blocks

You will want to vary activities.
- Use the Creative Teaching Activity for Chapter 7 as the basis for a 90-minute lesson. After completing the lesson, ask students to prepare a one-page magazine advertisement for their regions based on the information they researched for their radio announcements. Have volunteers present their advertisements and display them in the classroom.

The Northeast: PHYSICAL-POLITICAL

KEY
Elevation

Feet		Meters
14,000		4,270
7,000		2,135
1,500		457
700		213
(sea level) 0		0 (sea level)

- State capital
- Major city
- Mountain
- Waterfall

Lambert Azimuthal Equal-Area Projection

APPLYING THE GEOGRAPHIC THEMES

- **Place** In the Northeast, the most populous cities are located on or near the Atlantic coast.
  - *How has the topography of the Northeast affected population distribution?*
  - *How have rivers influenced the patterns of settlement in the Northeast? Explain.*

Natural Resources of the Northeast

Compared with other regions of the United States, the Northeast has few natural resources. The region's thin, rocky soils and steep hills are a challenge to the area's farmers. The northern reaches of the Appalachian Mountains make some parts of the Northeast quite rugged. Apart from the coal-rich area of Pennsylvania, the region has few mineral resources. But the Northeast has one major resource that has turned it into a center of trade, commerce, and industry—its waters.

Since Colonial times, people of the Northeast have engaged in commerce and fishing. The region's rocky and jagged shoreline provides many excellent harbors. Throughout the 1700s and 1800s, these natural harbors were used by merchant ships sailing to and from other regions of the world. Plentiful fish in the Grand Banks in the North Atlantic supported a thriving fishing industry.

A Leader in Industry

The Northeast's many rivers, including the Connecticut and the Hudson, have been vital to its history. The same hills that discouraged farming aided industrialists in the nineteenth century. The abundant precipitation, about 35 to 50 inches (89 to 127 cm) annually, combined with the hilly terrain, keeps the rivers of the region flowing swiftly. Industrialists harnessed the power of these rivers by building water wheels, which converted water power into machine power.

158 Chapter 7 ▪ Regions of the United States

RESOURCE DIRECTORY

Teaching Resources
Unit 2, Chapter 7
- Critical Thinking, p. 33
Mental Mapping booklet
- Chapter 7 Outline Map, p. 27

Prentice Hall Assessment System
Alternative Assessment booklet
- Oral Presentation Rubric, p. 20

Technology
World Geography Map and Photo Transparencies
- The United States and Canada: Maps and Photos

Throughout the 1800s—especially in Massachusetts, Rhode Island, and New Hampshire—factories were built at waterfalls along the region's many rivers. The factories produced shoes, cotton cloth, and other goods that were sold across the United States and shipped to markets around the world. The region's river valleys served as trade routes, railroad routes, and later as modern highway routes for the Northeast. By the early 1900s, the Northeast was the most productive manufacturing region in the world.

The Megalopolis

Cities along the Atlantic coast first grew in importance as harbors of international trade and as centers of shipbuilding. As manufacturing grew, those cities attracted industries that needed a large supply of workers. Decade after decade, new industries developed—and the Northeast's cities grew in population. Young people from the Northeastern countryside flocked to the factory towns to take industrial jobs.

Europeans were also attracted by the job opportunities in cities of the Northeast. In 1840, about 80,000 Europeans immigrated to the United States; by 1850 the number jumped to 308,000. Many came to escape political oppression and economic hardships. Today, many people in the Northeast are descendants of these earlier immigrants who came by sea.

Over time, coastal cities began to spread and run together. The far suburbs of one city in some cases stretched to the suburbs of the next. By the 1960s, the area from Boston to Washington, D.C., had earned a new name: **megalopolis** (mehg uh LAH puh lis), a word based on Greek roots meaning "a very large city." About 40 million people now live in this megalopolis—one seventh of the entire United States population. The map on page 135 shows the population density of this crowded part of the east coast.

While the east coast megalopolis remains one of the dominant centers of American business

GL🌐BAL CONNECTIONS

Migration In the 1840s, disease ruined the potato crop across Europe and a famine resulted in Ireland. Between 1845 and 1860, over 1.5 million Irish fled to the United States. Most of the Irish were too poor to buy farmland, so they settled in New York, Boston, and other cities where their ships landed. They crowded into poor neighborhoods and took whatever jobs they could find.

Skating in Central Park

Urbanization New York City is a world leader in industry, trade, and finance. It is also a cultural center of the United States and has more parks than any other U.S. city. Central Park provides a variety of recreational activities.

Place *Why are parks an important part of any city?*

Wildlife and Development

Ecosystems Many species of wildlife have adapted to life in populated areas. For example, the deer population in the Northeast is exploding. Landscaping provides deer with the luxury of feeding anytime.

Human-Environment Interaction *Why do you think some people might want to limit deer population?*

and industry, it faces serious problems, too. After decades of steady expansion, its inhabitants now have serious concerns that the area might run short of water or of facilities for waste disposal.

Another problem facing many cities in the Northeast is a decline in population. Between 1970 and 2000, for example, the population of the city of Philadelphia declined by more than 430,000. As a result, the city government must collect higher taxes from fewer residents and businesses. The city has to rely on other sources of revenue to pay for many basic services, such as street repairs and police protection.

Yet, the Northeast remains a vital area. Despite the destruction of the World Trade Center in 2001, New York is still the business capital of the world, and its population has grown to more than 8 million people. Businesses and industries that want to be near large numbers of consumers continue to thrive in the Northeast. Tax breaks have spurred the creation of new jobs. The natural beauty of less crowded parts of the region also attracts people.

SECTION 1 ASSESSMENT

1. **Key Term** Define megalopolis.

2. **Physical Characteristics** Describe how the physical characteristics and resources of the Northeast have benefited the region.

3. **Science and Technology** In the 1800s, how were rivers used to power factories of the Northeast?

4. **Urbanization (a)** What factors have played a key role in the development of cities in the Northeast? **(b)** What effect has steady expansion had on the region?

5. **Critical Thinking Analyzing Information** What are the advantages and disadvantages of living in a large Northeast urban area? Use information from the text, map, and pictures in this section.

Activity

Making a Chart Economic development leads to environmental and social change. Find a description of a major city in the Northeast in the 1800s and a description of that same city today. Make a chart comparing how the city has changed over time. Label the columns of the chart with topics such as population size and distribution, major businesses and industries, transportation, and forms of recreation.

2 The South

Reading Focus

• How have warm climates and rich soils affected vegetation in the South?

• What key natural resources have influenced industrial development?

• How have changes in the South led to the growth of cities?

Key Terms

mangrove

bayou

fall line

Sunbelt

 Main Idea The warm climate and abundant natural resources of the South continue to attract people and industry.

Ecosystems Grass grows tall in a coastal marsh off the shore of Georgia.

Many Americans think of the South as the old Confederacy. In 1860 and 1861, eleven states ranging from Texas to Virginia withdrew from the United States because of conflicts over economic and moral issues, including tariffs and, especially, slavery. These states formed the Confederate States of America. Between 1861 and 1865, however, United States military forces from the Northeast and Midwest fought a bloody war with the Confederacy—the Civil War, also known as the War Between the States. At the war's end, slavery was abolished and the South was drawn back into the Union.

As you can see from the map on page 162, the South, as we define it, does include the states of the old Confederacy, plus five others—Oklahoma, Kentucky, West Virginia, Maryland, and Delaware—as well as the District of Columbia. Together they make up a region rich in resources and culture that has become an increasingly popular place in which to live and work.

As a region, the South stands out from the rest of the country because of its humid, subtropical climate and the lush, mixed forests that are common to most of its areas.

American naturalist, explorer, and writer John Muir captured the essence of the climate and vegetation of the South in a diary he kept while on a trek through the region in 1867. Along the Savannah River in Georgia he saw magnificent, plumed grasses and "rich, dense, vine-clad forests." Commenting on a mysterious cypress swamp, he wrote:

> 66 This remarkable tree, called cypress, grows large and high. . . . The groves and thickets of smaller trees are full of blooming evergreen vines. These vines are arranged . . . in bossy walls and heavy, mound-like heaps and banks. Am made to feel that I am now in a strange land. 99

Linking Climate to Vegetation

The South's location closer to the Equator makes it warmer than other regions in the United States farther north. In addition, weather systems moving north from the Gulf of Mexico and the Caribbean Sea bring ample precipitation to most of the region. The coastal areas of Louisiana and Mississippi can receive over 60 inches (152 cm) of precipitation annually. Parts of Florida receive an average of 55 inches (140 cm) of rain per year.

Chapter 7 ▪ Section 2   **161**

Objectives

Upon completion of Section 2, students should be able to:

◆ explain how warm climates and rich soils have affected vegetation in the South;

◆ identify the key natural resources that have influenced industrial development in the South;

◆ discuss how changes in the South have led to the growth of cities.

National Geography Standards

The following National Geography Standards are highlighted in this section: 1, 2, 4, 5, 6, 8, 9, 10, 11, 12, 16, 17

Bellringer

Before reading the chapter, ask the class to preview the photos in Section 2. Ask: **What general statements about the South can you make after seeing these photos?** (Answers will vary, but students should be able to tell that the South is a region of great physical diversity.)

....

LESSON PLAN

1. Focus Write the following dates on the board: *mid-1500s* (European settlements in the South), *1790* (District of Columbia), *1840s* (textile mills in the Carolinas), *1901* (birth of the oil industry in Texas). Ask students to find the significance of each date in their textbooks. Then discuss how these events helped shape the South.

2. Instruct Refer students to the ecosystem map on page 133. Then list the various ecosystems of the South in columns on the board. Discuss how climate and vegetation of each ecosystem have affected the region's economic development. (A warm climate and rich soils have led to the development of agriculture.)

3. Close/Reteach Write the words *Farmer, Business Owner, Tourist,* and *Retiree* on the board. Have students prepare two or three sentences explaining what the South has to offer each group.

Chapter 7 ▪ Section 2   **161**

History

Oranges A great source of Vitamin C, the orange is a very popular fruit both in the United States and overseas. The United States is a leading producer of sweet and mandarin oranges—Brazil is the only nation that produces more of the fruit. Florida is the leading orange-growing state because its climate and soil are ideal for the citrus tree.

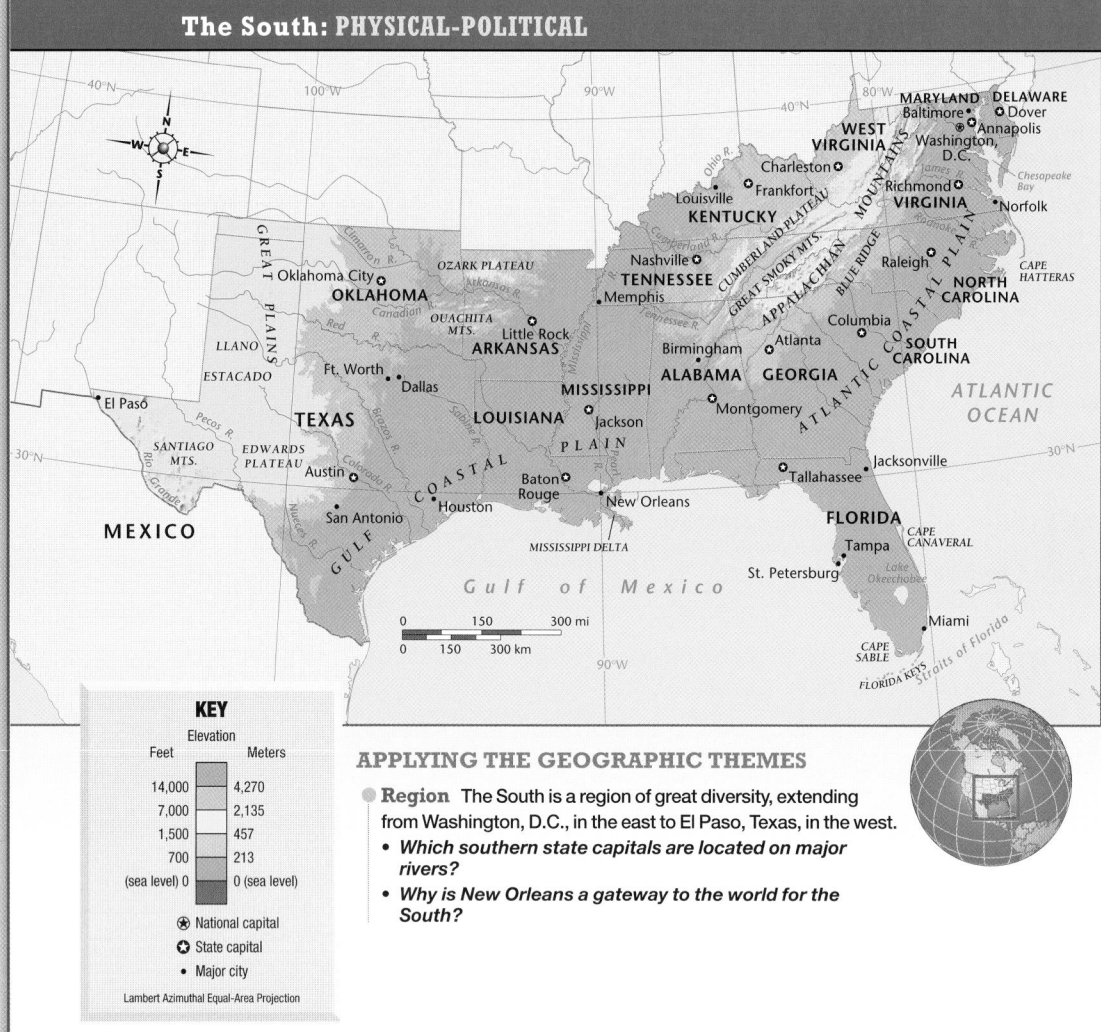

The South: PHYSICAL-POLITICAL

KEY

Elevation

Feet		Meters
14,000		4,270
7,000		2,135
1,500		457
700		213
(sea level) 0		0 (sea level)

⊛ National capital
✪ State capital
• Major city

Lambert Azimuthal Equal-Area Projection

APPLYING THE GEOGRAPHIC THEMES

● **Region** The South is a region of great diversity, extending from Washington, D.C., in the east to El Paso, Texas, in the west.
- *Which southern state capitals are located on major rivers?*
- *Why is New Orleans a gateway to the world for the South?*

The warm, wet climate produces thick, mixed forests of pine and other trees, or marshy stands of mangrove trees. **Mangroves** are tropical trees that grow in swampy ground along coastal areas. Other vegetation regions unique to the South include the marshy inlets of lakes and rivers of Louisiana called **bayous** (BY oos). In Florida, the Everglades—a large area of swampland covered in places with tall grass—provide a refuge for a wide variety of birds and animals.

In general, the farther west one moves within the South, the less the average annual precipitation. Oklahoma and western Texas have a warm,

semiarid climate. Parts of Oklahoma average 30 inches (76 cm) of rain per year; El Paso, Texas, only 8 inches (20 cm). Such a climate supports the temperate grasslands known as prairies.

Linking Climate, History, and Agriculture

The South's wide variety of plant and animal life is due not only to the subtropical climate of most of the region, but also to the rich soils of the wide coastal plains. People have taken advantage

---

Answers to Map Caption

Richmond, Nashville, Jackson, Montgomery, Little Rock, Baton Rouge, and Austin

It is located at the mouth of the Mississippi and has access to the Gulf of Mexico.

of these fertile soils for hundreds of years. Native American groups, such as the Natchez, Creek, and Cherokee, grew maize, melons, squash, beans, tobacco, and other crops. Later, by the mid-1500s, Europeans also began to settle in the South. The first permanent European settlements in the present-day United States were located in the South.

As word spread about the South's rich soils and long growing season, more and more Europeans migrated to the region. Some built huge plantations and used enslaved people from Africa and the West Indies to do the work of raising tobacco, rice, or cotton. Today, farming remains important to the South's economy.

Despite its mostly fertile soil and mild climate, parts of the South have large areas where people live in bleak poverty. For example, a rural area in the Appalachian Mountains, called Appalachia, is one of the poorest areas in the United States. Its rocky soil and steep slopes make it an unproductive site for farming. Little industry has located in the area.

Linking Resources to Industry

The traditional image of the South has been of a rural region, largely dependent on agriculture. But the South has long had a number of important industries, too.

In the 1840s, entrepreneurs built textile mills powered by the fast-moving streams of the Piedmont section of the Carolinas. These mills were built on the fall line. The **fall line** is an imaginary line between the Appalachian Mountains and the Atlantic coastal plain. It is the place where rivers and streams form waterfalls and rapids as they descend from plateau to coastal plain. Many cities sprang up along the waterfalls on the fall line in both the Northeast and the South. Textile mills were built close to farms that grew cotton. Even today, textile mills in the Carolinas produce a variety of fabrics.

The Columbian Exchange

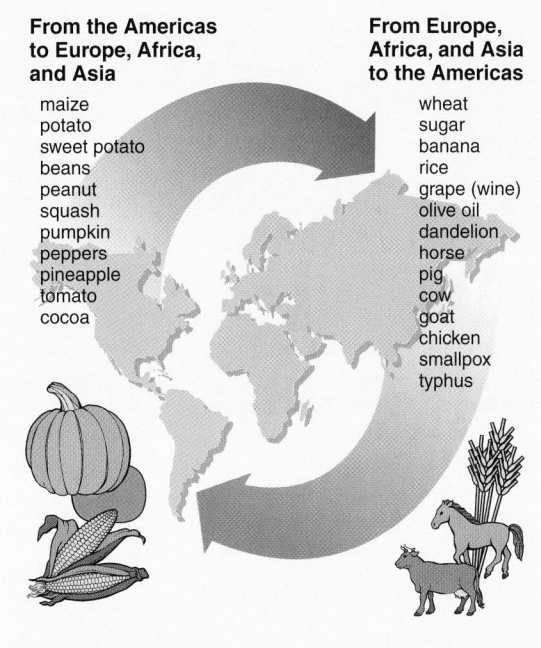

From the Americas to Europe, Africa, and Asia

maize
potato
sweet potato
beans
peanut
squash
pumpkin
peppers
pineapple
tomato
cocoa

From Europe, Africa, and Asia to the Americas

wheat
sugar
banana
rice
grape (wine)
olive oil
dandelion
horse
pig
cow
goat
chicken
smallpox
typhus

DIAGRAM SKILLS

Global Trade Patterns Agricultural products, livestock, and diseases crossed the Atlantic Ocean after Europeans came in contact with the Americas. This interchange has been called the Columbian Exchange, after Christopher Columbus.
• *How did this early global trade pattern affect the regions involved?*

The oil industry in the South began in eastern Texas in 1901. Some of the United States' largest oil reserves are located in this region. By the 1960s and 1970s, that industry was bringing great wealth to the region. A sharp decline in oil prices in the 1980s brought some economic hardship to the oil-producing states of Texas, Oklahoma, and Louisiana, but it also encouraged diversification.

The Gulf Coast has responded to the challenge. A large band of manufacturing borders the Gulf of Mexico. Available raw materials, sources of energy, and access to ocean ports have been key factors in the economic development of the region. The petrochemical industry is a leading source of industrial income. Texas has become

ACTIVITY

Vocabulary

Sunbelt Point out the Key Terms list on page 161. Have students look up *Sunbelt* in the Glossary. Have them name other "belts" that refer to regions. (cotton, wheat, corn, frost, rust, Bible) Ask: **What aspect of the area's geography does the term Sunbelt describe?** (climate)

ACTIVITY

Group Work

Activity: Designing posters

Purpose: Have each group pick a city in the South and work together to design a poster urging businesses to relocate there. The poster should highlight advantages of the South. It might also contain a slogan that emphasizes the unique attractions of the city.

Roles: Head designer, artists, copywriters

Result: Have groups display their posters on the bulletin board.

ACTIVITY

Reteach

Creating a Chart Make a two-column chart on the board with the headings *Opportunities* and *Problems.* Have students complete the chart by describing how the South has benefited from Sunbelt growth and by listing problems associated with growth. (Logical/Mathematical)

Answer to Photo Caption

It offers an easy and direct trade and transportation network.

GEOFacts

Along the Gulf of Mexico, erosion is cutting away at the South. Each year an average of 6 feet (183 cm) disappears from the shoreline, a rate that increases with each major storm along the coast.

one of the leading national producers of synthetic rubber, a petrochemical product.

A Changing Region

Until only recently, people often thought of the South as a slow-moving, slow-changing region. In the last few decades, that image has been shattered. As Joel Garreau, an author and editor, observed of the South, "Change has become [the South's] most identifiable characteristic."

Continued Growth of Industry Not all industry was related to agriculture or the landscape. In the 1950s, both large and small industries began taking root in the South. Some were brand-new, like the space industry that developed in the 1960s in Florida, Alabama, and Texas. But many industries were not new; they simply moved south from northern cities. Within several years, this migration of business became a steady wave.

The South attracted businesses for a number of reasons. Southern industrial plants often were newer, in better condition, and more efficient than those in the Northeast. New factories could be built on land that was cheaper than land in the megalopolis of the Northeast. Because labor unions were much less common in the South, labor costs were usually lower.

The Sunbelt Looking for job opportunities, thousands of people moved to the South. But business growth is not the only reason why the region has thrived. Thanks to the South's mild climate, it has grown enormously as a retirement and tourism center. Beaches along the Gulf of Mexico and the southern Atlantic provide welcome relief from northern winters. In fact, the band of southern states from the Carolinas to southern California became known as the **Sunbelt**. The Sunbelt region actually overlaps two regions—the South and the West.

Houston Highways

Economic Activities
This highway intersection is used every day by drivers traveling to and from Houston, Texas. The interstate highway system has encouraged economic growth in the South.

Movement *How does a highway system benefit economic growth?*

Latin Influence

Migration Immigration accounts for much of the South's diversity. About 12 percent of southern residents are of Hispanic origin. In Miami, about half of the population hails from Cuba. As this storefront window shows, the city has a distinctly Latin flavor.

Movement *How has movement of people within the United States contributed to the diversity of southern population?*

Southern Population

During the 1970s the South's population increased in number more than that of any other region of the country—an approximate increase of 7 million, or about 20 percent. By 1990, three of the largest cities in the nation were located in the South—Houston, Dallas, and San Antonio. By 1995, Texas was second only to California as the most populous state in the United States.

A Varied Population Today, the South has a diverse population. Over half of the nation's African American population lives in the South. The direction of African American migration is away from the industrial Northeast to southern cities. This reverses a century-long trend begun after the Civil War, during which thousands of African Americans migrated to the Northeast from the South in search of jobs.

Another large segment of the southern population is the hundreds of thousands of Hispanics who have moved there from Mexico and other Latin American countries. San Antonio, Texas, is one of the nation's largest cities, and one of the first major cities in the United States to have a Hispanic majority in its population.

Another large Hispanic group lives in southern Florida—the Cubans. Many Cubans have settled in the Miami area since 1960, after the Communist takeover of their homeland. One area of Miami is populated by a Cuban majority. Called Little Havana, it is the part of the city where Cuban restaurants and Spanish-language television and radio stations reflect Cuban heritage.

Many white Southerners have ancestors who came from England, Scotland, or Ireland. In Louisiana, many boast of French ancestry. The French settled the area in Colonial times and have made a lasting imprint on the region's culture. New Orleans, for example, is famous for its French cuisine.

Major Cities The South is home to many important cities. New Orleans is a major trading center near the mouth of the Mississippi River. Miami is the United States gateway to the Caribbean and South America. Atlanta, Georgia, once a major railroad center, is now a major airline hub, and its cable television stations are watched by people around the world.

Houston, Texas, is a large industrial and trading center. Much of the nation's space exploration is managed at the National Aeronautics and Space Administration (NASA), which is located there. Houston is also a center for the oil and banking industries. Fort Worth, about a four-hour drive north from Houston, is the heart of the Texas cattle industry, while Dallas is a business and electronics center.

Answers to
Section 2 Assessment

1. (a) mangrove, p. 162 **(b)** bayou, p. 162 **(c)** fall line, p. 163 **(d)** Sunbelt, p. 164

2. warm temperatures and ample precipitation

3. (a) Textile factories were built along the waterfalls on the fall line to harness the water power. **(b)** Oil reserves brought great wealth to the region until the sharp decline in oil prices in the 1980s. Today the petrochemical industry is a leading source of industrial income.

4. Possible answers: Industrial plants are newer and more efficient; land is cheaper and labor costs are lower; people are attracted to the job opportunities and milder climate.

5. The South's rich soils and long growing season attracted Native Americans and settlers from Europe. Settlers brought enslaved people from Africa and the West Indies to work on their plantations. Today, Miami is the gateway to the Caribbean and South America. Washington, D.C., is home to U.S. leaders and foreign diplomats.

Activity Rubrics Share rubrics with students before they begin.

Attempted The map contains erroneous information, is messy, or is incomplete.

Minimal The map does not indicate important changes to the city.

Adequate The map accurately identifies important changes to the city and is neatly done.

Exemplary The map is very well done and presents an accurate and thorough overview of changes to the city.

Capital City

Urbanization The South's most famous city is Washington, D.C., the nation's capital. The seat of the federal government and home of the Supreme Court, the capital also contains some of the nation's most important museums and monuments. Examine this aerial photograph of Washington, D.C.

Place *How does it differ from many other cities in the nation?*

The city of Washington is not located in any state, but rather in the District of Columbia. This district was carved from the states of Maryland and Virginia when it was chosen as the site for the nation's capital in 1790. Located on the shore of the Potomac River, Washington, D.C., was the first planned city in the nation. Because of its wide avenues, public buildings, and dramatic monuments, many people consider Washington to be one of the most beautiful cities in the world. As the nation's capital, it is home to the nation's leaders and to hundreds of foreign diplomats.

SECTION 2 ASSESSMENT

1. **Key Terms** Define **(a)** mangrove, **(b)** bayou, **(c)** fall line, **(d)** Sunbelt.

2. **Climates** What two climate characteristics have led to dense vegetation in the South?

3. **Natural Resources (a)** What role has water power played in the southern economy? **(b)** How have oil resources affected the economy of this region?

4. **Migration** Why have businesses and people from other countries or parts of the United States migrated to the South?

5. **Critical Thinking** **Drawing Conclusions** How has the geography and history of the South helped to create a diverse population that continues to grow?

Activity

Creating Maps Search the Internet for maps or descriptions of a southern city in the 1700s or 1800s as well as maps or descriptions of the same city today. Based on your research, create a map that shows how the city has changed over time.

RESOURCE DIRECTORY

Teaching Resources

Unit 2, Chapter 7
- Section 2 Quiz, p. 27
- Section 3 Guided Reading and Review, p. 28

Spanish Resources
- Section 2 Quiz, p. 17

Guide to the Essentials (English/Spanish)
- Section Summary, Chapter 7, Section 3

Mental Mapping booklet
- Unit 2 Checklist, p. 19

Technology

Guided Reading Audiotapes (English/Spanish), Chapter 7, Section 3

Section Reading Support Transparencies, Chapter 7, Section 3

World Geography Map and Photo Transparencies
- The United States and Canada: Maps and Photos

Book on CD, Chapter 7

Social Studies Skills Tutor CD-ROM

Companion Web site, www.phschool.com
- Chapter 7 Activities

Answer to Photo Caption

It is not located in any state, and it was the first planned city in the nation.

3 The Midwest

Reading Focus

- How does the climate of the Midwest support agriculture?
- Why has farming become big business?
- How have resources and transportation promoted industry in the Midwest?

Key Terms

humus
growing season
grain elevator
grain exchange

Main Idea Agriculture, manufacturing, and transportation form the backbone of the Midwestern economy.

Environmental Change The alternating patterns of strip cropping help prevent erosion.

What do you think of when you hear the term *Midwest*? The lush, wooded hills of the Ozarks in Missouri? The barren, eroded Badlands of South Dakota? The vast, blue-green Great Lakes? Or the acres of steel mills in the industrialized area around Gary, Indiana?

The Midwest is all of these and more, but a drive along any of the numerous highways crisscrossing the Midwest reveals that farms unite this region. Mile upon mile of fields and pastures stretch as far as the eye can see.

An Agricultural Economy

Most of the Midwest is relatively flat, and its soil is fertile. Long ago, melting glaciers deposited mineral-rich materials there that promote plant growth. In an ongoing soil-building process, the plants and animals that live in the soil die and decay. The dark-colored organic material that results is called **humus.** Humus combines with particles of weathered bedrock to help build more soil.

The Midwestern climate, which has promoted soil building, also favors agriculture. Although winters can be very cold, summers are usually long and hot. Most places receive at least 20 inches (51 cm) of precipitation annually.

Regional Variations Within the broad expanse of the Midwest are variations in climate and soil that affect farming. For example, eastern Ohio gets twice as much precipitation annually as central South Dakota. In southern Kansas, the **growing season**—the average number of days between the last frost of spring and the first frost of fall—is more than 200 days long. Near the Canadian border, the growing season is less than 120 days long.

In the warmer, wetter parts of Illinois, Indiana, and Iowa, corn and soybeans are the major crops. These states are also among the nation's leading producers of livestock, especially hogs. In the drier Great Plains states to the west, farmers are more likely to grow grains such as wheat or oats or sunflowers, which are a source of cooking oil. Along the northern margins of the region in states such as Wisconsin, cooler conditions and poorer soils favor the growth of hay and the raising of dairy cattle.

The Nation's Breadbasket Thanks to favorable natural conditions, Midwestern farms are among the most productive in the world. In

Articles From NATIONAL GEOGRAPHIC

The following article may be used to extend the content of this section.

Chadwick, Douglas, and Jim Brandenburg, photographer. "The American Prairie." *National Geographic*, Vol. 184, No. 4 (Oct. 1993), pp. 90–119.

The American prairie, once covering a ninth of the continent, has been reduced to a mere 10,000 square miles. Conservationists are working to preserve the remaining prairie land.

Objectives

Upon completion of Section 3, students should be able to:

- ◆ describe how climate supports the Midwest's agriculture;
- ◆ identify the reasons farming has become big business;
- ◆ explain how resources and transportation have promoted industry in the Midwest.

 National Geography Standards

The following National Geography Standards are highlighted in this section: 1, 2, 3, 4, 5, 8, 11, 12, 14, 16, 17, 18

 Bellringer

Early land surveys in the Midwest divided land into squares separated by roadways. A township was six miles on each side. How many one-mile-square "sections" would be in one township? (36)

LESSON PLAN

1. Focus Tell students they have just received a package with the words "Made in the Midwest" stamped across it. The package can be any shape or size. Ask: **From what you know of this region, what might you expect to find inside?** Make a list on the board of students' responses.

2. Instruct Write the following headings on the board: *Rainfall, Growing Season, Soil, Temperature.* For each heading, help students give two examples of the variations within the Midwest that create the variety of crops and livestock. (Example: Rich soil in Iowa and Illinois is good for corn and soybeans; poorer soil in Wisconsin is best for hay crops and dairy cattle.)

3. Close/Reteach Write the following statement on the board: *Business and industry in the Midwest are extensions of its agriculture.* Have students volunteer facts that explain or support the statement.

Vocabulary

Growing Season Point out the list of Key Terms on page 167. Have students look up *growing season* in the Glossary. Ask students: **Which region has a longer growing season—the Northeast or the South?** (the South) Then ask: **Why is knowing the length of the growing season important to farmers?** (Farmers need to know the length of the growing season to plan, plant, and harvest their crops.)

Asking Questions

Have students look over the sub-headings within the section The Changing Face of American Farms. Ask each student to use the subheadings as guides to write two questions that they think might be answered in the section. List the students' questions on the chalkboard. As students read the section, have them answer their questions.

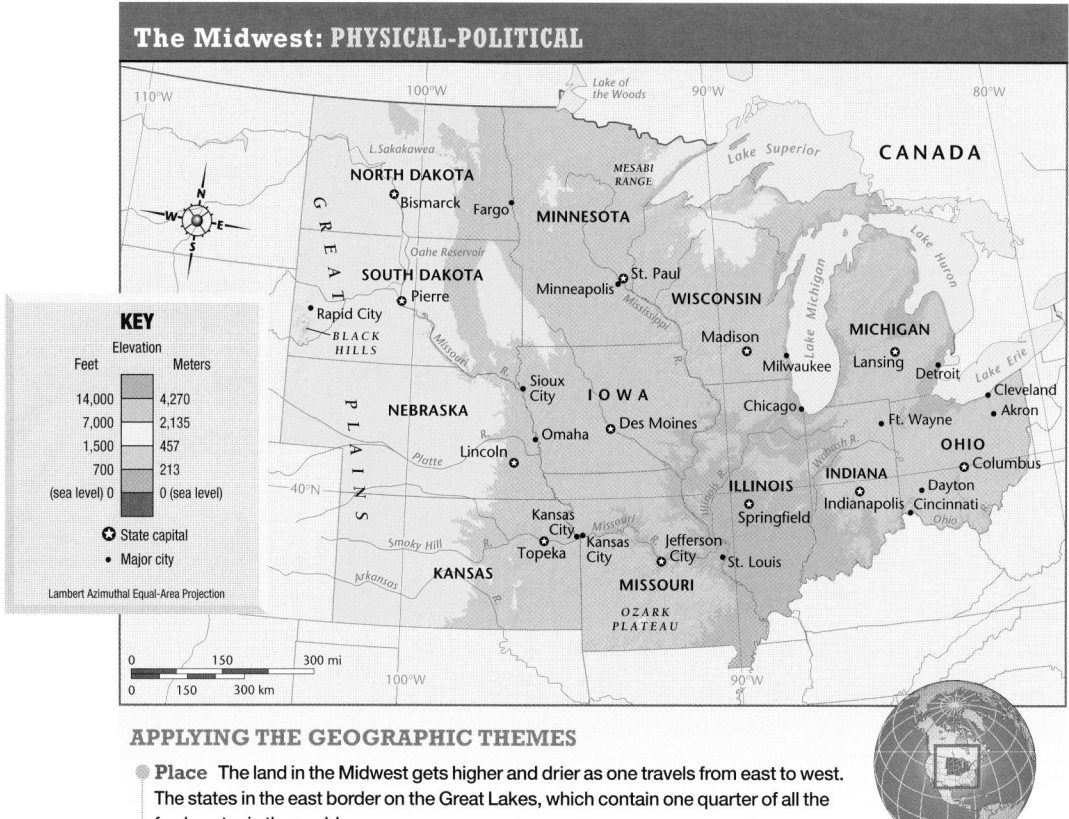

The Midwest: PHYSICAL-POLITICAL

KEY

Elevation

Feet	Meters
14,000	4,270
7,000	2,135
1,500	457
700	213
(sea level) 0	0 (sea level)

✪ State capital
• Major city

Lambert Azimuthal Equal-Area Projection

0   150   300 mi
0   150   300 km

APPLYING THE GEOGRAPHIC THEMES

● **Place** The land in the Midwest gets higher and drier as one travels from east to west. The states in the east border on the Great Lakes, which contain one quarter of all the fresh water in the world.
• *What physical characteristic forms the boundary between Illinois and Missouri?*

recent years, Iowa produced more corn, soybeans, and hogs than any other state in the nation. High wheat output has earned the Midwest the nickname "the nation's breadbasket."

Midwestern productivity is one factor responsible for the average American's being well fed. This remarkable productivity also allows the United States to export sizable amounts of its produce to other countries. Without the agricultural output of the farms of the Midwest region, the United States would be far less affluent.

The Changing Face of American Farms

In years past, American farms were mostly modest family enterprises. Single families usually ran them. People worked long days of hard physical labor. Few such farms remain in America. Today, farming has become big business, involving fewer people and more machinery.

Farming Technology By the 1800s, farmers had the ability to grow huge crops of grain, but had no way to harvest it quickly. In 1834, Cyrus McCormick patented a mechanical reaper, which revolutioned farming. Cyrus McCormick's reaper allowed farmers to harvest vast amounts of wheat in much less time than it took by hand. As more and more farm tasks were mechanized, farmers could produce more crops than ever before and with fewer workers. The number of farms has decreased year after year. Push-and-pull migration factors have played a role in reducing the number of workers on farms. Lower incomes have pushed people off

168 Chapter 7 ▪ Regions of the United States

Teaching Resources
Mental Mapping booklet
• Outline Map 7, p. 27

Technology
World Geography Map and Photo Transparencies
• The United States and Canada: Maps and Photos

Answer to Map Caption

Mississippi River

the farm as higher-paid jobs have attracted them to cities.

Despite the drop in the number of farms, farm size and output have increased dramatically. Large commercial farms use machinery, technology, and research to keep ahead.

Linking Farms to Cities Agriculture dominates the economy, even in many Midwestern towns and cities. Business activities center on dairies or on **grain elevators**—tall buildings equipped with machinery for loading, cleaning, mixing, and storing grain.

Large Midwestern cities, too, are closely linked to the countryside. Some of the tallest office buildings in Minneapolis, Kansas City, and Omaha are homes to companies whose names appear on flour bags and feed sacks. Radio stations broadcast frequent reports from the Chicago Mercantile Exchange and the Chicago Board of Trade.

The Mercantile Exchange is the world's busiest market for eggs, hogs, cattle, and other farm products; the Board of Trade is the largest **grain exchange**—a place where buyers and sellers deal for grain.

Linking Industries to Resources

Partly because of its rich supply of natural resources, the Midwest's cities are also home to much heavy manufacturing. Minnesota leads the states in iron ore production. Sizable coal deposits are found in Indiana and Illinois. Easy

A vast reservoir of groundwater lies below 170,000 square miles (440,300 sq km) of the Great Plains. The Ogallala aquifer, as it is called, supplies most of the water that transforms the drier parts of the Midwest into abundant cropland. Scientists estimate that 25 percent of Ogallala's water will be used up by the year 2020.

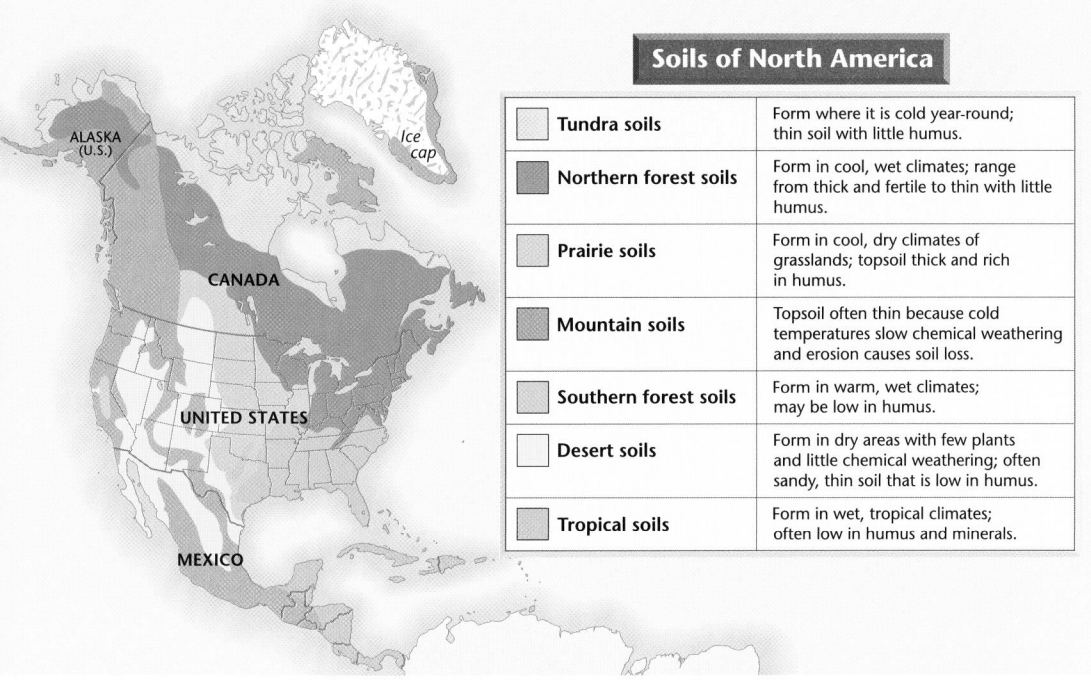

	Soils of North America	
	Tundra soils	Form where it is cold year-round; thin soil with little humus.
	Northern forest soils	Form in cool, wet climates; range from thick and fertile to thin with little humus.
	Prairie soils	Form in cool, dry climates of grasslands; topsoil thick and rich in humus.
	Mountain soils	Topsoil often thin because cold temperatures slow chemical weathering and erosion causes soil loss.
	Southern forest soils	Form in warm, wet climates; may be low in humus.
	Desert soils	Form in dry areas with few plants and little chemical weathering; often sandy, thin soil that is low in humus.
	Tropical soils	Form in wet, tropical climates; often low in humus and minerals.

CHART SKILLS

● **Natural Resources** An area's climate and plant life help to determine what type of soil is formed. Rich soil contributes to the productivity of American farms.
• *In which states do farmers benefit from prairie soils?*

Group Work

Activity: Food processing
Purpose: Ask each student to make a list of foods processed in the Midwest. (cereal, flour, corn syrup, vegetable oils, cake mixes, animal feeds, hot dogs) Have them use grocery store labels or library references to determine where these products are made and label each place on an outline map of the region.

Roles: Assign a leader for each group.

Result: Have groups share their maps with the class and identify major food-processing centers of the region.

Critical Thinking

Cause and Effect Relationships
Use the following questions to help students analyze some of the economics of farming: **How is Midwestern farming changing?** (Fewer farms produce more food.) **What accounts for the increased productivity?** (mechanization; Note that increased use of fertilizers and pesticides, new irrigation techniques, and bioengineered livestock also contribute to increased productivity.) **Why is farming more costly for a farmer today than in the past?** (A farmer today needs a higher initial investment and has greater expenses.) **Is the trend toward larger but fewer farms likely to continue?** (Yes, if improvements in technology continue to make large-scale farming more efficient.)

CUSTOMIZE FOR...

Students Acquiring English/ESL
Making a Collage Have students make and label a collage of foods and products grown or manufactured in the Midwest. Direct students to use old magazines, newspapers, and the Internet as resources. They may also photocopy pictures from books. Display collages in class.

TEST PREPARATION

Have students read the subsection Linking Farms to Cities on this page and complete the following sentence.
The Chicago Board of Trade is the largest _____ exchange.
 A dairy
 B produce
 Ⓒ grain
 D hog and cattle

Answer to Chart Skills

North Dakota, South Dakota, Minnesota, Nebraska, Iowa, Illinois, Wisconsin, Indiana, Missouri, Kansas, Oklahoma, Texas, New Mexico, and California

The Mighty Mississippi

Physical Characteristics
The Mississippi River flows
2,348 miles (3,787 km) from
Minnesota to the Gulf of Mexico. In this photograph you can
see where the Ohio River (right)
empties into the Mississippi.

Movement *Why have rivers
been important to the development of industry?*

access to these minerals spurred the development
of steel mills in northwestern Indiana and in Ohio.
The automobile industry grew up in the Detroit
area in part because of the city's location near
these steel-making centers.

Linking Transportation and Industry

Many Midwestern cities, such as Cleveland, Chicago, Minneapolis, St. Louis, Detroit, and Omaha, are located on the shores of the Great Lakes
or along major rivers. Water transportation aided
the growth of heavy industries, such as the manufacture of automobiles and machinery. Over
400 million tons (363 metric tons) of goods travel
through the Mississippi River system each year.

With the growth of the United States' railway
system, thousands of railroad cars were pulling
into Chicago every year. Freight cars brought millions of bushels of grain and head of livestock
from farms farther west. In Chicago, the grain was
processed and the livestock slaughtered. The meat
and grain were then shipped eastward by railroad.

SECTION 3 ASSESSMENT

1. **Key Terms** Define **(a)** humus, **(b)** growing
season, **(c)** grain elevator, **(d)** grain exchange.

2. **Climates** **(a)** How do variations in climate affect
agricultural production in the Midwest? **(b)** What
are some other geographic factors that affect
agricultural production in the region?

3. **Science and Technology** How has technology
changed farming into a big business?

4. **Economic Activities** Why has manufacturing
thrived in the Midwest?

5. **Critical Thinking** **Analyzing Causes and
Effects** How have natural resources had an
impact on the economy of the Midwest?

Activity

Take It to the NET

Creating a Brochure The United States
Department of Agriculture provides vital information
for American farmers. Research the role of the
Department of Agriculture and create a brochure
highlighting one or more of its key services. Visit the
World Geography section of **www.phschool.com**
for help in completing this activity.

Making Valid Generalizations

A generalization is a rational statement about an entire group based on common properties shared by the group. It requires a leap from what is known to a conclusion about the unknown. For example, after touching just a few hot stoves, a young child is able to generalize that touching any hot stove will be unpleasant. Throughout your life, you will use information to make generalizations about the world around you.

Learn the Skill Use the following steps to learn how to make valid generalizations.

1 *Determine known information.* Study the map below and the Regional Atlas maps of the United States and Canada. They will provide you with information that you can use to make generalizations. **(a)** *Which two states have the largest areas producing more than 150,000 harvested acres of wheat?* **(b)** *Describe the climate, physical characteristics, and other geographic conditions found in these two states.*

2 *Find similarities, relationships, or patterns.* In order to make a generalization, we need to find common elements or links among the different examples. *What geographic characteristics do the two wheat-producing states share in common?*

3 *Make general statements based on the similarities.* Use the similarities that you have found to make generalizations about the conditions that favor wheat production. **(a)** *What kind of terrain is*

best for growing wheat? **(b)** *What climate favors wheat production?* **(c)** *Does a wheat-farming region have many rivers?* **(d)** *What natural vegetation is most common in a wheat-farming region?*

4 *Check for faulty reasoning.* One of the four questions that you just answered will lead you to an invalid generalization. Generalizations need to be based on sufficient information. Here, for example, the best generalization would be based on data from other countries besides the United States. Generalizations also need to be based on sound reasoning. **(a)** *Can a region be unsuitable for growing wheat simply because it has many rivers? Explain.* **(b)** *Which generalization that you made in the previous step is an invalid generalization?*

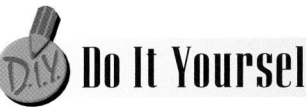

Practice the Skill Using reference works from a library or the Internet, make an economic activities map of your state. Gather other geographic data useful for making generalizations. Follow the steps above to make valid generalizations.

Apply the Skill See Chapter 7 Review and Assessment.

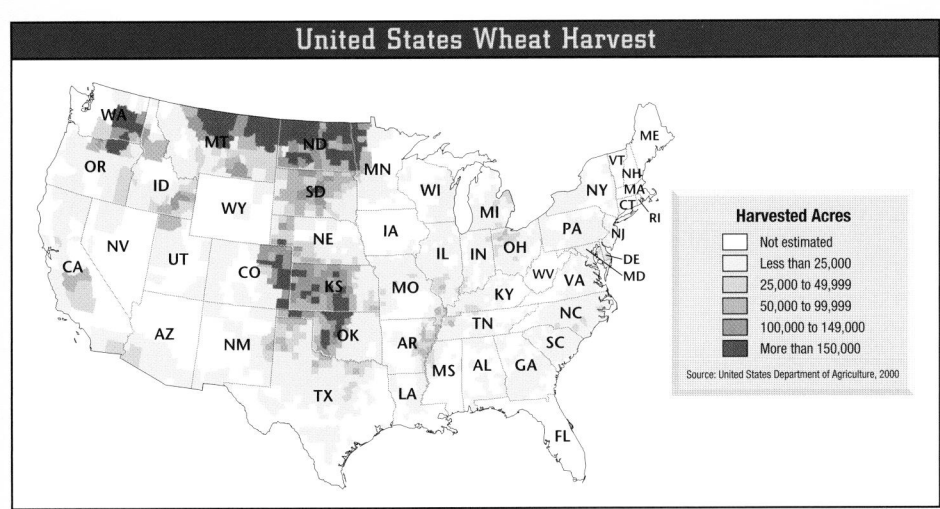

United States Wheat Harvest

Harvested Acres
- Not estimated
- Less than 25,000
- 25,000 to 49,999
- 50,000 to 99,999
- 100,000 to 149,000
- More than 150,000

Source: United States Department of Agriculture, 2000

Objectives

Upon completion of Section 4, students should be able to:

◆ explain how the abundance or scarcity of water resources affects natural vegetation in the West;

◆ list the major natural resources that have influenced the economy in the Western United States;

◆ describe how geography and distance have affected where people live and work in the West.

National Geography Standards

The following National Geography Standards are highlighted in this section: 1, 2, 3, 4, 8, 9, 11, 12, 15, 16, 17, 18

Bellringer

Refer students to the ecosystem map on page 133 and note that the region around southern California supports only chaparral or desert scrub. Then point out that it is also one of the most productive farming areas of the world. Ask students: **How can this be true?** (irrigation systems)

LESSON PLAN

1. Focus Ask students to locate the 100th meridian on the map on page 131. Tell students that this line serves as a rough boundary between wet and dry America. Much of the United States west of this line receives less than 20 inches (51 cm) of rainfall yearly. Despite this, many of the nation's largest cities and most productive farmlands are located here.

2. Instruct Write the following list on the board: *Mountains, Deserts, Volcanoes, Canyons, Plains, Glaciers, Rivers, Forests,* and *Ocean Coasts.* Work with the students to give at least one example of each type of landform found in the West.

3. Close/Reteach Ask students to make a regional score card comparing the West to other U.S. regions. Categories may include natural resources, economic activities, urbanization, cultural diversity, and scenic beauty.

4 The West

Reading Focus

• How does the abundance or scarcity of water resources affect natural vegetation in the West?

• What major natural resources have influenced economic activity in the western United States?

• How have geography and distance affected where people live and work in the region?

Key Terms

tundra

aqueduct

 Main Idea The availability and distribution of natural resources affect where people live and work in the West.

Natural Resources Much of the West's water comes from mountain streams.

A breathtaking natural landscape—this is the most memorable feature of much of the West. Towering snow-capped peaks rise throughout the Rocky Mountains. Rivers have carved spectacular canyons. Broad plains sweep on for hundreds of miles. Massive glaciers loom over icy Alaskan waters, while smoking volcanoes frequently spill red-hot lava over the Hawaiian land. The landscape of the West is varied and magnificent, but the physical characteristic that most affects the region is water.

Available Water

The abundance or scarcity of water is the major factor shaping the West's natural vegetation, economic activity, and population density. Looking again at the climate map on page 131, you will notice that most of the West has a semiarid or arid climate. San Diego, California, averages 9 inches (23 cm) of rain per year; Reno, Nevada, gets only 7 inches (18 cm). In dry areas such as these, the natural vegetation consists of short grasses, hardy shrubs, sagebrush, and cactus.

In contrast, other areas of the West generally receive adequate rainfall and contain rich deciduous and coniferous forests at lower elevations. In Seattle, Washington, for example, rainfall averages 39 inches (99 cm) per year. In the costal region of northern California, forests of giant redwood trees thrive.

Hawaii and Alaska, the nation's two remote states, offer another contrast. Much of Hawaii has a wet tropical climate and dense tropical rain forest vegetation. A world apart is northern Alaska's **tundra**—a dry, treeless plain that sprouts grasses and mosses only in summer, when the top layer of soil thaws.

Natural Resources and the Economy

Beneath the jagged peaks of the Rocky Mountains and the Sierra Nevada lies an immense storehouse of minerals—gold, silver, uranium, and other metals. When gold and silver deposits were discovered in the mid-1800s, fortune-seeking prospectors and settlers swarmed into the area. Few individuals struck it rich in these gold rushes. Most of the region's wealth was deep underground, out of reach of the average prospector. More successful were the huge mining companies that had the equipment

---

RESOURCE DIRECTORY

Teaching Resources

Creative Teaching Activities
• Regions of the United States, p. 9

Unit 2, Chapter 7
• Section 4 Guided Reading and Review, p. 30
• Map/Graph Skills, p. 34

Guide to the Essentials (English/Spanish)
• Section Summary, Chapter 7, Section 4

Mental Mapping booklet
• Unit 2 Checklist, p. 19

Social Studies Skills Handbook
• Checking Consistency of Ideas, p. 44

Technology

Guided Reading Audiotapes (English/Spanish),
Chapter 7, Section 4

Section Reading Support Transparencies,
Chapter 7, Section 4

World Geography Map and Photo Transparencies
• The United States and Canada: Maps and Photos

Book on CD, Chapter 7

Social Studies Skills Tutor CD-ROM

Companion Web site, www.phschool.com
• Chapter 7 Activities

The West: PHYSICAL-POLITICAL

KEY

Feet	Elevation	Meters
14,000		4,270
7,000		2,135
1,500		457
700		213
(sea level) 0		0 (sea level)

◉ State capital
• Major city
▲ Mountain
△ Volcano
~ Dam

Lambert Azimuthal Equal-Area Projection

APPLYING THE GEOGRAPHIC THEMES

● **Region** Mountains dominate the landscape of the West. Great distances separate Alaska and Hawaii from the 48 other states.
• *Why would you expect the population density to be greater along the West Coast?*

and resources to reach deep into the earth for not only gold and silver, but minerals such as copper and tin, as well.

Still, rumors of great strikes and dreams of wealth kept drawing people into the region. Along with the prospectors came enterprising people who set up business to provide goods and services to the miners. The population of the West grew rapidly.

Deeper still within their rugged surface, Western lands also contain valuable deposits of natural gas and oil. The discovery of a major oil field near Prudhoe Bay, Alaska, in the 1960s led to the transformation of that state's economy. The Trans-Alaska Pipeline carries crude oil, which is oil that has not been processed, across the tundra south to Alaska's Prince William Sound.

The natural resources of the West also support two other important economic activities—forestry and commercial fishing. Nearly half of the nation's construction lumber is harvested from the forests of the Pacific Northwest. The billions of tons of fish caught in the waters off Alaska, Hawaii, and other Pacific Coast states bring in billions of dollars annually from throughout the world.

Previewing

Before reading Section 4, read the headings for the section aloud with the class. Ask: **Judging from the headings, what do you think were two of the most pressing difficulties of settling in the West?** (the lack of water and the great distances)

Group Work

Activity: Investigating environmental issues

Purpose: Have each group research an environmental issue facing the West. (lumbering in the Pacific Northwest, smog in Los Angeles, offshore oil drilling, overcrowding at national parks, uranium mining)

Roles: Researchers and presenters

Result: Each group presents a panel discussion on its environmental issue.

Geography on Video

Yellowstone Yellowstone is located in the Northwest and is considered the "crown jewel" of our national parks. The film *Yellowstone's Burning Question* (NOVA series, Vestron Video, 1989) explains the formation of the park from within the earth and shows several aspects of its beauty. The film also dramatically portrays the impact of the summer fires of 1988 that affected over one million acres of the park.

Articles From NATIONAL GEOGRAPHIC

The following article may be used to extend the content in this section.

Mitchell, John G., and Peter Essick, photographer. "Wilderness: America's Lands Apart." *National Geographic*, Vol. 194, No. 5 (Nov. 1998), pp. 2–33.

In 1964, 54 acres of undeveloped land in the United States became protected under law from human influence. Today, this wilderness makes up more than 100 million acres.

TEST PREPARATION

Have students read the last two paragraphs in the section above and answer the following question.

Which of the following is *not* a natural resource of Alaska?

A Oil
B Forestry
Ⓒ Produce
D Fish

Answer to Map Caption

Possible answer: The terrain is less rugged, and the climate is milder.

Aqueduct Point out the list of Key Terms on page 172. Ask students to guess the meaning of *aqueduct* from its Latin roots: *aqua* (water) and *duct* (to carry or lead). Have students verify its meaning in a dictionary.

BACKGROUND

Physical World

National Parks The spectacular natural landscape of the West is preserved in 34 of the nation's parks, including the oldest (Yellowstone) and one of the newest (Great Basin, Nevada). The first international park, Waterton-Glacier International Peace Park, was established in 1932 on the Alberta-Montana border.

ACTIVITY

Reteach

Creating Postcards Have students imagine that they are traveling in the West. Ask them to use the text, maps, and photographs in Section 4 to design and draw a series of postcards. Ask students to write one or two sentences on the back of each postcard highlighting what they have seen on their trip. (Visual/Spatial)

Answer to Photo Caption

Possible answers: discovery of natural resources, growth of new industries, availability of transportation to a new region

174 Chapter 7

Change Over Time

Environmental Change

Population Growth In the 1850s (PAST), few houses and the first telegraph line in California dotted Telegraph Hill in San Francisco—a common stop for gold seekers and sea travelers. Today, the area is considered valuable real estate and is crowded with residences (PRESENT), many of whose inhabitants work in the nearby financial district.

Place *What are some processes that cause places to grow?*

PRESENT

PAST

The Growth of Western Cities

The completion of the first transcontinental railroad in 1869 spurred the growth of towns and cities along the ribbon of silvery track. In the 1880s, the railroads lowered the fare between the Midwest and Los Angeles to only one dollar. Thousands jumped at the opportunity to move out West. Because of the harsh landscape and climate, relatively few people settled in the region's countryside. Even today, a higher percentage of the West's population prefer to live in cities.

Anchoring the southwest corner of the continental United States is the nation's second-largest city, Los Angeles, California. It began as a cattle town, providing beef for prospectors in San Francisco during the Gold Rush. By the 1920s, the city was attracting new residents with the development of the military and civil aircraft industry and the motion picture industry.

To support its growing population, Los Angeles has to obtain huge amounts of water via **aqueducts**—large pipes that carry water over long distances. The California Aqueduct, completed in 1973, brings water from California's Sacramento Valley, 685 miles (1,102 km) farther north. Severe droughts, such as the one that lasted from 1987 to 1992, have prompted increased spending for recycling and conservation.

Conquering Western Distances

The two outlying states of the western region, Alaska and Hawaii, face challenges in surmounting distances.

Alaska Alaska is the largest state, but it is one of the least populated. Fewer than 630,000 people live in an area that is more than three times larger than all of the Northeast. Very few roads pass

GL BAL CONNECTIONS

Natural Resources
States and countries often make agreements to share natural resources. The Colorado River Compact divides the waters of the Colorado River between Colorado, New Mexico, Utah, Wyoming, California, Nevada, and Arizona. In the Mexican Water Treaty (1944), the United States agreed to deliver 1.5 million acre-feet of Colorado River water to Mexico annually.

RESOURCE DIRECTORY

Teaching Resources
Unit 2, Chapter 7
• Section 4 Quiz, p. 31
• Reviewing Main Ideas, p. 32
• Test Forms A and B, pp. 35–40
Spanish Resources
• Section 4 Quiz, p. 19
Guide to the Essentials (English/Spanish)
• Chapter 7 Test
Mental Mapping booklet
• Chapter 7 Map Test, p. 29
Simulations, Games, and Lab Activities
• Place Location Review Games, pp. 58–63

Social Studies Skills Handbook
• Study and Research Skills, pp. 94–108

Prentice Hall Assessment System
Alternative Assessment booklet
• Oral Presentation Evaluation Form, p. 21

Technology
ExamView Test Bank CD-ROM, Chapter 7 Test
Companion Web site, www.phschool.com
• Chapter 7 Self-Test

Alaskan Pipeline

Natural Resources
The Trans-Alaska Pipeline snakes across the fragile Arctic tundra. Millions of barrels of oil pass through the pipeline system each year. The pipes are elevated in order to prevent warm oil from thawing the permafrost.
Movement Why do you think oil is sent through the pipeline, instead of being trucked across Alaska?

through the rugged mountains, the Alaska Range and the Brooks Range, which cover much of Alaska. Juneau, the state capital, can be reached only by boat or airplane. Even Anchorage, a city with more than 250,000 residents, has only two roads leading out of town.

Hawaii The state of Hawaii is made up of eight main islands and more than 100 smaller islands in the central Pacific Ocean. The islands of Hawaii are located more than 2,000 miles (3,218 km) from the United States mainland. It was Hawaii's distant location, however, that first drew the attention of the United States government.

In the late nineteenth century, when the United States established trading relationships with China and Japan, it sought to control islands that it could use as refueling stations for its naval vessels. In 1898, the United States annexed Hawaii, and in 1959 Hawaii became the 50th state.

Today, technological improvements have shortened the distance between Hawaii and the rest of the nation. Jet travel has made Hawaii popular with tourists from North America and Asia. With the development of communications satellites and the Internet, Hawaiians no longer have to rely on radios for news from the mainland and around the world.

SECTION 4 ASSESSMENT

1. **Key Terms** Define **(a)** tundra, **(b)** aqueduct.

2. **Ecosystems** How does climate affect the variety and distribution of vegetation in the West?

3. **Natural Resources** What are three major industries in the West that rely most directly on natural resources?

4. **Patterns of Settlement** What geographic features have influenced where people live in the West?

5. **Critical Thinking Predicting Consequences** What might be the consequences of continued population growth in the West?

Activity

USING THE REGIONAL ATLAS

Creating a Dialogue Review the Regional Atlas for the United States and Canada and this section. Then, create a dialogue between two people who meet at a Chamber of Commerce convention and discuss why they think the population of the West is growing faster than the population of the Northeast.

CUSTOMIZE FOR...

Honors/PreAP
Making an Illustrated Map Have students research the natural resources and physical features of Hawaii. Have them trace a large map of Hawaii and then illustrate it with drawings or pictures from magazines of resources, products, or physical features representative of the state.

REVIEW AND ASSESSMENT
pp. 176–177

Creating a Chapter Summary
As a reteaching opportunity, pair a more able student with a less able student to complete this chapter summary.

Students may add the following entries:
Northeast—*Physical:* Thin, rocky soil, Steep hills *Resources:* Excellent harbors *Economic:* Manufacturing
South—*Physical:* Mild climate, Ample precipitation *Resources:* Rich soil, Oil reserves *Economic:* Petrochemicals
Midwest—*Physical:* Variations in climate *Resources:* Iron ore, Coal *Economic:* Manufacturing
West—*Physical:* Semiarid or arid climate, Jagged peaks *Resources:* Natural gas and oil, Forests *Economic:* Forestry, Fishing

Reviewing Key Terms
1–8. Students' puzzles should show a clear understanding of each term.

Understanding Key Ideas
9. The region's rocky and jagged coast creates many natural harbors. Its location along the Atlantic coast gave it access to shipping lanes.
10. Possible answers: Push factors included famine, political and economic hardships in Europe. Pull factors included jobs and freedom.
11. The region's growing industries have attracted people in search of jobs. Also, the mild climate has attracted retirees and tourists.
12. The population includes people of many ethnic groups, including Hispanic Americans and African Americans.
13. Long ago, glaciers deposited mineral-rich materials there that promote plant growth.
14. Mineral-rich soil, iron ore, and coal deposits provide industry with the raw materials it needs. Major rivers and bodies of water provided transportation for manufactured goods.
15. The government can fund projects to build aqueducts and reservoirs.

CHAPTER 7 REVIEW AND ASSESSMENT

Creating a Chapter Summary

Copy this chart on a sheet of paper. Add information about the regions of the United States. Some entries have been filled in to help you get started.

REGION	PHYSICAL CHARACTERISTICS	NATURAL RESOURCES	ECONOMIC ACTIVITIES
NORTHEAST	• •	• Swift rivers •	•
SOUTH	• •	• •	• Farming •
MIDWEST	• Flat terrain •	• •	• Farming •
WEST	• •	• Minerals •	• Mining •

Take It to the NET
Chapter Self-Test For practice test questions for Chapter 7, go to the World Geography section of **www.phschool.com**.

Reviewing Key Terms

Use the key terms listed below to create a crossword puzzle. Exchange puzzles with a classmate. Complete the puzzles and then check each other's answers.

1. megalopolis
2. mangrove
3. bayou
4. Sunbelt
5. humus
6. growing season
7. grain elevator
8. aqueduct

Understanding Key Ideas

9. Global Trade Patterns How did geographic characteristics of the Northeast help people of the region to trade with other regions of the world?

10. Migration What were some of the push-and-pull factors that stimulated immigration to the Northeast?

11. Patterns of Settlement Why has the Sunbelt experienced growing population over the past few decades?

12. Cultures Why might the South be described as a culturally diverse region?

13. Physical Processes How did physical processes of the past add minerals and nutrients to the soil of the Midwest?

14. Natural Resources What natural resources encouraged the development of industry in parts of the Midwest?

15. Government and Citizenship How can government projects help provide adequate water supplies to people of the West?

Critical Thinking and Writing

16. Making Comparisons Explain how agriculture in the South was different from agriculture in the Northeast.

17. Synthesizing Information Is the Sunbelt a functional, formal, or perceptual region? Explain.

18. Analyzing Causes and Effects Why did Chicago emerge as a leading Midwestern city?

19. Recognizing Points of View Describe two different points of view about drilling more oil wells in Alaska.

Critical Thinking and Writing
16. The climates and soil are different. In the Northeast, the land is rocky and uneven and the climate is colder. In the South, the climate is more mild and the soil more fertile, making it easier to grow commercial crops.
17. Perceptual—its boundaries depend on one's point of view. For example, some people consider Maryland a northern state.
18. Chicago is located near water transportation. Later, the city became a major railroad hub, where freight cars brought grain and livestock to be processed. These products were then shipped to the East for sale.
19. Possible answers: One point of view is that because oil is in short supply, the United States should tap what resources it has. The other point of view is that because oil drilling spoils the natural environment and causes pollution, no more wells should be drilled in Alaska.

Applying Skills

Making Valid Generalizations Refer to the Skills for Life lesson on page 171, the map of the Midwest on page 168, and the map of the West on page 173 to answer these questions:

20. Which region of the United States is best suited to wheat production?

21. How important are major river systems to wheat farms? Explain.

Reading a Diagram Study the diagram below, and answer the following questions:

22. Name three food crops that spread from the Americas to Europe, Africa, and Asia.

23. Does the diagram illustrate cultural convergence, cultural divergence, or both? Explain.

The Columbian Exchange

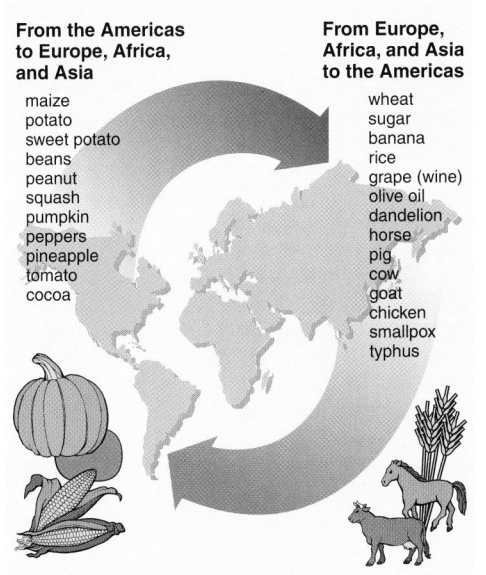

From the Americas to Europe, Africa, and Asia	From Europe, Africa, and Asia to the Americas
maize	wheat
potato	sugar
sweet potato	banana
beans	rice
peanut	grape (wine)
squash	olive oil
pumpkin	dandelion
peppers	horse
pineapple	pig
tomato	cow
cocoa	goat
	chicken
	smallpox
	typhus

Test Preparation

Read the question below and choose the best answer.

24. What is one reason why many businesses moved to the Sunbelt?

   A Railways are plentiful in the North.

   B Land was cheap in parts of the South.

   C Labor costs were high in the West.

   D The Midwest has rich soil for farming.

Activities

USING THE REGIONAL ATLAS

Review this chapter and the Regional Atlas for the United States and Canada. Create a table that describes the climate conditions in each region of the United States and the effects of those climate conditions. Include effects related to ecosystems, economic activities, migration, and other topics.

MENTAL MAPPING

Review a map of the United States. On a separate sheet of paper, draw a sketch map of the United States from memory. Label the following places on your map:

• Northeast	• Washington, D.C.	• Phoenix
• South	• Atlanta	• Los Angeles
• Midwest	• Dallas	• San Francisco
• West	• Chicago	• Seattle
• Boston	• Minneapolis	
• New York	• St. Louis	

Take It to the NET

Analyzing Causes and Effects Do research on the Internet to learn about the causes and effects of regulations on water use and conservation in your local community or state. Display your findings in some kind of a chart or other graphic organizer. Visit the World Geography section of **www.phschool.com** for help in completing this activity.

Applying Skills
20. Midwest

21. Major river systems are not very important to wheat farms, since rivers are physical characteristics that do not greatly influence vegetation or climate.

22. Possible answers: maize, potato, sweet potato, beans, peanut, squash, pumpkin, pineapple, tomato, cocoa

23. The diagram illustrates convergence because Europeans and Native Americans each adapted and used goods from other continents, essentially taking the goods and making them their own. Examples include tomato sauce in Italy and wineries in the United States.

Test Preparation
24. B

Activities

Using the Regional Atlas
Students' work should provide accurate descriptions of the climate conditions and their effects, and their tables should be clear and easy to read.

Mental Mapping
Review students' maps for relative and absolute location. Refer to the Regions map of the United States on page 156.

Take It to the Net
Students' work should reflect sound research on the causes and effects of water use regulations and conservation within the local community or the state. Information should be organized in a chart or other type of graphic organizer.

MENTAL MAPPING

Games for Review See pages 58–63 of the Simulations, Games, and Lab Activities booklet for games to review place names in preparation for the Chapter 7 Map Test.

Chapter Map Test Students should use the completed Chapter 7 outline map and the Unit 2 Checklist in their Atlas Portfolios to prepare for the Chapter 7 Map Test. Point out to students that the test will cover only Parts I and III of the Unit 2 Checklist.

Alternative Assessment

Final Evaluation
Oral Presentation Use the Oral Presentation Evaluation Form on page 21 of the Alternative Assessment booklet in the Prentice Hall Assessment System to evaluate students' oral presentations. Either teachers or students can complete the forms to indicate which level of work was achieved for each of the criteria. The evaluation should include specific examples and comments.

Objectives

Upon completion of this feature, students should be able to:

◆ explain what an invasive species is and give examples of invasive species in the United States;

◆ describe the problems caused by kudzu in the American South;

◆ explain how zebra mussels arrived in the United States and state the threats they pose.

National Geography Standards

The following National Geography Standards are highlighted in this feature: 1, 4, 8, 14, 15, 18

Bellringer

Ask students to define *species*. Ask students to list as many species of plants and animals as they can that live in their region. Discuss what might happen to the species if it was moved to a different region.

LESSON PLAN

1. Focus Write the word *invasive* on the board. Discuss the meaning, and have students offer theories to explain why some species are called *invasive*.

2. Instruct Draw a Venn diagram on the board. Label one circle *kudzu* and the other circle *zebra mussels*. Where the circles overlap, have students list common problems caused by the two species. Tell students to list the differences between the two species in the parts that do not overlap. Ask students which species is causing the most serious problem.

Answer to Map Caption

Northeast, Midwest, and South

Answer to Photo Caption

It will eventually kill them by blocking out the sunlight.

178 Chapter 7

People and Geography

Invasive Species and the United States

The Issue

An invasive species is a nonnative plant, animal, or microscopic organism whose introduction to a region threatens to harm people, the economy, or the environment. Human activities are the primary means of invasive species introductions. Nonnative, or alien, species can multiply rapidly if they have no natural enemies in their new environment. As a result, invasive species threaten nearly half of the plants and animals that are listed by the United States government as threatened or endangered species. Economic damage and control efforts cost the nation more than $100 billion every year.

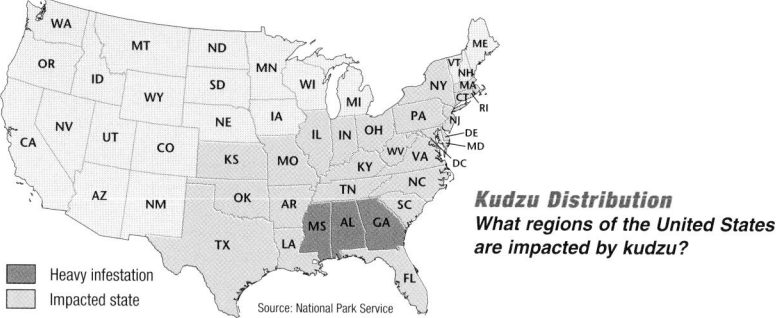

Kudzu Distribution
What regions of the United States are impacted by kudzu?

Heavy infestation
Impacted state

Source: National Park Service

Environmental Threat
How will kudzu probably affect the native plants and trees in this photograph?

Kudzu

Kudzu is a vine that is native to Japan and China. In the early 1900s, farmers in the American South planted the vine to control erosion and to provide feed for animals. However, a problem quickly emerged. Lacking its natural predators, kudzu grows too well. The vines climb over native plants and trees and eventually kill them by blocking out the sunlight. Kudzu also climbs on utility poles, causing electrical short circuits. It can hide open wells and other hazards in the landscape. Control efforts, including burning and the use of herbicides, have been largely unsuccessful. Today, nearly 7 million acres of the Southeast is infested with kudzu. Recently, government researchers have discovered a common fungus that kills kudzu. They are hopeful that this new weapon will win the war against a plant that some call "the vine that ate the South."

RESOURCE DIRECTORY

Teaching Resources
People and Geography
• Global Interdependence, pp. 8–13

Technology
World Geography Map and Photo Transparencies
• The United States and Canada: Political

Zebra Mussels

The zebra mussel is a tiny shelled mollusk native to Eastern Europe. In the 1700s and 1800s, the mussels spread across the continent by attaching themselves to canal boats. The mussels reached the Great Lakes of North America in the 1980s—probably when transoceanic ships discharged ballast water containing the mussels. Since then, they have spread to rivers and lakes in more than a dozen states. Young mussels can swim. Older mussels attach themselves to the hulls of boats and may be moved overland by boats carried on trailers.

Zebra mussels pose significant problems. They interrupt the food chain by eating huge amounts of organisms in the water, thus starving other species. Additionally, the mussels attach themselves to water-intake pipes in layers up to 8 inches (20 cm) thick. As a result, they restrict the flow of water to cities, factories, power plants, and irrigation canals.

There are various ways of removing mussels. Chlorine treatments can be used, but the chemical endangers people and native wildlife. Mussels can be dislodged by spraying them with hot water or by scraping them away, but these methods are costly. Loud noises, electrical shocks, ultraviolet light, and biological predators have also shown some success. In 1999, the United States federal government formed the Invasive Species Council to find new ways to limit these and other invasive species.

Economic Threat
Why does this worker need to remove zebra mussels from the water-intake pipe?

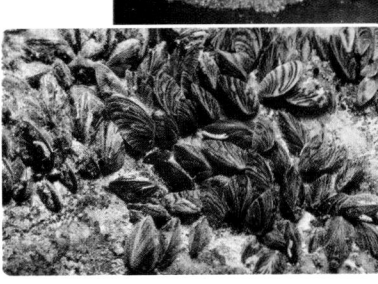

Zebra Mussel Distribution
How have zebra mussels migrated from the Great Lakes to other parts of North America?

Source: U.S. Geological Survey

☐ Infested state

ASSESSMENT: Solving Problems

1. **Identify the Problem** Why are invasive species sometimes a problem?

2. **Gather Information (a)** How are species introduced into new environments? **(b)** How are zebra mussels spreading in the United States?

3. **Identify Options (a)** What do you think that governments can do to reduce the spread of nonnative species? **(b)** What methods are used to control zebra mussels?

4. **Choose a Solution** Why is chlorine treatment usually not chosen as a way to control zebra mussels?

5. **Plan for the Future** Do research to learn about another invasive species. List options, recommend a solution, and explain your reasoning.

CUSTOMIZE FOR...

Gifted and Talented

Creating a Pamphlet Have students find out what invasive plants and animals are most common in your region. Have them create a pamphlet that illustrates the species and explains the threats they pose. Post pamphlets on the class bulletin board where students can examine them.

---

3. Close/Reteach Discuss the difficulties of removing invasive species from an area. Have students use information that they have gathered about kudzu and zebra mussels to help them participate in the discussion.

ACTIVITY

Reteach

Making a Chart Ask students to make a chart that lists information about kudzu and zebra mussels. Headings might include *Native Country, Description, Problems,* and *Control Measures.* (Visual/Spatial)

Answers to Assessment

1. Invasive species can kill off native species, interrupt the food chain, and disrupt the infrastructure of a city or town.

2. (a) usually by human activities **(b)** Young mussels can swim. Older mussels spread to rivers and lakes by attaching themselves to recreational boats that are transported on trailers.

3. (a) Possible answer: They can more carefully monitor plants and animals that are brought to the United States. **(b)** spraying them with hot water; using loud noises, electrical shocks, ultraviolet light, and biological predators

4. Chlorine endangers people and native wildlife.

5. The United States federal government formed the Invasive Species Council to study methods of controlling invasive species.

Answer to Photo Caption

The mussels attach themselves to the inside of water intake pipes and restrict the flow of water.

Answer to Map Caption

The mussels attach themselves to recreational boats and are carried from place to place by trailer.

Resource Manager

Chapter-Level Resources	CORE INSTRUCTION	READING/SKILLS
	Teaching Resources 📖 **Unit 2**/Ch. 8 • Reviewing Main Ideas, p. 47 📖 **Mental Mapping booklet** • Unit 2 Checklist, p. 19 📖 **Simulations, Games, and Lab Activities** • Place Location Review Games, pp. 58–63 📖 **Creative Teaching Activities** • Searching for the Northwest Passage, p. 10 💿 **TeacherExpress™ CD-ROM**, Ch. 8 💻 **Companion Web site,** **www.phschool.com** • eTeach	**Teaching Resources** 📖 **Unit 2**/Ch. 8 • Map/Graph Skills, p. 49 📖 **Social Studies Skills Handbook** • Identifying the Main Idea, p. 41 💿 **Book on CD,** Ch. 8 💿 **Social Studies Skills Tutor CD-ROM**
1 Regions of Canada 1. List the main economic activities in the Atlantic Provinces. 2. Explain why the Great Lakes–St. Lawrence Provinces have become Canada's heartland. 3. Describe economic activities and patterns of settlement in the Prairie Provinces and British Columbia. 4. Explain how climate and location have affected the development of the northern territories.	**Teaching Resources** 📖 **Unit 2**/Ch. 8 • Guided Reading and Review, p. 41 💿 **Prentice Hall Presentation Pro CD-ROM**, Ch. 8, Sec. 1	**Teaching Resources** 📖 **Guide to the Essentials (English/Spanish)** • Section Summary, Ch. 8, Sec. 1 📖 **Mental Mapping booklet** • Outline Map 8, p. 30 📖 **Social Studies Skills Handbook** • Elevation on a Map, p. 20 📼 **Guided Reading Audiotapes (English/Spanish)**, Ch. 8, Sec. 1 📄 **Section Reading Support Transparencies**, Ch. 8, Sec. 1
2 The Search for a National Identity 1. Identify the historical roots of Canada's major culture groups. 2. Explain why Quebec is the scene of conflict between two cultures. 3. Discuss how the multicultural nature of Canada's population represents its policy of welcoming diversity while promoting unity.	**Teaching Resources** 📖 **Unit 2**/Ch. 8 • Guided Reading and Review, p. 43 💿 **Prentice Hall Presentation Pro CD-ROM**, Ch. 8, Sec. 2	**Teaching Resources** 📖 **Guide to the Essentials (English/Spanish)** • Section Summary, Ch. 8, Sec. 2 📼 **Guided Reading Audiotapes (English/Spanish)**, Ch. 8, Sec. 2 📄 **Section Reading Support Transparencies**, Ch. 8, Sec. 2
3 Canada Today 1. Identify the challenges to future development that Canada faces today. 2. Describe Canada's relationship with the United States. 3. Explain Canada's relationship with other countries.	**Teaching Resources** 📖 **Unit 2**/Ch. 8 • Guided Reading and Review, p. 45 💿 **Prentice Hall Presentation Pro CD-ROM**, Ch. 8, Sec. 3	**Teaching Resources** 📖 **Guide to the Essentials (English/Spanish)** • Section Summary, Ch. 8, Sec. 3 📼 **Guided Reading Audiotapes (English/Spanish)**, Ch. 8, Sec. 3 📄 **Section Reading Support Transparencies**, Ch. 8, Sec. 3

ENRICHMENT/HONORS/PREAP

📦 **Teaching Resources**

📘 **Unit 2**/Ch. 8
- Critical Thinking, p. 48

📘 **Mental Mapping booklet**
- Atlas Activity, p. 31

📘 **Social Studies Skills Handbook**
- Study and Research Skills, pp. 94–108

📖 **World Geography Map and Photo Transparencies**
- The United States and Canada: Maps and Photos

📹 **World Geography Videos**
- Place: Canada, Tape 1

💻 **Companion Web site, www.phschool.com**
- Chapter 8 Activities

💻 **Companion Web site, www.phschool.com**
- Chapter 8 Activities

💻 **Companion Web site, www.phschool.com**
- Chapter 8 Activities

💻 **Companion Web site, www.phschool.com**
- Chapter 8 Activities

ASSESSMENT

PRENTICE HALL
ASSESSMENT *SYSTEM*

Core Assessment

📘 ExamView Test Bank booklet, Ch. 8

💿 ExamView Test Bank CD-ROM, Ch. 8

💿 ExamView Test Bank CD-ROM, Unit 2

Standardized Test Preparation

Review and Reteach

📘 Review Book for World Geography, pp. 5–6

Practice and Assess

📘 Test-taking Strategies With Transparencies for High School

Test-taking Strategy Poster

📘 Alternative Assessment booklet

📘 Test Prep Book for World Geography

📦 **Teaching Resources**

📘 **Unit 2**/Ch. 8
- Section Quizzes, pp. 42, 44, 46
- Test Forms A and B, pp. 50–56

📘 **Guide to the Essentials (English/Spanish)**
- Chapter 8 Test

📘 **Spanish Resources**, Ch. 8
- Section Quizzes, pp. 20–22

📘 **Mental Mapping booklet**
- Chapter 8 Map Test, p. 32
- Unit 2 Map Test, p. 33

💻 **Companion Web site, www.phschool.com**
- Chapter 8 Self-Test

CUSTOMIZE FOR INDIVIDUAL NEEDS

Gifted and Talented
- Teacher's Edition, Customize for . . . , pp. 187, 189

Honors/PreAP
- Teacher's Edition, Customize for . . . , p. 199

Less Proficient Readers
- Guide to the Essentials (English), Ch. 8, Section Summaries
- Social Studies Skills Handbook, p. 75
- Guided Reading Audiotapes (English), Ch. 8
- Section Reading Support Transparencies, Ch. 8
- Book on CD, Ch. 8
- Teacher's Edition, Reading Strategy, pp. 185, 190, 194
- Teacher's Edition, Activity: Vocabulary, p. 183
- Teacher's Edition, Customize for . . . , p. 195

Students Acquiring English/ESL
- Guide to the Essentials (English/Spanish), Ch. 8
- Guided Reading Audiotapes (English/Spanish), Ch. 8
- Section Reading Support Transparencies, Ch. 8
- Book on CD, Ch. 8

Less Proficient Writers
- Social Studies Skills Handbook, p. 84
- Alternative Assessment, Writing Assignment Rubric, p. 6

MENTAL MAPPING

Referring to the map on this page, point out that Canada lies within the Northern Hemisphere. It is a very large country, exceeded in size only by Russia. Have students use the map to name the oceans bordering Canada. (Pacific Ocean, Arctic Ocean, Atlantic Ocean)

Mapping the Region Have students create a map like the one on this page. Either have them draw their own sketch maps, or distribute the Chapter 8 Outline Map on page 30 of the Mental Mapping booklet in the Teaching Resources. Have students lightly shade each province and territory a different color. Then ask them to label the major Canadian cities listed under Part I of the Unit 2 Checklist and the provinces and territories listed under Part IV of the Checklist.

eTeach

Be sure to check out this month's online forum with a Master Teacher to join in an exchange of teaching ideas. **www.phschool.com**

C H A P T E R

8

Canada

SECTIONS

1 **Regions of Canada**

2 **The Search for a National Identity**

3 **Canada Today**

Canada: POLITICAL

KEY

⊕ National capital
⊙ Provincial capital
• Other city

Lambert Azimuthal Equal-Area Projection

(Map of Canada showing provinces, territories, cities, and surrounding oceans: Arctic Ocean, Pacific Ocean, Atlantic Ocean, Bering Sea, Beaufort Sea, Baffin Bay, Hudson Bay, Labrador Sea; Alaska (U.S.), Greenland (Den.); Yukon, Northwest Territories, Nunavut, British Columbia, Alberta, Saskatchewan, Manitoba, Ontario, Quebec, Newfoundland and Labrador, New Brunswick, Prince Edward Island, Nova Scotia; cities including Whitehorse, Yellowknife, Iqaluit, Edmonton, Calgary, Vancouver, Victoria, Saskatoon, Regina, Winnipeg, St. John's, Quebec, Charlottetown, Fredericton, Halifax, Hull, Ottawa, Montreal, Toronto; United States to the south)

Go Online
PHSchool.com

For: More information about Canada and access to the Take It to the Net activities
Visit: phschool.com
Web Code: mjk-0009

RESOURCE DIRECTORY

Teaching Resources
Unit 2, Chapter 8
• Section 1 Guided Reading and Review, p. 41
Guide to the Essentials (English/Spanish)
• Section Summary, Chapter 8, Section 1
Mental Mapping booklet
• Atlas Activity, p. 31
• Unit 2 Checklist, p. 19

Technology
Guided Reading Audiotapes (English/Spanish),
  Chapter 8, Section 1

Section Reading Support Transparencies,
  Chapter 8, Section 1
World Geography Map and Photo Transparencies
• The United States and Canada: Maps and Photos
Book on CD, Chapter 8
World Geography Videos
• Place: Canada, Tape 1
TeacherExpress™ CD-ROM, Chapter 8
Prentice Hall Presentation Pro CD-ROM, Chapter 8
Social Studies Skills Tutor CD-ROM
Companion Web site, www.phschool.com
• Chapter 8 Activities

1 Regions of Canada

Reading Focus

- **What are the main economic activities in the Atlantic Provinces?**
- **Why have the Great Lakes–St. Lawrence Provinces become Canada's heartland?**
- **What economic activities and patterns of settlement are found in the Prairie Provinces and British Columbia?**
- **How have climate and location affected the development of the northern territories?**

Key Terms

province   lock
maritime   bedrock

Main Idea Canada can be divided into five distinct regions based on physical features, cultural characteristics, and economic activities.

Economic Activities Small fishing villages line the coast of the Atlantic Provinces.

◀ **British Columbia** (photo left)

anada is a vast land that covers most of the northern half of North America. Canada shares many physical characteristics with the United States, yet it is a distinct nation with its own unique cultural characteristics, opportunities, and challenges.

Canada's ten **provinces,** or political divisions, and three territories can be divided into five regions based on physical features, culture, and economy. As you read in Chapter 7, the regions of the United States overlap one another. The regions of Canada, however, are more distinct than those of the United States. Two reasons for this clear separation are the country's relatively small population and the structure of its government, which gives a great deal of power to the provinces.

The Atlantic Provinces

Tucked into the southeastern corner of Canada are the four Atlantic Provinces of Newfoundland and Labrador, Prince Edward Island, Nova Scotia, and New Brunswick. Locate these provinces on the map on page 180. All four provinces border on the Atlantic Ocean. The land in this region forms part of the Appalachian Mountains, which extend southward into the eastern United States. Hills covered with thick mixed deciduous forest and rugged mountaintops highlight the landscape in most of the region. Thousands of lakes and small ponds dot the rugged terrain. As in New England, glaciers once moved across the area, leaving the soil thin and strewn with rocks and boulders.

Links to the Sea The Atlantic Provinces are often called the Maritimes because of their close ties with the sea. The word **maritime** means "bordering on or related to the sea." The coastlines of these provinces are marked by hundreds of bays and inlets, providing excellent harbors for fishing fleets. Most residents of this region live along the coast.

The Atlantic Provinces are the smallest of Canada's regions, including only about 5 percent of Canada's land and only about 8 percent of its people. Although small in area, the Atlantic Provinces

Chapter 8 ▪ Section 1   **181**

Objectives

Upon completion of Section 1, students should be able to:

- ◆ list the main economic activities in the Atlantic Provinces;
- ◆ explain why the Great Lakes–St. Lawrence Provinces have become Canada's heartland;
- ◆ describe economic activities and patterns of settlement in the Prairie Provinces and British Columbia;
- ◆ explain how climate and location have affected the development of the northern territories.

National Geography Standards

The following National Geography Standards are highlighted in this section: 1, 2, 3, 4, 5, 8, 9, 10, 11, 12, 13, 14, 16, 17

Bellringer

Recite this limerick: There was an old man from Quebec,/Who was buried in snow to his neck./When asked, "Are you friz?" [frozen]/He replied, "Yes, I is,/But we don't call this cold in Quebec." Ask what this suggests about Canada's climate.

LESSON PLAN

1. Focus Refer students to the population density map on page 135. Have students focus on the Northwest Territories, and note that all of the residents in that vast area could be seated inside an average-size baseball stadium.

2. Instruct Ask students how Quebec and Ontario are Canada's heartland in terms of Location, Economic Activity, Population, Land Area, Government, and Transportation.

3. Close/Reteach Have students explain how location and resources have influenced economic activities and population density in each region of Canada.

Pacing Suggestions

For 90-minute Blocks

You will want to vary activities.

- Use the Creative Teaching Activity for Chapter 8 as the basis for a 90-minute lesson. Once all the groups have given their oral reports, ask students to imagine that they are members of the expedition they researched. Instruct them to create journal entries recounting adventures or discoveries from their journeys. Ask volunteers to share their entries with the class.

have been fundamental to Canada's settlement and development.

Economic Activities The Grand Banks area off the coasts of Newfoundland and Nova Scotia was long one of the world's richest fishing areas. However, years of overfishing depleted the supply so profoundly that Canada suspended cod fishing in 1992. Many people in the fishing and fish-processing industries lost their livelihoods. By 1999, the cod stocks still had not recovered. However, many people found new livelihoods catching shrimp and crab.

Forestry and farming are also important in the Maritimes. Some fruit, vegetable, and dairy farming takes place where the soil and local climate permit. The gentle, rolling plains and fertile soil of Prince Edward Island are particularly well suited to farming. Because it is a small island, and more of its land is close to the moderating influences of water, Prince Edward Island has a milder climate and a longer growing season than the mainland provinces.

In recent years, many Maritime residents have found work in newly developing industries. Rugged coastlines and scenic hills make the region a popular vacation spot. Consequently, many in the Atlantic Provinces are turning to tourism for their livelihoods. In addition, offshore oil discoveries are drawing many workers. After a few years of a slump, the economy of the Atlantic Provinces has rebounded.

Canada: PHYSICAL-POLITICAL

APPLYING THE GEOGRAPHIC THEMES

Regions Canada is politically divided into ten provinces and three territories.
• *Which province borders the Pacific Ocean?*

The Great Lakes–St. Lawrence Waterway

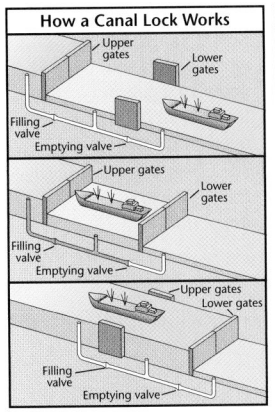

How a Canal Lock Works

Upper gates
Lower gates
Filling valve
Emptying valve

Upper gates
Lower gates
Filling valve
Emptying valve

Upper gates
Lower gates
Filling valve
Emptying valve

DIAGRAM SKILLS

● **Science and Technology** A system of locks and canals links the St. Lawrence River and the Great Lakes, making the waterway usable to ships.
  • *How do the canal locks make up for the varying elevations between the Great Lakes?*

The Great Lakes and St. Lawrence Provinces

In sharp contrast to the Atlantic Provinces, the two provinces surrounding the Great Lakes and the St. Lawrence River are the core of Canada's population and its economic activity. The large provinces of Quebec and Ontario are the heartland of Canada. These provinces are distinguished by three distinct landscapes. The first is the Canadian Shield. It has poor soil and a cold climate but contains rich mineral deposits. The Canadian Shield covers most of Quebec and Ontario. The second landscape is the Hudson Bay Lowlands—a flat, sparsely populated, swampy region between the Canadian Shield and Hudson Bay. The St. Lawrence Lowlands—third of the landscapes—have rich soil and a relatively mild

climate. Sixty percent of Canada's population lives in this region around the Great Lakes and the St. Lawrence River valley.

Characteristics of Ontario One of Ontario's most important features is its system of waterways. The St. Lawrence Seaway, which connects the Great Lakes to the St. Lawrence River, has been called Canada's highway to the sea because of the volume of goods that travels its length.

The Great Lakes differ greatly in elevation. Lake Superior is the highest at 600 feet (183 m) above sea level, while Lake Ontario is the lowest, at 245 feet (75 m) above sea level. To make up for the differences in water levels, the Great Lakes–St. Lawrence waterway system has a series of locks. A **lock** is an enclosed area on a canal that raises

Vocabulary

Lock Refer to the Key Terms list on page 181. Have students locate the term *lock* in the chapter and restate the definition in their own words. Ask students to name canals where locks are used other than the Great Lakes–St. Lawrence waterway system. (Erie, Panama)

BACKGROUND

Word Origin

Ontario The name *Ontario* comes from an Indian term meaning "beautiful water." This name is most appropriate for the province because rivers and lakes cover one sixth of its total area.

Alternative Assessment

Introduce the Activity

Writing a Position Paper Ask students to conduct research and to write a two-page position paper agreeing or disagreeing with the following statement: "The separatist movement in Canada will probably gain strength in the next 20 years and result in splitting Canada into two countries." Distribute the Position Paper Rubric on page 8 of the Alternative Assessment booklet in the Prentice Hall Assessment System for student reference during the project.

TEST PREPARATION

Have students use the diagram on this page to complete the following statement.
A ship headed from Quebec to Thunder Bay would pass first through the —
(A) St. Lawrence Seaway
B Welland Canal
C Gulf of St. Lawrence
D Soo Locks

Answer to Diagram Skills

Inside locks, the water level can be changed to raise or lower ships.

Word Origin

Toronto During the 1600s and 1700s, the Huron Indians used the Toronto area as an overland route between Lake Ontario and Lake Huron. *Toronto* is a Huron Indian word meaning "meeting place."

Environmental Issues

Acid Rain Some experts maintain that the U.S. government emission standards set in 1970 unintentionally made southeastern Canada's acid rain problem greater. These standards required taller smokestacks on factories producing sulfur and nitrogen oxide wastes. The taller smokestacks send pollutants higher into the atmosphere where they can be picked up by upper-level winds. They mix with water and fall to the ground as acid rain in areas distant from their original sources.

The Canadian Shield

Physical Processes To the northeast of the Interior Plains lies an area of exposed bedrock called the Canadian Shield. During the Ice Age, which ended about 10,000 years ago, glaciers scraped the ancient bedrock clear of overlying materials.

Regions *Why do you think this region is so sparsely populated?*

or lowers ships from one water level to another. (See the diagram on page 183.) Canada and the United States have taken advantage of the difference in height between the Great Lakes and sea level by jointly constructing a hydroelectric plant along the seaway.

In addition to a central location and excellent waterways, Ontario has rich soil and abundant mineral resources. Much of the land in the southeastern part of the province is used for farming, and it is here that most of the province's people live. A network of cities has developed in which a wide variety of products—cars, food products, clothing, and building materials—are manufactured and distributed. Because of the province's location, industries based on processing minerals or manufacturing goods can easily ship their products to other parts of Canada and to the United States.

Toronto, Ontario's capital, is the largest metropolitan area in Canada. More than one third of Canada's largest companies now have their main offices in Toronto. This city also contains Canada's banking and financial center, as important to Canada as New York's Wall Street is to the United States.

Ottawa, the national capital of Canada, is located on the Ottawa River in southeastern Ontario. Together, Ottawa and its neighbor across the river, Hull, Quebec, make up Canada's fourth-largest metropolitan area.

Characteristics of Quebec Although Quebec is Canada's largest province in terms of area, its population is not equally distributed. Most residents live in the cities in and around the St. Lawrence River valley. Few people live on the Canadian Shield, an area of exposed bedrock which covers the northern four fifths of the province. **Bedrock** is solid rock that is usually covered by soil, gravel, and sand. Most of this region has remained a wilderness of forests, rivers, lakes, and streams. Treeless tundra with lichens and mosses covers the northernmost parts of Quebec.

The Appalachian Mountains rise gently along the southeastern border of the province. Both of these regions, the southeast and the Canadian Shield, are centers of mining and forestry. Farming remains an important activity in the fertile plains of the St. Lawrence Valley. In recent decades, however, increasing numbers of Quebec's residents have been attracted to manufacturing and service jobs.

Quebec's largest city is Montreal, a beautiful metropolis at the Lachine Rapids of the St. Lawrence. Development that began when Montreal hosted Expo '67 transformed it from a provincial city into a dynamic urban center.

184 Chapter 8 ▪ Canada

Answer to Photo Caption

The climate is cold and there is little soil for agriculture. Building and land transportation are difficult.

The capital of the province, also called Quebec, is the oldest city in Canada. It was founded in 1608 by Samuel de Champlain, who was sent by France to establish a colony. The historic sites and European charm of Quebec make it a popular tourist attraction. Section 2 describes the province of Quebec's unique culture as the center of Canada's French-Canadian population.

The Prairie Provinces

The provinces of Alberta, Manitoba, and Saskatchewan lie in southwestern Canada between the Rocky Mountains and the Canadian Shield. Known as the Prairie Provinces, they have long been associated with rolling fields of wheat. One writer described the landscape as looking "as if someone had taken a colossal pencil to the countryside and erased anything taller than a bush." The prairies are more than crop-covered flatlands, however. For the traveler who leaves the main highways, the prairies also offer clear, cool lakes; lazy rivers; and mysterious badlands filled with strange, eroded sand and rock formations. Huge tracts of sand dunes are also found stretching across these broad, semiarid plains.

Patterns of Settlement Half or more of the people in each of the three Prairie Provinces live in cities. The largest cities in the region are located at strategic points along the railroads that were built in the late 1800s. Winnipeg was established at an important river crossing as railroad tracks were laid from the east through the Canadian Shield. From Winnipeg, two rail lines were built to the west, each taking a different set of passes through the Rocky Mountains. The cities of Edmonton and Calgary in Alberta were established at points where each rail line headed into the mountains. Roughly midway between those cities and Winnipeg, the Saskatchewan cities of Saskatoon and Regina were founded as major service centers along the rail lines. The large number of rail lines reflects the importance of agriculture to the province. Accordingly, the Prairie Provinces have been described as a region where "grains and trains dominate life."

GEOFacts

Lakes and rivers cover about 7.6 percent of Canada's vast landmass. There is enough water in these lakes and rivers to flood the entire country to a depth of more than 6 feet (2 m).

READING STRATEGY

Making Inferences

Write these questions on the board: *Why are railroads a necessity in the Prairie Provinces? What is the relationship between railroads and urbanization? What special services and products are most likely provided by cities?* Instruct students to answer the questions as they read the subsection The Prairie Provinces on this page.

Prairie Wheat Fields

Economic Activities
Fields of wheat cover the flatlands of the Prairie Provinces. The growing season there is short, but long summer days provide lots of sunshine for crops.

Place *Explain one advantage and one disadvantage of living in a farming community such as this one.*

Articles From NATIONAL GEOGRAPHIC

The following article may be used to extend the content in this section.

Vesilind, Priit J., and Maria Stenzel, photographer. "David Thomas: The Man Who Measured Canada." *National Geographic,* Vol. 189, No. 5 (May 1996), pp. 112–137.

Exploring over 80,000 miles of Canadian land in the late 1700s and early 1800s, David Thomas created the first maps of the nation's interior.

Answer to Photo Caption

Possible answer: One advantage is lack of industrial pollution. One disadvantage is limited cultural and entertainment opportunities.

Global Economy

Lumber Industry British Columbia contains some of the world's most magnificent stands of timber. These forests of Douglas fir and hemlock have made British Columbia the leading lumber producer in Canada. Much of this lumber is exported from Vancouver to Asian countries. The timber is sometimes harvested with controversial clear-cutting techniques in which all the trees in a given area of perhaps several hundred acres are cut at one time. Loggers say this is the most efficient way to log trees and enhance reforestation. Conservation groups say the process leaves the land ugly and devastated and contributes to erosion, stream pollution, and the destruction of forest ecosystems.

History

Victoria Victoria, western Canada's oldest city, is a good case study in how natural resources affect human settlement and economic activities. British Columbia's wildlife attracted fur traders, who established Victoria (then Fort Victoria) as a trading post in 1843. Gold was discovered in British Columbia's mainland in 1858. That year, gold fever drew 20,000 prospectors to Victoria Bay. Because of the gold rush, Victoria's population exploded, its real estate values skyrocketed, and it became the capital of British Columbia. Today, Victoria's mild climate and scenic vistas draw retirees, who make up a quarter of its population, and support its largest industry—tourism. Victoria's waterways are home to a naval base and a major fishing fleet.

Answer to Photo Caption

Possible answers: salmon, minerals, water

Logging Industry

Natural Resources The forests of British Columbia yield a rich harvest of timber. These logs are being floated to mills downriver, where they will be turned into lumber, paper, wood pulp, and other products.
Place *What other natural resources are found in British Columbia?*

Economic Activities The Prairie Provinces provide most of Canada's grain and cattle. Wheat is the major agricultural crop. Most grain is exported and is transported by rail to ports on the Pacific Ocean, the Great Lakes, or Hudson Bay.

Tourism is an important economic activity in many of the region's magnificent parks. The

snowcapped Rocky Mountains of western Alberta have some of North America's most spectacular scenery. The discovery of oil and natural gas in Alberta provided a new source of wealth for the region. The oil industry also had a major effect on the growth of cities like Calgary and Edmonton.

British Columbia

The natural beauty of the Rockies stretches farther west into British Columbia. Canada's westernmost province is unlike any other region in Canada. The Inside Passage, a waterway between the long string of offshore islands and the Coast Mountains of British Columbia, provides travelers with many scenic wonders:

> 66 Always the ultimate backdrop is rank on rank of mountains, some velvety green, some topped with snow, some populated with giant trees on the lower slopes but turning to sheer rock decorated with sheets of ageless ice. Here and there, like a silver thread in the mountain distance, is a glimpse of plunging river, disappearing into the green as if into a deep sponge. 99

Notice on the map on page 182 that mountains of several ranges cover nearly all of British Columbia. As a result, more than four fifths of the province's residents live in or near the city of Vancouver.

Plentiful natural resources, including salmon, forests, and minerals, have helped British Columbia become one of Canada's wealthiest provinces. But for many residents and visitors, its cities are its most memorable attractions. Victoria, the capital, is located at the southeastern tip of Vancouver Island. It has the relaxed charm of a small British city, with manicured gardens that bloom year-round in the mild, wet, marine west coast climate.

Vancouver, the province's largest city, occupies a site by an excellent harbor. It is Canada's major port on the Pacific Ocean, and has grown rapidly during recent decades as trade with Asia increased. Immigration from Asia has increased Vancouver's population. Vancouver's population has also swelled due to the many Canadians from other provinces who are moving to Vancouver

RESOURCE DIRECTORY

Teaching Resources
Creative Teaching Activities
• Searching for the Northwest Passage, p. 10
Unit 2, Chapter 8
• Map/Graph Skills, p. 49
Social Studies Skills Handbook
• Elevation on a Map, p. 20

when they retire because of its desirable climate and scenic beauty.

The Northern Territories

The northern 40 percent of Canada consists of the Yukon Territory, Northwest Territories, and Nunavut, Canada's newest territory. Nunavut was established in 1999, when it was carved from the Northwest Territories as part of a land claim settlement with the native peoples.

These cold, largely treeless lands are sparsely settled. Together, they are home to fewer than 1 percent of Canada's population. Nearly all the population live in small settlements along the Mackenzie River and the Arctic coastline.

A Changing Culture Many residents of the northern territories are native people who call themselves Inuit, a term that means "the people." Inuit, rather than Eskimo, is the name by which these people prefer to be known. The Inuit generally live north of the forests, while other Native Canadian groups live farther south. Recently, a writer who traveled from one end of Canada to the other told of the Inuit's attitude toward the land.

66 Of all Canadians . . . [the Inuit] have developed . . . [and] maintained perhaps the closest relationship with the geography. They have a saying: "Our land is our life." Recognizing they are but one of the land's many elements—and certainly not the most important—the Inuit use the harsh geography to survive, as an astute judo student turns the momentum of an onrushing attacker to his own advantage. 99

Contact with persons of European ancestry has changed the ways in which the Inuit live. Although seal hunting is still an important economic activity, modern Inuit hunters now use snowmobiles instead of dog sleds to cross the frozen lands. Modern technology is used to overcome vast distances in other ways as well. Some Inuit children remain at home, taking classes transmitted by satellite over radio and television systems, and their teachers may be thousands of miles away.

A Difficult Environment The northern territories contain rich deposits of minerals. A wealth of gold, silver, copper, zinc, lead, iron ore, and uranium can be found in the region. So can

Electronic Education

Science and Technology Schools in Canada's remote northern areas are using modern technology, such as videoconferencing and the Internet, to reduce their isolation.

Place *How does technology affect the impact of distance on remote places?*

GLOBAL CONNECTIONS

Migration

Inuit Homelands About 41,000 of the Inuit live in Canada and a little more than 44,000 live in Alaska. The largest population lives in Greenland (nearly 49,000), where most of the people have mixed European and Inuit ancestry. The northeastern tip of Russia is home to fewer than 2,000 Inuit people. While the traditional Inuit language is losing ground in Alaska, it is an official language in both Nunavut and Greenland.

ACTIVITY

Group Work

Activity: Developing an outline for a television documentary

Purpose: Groups will research these topics related to the northern territories: physical environment, modern life of present-day Inuit, traditional life of historic Inuit, mining in the northern territories. Instruct each group to develop an outline for a television documentary based on its topic. Outlines should include ideas for narration as well as maps, photos, diagrams, or other visuals. Students may videotape their documentaries if the resources are available.

Roles: One or more lecturers/narrators, researchers, writers, artists, and possibly camera operators

Result: Each group presents the outline for a television documentary to the class and, if possible, presents a videotape of portions of the documentary.

CUSTOMIZE FOR...

Gifted and Talented

Traveling by Rail Have students create an itinerary for a five-day trip across Canada by railroad. They should decide what time of year they want to travel, where to get on and off trains, and what side trips to take along the way. Have them consult travel books and brochures to find out about special events, major cities, and scenic national parks. You may also want them to make maps showing their stops and the highway routes to any side trips.

Answer to Photo Caption

Technology allows people in remote areas to have access to the information and services available in more densely populated regions.

Answers to
Section 1 Assessment

1. (a) province, p. 181
(b) maritime, p. 181 **(c)** lock, p. 183
(d) bedrock, p. 184
2. catching fish and shellfish, forestry, farming, tourism, offshore oil development
3. Possible answers: factors such as their central location, excellent waterways, rich soil, and abundant mineral resources
4. (a) The flatlands of the Prairie Provinces are well suited to raising grain and cattle. The region's parks attract tourists. The oil industry also became important after oil and natural gas were discovered in Alberta.
(b) British Columbia's plentiful forests have spurred the growth of logging and related industries. The scenic beauty has also made tourism an important economic activity. Because of its location on the Pacific, trade with Asia has increased.
5. The northern territories are sparsely settled. The indigenous people who live there have a deep appreciation for the land and use the harsh geography to survive. Modern technology has helped to overcome the vast distances and harshness of the climate.
6. Students should be evaluated on the level of detail they use in comparing the two regions.

Activity Rubrics Share rubrics with students before they begin their maps.
Attempted The map is messy or incomplete.
Minimal The map includes the required information, but the labeling is unclear or inaccurate.
Adequate The map is accurately labeled, the route is correctly plotted, and the approximate elevation change is reasonable.
Exemplary The map includes all the required elements, is very well executed, and is visually appealing.

Answer to Photo Caption

Canada's northern resources are difficult to develop because of the harsh climate and difficult terrain.

Tapping Canada's Resources

Natural Resources Much of Canada's northern territories is a vast expanse of tundra (left). Beneath this treeless landscape lie deposits of valuable minerals. Oil riggers (above) work to tap the large reserves of petroleum that are also found in the region.

Human-Environment Interaction *Why has development of Canada's northern resources been limited?*

large reserves of petroleum and natural gas. For example, in the mid-1980s, an oil pipeline was constructed. It delivers oil to southern markets. However, most of this wealth remains buried within the earth. Many deposits have not been developed because the harsh climate and rugged terrain make it difficult to mine and transport these materials.

In spite of the difficulties of life in the north, the people who reside there live with a knowledge of the hardships and a deep appreciation for the beauty and bounty that the land offers.

SECTION 1 ASSESSMENT

1. Key Terms Define **(a)** province, **(b)** maritime, **(c)** lock, **(d)** bedrock.

2. Economic Activities What economic activities are important in the Atlantic Provinces?

3. Physical Characteristics What factors led to the emergence of the Great Lakes–St. Lawrence Provinces as Canada's heartland?

4. Economic Activities How have location and resources influenced economic activities in **(a)** the Prairie Provinces, **(b)** British Columbia?

5. Cultures How has climate affected culture in the northern territories?

6. Critical Thinking Making Comparisons Choose two of Canada's regions and compare their physical features, economic activities, and population distribution.

Activity

Planning a Route Review the diagram and map on page 183. On an outline map of North America, trace a water route from Thunder Bay to Montreal. Label the start and end points of your journey and the lakes you would pass through. What is the approximate elevation change during your trip?

RESOURCE DIRECTORY

Teaching Resources

Unit 2, Chapter 8
• Section 1 Quiz, p. 42
• Section 2 Guided Reading and Review, p. 43

Spanish Resources
• Section 1 Quiz, p. 20

Guide to the Essentials (English/Spanish)
• Section Summary, Chapter 8, Section 2

Mental Mapping booklet
• Unit 2 Checklist, p. 19

Technology

Guided Reading Audiotapes (English/Spanish), Chapter 8, Section 2

Section Reading Support Transparencies, Chapter 8, Section 2

World Geography Map and Photo Transparencies
• The United States and Canada: Maps and Photos

Book on CD, Chapter 8

Social Studies Skills Tutor CD-ROM

Companion Web site, www.phschool.com
• Chapter 8 Activities

2 The Search for a National Identity

Reading Focus

- What are the historical roots of Canada's major culture groups?
- Why is Quebec the scene of conflict between two cultures?
- How does the multicultural nature of Canada's population represent its policy of welcoming diversity while promoting unity?

Key Terms

separatism
secede

Main Idea Conflict between the diverse culture groups of Canada has made national unity a challenge to achieve.

Cultures Like these modern Inuit, some of Canada's earliest inhabitants lived in the arctic north.

Like Canada's landscapes, the nation's population is extremely varied. Canada has come to define itself as a multicultural country—a mosaic of many pieces with varying colors. Unity is difficult to achieve because the country is so vast and there are such great differences among the provinces and territories as well as among the people. This lack of unity is partly explained by the history of Canada.

Understanding the Past

Canada has had to struggle to develop a single national identity. One reason is that many of its people identify more strongly with regional and ethnic groups than with the nation as a whole. Most of the population are of British and French ancestry. About 40 percent of all Canadians have British ancestors; another 27 percent are of French descent.

The First Canadians The first people to live in what is now Canada were the Inuit and Native Americans whose ancestors migrated to North America thousands of years ago. These first Canadians developed stable societies and adapted to a wide range of environments. Many

lived in villages along the Pacific coast, enjoying the abundance of resources in the forests, bays, and rivers. Others were nomadic, gathering food and hunting game, such as walruses and seals in the arctic north, moose and caribou along the Canadian Shield, and buffalo in the plains. Many in the Great Lakes–St. Lawrence Lowlands lived in permanent settlements and raised maize, squash, and other crops.

Beginning in the 1500s, the rival European empires of England and France began colonizing the region, devastating the native population with European diseases and warfare. Soon England and France were battling each other for control of the land.

Colonial Rivalries French and English colonists competed with each other for the prosperous North American fur trade and clashed over land claims. Between 1689 and 1763, British and French colonists fought four wars in North America. Finally, British troops defeated the French in the Battle of Quebec in 1759, and by 1763 France surrendered all of its empire in what is now Canada. Britain then assumed control over the entire region.

Chapter 8 ▪ Section 2 **189**

CUSTOMIZE FOR...

Gifted and Talented

Battle of Quebec Have students work as a group to research the Battle of Quebec, 1759, and create an illustrated, multipaneled mural depicting the stages, strategies, and final outcome of the battle. The panels should contain information about what was at stake for both the French and the British, the treaty concluding the war, and generals Wolfe and Montcalm and their fates.

Section 2 *pp. 189–191*

Objectives

Upon completion of Section 2, students should be able to:

- identify the historical roots of Canada's major culture groups;
- explain why Quebec is the scene of conflict between two cultures;
- describe Canada's policy of welcoming diversity while promoting unity.

 National Geography Standards

The following National Geography Standards are highlighted in this section: 1, 3, 4, 5, 6, 9, 10, 13, 17

 Bellringer

Tell students that the origin of the name *Canada* is uncertain. It may have originated from the word *kanata*—a Huron-Iroquois word for "village." Or it may have come from Portuguese sailors who, on visiting the Canadian shore around 1500, may have exclaimed, "Cá nada!" which means "Here, nothing!"

LESSON PLAN

1. Focus Discuss the factors that help build a sense of national identity. (shared government, history, language, culture, media, education) Explain that Canada has been called a "landscape in search of a country." Have students speculate about what this means.

2. Instruct Write the following dates on the board and ask students to identify events that helped shape the conflict between French and English colonists during these years: *1500s* (competition between fur traders for control of the region), *1689–1763* (French and English fight four wars), *1763* (British gain control over Canada), *1867* (British establish Dominion of Canada but retain decision-making powers), *1931* (Canada becomes fully independent but remains a member of the British Commonwealth).

3. Close/Reteach Make a two-column chart on the board. Label the columns *Obstacles to Unity* and *Forces for Unity*. Have students fill in the chart.

Group Work

Activity: Preparing a panel discussion

Purpose: Groups prepare panel discussions on how life would change if Quebec became a separate nation. Remind students to consider both positive and negative effects.

Roles: Assign a group leader for each group.

Result: The groups present their discussions to the rest of the class.

READING STRATEGY

Building Vocabulary

As students read the subsection Conflict Between Two Cultures, refer them to the two bolded key terms within the subsection—separatism and secede. Instruct them to use context clues to create a definition for each of the words. Have them compare their definitions with the Glossary's definitions for the words. Then ask them to write new sentences that use the words correctly.

BACKGROUND

Connecting With . . .

History Canada's history has been wrought by conflict between the British and the French. In 1774, 11 years after winning the French and Indian War, the British guaranteed the French settlers in Canada the right to retain their language and Roman Catholic religion. Despite these assurances, French Canadians endured generations of discrimination. "Je me souviens"—on the license plates that the province of Quebec issues—means "I remember" and refers to the violence and discrimination that the French Canadians have suffered and are determined never to let happen again.

Answer to Photo Caption

Many Quebecois feel discriminated against by the English-speaking majority. They want to assure the preservation of French culture.

GLOBAL CONNECTIONS

Migration In the 1750s, British troops drove settlers out of the French colony of Acadia, which was centered in what is now Nova Scotia. Many Acadians eventually settled in the bayous of Louisiana. Living in isolation, they developed a unique culture. Over the years, the name Acadian became Cajun. Today, Cajuns speak their own language, a combination of English and a French dialect. They are known for their spicy cooking and zydeco music.

Ties to Britain Canada remained under direct British rule until 1867 when the British created the Dominion of Canada. This act gave Canada its own government, but foreign policy and military decisions were still made by the British. Canada became a completely independent country in 1931, when the last British controls ended. Even today, however, Canada's symbolic ruler is the British monarch.

Conflict Between Two Cultures

When France lost its empire in what is now Canada to Britain, about 70,000 French colonists lived in the area. Since then Canada's French-Canadian population has grown to over one quarter of the country's total population. The great majority of French-speaking Canadians live in the province of Quebec.

In 1774 the British government passed laws to ensure that French Canadians, many of whom also lived in Ontario, would be able to maintain their own language, laws, and culture. When Canada became an independent country, the government continued to protect the rights of French-speaking citizens. Both English and French are official languages in Canada. However, only about 15 percent of Canadians speak both languages.

Many French Canadians today feel discriminated against by the English-speaking majority. They claim that they are denied jobs in government or industry because they are of French descent.

The Quebecois (kay-beh-KWAH), Quebec's French-speaking citizens, consider themselves the guardians of French culture in Canada. Starting in the 1960s, many Quebecois began to press for changes that would assure the preservation of French culture. Some people favored **separatism,** that is, making Quebec an independent country.

In 1974 the government of Quebec made French the official language of the province. Many English-speaking residents and businesses left Quebec, and the province suffered economically. In 1995, a referendum allowing residents to decide whether Quebec should **secede,** or withdraw, from the rest of Canada, failed by a

190

Separatist Protest in Quebec

Cooperation and Conflict Canada's attempt at fostering a bilingual, multicultural society has not been enough for many Quebecois. Despite impassioned efforts of the separatists, Quebec remains part of Canada.

Place *Why do so many Quebecois want Quebec to secede?*

RESOURCE DIRECTORY

Teaching Resources
Unit 2, Chapter 8
• Section 2 Quiz, p. 44
Spanish Resources
• Section 2 Quiz, p. 21

narrow margin. Those dedicated to separatism pledged to continue their efforts. However, in 1998, Canada's highest court declared that Quebec cannot legally secede on its own, even if a referendum passes.

Welcoming Diversity, Promoting Unity

The multicultural nature of Canada's population is one of its most distinctive characteristics. Although most Canadians have British or French ancestors, many other groups are represented in the population.

A Multicultural Society Inuit and Native Americans had been living in what is now Canada for thousands of years before Europeans arrived. Today, most of Canada's 41,000 Inuit live in the territories and in northern areas of Newfoundland, Ontario, and Quebec. Canada has nearly 554,000 Native Canadians, the majority of whom live on reserves.

Canada has welcomed immigrants from all over the world. The largest numbers have come from Europe. In recent years, increasing numbers of immigrants from Asia have settled in Canada, particularly in British Columbia.

Uniting Canada's Regions Canada has been successful in uniting its regions and its people through transportation and communication links. Canada's modern leadership in

Ethnic Composition of Canada

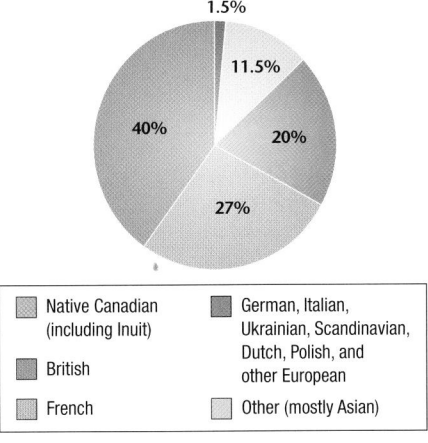

- Native Canadian (including Inuit)
- British
- French
- German, Italian, Ukrainian, Scandinavian, Dutch, Polish, and other European
- Other (mostly Asian)

Source: *The World Almanac and Book of Facts*

GRAPH SKILLS

● **Cultures** Canada's historical ties to Europe can be seen in its ethnic composition.
- *To which European country do most Canadians trace their heritage?*

telecommunications largely results from efforts to communicate with residents in its remote, northern regions. Yet, establishing a truly national identity is proving difficult to achieve.

SECTION 2 ASSESSMENT

1. **Key Terms** Define **(a)** separatism, **(b)** secede.

2. **Understanding the Past** What are the historical roots of the conflict between French-speaking and English-speaking Canadians?

3. **Cultures** How does Canada's diversity affect its efforts to achieve national unity?

4. **Migration (a)** How has recent migration added to the diversity of Canada's population? **(b)** What technological advances has Canada used successfully to unite its diverse and remote regions?

5. **Critical Thinking Synthesizing Information** Why is Canada's multicultural nature characterized as a "mosaic" rather than a "melting pot"?

Activity

Take It to the NET

Creating a Bulletin Board Display Do research on the Internet to find out about the origins of Canadian place names. Include geographic features such as rivers and cities. How do the names reflect Canada's diverse population? Present your findings in a bulletin board display. Visit the World Geography section of **www.phschool.com** for help in completing this activity.

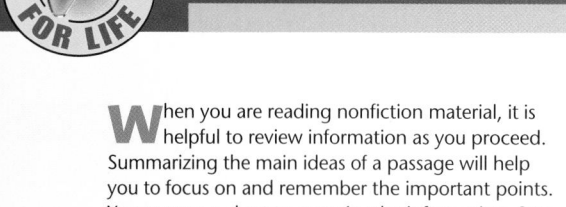
Teaching the Skill

Ask students to read the paragraph introducing the lesson and to write one sentence summarizing its content. Call on two or three volunteers to write their sentences on the board. Discuss the sentences with the class. Note that stopping to summarize paragraph by paragraph may not always be the most efficient reading strategy. Point out that this lesson presents strategies for summarizing longer passages. Then work through the steps in the lesson with the students.

Answers to Learn the Skill

1. developing its natural resources
2. Possible answer: Canada's future development presents challenges and opportunities that involve human-environment interaction and movement.
3. Details: Oil pipelines can interfere with the migration of arctic animals; the harvesting of some fish species has been banned to prevent overfishing.
4. pollution, need for housing and services
5. Possible answer: Canada faces challenges in its future development. The opportunities offered by its natural resources must be balanced with the need to preserve the environment. Similarly, Canada's increasing urbanization has created many challenges, including pollution and overcrowding.

Answers to Practice the Skill

Check that students' graphic organizers correctly identify the main idea and supporting details. Check their summaries for accuracy.

When you are reading nonfiction material, it is helpful to review information as you proceed. Summarizing the main ideas of a passage will help you to focus on and remember the important points. You can use a chart to organize the information. Summarizing is a useful skill whether you are reading a book about your favorite hobby, a newspaper article, or a textbook.

Learn the Skill Use the following steps to learn how to summarize main ideas.

1 *Skim the selection to get an overview of the material.* If the selection contains headings, they will give you an idea of what topics are covered and how the information is organized. The main head indicates the overall topic, while subheadings indicate the subtopics under that general topic. Look at the section on page 193 titled Challenges for Canada Today. *Besides urbanization, what is another major challenge for Canada today?*

2 *Identify the main ideas.* As you read each paragraph, look for sentences that state or suggest the main idea of that paragraph. Keep in mind that the main points are not always clearly stated. Instead, they may be implied. Read the first paragraph under the head Challenges for Canada Today. *Restate the main idea in your own words.*

3 *Look for supporting evidence.* Watch for details, examples, explanations, descriptions, and statistics that expand the main ideas. *What supporting details are provided about the challenges Canada faces with regard to natural resources?*

4 *Compile the main ideas and supporting information in a graphic organizer.* The graphic organizer on this page shows how you can outline main ideas and supporting information. *What are two more details you could add to the chart under Urbanization?*

5 *Summarize the important information.* Use the main ideas and details you have identified to help you formulate a brief summary of what you have read. *How would you summarize the section you read on page 193?*

Practice the Skill Select a section from a nonfiction book or publication on a topic that interests you. Make a graphic organizer identifying the main ideas and supporting evidence that you find. Then, use the graphic organizer to prepare a brief summary of the passage.

Apply the Skill See Chapter 8 Review and Assessment.

RESOURCE DIRECTORY

Teaching Resources

Unit 2, Chapter 8
• Section 3 Guided Reading and Review, p. 45

Guide to the Essentials (English/Spanish)
• Section Summary, Chapter 8, Section 3

Mental Mapping booklet
• Unit 2 Checklist, p. 19

Social Studies Skills Handbook
• Identifying the Main Idea, p. 41

Technology

Guided Reading Audiotapes (English/Spanish), Chapter 8, Section 3

Section Reading Support Transparencies, Chapter 8, Section 3

World Geography Map and Photo Transparencies
• The United States and Canada: Maps and Photos

Book on CD, Chapter 8

Social Studies Skills Tutor CD-ROM, Identifying Main Ideas

Companion Web site, www.phschool.com
• Chapter 8 Activities

3 Canada Today

Reading Focus
- **What geographic challenges does Canada face today with respect to its future development?**
- **What is Canada's relationship with the United States?**
- **How is Canada linked to other countries in the rest of the world?**

Key Terms
customs
tariff
NAFTA

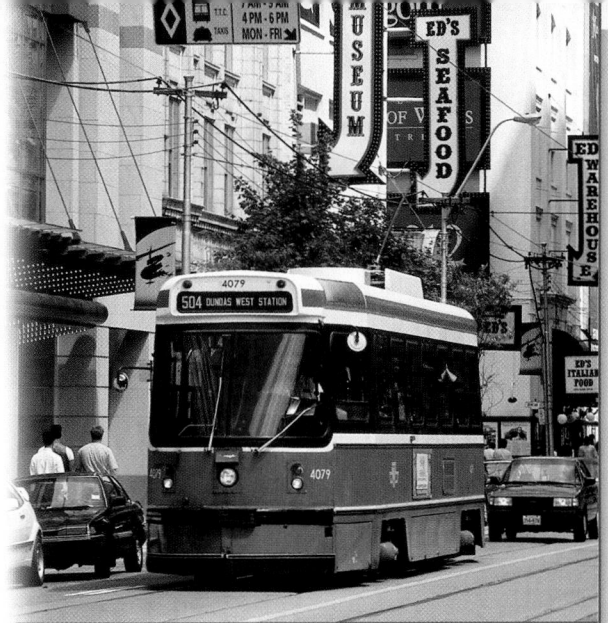

Main Idea — Canada faces challenges and opportunities as it seeks to maintain peaceful relationships with the United States and with other nations.

Science and Technology Trolley cars ease transportation through downtown Toronto.

The history of Canada has centered on the struggle to overcome a harsh environment. Canada has emerged from that struggle to become a prosperous nation. Its gross national product is among the top twenty in the world. Its stable government and high standard of living attracted millions of immigrants in recent decades. Canada has developed a blend of cultures while becoming a leader in worldwide organizations.

Challenges for Canada Today

In its continuing progress, Canada faces challenges as well as opportunities. Canada's future, like its past, largely depends on its geography. The themes of human-environment interaction and movement are of basic importance in understanding Canada's future development.

Natural Resources Canada must balance the opportunities offered by its natural resources with the need to preserve the environment. While an aboveground pipeline minimizes destruction of arctic permafrost, it creates barriers to the migration of caribou and causes habitat loss for

other arctic animals. Some lumber companies seek ways to produce wood products without destroying entire forests. Similarly, concerns about overfishing have led to bans on harvesting some species of fish.

Urbanization In 1900 only about one third of Canada's people lived in urban areas. Today, 77 percent of the nation's people live in cities. Canada has more than 20 metropolitan areas with a population of 100,000 or more. Urbanization has created many challenges: providing housing and services, controlling pollution, and preventing overcrowding.

Links With the United States

The border between Canada and the United States is the longest undefended border in the world—more than 5,000 miles (8,045 km) long. Travelers between the two countries pay **customs**—fees charged by one country's government on goods people bring in from the other country. But no fence exists along the Canadian–United States border.

Chapter 8 ▪ Section 3   **193**

▶▶▶ *Career Prep*

Careers in Geography
Policy Planner Policy planners specialize in helping cities make informed decisions about issues related to future growth. For example, policy planners might predict population growth of certain age groups and advise on policy matters related to building schools or senior citizen centers.

TEST PREPARATION

Have students read the section Links With the United States on this page to complete the following sentence.

After traveling in Canada, U.S. citizens re-entering the United States at the border can expect to —

A   go through an aboveground pipeline

B   pay a fee for goods they bought in Canada

C   be stopped by Canadian soldiers

D   board a trolley to cross the boundary line

Objectives
Upon completion of Section 3, students should be able to:
◆ identify the challenges to future development that Canada faces today;
◆ describe Canada's relationship with the United States;
◆ explain Canada's relationship with other countries.

 National Geography Standards
The following National Geography Standards are highlighted in this section: 1, 4, 6, 11, 12, 13, 16

 Bellringer
Writer Mordecai Richler referred to Canada as more than "this continent's attic" as he talked about how little the people of the United States think about Canada. Ask students what they know about recent events in Canada. Then note that most Canadians are much more informed about U.S. events than average Americans are about Canadian events.

LESSON PLAN

1. Focus Read aloud the following quote from former Canadian prime minister Pierre Trudeau: "Living next to you is in some ways like sleeping [next to] an elephant. No matter how friendly and even-tempered is the beast . . . one is affected by every twitch and grunt." Ask students who the elephant is, and suggest why the United States might sometimes seem like an overpowering neighbor. (wealth, population size, superpower status)

2. Instruct Discuss why American cultural influence might make it more difficult for Canada to establish a strong national identity. Remind students that most Canadians live within a 100-mile-wide zone along the border with the United States.

3. Close/Reteach Have students identify advantages in location that have helped Toronto, Montreal, and Vancouver become successful urban centers.

Chapter 8 ▪ Section 3   **193**

Point out the Key Terms list on page 193. Have students locate the definition of *tariff* in the chapter and paraphrase it. Discuss why governments put tariffs on goods. (to protect local industries, discourage foreign competition, earn revenues)

Group Work

Activity: Holding a press conference

Purpose: Divide the class into small groups. Have each group create four questions for a mock press conference on U.S.-Canadian relations.

Roles: For each group, assign a Canadian prime minister and a U.S. President. The remaining group members will act as reporters.

Result: Have groups take turns holding mock press conferences in which the students playing the Canadian prime minister and the U.S. President answer questions posed by the reporters.

Niagara Falls

Natural Resources On the border between Canada and the United States is a pair of waterfalls known as Niagara Falls. Water thunders over the falls at an average rate of 202,000 cubic feet (5,720 cubic meters) per second. Some of the waterflow is diverted upstream to generate hydroelectric power at power plants in New York State and Ontario.

Regions *What other kinds of links does Canada have with the United States?*

Cultural Links Some of Canada's links with the United States are cultural. People living close to the border can enjoy radio and television programs from stations in both countries. Professional baseball and hockey leagues include teams from both nations.

Economic Links Canada and the United States have important economic links. Canada buys nearly 25 percent of all United States exports, and the United States buys about 85 percent of Canadian exports.

In recent years, Canada and the United States negotiated two important trade agreements. The first, the Free Trade Agreement (FTA), was signed in 1988. It called for an end to export barriers, including the elimination of all tariffs by the year 1999. **Tariffs** are taxes on imports. They cause the prices of imported goods to rise.

The FTA produced mixed reactions. On the one hand, Canadians were able to take advantage of lower prices by shopping across the border. On the other hand, many Canadians blamed the FTA for plant closings and rising unemployment, as major firms relocated south of the border where costs were lower.

Canada and the United States extended the FTA in 1993 to include Mexico. This new pact, the North American Free Trade Agreement (**NAFTA**), was designed to establish a free-trade zone across all of North America. The agreement marked a giant step toward creating the world's largest trading bloc, with about 380 million consumers.

An Uneven Relationship Although there are many positive links between Canada and the United States, some Canadians are uncomfortable because the relationship between the two nations is so uneven.

Canada's location relative to the United States provides its people with great opportunities. At the same time, Canada still struggles to prevent its identity from being overshadowed by the United States. Canadians are generally aware of what's happening in the United States, while Americans tend to give little thought to their northern neighbors. Mordecai Richler, a well-known Canadian writer, spoke for many Canadians when he declared that he wanted his country to be "something more than this continent's attic."

GLOBAL CONNECTIONS

Cooperation and Conflict Canadian and American forces cooperate in NORAD, the North American Aerospace Defense Command. This military unit uses a network of radar stations to detect any missile threat to the United States or Canada. In addition, NORAD monitors any aircraft suspected of illegal drug trafficking. This information is then passed to local enforcement agencies.

Answer to Photo Caption
cultural and economic links

Canada and the United States
Transportation Data

Country	Motor Vehicles (per 1,000 people)	Total Highway Length (miles)	Total Airports
Canada	563	560,081	1,411
United States	773	3,942,249	14,572

Sources: *Encarta World Atlas; The World Factbook*

CHART SKILLS

● **Science and Technology** *Which country has more motor vehicles per thousand people?*

● **Patterns of Settlement** *Which country has fewer highways and airports? How might population distribution account for this?*

Links With the World

In contrast to the United States, often called a superpower, Canada plays the role of a middle power in the global community. Middle powers often join together to achieve their common goals. Because of its location, size, and multicultural population, Canada is very well suited to working with other nations.

The Importance of Location Canada has a unique position with regard to other nations because of its location. With major ports on both the Atlantic and Pacific coasts, Canada has access to trade with Japan and other Asian countries as well as with Europe.

Member of the Commonwealth Canada maintains links with many nations through its membership in the Commonwealth of Nations. This is a group of countries, mostly former British colonies, that now have independence under the symbolic protection of the British crown. Commonwealth nations often work together to promote better trade, health, and education in their countries.

As a member of the Commonwealth of Nations, Canada has links with developing countries. Membership also puts Canada in a favorable position with regard to trade with the European Community, a group of Western European countries that have united their economic resources.

The Role of Peacekeeper Lester Pearson, Canada's prime minister from 1963 to 1968, once said:

> 66 The best defense of peace is not power, but the removal of the causes of war, and international agreements which will put peace on a stronger foundation than the terror of destruction. 99

Much of Canada's international policy has been based on Pearson's ideas. Canada has taken an active part in promoting arms control and disarmament among other nations of the world.

SECTION 3 ASSESSMENT

1. **Key Terms** Define **(a)** customs, **(b)** tariff, **(c)** NAFTA.

2. **Natural Resources** What challenges must Canada face as it tries to use its natural resources?

3. **Global Trade Patterns (a)** What economic links does Canada have with the United States? **(b)** Why did some Canadians have concerns about the FTA?

4. **Cooperation and Conflict** What role does Canada play in world affairs?

5. **Critical Thinking** **Predicting Consequences** What long-term effects do you think NAFTA will have on the Canadian economy and the nation's role as international peacekeeper?

Activity

USING THE **REGIONAL ATLAS**

Review the information in this section and in the Regional Atlas. Create a poster illustrating the ties between Canada and the United States. Include information on cultural similarities, economic links, and shared physical features.

Answers to Section 3 Assessment
1. **(a)** customs, p. 193 **(b)** tariff, p. 194 **(c)** NAFTA, p. 194
2. Canada faces the challenge of developing its resources while at the same time protecting the environment.
3. **(a)** Canada and the United States are trade partners. The two countries have negotiated agreements to remove barriers to free trade. **(b)** Some Canadians blamed the FTA for plant closings and unemployment, as firms relocated south of the border where costs were lower.
4. Canada is a middle power in the global community. It maintains links with many nations through its membership in the Commonwealth of Nations.
5. Answers will vary. Some students may suggest that NAFTA will have positive effects on the Canadian economy because of the large trading bloc it creates. Others may predict unemployment and other negative effects as firms relocate south of the border where costs are lower. According to Pearson, international agreements (in this case, NAFTA) help to promote peace.

Activity Rubrics Share rubrics with students before they begin their posters.
Attempted The poster is attempted but is sketchy or incomplete.
Minimal The poster shows limited understanding of the ties between Canada and the United States.
Adequate The poster is well presented and reflects a good understanding of the relationship between Canada and the United States.
Exemplary The poster is very well executed and includes a variety of examples of cultural, economic, and physical links between the two countries.

Answers to Chart Skills

United States

Canada; its population is concentrated in the southern part of the country.

Creating a Chapter Summary

As a reteaching opportunity, pair a more able student with a less able student to complete this chapter summary.

Possible answers: **Cultures:** British, Asian, Native Canadian **Natural Resources:** Minerals, Forests, Fish **Global Trade Patterns:** NAFTA

Reviewing Key Terms

1–7. Students' sentences and answers should demonstrate a clear understanding of the key terms.

Understanding Key Ideas

8. The Maritimes have few natural resources other than the sea.
9. (a) The Canadian Shield has poor soil and a cold climate.
(b) The Hudson Bay Lowlands are flat and swampy. **(c)** The St. Lawrence Lowlands have rich soil and a relatively mild climate.
10. The country is vast, and great differences exist among the provinces and territories, as well as among the people.
11. Canada was under direct British rule from 1763 until 1867, when it gained limited self-rule. It became completely independent in 1931, although the British monarch remains the symbolic ruler.
12. providing housing and services, controlling pollution, and preventing overcrowding
13. Because it has major ports on both the Atlantic and the Pacific, Canada has trade access to both Asia and Europe.

Critical Thinking and Writing

14. Quebec, the oldest city in Canada, is a popular tourist attraction because of its historic sites and European charm. It is the center of Canada's French Canadian population. Vancouver has an excellent harbor and is Canada's major Pacific port. Many immigrants from Asia, as well as Canadians from other provinces, have moved there.
15. The Great Lakes–St. Lawrence waterway system is known as Canada's highway to the sea because of the volume of goods that travel its length.

Creating a Chapter Summary

Copy this concept web on a piece of paper. Fill in each circle with supporting details about each topic. Some information has been filled in to help you get started.

Take It to the NET
Chapter Self-Test For practice test questions for Chapter 8, go to the World Geography section of **www.phschool.com**.

Reviewing Key Terms

Write sentences using the chapter key terms listed below, leaving blanks where the key terms would go. Exchange your sentences with those of another student and fill in the blanks in each other's sentences.

1. province
2. maritime
3. lock
4. bedrock
5. separatism
6. secede
7. customs

Understanding Key Ideas

8. Patterns of Settlement Why do most residents of the Maritimes live along the coast?

9. Physical Characteristics Describe the landscape and climate of **(a)** the Canadian Shield, **(b)** the Hudson Bay Lowlands, **(c)** the St. Lawrence Lowlands.

10. Cultures Why has it been difficult for Canada to establish a single national identity?

11. Understanding the Past What historical ties does Canada have with Britain?

12. Planning for the Future What challenges does Canada face as a result of urbanization?

13. Global Trade Patterns How does Canada's location influence its role in international trade?

Critical Thinking and Writing

14. Making Comparisons Compare the characteristics of the cities of Quebec and Vancouver.

15. Identifying Relationships How does southern Canada's economy rely on waterways and railroads?

16. Analyzing Causes and Effects How do Canada's ethnic composition and official languages reflect its history?

17. Drawing Conclusions How does climate affect patterns of settlement in Canada?

18. Defending a Position Suppose that you are an industrialist seeking to mine and transport large reserves of natural resources from beneath the Canadian tundra. Write a proposal for your plan, including possible economic and environmental effects.

Railroads transport Canada's agricultural products to market.
16. England and France colonized much of Canada. Today, 40 percent of Canadians are of British ancestry; 27 percent are of French ancestry. English and French are the official languages.
17. Few people live in Canada's northern latitudes, where the climate is cold. The population is concentrated in the southern part of the country. Sixty percent of Canada's population lives in the St. Lawrence Lowlands, where the climate is relatively mild.
18. Answers will vary. Students' proposals should point out the northern territories' wealth of minerals and large reserves of petroleum and natural gas, while emphasizing the need to protect the tundra and wildlife.

Applying Skills

Summarizing Main Ideas Review what you learned in the Skills for Life lesson on page 192. Follow the steps there to summarize the main ideas in the section The Prairie Provinces on pages 185–186.

19. Based on the section subheads, what topics does the section cover?

20. What details are provided about economic activities in the Prairie Provinces?

21. Create a graphic organizer that summarizes the main ideas of this section.

Analyzing a Photograph Study the photograph below, and answer the following questions:

22. What might be one reason why these logs are being transported by water rather than on trucks or trains?

23. What secondary economic activities are based on the primary activity shown in the photograph?

Test Preparation

Read the question and choose the best answer.

24. Many English-speaking residents and businesses left Quebec when the —

A province suffered economically in 1976

B French-Canadian population spoke out in favor of NAFTA

C Quebecois voted to secede from the rest of Canada

D government of Quebec made French the official language of the province

Activities

USING THE REGIONAL ATLAS

Review the information in this chapter and in the Regional Atlas for the United States and Canada. Suppose that a new city was being built in Canada and you are to decide where it should be located. Draw up a proposal, giving reasons for your choice of location. Consider such factors as climate, natural resources, and access to transportation.

 MENTAL MAPPING

Review a political map of Canada. On a separate piece of paper, draw a sketch map of Canada from memory. Label the following places on your map:

- Halifax
- Hudson Bay
- Toronto
- Ontario
- Victoria
- Great Lakes
- Yukon Territory
- Northwest Territories
- Newfoundland
- Winnipeg

 Take It to the NET

Solving Problems Search the Internet for information about modern technology to extract oil and mineral resources from Canada's northern territories. Explain how technology is reducing the negative impact on the environment. Visit the World Geography section of **www.phschool.com** for help in completing this activity.

Applying Skills

19. Patterns of Settlement, Economic Activities

20. Details: Most of Canada's grain and cattle comes from the Prairie Provinces; tourism and the oil industry are also important economic activities.

21. Check that students' graphic organizers accurately reflect the main ideas of the section.

22. Possible answer: The mountainous terrain makes water transport more practical than train or truck transport.

23. Answers include producing lumber, wood pulp, plywood, and other products.

Test Preparation
24. D

Activities

Using the Regional Atlas
Check that students have given valid reasons supporting their choice of location.

Mental Mapping
Review students' maps for relative and absolute locations.

Take It to the Net
Students' work should reflect sound research and accurately convey the role of technology in the development of Canada's northern resources.

MENTAL MAPPING

Games for Review See pages 58–63 of the Simulations, Games, and Lab Activities booklet for games to review place names.
Chapter Map Test Students should use their completed Chapter 8 Outline Map and the Unit 2 Checklist in their Atlas Portfolios to prepare for the Chapter 8 Map Test.
Unit Map Test To prepare for the Unit 2 Map Test, students will need to study the locations of the place names on the Unit 2 Checklist.

Alternative Assessment

Final Evaluation

Writing a Position Paper Use the Position Paper Evaluation Form on page 9 of the Alternative Assessment booklet in the Prentice Hall Assessment System to evaluate students' papers. Either teachers or students can complete the forms to indicate which level of work was achieved for each of the criteria. The evaluation should include specific examples and comments.

Objectives

Upon completion of this feature, students should be able to:

◆ describe where the world's coniferous forests are located;

◆ recognize the features that enable conifers to withstand long, cold winters;

◆ identify the behaviors and adaptations that enable animals to survive in northern coniferous forests.

 National Geography Standards

The following National Geography Standards are highlighted in this feature: 1, 4, 7, 8

 Bellringer

Have students list three features that make evergreen trees different from other trees. Examples might include pointy leaves or needles, pine cones, and staying green all year. Have students list types of trees found in their region. Then ask: **Are the trees you listed conifers or deciduous trees? How do you know?**

LESSON PLAN

1. Focus Have students read the introductory paragraph. Ask: **What is the feature that all conifers share?** (They carry their seeds in cones.) Then make a list on the board of all the conifers they can name. (Spruce, pine, juniper, cedar, sequoia, redwood, fir, and cypress are some possible answers.)

2. Instruct Create a three-column chart about the types of animals that live in coniferous forests. Label the columns: *Type of Animal, Feature or Habit,* and *How It Promotes Survival.* Have students complete the chart using information from the feature.

3. Close/Reteach Have students review the feature and their completed charts. Ask them to write a paragraph describing the plant and animal life in a coniferous forest.

How the Earth Works

Coniferous Forests

The world's largest forests extend across the far north, where winters can last for eight months. These dense **coniferous forests** consist of spruces, pines, and other trees that carry their seeds in cones. They are particularly suited for coping with cold conditions. Animals in northern forests find plentiful food during the long days of summer, but the season is brief and cold weather soon returns. To survive the harsh winter, many animals migrate south, while others hibernate.

Distribution of northern coniferous forests

FORESTS AND LAKES
Coniferous forests often grow on land once covered by ice age glaciers. These glaciers scoured the ground, scraping away soil and creating rounded hills and hollows. When the glaciers melted, the hills became covered with trees and the hollows turned into lakes.

CONIFER LEAVES
Most conifers have small evergreen leaves that are tough enough to withstand the colde winters. A narrow shape helps the leaves to cope with strong winds.

White spruce

Waterlogged soil beneath trees is acidic and infertile.

Bobcat

PREDATORS
Mammals are relatively scarce in northern forests, so the **predators** that feed upon other animals sometimes ha to cover vast distances to fin food. Bobcats may roam many miles searching for small prey. Wolves hunt in packs for deer and other large mammals.

198   Chapter 8 ▪ Canada

RESOURCE DIRECTORY

Technology
World Geography Map and Photo Transparencies
• How the Earth Works, Unit 2
Companion Web site, www.phschool.com
• Chapter 8 Activities

1. A horntail lays eggs deep in a tree trunk.

2. Young larvae bore away from the drill-hole.

3. Each larva matures inside a chamber near the bark of the tree.

EATING WOOD

Several insects of northern forests feed on wood. The horntail, or giant wood wasp, lays eggs by drilling deep beneath tree bark with a long egg-laying tube. The larvae hatch and mature inside the tree while feeding on the wood.

ed crossbill

SEED EATERS

Some birds rely on conifer seeds for food. Crossbill finches have unique bills that are crossed at the tips. This helps them remove seeds from cones. Clark's nutcracker, a member of the crow family, hides 20,000 or more seeds each fall. It is able to remember the locations of many of these seeds for up to nine months.

Spruce cone

Cold lake water contains few nutrients but is often rich in oxygen.

Caribou

ADAPTED FOR TRAVEL

To help them walk across thick layers of snow without sinking, caribou and elk have hooves with broadly splayed toes that help to distribute their weight. Lynx and snowshoe hares have similar adaptations.

Caribou hooves act as snowshoes.

COPING WITH COLD

To avoid extreme winter temperatures, bears, woodchucks, and other mammals hibernate. During the fall, they build up a store of fat in their bodies that will last until spring. They then go into **hibernation,** which slows their bodily functions to a minimum.

Woodchuck

ASSESSMENT

1. **Key Terms** Define **(a)** coniferous forest, **(b)** predator, **(c)** hibernation.

2. **Climates** Describe the climatic conditions that are generally found in northern coniferous forests.

3. **Ecosystems** How do trees serve as a food source for birds and insects?

4. **Ecosystems** How are mammals of northern coniferous forests well suited for survival in their natural environment?

5. **Critical Thinking Developing a Hypothesis** Deforestation has not reduced northern coniferous forests to the same degree that it has reduced mid-latitude deciduous forests. Why do you think that northern coniferous forests have fared better than deciduous forests to the south?

Chapter 8   **199**

CUSTOMIZE FOR...

Honors/PreAP

Hibernation Mammals are not the only animals that hibernate in winter. Many fish, amphibians, and reptiles are also hibernators. Divide the class into groups and have each find out how one type of animal hibernates. Have each group explain how that type of hibernation differs from mammal hibernation.

ACTIVITY

Vocabulary

Coniferous Point out to students that *coniferous* sounds very much like another scientific term, *carnivorous.* Have them contrast the origins of these words. (*Coniferous* comes from Latin and Greek roots that mean "cone-bearing." *Carnivorous* comes from the Latin words *caro,* which means "flesh," and *vorare,* which means "to swallow up.") Encourage students to use both words correctly in sentences.

ACTIVITY

Reteach

Conifer Needles Have students collect or draw the needles of different kinds of conifers. Then have them write a paragraph that explains how the leaves are well adapted for cold climates. Display collections and paragraphs in the classroom. (Bodily/Kinesthetic; Visual/Spatial)

Answers to Assessment

1. (a) coniferous forest, p. 198 **(b)** predator, p. 198 **(c)** hibernation, p. 199

2. Winters are long and cold; summers are brief.

3. Some insects eat wood. Some birds eat conifer seeds.

4. Some mammals, such as elk, have splayed toes that help them walk on snow. Other mammals build up stores of fat during the fall that will last until spring. In winter they hibernate.

5. Possible answer: Fewer people have wanted to settle in cold, northern areas. The land is not suited to farming so humans have not cut these forests to clear land.

Use this sample exam to help your students prepare for standardized tests.

You might want to remind your students of the following:

Tips for Test Taking

1. Read the directions carefully.
2. Read each question carefully.
3. For multiple choice questions, try to answer the question before you look at the choices. Read all the choices. Then, eliminate those that are absolutely incorrect.
4. For short answer questions, be sure to answer the question completely if there is more than one part.
5. Answer the easy questions first. Then, go back to the ones that will take more time.
6. Pace yourself. Be sure to set aside enough time for the writing questions.

Write answers on a separate sheet of paper.

Multiple Choice

1 In which region of the United States are arid and semiarid climate conditions most prevalent?

   A Northeast

   B South

   C Midwest

   D West

Use the graph <u>and</u> your knowledge of social studies to answer the following question.

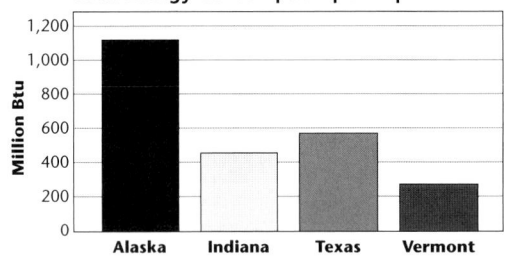

Total Energy Consumption per Capita

Sources: Energy Information Administration, U.S. Department of Energy

2 Which of the following statements is supported by the data in this bar graph?

   A Climate conditions require people in Alaska to use great amounts of energy for heat.

   B Alaska's per capita energy use is high because it is separated from the rest of the United States by British Columbia.

   C Texas uses more energy per capita than any other state.

   D Vermont has used tough conservation measures to keep its per capita energy use low.

3 Which of the following was a national human activity that led to modifications of the environment of the Great Plains?

   A Invention of the telegraph

   B Use of rivers for transportation

   C Reliance on free enterprise

   D Passage of the Homestead Act in 1862

4 Hibernation is a way some animals have adapted to —

   A a climate with extremely cold winter conditions

   B an ecosytem that is difficult to move through because of the abundance of trees

   C the clearing of forest lands as a result of human settlement and development

   D a physical landscape that has been shaped by the effects of glacial erosion

5 The key element in the growth of the cities of Edmonton, Calgary, Winnipeg, Saskatoon, and Regina was —

   A introduction of the interstate highway system

   B construction of rail lines across Canada

   C expansion of the lumber industry

   D location along the Atlantic coast

6 Which of the following is a distinctive cultural pattern of the United States that has encouraged immigration?

   A Innovations in transportation

   B Establishment of national parks

   C Expansion of suburbs

   D Support for free enterprise

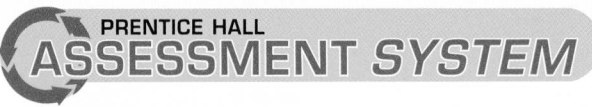

PRENTICE HALL

ASSESSMENT *SYSTEM*

Diagnose and Prescribe
- Profile student skills with Diagnostic Tests A&B.
- Address student needs with program materials identified in the test.

Review and Reteach
- Provide cumulative content review with the Review Book.

Practice and Assess
- Build test-taking skills with Test-Taking Strategies on Transparencies.

Use the map <u>and</u> your knowledge of social studies to answer the following question.

Source: New York State Canal Corporation

7 Which result of the Erie Canal is best supported by the map?

A A more direct route was established between New York City and Rochester.

B The Erie Canal created a waterway that connected Lake Ontario and Lake Erie.

C Easier transportation between inland and coastal cities encouraged economic growth.

D The Erie Canal made the city of Albany so important that it became the capital of the state of New York.

8 In the early 1900s, Americans perceived kudzu as a valuable resource for controlling erosion. Which statement best summarizes the general perception of kudzu today?

A Kudzu is a popular food in restaurants and a good source of iron and calcium.

B Kudzu is a valuable resource because it can be used in the battle against zebra mussels.

C Kudzu is a problem because it has been affected by a disease and is on the verge of extinction.

D Kudzu is a problem because it overwhelms and kills many native plants.

Use the quotation <u>and</u> your knowledge of social studies to answer the following question.

> I have one love—Canada; one purpose—Canada's greatness; one aim—Canadian unity from the Atlantic to the Pacific.
>
> –John Diefenbaker, Prime Minister of Canada, 1957–1963

9 Based on this statement, which of the following political movements would Diefenbaker have been most likely to oppose?

A Creation of the Dominion of Canada

B Separatism in Quebec

C Canadian independence

D Establishment of Nunavut

10 How did the northeastern United States become an important economic center in spite of its thin, rocky soil and few mineral resources?

A Industrialists used the region's waterways to build factories and establish trade routes.

B The region's population grew as people moved away from cities in the South and West.

C Long-established businesses in cities of the Northeast had an edge over those in newly developed parts of the country.

D Businesses took advantage of their colonial ties to secure foreign capital for expansion.

Writing Practice

11 What secondary and tertiary economic activities might you expect to find in an area dominated by the primary economic activity of gold mining?

12 Explain the term *megalopolis*. Then, discuss the main advantages and disadvantages of living in a megalopolis.

13 How has climate encouraged changes in population density in the United States since the 1960s?

Multiple Choice

1 D

2 A

3 D

4 A

5 B

6 D

7 B

8 D

9 B

10 A

Writing Practice

11 Possible answer: Secondary economic activities might include the work of jewelers and goldsmiths. Tertiary economic activities might include businesses providing miners with food, housing, clothing, or supplies.

12 *Megalopolis* means "a very large city"; geographically, the term refers to a phenomenon in which neighboring cities grow so large that they run together. Some advantages of living in a megalopolis are that it allows a person to participate in the area's business and cultural opportunities. Disadvantages include periodic shortages of water, electricity, and services such as waste disposal, mass transportation, and law enforcement.

13 Mild climates have attracted people from colder climates to the Sunbelt, a region that includes states that stretch from the Carolinas to southern California.

Introducing

Latin America

Activating Prior Knowledge

Ask students to list as many Latin American nations as they can without looking at a map. Students may not realize that much of South America is farther east than North America. Ask students to look at the World Political map in the Atlas to point this out.

Photo Study

The Amazon River

The Amazon River of South America is the longest river in the Western Hemisphere. The Amazon carries more water than any other river. It is estimated that one sixth to one fifth of all the water that runs off the surface of the earth flows through the Amazon. **Drawing Conclusions** Ask students to use the map on page 207 to locate the source and mouth of the Amazon. (source: in the Andes not far from the Pacific Ocean; mouth: in northeast Brazil into the Atlantic Ocean)

eTeach

Be sure to check out this month's online forum with a Master Teacher to join in an exchange of teaching ideas. **www.phschool.com**

Latin America

Locating the Region

Latin America begins at the southern border of the United States and stretches southward to the tip of stormy Cape Horn, almost to Antarctica. The countries of this large region are located in North, South, and Central America and on many islands in the Caribbean Sea.

Robinson Projection

RESOURCE DIRECTORY

Teaching Resources

Unit 3
• Geography and World Literature, The Younger Brother, p. 65

Mental Mapping booklet
• Unit 3 Checklist, p. 34
• Unit 3 Map Test, p. 38

Simulations, Games, and Lab Activities
• Where on Earth? Games, pp. 68–69

Global Environmental Posters

Technology

TeacherExpress™ CD-ROM
World Geography: Building a Global Perspective Teaching Resources on CD-ROM offers lesson planning flexibility, test-generation capability, and resource manageability.

Prentice Hall Presentation Pro CD-ROM
This CD-ROM allows you to create custom lessons for instruction or review for every chapter.

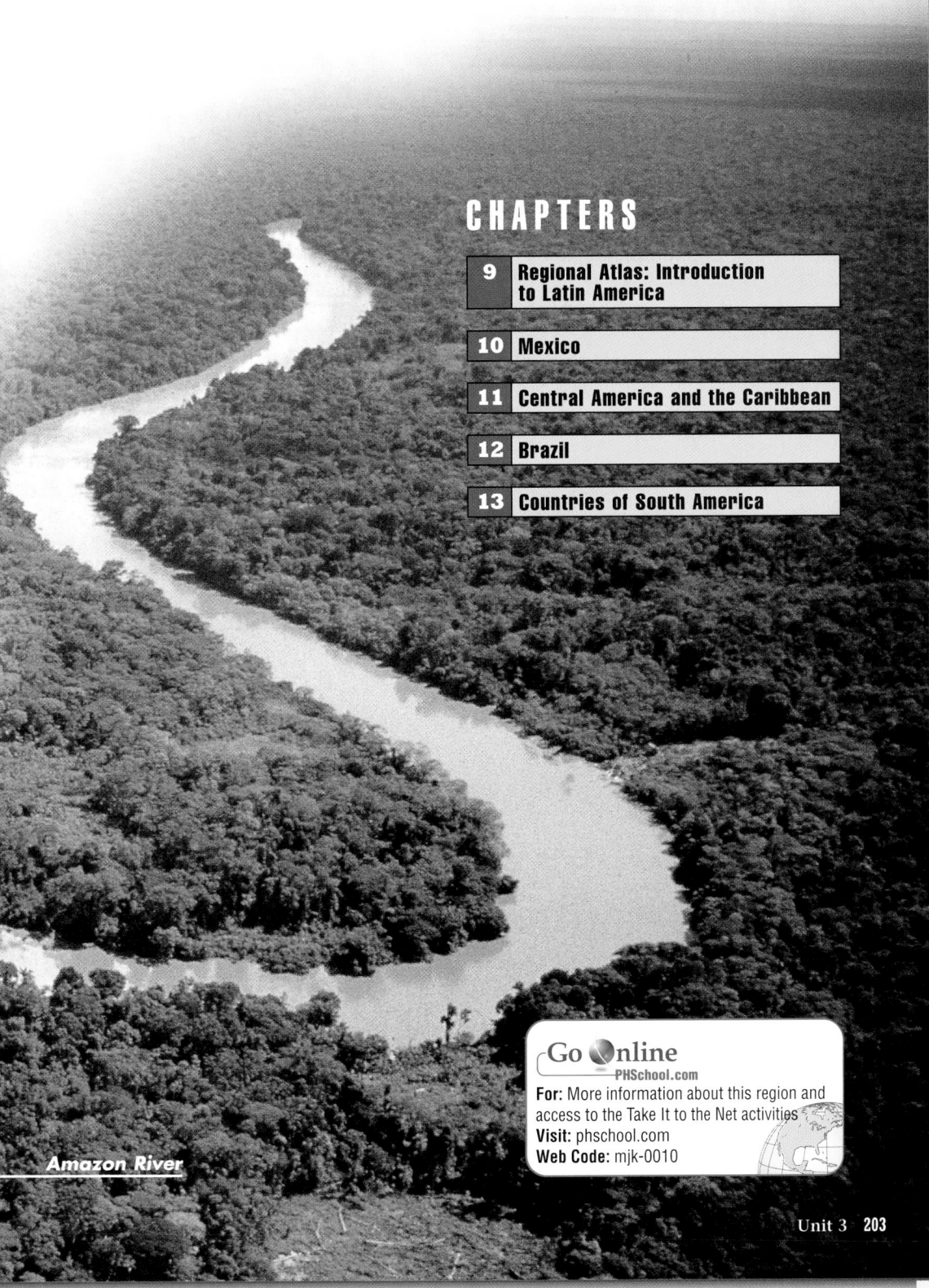

CHAPTERS

Go Online
PHSchool.com
For: More information about this region and access to the Take It to the Net activities
Visit: phschool.com
Web Code: mjk-0010

Amazon River

Unit 3   203

Promoting Geographic Understanding

Introduce the unit by using the themes below.

1. Location Direct students to the Robinson projection map on the facing page. Ask students to name the bodies of water that border Latin America. (Atlantic Ocean, Pacific Ocean, Caribbean Sea, Gulf of Mexico) Ask: **What continent borders South America to the north?** (North America)

2. Region Point out that Mexico, the seven countries of Central America, the Caribbean islands, and the twelve countries of South America — as well as the French overseas department of French Guiana—make up the region called Latin America. Ask students: **What language do most people in Latin America speak?** (Spanish) **What clue does this give about the history of Latin America?** (There must have been contact between the people of Latin America and Spain at some time.) Tell the students that the reason the region is called Latin America is because the major languages of the region (Spanish, Portuguese, and French) are based on Latin, which was the language of ancient Rome.

Resource Manager

	CORE INSTRUCTION	READING/SKILLS
Chapter-Level Resources	📘 Teaching Resources 📗 **Unit 3**/Ch. 9 • Regional Atlas Study Guide, p. 2 📖 **Mental Mapping booklet** • Unit 3 Checklist, p. 34 📖 **Simulations, Games, and Lab Activities** • Place Location Review Games, pp. 58–63 💿 **TeacherExpress™ CD-ROM**, Ch. 9 💻 **Companion Web site, www.phschool.com** • eTeach	📘 Teaching Resources 📗 **Unit 3**/Ch. 9 • Regional Atlas Review, p. 3 📖 **Guide to the Essentials (English/Spanish)** • Chapter 9 Summary 📖 **Spanish Resources** • Regional Atlas Review, p. 23 📼 **Guided Reading Audiotapes (English/Spanish)**, Ch. 9 📖 **Section Reading Support Transparencies**, Ch. 9 💿 **Book on CD**, Ch. 9 💿 **Social Studies Skills Tutor CD-ROM**
Historical Overview Describe significant events and developments in the history of Latin America.	📘 Teaching Resources 📖 **Mental Mapping booklet** • Outline Map 9A, p. 35 💿 **Prentice Hall Presentation Pro CD-ROM**, Ch. 9	📘 Teaching Resources 📖 **Social Studies Skills Handbook** • Reading a Political Map, p. 19
Physical Characteristics Identify major physical characteristics of Latin America.	📘 Teaching Resources 📖 **Mental Mapping booklet** • Outline Map 9B, p. 36 💿 **Prentice Hall Presentation Pro CD-ROM**, Ch. 9	📘 Teaching Resources 📖 **Social Studies Skills Handbook** • Elevation on a Map, p. 20 • Four Types of Landforms, p. 21 • Relief on a Map, p. 22
Climates Compare climate regions in Latin America.	💿 **Prentice Hall Presentation Pro CD-ROM**, Ch. 9	📘 Teaching Resources 📖 **Social Studies Skills Handbook** • Reading a Climate Map, p. 26 • Reading a Climate Graph, p. 65 • Comparing Climate Graphs, p. 66
Ecosystems Describe characteristics of major ecosystems in Latin America.	💿 **Prentice Hall Presentation Pro CD-ROM**, Ch. 9	📘 Teaching Resources 📖 **Social Studies Skills Handbook** • Reading a Natural Vegetation Map, p. 25
People and Cultures Discuss elements of culture in Latin America.	📘 Teaching Resources 📖 **Creative Teaching Activities** • Latin American Music, p. 11 💿 **Prentice Hall Presentation Pro CD-ROM**, Ch. 9	📘 Teaching Resources 📖 **Social Studies Skills Handbook** • Reading a Population Density Map, p. 31
Economics, Technology, and Environment Identify how the economy, technology, and environment interact in Latin America.	💿 **Prentice Hall Presentation Pro CD-ROM**, Ch. 9	📘 Teaching Resources 📖 **Social Studies Skills Handbook** • Reading an Economic Activity Map, p. 27 • Reading a Natural Resources Map, p. 34
Database • Understand how a country's GDP per capita is determined. • Describe the various economic systems found within Latin America. • Compare the economies of Latin American countries to that of the United States.	📘 Teaching Resources 📗 **Unit 3**/Ch. 9 • Regional Atlas Database Skills, p. 4 💿 **Prentice Hall Presentation Pro CD-ROM**, Ch. 9	📘 Teaching Resources 📗 **Unit 3**/Ch. 9 • Regional Atlas Database Skills, p. 4 📖 **Social Studies Skills Handbook** • Reading a Table, p. 62

ENRICHMENT/HONORS/PREAP

Teaching Resources

Mental Mapping booklet
• Atlas Activity, p. 37

Social Studies Skills Handbook
• Study and Research Skills, pp. 94–108

World Geography Map and Photo Transparencies
• Latin America: Maps and Photos

World Geography Videos
• Regional Atlas: Latin America, Tape 1

Companion Web site, www.phschool.com
• Chapter 9 Activities

World Geography Map and Photo Transparencies
• Latin America: Political

World Geography Map and Photo Transparencies
• Latin America: Physical

Teaching Resources

Simulations, Games, and Lab Activities
• Where on Earth?, The Vanished Expedition, pp. 68–69

World Geography Map and Photo Transparencies
• World Climate Zones

Teaching Resources

Simulations, Games, and Lab Activities
• Should Cooper's Point Be Developed?, pp. 17–22

World Geography Map and Photo Transparencies
• Latin America: Natural Hazards

World Geography Map and Photo Transparencies
• Latin America: Population Density

World Geography Map and Photo Transparencies
• Latin America: Economic Activities

World Geography Map and Photo Transparencies
• Per Capita GDP

ASSESSMENT

PRENTICE HALL
ASSESSMENT SYSTEM

Core Assessment

ExamView Test Bank booklet, Ch. 9

ExamView Test Bank CD-ROM, Ch. 9

Standardized Test Preparation

Diagnose and Prescribe

Diagnostic Tests for High School Social Studies Skills

Review and Reteach

Review Book for World Geography, pp. 7–8

Practice and Assess

Test-taking Strategies With Transparencies for High School

Test-taking Strategy Poster

Alternative Assessment booklet

Test Prep Book for World Geography

Teaching Resources

Unit 3/Ch. 9
• Test Forms A and B, pp. 5–10

Guide to the Essentials (English/Spanish)
• Chapter 9 Test

Mental Mapping booklet
• Chapter 9 Map Test, p. 38

Companion Web site, www.phschool.com
• Chapter 9 Self-Test

CUSTOMIZE FOR INDIVIDUAL NEEDS

Gifted and Talented
• Teacher's Edition, Customize for . . . , p. 213

Less Proficient Readers
• Guide to the Essentials (English), Ch. 9
• Social Studies Skills Handbook, p. 76
• Guided Reading Audiotapes (English), Ch. 9
• Section Reading Support Transparencies, Ch. 9
• Book on CD, Ch. 9

Students Acquiring English/ESL
• Guide to the Essentials (English/Spanish), Ch. 9
• Guided Reading Audiotapes (English/Spanish), Ch. 9
• Section Reading Support Transparencies, Ch. 9
• Book on CD, Ch. 9

Less Proficient Writers
• Social Studies Skills Handbook, p. 85
• Alternative Assessment, Writing Assignment Rubric, p. 6

Objectives

Upon completion of this Regional Atlas, students should be able to:

◆ describe significant events and developments in the history of Latin America;

◆ identify major physical characteristics of Latin America;

◆ compare climate regions in Latin America;

◆ describe characteristics of major ecosystems in Latin America;

◆ discuss elements of culture in Latin America;

◆ identify how the economy, technology, and the environment interact in Latin America.

National Geography Standards

The following National Geography Standards are highlighted in this section: 1, 2, 3, 4, 5, 8, 9, 14, 15

Bellringer

Write the following words on the board: *tango, rumba, samba, reggae, mariachi, tortilla, taco, plaza, patio.* Then put the headings *Music/Dance, Food,* and *Place* on the board at the top of three columns. Ask the students to identify into which of these categories each of the words fits. Point out that these are just a few of the cultural imports to the United States from Latin America.

Answers to Assessment

1. (a) conquistador, p. 204
(b) cultural convergence, p. 204
(c) *caudillo,* p. 204

2. Possible answers: Martinique, Guadeloupe, French Guiana

3. Check students' answers for grammar and content

Historical Overview

Thousands of years ago, people migrated to the Americas. There, some people organized complex societies and developed agriculture. The Mayas and Aztecs established civilizations in Mexico, while the Incas conquered a vast territory in South America. The people in these areas were skilled farmers and developed advanced knowledge in many fields.

New Cultures   After Christopher Columbus landed in the West Indies in 1492, Spanish explorers called **conquistadors,** or conquerors, came from Europe. Soon, much of Latin America became part of the Spanish or Portuguese empires. The Europeans brought enslaved Africans to work on plantations in the Americas. This **cultural convergence,** or merging of cultures, led to a new culture that combined Native American, European, and African traditions. A colonial class structure also developed, with people of European descent at the top.

Independent Republics   In the late 1700s and early 1800s, people of Latin America fought successfully for independence. Toussaint L'Ouverture, a self-educated former slave, led the revolt against French rule in Haiti. In South America, Simón Bolívar led resistance against the Spanish. He waged a series of military campaigns that won independence for present-day Venezuela, Colombia, Panama, Ecuador, Peru, and Bolivia. José de San Martín defeated the Spanish in Argentina and Chile.

A number of Latin American republics were established, but democracy did not follow. One problem was that the colonial class structure and economy remained largely intact. Latin American economies were dependent on cash crops and trade with Europe. If a crop failure occurred, or if prices for the products fell, economic ruin followed. Local military rulers called **caudillos** often seized power. These dictators usually favored the upper classes.

Struggles for Reform   In the 1900s, Latin Americans struggled for reform. Mexicans rebelled against dictator Porfirio Díaz, whose brutal rule left most Mexicans landless and poor. In 1917, a new Mexican constitution called for land reform and more rights for workers and women. Even so, injustices continued. Elsewhere, Cuba underwent a revolution in 1959 that led to a communist dictatorship. In Argentina, a series of military regimes ruled with an iron hand. Military rule finally gave way to democracy in the last decades of the century. Other countries that seemed to be moving toward more democratic government included Brazil, Guatemala, and Nicaragua.

Economic Gains   Latin Americans also worked to achieve substantial economic gains. In various countries, governments pursued economic policies that reduced dependence on a single crop, promoted modern technology and industry, and eased debt. They also took measures to reduce foreign control of businesses. Today, foreign companies still invest in the region, but they must abide by laws and regulations set by the Latin American governments.

ASSESSMENT

1. **Key Terms**   Define **(a)** conquistador, **(b)** cultural convergence, **(c)** *caudillo.*

2. **Map Skills**   **Regions**   What Latin American territories are still owned by France (Fr.)?

3. **Critical Thinking**   **Identifying Main Ideas**   For each paragraph in the above overview, write an original sentence that summarizes the main idea of the paragraph.

RESOURCE DIRECTORY

Teaching Resources

Unit 3, Chapter 9
• Regional Atlas Study Guide, p. 2
Guide to the Essentials (English/Spanish)
• Chapter 9 Summary
Mental Mapping booklet
• Unit 3 Checklist, p. 34
• Outline Map 9A, p. 35
Social Studies Skills Handbook
• Reading a Political Map, p. 19

Technology

Guided Reading Audiotapes (English/Spanish),
   Chapter 9
Section Reading Support Transparencies, Chapter 9
World Geography Map and Photo Transparencies
• Latin America: Maps and Photos
World Geography Videos
• Regional Atlas: Latin America, Tape 1
Book on CD, Chapter 9

REGIONAL ATLAS

Latin America: POLITICAL

UNITED STATES

Gulf of Mexico

ATLANTIC OCEAN

Tropic of Cancer

Nassau
BAHAMAS

MEXICO

Havana
CUBA

Mexico City

DOMINICAN REPUBLIC
PUERTO RICO (U.S.)
San Juan
HAITI
Port-au-Prince
Santo Domingo

VIRGIN IS. (U.K and U.S.)
ST. KITTS & NEVIS
ANTIGUA & BARBUDA
GUADELOUPE (FR.)
DOMINICA
MARTINIQUE (FR.)
BARBADOS
GRENADA
TRINIDAD & TOBAGO

BELIZE
Belmopan
GUATEMALA
Guatemala
San Salvador
EL SALVADOR

Kingston JAMAICA

HONDURAS
Tegucigalpa
NICARAGUA
Managua

Caribbean Sea

ST. LUCIA
ST. VINCENT AND THE GRENADINES

L. Nicaragua

Caracas

San José
COSTA RICA
Panama
PANAMA

L. Maracaibo

VENEZUELA

GUYANA
Georgetown
SURINAME
Paramaribo
Cayenne
FRENCH GUIANA (FR.)

PACIFIC OCEAN

Equator

Bogotá
COLOMBIA

Galápagos Islands (Ec.)

Quito
ECUADOR

PERU

BRAZIL

Lima

KEY
— National boundary
⊛ National capital
• Other city

Lambert Azimuthal Equal-Area Projection

Titicaca
La Paz
BOLIVIA
Sucre

Brasília

Tropic of Capricorn

CHILE

PARAGUAY
Asunción

Rio de Janeiro
São Paulo

Santiago
ARGENTINA
URUGUAY
Buenos Aires
Montevideo

0   500   1,000 mi
0   500   1,000 km

ATLANTIC OCEAN

Falkland Islands (U.K.)
Tierra del Fuego
South Georgia Island (U.K.)

MENTAL MAPPING

Making a Political Map Study this political map and then draw your own sketch map of Latin America. Label the countries and major cities of the region. Use various colors to outline and shade each country.

1. Focus Point out that South America is a continent of superlatives: the world's second highest mountain range, largest rain forest, and the largest river by volume. Ask students to make a list of superlatives for South America as they study the continent.

2. Instruct Have students complete the Assessment questions and Mental Mapping activities as a class.

3. Close/Reteach Ask students to plan a trip to Latin America. Ask them to use the Regional Atlas to choose five different places they would like to visit and explain why.

Map Study Extension
Use the question below to develop an additional geographic theme.

Movement Help students understand the location of the United States in relation to the Caribbean islands. Ask: **If you wanted to reach the mainland United States from a Caribbean island, where would be your closest landing point?** (Florida)

Unit Checklist Distribute the Unit 3 Checklist on page 34 of the Mental Mapping booklet in the Teaching Resources. This checklist includes a list of all the place names, bodies of water, and physical features that students should learn in this unit.

Making a Political Map Students can complete the mapping activity on this page either by sketching their own maps or by coloring and labeling the Chapter 9A Outline Map on page 35 of the Mental Mapping booklet in the Teaching Resources. Ask students to label all of the countries and major cities listed under Part I of the Unit 3 Checklist.

Alternative Assessment

Introduce the Activity

Making Maps You may wish to distribute the Map Rubric found on page 14 of the Alternative Assessment booklet in the Prentice Hall Assessment System.

TEACHING TIP
From a Master Teacher

Latin America You will want to help students understand that the value of a region's resources changes over time. When the Portuguese and Spanish first made contact with Latin America, the world most valued its minerals, forest products, and crops. Latin American ecosystems and environments are now of great interest. Balance is sought between the needs for economic development and policies to preserve biodiversity, particularly in the dwindling rain forests.

Map Study Extension

Use the questions below to develop additional geographic themes.

1. Movement Instruct students to think about the effects of the mountain ranges of Latin America on transportation and communication. Ask: **If you planned to travel from Buenos Aires to Santiago, what would be your greatest obstacle?** (the Andes)

2. Human-Environment Interaction The population of Latin America tends to be concentrated in certain areas. Ask: **Name some of the physical features of Latin America that will not support large populations.** (People find it difficult to live in high mountain regions, rain forests, or deserts.)

Answers to Assessment

1. (a) pampas, p. 206 **(b)** cay, p. 206 **(c)** coral, p. 206

2. the Andes and along the Pacific Coast

3. Possible answer: It is the narrowest point between the Pacific Ocean and the Caribbean Sea.

Physical Characteristics

The Andes and other mountain ranges run the length of Mexico, Central America, and South America. They are part of the Ring of Fire that encircles the Pacific Ocean. Along the ring, earthquakes and volcanoes are common. The largest lowland areas are the Amazon River basin and the **pampas,** which are grassy plains in southeastern South America. Many islands are found in the Caribbean Sea. Some are the tops of underground mountains. Others are **cays** (KĒZ), formed over thousands of years from the accumulation of **coral,** the skeletons of tiny sea animals.

Andes Mountains

The rugged Andes are the highest mountains of Latin America. Like other mountain ranges, the Andes were formed when tectonic plates collided. **PHYSICAL CHARACTERISTICS** *Based on the map, along which coast do these mountains run?*

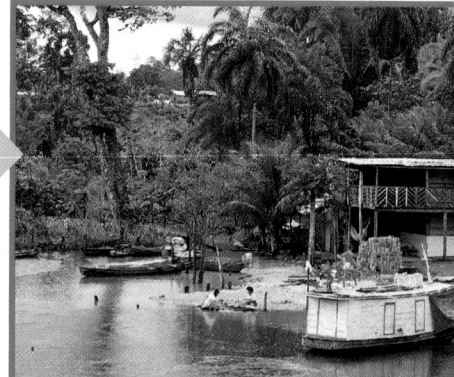

Amazon Lowlands

The Amazon Basin is the lowland area drained by the huge Amazon River and its many tributaries. High levels of rainfall and constant temperatures provide an endless growing season. These conditions encourage diverse plant and animal life. **PHYSICAL PROCESSES** *Look at the map and identify the ocean into which this river flows.*

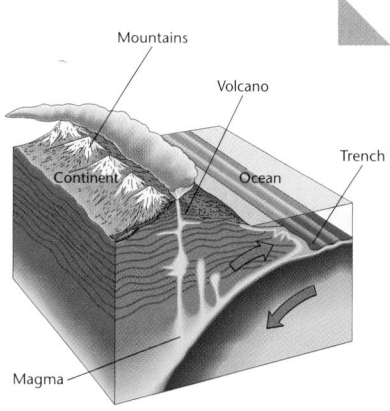

Mountains

Volcano

Trench

Continent

Ocean

Magma

Earthquakes and Volcanoes

Earthquakes are common where tectonic plates collide. In a volcanic eruption, magma is forced to the surface and is spewed out as molten lava. **NATURAL HAZARDS** *Why are earthquakes and volcanoes common along the Ring of Fire?*

ASSESSMENT

1. **Key Terms** Define **(a)** pampas, **(b)** cay, **(c)** coral.

2. **Map Skills** **Regions** Where would you expect to find tectonic plate boundaries in Latin America?

3. **Critical Thinking** **Analyzing Information** Based on the map, why do you think engineers chose the Isthmus of Panama as the location for a canal?

206 Chapter 9 ▪ Regional Atlas: Latin America

Answers to Photo Captions

Andes Mountains the west, or Pacific, coast

Amazon Lowlands the Atlantic Ocean

Earthquakes and Volcanoes because that is where tectonic plates meet and collide

RESOURCE DIRECTORY

Teaching Resources
Mental Mapping booklet
• Outline Map 9B, p. 36
• Unit 3 Checklist, p. 34
Social Studies Skills Handbook
• Elevation on a Map, p. 20
• Four Types of Landforms, p. 21
• Relief on a Map, p. 22

Technology
World Geography Map and Photo Transparencies
• Latin America: Maps and Photos
TeacherExpress™ CD-ROM, Chapter 9
Prentice Hall Presentation Pro CD-ROM, Chapter 9
Social Studies Skills Tutor CD-ROM
Companion Web site, www.phschool.com
• Chapter 9 Activities

REGIONAL ATLAS

Latin America: PHYSICAL

UNITED STATES

ATLANTIC OCEAN

Gulf of Mexico

Tropic of Cancer

BAHAMAS

Monterrey

Straits of Florida

Havana

GREATER ANTILLES

CUBA

DOMINICAN REPUBLIC

PUERTO RICO (U.S.)

VIRGIN IS. (U.K. and U.S.)

ST. KITTS & NEVIS

ANTIGUA & BARBUDA

GUADELOUPE (FR.)

DOMINICA

MARTINIQUE (FR.)

BARBADOS

Orizaba 18,406 ft. (5,610 m)

Guadalajara

YUCATÁN PENINSULA

Mexico City

MEXICO

BELIZE

JAMAICA

HAITI

Hispaniola

San Juan

Caribbean Sea

ST. LUCIA

ST. VINCENT AND THE GRENADINES

GRENADA

GUATEMALA

HONDURAS

EL SALVADOR

NICARAGUA

ISTHMUS OF PANAMA

Panama Canal

Caracas

TRINIDAD & TOBAGO

L. Nicaragua

COSTA RICA

PANAMA

Bogotá

Maracaibo

COLOMBIA

Orinoco R.

VENEZUELA

GUIANA HIGHLANDS

GUYANA

SURINAME

FRENCH GUIANA (FR.)

PACIFIC OCEAN

Quito

ECUADOR

Galápagos Islands (Ec.)

Chimborazo 20,697 ft. (6,310 m)

Equator

AMAZON BASIN

Manaus

Amazon R.

PERU

Madeira R.

Xingu R.

Tocantins R.

São Francisco R.

BRAZIL

Lima

L. Titicaca

BOLIVIA

Brasília

Guallatiri 19,882 ft. (6,060 m)

BRAZILIAN HIGHLANDS

Llullaillaco 22,057 ft. (6,723 m)

GRAN CHACO

PARAGUAY

Paraguay R.

São Paulo

Rio de Janeiro

Paraná R.

CHILE

Aconcagua 22,834 ft. (6,960 m)

Santiago

URUGUAY

Uruguay R.

Buenos Aires

PAMPAS

ARGENTINA

Río de la Plata

Tropic of Capricorn

ATLANTIC OCEAN

PATAGONIA

Falkland Islands (U.K.)

Strait of Magellan

Tierra del Fuego

Cape Horn

South Georgia Island (U.K.)

KEY

Elevation

Feet		Meters
14,000		4,268
7,000		2,134
1,500		457
700		213
(sea level) 0		0 (sea level)

• Major city
▲ Mountain
△ Volcano

Lambert Azimuthal Equal-Area Projection

| 0 | 500 | 1,000 mi |
| 0 | 500 | 1,000 km |

Making a Physical Map Study this physical map and then draw your own sketch map of Latin America. Label the major physical features, including rivers and other bodies of water.

Mapping Physical Features Students can complete the mapping activity on this page either by adding labels to the political maps they have already completed or by coloring and labeling the Chapter 9B Outline Map on page 36 of the Mental Mapping booklet in the Teaching Resources. Ask students to label all of the bodies of water and landforms listed under Part II of the Unit 3 Checklist.

ACTIVITY

Connecting With . . .

Science South America is home to many diverse species of animal life. Have students prepare reports on the animals of the Pampas (rhea, Patagonian weasel), Andes (chinchilla, alpaca, llama, vicuna), or Amazon basin (spider monkey, fruit-eating bat, sloth, South American tapir, jaguarundi). Reports can focus on specific adaptations the animals have made to the habitats in which they live.

BACKGROUND

Word Origin

Tierra del Fuego The archipelago Tierra del Fuego ("Land of Fire") was named by European explorer Ferdinand Magellan. He named the place for the constant fires kept burning by the area's indigenous people, the Ona and Yahgan, to ward off the constant cold.

Articles From
NATIONAL GEOGRAPHIC

The following article may be used to extend the content in this section.

Van Dyk, Jere, and Alex Webb, photographer. "The Amazon." *National Geographic*, Vol. 187, No. 2 (Feb. 1995), pp. 2–39.

Meet the diverse peoples who live along the banks of the Amazon in this firsthand account of a dangerous voyage on this enormous river.

Map Study Extension

Use the questions below to develop additional geographic themes.

1. Location Instruct students to use the key of the climate map to explore the continent's many different climates. Ask: **Which countries have arid climates?** (Mexico, Venezuela, Peru, Chile, and Argentina)

2. Place Help students understand that most Latin American countries have more than one climate region. Ask: **Which Latin American countries have only one climate region?** (Uruguay, Suriname, and French Guiana, and many of the smaller island nations)

Answers to Assessment

1. (a) tropical storm, p. 208
(b) hurricane, p. 208 **(c)** El Niño, p. 208

2. Possible answers: Bogotá and Rio de Janeiro

3. El Niño, because it is located on the western coast of Latin America, below Peru, and El Niño always begins off the coast of Peru

Climates

Atmospheric and ocean currents affect climate conditions in Latin America. In summer and early fall, when ocean waters are warmest, storms form off West Africa. As they move west, some of them become **tropical storms** with winds of at least 39 miles per hour, or gain even more power and become **hurricanes** with winds of at least 74 miles per hour. About every three years, an ocean current known as **El Niño** warms the Pacific waters off the coast of Peru. El Niño causes droughts and floods around the world.

Source: www.worldclimate.com
Curved lines show temperatures in Fahrenheit degrees.
Bars show rainfall in inches.

Tropical Climates

The coastal desert city of Lima has an arid climate, whereas the Amazon Basin city of Manaus has a tropical wet climate. Factors such as wind patterns and precipitation influence climate regions. **CLIMATES** *Based on the maps on pages 207 and 209, what physical feature separates Lima from the warm, moisture-laden air to the east?*

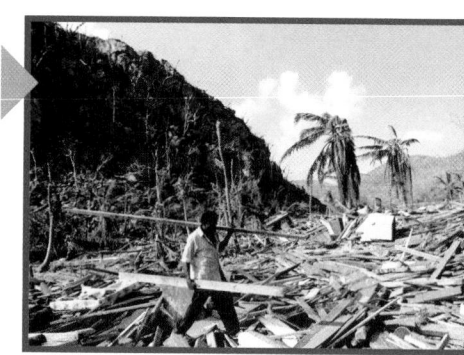

Hurricanes

Hurricanes can sweep westward across the Atlantic to devastate islands and coastal regions. They are particularly hazardous to low-lying areas along the Atlantic Ocean, Caribbean Sea, and Gulf of Mexico. **NATURAL HAZARDS** *Based on the map, which climate regions in Latin America are likely to experience hurricanes?*

27 DEC 1997

El Niño

This satellite image shows that humidity is higher than normal in the eastern Pacific and lower than normal in the western Pacific. These changes indicate that an El Niño condition is occurring. **GEOGRAPHIC TOOLS** *How does the image use color to show humidity levels?*

ASSESSMENT

1. **Key Terms** Define **(a)** tropical storm, **(b)** hurricane, **(c)** El Niño.

2. **Map Skills Regions** Name two cities of Latin America that lie within a tropical wet climate region.

3. **Critical Thinking Drawing Conclusions** Would you expect Bolivia to be more strongly affected by hurricanes or by El Niño? Explain.

Answers to Photo Captions

Tropical Climates the Andes
Hurricanes tropical wet and tropical wet and dry
El Niño Blue indicates lower than normal humidity (the deeper the blue, the lower the humidity); green indicates normal humidity; yellow, orange, and red indicate high, higher, and highest humidity, respectively.

RESOURCE DIRECTORY

Teaching Resources
Social Studies Skills Handbook
• Reading a Climate Map, p. 26
• Reading a Climate Graph, p. 65
• Comparing Climate Graphs, p. 66
Simulations, Games, and Lab Activities
• Where on Earth?, The Vanished Expedition, pp. 68–69

Technology
World Geography Map and Photo Transparencies
• Latin America: Maps and Photos

Latin America: CLIMATE REGIONS

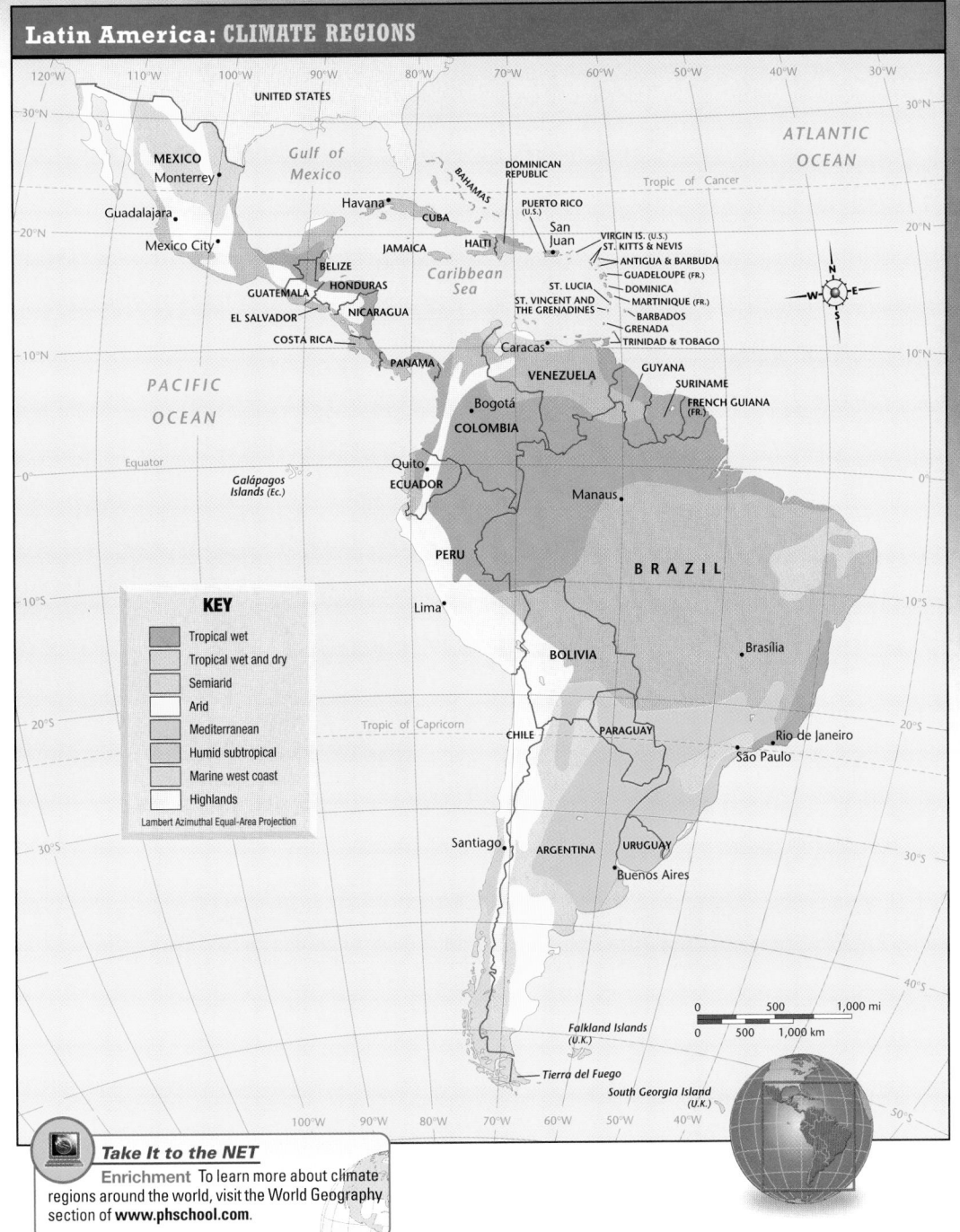

KEY

- Tropical wet
- Tropical wet and dry
- Semiarid
- Arid
- Mediterranean
- Humid subtropical
- Marine west coast
- Highlands

Lambert Azimuthal Equal-Area Projection

Take It to the NET
Enrichment To learn more about climate regions around the world, visit the World Geography section of **www.phschool.com**.

Chapter 9 ■ Regional Atlas: Latin America **209**

GLOBAL CONNECTIONS

Natural Hazards

El Niño The El Niño current of 1997–1998 had an especially strong effect on global weather patterns. Indonesia experienced wildfires brought on by shifting winds that carried extremely high temperatures across the Pacific. In the United States, southeastern states had record rainfalls, while California suffered serious mudslides.

BACKGROUND

The Physical World

A Foggy Desert The Peru current is a cold ocean current that consistently flows along the west coast of South America toward the Equator. The current cools warm Pacific winds passing over it. The cooled air condenses moisture and rises as it reaches the Peruvian and Chilean coasts. The result is the Atacama Desert—one of the driest places on earth shrouded in fog.

Ecosystems

The Amazon rain forest is one of the largest ecosystems in the world. Other tropical rain forests are found in Central America, Mexico, and various islands of the Caribbean. To the north and south of the Amazon rain forest are tropical grasslands. Arid regions of Mexico and South America support desert and desert scrub. In the Andes, ecosystems change with the elevation.

South American Grasslands
The pampas of South America have long been used for raising livestock. Recently, more farmers have been growing grain in the pampas. **ECONOMIC ACTIVITIES** *How might this shift in land use affect cattle ranchers?*

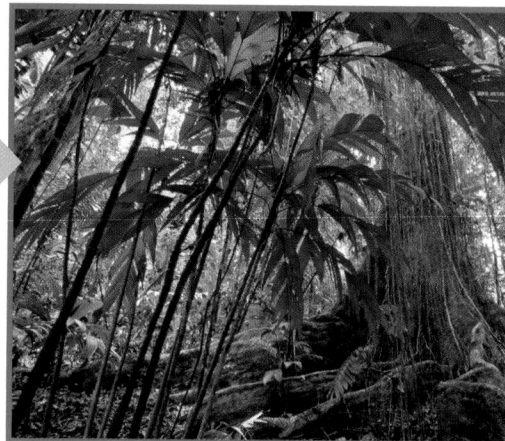

Costa Rican Rain Forest
The **canopy** of a rain forest is the uppermost layer where tree branches meet. Only small plants grow on the forest floor because little sunlight penetrates the canopy. **ECOSYSTEMS** *Do you think animal life is plentiful in the rain forest? Why or why not?*

Mexican Desert
Most desert ecosystems support many types of life. Infrequent and unpredictable rainfall forces plants and animals to adapt to very dry conditions. **ECOSYSTEMS** *Based on the map, which countries in Latin America include desert ecosystems?*

ASSESSMENT

1. **Key Terms** Define canopy.

2. **Map Skills** **Human-Environment Interaction** **(a)** What ecosystem is most widespread in Paraguay? **(b)** How do you think this affects economic activities in Paraguay? Explain.

3. **Critical Thinking** **Making Comparisons** How do the pampas of South America differ from the desert lands of Mexico?

REGIONAL ATLAS

Latin America: ECOSYSTEMS

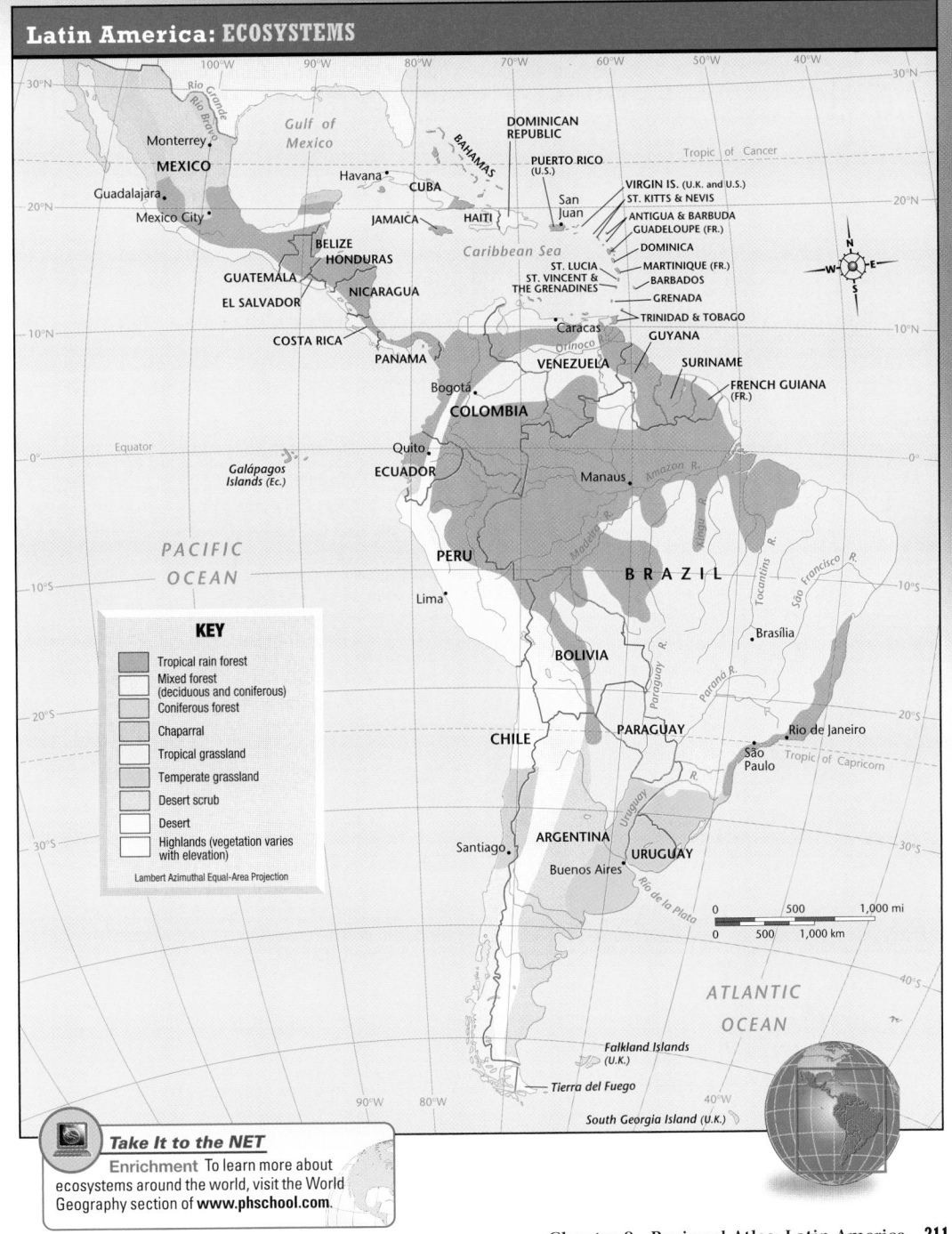

KEY

- Tropical rain forest
- Mixed forest (deciduous and coniferous)
- Coniferous forest
- Chaparral
- Tropical grassland
- Temperate grassland
- Desert scrub
- Desert
- Highlands (vegetation varies with elevation)

Lambert Azimuthal Equal-Area Projection

Take It to the NET
Enrichment To learn more about ecosystems around the world, visit the World Geography section of **www.phschool.com**.

ACTIVITY

Reteach

What Region Am I? Divide the students into two teams or into pairs. One team or player picks a South American country or dependency and writes its name on a piece of paper. The other team or player then compiles a list of questions to ask about the physical setting, climate, and vegetation of the political region. The object of the game is to gather enough clues to identify the region in the fewest number of questions. (Logical/Mathematical)

ACTIVITY

Enrichment

Creating Latin American Postcards Arrange students in pairs and assign each pair a different Latin American country to "tour." Instruct each pair to create a postcard to send to a friend at home. The illustrated side of the card will depict an ecosystem, and the message side will comment on the scene and its setting. Students may use glossaries, dictionaries, travel guides, and library resources for more detailed descriptions of assigned countries and ecosystems. Display cards in the classroom. (Visual/Spatial, Verbal/Linguistic).

Chapter 9 ▪ Regional Atlas: Latin America **211**

TEST PREPARATION

Have students use the map on this page to answer the following question.

What are the predominant ecosystems found in countries of Central America and the Caribbean?

A Desert and desert scrub

B Tropical grassland and temperate grassland

C Tropical rain forest and tropical grassland

D Mixed forest and highlands

People and Cultures

Latin Americans trace their ancestry to Native Americans, Africans, and Europeans. Most people have a mixed ethnic heritage. **Mestizos,** for example, are people of both Native American and European descent. People whose ancestry is African and European are known as **mulattoes.** Today, ethnic and cultural diversity is evident in Latin America's growing cities.

Urbanization

The city of São Paulo, Brazil, lies upstream from the nation's busiest port. While highways provide Brazil's main transportation networks, in some areas rivers serve as travel and shipping routes. **PATTERNS OF SETTLEMENT** *(a) Are most South American cities located near the coast or in the interior of the continent? (b) What do you think are the reasons for this pattern?*

Migration in Brazil

Over the past few decades, Brazilian cities have grown dramatically as people have moved in search of jobs and other benefits. **MIGRATION** *(a) What percentage of Brazilians lived in rural areas in 1974? (b) How is migration affecting rural communities in Brazil?*

1974

60% urban

2025 (estimate)

89% urban

Sources: UN Population Division; *Chicago Tribune*

Ethnic Diversity

These three girls reflect the Native American, European, and African heritage of Puerto Rico. Migration patterns have led to great diversity in the Caribbean. **CULTURES** *Do you think ethnic diversity affects culture in Latin America? Explain.*

ASSESSMENT

1. **Key Terms** Define **(a)** mestizo, **(b)** mulatto.

2. **Map Skills** **Location** **(a)** What are the four largest cities in Latin America? **(b)** Describe the relative location of each of these cities.

3. **Critical Thinking** **Drawing Conclusions** If Brazilians continue to migrate from rural areas to urban areas, how might the map on page 213 look different in the future? Explain.

REGIONAL ATLAS

Latin America: POPULATION DENSITY

UNITED STATES

ATLANTIC OCEAN

Tropic of Cancer

Monterrey
Guadalajara
Mexico City
Havana
Port-au-Prince
Kingston
San Juan
Santo Domingo
Guatemala
San Salvador
Tegucigalpa
Caracas
San José
Maracaibo
Medellín
Bogota
Cali
Quito
Guayaquil
Belém
Fortaleza
PACIFIC OCEAN
Equator
Lima
Recife
La Paz
Brasília
Salvador
Belo Horizonte
São Paulo
Río de Janeiro
Asunción
Curitiba
Valparaíso
Santiago
Rosario
Pôrto Alegre
Buenos Aires
Montevideo
Tropic of Capricorn

KEY

Persons per sq mi	Persons per sq km
520 and over	200 and over
260–519	100–199
130–259	50–99
25–129	10–49
1–24	1–9
Less than 1	Less than 1

Metropolitan areas
□ 10,000,000 and over
■ 5,000,000–9,999,999
○ 2,000,000–4,999,999
◉ 1,000,000–1,999,999
• 250,000–999,999

Lambert Azimuthal Equal-Area Projection

0   500   1,000 mi
0   500 1,000 km

ATLANTIC OCEAN

GET THE FACTS . . .
Go to the **Table of Countries** at the back of this book for additional population data.

Chapter 9 ▪ Regional Atlas: Latin America **213**

Economics, Technology, and Environment

Traditionally, the economies of most Latin American countries have been based on cash crops such as coffee and bananas. Mining has also been important. In recent years, however, diversification has occurred. Modern industry is expanding in the cities. As in other regions, people try to balance economic growth and protection of the environment. Environmental concerns include air pollution and destruction of rain forests.

Commercial Agriculture

Many Latin American farmers rely on subsistence farming practices to provide food for their families. Increasingly, however, large commercial farms use mechanized equipment such as electric pumps for irrigation. **SCIENCE AND TECHNOLOGY** *How might modern agricultural practices affect employment?*

Automobile Industry

In this Brazilian factory, robots are used to assemble automobiles. Manufacturing makes up one third of the nation's yearly production of goods and services. **NATURAL RESOURCES** *Based on the map, what is one of Brazil's main sources of energy?*

Destruction of Rain Forests

This tractor is clearing trees in the Amazon rain forest. Many farms in the Amazon are unsuccessful because the soil and its nutrients are washed away when the vegetation is cleared. **ENVIRONMENTAL CHANGE** *Which of the economic activities shown on the map is most likely to decline as the rain forest is cleared?*

ASSESSMENT

1. **Map Skills** **Human-Environment Interaction** What effect might agricultural expansion have on the rain forests?

2. **Critical Thinking** **Drawing Conclusions** Based on climate and topography, how would you explain the distribution of economic activities in Latin America?

Latin America: ECONOMIC ACTIVITIES AND RESOURCES

KEY

Forestry		Hydroelectric power	
Livestock raising		Iron	
Commercial farming		Copper	
Subsistence farming		Bauxite	
Manufacturing and trade		Gold	
Commercial fishing		Silver	
Little or no activity		Uranium	
Coal		Tin	
Petroleum		Lead	
		Nickel	

Lambert Azimuthal Equal-Area Projection

0   500   1,000 mi
0   500   1,000 km

Take It to the NET
Enrichment To learn more about the economic activities and resources of this region, visit the World Geography section of **www.phschool.com**.

BACKGROUND

Daily Life

The Plaza The hub of daily life in cities and towns throughout Latin America is the plaza—the main square of the town. Usually the church occupies one end of the plaza, while shops, stores, and cafes face along its other sides. Lingering over coffee and visiting with friends is a time-honored tradition. You may wish to ask students if there is anything equivalent in their community.

ACTIVITY

Connecting With . . .

Mathematics Supply students with the following data. The estimated global oil reserves for the total world are 1,016 billion barrels; for Latin America, 115 billion barrels; and for the United States, 21 billion barrels. Have students work in pairs to create two graphs: a circle graph illustrating Latin American oil reserves in relation to the world's total, and a bar pictograph comparing Latin American reserves with those of the United States. Select one set of completed graphs to display on the bulletin board.

Chapter 9 ▪ Regional Atlas: Latin America **215**

Database:
Comparing Economies
pp. 216–217

Objectives
Upon completion of this lesson, students should be able to:
- understand how a country's GDP per capita is determined;
- describe the various economic systems found within Latin America;
- compare the economies of Latin American countries to that of the United States.

National Geography Standards
The following National Geography Standards are highlighted in this feature: 11, 18

Bellringer
Have students talk about the U.S. economy. What words would they use to describe the type of economy found in the United States? (capitalism, market, private business, etc.) Ask if they are aware of other types of economies.

LESSON PLAN

1. Focus Write *supply and demand* on the chalkboard. Ask volunteers to use the phrase to explain how the owner of a pizza parlor would decide how many pizzas to make each day.

2. Instruct After the students have read pages 216 and 217, have them create charts comparing market, command, and traditional economies. Review the meanings of terms as needed.

3. Close/Reteach Use the Assessment questions as a basis for class discussion. Ask students: **Do you think geography (climate, physical features, and ecosystems) or people have a greater influence on the type of economy a country adopts?**

LATIN AMERICA
Database: Comparing Economies

By comparing the data below, you will learn that three very different economic systems exist in Latin America. You will also note that some countries are more prosperous than others. Mexico, for example, is one of the wealthiest countries of the region, whereas Cuba is one of the poorest. You will note even greater differences when you compare the Latin American data with the United States data on page 217.

Source: *The World Factbook*

Key Terms: market economy, GDP per capita, command economy, traditional economy

GET THE FACTS . . .
Go to the Table of Countries at the back of this book to view additional data for the countries of Latin America.

Take It to the NET
Data Update For the most recent update of this database, visit the World Geography section of www.phschool.com.

Mexico

GDP per Capita	$9,000
Inflation	6.5%
Unemployment	3.0%
Population Below Poverty Line	40%
GDP by Sector	Agriculture: 5%
	Industry: 26%
	Services: 69%
Leading Import	Machinery
Leading Export	Manufactured goods

Mexico has a **market economy.** In this type of economy, decisions about production, price, and other economic factors are determined by the law of supply and demand. From the 1980s to the 1990s, the number of state-owned businesses fell from more than 1,000 to fewer than 200. Income distribution is unequal, with the top 20% of income earners accounting for 55% of income. In recent years, Mexico has enjoyed a growing per capita gross domestic product (GDP). **GDP per capita** is the total value of goods and services produced in a country in a year, divided by the country's total population.

Cuba

GDP per Capita	$2,300
Inflation	7.1%
Unemployment	4.1%
Population Below Poverty Line	NA
GDP by Sector	Agriculture: 8%
	Industry: 35%
	Services: 58%
Leading Import	Petroleum
Leading Export	Sugar

NA = information not available.

The Communist government of Cuba dominates the nation's command economy. In a planned, or **command economy,** a single central government makes economic decisions such as what to produce, how much to produce, and what price to charge. As a result of lost aid from the Soviet Union, Cuba's GDP declined by 35% from 1989 to 1993. To combat serious shortages of food and consumer goods, the government reduced the support it provides to unprofitable businesses.

RESOURCE DIRECTORY

Teaching Resources
Unit 3, Chapter 9
- Regional Atlas Review, p. 3
- Regional Atlas Database Skills, p. 4
- Test Forms A and B, pp. 5–10

Spanish Resources
- Regional Atlas Review, p. 23

Guide to the Essentials (English/Spanish)
- Chapter 9 Test

Mental Mapping booklet
- Chapter 9 Map Test, p. 38

Simulations, Games, and Lab Activities
- Place Location Review Games, pp. 58–63

Social Studies Skills Handbook
- Study and Research Skills, pp. 94–108

Prentice Hall Assessment System
Alternative Assessment booklet
- Map Evaluation Form, p. 15

Technology
ExamView Test Bank CD-ROM, Chapter 9 Test
Companion Web site, www.phschool.com
- Chapter 9 Self-Test

Brazil

GDP per Capita	$7,400
Inflation	7.7%
Unemployment	6.4%
Population Below Poverty Line	22%
GDP by Sector	Agriculture: 9% Industry: 32% Services: 59%
Leading Import	Machinery
Leading Export	Manufactured goods

Brazil has one of the world's major economies. During the 1960s and 1970s, the economy underwent diversification and industrialization. Economic growth was boosted in 1994 by the launch of MERCOSUR, the common market with neighboring Argentina, Paraguay, and Uruguay. However, excessive spending resulted in rising debt and budget deficits, which contributed to economic recessions in the 1990s.

Honduras

GDP per Capita	$2,600
Inflation	9.7%
Unemployment	28%
Population Below Poverty Line	53%
GDP by Sector	Agriculture: 18% Industry: 32% Services: 50%
Leading Import	Machinery
Leading Export	Manufactured goods

Honduras has mainly a **traditional economy**, a system that is most often found in rural areas of less developed countries. In a traditional, or subsistence, economy, families produce goods and services for their own use. There is little surplus and exchange of goods. The Honduran economy was growing at a moderate pace until Hurricane Mitch struck in 1998. The storm resulted in about $3 billion in damages. In 1999, the GDP shrank, unemployment rose, and the trade deficit grew to more than $400 million.

ASSESSMENT

Use the data for Latin America and the United States (at right) to answer the following questions.

1. **Key Terms** Define **(a)** market economy, **(b)** GDP per capita, **(c)** command economy, **(d)** traditional economy.
2. **Economic Systems** How much does the Cuban economy differ from the Mexican economy?
3. **Economic Activities** **(a)** Which of the five nations has the highest per capita income? **(b)** What economic sector makes up the largest part of each nation's GDP?
4. **Critical Thinking Drawing Conclusions** Why do you think the per capita GDP of Cuba is among the lowest in Latin America?

United States

GDP per Capita	$36,300
Inflation	2.8%
Unemployment	5.0%
Population Below Poverty Line	13%
GDP by Sector	Agriculture: 2% Industry: 18% Services: 80%
Leading Import	Petroleum
Leading Export	Manufactured goods

Games for Review See pages 58–63 of the Simulations, Games, and Lab Activities in the Teaching Resources for games to review place names in preparation for the Chapter 9 Map Test.

Chapter Map Test Students should use the completed Chapter 9 outline maps and the Unit 3 Checklist in their Atlas Portfolios to prepare for the Chapter 9 Map Test. Point out to students that the test will cover all of the place names listed on the Unit 3 Checklist.

 Alternative Assessment

Final Evaluation

Making Maps Use the Map Evaluation Form on page 15 of the Alternative Assessment booklet in the Prentice Hall Assessment System to evaluate students' map.

Answers to Assessment

1. (a) market economy, p. 216
(b) GDP per capita, p. 216
(c) command economy, p. 216
(d) traditional economy, p. 217

2. Mexico has a market economy under which supply and demand determine production. Cuba has a command economy under which the central government makes most of the economic decisions.

3. (a) the United States **(b)** services

4. Possible answer: Command economies tend to be less efficient; however, wealth is usually distributed more equally. When the Soviet Union collapsed, Cuba lost a great deal of aid, and this caused a dramatic decline in its economy.

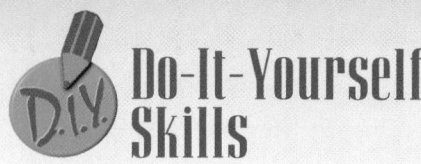

Do-It-Yourself Skills

pp. 218–219

Objectives

Upon completion of this feature, students should be able to:

◆ explain the purpose of a population pyramid;

◆ create a population pyramid;

◆ analyze a population pyramid and draw conclusions from the data.

National Geography Standards

The following National Geography Standards are highlighted in this feature: 1, 15

Bellringer

Ask students what they think of when they hear the word *pyramid*. Discuss the different associations students have with that word.

LESSON PLAN

1. Focus Have students look at the population density map on page 213. Explain that it shows where the population is greatest in a country, as opposed to a population pyramid, which shows the gender/age composition of a population.

2. Instruct To help students plan the length of the bars in their graph, draw a model axis on the board. Show them that if they draw bars to represent the largest and smallest populations first, it will be easier to decide how long the other bars should be.

3. Close/Reteach Help students compare the two Mexico population pyramids. Have them describe the population changes in the male and female population in Mexico between 2000 and 2025.

Do-It-Yourself Skills

Making and Analyzing Population Pyramids

What Is a Population Pyramid?

A population pyramid is a graphic model that shows the gender/age composition of a population at a specific time. Basically, it consists of two horizontal bar graphs. Usually, the right bar graph represents the number of females in a country and the left bar graph represents the number of males. Each individual bar represents the number of men or women in a particular age range.

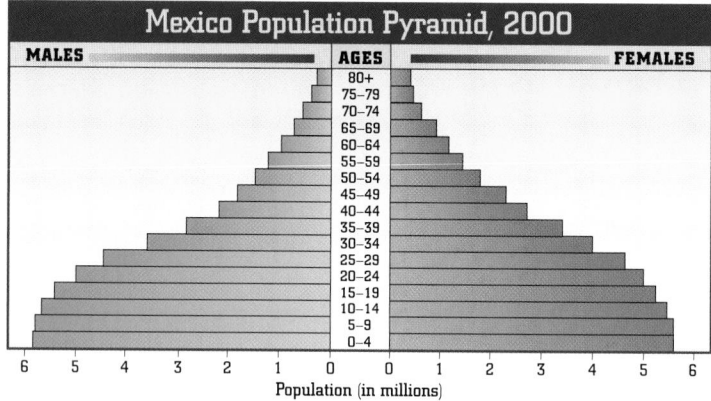

Source: U.S. Census Bureau, International Data Base

How Can I Use This Skill?

By making a population pyramid, you can view a visual model of a population. By studying the pyramid, you can analyze a community's needs and then support policies to best address those needs. Knowing how to make and analyze population pyramids will enable you to make informed decisions.

Step by Step

Follow these steps to make and analyze a population pyramid. As you proceed, use the population pyramid for Mexico in 2000 (above) as a model.

 Select a specific population. Pick a country or other community whose population you wish to study. (For this lesson, we have selected Mexico in 2025.)

RESOURCE DIRECTORY

Teaching Resources
Social Studies Skills Handbook
• Reading a Bar Graph, p. 53

Technology
Social Studies Skills Tutor CD-ROM, Analyzing Graphic Data

Collect the statistics from a reliable source for population statistics, such as an atlas or almanac. For this exercise, use the table below.

Make a vertical axis and write labels for specific age groups. Start with 0–4 at the base of the axis and end with the oldest age group at the top. The labels should be evenly spaced and represent the same number of years.

Make a horizontal axis and write labels for numbers of people. Start with 0 near the center of the axis and add numbers to the right that will represent the statistics you have collected. The labels should be evenly spaced. Do the same for the left side of the axis.

Provide all other labels for the pyramid. Write the title of the pyramid and the data source. Indicate which side of the pyramid is for the female population and which side is for the male population. Also, write labels to show what the numbers on the two axes represent.

Use the statistics you have collected to draw horizontal bars. Each bar should accurately represent the number of men or women in a specific age group, sometimes called an age-gender cohort.

Analyze the pyramid you have made. In general, a pyramid with a wide bottom indicates a growing population with many young people. A pyramid with a wide top indicates an older population that will probably decline in number. You might also compare pyramids.

MEXICO: Population (in millions) 2025*

AGES	TOTAL	MALES	FEMALES
0–4	10.469	5.351	5.117
5–9	10.564	5.396	5.167
10–14	10.666	5.445	5.221
15–19	10.672	5.434	5.238
20–24	10.547	5.336	5.211
25–29	10.366	5.203	5.163
30–34	10.157	5.064	5.093
35–39	9.832	4.873	4.958
40–44	9.404	4.628	4.776
45–49	8.980	4.384	4.596
50–54	8.316	4.019	4.297
55–59	6.876	3.191	3.684
60–64	5.542	2.491	3.050
65–69	4.139	1.808	2.331
70–74	3.138	1.343	1.795
75–79	2.096	0.862	1.234
80+	2.074	0.759	1.314
TOTAL	133.835	65.589	68.246

Source: U.S. Census Bureau, International Data Base
*Estimate.

TIP

Collecting Information

The United States Census Bureau is an excellent source for population data. Link to the World Geography section of **www.phschool.com** for help in collecting government data.

APPLY YOUR SKILL

Select another country in Latin America or any other region. Create a population pyramid for that country. Then, write some questions to help you analyze the pyramid and compare it to others. Your questions might include:
- Which age-gender cohorts are the largest?
- Which age-gender cohorts are the smallest?
- How are the pyramids different?
- Which pyramid shows a greater rate of population growth? Explain.

Next, offer theories, predictions, and recommendations based on the pyramid you created.

Resource Manager

	CORE INSTRUCTION	READING/SKILLS
Chapter-Level Resources	📗 Teaching Resources 📕 **Unit 3**/Ch. 10 • Reviewing Main Ideas, p. 15 📖 **Mental Mapping booklet** • Unit 3 Checklist, p. 34 📖 **Simulations, Games, and Lab Activities** • Exploring Local Geography, Environmental Problems, p. 4 • Place Location Review Games, pp. 58–63 💿 **TeacherExpress™ CD-ROM**, Ch. 10 💻 **Companion Web site,** **www.phschool.com** • eTeach	📗 Teaching Resources 📕 **Unit 3**/Ch. 10 • Map/Graph Skills, p. 17 💿 **Book on CD**, Ch. 10 💿 **Social Studies Skills Tutor CD-ROM**
1 Geography of Mexico 1. Identify the main physical characteristics that affect daily life in Mexico's heartland region. 2. Differentiate between Mexico's four coastal regions.	📗 Teaching Resources 📕 **Unit 3**/Ch. 10 • Guided Reading and Review, p. 11 📖 **Creative Teaching Activities** • Using a Physical Map, p. 12 💿 **Prentice Hall Presentation Pro CD-ROM**, Ch. 10, Sec. 1	📗 Teaching Resources 📖 **Guide to the Essentials (English/Spanish)** • Section Summary, Ch. 10, Sec. 1 📖 **Mental Mapping booklet** • Outline Map 10, p. 39 📖 **Social Studies Skills Handbook** • Reading a Population Distribution Map, p. 33 📼 **Guided Reading Audiotapes (English/Spanish)**, Ch. 10, Sec. 1 📺 **Section Reading Support Transparencies**, Ch. 10, Sec. 1
2 A Place of Three Cultures 1. Explain how Mexico became a Spanish colony. 2. Trace the key political events in the development of democracy in Mexico. 3. Identify Mexico's current social problems. 4. Give the main characteristics of the Mexican economy.	📗 Teaching Resources 📕 **Unit 3**/Ch. 10 • Guided Reading and Review, p. 13 💿 **Prentice Hall Presentation Pro CD-ROM**, Ch. 10, Sec. 2	📗 Teaching Resources 📖 **Guide to the Essentials (English/Spanish)** • Section Summary, Ch. 10, Sec. 2 📖 **Social Studies Skills Handbook** • Analyzing a Photograph, p. 58 📼 **Guided Reading Audiotapes (English/Spanish)**, Ch. 10, Sec. 2 📺 **Section Reading Support Transparencies**, Ch. 10, Sec. 2

ENRICHMENT/HONORS/PREAP

Teaching Resources
Unit 3/Ch. 10
- Critical Thinking, p. 16

Mental Mapping booklet
- Atlas Activity, p. 40

Social Studies Skills Handbook
- Study and Research Skills, pp. 94–108

People and Geography
- Urbanization, pp. 14–18

World Geography Map and Photo Transparencies
- Latin America: Maps and Photos
- World Population Growth

World Geography Videos
- Natural Hazards: Mexico, Tape 1

Companion Web site, www.phschool.com
- Chapter 10 Activities

Companion Web site, www.phschool.com
- Chapter 10 Activities

Teaching Resources
Social Studies Skills Handbook
- Identifying Assumptions, p. 46

Companion Web site, www.phschool.com
- Chapter 10 Activities

ASSESSMENT

PRENTICE HALL ASSESSMENT SYSTEM

Core Assessment
- ExamView Test Bank booklet, Ch. 10
- ExamView Test Bank CD-ROM, Ch. 10

Standardized Test Preparation

Review and Reteach
- Review Book for World Geography, pp. 7–8

Practice and Assess
- Test-taking Strategies With Transparencies for High School
- Test-taking Strategy Poster
- Alternative Assessment booklet
- Test Prep Book for World Geography

Teaching Resources
Unit 3/Ch. 10
- Section Quizzes, pp. 12, 14
- Test Forms A and B, pp. 18–23

Guide to the Essentials (English/Spanish)
- Chapter 10 Test

Spanish Resources, Ch. 10
- Section Quizzes, pp. 24–25

Mental Mapping booklet
- Chapter 10 Map Test, p. 41

Companion Web site, www.phschool.com
- Chapter 10 Self-Test

CUSTOMIZE FOR INDIVIDUAL NEEDS

Less Proficient Readers
- Guide to the Essentials (English), Ch. 10, Section Summaries
- Guided Reading Audiotapes (English), Ch. 10
- Section Reading Support Transparencies, Ch. 10
- Book on CD, Ch. 10
- Teacher's Edition, Reading Strategy, pp. 222, 228
- Teacher's Edition, Activity: Vocabulary, p. 229

Students Acquiring English/ESL
- Guide to the Essentials (English/Spanish), Ch. 10
- Guided Reading Audiotapes (English/Spanish), Ch. 10
- Section Reading Support Transparencies, Ch. 10
- Book on CD, Ch. 10
- Teacher's Edition, Customize for . . . , p. 227

Less Proficient Writers
- Social Studies Skills Handbook, p. 86
- Alternative Assessment, Writing Assignment Rubric, p. 6
- Teacher's Edition, Customize for . . . , p. 223

MENTAL MAPPING

Ask students to look at the map on this page. Point out that Mexico is located in the southern part of North America, south of the United States and north of Central America. Indicate that the Pacific Ocean lies to the west of Mexico and the Gulf of Mexico lies to the east.

Mapping the Region Have students study this map. Then ask them to close their books and draw a sketch map of Mexico. Sketches should include the following items:
• **Mexico**
• **Mexico City**
• **Pacific Ocean**
• **Gulf of Mexico**
• **United States**
• **Central America**
Students needing extra assistance may label outline maps of Mexico. Remind students to keep their maps in their Atlas Portfolios to prepare for the Chapter Map Test.

C H A P T E R

10

*M*exico

Mexico: POLITICAL

KEY

⊛ State boundary
⊛ National capital
• Other city

Lambert Azimuthal Equal-Area Projection

0   200   400 mi
0   200   400 km

Tijuana · BAJA CALIFORNIA · SONORA · Ciudad Juárez · UNITED STATES · CHIHUAHUA · COAHUILA · BAJA CALIFORNIA SUR · NUEVO LEÓN · Monterrey · Matamoros · Gulf of Mexico · SINALOA · DURANGO · Mazatlán · MEXICO · ZACATECAS · TAMAULIPAS · Tropic of Cancer · PACIFIC OCEAN · AGUASCALIENTES · NAYARIT · SAN LUIS POTOSÍ · Puerto Vallarta · GUANAJUATO · QUERÉTARO · Bay of Campeche · YUCATÁN · Guadalajara · JALISCO · HIDALGO · Mexico City · QUINTANA ROO · Manzanillo · COLIMA · MICHOACÁN · MÉXICO · TLAXCALA · Veracruz · CAMPECHE · MORELOS · PUEBLA · VERACRUZ · TABASCO · GUERRERO · Acapulco · OAXACA · CHIAPAS · CENTRAL AMERICA

Go Online
PHSchool.com

For: More information about Mexico and access to the Take It to the Net activities
Visit: phschool.com
Web Code: mjk-0011

eTeach

Be sure to check out this month's online forum with a Master Teacher to join in an exchange of teaching ideas. **www.phschool.com**

RESOURCE DIRECTORY

Teaching Resources
Unit 3, Chapter 10
• Section 1 Guided Reading and Review, p. 11
Guide to the Essentials (English/Spanish)
• Section Summary, Chapter 10, Section 1
Mental Mapping booklet
• Atlas Activity, p. 40
• Unit 3 Checklist, p. 34

Technology
Guided Reading Audiotapes (English/Spanish),
Chapter 10, Section 1

Section Reading Support Transparencies,
Chapter 10, Section 1
World Geography Map and Photo Transparencies
• Latin America: Maps and Photos
Book on CD, Chapter 10
World Geography Videos
• Natural Hazards: Mexico, Tape 1
TeacherExpress™ CD-ROM, Chapter 10
Prentice Hall Presentation Pro CD-ROM, Chapter 10
Social Studies Skills Tutor CD-ROM
Companion Web site, www.phschool.com
• Chapter 10 Activities

1 Geography of Mexico

Reading Focus

- **What are the main physical characteristics that affect daily life in Mexico's heartland region?**
- **How do Mexico's four coastal plains regions differ?**

Key Terms

plateau

peninsula

irrigation

sinkhole

Main Idea In each region of Mexico, climate, landforms, and other geographic factors affect economic activities.

Physical Characteristics The state of Chiapas, in southern Mexico, is noted for its mountains and lush vegetation.

According to an old story, Charles V, the ruler of Spain, asked Hernán Cortés, the Spanish explorer who conquered Mexico, to describe the country's physical features. Cortés answered by crumpling a piece of paper and throwing it on the table. The wrinkled paper represented what Cortés could not describe in words: Mexico's rugged terrain.

Mountains dominate Mexico's physical setting. The largest mountain range, the Sierra Madre (see EHR uh MAH dray) Occidental, extends along the western coast. Mexico's second great mountain range, the Sierra Madre Oriental, runs parallel to the eastern coast, along the Gulf of Mexico. Between the Sierra Madres—which means "mother ranges"—lies Mexico's central **plateau,** an area of high, flat land.

Between the mountains and the ocean are Mexico's different coastal plains regions. The northern Pacific coast includes Baja (BAH hah) California, a **peninsula,** or strip of land that juts out into the Pacific Ocean. In spite of its name, which means "Lower California," it is part of Mexico. The southern Pacific coast, south of the central plateau, is a narrow strip of tropical coastline. The resort city of Acapulco is located

at the midpoint of the southern Pacific coast. On the east, the Gulf coastal plain curves around the Gulf of Mexico into the Yucatán Peninsula. The Yucatán, set apart from the rest of Mexico, sticks out into the Gulf like a thumb.

The Heartland Region

The central plateau is Mexico's most important and populous region, with several large cities. The southern part of the plateau, nourished by rich soil and plenty of rainfall, has Mexico's best farmland. About four fifths of the country's people live here.

Natural Hazards Mexico's central plateau is geologically unstable, however. The reason, as the plate tectonics map on page 47 shows, is that Mexico is located at the intersection of four tectonic plates—the North American Plate, the Caribbean Plate, the Pacific Plate, and the Cocos Plate. These tectonic plates move against one another and push jagged mountain ranges. Some of the mountains on the southern edge of the plateau are active volcanoes. In addition, earthquakes often shake the land. In 1985,

◄ Mexico City, Mexico *(photo left)*

Objectives

Upon completion of Section 1, students should be able to:

◆ identify the main physical characteristics that affect daily life in Mexico's heartland region;

◆ differentiate between Mexico's four coastal regions.

 National Geography Standards

The following National Geography Standards are highlighted in this section: 1, 2, 4, 5, 7, 12, 16, 18

 Bellringer

Ask students to think of words or phrases they associate with the word *neighbor.* Remind them that Mexico is one of the two immediate neighbors of the United States, along with Canada.

LESSON PLAN

1. Focus Have students use the map of Mexico on page 222 to help them understand how mountains divide Mexico into five physical regions: (1) central plateau, (2) northern Pacific coast, (3) southern Pacific coast, (4) Gulf coastal plain, (5) the Yucatán Peninsula.

2. Instruct Have groups of students list the characteristics of each of the five physical regions of Mexico. Ask a spokesperson from each group to present its list so that the rest of the class can take notes.

3. Close/Reteach Have students compare the characteristics of Mexico's five regions from the lists they made. Students should determine that each region is unique, with few characteristics in common.

Pacing Suggestions

 For 90-minute Blocks

You will want to vary activities.

- Use the Creative Teaching Activity on page 12 in the Creative Teaching Activities booklet. Enrich the activity by incorporating other maps from the Latin America Regional Atlas. Ask students to formulate questions that compare Mexico to the rest of Latin America in terms of physical characteristics, population, climate, natural vegetation, economic activity, and resources.

a strong earthquake struck Mexico City, killing an estimated 10,000 people and causing $4.1 billion in damage.

Climate Factors In spite of these dangers, other factors make Mexico's central plateau an attractive place to live. Climate is a major reason. In much of northern Mexico, the towering Sierra Madres block rainfall coming from the ocean. Some arid sections receive less than 4 inches (10 cm) of precipitation each year. Farther south, though, moist ocean winds find their way through the mountains to bring rain to the lower end of the plateau. Compare the annual precipitation and population maps on page 223, noticing where population is densest.

Elevation is a key factor in the climate of the central plateau. Although the southern part of the plateau is in the tropics, its climate is not tropical. The high elevation, averaging about 7,000 feet (2,100 m), keeps temperatures mild and makes the climate pleasant year-round. Mexico City, at about 7,340 feet (2,240 m) above sea level, enjoys moderate temperatures. The average high temperature is about 74°F (23°C) in July, 70°F (21°C) in January.

Drawn partly by Mexico City's attractive climate, scores of people have flocked to the city in

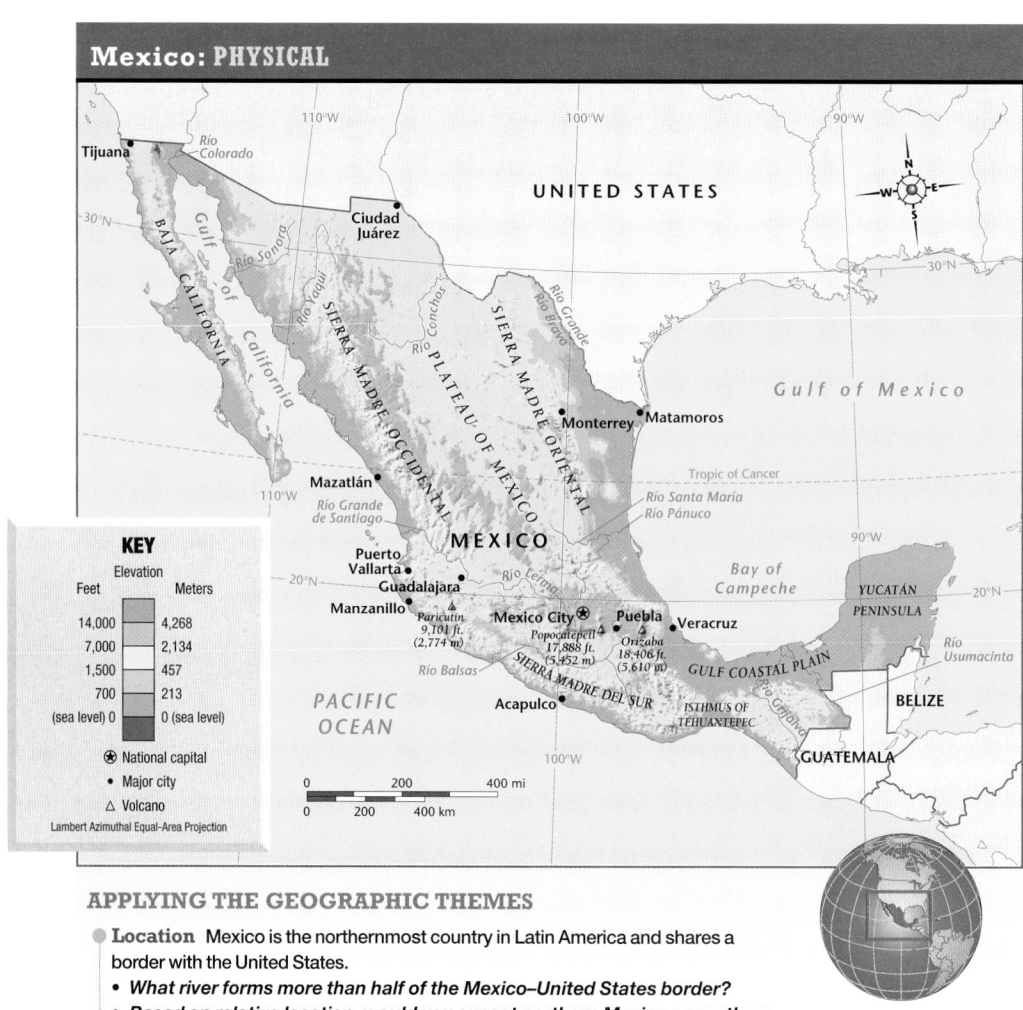

Mexico: PHYSICAL

KEY

Elevation

Feet	Meters
14,000	4,268
7,000	2,134
1,500	457
700	213
(sea level) 0	0 (sea level)

⊛ National capital
• Major city
△ Volcano

Lambert Azimuthal Equal-Area Projection

0   200   400 mi
0   200   400 km

APPLYING THE GEOGRAPHIC THEMES

● **Location** Mexico is the northernmost country in Latin America and shares a border with the United States.
  • *What river forms more than half of the Mexico–United States border?*
  • *Based on relative location, would you expect northern Mexico or southern Mexico to be more strongly influenced by United States culture? Explain.*

222   Chapter 10 ▪ Mexico

search of a better life. The city is now encircled by *ciudades perdidas* or "lost cities." Many of the city's arrivals are underemployed—working, but earning little money. Mexico City's poor live in vast slums, often without sewage and running water.

In the past such newcomers were treated as illegal squatters. Today they are legally allowed to own small parcels of land after having lived on them for five years. Schools have improved and electrical services are now provided.

The Coastal Regions

Mexico's coastal plains regions are a study in contrasts. As the map on page 222 shows, the rugged mountains dictate the width of the plains. The plains are widest along the Gulf coast and the northern Pacific coast, stretching inland as much as 80 miles (130 km) before rising up to meet the mountains. On the southern Pacific coast, mountains crowd close to the ocean, leaving a coastal plain that is often only 15 miles (24 km) wide.

Northern Pacific Coast Dry, hot, and for the most part thinly populated describes Mexico's northern Pacific coast. The city of Tijuana (tee WAH nuh), just across the border from the state of California, is one of Mexico's fastest-growing cities. Despite its arid climate, this region has some of the best farmland in the country. The reason is **irrigation,** the artificial watering of farmland by storing and distributing water drawn from reservoirs or rivers. Dams have been built on three rivers—the Colorado, the Sonora, and the Yaqui (yah KEE)—enabling farmers to raise wheat, cotton, and other crops.

By contrast, the Baja California peninsula is a long, thin arm—760 miles (1,223 km) in length—of mostly mountainous desert. An American described a trip into Baja's desert in August in this way:

> ❝As we drove south . . . we passed the canteen back and forth in a kind of trance, lulled by heat waves rising off the pavement. I wiped dust from the little plastic thermometer I'd clipped to my bag; it read 110 degrees. The scene out our window was a no-man's-land of reddish volcanic mountains and scorched vegetation. Mars with cactus.❞

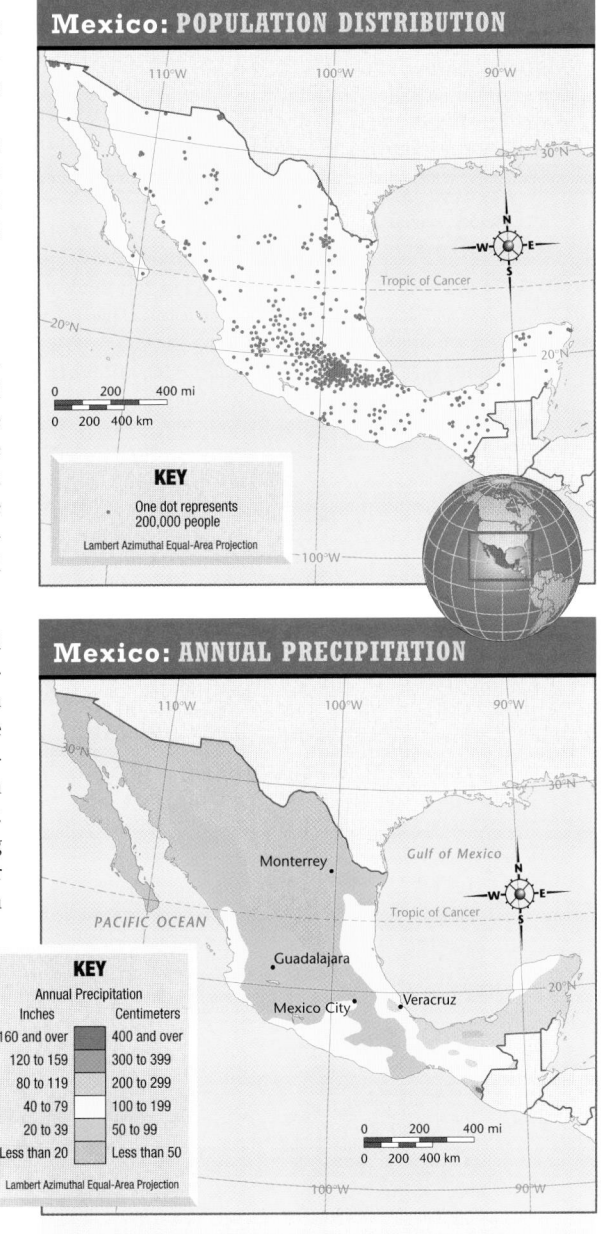

Mexico: POPULATION DISTRIBUTION

KEY
One dot represents 200,000 people
Lambert Azimuthal Equal-Area Projection

Mexico: ANNUAL PRECIPITATION

KEY

Annual Precipitation	
Inches	Centimeters
160 and over	400 and over
120 to 159	300 to 399
80 to 119	200 to 299
40 to 79	100 to 199
20 to 39	50 to 99
Less than 20	Less than 50

Lambert Azimuthal Equal-Area Projection

APPLYING THE GEOGRAPHIC THEMES

● **Human-Environment Interaction** Rainfall can influence patterns of settlement in a nation or region.
- *How is the distribution of Mexico's population related to the amount of annual rainfall?*
- *What might account for this relationship between rainfall and population?*

GEOFacts

In the 1600s and 1700s, a Spanish treasure ship sailed each year from Asia to Acapulco. Merchants flocked to the city to buy Asian silks, ivory, porcelain, and lacquerware.

Southern Pacific Coast

A smaller mountain range, the steep-sided Sierra Madre del Sur, edges the narrow southern Pacific coast. There is little farmland, but the region's spectacular natural setting and tropical climate favor another kind of economic activity—tourism. The sunny, wave-washed beaches of resort cities such as Acapulco, Mazatlán (mah sah TLAHN), and Puerto Vallarta (pwer toh vah YAR tuh) draw thousands of visitors each year from around the world.

Gulf Coastal Plain

The Gulf coastal plain is vitally important to Mexico's economy in a different way. Along the plain and offshore, beneath the waters of the Gulf of Mexico, are vast deposits of petroleum and natural gas. These geological riches have made the Gulf coastal plain one of the world's major oil-producing regions.

The Yucatán Peninsula

The Yucatán Peninsula is generally flat, in contrast to the mountains that cover much of Mexico. Unlike the volcanic soil that covers the land in other regions, the bedrock that underlies the Yucatán is porous limestone. When rain falls here, it seeps through the surface of the land, working its way into the rock. The limestone is gradually dissolved, creating underground caverns. Periodically the roof of a cavern collapses, and a **sinkhole** is formed. The landscape of the Yucatán is dotted with sinkholes, which the ancient Maya used as wells.

Country	Total Exports (billions of dollars)	Total Imports (billions of dollars)	Trade Balance (billions of dollars)
Mexico	136.8	142.1	−5.3
United States	663.0	912.0	−249.0

Mexico and the United States Trade Data

Source: *The World Factbook*

CHART SKILLS

● **Economic Activities** *Which country's total imports are higher?*

● **Global Trade Patterns** *Would a country be likely to encourage or discourage a negative balance of trade? Explain.*

Petroleum Extraction

Economic Activities The state of Tabasco, along the Gulf coastal plain, is one of Mexico's important sources of petroleum.

Regions *How does the economy of the Gulf coastal plain contrast with that of the southern Pacific coast?*

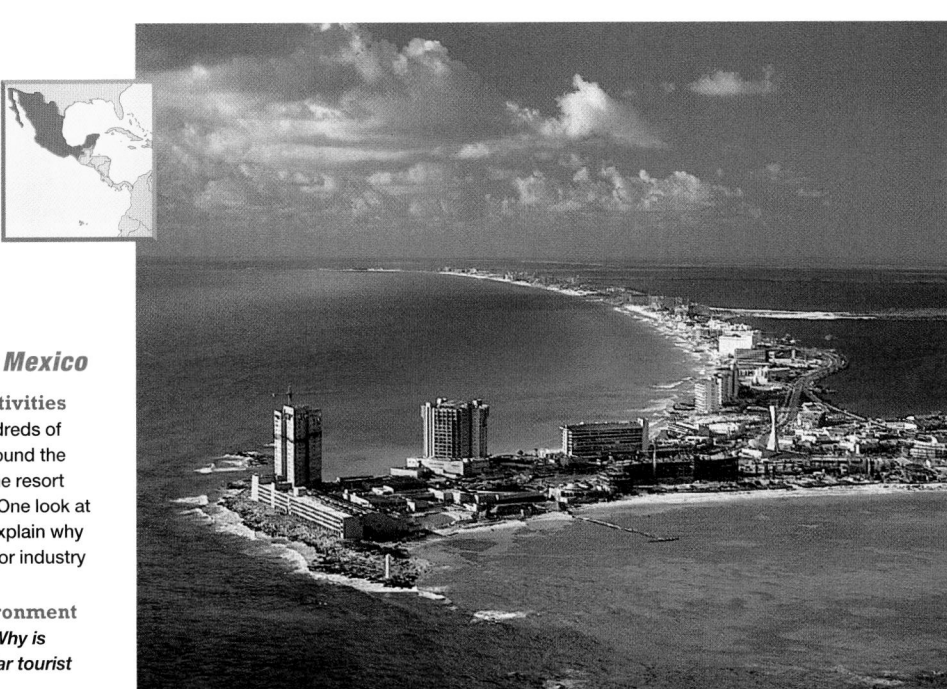

Tourism in Mexico

Economic Activities
Every year, hundreds of tourists from around the world flock to the resort city of Cancún. One look at Cancún helps explain why tourism is a major industry in Mexico.

Human-Environment Interaction *Why is Mexico a popular tourist destination?*

Despite its level terrain, the population is fairly sparse in the Yucatán. Mérida, with a population of more than 500,000 people, is the largest city in the region. Tourism along the Caribbean coastline and the building of better roads has greatly contributed to economic development in cities such as Cancún. The streets of these cities are lined with towering hotels and lavish resorts, and many people work in service industries that support tourism. Throughout the Yucatán, ancient Mayan ruins attract tourists and archaeologists seeking to learn more about the rise and fall of civilizations and about the lives of people who once populated the area.

SECTION 1 ASSESSMENT

1. **Key Terms** Define **(a)** plateau, **(b)** peninsula, **(c)** irrigation, **(d)** sinkhole.

2. **Physical Characteristics** How do natural hazards and climate affect the heartland region of Mexico?

3. **Economic Activities** How do conditions in the coastal regions of Mexico influence economic activities?

4. **Critical Thinking Analyzing Causes and Effects** How might worldwide demand for gasoline affect the economy of the Gulf coastal plain? Explain.

5. **Critical Thinking Asking Geographic Questions** What questions might a geographer ask about the development of resort cities such as Cancún?

Activity

USING THE **REGIONAL ATLAS**

Review the Regional Atlas for Latin America and this section. Then, create a full-page magazine advertisement urging business owners to move their companies to Mexico. Your advertisement should point out how geographic conditions help support a variety of economic activities in Mexico.

Answers to Section 1 Assessment

1. (a) plateau, p. 221 **(b)** peninsula, p. 221 **(c)** irrigation, p. 223 **(d)** sinkhole, p. 224

2. The Mexican heartland is geologically unstable because it is located at the intersection of four tectonic plates; it has many earthquakes and volcanoes. The climate in the north is arid with very little rainfall, but in the south the climate is pleasant, with moist ocean winds causing moderate levels of precipitation.

3. The northern Pacific coast has good farmland, the southern Pacific coast attracts tourism, and the Gulf coastal plain contains large deposits of petroleum and natural gas.

4. Increased worldwide demand for gasoline would increase the export of petroleum from the Gulf coastal plain. This would benefit the economy. Decreased demand for gasoline would have the opposite effect.

5. Possible answers: What geographical qualities would make a city a good site for a resort? How will development of the resort city affect its physical characteristics and natural resources?

Activity Rubrics Share rubrics with students before they begin their advertisements.

Attempted The advertisement is incomplete or reveals little understanding of how geographic conditions support economic activities.

Minimal The advertisement shows some understanding but is poorly executed.

Adequate The advertisement is well conceived and shows good understanding.

Exemplary The advertisement is well executed and shows a thorough understanding of how geographic conditions help support economic activities.

TEST PREPARATION

Have students read the subsection The Yucatán Peninsula beginning on the opposite page to answer the following question.

Which one of the following cities might a tourist in the Yucatán visit?

A   Puerto Vallarta
B   Acapulco
C   Mazatlán
Ⓓ   Cancún

Answer to Photo Caption

Possible answer: Tourist attractions include the coastal climate; the warm, sandy beaches; and the Mayan and Aztec ruins.

Teaching the Skill

Ask students to imagine that earth-moving crews and equipment have just arrived at an empty lot in their neighborhood. Call on volunteers to predict what is about to happen with this property. Next, have students read the description of *making inferences* in the lesson. Help them relate the description to the inferences they made about the empty lot. Then complete the skill steps with the students.

Answers to Learn the Skill

1. (a) The people are harvesting a crop. **(b)** They are using a tractor and modern farm equipment. **(c)** The land is green and cultivated in the foreground and the land in the background looks like desert.
2. This photo shows the effects of irrigation. One can see that the field ends where the desert begins.
3. Although people tend to swim outdoors in summer, they may swim outdoors during other seasons as well. Other details in the picture, such as snow on the ground, could also lead a viewer to believe it was a different season.
4. (a) It looks like a large farm because of the size of the field and the farm equipment. It seems to be a cash crop because the produce is being packed into crates like the ones delivered to grocery stores. **(b)** The farm uses irrigation because it borders the desert.

Answer to Practice the Skill

Student work should reflect reasonable assumptions about what might have happened before the picture was taken. These assumptions should be based on the picture's content.

You make inferences all day without realizing it. You look at the world around you and come to conclusions about what you think is happening. This process of "reading" what you see and drawing conclusions is making an inference. These inferences are based on what you know; they are not necessarily fact.

Learn the Skill Use the following steps to analyze the photograph below and make inferences.

1 Notice the details of the photograph. Identify the elements of the picture and the action that you recognize. **(a)** *What are the people doing?* **(b)** *What kind of equipment are they using?* **(c)** *How does the land in the front, or foreground, of the picture differ from the dry region in the back?*

2 *Read any accompanying information.* Sometimes a photograph has a title and caption, which can be an important source of information. When a photograph is used to illustrate written text, the two elements work together to increase understanding. *How does this photograph help you to better understand the information in Section 1 about farming in Mexico?*

3 *Apply what you already know.* You will depend upon your own knowledge to help draw valid

conclusions. For example, if you saw a photograph of a person swimming in a lake, based on your experience you might assume it was summer. *What reasons can you think of that would make this inference inaccurate?*

4 *Make your best guess.* Based on your knowledge and the photograph below, make your best inference about what is happening. **(a)** *Is this a large farm? Why do you think so?* **(b)** *Does this farm depend on irrigation? Explain.*

 # Do It Yourself

Practice the Skill Find a photograph of people in action in your school textbooks or possibly among photographs that you have at home. Then, work in pairs or individually to create a caption for the photograph. In the caption, describe what you think was happening when the picture was taken. Base your response on the clues given in the picture.

Apply the Skill See Chapter 10 Review and Assessment.

RESOURCE DIRECTORY

Teaching Resources

Unit 3, Chapter 10
• Section 2 Guided Reading and Review, p. 13
• Map/Graph Skills, p. 17

Guide to the Essentials (English/Spanish)
• Section Summary, Chapter 10, Section 2

Mental Mapping booklet
• Unit 3 Checklist, p. 34

Social Studies Skills Handbook
• Analyzing a Photograph, p. 58

Technology

Guided Reading Audiotapes (English/Spanish), Chapter 10, Section 2

Section Reading Support Transparencies, Chapter 10, Section 2

World Geography Map and Photo Transparencies
• Latin America: Maps and Photos

Book on CD, Chapter 10

Social Studies Skills Tutor CD-ROM, Making Inferences/Drawing Conclusions

Companion Web site, www.phschool.com
• Chapter 10 Activities

2 A Place of Three Cultures

Reading Focus

- How did Mexico become a Spanish colony?
- What were key political events in the development of democracy in Mexico?
- What social problems face Mexico today?
- What are the main characteristics of the Mexican economy?

Key Terms

hacienda
land redistribution
ejido
subsistence farming
latifundio

cash crop
migrant worker
NAFTA
maquiladora

Main Idea Historical developments and current social conditions affect economic activities in Mexico.

Understanding the Past Unearthed during subway construction, an Aztec temple gives testimony to Mexico's past.

A broad square in Mexico City stands as a symbol of the complexity of Mexican culture. The Plaza de las Tres Culturas—the Three Cultures—is located on the site of an Aztec center that fell to the Spanish in a 1521 battle. In the center are the restored ruins of an Aztec temple pyramid. On one side of the square is a church built by the Spanish conquerors in 1609. On another side, twin office buildings of glass and concrete represent Mexico's modern culture. A busy eight-lane highway runs past the plaza.

Together, these three cultures—Indian, Spanish, and modern—make up modern Mexico. The result is a nation aware of the traditions of the past and the possibilities of the future.

Aztecs and Spaniards

Drawing on elements from earlier cultures, the Aztecs built the most powerful empire in early Mexico. By the early 1400s, their capital city of Tenochtitlán (teh noch tee TLAHN) was the center of an empire that spread over much of south-central Mexico. Tenochtitlán, built on an island in a lake, occupied the site of modern Mexico City. On its main square were great temples and

the palaces of Aztec royalty. The city had open plazas and huge marketplaces. In the 1400s, it was one of the largest cities in the world. An estimated 60,000 Aztecs gathered each day to trade goods.

The Spanish Conquest Spanish adventurer Hernán Cortés, with six hundred Spanish soldiers, marched into Tenochtitlán in 1519. The Spaniards had come inland from Mexico's Gulf coast, making allies of the Aztecs' enemies along the way. Within two years, the conquistadors, or conquerors, destroyed the Aztec empire. Tenochtitlán and other Aztec towns lay in ruins. The Spanish then went on to conquer the remaining Indian groups in Mexico. The territory won by Cortés became the colony of New Spain.

New Spain Four social classes emerged as the Spanish settled New Spain. At the top were the *peninsulares* (peh nin suh LAHR es). This group, those born in Spain, held high official positions. The next highest group were the *criollos* (cree OHL yos), people of Spanish ancestry born in the Americas. Mestizos, people of mixed ancestry, ranked third, and the Indians ranked lowest. Over the next three hundred

---

Objectives

Upon completion of Section 2, students should be able to:

◆ explain how Mexico became a Spanish colony;
◆ trace the development of democracy in Mexico;
◆ identify Mexico's social problems;
◆ give the main characteristics of the Mexican economy.

National Geography Standards

The following National Geography Standards are highlighted in this section: 1, 4, 6, 10, 12, 13, 14, 17

Bellringer

Have students list at least ten things that they associate with life in Mexico today that are found in the United States. Examples may include the Spanish language, foods such as tacos and tortillas, and sports such as soccer. Have students explain why they think U.S. culture is influenced by Mexican culture. Encourage a discussion of cultural diffusion.

LESSON PLAN

1. Focus Read the following quotation by Hernán Cortés describing his impressions of Tenochtitlán, the Aztec capital. "The city has many squares where . . . every kind of merchandise . . . is found. . . . There are . . . many temples. . . . They are all very beautiful buildings." Remind students that the Spaniards destroyed Tenochtitlán during their conquest of the Aztecs.

2. Instruct Organize the class into three groups: ancient Indian, Spanish, and modern. Ask each group to read and summarize the material in the text about their topic. Ask for volunteers to share their summaries with the class.

3. Close/Reteach Have students read the following terms aloud and decide if each is associated with Mexico's Indian culture, its Spanish culture, or its modern culture: *hacienda, Tenochtitlán, democratic republic, peninsulares, PRI, ejidos.*

CUSTOMIZE FOR...

Students Acquiring English/ESL
Postcards From Mexico On an index card, have students make a quick sketch of one Mexican attraction. Instruct each student to write a brief description of the place he or she drew. Display the cards and descriptions on the bulletin board.

Activity: Creating "Mexican Fair" posters

Purpose: Have each group create a poster for a Mexican fair. Posters should highlight a specific cultural characteristic of Mexico, such as life in Mexico City, traditional foods, clothing, or fine art. Each poster should have a title.

Roles: Researchers, artists, writers, spokesperson

Result: Use the posters to decorate the classroom for a "Mexican Fair," at which a volunteer from each group explains his or her group's poster to the class.

READING STRATEGY

Predicting

Before students read the section, have them examine its four main headings and their subheadings. Instruct students to use this information to predict one fact they might learn in each of the four main parts. Have students record their predictions in their notebooks. Direct them to look for the facts that match their predictions as they read the section.

Alternative Assessment

Introduce the Activity

Creating a Time Line Ask students to create a time line showing the events in the development and interaction of the three cultures of Mexico: ancient Indian, colonial Spanish, and modern. Distribute the Time Line Rubric found on page 12 of the Alternative Assessment booklet in the Prentice Hall Assessment System for student reference during the project.

Answer to Photo Caption

A system with a single party gives voters little choice of candidates and political philosophy. Citizens who do not agree with the philosophy of the dominant political party are not represented in government.

Change Over Time

Political Change

Changing Governments During the Mexican Revolution, guerrilla leaders like Pancho Villa (PAST) resorted to armed uprisings to force governmental change. In 2000, Vicente Fox (PRESENT), following a peaceful election, became the first Mexican president in more than 70 years who was not nominated by the Institutional Revolutionary Party (PRI).

Place *Why might people object to having a single political party?*

PRESENT

PAST

years, life in New Spain followed these strict social lines.

As in other Spanish colonies in the Americas, Indians provided the labor on **haciendas** (hah see EN duhs). These were large, Spanish-owned estates of land, usually run as farms or cattle ranches. Both the haciendas and the Indians who worked on them were granted to the conquistadors as rewards by the Spanish king. Under this system, known as the *encomienda*, landowners were supposed to care for their workers' welfare. But in fact low wages and constant debt forced most Indians to live a slave-like existence.

Road to Democracy

Spanish colonial rule continued into the early 1800s. Then the resentment the *criollos* felt for the privileged *peninsulares* erupted into conflict. In 1810 a *criollo* priest named Miguel Hidalgo called for a rebellion against Spanish rule. His cry sparked a war of independence. By 1821, the independent nation of Mexico was established.

But while Mexico had finally achieved independence, the new nation was not democratic. The search for democracy took about another

hundred years. During that time, the country went through a series of political struggles and even a civil war. Strong military leaders ruled as dictators, while the people wanted democracy.

By the end of the 1800s, Mexico was stable enough to attract large amounts of foreign capital and industry. Railroads were built, ranches were expanded, and Mexico's valuable oil reserves were developed. Such efforts to modernize the country, however, mainly helped wealthy Mexicans become even wealthier. The gap between rich and poor, established in colonial times, continued unchanged.

The Mexican Revolution In 1910, peasants and middle-class Mexicans rebelled. In the Mexican Revolution, they stood up to the military dictator and the landlords who together controlled the country. By the time the fighting ended in 1920, Mexico had a new president and a new constitution. The new government promised "land, bread, and justice for all."

The democratic republic established by the Mexican Revolution remains in place today. Mexico, like the United States, is a federal republic headed by an elected president and congress.

RESOURCE DIRECTORY

Prentice Hall Assessment System
Alternative Assessment booklet
• Time Line Rubric, p. 12

Unlike the United States, however, one political party held power. Called the Institutional Revolutionary Party (PRI), this party maintained control of Mexican politics for decades. PRI power diminished in 2000, when Vicente Fox of the National Action Party was elected president.

Social Conditions

Mexico has worked to preserve both its Indian and Spanish heritages. Nearly all Mexicans use Spanish as their official language. People of Indian descent, however, often speak their ancestral languages at home. The constitution grants freedom of religion, but most Mexicans are Roman Catholics.

Although Mexico has made great economic strides in modern times, a minority still holds much of the country's wealth. The country is still working to achieve social justice and create economic opportunities for more people.

Rural Life Most people in the Mexican countryside work in agriculture. In 1910 nearly all Mexican land that could be used for farming was part of about 8,000 haciendas. After the revolution, the government began a program of buying out landowners and breaking up their large haciendas. The estates were divided among landless peasants. The government still follows this policy

of **land redistribution.** About half of the haciendas have been broken up in this way.

The government awarded most of the reclaimed land in the form of *ejidos* (ay HEE doz), farmland owned collectively by members of a rural community. Many *ejido* farmers practice **subsistence farming.** They grow only enough crops to meet their family's needs.

Approximately one third of Mexican farms, however, are huge commercial farms owned by individuals or by farming companies. These commercial farms are called *latifundios.* Mexico's commercial farms and some *ejidos* raise **cash crops,** farm crops grown for sale and profit, such as corn, sugar cane, coffee, and fruit.

An estimated 3 to 4 million rural Mexican families have neither the land nor opportunities for work. Some try to coax crops from land unsuitable for farming. Many landless, jobless peasants become **migrant workers.** That is, they travel from place to place where extra workers are needed to cultivate or harvest crops. At harvest time many migrant workers also cross the Rio Grande into the United States. While some have permits to cross the border, others cross illegally.

Urban Life The heart of modern Mexican culture is its urban areas, where three quarters of Mexico's population lives. Mexico City is one of the largest urban areas in the world and is still

Village Life

Cultures In rural Mexican villages, many people maintain traditional lifestyles. The church in the center of the village shows the importance of religion in Mexican culture.

Human-Environment Interaction *How does the photograph indicate that villagers grow their own food?*

229

Articles From
NATIONAL GEOGRAPHIC

The following article may be used to extend the content in this section.

Cobb Jr., Charles E., and Danny Lehman, photographer. "Mexico's Bajio—The Heartland." *National Geographic*, Vol. 178, No. 6 (Dec. 1990), pp. 122–143.

Birthplace of the revolution that overthrew imperial Spain's rule in Mexico, Bajio is both the historical center and the mother of modern Mexico.

ACTIVITY

Vocabulary

Latifundio Point out the word *latifundio* on the list of Key Terms on page 227. Explain that this term refers to large commercial farms in Mexico. Ask students to suggest what crops might be grown on Mexican *latifundios.* (Answers may include corn, sugar cane, coffee, fruit.)

ACTIVITY

Critical Thinking

Making Comparisons Write the headings *Rural* and *Urban* across the top of the chalkboard. Ask students to list characteristics of rural and urban Mexico under the appropriate heading. Have students compare these characteristics. Then have students list the urban and rural characteristics of the United States and compare that list to the one for Mexico.

BACKGROUND

Daily Life

Mealtimes Most Mexicans follow a daily schedule that includes coffee or hot chocolate and rolls early in the morning and a fuller breakfast around 9:00 A.M. The main meal of the day, called *comida,* is served around 2:00 P.M. An afternoon snack at around 6:00 P.M. and a late supper at around 10:00 P.M. complete the meals of the day.

Answer to Photo Caption

Crops are growing next to the houses and along the street instead of on farms.

Environmental Issues

The Shrinking Sierra Madre Occidental New roads are bringing traffic, ranching, and lumbering to the once almost inaccessible reaches of the Sierra Madre Occidental. Environmentalists note with dismay that overgrazing and logging are driving out some forms of wildlife, including the grizzly bear.

Critical Thinking

Land and Culture Use the following questions to help students see the links between land and culture in Mexico: **Of the four social classes of New Spain, which groups were likely to hold large amounts of land?** (*peninsulares* and *criollos*) **When did land reform begin in Mexico?** (after the revolution of 1910) **To what degree have commercial farms taken the place of haciendas?** (Huge commercial farms owned by individuals or farming companies now own about one third of Mexico's farms.) **How have the peasants who were not included in land reform found work?** (as migrant workers and in the cities) **How are urban dwellers divided into economic levels?** (an elite upper class, growing middle class, the working class, and a large lower class)

Alternative Assessment

Mid-Point Monitoring

Creating a Time Line You may wish to monitor students' progress on creating their time lines by conferring with them. Have they completed their research, chosen the items for their time lines, and begun to plan scale and sequence?

Answer to Photo Caption

Urban areas may offer more job opportunities as well as better opportunities for education and social contact.

GLOBAL CONNECTIONS

Migration Villages of mostly women are common in rural Mexico, as the men travel to other areas for work. Many enter the United States, where they hope to earn enough money to buy land at home.

growing. For many Mexicans, city life means better job opportunities than those found in the countryside. Cities also offer chances for education and excitement.

Although there is a small, wealthy, educated upper class in the cities, most urban dwellers in Mexico are the very poor and must struggle to survive. A growing middle class includes government workers, professionals, and business owners. Mexico's working-class citizens are generally skilled workers who maintain strong ties to traditional Mexican culture. They may live in adobe-block houses in older neighborhoods or in new worker apartment complexes.

Economic Activities

In 1993, the United States, Canada, and Mexico formed the North American Free Trade Agreement **(NAFTA),** which was designed to compete with the European Union, a free-trade network in Europe. NAFTA phased out trade barriers among the three countries. By 1999, Mexico's trade with the United States and Canada had nearly doubled. Manufacturing increased and unemployment declined. Encouraged by its experience in NAFTA, Mexico pursued new trade agreements with other countries.

Major Industries Two of Mexico's most important economic activities are petroleum extraction and tourism. Great reserves of petroleum lie off Mexico's Gulf coast near the city of Tampico. However, because Pemex (Petroleos Mexicanos) is a state-owned company, government revenues rise and fall along with oil prices.

Climate, scenery, tropical beaches, and a rich cultural history make tourism another major source of income for Mexico. Resort cities such as Acapulco and Cancún draw tourists from all over the world. Investment dollars pour into these resort cities.

Tourism is important for another reason. Manufacturing has long contributed to Mexico's economy, with Mexico City as the country's leading industrial center. But factories create a heavy load of pollution. In Mexico City, particularly, polluted air from factories and cars collects over the city because mountains trap the air on three sides. Tourism is a cleaner economic alternative. In fact, Mexicans call it the "smokeless industry."

Border Industries Clustered along the United States–Mexico border are more than two

Mexico City

Urbanization The Independence Monument towers above the Paseo de la Reforma. Beyond, the city stretches for miles in all directions.

Movement *Why do many people move to urban areas?*

Border Industry

Economic Activities
Maquiladoras have spurred economic growth along Mexico's border with the United States.

Human-Environment Interaction *What concerns do some people have about* maquiladoras?

PRODUCTOS ELECTROMECANICOS BAC, S.A. DE C.V.

thousand **maquiladoras** (mah kee luh DOHR uhs). These are factories that assemble products almost exclusively for consumers in the United States. In 1980, these factories employed approximately 200,000 workers. Today, more than a million people work in *maquiladoras*.

When *maquiladoras* first appeared in the Mexican economy, many people expressed concerns that the work was tedious and the pay was quite low. However, as employment in *maquiladoras* has increased, so have the skills of the workers.

Maquiladoras have also profoundly changed the appearance of cities in northern Mexico. Manufacturers have sprung up all across the region. The increase of pollutants from *maquiladoras* has raised concerns about damage to health and the environment.

Many factories have been accused of air and water pollution and improper disposal of waste products. The Mexican government continues to encourage job growth while monitoring the impact of industry on the environment.

SECTION 2 ASSESSMENT

1. **Key Terms** Define **(a)** hacienda, **(b)** land redistribution, **(c)** *ejido*, **(d)** subsistence farming, **(e)** *latifundio*, **(f)** cash crop, **(g)** migrant worker, **(h)** NAFTA, **(i)** *maquiladora*.

2. **Understanding the Past** How did Spanish conquest affect social structure in Mexico?

3. **Government and Citizenship** In what way was the presidential election of 2000 a turning point for Mexican government?

4. **Migration** What social conditions cause many Mexicans to become migrant workers?

5. **Global Trade Patterns** Why are many factories clustered along the United States–Mexico border?

6. **Critical Thinking Predicting Consequences** Based on the information in this section, how do you think that Mexico would be affected by a worldwide increase in the demand for oil? Explain.

Activity

Take It to the NET

Making a Graph Use economic statistics from the Internet to make a graph on one or more of the following topics concerning Mexico: imports, exports, agricultural products, industrial products. Visit the World Geography section of **www.phschool.com** for help in completing this activity.

TEST PREPARATION

Have students read the subsection Border Industries beginning on the opposite page to answer the following question.
Maquiladoras have provided all of the following *except*—
 A   products for the United States
 B   cleaner air and water
 C   increased employment
 D   improved skills among workers

Creating a Chapter Summary
As a reteaching opportunity, pair a more able student with a less able student to complete this chapter summary.

Possible answers: **Regions:** Central plateau, Northern Pacific coast, Southern Pacific coast, Gulf coastal plain, Yucatán Peninsula **Economy:** Petroleum extraction, Tourism, *Maquiladoras* **Culture:** Native American, Spanish, Mestizo

Reviewing Key Terms
1–10. Students' sentences should show a clear understanding of each word.

Understanding Key Ideas
11. Plate movement has pushed up jagged mountain ranges. Some of these mountains are active volcanoes. Plate movement also causes earthquakes in some places.
12. The central plateau's mild climate has attracted many Mexicans to this region and has contributed to the growth of Mexico City, one of the world's largest urban areas.
13. It is flat and the bedrock is limestone, which dissolves and turns into sinkholes.
14. The Spanish created a social system with four categories: Spanish-born people were at the top and were eligible for the best jobs. Those of Spanish ancestry born in America were next. Mestizos ranked third. Indians were at the bottom of the social structure.
15. Contributing factors to the Mexican Revolution include the gap between the rich and poor, resentment against the wealthy landowners who held all political and economic power, and social injustices suffered by indigenous peoples and mestizos.
16. Students should recognize that although political change has brought about programs to help poor Mexicans—for example, land redistribution—the gap between rich and poor is wide.
17. (a) Workers may gain new skills. **(b)** The work is usually tedious, the pay is low, and some *maquiladoras* pollute the environment.

Creating a Chapter Summary

Copy this concept web on a piece of paper. Add supporting details about each topic shown. You may need to add more circles. Some entries have been completed to serve as a sample.

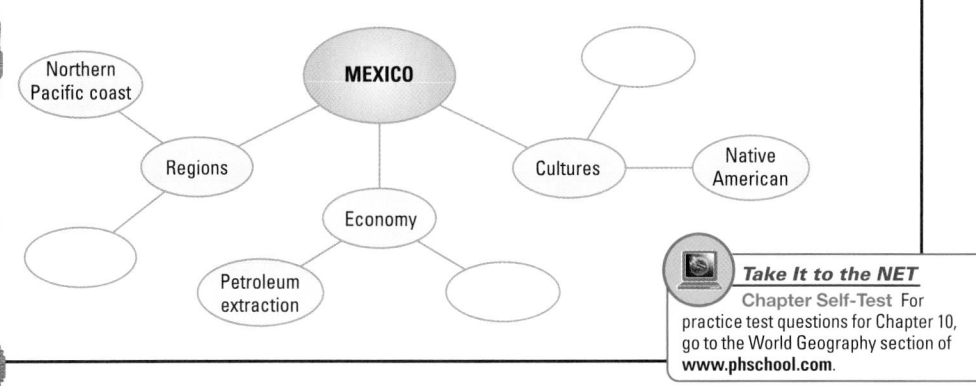

Take It to the NET
Chapter Self-Test For practice test questions for Chapter 10, go to the World Geography section of **www.phschool.com**.

Reviewing Key Terms

Write each of the following terms in a sentence that shows its meaning. You may use two terms in one sentence.

1. peninsula
2. irrigation
3. sinkhole
4. hacienda
5. land redistribution

6. *ejido*
7. *latifundio*
8. cash crop
9. migrant worker
10. NAFTA

Understanding Key Ideas

11. **Physical Processes** How have tectonic plates influenced Mexico's geographic features?
12. **Climates** How has climate influenced urban growth in the heartland of Mexico?
13. **Physical Characteristics** How is the Yucatán Peninsula different from Mexico's other regions?
14. **Cultures** How did the arrival of Spanish conquistadors and settlers lead to a new social structure in Mexico?

15. **Understanding the Past** What factors contributed to revolution in Mexico?
16. **Government and Citizenship** How have political changes in Mexico affected ownership of resources?
17. **Economic Activities** (a) How do *maquiladoras* benefit workers? (b) What are some drawbacks of *maquiladoras*?

Critical Thinking and Writing

18. **Defending a Position** How might you support the idea that the Mexican Revolution continued for decades after 1920?
19. **Recognizing Points of View** (a) What benefits to Mexico have resulted from passage of NAFTA? (b) Why might some people oppose NAFTA?
20. **Making Decisions** Suppose that you are developing a new resort city in one of the regions discussed in this chapter. Write a one-page proposal for your plan, including reasons for choosing that site, possible environmental effects, and possible economic effects.

Critical Thinking and Writing
18. Students might suggest that the Mexican Revolution continued after 1920 through the efforts of indigenous peoples to fight for equal rights and for all Mexicans to struggle to make their government accountable.
19. (a) NAFTA eliminated trade barriers among Mexico, the United States, and Canada. Trade with the United States and Canada doubled and unemployment in Mexico declined. **(b)** Some U.S. citizens opposed NAFTA because they were concerned that U.S. companies would move U.S.-based factories to Mexico where wages are lower and there are fewer laws about pollution.
20. Students' answers should reflect knowledge about the regions of Mexico and about place and location. Their answers should show an understanding of the impact of people on the environment and on the economy.

Applying Skills

Making Inferences Refer to the Skills for Life lesson on page 226 to answer these questions:

21. Is this farm more likely to be an *ejido* or a *latifundio*? Explain.

22. Are the people in the photograph likely to be the farm owners? Explain.

23. Are the products of this farm likely to be sold locally? Explain.

Reading a Map Study the map below, and answer the following questions:

24. What area shows the highest concentration of people?

25. What area appears to have the lowest concentration of people?

26. In general, do more people live along the east coast or the west coast of Mexico?

27. Is the population more evenly distributed along the southern or the northern border of Mexico?

Mexico: POPULATION DISTRIBUTION

KEY

One dot represents 200,000 people

Lambert Azimuthal Equal-Area Projection

Test Preparation

Read the question and choose the best answer.

28. The Mexican war for independence began in 1810 when —

A Mexican peasants rebelled against French rule

B the *encomienda* system was put into place

C Miguel Hidalgo, a priest, called for rebellion against Spanish rule

D Hernán Cortés defeated the Aztecs

Activities

USING THE REGIONAL ATLAS

Make or copy an outline map of Latin America. Then, review the Regional Atlas for Latin America and Chapter 10. Develop a map key identifying natural hazards that affect Latin America. Color or shade your map to indicate which regions of Latin America are affected.

 MENTAL MAPPING

Review a map of Mexico. On a separate piece of paper, draw a sketch map of Mexico from memory. Label the following places on your map:

- Guadalajara
- Acapulco
- Gulf of Mexico
- Yucatán Peninsula
- Mexico City
- Baja California
- Gulf of California
- Bay of Campeche
- Sierra Madre Oriental
- Sierra Madre Occidental

Take It to the NET

Making a Map Explore Mexican travel sites to identify places in Mexico that reflect the influence of ancient Indian culture, colonial Spanish culture, and modern Mexico. On an outline map of Mexico, locate each place and write a caption that explains its importance. Visit the World Geography section of **www.phschool.com** for help in completing this activity.

Applying Skills

21. *latifundio;* it looks like a commercial crop is being grown

22. No. The owners of a *latifundio* hire others to work the land.

23. The owners of a *latifundio* are likely to sell cash crops outside the local area.

24. the central region

25. the Baja peninsula

26. east coast

27. southern border

Test Preparation

28. C

Activities

Using the Regional Atlas
Check students' map and map key for accuracy. Check that students have correctly identified the location and type of natural hazards that affect Latin America.

Mental Mapping
Review students' maps for relative and absolute location.

Take It to the Net
Students' work should reflect sound research. Check students' work for accurate location of places and captions that reflect an understanding of influences on Mexican culture.

 MENTAL MAPPING

Games for Review See pages 58–63 of the Simulations, Games, and Lab Activities booklet for games to help students review for the chapter map test.

Chapter Map Test Students should use the completed outline maps and the Unit 3 Checklist in their Atlas Portfolios to prepare for the chapter map test. The test will cover only those names on the Unit Checklist related to Mexico.

Alternative Assessment

Final Evaluation

Creating a Time Line Use the Time Line Evaluation Form on page 13 of the Alternative Assessment booklet in the Prentice Hall Assessment System to evaluate students' papers. Either teachers or students can complete the forms to indicate which level of work was achieved for each of the criteria. The evaluations should include specific comments.

People and Geography

pp. 234–235

Objectives

Upon completion of this feature, students should be able to:

◆ identify the causes and effects of air pollution in Mexico City;

◆ explain Mexico City's efforts to decrease pollution levels.

 ### National Geography Standards

The following National Geography standards are highlighted in this feature: 1, 3, 4, 9, 12, 14

 ### Bellringer

Ask the students to brainstorm adjectives that describe polluted air. For example, students might say that polluted air is not only *ugly* and *smelly* but also *unhealthy* and *preventable*.

....

LESSON PLAN

1. Focus Tell students to read pages 234–235. Ask: **Why is pollution a concern for everyone?** (Its effects are not limited to those who create it. Wind moves air pollution across regions.)

2. Instruct Make a three-column chart on the chalkboard. In the first column, list the major causes of Mexico City's air pollution. In the second column, list the effects. In the final column, record Mexico City's control strategies.

3. Close/Reteach Review the chart with the class. Ask students: **What other control strategies could Mexico City use to improve its air quality?** (Possible answer: encourage the use of alternative energy sources and reward efforts to reduce emissions)

Answers to Photo Captions

Smog Over Mexico City A larger population uses more utilities and vehicles, increasing air pollution.

Sources of Air Pollution Human processes include the use of emissions-producing vehicles and factories. Physical processes include the inversion that traps polluted air in Mexico City.

234 Chapter 10

People and Geography
Air Pollution in Mexico City

The Issue

Mexico City has grown to be one of the ten most populous cities in the world. Within its sprawling metropolitan area, there are more than 15 million people. Like other cities its size, it has a serious air pollution problem. In fact, Mexico City has one of the most severe cases of atmospheric pollution in the world.

Smog Over Mexico City
How do you think population size might affect air pollution?

The Causes

Both physical and human processes contribute to Mexico City's atmospheric pollution problem. The main sources of pollutants are emissions from cars and trucks. Natural sources, such as soil erosion and forest fires, are also major contributing factors. During drought periods, when forest fires become common, winds can carry smoke to the capital city from other parts of Mexico. The location of Mexico City further aggravates the problem. The city is largely surrounded by mountains. This creates a basin where cooler air can be trapped by warmer air above, in a process called inversion. Pollution collects in the air over four-to-six-day cycles, similar to cycles experienced by some cities in the western United States.

Sources of Air Pollution
What human and physical processes affect air pollution in Mexico City?

Industry 3%
Soil and vegetation 12%
Services 10%
Transportation 75%

Solar energy

Warmer air

Cooler air

Trapped pollutants

Mexico City

RESOURCE DIRECTORY

Teaching Resources
Simulations, Games, and Lab Activities
• Exploring Local Geography, Environmental Problems, p. 4
People and Geography
• Urbanization, pp. 14–18

Technology
World Geography Map and Photo Transparencies
• World Population Growth
• Latin America: Maps

The Effects

The combustion of fuels in cars, trucks, and jets produces primary pollutants such as nitrogen oxides, hydrocarbons, and carbon monoxide. In the presence of sunlight, nitrogen oxides combine with hydrocarbons to form secondary pollutants, such as ozone. The effects of pollution on people can range from slight irritation to serious illness or even death, depending on the nature of the pollutant and the length of exposure. As winds carry urban pollution beyond city limits, crops and other plant life are affected. Ground-level ozone interferes with a plant's ability to produce and store food. As a result, plants become more vulnerable to pests, diseases, and environmental stresses.

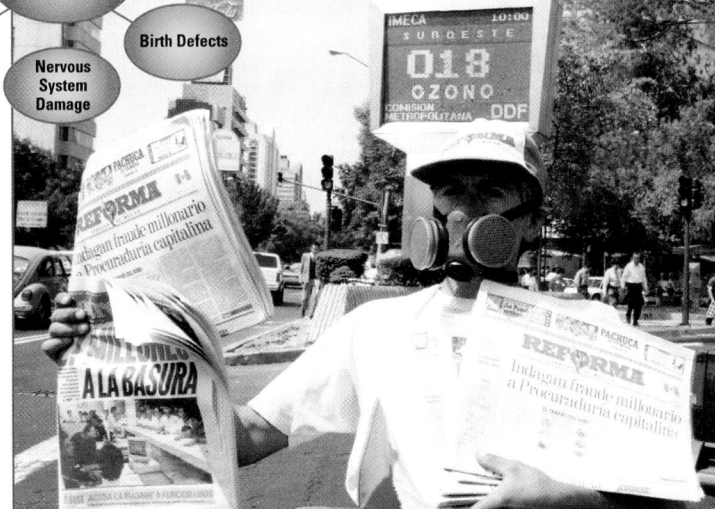

Asthma, Bronchitis — Kidney and Liver Damage — Cancer — AIR POLLUTION — Skin Rashes — Nervous System Damage — Birth Defects

Effects on People
How can people be affected by air pollution, and what can they do to protect themselves?

Control Strategies

In recent years, Mexico City has made serious efforts to reduce air pollution. To promote the use of public transportation and car pooling, the government has enacted a program called Today My Car Stops. Depending on its license plate, every car is banned from city streets at least one day a week. Government regulations have also mandated the use of cleaner fuels. In addition, cars must be equipped with catalytic converters that reduce emissions. When air pollution levels rise, the government may take emergency measures to reduce emissions and protect residents. These may include ordering a decrease in production rates in factories and limiting outdoor activities at schools.

ASSESSMENT: Solving Problems

1. **Identify the Problem** Based on this case study, describe the atmospheric problem faced by cities around the world.

2. **Gather Information** **(a)** What are some causes of the problem? **(b)** What are some effects?

3. **Identify Options** **(a)** What can the government do to reduce or solve the problem? **(b)** What can scientists and engineers do to ease the problem? **(c)** What can ordinary citizens do?

4. **Choose a Solution** Which option or group of options seems best to you? Why?

5. **Plan for the Future** **(a)** What has been done in Mexico City to ease pollution? **(b)** Do you think the solution is adequate for the future? Why or why not?

CUSTOMIZE FOR...

Gifted and Talented

Creating Posters Explain that although ozone can be a damaging pollutant at ground level, the layer of ozone in the earth's stratosphere (outer atmosphere) protects us from the sun's harmful rays. Organize the class into pairs. Have half of the groups research "good" ozone and the others research "bad" ozone. Each pair should produce a poster about its type of ozone that explains chemical content, formation, and benefits or dangers for life on earth. The posters should also explain current issues connected with the students' type of ozone. Display students' posters.

Chapter 11 Planning Guide

Resource Manager

	CORE INSTRUCTION	READING/SKILLS
Chapter-Level Resources	**Teaching Resources** **Unit 3**/Ch. 11 • Reviewing Main Ideas, p. 28 **Mental Mapping booklet** • Unit 3 Checklist, p. 34 **Simulations, Games, and Lab Activities** • Place Location Review Games, pp. 58–63 **Creative Teaching Activities** • Island or Mainland?, p. 13 **TeacherExpress™ CD-ROM**, Ch. 11 **Companion Web site,** **www.phschool.com** • eTeach	**Teaching Resources** **Unit 3**/Ch. 11 • Map/Graph Skills, p. 30 **Social Studies Skills Handbook** • Using the Internet, p. 100 • Doing Searches on the Internet, p. 101 **Book on CD**, Ch. 11 **Social Studies Skills Tutor CD-ROM**
1 Central America 1. Identify the major landforms and climates of Central America. 2. Describe the peoples and cultures found in Central America. 3. Explain how social and economic conditions have sometimes led to political conflicts in the nations of Central America.	**Teaching Resources** **Unit 3**/Ch. 11 • Guided Reading and Review, p. 24 **Prentice Hall Presentation Pro CD-ROM**, Ch. 11, Sec. 1	**Teaching Resources** **Guide to the Essentials (English/Spanish)** • Section Summary, Ch. 11, Sec. 1 **Mental Mapping booklet** • Outline Map 11, p. 42 **Guided Reading Audiotapes (English/Spanish)**, Ch. 11, Sec. 1 **Section Reading Support Transparencies**, Ch. 11, Sec. 1
2 The Caribbean Islands 1. Describe the major physical characteristics of the Caribbean islands. 2. Identify the ethnic roots of Caribbean culture. 3. Describe the political and economic status of the Caribbean islands today. 4. Explain why migration is so common among Caribbean islanders.	**Teaching Resources** **Unit 3**/Ch. 11 • Guided Reading and Review, p. 26 **Prentice Hall Presentation Pro CD-ROM**, Ch. 11, Sec. 2	**Teaching Resources** **Guide to the Essentials (English/Spanish)** • Section Summary, Ch. 11, Sec. 2 **Social Studies Skills Handbook** • Reading a Table, p. 62 **Guided Reading Audiotapes (English/Spanish)**, Ch. 11, Sec. 2 **Section Reading Support Transparencies**, Ch. 11, Sec. 2

ENRICHMENT/HONORS/PREAP

Teaching Resources

Unit 3/Ch. 11
- Critical Thinking, p. 29

Mental Mapping booklet
- Atlas Activity, p. 43

Social Studies Skills Handbook
- Study and Research Skills, pp. 94–108
- Recognizing Cause and Effect, p. 49

World Geography Map and Photo Transparencies
- Latin America: Maps and Photos
- How the Earth Works, Unit 3
- Tectonic Plates

World Geography Videos
- Planning for the Future: Central America and the Caribbean, Tape 1

Companion Web site, www.phschool.com
- Chapter 11 Activities

Companion Web site, www.phschool.com
- Chapter 11 Activities

Teaching Resources

Social Studies Skills Handbook
- Distinguishing False From Accurate Images, p. 45

Companion Web site, www.phschool.com
- Chapter 11 Activities

ASSESSMENT

PRENTICE HALL ASSESSMENT SYSTEM

Core Assessment
- ExamView Test Bank booklet, Ch. 11
- ExamView Test Bank CD-ROM, Ch. 11

Standardized Test Preparation

Review and Reteach
- Review Book for World Geography, pp. 7–8

Practice and Assess
- Test-taking Strategies With Transparencies for High School

  Test-taking Strategy Poster

- Alternative Assessment booklet
- Test Prep Book for World Geography

Teaching Resources

Unit 3/Ch. 11
- Section Quizzes, pp. 25, 27
- Test Forms A and B, pp. 31–36

Guide to the Essentials (English/Spanish)
- Chapter 11 Test

Spanish Resources, Ch. 11
- Section Quizzes, pp. 26–27

Mental Mapping booklet
- Chapter 11 Map Test, p. 44

Companion Web site, www.phschool.com
- Chapter 11 Self-Test

CUSTOMIZE FOR INDIVIDUAL NEEDS

Gifted and Talented
- Teacher's Edition, Customize for . . . , p. 243

Honors/PreAP
- Teacher's Edition, Customize for . . . , pp. 239, 245

Less Proficient Readers
- Guide to the Essentials (English), Ch. 11, Section Summaries
- Guided Reading Audiotapes (English), Ch. 11
- Section Reading Support Transparencies, Ch. 11
- Book on CD, Ch. 11
- Teacher's Edition, Reading Strategy, pp. 238, 247
- Teacher's Edition, Activity: Vocabulary, p. 238
- Teacher's Edition, Customize for . . . , p. 251

Students Acquiring English/ESL
- Guide to the Essentials (English/Spanish), Ch. 11
- Guided Reading Audiotapes (English/Spanish), Ch. 11
- Section Reading Support Transparencies, Ch. 11
- Book on CD, Ch. 11

Less Proficient Writers
- Social Studies Skills Handbook, p. 87
- Alternative Assessment, Writing Assignment Rubric, p. 6

Introducing
CHAPTER
11
pp. 236–253

MENTAL MAPPING

Referring to the map on this page, point out that Central America is an isthmus connecting North and South America. It is bound by the Pacific Ocean on the west and the Caribbean Sea on the east. In the Caribbean lies a long chain of islands arching from the southern tip of Florida to the coast of Venezuela.

Mapping the Region Ask students to create a map like the one on this page. Either have them sketch their own outline maps or distribute the Chapter 11 Outline Map on page 42 of the Mental Mapping booklet in the Teaching Resources. Ask students to shade each country a different color, and have them add labels for countries and bodies of water that are shown on the map. Students should keep their maps in their Atlas Portfolios in order to prepare for the Chapter 11 Map Test.

eTeach

Be sure to check out this month's online forum with a Master Teacher to join in an exchange of teaching ideas. **www.phschool.com**

CHAPTER
11

Central America and the Caribbean

SECTIONS

1	Central America

2	The Caribbean Islands

Central America and the Caribbean: POLITICAL

(Map showing Central America and the Caribbean with labels including Gulf of Mexico, ATLANTIC OCEAN, Tropic of Cancer, Havana, Nassau, BAHAMAS, CUBA, HAITI, Port-au-Prince, DOMINICAN REPUBLIC, San Juan, Santo Domingo, VIRGIN IS. (U.S.) (U.K.), Anguilla (U.K.), ST. KITTS AND NEVIS, ANTIGUA AND BARBUDA, PUERTO RICO (U.S.), St. Croix, Guadeloupe (Fr.), Roseau, DOMINICA, ST. LUCIA, Martinique (Fr.), Castries, ST. VINCENT AND THE GRENADINES, Kingstown, BARBADOS, Bridgetown, St. George's, GRENADA, Port of Spain, TRINIDAD AND TOBAGO, Caribbean Sea, JAMAICA, Kingston, Belmopan, BELIZE, GUATEMALA, Guatemala, HONDURAS, Tegucigalpa, San Salvador, EL SALVADOR, NICARAGUA, Managua, San José, COSTA RICA, PACIFIC OCEAN, Panama, PANAMA, SOUTH AMERICA, Aruba (Neth.), Curaçao (Neth.))

KEY
— National boundary
⊛ National capital
• Other city
Lambert Conformal Conic Projection

0 200 400 mi
0 200 400 km

Go Online
PHSchool.com
For: More information about Central America and the Caribbean and access to the Take It to the Net activities
Visit: phschool.com
Web Code: mjk-0012

RESOURCE DIRECTORY

Teaching Resources
Unit 3, Chapter 11
• Section 1 Guided Reading and Review, p. 24
Guide to the Essentials (English/Spanish)
• Section Summary, Chapter 11, Section 1
Mental Mapping booklet
• Atlas Activity, p. 43
• Unit 3 Checklist, p. 34
Technology
Guided Reading Audiotapes (English/Spanish), Chapter 11, Section 1
Section Reading Support Transparencies, Chapter 11, Section 1

World Geography Map and Photo Transparencies
• Latin America: Maps and Photos
Book on CD, Chapter 11
World Geography Videos
• Planning for the Future: Central America and the Caribbean, Tape 1
TeacherExpress™ CD-ROM, Chapter 11
Prentice Hall Presentation Pro CD-ROM, Chapter 11
Social Studies Skills Tutor CD-ROM
Companion Web site, www.phschool.com
• Chapter 11 Activities

1 Central America

Reading Focus

- What are the major landforms and climates of Central America?
- What peoples and cultures are found in Central America?
- How have social and economic conditions sometimes led to political conflicts in the nations of Central America?

Key Terms

isthmus

guerrilla

 Main Idea Central America, a region of widely varied physical and human features, has often been the scene of political conflict.

Global Trade Patterns The Panama Canal links the Pacific Ocean and the Caribbean Sea.

The small region of Central America curves between the giant land masses of North America and South America. Central America is an **isthmus**—a narrow strip of land, with water on both sides, that connects two larger bodies of land. Central America thus forms a land bridge between the two continents.

Until 1914, Central America greatly hindered movement of people and goods between the Atlantic and Pacific oceans. In that year, the opening of the Panama Canal made it possible for ships to cross the isthmus and sail between the two oceans. Many days were saved because ships did not have to travel thousands of extra miles around the tip of South America.

Seven countries occupy this narrow, curving strip of land between Mexico and Colombia. Beginning in the north, they are Belize, Guatemala, Honduras, El Salvador, Nicaragua, Costa Rica, and Panama. As the map on page 238 shows, these countries are small in area, with a combined land area only about one fourth the size of Mexico. However, packed into this small region is a diverse physical and human landscape as complex as the designs in traditional Indian clothing. This great cultural complexity explains

many of the political, social, and economic challenges that Central America faces today.

Landforms and Climates

Naturalist Jonathan Evan Maslow captured the physical diversity of Central America in this description of Guatemala:

> ❝Up and down, round and round, the countryside never stayed the same more than a few miles at a stretch. . . . Granite heights that looked clawed by blind and angry titans [giants] pitched into patches of lowland rain forest. . . . It was like an entire continent stuffed as in an expertly packed suitcase into a country the size of Massachusetts.❞

This narrative could be used to describe many of the countries in this region. While the landscape of most of Central America is widely varied, even this diverse landscape can be divided into regions. Three major landform regions make up Central America—the mountainous core, the

 ◀ **Half Moon Bay, Antigua Island** (photo left)

Chapter 11 ▪ Section 1 **237**

Section 1 *pp. 237–242*

Objectives

Upon completion of Section 1, students should be able to:

◆ identify the major landforms and climates of Central America;

◆ describe the peoples and cultures found in Central America;

◆ explain how social and economic conditions have sometimes led to political conflicts in the nations of Central America.

 ## National Geography Standards

The following National Geography Standards are highlighted in this section: 1, 2, 4, 5, 7, 10

 ## Bellringer

Ask students to make a rough sketch of the Western Hemisphere with the south at the top of the page, that is, with Greenland and Alaska at the bottom of the page and Tierra del Fuego and Cape Horn at the top. Ask students if this view changes their perception of Central America.

LESSON PLAN

1. Focus Present students with this situation: two thirds of the class are Central American peasants who barely grow enough food to eat. The other one third of the class are very wealthy landowners who control the government. Ask students to think about events that might trigger conflict between the two groups.

2. Instruct As the class reads Section 1, have students discuss the following causes of political conflict in Central America: geographic limits to land available for farming, population growth, and division of the population into racial and economic groups.

(continued on next page)

(continued on next page)

TEACHING TIP
From A Master Teacher

Push-Pull Factors A study of the Caribbean and Central America offers students an opportunity to understand the push-pull factors of migration. You may note that Europeans were pulled to the resource-rich region. Later, Africans were brought involuntarily. Still later, Asians came seeking job opportunities. Today, people are being pushed from the region by political conflicts and natural hazards and pulled to regions with higher living standards.

Pacing Suggestions

▪ For 60-minute Blocks

You will want to vary activities.

- Have students complete the Critical Thinking activity on page 29 in the Unit 3 booklet. Then divide the students into four groups and assign each group one of the following topics: Poverty in Central America, Political Conflict in Central America, Unemployment in the Caribbean Islands, and Political Unrest in the Caribbean Islands. Ask each group to discuss and record the causes and effects of its assigned problem.

Chapter 11 ▪ Section 1 **237**

Section 1—*Landforms and Climates,
People and Cultures, Wealth and
Poverty, Economic Activities,* and
Political Conflict—on the board.
After students finish reading the
chapter, ask the class to brainstorm the main ideas of each of
these subsections. Write students'
main ideas on the board under
the appropriate headings. Instruct
students to use this chart as a
study aid.

ACTIVITY

Vocabulary

Isthmus Refer to the key terms list
on page 237. Write the term *isthmus*
on the board. Ask students to look
up *isthmus* in the Glossary and paraphrase the definition. Ask: **How
could an isthmus affect trade?**
(An isthmus might promote trade
between the connected land areas
but might also hinder travel between
two bodies of water.)

READING STRATEGY

Summarizing Main Ideas

As the class reads this page and the
next, instruct students to write two
or three sentences summarizing the
three major types of landforms in
Central America. Have them use
their sentences to create a paragraph
describing the physical features.

Caribbean lowlands, and the Pacific coastal plain.
Each landform region has its own climate.

The Mountainous Core As in Mexico,
mountains run the length of Central America,
some towering more than 13,000 feet (4,000 m)
above sea level. These rugged mountains are difficult to cross, causing serious problems for transportation in the region. Many of these mountains
are active volcanoes.

Two climate zones exist in the high elevations of Central America's mountainous core. Elevations between 3,000 and 6,000 feet (900 and
1,800 m) have a year-round, springlike climate,
free of frosts but cool enough to grow corn and
coffee. Above 6,000 feet (1,800 m) the climate is
cold. Because of frequent frosts, few crops other
than potatoes and barley can grow at these high
elevations.

Caribbean Lowlands On the eastern
side of Central America, the mountainous core
gives way to lowlands that edge the Caribbean
Sea. The Caribbean lowlands have a tropical wet
climate—hot and humid with year-round high
temperatures and heavy rainfall. Northeast trade
winds may bring more than 80 inches (203 cm)
of rain in a year. Dense rain forest vegetation
covers much of the land. The rain forest soil is
not very fertile, limiting the crops that can be
grown there.

Pacific Coastal Plain Unlike the Caribbean coast, the Pacific coast has a tropical wet and
dry climate with savanna, or grassland, vegetation. The difference in climate on the two coasts is
due to the moist winds that sweep from the northeast across the Caribbean toward Central America.
These winds drop rain on the Caribbean coast and

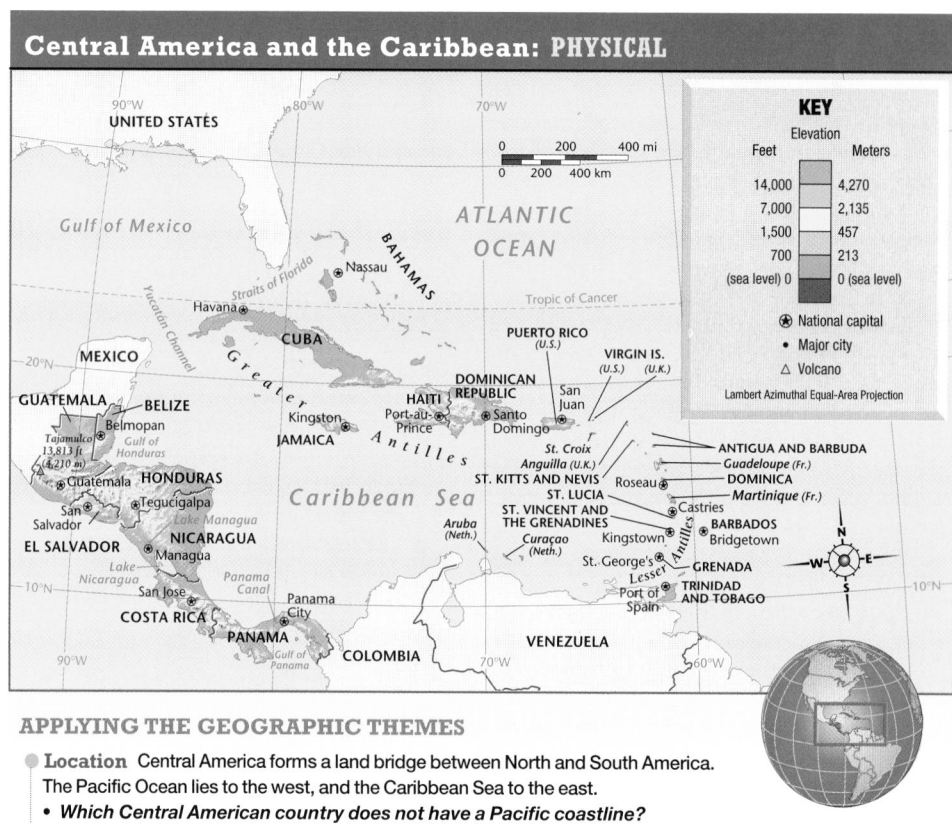

Central America and the Caribbean: PHYSICAL

APPLYING THE GEOGRAPHIC THEMES

● **Location** Central America forms a land bridge between North and South America.
The Pacific Ocean lies to the west, and the Caribbean Sea to the east.
• *Which Central American country does not have a Pacific coastline?*

RESOURCE DIRECTORY

Teaching Resources
Unit 3, Chapter 11
• Critical Thinking, p. 29
• Map/Graph Skills, p. 30
Mental Mapping booklet
• Outline Map 11, p. 42

Technology
World Geography Map and Photo Transparencies
• Latin America: Maps and Photos

Answer to Map Caption

Belize

the eastern mountain slopes throughout the year. In contrast, the Pacific coast can depend on rain only in the summer. Volcanoes high in the mountains above the Pacific coastal plain affect the land. Lava flows and deposits of volcanic ash make Pacific coast soils extremely fertile.

Nicaragua's Pacific coastal plain has several freshwater lakes. The largest is Lake Nicaragua, a large oval lake scattered with small islands. Scientists believe that it was once a bay, cut off from the Pacific Ocean when a volcanic eruption created a ridge of mountains. Although the lake is fresh water, ocean creatures such as sharks and swordfish swim in its deep blue waters.

Climatic Hazards In summer and early fall, tropical storms and hurricanes can strike. One of the most deadly was Hurricane Mitch, in October 1998. Hardest hit was Honduras, where torrents of rain caused flooding and mudslides. In some areas, entire villages were washed away.

People and Cultures

As the map on page 247 shows, Central America is home to several ethnic groups. Each group tends to be concentrated in a specific location. One reason for this is that throughout the region's history, the mountains have made it difficult for people to travel between areas and mingle with other groups.

Indians The people who have lived longest in Central America are the Indians. Each Indian group has its own distinct history, culture, and language. The largest number of Central American Indians live in Guatemala. There they make up more than half the population.

Europeans and Mestizos Europeans arrived in Central America in the 1500s, when Spaniards conquered and colonized the region. Because of this history, Spanish is the official language in almost all of Central America.

The largest European settlement today is in Costa Rica, where 90 percent of the people are of European—mostly Spanish—descent. Another large group in Central America's population consists of people of mixed European and Indian background called mestizos. Both El Salvador and Nicaragua have large mestizo populations.

Arts and Culture

Cultures This Guatemalan woman is weaving a blanket with a colorful design. Weaving is an ancient Indian art.

Place *Why might you expect traditional weaving to be important in Guatemala?*

African Descent People of African descent are an important population group on Central America's Caribbean coast. Some are descendants of African slaves, who were brought to Central America as early as the 1500s. Most, however, are descended from people who migrated to the region from the Caribbean islands in the early 1900s. They came to work on banana plantations or to help build the Panama Canal.

Wealth and Poverty

Most of the people of Central America are very poor. The wealthy constitute only a tiny percentage of the total population. Most of them are

Cutting Sugar Cane

Economic Activities
Agricultural workers in El Salvador often work long hours for little pay, like the sugar cane cutter shown here. El Salvador is facing a shortage of skilled workers but has a large pool of unskilled labor.

Place *How might the size of the unskilled-labor pool affect the wages of farm laborers in El Salvador?*

plantation owners and are European or mestizo. The rich dominate government and politics in the region.

At least two thirds of all Central Americans are poor, with little political power. They include millions of farmers who have little or no land, and laborers who earn low wages on plantations or in factories. Most are people of Indian and African descent.

The middle class is a small but very important third category in Central America's social structure. This group includes farmers who own small, noncommercial farmland and some employees of urban industries and services. Central America's middle class is a growing population, but it remains small in comparison with the millions of poor people.

Economic Activities

The majority of Central America's people earn their living by some kind of farming. In Guatemala and Honduras, farming employs more than 50 percent of the people. Most of the rural population of Central America lives by subsistence farming. On small farms, using only their hands and a few basic tools, families labor to grow enough corn, beans, and squash to stay alive.

In sharp contrast are the large plantations owned by wealthy families and corporations. Plantation owners hire workers at very low wages and bring in the newest machines, fertilizers, and pesticides to produce cash crops of coffee, bananas, or cotton. Most of these crops are shipped to the United States or Europe. These cash crops account for well over half of Central America's income from exports.

Political Conflict

Picture deep-red coffee beans ripening in the warm sun and workers on ladders reaching to cut clumps of bananas from the trees. Now imagine the crack of gunfire and the sound of soldiers scrambling through mountain forests. For years, these two images have contributed to the nature of Central America.

Armed conflicts have troubled Central America for much of its history. Each nation has specific problems, but some causes for conflict apply to the region as a whole. One important problem is the shortage of available farmland to meet

GLOBAL CONNECTIONS

Global Trade Patterns
In 1999, a dispute over Caribbean bananas threatened cashmere factories halfway across the world. As part of a trade dispute with European governments over banana imports, the United States placed new tariffs on many items, including cashmere from Scotland. The tariffs made the cashmere much more expensive for American customers.

the needs of a growing population, made worse by the unequal distribution of usable land and limited access to productive technology and methods.

In addition, recent governments in Central America have mainly served the interests of the wealthy. Opponents of those governments have sometimes organized **guerrilla** movements, armed forces outside the regular army, who often fight in small bands.

Nicaragua From 1936 to 1979, the Somoza family controlled Nicaragua through corrupt means, changing election results and manipulating the economy. In 1979, a group called the Sandinistas (Sandinista Front for National Liberation) led a movement that overthrew the Somoza government. The Sandinistas governed the country under a socialist system, taking property from landowners and giving it to their supporters. Government control of agriculture and industry caused lower production and a drop in exports.

Soon other Nicaraguans, dissatisfied with these moves, tried to overthrow the Sandinista government, claiming it was turning the country toward communism. These guerrilla fighters were known as the contras, from the Spanish word for "against." Fighting between the two factions raged in Nicaragua and the borders of neighboring countries throughout the 1980s, causing thousands of deaths.

A cease-fire brought a measure of peace in 1990. For the first time in the country's history, power passed peacefully in a free election in 1990. Another election took place in 1996. Nicaragua made slow but steady progress in rebuilding its economy until Hurricane Mitch struck in 1998, devastating crops and destroying many roads and buildings.

El Salvador Political instability and violence have troubled other countries in Central America. In El Salvador, as landlessness among ordinary people increased, wealthy landowners feared a popular revolution. They hired "death squads" to eliminate political opponents who wanted reform. Between 1979 and 1992, El Salvador was the scene of a bloody civil war that involved the army, the death squads, and anti-government guerrillas. More than 70,000 people, many of them civilians, died. In 1992 a peace

El Salvador Earthquake

Natural Hazards In 2001 a series of earthquakes struck El Salvador, destroying more than 100,000 homes and businesses. This town was devastated by a landslide that was caused by the earthquake.

Human-Environment Interaction *How can natural disasters cause economic setbacks in nations such as El Salvador?*

241

1. (a) isthmus, p. 237 **(b)** guerrilla, p. 241

2. In the mountainous core, elevations between 3,000 and 6,000 feet have a year-round springlike climate. At higher elevations, the climate is cold. The Caribbean lowlands have a tropical wet climate. The Pacific coast has a tropical wet and dry climate.

3. (a) The main ethnic groups are Indians, Europeans, mestizos, and people of African descent. **(b)** Guatemala has the highest number of Central American Indians. The largest European settlement is in Costa Rica. El Salvador and Nicaragua have large mestizo populations. People of African descent are an important population group on the Caribbean coast.

4. Land, wealth, and political power are unequally distributed.

5. Possible answer: Europeans conquered and colonized the region in the 1500s. Today, the small upper class, mainly people of European descent or mestizos, continues to dominate government and politics. People of Indian or African ancestry have generally suffered from European domination.

Activity Rubrics Share rubrics with students before they begin their maps.
Attempted The map is incomplete and is messy or difficult to read.
Minimal The map contains basic information on the three landform regions and the climate in each region.
Adequate The map is complete and easily readable. It contains a full paragraph on climate variations.
Exemplary The map is complete, easy to read, and visually attractive. The paragraph is well written and clearly explains the climate variations.

Answers to Chart Skills

El Salvador has more television receivers than radio receivers per 1,000 people.

Costa Rica has the highest level of newspaper circulation.

---

agreement mediated by the United Nations ended the war. After peace returned, the economic horizon looked a little brighter, although El Salvador, too, was hard hit by Hurricane Mitch.

Guatemala The most populous country in Central America, Guatemala has a political history similar to that of El Salvador and Nicaragua. After gaining independence from Spain in 1821, Guatemala was ruled by a series of caudillos, or military dictators. Following World War II, a liberal government was elected, ending the long-term dictatorship of Jorge Ubico.

In the decades that followed, the military gained power. Civil war erupted in the 1960s as leftist guerrilla movements challenged the harsh military regime. During the civil war, the government ruled through the heavy hand of "death squads" who routinely tortured and murdered critics, including student and labor leaders. More than 150,000 people were killed and another 40,000 "disappeared."

Guatemala returned to civilian rule in the mid-1980s, although the military remained a powerful force behind the scenes. The crisis-ridden government of President Jorge Serrano Elías was ousted by the military in 1993. Congress then elected Ramiro de León Carpio to complete the term. A champion of human rights, De León worked to end government corruption and restore peace to Guatemala.

The 30-year war tapered off in the 1990s. In 1995, a UN report blamed Guatemalan authorities for the majority of human rights violations. A peace accord was signed in 1996, ending the war, and a number of police and military personnel were arrested for their "death squad" activities. Free elections were held in 1999. The new president, Alfonso Portillo, promised to continue the reform movement.

Central America and the United States
Communications Data

Country	Radio Receivers (per 1,000 people)	Television Receivers (per 1,000 people)	Newspaper Circulation (per 1,000 people)
Belize	589	183	18
Costa Rica	271	143	91
El Salvador	461	675	48
Guatemala	73	57	31
Honduras	409	95	55
Nicaragua	283	73	32
Panama	299	187	62
United States	2,115	805	212

Source: *Encarta World Atlas*

CHART SKILLS

- **Science and Technology** *Which Central American country has more television receivers than radio receivers per 1,000 people?*
- **Cultures** *Which country in Central America has the highest level of newspaper circulation?*

SECTION 1 ASSESSMENT

1. **Key Terms** Define **(a)** isthmus, **(b)** guerrilla.

2. **Physical Characteristics** What landforms and climates are found in Central America?

3. **Cultures (a)** What are the main ethnic groups in Central America? **(b)** Where is each group concentrated?

4. **Cooperation and Conflict** What are some of the causes of political conflict in Central America?

5. **Critical Thinking Analyzing Causes and Effects** How has Central America's history affected the four main ethnic groups and their positions in society?

Activity

USING THE REGIONAL ATLAS

Review the information on Central America's physical characteristics in this section and in the Regional Atlas. On an outline map, indicate the three landform regions and the climate in each region. Add arrows to show wind patterns and ocean currents. Write a brief paragraph explaining the climate variations between the two coastal regions.

RESOURCE DIRECTORY

Teaching Resources
Unit 3, Chapter 11
- Section 1 Quiz, p. 25

Spanish Resources
- Section 1 Quiz, p. 26

Social Studies Skills Handbook
- Using the Internet, p. 100
- Doing Searches on the Internet, p. 101

Technology
Social Studies Skills Tutor CD-ROM, Using Reliable Information

Evaluating Sources on the Internet

The Internet can be a valuable research tool. By "surfing the Web," you can link to millions of Web sites. However, not all sites present information that is worthwhile—or even accurate. To make the Internet a useful research tool, you must learn how to identify sites that are relevant and factual. For this lesson, assume that you are searching for information about animal life in Central American rain forests.

Learn the Skill Use the following steps to learn how to evaluate sources on the Internet.

1 *Choose a search tool.* If you do not know the Internet site you need, you will need to use a search tool. A search tool is a Web site that helps you find other Internet sites. Some search tools are directories that list sites by category. Others are search engines, which look for sites based on key words that you choose and input yourself. Still others provide both a directory and an engine. **(a)** *What are the advantages of using a directory?* **(b)** *What are the advantages of using a search engine?*

2 *Select key words.* To use a search engine, select key words that summarize your topic, and type them into the text box on the search engine page. Avoid key words that are too broad or too narrow. If you type in "Central America," you will find links to pages that have nothing to do with rain forests. On the other hand, the key word "coati" may lead to sites that deal only with that animal. *What key words might lead to sites about animal life in Central American rain forests?*

3 *Evaluate the quality of sites.* When the search results page comes up, read the summaries. Note how recently the information was posted on the site. Examine the Universal Research Locator (URL) to determine the sponsor of the site. The .edu domain indicates universities and other education sites, the .gov domain indicates government sites, and .com indicates commercial sites. Sites run by governments, universities, libraries, and museums often are reliable because they tend to provide official or scholarly information, rather than one person's opinion. **(a)** *Which of the sites shown below would you expect to be most reliable?* **(b)** *Which site appears to be selling something?* **(c)** *Why might some sites present accurate information in a biased way?*

Do It Yourself

Practice the Skill Choose a topic from Section 1 of this chapter. Identify key words to help you find sources. When you have found several sites, determine if any seem to be reliable sources of information. Write a paragraph explaining why you think a particular site will be useful, based on the site descriptions. Now review the sites to see if you were correct. Write a second paragraph comparing your analysis of the site description to the site itself.

Apply the Skill See Chapter 11 Review and Assessment.

Objectives
Upon completion of this feature, students should be able to:
◆ explain what causes an earthquake;
◆ describe the possible physical effects of an earthquake.

 ### National Geography Standards
The following National Geography Standards are highlighted in this feature: 4, 7, 15, 18

 ### Bellringer
Ask students what comes to mind when they think of earthquakes. Discuss earthquake experiences they may have had or heard about.

LESSON PLAN

1. Focus Have students read and examine the photos on this page and the next. Ask: **What do you suppose people in these regions had to do after the earthquake?** (They had to re-build buildings, fix streets, and find people who were trapped under snow and rubble.)

2. Instruct Write the key terms on the board. Ask volunteers to write definitions beside them. Then have the class work together to use the words in sentences that describe the causes and effects of earthquakes.

3. Close/Reteach Work with students to model how an earthquake happens. Encourage them to build models using everyday classroom materials, such as books for tectonic plates and paper strips for seismic waves.

Effects of Earthquakes

An **earthquake** is a shaking of the ground caused by sudden movements in the earth's crust. The biggest quakes are set off by the movement of tectonic plates. Some plates slide past one another gently. However, others get stuck, and the forces pushing the plates build up. The stress mounts until the plates suddenly shift their positions and cause the earth to shake. Most earthquakes last less than one minute. Even so, the effects of an earthquake can be devastating and long-lasting.

TSUNAMI
In 1755, an earthquake in Lisbon, Portugal, caused a tsunami, as illustrated in this painting. A **tsunami** is a huge sea wave that is set off by an undersea earthquake or volcanic eruption. When tsunamis break on shore, they often devastate coastal areas. Tsunamis can race at speeds of about 450 miles per hour and may reach heights of about 100 feet (30.5 m).

LANDSLIDE
In January 2001, an earthquake struck El Salvador. It caused the landslide that left these Salvadoran women homeless. A **landslide** is a sudden drop of a mass of land down a mountainside or hillside. Emergency relief workers from around the world often rush to the site of an earthquake disaster like the one that occurred in El Salvador.

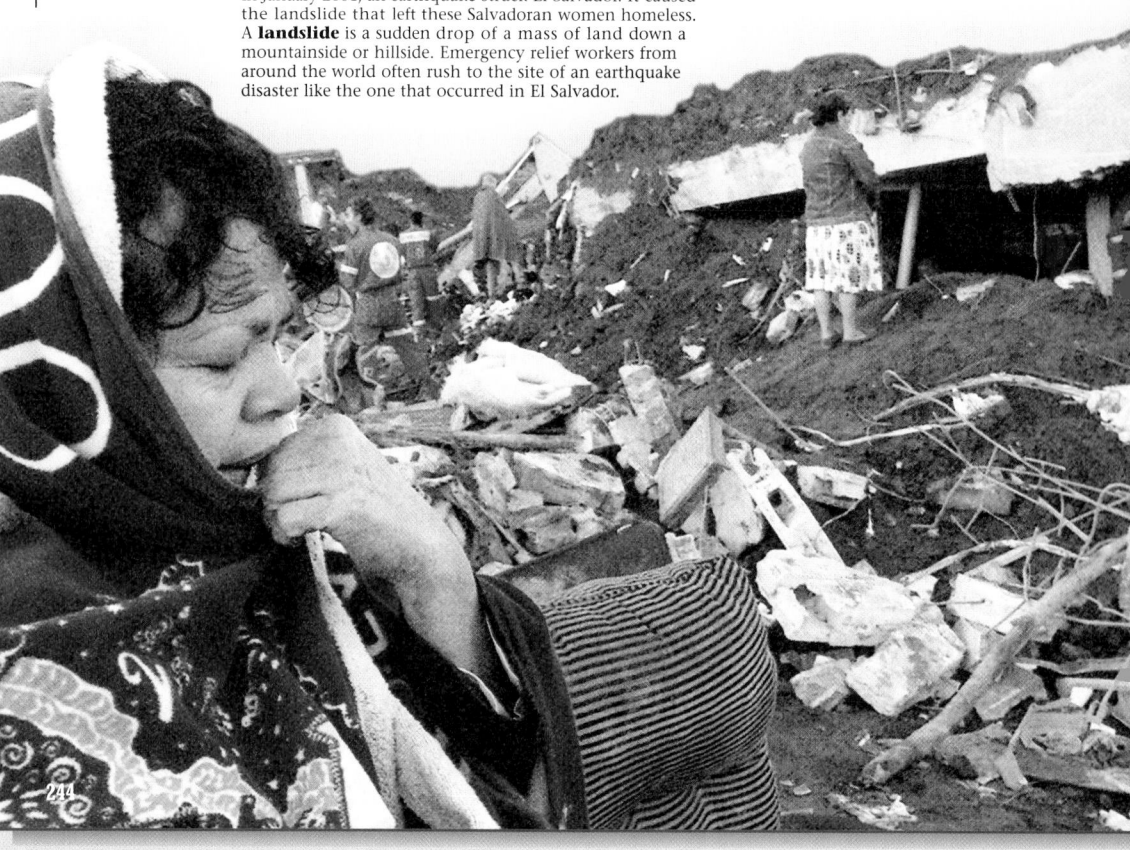

RESOURCE DIRECTORY

Teaching Resources
Social Studies Skills Handbook
• Recognizing Cause and Effect, p. 49

Technology
World Geography Map and Photo Transparencies
• How the Earth Works, Unit 3
• Tectonic Plates
Companion Web site, www.phschool.com
• Chapter 11 Activities

INFRASTRUCTURE DAMAGE
When an earthquake occurred in Los Angeles in 1994, underground gas and water lines burst, causing fires and floods. Earthquakes often cause tremendous damage to the **infrastructure**—the network of services that supports a community. Infrastructure includes power utilities, water supplies, and transportation and communication facilities.

WHEN THE EARTH CRACKS
Most people killed or injured by an earthquake are hit by debris from buildings. Additional damage can be caused by **aftershocks**—tremors that can occur hours, days, or even months after an earthquake. The scene above shows the city of Anchorage, Alaska, after a major earthquake. Extensive ground tremors caused the street to break up as the soil below it collapsed. Buildings and cars were dropped more than 10 feet (3 m) below street level.

AVALANCHE
Earthquakes may trigger an **avalanche**—a sudden fall of a mass of ice and snow. In 1970, a severe earthquake off the coast of Peru caused a disastrous slide of snow and rock that killed some 18,000 people in the valley below.

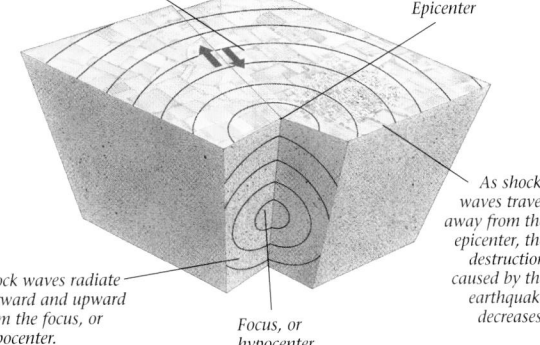

When two tectonic plates suddenly move past each other, waves of built-up energy are released.

Epicenter

As shock waves travel away from the epicenter, the destruction caused by the earthquake decreases.

Shock waves radiate outward and upward from the focus, or hypocenter.

Focus, or hypocenter

SEISMIC WAVES
As tectonic forces build, rock beneath the surface bends until it finally breaks. The tectonic plates suddenly move, causing **seismic waves**, or vibrations, to travel through the ground. The waves radiate outward from an underground area called the focus, or hypocenter. Damage is usually greatest near the **epicenter**, the point on the surface directly above the focus.

ASSESSMENT

1. **Key Terms** Define **(a)** earthquake, **(b)** tsunami, **(c)** landslide, **(d)** infrastructure, **(e)** avalanche, **(f)** aftershock, **(g)** seismic wave, **(h)** epicenter.

2. **Physical Processes** What physical processes cause an earthquake to occur?

3. **Environmental Change** How can an earthquake cause changes to the physical characteristics of a place?

4. **Natural Hazards** **(a)** How can an earthquake change the human characteristics of a place? **(b)** How does the international community respond to a devastating earthquake?

5. **Critical Thinking** **Solving Problems** What can a community do to reduce the amount of earthquake damage that might occur in the future?

The Physical World

Faults A place where tectonic plates move past each other and cause earthquakes is called a *fault*. A fault is a large fracture in the earth's crust. A long fault in North America is the San Andreas Fault, which stretches from the Gulf of California to an area off the shore of San Francisco. In the twentieth century, three large earthquakes occurred along the San Andreas fault—in 1906, 1989, and 1994.

ACTIVITY

Group Work

Activity: Creating safety pamphlets

Purpose: Tell students to find out the recommended ways to protect themselves during an earthquake. Have them create a pamphlet that explains and illustrates safety instructions.

Roles: Each group should have researchers, an editor to compile the explanations, and an illustrator to create the pictures.

Result: Post completed safety pamphlets on your class bulletin board.

Answers to Assessment

1. (a) earthquake, p. 244 **(b)** tsunami, p. 244 **(c)** landslide, p. 244 **(d)** infrastructure, p. 245 **(e)** avalanche, p. 245 **(f)** aftershock, p. 245 **(g)** seismic wave, p. 245 **(h)** epicenter, p. 245

2. sudden movements in the earth's crust

3. Earthquakes can change the level of the land, cause fires and floods, and cover areas with snow and ice.

4. (a) Possible answer: Damage from an earthquake can destroy buildings and make a place uninhabitable. **(b)** Emergency relief workers from around the world may arrive to help with rescue and cleanup efforts. People around the world may donate money to help victims survive until they rebuild their lives.

5. Possible answers: Design buildings to withstand the shock of an earthquake. Build villages, towns, and cities far from fault lines.

CUSTOMIZE FOR...

Honors/PreAP

An Account of an Earthquake Ask students to research a historic earthquake, like the one that hit Lisbon in 1755. Have them imagine that they survived it and are writing a story about it for a foreign newspaper. Encourage them to use factual details and fictional interviews in their stories. Before they begin, remind them that the first paragraph should answer these questions: *Who? What? Where? When?* and *Why?*

Objectives

Upon completion of Section 2, students should be able to:

◆ describe the major physical characteristics of the Caribbean islands;

◆ identify the ethnic roots of Caribbean culture;

◆ describe the political and economic status of the Caribbean islands today;

◆ explain why migration is so common among Caribbean islanders.

National Geography Standards

The following National Geography Standards are highlighted in this section: 9, 10, 12, 18

Bellringer

Have students describe television commercials or print advertisements they may have seen for any of the Caribbean islands.

LESSON PLAN

1. Focus Tell students to make a list of the qualities and features they associate with the Caribbean islands, such as physical features, culture, arts, history, economy, and politics. Have them add information to these lists as they read.

2. Instruct Write the phrase *colonial history* on the board. As the class reads the chapter, ask students to describe political, economic, social, and cultural effects of the colonial history of the Caribbean islands. When the class has completed the chapter, ask students to arrange these effects into a graphic organizer showing the effects of colonial history.

3. Close/Reteach Ask students to explain which aspects of European colonization (if any) they think have had a positive influence on the Caribbean islands.

2 The Caribbean Islands

Reading Focus

- **What are the major physical characteristics of the Caribbean islands?**
- **What are the ethnic roots of Caribbean culture?**
- **What is the political and economic status of the Caribbean islands today?**
- **Why is migration so common among Caribbean islanders?**

Key Terms

archipelago
coral island
windward
leeward

Main Idea The Caribbean islands depend on agriculture and tourism. Many islanders have emigrated in search of other opportunities.

Economic Activities The islands of the Caribbean attract tourists from all over the world.

A large billboard looms over the highway that connects the city of Santo Domingo with its airport. The billboard often features baseball players from the Dominican Republic endorsing soft drinks and other products. These players, though, have gained fame by playing baseball in the United States and Canada, not in their native land. The billboard symbolizes the predicament of many Caribbean islanders who have had to travel to wealthier countries in search of opportunity.

The Caribbean is a beautiful region of forest-covered mountains, warm temperatures, and clear, blue waters. However, many Caribbean nations are struggling to develop their economies. That is one reason why some of their people have left the islands to find opportunities their homelands cannot yet offer.

Physical Characteristics

The Caribbean islands consist of three island groups: the Greater Antilles, the Lesser Antilles, and the Bahamas. Except for some of the islands in the Bahamas, all of the islands are located in the tropics.

The Greater Antilles include the four largest islands of the region—Cuba, Jamaica, Hispaniola (divided into the countries of Haiti and the Dominican Republic), and Puerto Rico. The Bahama **archipelago** (ar kih PEHL ih goh), or group of islands, includes nearly 700 islands northeast of Cuba. Most of the Lesser Antilles form another archipelago, a curving arc that separates the Caribbean Sea from the Atlantic Ocean. The rest, including Aruba, Trinidad and Tobago, and the Netherlands Antilles, hug the coast of South America.

Island Formations If you were to fly over the Caribbean islands, you would notice mountainous islands as well as islands with fairly level land. The varying landforms are the result of differing physical forces that shaped the islands. The Greater Antilles and some of the Lesser Antilles, including those just off the coast of South America, are the tops of volcanic mountains that have been pushed up from the ocean

246   Chapter 11 ▪ Central America and the Caribbean

floor. These rugged islands generally slope from a central mountain to coastal plains. The western arc of islands in the Lesser Antilles were formed by more recent volcanoes, some of which are still active. Violent eruptions have taken place on islands such as Martinique and St. Vincent in the last 120 years. The volcanic islands have rich soil, but their slopes are quickly drained of nutrients and easily eroded.

The islands with flatter terrain are **coral islands.** They were created by the remains of colonies of tiny, soft-bodied sea animals called coral polyps. Coral polyps take in water and nutrients and release calcium carbonate, or limestone, to form a hard outer skeleton. As the corals die, the limestone skeletons form a coral reef. Sand and sediment begin to pile on top of it, and the new island emerges from the water. Eventually soil forms, plants take root, and an ecosystem develops. The sandy soil, however, cannot support much agriculture. All of the Bahamas are coral islands.

Marine Climate The climate of the Caribbean islands is affected more by sea and wind than by elevation. As you know, nearness to water affects the climate of coastal areas. As light breezes blow over the Caribbean Sea, they take on the temperature of the cooler water beneath them. When the winds blow onshore, they moderate the higher temperature of the land. Even though most of the Caribbean islands lie within the tropics, where the sun's rays are most direct, year-round temperatures reach only an average high of 80°F (27°C). However, humidity levels can be high.

APPLYING THE GEOGRAPHIC THEMES

- **Regions** European colonization and slavery have left their mark on the human geography of this region.
  - *Which countries have a population of predominantly African descent?*
  - *Which countries have a population of predominantly European descent?*

Articles From
NATIONAL GEOGRAPHIC

The following article may be used to extend the content of this section.

A. R. Williams and Vincent J. Musi, photographer. "Montserrat: Under the Volcano." *National Geographic*, Vol. 192, No. 1 (July 1997), pp. 58–75.

A small Caribbean island is threatened by volcanic eruptions. Major towns are evacuated but many islanders remain, hopeful that the once-dormant volcano will return to its slumber.

ACTIVITY

Reteach

Windward and Leeward Ask students to illustrate the key terms *windward* and *leeward* using a small oscillating fan. (Bodily/Kinesthetic)

ACTIVITY

Enrichment

Culture Map Use Outline Map 11 on page 42 of the Mental Mapping booklet in the Teaching Resources to show how Caribbean culture spread in three directions: northward in the Atlantic to the Bahamas and Bermuda, westward to Belize (former British Honduras) in Central America, and south to Guyana, Suriname, and French Guiana on the South American mainland. Explain that people in these locations share a common heritage as descendants of people—African, Asian, and Aboriginal—who survived centuries of enslavement and indenture under European colonists. Ask students to illustrate their maps to show the spread of some aspects of Caribbean culture. (Visual/Spatial)

BACKGROUND

Connecting With . . .

Music The popular Jamaican singer Bob Marley popularized the music of the Rastafarians, a Jamaican religious group. Marley, who died in 1981 at the age of 36, is a hero to many Jamaicans for his efforts to bring about social change.

Calypso Performers

Cultures Calypso songs owe their vitality to timely topics, improvisation, and their constant updating for each year's Carnival. Their strength is their connection to tradition and culture.

Movement *How does calypso music reflect the African roots of Caribbean culture?*

Prevailing winds also affect the amount of rainfall in the Caribbean. On the **windward** northern and eastern sides of the islands—facing the wind—rain can fall in torrents, reaching as much as 200 inches (500 cm) a year. On the **leeward** sides—facing away from the wind—rainfall may be only 30 inches (75 cm) a year.

Ethnic Roots

Visitors to the Caribbean islands today find little evidence of the original inhabitants. European colonists arrived with Columbus in 1492, and within a century, most of the Indians had vanished. Many died from diseases brought by the foreigners, others from their cruel treatment.

African Descent European colonists in what were then called the West Indies needed laborers to do the hard work on their plantations, growing and harvesting sugar cane. They brought millions of Africans to work as slaves. Most of the region's present population is descended from those enslaved Africans or from Europeans and native Indians.

Caribbean culture has been greatly influenced by its African roots. One example is calypso music, a form of folk music that spread from Trinidad throughout the Caribbean. Calypso features witty lyrics and clever satire, set to a rhythmic beat and accompanied by a band of steel drums. The music traces its roots to the songs sung by enslaved Africans who worked on the plantations of Trinidad.

Asian Immigrants The Caribbean islands today also have a sizable Asian population. Most are descendants of immigrants from East Asia and South Asia who came voluntarily to work in the Caribbean islands in the nineteenth century. When slavery was abolished, plantation owners searched halfway around the world for replacement laborers.

RESOURCE DIRECTORY

Teaching Resources
Creative Teaching Activities, Island or Mainland?, p. 13
Social Studies Skills Handbook
• Distinguishing False From Accurate Images, p. 45

Answer to Photo Caption

Calypso derived from the songs of enslaved Africans working on plantations.

Caribbean Nations Today

Today the Caribbean reflects its past. About 90 percent of the Caribbean's population live in independent countries. They include Cuba, Haiti, the Dominican Republic, Barbados, Jamaica, the Bahamas, and Trinidad and Tobago (one country made up of two islands).

Many other Caribbean islands are still politically linked to European countries or the United States. The British Virgin Islands, the Cayman Islands, Montserrat, and several others remain colonies of the United Kingdom. Others, such as Jamaica and the Bahamas, are independent members of the British Commonwealth. The U.S. Virgin Islands is United States territory. Puerto Rico is a United States commonwealth. Residents of both Puerto Rico and the U.S. Virgin Islands are American citizens. The islands of Guadeloupe and Martinique are overseas departments of France. The Netherlands Antilles and Aruba are associated with the Netherlands but govern themselves.

Economic Activities

The economies of many Caribbean islands depend on agriculture. Because of the extremely fertile soil in the volcanic islands, much of the world's sugar, bananas, coconuts, cocoa, rice, and cotton are produced in the region. Besides farm laborers, many others work in industries related to agriculture—refining sugar, packaging coconut and rice products, and making textiles. Still others work on the docks, loading and shipping exports to North America, Europe, or Northern Eurasia.

Because of their natural beauty, the islands draw tourists from all over the world. Visitors flock there to enjoy the tropical climate, relax on white sandy beaches, and sail, snorkel, and scuba dive in the warm turquoise water.

Yet, while tourism thrives, the islanders themselves reap few benefits. Most of the hotels, airlines, and cruise ships are owned by foreign corporations, not by people of the Caribbean islands. Most of the profits end up overseas. Local people hired for unskilled jobs in the tourist

GE◉Facts

Among the remnants of English colonialism in Barbados is cricket, the national sport. The Caribbean island claims to have more world-class cricket players per capita than any other nation in the world. One of Barbados's most famous cricket players, Sir Frank Worrell, appears on the five-dollar bill of Barbados.

Farming in Haiti

Economic Activities Agriculture is the chief economic activity in Haiti. Most Haitian workers are subsistence farmers, growing only enough food to feed their families. Others work on plantations that raise cash crops. Some crops, such as the rice shown here, face competition from cheap imports.

Place *What physical features make Haiti well suited for agriculture?*

ACTIVITY

Connecting With . . .

Mathematics Ask students to use the data from the chart on this page to make bar graphs comparing the populations of the following Caribbean countries: Barbados, Cuba, Grenada, Haiti, and Trinidad and Tobago.

Alternative Assessment

Mid-Point Monitoring

Making an Oral Presentation
You may wish to monitor students' progress on their oral reports. Confer with students to see if they will soon complete their research, develop a draft, and begin to create their multimedia materials.

industry are poorly paid and face layoffs in the off-season. But since jobs are scarce, even these jobs are better than none.

Migration

Since the first European colonization, Caribbean islanders have been ready to move. Most often, they have migrated in search of jobs. Traditionally, sugar plantations have been the major employers, but the plantation's busy season lasts only four months. The other eight months are called the *tiempo muerto*—the dead season. During the dead season, idle workers pack up and head to other islands, to Central America, or to the United States to find work. When they receive a paycheck they send money to their families back home.

At the start of the twentieth century, many islanders found work in Panama, helping to build the Panama Canal. Once the canal opened, most migrants returned to their homes.

Starting in the 1940s, large numbers of Puerto Ricans began moving to cities in the United States. A large percentage of these migrants have settled in New York City, where they have built a large and vibrant Hispanic community.

Unhappiness at Home Political changes have promoted movement away from some Caribbean nations. In the 1800s, many Cubans left the island for the United States. Some of these emigrants raised money and trained troops in hopes of helping Cuba gain independence from Spain. In 1959, Fidel Castro led a revolution that toppled Cuba's dictatorial government. Castro set up a communist government supported by the Soviet Union. Unhappy with the new order, many Cubans fled to the United States, especially Florida. When the Soviet Union fell in 1991, Cuba lost financial support and plunged deeper into poverty, causing more emigrants to flee.

Between 1957 and 1986, Haiti was ruled by military dictators. Thousands of people fled to the United States to escape the cruelty. Haitians ousted their dictator in 1986, but democracy has been troubled since then, with contested elections and one brief period of military control. Today, many more Haitians look to depart their island home, but their reasons now are economic. About 80 percent of the nation's population lives in poverty. Because soil erosion makes

Caribbean Countries and the United States
Population Data

Country	Total Population	Population Density (persons per square mile)	Urban Population (percent)
Antigua and Barbuda	71,500	419	37
Bahamas	298,000	77	88
Barbados	269,000	1,618	49
Cuba	11,190,000	261	75
Dominica	71,700	247	70
Dominican Republic	8,693,000	462	65
Grenada	102,000	767	38
Haiti	6,965,000	651	35
Jamaica	2,624,000	618	55
St. Kitts and Nevis	38,800	373	34
St. Lucia	158,000	664	37
St. Vincent and the Grenadines	113,000	752	54
Trinidad and Tobago	1,298,000	655	73
United States	290,342,550	78	77

Sources: *Encyclopedia Britannica Almanac; Encarta World Atlas*

CHART SKILLS

● **Urbanization** *Which island has the largest percentage of urban population?*

● **Patterns of Settlement** **(a)** *Do most island nations of the Caribbean have a lower or higher population density than the United States?* **(b)** *What do you think is the reason for this difference?*

agricultural production difficult, many Haitians move to the capital city, Port-au-Prince, or they seek better opportunities in other nations.

Environmental conditions can also encourage emigration. More than half of the residents of the small island of Montserrat left after violent volcanic eruptions in 1995.

Economic Benefits The Caribbean islands have lost many people to emigration, but

Answers to Chart Skills

the Bahamas

(a) Most Caribbean island nations have a higher population density. **(b)** They are much smaller in area than the United States.

Puerto Rican Coastline

Economic Activities In San Juan, Puerto Rico, new high-rise hotels offer views of the island's past. Tourism plays a significant role in the Caribbean economy.

Place *Why are hurricanes a significant threat to the tourism industry in the Caribbean?*

they have also benefited from it. The hundreds of millions of dollars that emigrants have sent home—not all of it from the United States—have helped reduce the burden of poverty throughout the Caribbean. With that money, the people at home have bought consumer goods such as radios and televisions. The resulting changes are so great that returning migrants are often amazed to

find their island home has been transformed. Their feelings of bewilderment are captured by Puerto Rican poet Tato Laviera, who wrote:

> 66 I fight for you, Puerto Rico, do you know that?
> I defend your name, do you know that?
> When I come to the island, I feel like a
> stranger, do you know that? 99

SECTION 2 ASSESSMENT

1. **Key Terms** Define **(a)** archipelago, **(b)** coral island, **(c)** windward, **(d)** leeward.
2. **Physical Processes** What physical forces shaped the two types of Caribbean islands?
3. **Cultures** Why does Caribbean culture reflect a variety of different influences?
4. **Economic Activities** What are the main economic activities in the Caribbean islands?
5. **Migration** Why have Caribbean islanders frequently migrated, both within the islands and outside the region?
6. **Critical Thinking** **Recognizing Points of View** Why might many people who live in the

Caribbean have mixed feelings about the tourism industry?

Activity

Take It to the NET

Planning a Trip Use Internet resources to plan a trip to the Caribbean islands. Select at least ten specific locations to visit, including natural wonders, historical sites, and other points of interest. Prepare a travel itinerary. Illustrate your itinerary with a map and drawings or photographs of some of the places you will visit during the trip. Visit the World Geography section of **www.phschool.com** for help in completing this activity.

CHAPTER **11**

REVIEW AND ASSESSMENT

pp. 252–253

Creating a Chapter Summary

As a reteaching opportunity, pair a more able student with a less able student to complete this chapter summary.

Central America *Physical Characteristics:* Mountainous core, Caribbean lowlands, Pacific coastal plain *Climate:* Springlike and cold, Tropical wet, Tropical wet and dry *People:* Indians, Europeans, Mestizos, People of African descent *Economies:* Most people are very poor. **Caribbean** *Physical Characteristics:* Varying landforms, Volcanic and coral islands *Climate:* Marine *People:* Descendants of Africans, Europeans, and Asians *Economies:* Most depend on agriculture and tourism. *Politics:* Many islands are still linked to Europe or the United States. Some independent countries have experienced political upheaval or military dictatorships.

Reviewing Key Terms

1–5. Students' sentences should demonstrate a clear understanding of each of the key terms.

Understanding Key Ideas

6. Each landform region has its own climate. In the mountainous core, the climate is cold, while the mid-level climate is springlike. The Caribbean lowlands have a tropical wet climate, and the Pacific coast a tropical wet and dry climate.
7. Many Africans were brought to Central America as slaves. Others came to work on banana plantations or to help build the Panama Canal.
8. The majority of Central America's people earn their living from agriculture.
9. Nicaragua now has democratically elected governments. In El Salvador, a peace agreement was mediated by the UN. Guatemala held free elections in 1999. All three struggled to rebuild their economies.
10. Land temperatures and rainfall are affected by winds from the sea. The sides of the islands that face the wind get much more rainfall than the sides facing away from the wind.
11. As people from Africa, Europe, and Asia settled in the Caribbean, they brought their cultures with them. Caribbean culture now includes elements of these cultures.

252 Chapter 11

Creating a Chapter Summary

On a sheet of paper, draw a table like the one shown here. Add supporting details about the physical characteristics, climates, people, economies, and politics of Central America and the Caribbean. Some entries have been filled in to help you get started.

	CENTRAL AMERICA	CARIBBEAN
PHYSICAL CHARACTERISTICS		• Three island groups •
CLIMATES		
PEOPLE		
ECONOMIES		
POLITICS	• Political unrest and armed conflict have been common.	

Take It to the NET
Chapter Self-Test For practice test questions for Chapter 11, go to the World Geography section of **www.phschool.com**.

Reviewing Key Terms

Write sentences, using the chapter key terms listed below, leaving blanks where the key terms would go. Exchange your sentences with those of another student and fill in the blanks in each other's sentences.

1. isthmus
2. guerrilla
3. archipelago
4. windward
5. leeward

Understanding Key Ideas

6. Physical Characteristics How are landform regions and climates related in Central America?

7. Understanding the Past Why did many Africans migrate to Central America?

8. Economic Activities What role does agriculture play in the economy of Central America?

9. Government and Citizenship What was the outcome of civil wars in Nicaragua, El Salvador, and Guatemala?

10. Physical Processes How do the sea and wind affect the climate of the Caribbean islands?

11. Cultures How has migration from around the world affected culture in the Caribbean?

12. Global Trade Patterns How does tourism both help and hurt Caribbean islanders?

Critical Thinking and Writing

13. Asking Geographic Questions In which region of Central America would it be most difficult to make a living from farming? Why?

14. Solving Problems With a shortage of available farmland and growing populations, what can the governments of Central America do to prevent poverty and unemployment from increasing in the future?

15. Analyzing Causes and Effects Why have democratic governments been difficult to establish and maintain in Central America?

16. Drawing Conclusions How does the fact that the Bahamas are coral islands affect the area's economy?

---

12. Many islanders find work in tourism-related industries, but the jobs require few skills, pay little, and provide work only part-time. Most of the profits end up overseas.

Critical Thinking and Writing

13. Possible answers: In the mountainous region, the climate is too cold for most crops except potatoes and barley. In the Caribbean lowlands, dense forest vegetation covers much of the land and the soil is not very fertile.

14. Possible answers: develop new industries, educate people for skilled jobs, encourage corporations to build plants in Central America
15. Possible answer: Wealth and political power are concentrated.
16. The Bahamas are coral islands with sandy soil that cannot support much agriculture. Other economic activities, such as tourism, have become important.

(Continued on next page.)

17. Drawing Conclusions Why have some Caribbean islands remained politically linked to European countries or the United States instead of seeking their independence?

18. Defending a Position Should the United States open its doors to all Caribbean emigrants who are seeking protection from political persecution? Write a letter to the editor explaining your opinion.

Applying Skills

Evaluating Sources on the Internet Refer to the Skills for Life lesson on page 243 to answer these questions:

19. How can one tell whether a Web site is run by an educational institution or a commercial enterprise?

20. Suppose that you are looking for information about the effects of tourism on the rain forest in Central America. Which of these sites would you expect to be more helpful: a Web site run by a travel agency, or a Web site run by a geography professor? Explain.

Analyzing a Photograph Study the photograph below, and answer the following questions:

21. Based on this photograph, how do you think traditional weaving skills are passed along from one group to another?

22. What uses might there be for fabric such as that being woven in the photograph?

Test Preparation

Read the question and choose the best answer.

23. In the nineteenth century, many East Asian and South Asian migrants came to the Caribbean to find work after —

A the abolition of slavery

B Castro took control of Cuba

C the Panama Canal opened

D tourism became popular

Activities

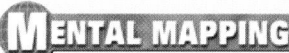

USING THE REGIONAL ATLAS

Review this chapter and the Regional Atlas for Latin America. Create a time line that shows major events in the history of Central America. Write detailed captions for each event, including information about how the events were related to geography. Present your time line to the class.

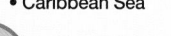 **MENTAL MAPPING**

Review a map of Central America. On a separate piece of paper, draw a map of Central America from memory. Label the following places on your map:

- Honduras
- Pacific Ocean
- El Salvador
- Belize
- Caribbean Sea
- Panama
- Lake Nicaragua
- Guatemala
- Costa Rica
- Nicaragua

Take It to the NET

Making a Map Explore the impact of volcanoes on the countries of Central America and the Caribbean islands by researching eruptions since 1900. On an outline map of this region, locate where volcanic eruptions have taken place, and label each location with the appropriate date. Write a caption for each volcanic eruption, describing its effects on the surrounding area. Visit the World Geography section of **www.phschool.com** for help in completing this activity.

---

17. Possible answer: Many of the islands have such small populations or limited resources that survival as independent nations would be difficult. By maintaining political links with European countries or the United States, they receive economic assistance and political protection.

18. Some students may say that people seeking protection from political persecution should be able to take refuge in the United States. Political refugees need protection because their lives are being threatened. Other students may argue that the United States is not obligated to open its doors to people from other countries, no matter what the circumstances. The American economy cannot provide jobs for everyone who wants to come here.

Applying Skills

19. Sites run by educational institutions are in the *.edu* domain. Commercial sites are indicated by *.com*.

20. A Web site run by a geography professor would probably be more informative. The travel agency's Web site would be more geared to promoting the agency's services.

21. The older generation teaches the skills to the younger generation.

22. Possible answers: clothing, blankets, rugs, wall hangings

Test Preparation

23. A

Activities

Using the Regional Atlas

Check students' time lines for accuracy. Check that students have correctly identified the major events in the history of the Caribbean and included accurate, detailed captions that link these events to geography.

Mental Mapping

Review students' maps for relative and absolute location. Refer to the Political Map on page 236.

Take It to the Net

Students' maps should reflect sound research on volcanic eruptions since 1900 and should include a caption for each eruption, as well as the date it occurred.

MENTAL MAPPING

Games for Review See pages 58–63 of the Simulations, Games, and Lab Activities booklet for games to review place names in preparation for the Chapter 11 Map Test.

Chapter Map Test Students should use the completed outline maps and the Unit 3 Checklist in their Atlas Portfolios to prepare for the Chapter 11 Map Test. The test will cover only those place names on the Unit 3 Checklist relating to Central America and the Caribbean.

Alternative Assessment

Final Evaluation

Making an Oral Presentation Use the Oral Presentation Evaluation Form on page 21 of the Alternative Assessment booklet in the Prentice Hall Alternative Assessment System to evaluate presentations. Either teachers or students can complete the forms to indicate which level of work was achieved for each of the criteria. The evaluation should include specific comments.

Chapter 12 Planning Guide

Resource Manager

	CORE INSTRUCTION	READING/SKILLS
Chapter-Level Resources	**Teaching Resources** ▪ **Unit 3**/Ch. 12 • Reviewing Main Ideas, p. 41 ▪ **Mental Mapping booklet** • Unit 3 Checklist, p. 34 ▪ **Simulations, Games, and Lab Activities** • Place Location Review Games, pp. 58–63 ▪ **Creative Teaching Activities** • The Amazon River and Basin, p. 14 ▪ **TeacherExpress™ CD-ROM**, Ch. 12 ▪ **Companion Web site,** **www.phschool.com** • eTeach	**Teaching Resources** ▪ **Unit 3**/Ch. 12 • Map/Graph Skills, p. 43 ▪ **Social Studies Skills Handbook** • Analyzing a Photograph, p. 58 ▪ **Book on CD**, Ch. 12 ▪ **Social Studies Skills Tutor CD-ROM**
1 The Land and Its Regions 1. Identify existing environmental and economic challenges in the northeast. 2. Describe the effects of urbanization on the southeast region. 3. Explain why the government has encouraged urban growth and economic development in the Brazilian Highlands. 4. List the main characteristics of the Amazon River basin ecosystem.	**Teaching Resources** ▪ **Unit 3**/Ch. 12 • Guided Reading and Review, p. 37 ▪ **Prentice Hall Presentation Pro CD-ROM**, Ch. 12, Sec. 1	**Teaching Resources** ▪ **Guide to the Essentials (English/Spanish)** • Section Summary, Ch. 12, Sec. 1 ▪ **Mental Mapping booklet** • Outline Map 12, p. 45 ▪ **Guided Reading Audiotapes (English/Spanish)**, Ch. 12, Sec. 1 ▪ **Section Reading Support Transparencies**, Ch. 12, Sec. 1
2 Brazil's Quest for Economic Growth 1. Identify the economic challenges the urban and rural poor in Brazil face. 2. Explain how Brazilian government policies have affected the economy. 3. List the effects of economic growth on the Brazilian labor force. 4. Describe how economic development has contributed to environmental change.	**Teaching Resources** ▪ **Unit 3**/Ch. 12 • Guided Reading and Review, p. 39 ▪ **Prentice Hall Presentation Pro CD-ROM**, Ch. 12, Sec. 2	**Teaching Resources** ▪ **Guide to the Essentials (English/Spanish)** • Section Summary, Ch. 12, Sec. 2 ▪ **Guided Reading Audiotapes (English/Spanish)**, Ch. 12, Sec. 2 ▪ **Section Reading Support Transparencies**, Ch. 12, Sec. 2

ENRICHMENT/HONORS/PREAP

Teaching Resources

Unit 3/Ch. 12
- Critical Thinking, p. 42

Mental Mapping booklet
- Atlas Activity, p. 46

Social Studies Skills Handbook
- Study and Research Skills, pp. 94–108

World Geography Map and Photo Transparencies
- Latin America: Maps and Photos

World Geography Videos
- Patterns of Settlement: Brazil, Tape 1

Companion Web site, www.phschool.com
- Chapter 12 Activities

Companion Web site, www.phschool.com
- Chapter 12 Activities

Companion Web site, www.phschool.com
- Chapter 12 Activities

ASSESSMENT

PRENTICE HALL
ASSESSMENT SYSTEM

Core Assessment

ExamView Test Bank booklet, Ch. 12

ExamView Test Bank CD-ROM, Ch. 12

Standardized Test Preparation

Review and Reteach

Review Book for World Geography, pp. 7–8

Practice and Assess

Test-taking Strategies With Transparencies for High School

Test-taking Strategy Poster

Alternative Assessment booklet

Test Prep Book for World Geography

Teaching Resources

Unit 3/Ch. 12
- Section Quizzes, pp. 38, 40
- Test Forms A and B, pp. 44–49

Guide to the Essentials (English/Spanish)
- Chapter 12 Test

Spanish Resources, Ch. 12
- Section Quizzes, pp. 28–29

Mental Mapping booklet
- Chapter 12 Map Test, p. 47

Companion Web site, www.phschool.com
- Chapter 12 Self-Test

CUSTOMIZE FOR INDIVIDUAL NEEDS

Gifted and Talented
- Teacher's Edition, Customize for . . . , p. 261

Less Proficient Readers
- Guide to the Essentials (English), Ch. 12, Section Summaries
- Guided Reading Audiotapes (English), Ch. 12
- Section Reading Support Transparencies, Ch. 12
- Book on CD, Ch. 12
- Teacher's Edition, Reading Strategy, pp. 256, 261
- Teacher's Edition, Activity: Vocabulary, p. 261

Students Acquiring English/ESL
- Guide to the Essentials (English/Spanish), Ch. 12
- Guided Reading Audiotapes (English/Spanish), Ch. 12
- Section Reading Support Transparencies, Ch. 12
- Book on CD, Ch. 12

Less Proficient Writers
- Social Studies Skills Handbook, p. 88
- Alternative Assessment, Writing Assignment Rubric, p. 6
- Teacher's Edition, Customize for . . . , p. 257

Introducing
CHAPTER
12
pp. 254–265

MENTAL MAPPING

Have students study the map on this page. Ask: **In which hemispheres is Brazil?** (Western, Northern, and Southern)

Mapping the Region Have students create a map like the one on this page, adding labels for cities and bodies of water. Distribute the Chapter 12 Outline Map on page 45 of the Mental Mapping booklet in the Teaching Resources, or instruct students to sketch their own maps of Brazil. Students should keep their maps in their Atlas Portfolios in order to prepare for the Chapter 12 Map Test.

eTeach

Be sure to check out this month's online forum with a Master Teacher to join in an exchange of teaching ideas. **www.phschool.com**

CHAPTER
12
Brazil

SECTIONS

1 The Land and Its Regions

2 Brazil's Quest for Economic Growth

Brazil: POLITICAL

80°W 70°W VENEZUELA 60°W SURINAME 50°W 40°W
COLOMBIA GUYANA FRENCH GUIANA (FR.)
Equator
ECUADOR Manaus Amazon R. Fortaleza
Tapajós R. Tocantins R.
PERU BRAZIL Recife
10°S 10°S
BOLIVIA • Salvador
PACIFIC OCEAN ⊛ Brasília
Belo Horizonte •
20°S PARAGUAY Paraná R. 20°S
São Paulo • Rio de Janeiro Tropic of Capricorn
ATLANTIC OCEAN
ARGENTINA • Pôrto Alegre
30°S
URUGUAY
70°W 60°W 50°W

KEY
— National boundary
⊛ National capital
• Other city
Lambert Azimuthal Equal-Area Projection

0 300 600 mi
0 300 600 km

254 Chapter 12

Go Online
PHSchool.com
For: More information about Brazil and access to the Take It to the Net activities
Visit: phschool.com
Web Code: mjk-0013

RESOURCE DIRECTORY

Teaching Resources
Unit 3, Chapter 12
- Section 1 Guided Reading and Review, p. 37

Guide to the Essentials (English/Spanish)
- Section Summary, Chapter 12, Section 1

Mental Mapping booklet
- Atlas Activity, p. 46
- Unit 3 Checklist, p. 34

Technology
Guided Reading Audiotapes (English/Spanish), Chapter 12, Section 1

Section Reading Support Transparencies, Chapter 12, Section 1

World Geography Map and Photo Transparencies
- Latin America: Maps and Photos

Book on CD, Chapter 12

World Geography Videos
- Patterns of Settlement: Brazil, Tape 1

TeacherExpress™ CD-ROM, Chapter 12

Prentice Hall Presentation Pro CD-ROM, Chapter 12

Social Studies Skills Tutor CD-ROM

Companion Web site, www.phschool.com
- Chapter 12 Activities

1 The Land and Its Regions

Reading Focus

- **What environmental and economic challenges exist in the northeast?**
- **How has urbanization affected the southeast region?**
- **Why has the government encouraged urban growth and economic development in the Brazilian Highlands?**
- **What are the main characteristics of the Amazon River basin ecosystem?**

Key Terms

escarpment

sertão

favela

Main Idea Brazil's various regions have very different physical and human characteristics and face many challenges.

Economic Activities Laborers make bricks from the hard soil of the *sertão*.

B razil is the giant of South America. Nearly half the continent's people and land lie within its borders. Despite its huge land area, Brazil has just two major types of landforms—plains and plateaus. A fertile ribbon of lowlands, 10 to 30 miles (16 to 48 km) wide, winds along the curving Atlantic coastline. The immense Amazon River basin is also a plains region.

Behind the coastal plains is a huge interior plateau. As it drops sharply to the plains, it forms an **escarpment**—a steep cliff between two level areas at different heights. In past centuries, the escarpment was a natural barrier. As a result, much of the interior of Brazil was undeveloped and sparsely populated.

Northeast Region

Brazil's northeast region bulges out into the Atlantic Ocean. The Portuguese colonists who landed on its shores in 1500 built large sugar plantations along the fertile coastal plain. They established port cities from which to ship the valuable crop to Europe. Brazil became the world's major producer of sugar.

Over the next 300 years, Brazil's colonists brought in more than 3 million enslaved Africans to work on the plantations. The folktales, food, and religion of the northeast still reflect this African heritage.

Inland from the northeast's coastal plains lies the *sertão* (ser TY oh), or interior plateau. With a tropical wet and dry climate, the *sertão* often bakes through a year or more of drought. When the rains eventually come, the land is devastated because the hard soil cannot absorb the heavy rainfall.

Poverty is severe in the northeast. Because of their impoverished lives and chronic malnutrition, the people of this region have an average life expectancy at birth of only 49 years—well below the rest of Brazil. Here, a family's average

◀ Rio de Janeiro, Brazil *(photo left)*

Chapter 12 ▪ Section 1 **255**

Objectives

Upon completion of Section 1, students should be able to:

◆ identify existing environmental and economic challenges in the northeast;

◆ describe the effects of urbanization on the southeast region;

◆ explain why the government has encouraged economic development in the Brazilian Highlands;

◆ list the main characteristics of the Amazon River basin ecosystem.

 National Geography Standards

The following National Geography Standards are highlighted in this section: 1, 4, 5, 8, 9, 11, 12, 16, 17, 18

Bellringer

Ask students to think about a trip down the Amazon River in a small boat. Using their knowledge of the rain forest, have students make a list of some of the things they would see, hear, smell, and feel on such a trip. As students study the chapter, ask them to revise their lists.

LESSON PLAN

1. Focus Explain that each of Brazil's four regions has developed differently based on its resources. As students read the text, ask them to make a graphic organizer showing the cause-and-effect relationship between each region's resources and its development.

2. Instruct Discuss the following questions: **Which region of Brazil is the largest?** (Amazon River basin) **Which region has the richest farmlands?** (southeast) **What is the *sertão*?** (interior plateau) **In which region do 40 percent of all Brazilians live?** (southeast) **Which region contains a huge rain forest?** (Amazon River basin)

3. Close/Reteach Have students write the names of the four regions of Brazil as headings for a chart. Under each heading, students should write phrases indicating the region's location, major cities, and main resources.

TEACHING TIP
From A Master Teacher

Brazil A study of Brazil offers students a chance to see how settlement patterns and migration are linked to the distribution of resources and economic prosperity. People are drawn to cities because they offer many job opportunities. In Brazil, too many people and resources were concentrated in Rio de Janeiro and São Paulo. Have students explain how the government of Brazil tried to redistribute the population and to decentralize economic and political power by building the new capital of Brasília.

Pacing Suggestions

For 60-minute Blocks

You will want to vary activities.

- Have students pair up and complete the Atlas Activity on page 46 of the Mental Mapping booklet in the Teaching Resources. Focus on question 5 in the activity regarding the deforestation of Brazil's rain forests. Get students thinking about the impact of deforestation by asking: **What happens to the plants and animals that live in a region that is becoming deforested?** (They lose their homes.) Have students sketch a rain forest and its inhabitants before and after deforestation.

Chapter 12 ▪ Section 1 **255**

As students read this chapter, have them make lists of words that are unfamiliar to them. Encourage them to use context clues to define the words. Instruct them to record both their guesses and the correct definitions (from a dictionary) on their lists. Discuss which sentences provided the best clues.

BACKGROUND

Environmental Issues

Drought Northeastern Brazil is often referred to as the "Polygon of Drought" because of the frequency and duration of the dry periods. During the early 1980s, the region received almost no precipitation for four years. When the rains finally did return in 1985, they were so torrential that much of the northeast was devastated by floods.

Alternative Assessment

Introduce the Activity

Writing a Position Paper Ask the students to research current events in Brazil and write a two-page position paper agreeing or disagreeing with the following statement by a Brazilian business owner: "Brazil seemed more the country of the future twenty years ago than it does today." Distribute the Position Paper Rubric found on page 8 of the Alternative Assessment booklet in the Prentice Hall Assessment System for student reference during the project.

Answers to Map Caption

Xinju, Tapajós, Madeira, Purus, Juruá, and Rio Negro

Possible answers: Brazilian Highlands and southeast; they have higher elevations and are farther from the Equator.

Brazil: PHYSICAL

APPLYING THE GEOGRAPHIC THEMES

Regions The Amazon River is the world's largest river by volume.
- *What other major rivers drain through the Amazon Basin?*
- *In which region of Brazil would you expect to find the coolest climate? Explain.*

yearly income may be only one third the income of a similar family living in the southeast.

Southeast Region

The southeast, Brazil's smallest region, is its economic heartland. With only 10.9 percent of the country's area, it is home to 40 percent of the population. Because of the region's mostly humid subtropical climate and fertile soil, farmers can easily grow great quantities of cash crops such as cotton, sugar cane, rice, and cacao, the base of chocolate.

The southeast's biggest and most important crop, however, is coffee. In the 1800s, thousands of people migrated from various parts of the world to this region in Brazil to work on coffee plantations. Today, Brazil is often referred to as the world's "coffeepot," growing one fourth of the world's supply.

Despite the southeast's healthy agriculture, most people live in or near the cities of São Paulo and Rio de Janeiro. The beauty, excitement, and economic health of Rio and São Paulo draw rural Brazilians looking for a better life. Undereducated and without much experience, many find no jobs or settle for low-paying ones. Most end up in slum communities called *favelas.* A journalist who visited Rio de Janeiro described its *favelas:*

RESOURCE DIRECTORY

Teaching Resources
Creative Teaching Activities, The Amazon River and Basin, p. 14
Unit 3, Chapter 12
- Map/Graph Skills, p. 43
Mental Mapping booklet
- Outline Map 12, p. 45

Prentice Hall Assessment System
Alternative Assessment booklet
- Position Paper Rubric, p. 8

Technology
World Geography Map and Photo Transparencies
- Latin America: Maps and Photos

"The houses [of the *favelas*], built illegally on hillsides or swampland, generally consist of wood planks, mud, tin cans, corrugated iron and anything that comes to hand. Some cling to slopes so [steep] that the dwellings are in constant danger of being swept away in the heavy tropical rain storms that burst over the city.**"**

Every Brazilian city has *favelas,* although the government has tried to improve the situation. Some *favelas* have been torn down and replaced by affordable public housing.

Urbanization of Brazil

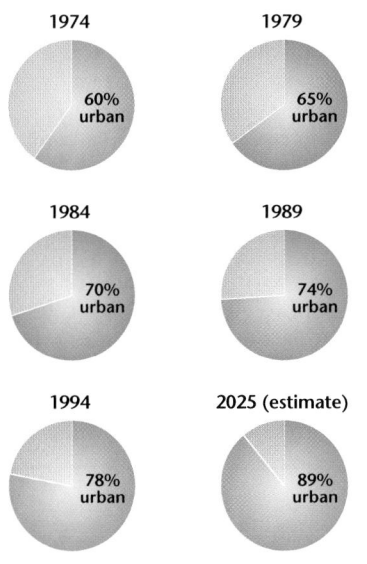

1974 — 60% urban
1979 — 65% urban
1984 — 70% urban
1989 — 74% urban
1994 — 78% urban
2025 (estimate) — 89% urban

Sources: UN Population Division; *Chicago Tribune*

GRAPH STUDY

● **Urbanization** Since 1974, there has been a steady movement of people from the rural to the urban areas of Brazil.

- *What percentage of the population was urban in 1974?*
- *What percentage is expected to be urban in 2025?*
- *How would you expect rapid urbanization to affect housing conditions for new city dwellers?*

Despite its poverty, most people around the world associate Rio de Janeiro with its famous festival known as Carnival. Carnival takes place during the four days preceding Lent— a period of 40 days of fasting and penitence before the Christian celebration of Easter. A year of planning, rehearsing dance steps, sewing costumes, and designing floats culminates in four days and nights of music and dancing. During Carnival, Brazilians take part in dance competitions and perform the samba—Brazil's national dance.

GL○BAL CONNECTIONS

Cultures The tradition of holding a festival before Lent stretches back to the Roman Empire. In the United States, the city of New Orleans has held Mardi Gras celebrations since 1827. Each year, more than 1 million costumed revelers attend parades and parties over several weeks. Similar festivities are held in countries such as Germany, Slovenia, and Spain.

Brazilian Highlands

North of the southeast region lie the Brazilian Highlands, an interior area of hills on the country's central plateau. Brazil's capital, Brasília, is located in the Highlands, far from the country's other large cities. For years, overcrowded Rio de Janeiro was the capital of Brazil. In 1956, hoping to boost development of the interior and to draw people away from the coastal cities, the national government decided to build a new capital city 600 miles (960 km) inland. Officially "inaugurated" in 1960, Brasília in the mid-1990s had a population of about 1.8 million.

Amazon River Region

Of Brazil's major regions, the largest and least explored is the Amazon River basin, which spreads across more than half of the country. Moist trade winds that blow from the Atlantic Ocean drop more than 80 inches (200 cm) of rain on the region each year. With heavy rainfall and constant temperatures of about 80°F (27°C), the growing season never ends. As a result, the Amazon rain forest is home to thousands of species of plants and animals, including orchids, palms, monkeys, jaguars, and toucans. Piranha and dolphins live in the river.

GLOBAL CONNECTIONS

Global Trade Patterns

Coffee Each year, people around the globe drink over 400 billion cups of coffee, the most popular drink in the world. This makes Brazil's 3 billion coffee trees important to the world economy: The only worldwide industry that is considered more valuable than coffee is oil.

BACKGROUND

Daily Life

Ethnic Groups in Brazil The three main ethnic groups in Brazil are people of Portuguese descent, those of African descent, and mulattoes—people of mixed ancestry. The Japanese population is also high: More people of Japanese descent live in Brazil than in any other country except Japan. There are also Arab and Jewish minorities in Brazil.

ACTIVITY

Enrichment

Brazilian Role Play Assign students the roles of the following Brazilians: a rain forest farmer, a sugar plantation worker, a São Paulo banker, a Rio de Janeiro hotel worker, and a *favela* dweller. Have the five Brazilians describe to the class the region in which they live and what their lives are like. (Verbal/Linguistic)

ACTIVITY

Group Work

Activity: Making a poster
Purpose: Instruct each group to create a poster illustrating one of the regions of Brazil. Groups may use original drawings or magazine and brochure photographs along with information from their textbooks or other sources.
Roles: Researchers, writers, artists
Result: Display posters.

CUSTOMIZE FOR...

Less Proficient Writers
A Brazilian Webbing Activity Begin a webbing activity by writing the name of one of Brazil's four regions on the board. Draw a circle around it, and draw spokes around the circle. On each spoke, write a different fact about this region. Ask students to prepare similar wheels for another region. Allow students to share their wheels. Instruct each student to use one of his or her wheels to write a paragraph that describes that region.

TEST PREPARATION

Have students read the section Brazilian Highlands on this page to answer the following question.
Why did the government make Brasília the capital of Brazil?

- **(A)** The government wanted to develop the interior of Brazil.
- **B** Many people lived in Brasília.
- **C** Brasília is in southeastern Brazil, where most Brazilians live.
- **D** Brasília is in a better location than Rio de Janeiro.

Answers to Graph Study

60 percent
89 percent
Rapid urbanization will likely cause housing conditions to deteriorate.

Answers to
Section 1 Assessment

1. **(a)** escarpment, p. 255 **(b)** *sertão*, p. 255 **(c)** *favela*, p. 256

2. Due to scarce grazing lands, flooding, and droughts, the people of this region are impoverished and suffer from malnutrition.

3. Poverty and other harsh conditions push rural Brazilians from their homelands. The beauty, excitement, and economic health of Rio de Janeiro and São Paulo pull them to the cities.

4. The government hoped to boost development of the interior and draw people away from the overcrowded coastal cities.

5. heavy rainfall and constant temperatures of about 80°F

6. **(a)** The reservations are designed to keep Indian communities together and guarantee that some land remains available to Indians. **(b)** Reservations actually contribute to the disappearance of language, customs, and religion. Many tribes will disappear as Indians become part of the country's majority culture.

Activity Rubrics Share rubrics with students before they begin their tables.

Attempted The table shows little research, is poorly organized, and is incomplete.

Minimal The table reveals some research but is poorly organized and has many errors.

Adequate The table is complete, addresses the major issues, has few mechanical errors, and is well organized.

Exemplary The table reveals extensive research, is well organized, has no errors, and shows insight into the issues.

Answer to Photo Caption

The indigenous population has suffered from newly introduced diseases and loss of habitat and natural resources.

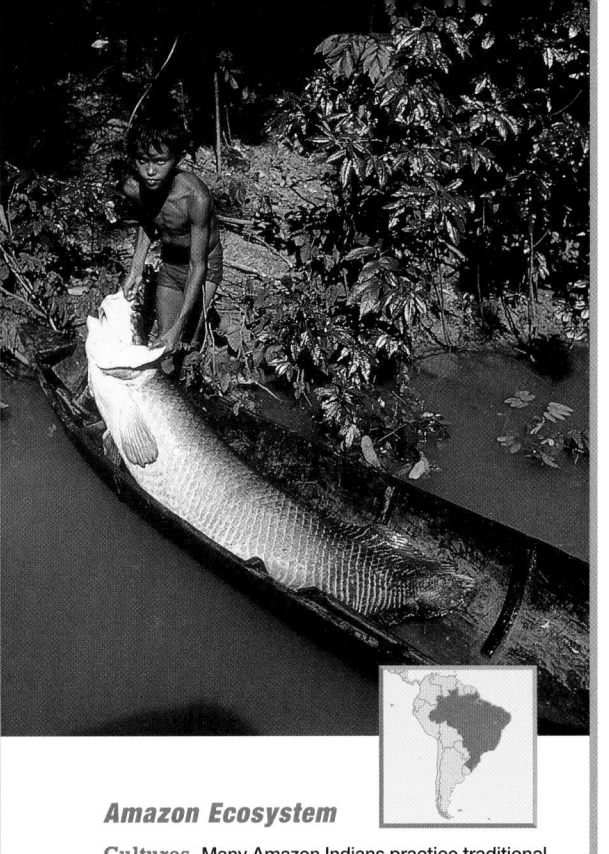

Amazon Ecosystem

Cultures Many Amazon Indians practice traditional ways of life. The region's rivers supply a wide variety of fish, including the pirarucu shown here.

Human-Environment Interaction *How has economic development in Brazil affected the lives of Amazon Indians?*

The Amazon Indians Only about 10 percent of Brazilians live in the Amazon Basin, including about 200,000 Indians from 180 different tribes. Although many Amazon Indians live in small groups, they are linked through broad trade networks.

Brazil's original Indian population was much larger. When the Portuguese arrived in the 1500s, between 2 and 5 million Indians were living in what is now Brazil. Over the years, many were killed by settlers or by diseases that Europeans brought with them.

Although medical science has improved life for many people, disease continues to pose problems for some groups. In an effort to improve access to the interior of the country, roads have been built across Brazil. One of these roads cut through territory of the Panara tribe. For the first time, the Panara people were exposed to diseases from the outside world. Lacking any natural immunity, the Panara population was devastated. In 2000, a Brazilian court issued a ruling that ordered the government to compensate the Panara.

To help preserve Indian communities, the government has set up reservations. The reservations are designed to keep groups together and guarantee that some land remains available to Indians. Opponents argue that this system causes Indians to lose their culture as their way of life changes. These people assert that reservations actually contribute to the disappearance of language, customs, and religion. Over time, they fear, many tribes will disappear as Indians become part of the country's majority culture.

SECTION 1 ASSESSMENT

1. **Key Terms** Define **(a)** escarpment, **(b)** *sertão*, **(c)** *favela*.

2. **Physical Characteristics** Describe how conditions in the *sertão* affect daily life in northeastern Brazil.

3. **Urbanization** What push-pull factors draw people to São Paulo and Rio de Janeiro in the southeast?

4. **Patterns of Settlement** Why did the Brazilian government build a new capital city in the Highlands?

5. **Ecosystems** What factors contribute to the diverse plant and animal life in the Amazon River basin?

6. **Critical Thinking** **Recognizing Points of View** **(a)** What does the Brazilian government hope to achieve by establishing reservations? **(b)** Why do some people disagree with this policy?

Activity

Take It to the NET

Making a Table Search the Internet to learn more about *favelas* in Brazil. Identify the major issues that affect quality of life in *favelas*, such as education. Create a two-column table. The left column should be titled Quality-of-Life Issue. The right column should be titled Impact of Issue. Visit the World Geography section of **www.phschool.com** for help in completing this activity.

RESOURCE DIRECTORY

Teaching Resources

Unit 3, Chapter 12
• Section 1 Quiz, p. 38

Spanish Resources
• Section 1 Quiz, p. 28

Social Studies Skills Handbook
• Graph and Chart Skills, p. 58

Technology

Social Studies Skills Tutor CD-ROM

Analyzing Aerial Photographs

Photographs taken from air and space provide information about a planet's landforms, vegetation, and resources. They permit accurate mapping and make landscape features understandable on a regional, continental, or global scale. In today's "information age," literacy means not only the ability to read and write, but also the ability to understand and interpret visuals such as aerial photographs.

Learn the Skill Use the following steps to learn how to understand and analyze aerial photographs.

1 *Identify the content of the photograph.* The content of an aerial photograph includes all the individual images that make up the photo. *What does the photograph below show?*

2 *Read any text that accompanies the photograph.* An aerial photograph often has a title, caption, or other accompanying text that identifies the photo. **(a)** *What is the subject of this photograph?* **(b)** *What do the brown areas represent?*

3 *Consider the purpose of the photograph.* A good starting point for identifying the purpose of a photograph is to consider the individual or group that produced it. **(a)** *Who do you think produced this aerial photograph?* **(b)** *Why do you think this photograph was taken?*

4 *Learn more about the visual or its subject.* Since the 1960s, large areas of the rain forest

have been cleared and burned to create new farm and ranch land. **(a)** *How does this photograph show deforestation? Explain.* **(b)** *Where in the photograph does the forest seem unharmed?*

5 *Make predictions and recommendations.* Suppose that a series of aerial photographs taken over several years shows an increase in the size of the Sahara. A reasonable prediction is that this expansion will result in the loss of valuable farmland. You might recommend that governments in Africa take steps to protect their farmland from disappearing. *Based on the aerial photograph below and your knowledge of the Amazon, what might you expect to find in a more recent aerial photograph of the same region? Explain.*

 Do It Yourself

Practice the Skill Find an aerial photograph that appears in print or online. Copy the photograph and any accompanying labels or captions. Use the steps in this skill lesson to write an interpretation of the visual.

Apply the Skill To apply this skill, go to the Chapter 12 Review and Assessment.

Amazon River Basin

▶▶▶ *Career Prep*

Careers in Geography
Remote Sensing Specialist The U.S. government hires remote sensing specialists to analyze satellite images and aerial photos taken by high-flying aircraft. Remote sensing specialists study land use and sometimes foreign military movements.

Objectives

Upon completion of Section 2, students should be able to:

♦ identify the economic challenges the urban and rural poor in Brazil face;

♦ explain how Brazilian government policies have affected the economy;

♦ list the effects of economic growth on the Brazilian labor force;

♦ describe how economic development has contributed to environmental change.

National Geography Standards

The following National Geography Standards are highlighted in this section: 3, 9, 11, 12, 14, 15, 16, 18

Bellringer

Ask students to name a river in or near their community. Ask them to think of ways that the river affects them. Ask: **Why are rivers important?** (transportation; wildlife; source of water for agriculture, drinking)

LESSON PLAN

1. Focus Tell students that only 2 percent of the farmers in Brazil control most of the arable land. Many farming families live in poverty because they have no rights to the land they work or the earnings their harvests yield. Ask students to think of ways in which they would reduce poverty in Brazil while improving its economy. Have them share their suggestions with the class.

2. Instruct Have students make a list of the positive and negative aspects of Brazil's development. Ask several volunteers to read their lists. Summarize the findings for the class.

3. Close/Reteach Read the following list of words to the class. Ask students to explain whether each term relates to the positive or the negative aspects of Brazil's economic development: *favelas, sertão, Brasília, ethanol, service industries, deforestation, ecotourism.*

2 Brazil's Quest for Economic Growth

Reading Focus

• **What economic challenges are faced by the urban and rural poor?**

• **How have Brazilian government policies affected the economy?**

• **What effects has economic growth had on the labor force in Brazil?**

• **How has economic development contributed to environmental change?**

Key Terms

plantation

gasohol

deforestation

ecotourism

| **Main Idea** | Many Brazilians have benefited from economic development, but poverty and environmental harm are major problems. |

Urbanization Government and individuals struggle to improve life in the *favelas*.

Brazil is a country of extremes. It is a huge country rich in natural resources, and it is also a country with much poverty. In the past few decades, Brazil has begun to realize its potential. The government has taken steps to modernize the economy and improve the lives of its people. Many have benefited, but some have not.

Brazil today, like much of Latin America, is no longer a society of only rich and poor. The growth of industry and manufacturing has helped to create a middle class, as people have been needed to manage and work in factories and offices. Likewise, as cities have grown, doctors, teachers, government workers, and others have moved in to fill the needs of a growing urban population.

Economic Challenges

Most of Brazil's poorest people live in the urban *favelas* or the rural northeast. Many parents in the *favelas* cannot feed or house their children, much less provide them with schooling. Hungry, homeless children live dangerously on the streets,

seeking menial jobs or begging for coins with which to buy food.

Conditions in agriculture contribute to poverty. A handful of wealthy families own the profitable **plantations** or large commercial farms. Most rural workers find work on plantations, or become subsistence farmers working small plots of land that barely support a family. In the late 1990s, thousands of people across the country protested these conditions. President Cardoso promised land redistribution, but millions of families remained without land.

Many of Brazil's farmers live in the inhospitable region of the *sertão*. The conditions there—poor soil, scarce grazing land, and droughts—also contribute to the country's poverty. Few can afford the expensive farm equipment that would improve productivity.

Government Policies

Since the mid-1940s, the Brazilian government has undertaken several massive programs to ease the burden of poverty for its people. These programs

---

have had two major aims: to boost the growth of industry and to encourage settlement and development in the country's interior.

Economic Activities During the 1940s and early 1950s, the Brazilian government built the country's first steel mill and oil refinery. It also began to build a series of huge hydroelectric dams to produce power for the planned industrial expansion. The dams were built where rivers dropped over the steep escarpment. To further encourage the growth of industry, the government established a bank that loaned money to people who wanted to start new businesses.

Manufacturing began to thrive in the 1950s with tremendous growth in the automobile, chemical, and steel industries. Within ten years, millions of Brazilians began to move from rural to urban areas, seeking jobs in the new factories. Coastal area cities, especially São Paulo, became crowded industrial centers.

Patterns of Settlement With São Paulo and Rio de Janeiro rapidly becoming overcrowded, Brazil's leaders recognized the need to develop the country's vast interior. In the late 1950s the new capital city, Brasília, was "planted" in the Brazilian Highlands, 600 miles (960 km) inland from the Atlantic coast. The city was to be a showplace of shiny glass and gleaming steel architecture. When viewed from the air, the city has the shape of a bow

and arrow or, some say, an airplane. Either way, Brasília's shape symbolizes movement—the readiness of the country to take off.

Brasília represented movement in another way. Because the country as a whole had few roads except along the coast, the government began a massive road-building project with Brasília at its center. By the 1970s the country boasted thousands of miles of new roads, including one that stretched across the Amazon Basin for about 3,000 miles (4,800 km).

To promote settlement in the north, the government gave away thousands of plots of land in the Amazon region, as well as thousands of mining or prospecting permits. New roads and free land grants drew many settlers to the Brazilian Highlands and Amazon regions. Between 1970 and 1985, more than 1 million people migrated to the Amazon region.

Economic Growth

Brazil's development programs have had remarkable success. Industry now accounts for more than one third of Brazil's gross domestic product. The country ranks among the world's leading industrial nations.

One major step was the successful development of a new alcohol-based fuel called **gasohol,** a mix of gasoline and ethanol, in response to the high cost of imported oil in the 1970s. Ethanol,

Industry Takes Off

Economic Activities Industry accounts for about one third of Brazil's gross domestic product and employs about one quarter of its workers. Major products are airplanes, motor vehicles, textiles, and chemistry. Many products are consumed by the nation's nearly 180 million residents. The United States purchases more Brazilian exports than does any other nation.

Movement *How did the development of industry affect Brazil's cities?*

Chapter 12 Section 2 **261**

Chapter 12 ▪ Section 2 **261**

The Physical World

Water Brazil's rapid industrial expansion has run on water power. Ninety percent of Brazil's electricity is generated by falling water. Large power plants operate on several rivers in Brazil, but much of the country's vast hydroelectric power remains untapped.

Connecting With . . .

Science Remind students that Brazil's rain forest contains unknown species of plants and animals. Have students inventory the living species they can collect or observe in an area of one square yard (1.2 square meters). Ask students to complete inventories in different areas such as by a pond, in their backyards, in a garden, or at a beach. Ask students to describe the difficulties in taking such an inventory.

Group Work

Activity: Writing a script

Purpose: Ask each group to write a script about an urban family considering a move to the Amazon River basin to farm. In the script, family members should discuss the pros and cons of the move and decide whether they should move.

Roles: Scriptwriter, parents, and children

Result: Select several groups to read their scripts to the class.

Answer to Map Caption

Southeast Asia or Africa

GEOFacts

Rain forests are often called jungles, which are noted for tangled undergrowth that makes movement difficult. Actually, jungle develops only when the rain forest canopy is removed and sunlight encourages new plant growth at ground level.

a type of alcohol, is made from Brazil's own sugar cane. In a sense, Brazilian farmers are *growing* fuel. Brazil no longer has to import expensive foreign oil.

These and other industrial developments have changed the way Brazilians earn a living. In 1940, two thirds of the work force was employed in agriculture. By 2000, over one third worked in manufacturing, construction, or mining. About half of the labor force now works in service industries, such as hotels and restaurants, retail stores, and government, that have sprung up as offshoots of the nation's industrial growth.

The new jobs usually pay more than agricultural work. They have given Brazil a skilled, educated, growing middle class, something that scarcely existed before the 1940s. Yet much poverty still remains, mainly in the cities and in the agricultural northeast.

Environmental Changes

Although economic development has brought positive changes, it has had some unintended effects. In the big cities, poverty has increased. Rural Brazilians have flocked to cities in search of work, resulting in more migrants than jobs. As a result, the *favelas* have become a growing part of these cities. The government has tried to provide low-cost housing for Brazil's urban poor, but the plan has backfired. Because of strict regulations, fewer rental units are being built, which pushes more and more people into *favelas*.

Challenges and Opportunities Economic development in the Amazon has also yielded surprises. Many settlers moved to the region to farm or ranch. But after clearing the forest to plant crops, they found that only the thick vegetation had kept the soil and nutrients from washing away during heavy rains. Despite the lush vegetation, the soil was thin and not very fertile. After a few years of farming and erosion, the soil was no longer usable. To keep their farms running, settlers had to clear more land.

The World: TROPICAL RAIN FOREST DEPLETION

KEY
Remaining rain forest
Area of depletion
Robinson Projection

APPLYING THE GEOGRAPHIC THEMES

● **Regions** The map above compares the land area covered by rain forests during the 1970s with the area covered by rain forests today.
• *What part of the world has suffered the greatest loss of rain forest?*

Teaching Resources

Unit 3, Chapter 12
• Section 2 Quiz, p. 40
• Reviewing Main Ideas, p. 41
• Test Forms A and B, pp. 44–49

Spanish Resources
• Section 2 Quiz, p. 29

Guide to the Essentials (English/Spanish)
• Chapter 12 Test

Mental Mapping booklet
• Chapter 12 Map Test, p. 47

Simulations, Games, and Lab Activities
• Place Location Review Games, pp. 58–63

Social Studies Skills Handbook
• Study and Research Skills, pp. 94–108

Prentice Hall Assessment System
Alternative Assessment booklet, Position Paper Evaluation Form, p. 9

Technology
ExamView Test Bank CD-ROM, Chapter 12 Test
Companion Web site, www.phschool.com
• Chapter 12 Self-Test

Tourism in the Amazon

Planning for the Future
Investment in the Amazon sometimes takes the form of hotel construction, as shown here near the Brazilian city of Manaus. The government promotes tourism as a way to provide economic opportunities that will leave more of the rain forest intact.

Human-Environment Interaction *Does ecotourism change the natural environment as much as agriculture? Explain.*

New Efforts **Deforestation**, or the permanent removal of woodland, threatens vast numbers of plant and animal species in the Amazon. However, many scientists and entrepreneurs recognize that the region's biological diversity offers opportunities for advances in medicine. The Amazon basin contains some 1,300 plants that can be used in the treatment of a variety of illnesses.

To avoid destroying this potential source of life-saving materials, the Brazilian government is working to combat deforestation. Each year during the dry season, military personnel and police combine forces to seize illegally logged timber. Taxation policies encourage farmers, ranchers, and foresters to maintain rain forest areas. The government also encourages **ecotourism**, or tourism that encourages environmental awareness and has little effect on the ecosystem. The Brazilian government hopes such policies will encourage economic growth while avoiding destruction of the rain forest.

SECTION 2 ASSESSMENT

1. **Key Terms** Define **(a)** plantation, **(b)** gasohol, **(c)** deforestation, **(d)** ecotourism.

2. **Economic Activities** Why do many Brazilian farmers suffer from poverty?

3. **Government and Citizenship** How has the Brazilian government worked to promote economic development?

4. **Economic Activities** How has industrial growth improved the Brazilian economy?

5. **Ecosystems** How is the government working to limit destruction of the rain forest?

6. **Critical Thinking** **Asking Geographic Questions** What questions might a news reporter ask a Brazilian official in order to learn how economic development affects the rain forest?

Activity

USING THE **REGIONAL ATLAS**

Review the Regional Atlas for Latin America and this section. Then, create a map that identifies the locations of Brazil's major economic activities. You may wish to use a combination of shading and symbols, depending on how the activities are distributed. Next, locate and label Brazilian cities discussed in this section. Write a caption for your map, pointing out which economic activities tend to be located near cities.

TEST PREPARATION

Have students read the subsection Challenges and Opportunities on the previous page and New Efforts on this page to answer the following question.
All of the following are results of deforestation in the Amazon rain forest *except* —

A destruction of plants and animals
B threatening of medical research
C promotion of ecotourism
(D) overabundance of nutrient-rich soil

REVIEW AND ASSESSMENT
pp. 264–265

Creating a Chapter Summary
As a reteaching opportunity, pair a more able student with a less able student to complete this chapter summary.

Students may add the following entries: **Regions:** Northeast, Southeast, Brazilian Highlands, Amazon River Region **Economic Issues:** Poverty, Unemployment **Environmental Issues:** Soil erosion, Depletion of the rain forest

Reviewing Key Terms
1–5. Students' quiz items should show a clear understanding of each term.

Understanding Key Ideas
6. Northeast: Most of Brazil's poor live in the *favelas* of the coastal cities or in the dry interior *sertão*. Southeast: The country's heartland has both rich agriculture and the major cities of Rio de Janeiro and São Paulo. Brazilian Highlands: The country's barren interior is home to Brazil's capital, Brasília. Amazon River Region: This huge interior plain is rich in tropical vegetation and animal life.
7. With increasing poverty and unemployment, many urban dwellers end up in the slum communities of the *favelas*.
8. The government hoped to boost development of the interior and draw people away from the overcrowded coastal cities.
9. The indigenous population has suffered from newly introduced diseases.
10. The government built hydroelectric dams to provide for industry, established a bank to lend money for new businesses, developed gasohol, designed taxation policies to encourage maintenance of the rain forest areas, and encouraged ecotourism.
11. Hydroelectric dams make use of Brazil's rivers to provide electricity.

Critical Thinking and Writing
12. The tropical wet and dry climate contributes to poor soil and scarce grazing land, making agriculture unprofitable in this area.

Creating a Chapter Summary
Copy this concept web on a piece of paper. Include supporting details about Brazil, adding more circles as needed. Some entries have been completed to serve as a sample.

Take It to the NET
Chapter Self-Test For practice test questions for Chapter 12, go to the World Geography section of **www.phschool.com**.

Reviewing Key Terms

Review the key terms listed below. Then, use the words and their definitions to create a matching quiz. Exchange quizzes with another student. Check each other's answers when you are finished.

1. escarpment
2. *sertão*
3. *favela*
4. gasohol
5. ecotourism

Understanding Key Ideas

6. **Physical Characteristics** What are the key characteristics of each of Brazil's four main regions?
7. **Urbanization** What challenges face many city residents in Brazil?
8. **Patterns of Settlement** Why did Brazil move the nation's capital away from Rio de Janeiro?
9. **Cultures** How has economic development affected many Indians in the Amazon Basin?

10. **Government and Citizenship** Identify government policies and programs designed to encourage industrial and agricultural development in Brazil.
11. **Science and Technology** How have Brazilians used technology to produce electricity from natural resources?

Critical Thinking and Writing

12. **Analyzing Causes and Effects** How does climate influence income in the *sertão*?
13. **Interpreting Maps** Study the map on page 256. Why would transportation between the Amazon Basin and the cities of the southeast be difficult?
14. **Analyzing Change** How have changing perceptions of the Amazon rain forest region led to changes in government policies and economic activities?
15. **Defending a Position** Write a letter to the editor explaining whether you feel the government should continue programs to limit rain forest removal.

13. Transportation would have to cross a vast mountainous region.
14. Scientists and entrepreneurs have recognized that the region's biological diversity offers opportunities for advances in medicine. The government has implemented a series of policies to maintain the rain forest for these purposes.
15. Answers will vary, but students should be able to support their arguments.

Applying Skills

Analyzing Aerial Photographs Refer to the aerial photograph on page 259 to answer these questions:

16. How might this photograph show planned deforestation for agricultural purposes?

17. (a) What else, besides agriculture, might cause the deforestation shown in this photo? (b) Do you think any of these causes is more likely than agricultural development? Explain.

Analyzing Graphs Study the graphs below, and answer the following questions:

18. Did urbanization increase more quickly between 1974 and 1984, or between 1984 and 1994?

19. What do these graphs suggest about agricultural employment in Brazil since 1974?

Urbanization of Brazil

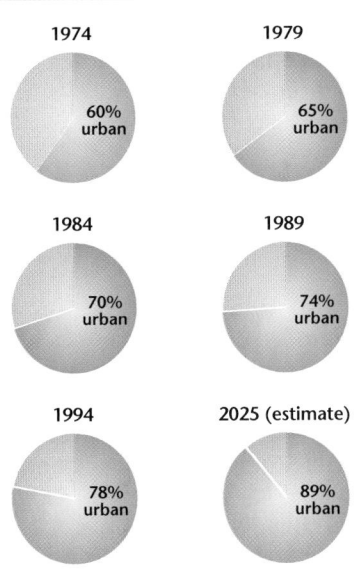

Sources: UN Population Division; *Chicago Tribune*

Test Preparation

Read the question and choose the best answer.

20. New jobs in manufacturing, construction, mining and service industries have encouraged —

A an expanding middle class

B people to leave Rio de Janeiro for Brasília

C the development of gasohol

D migration into the *sertão*

Activities

USING THE REGIONAL ATLAS

Review the Regional Atlas for Latin America and Chapter 12. On an outline map of Brazil, indicate elevation and climate regions. You may wish to use a combination of shading and outlining. Present your map to the class, noting the relationships between climate and elevation in Brazil.

 MENTAL MAPPING

Review the map of Brazil on page 254. On a separate piece of paper, draw a sketch map of Brazil from memory. Label the following places on your map:

- Brazil
- Pôrto Alegre
- São Paulo
- Rio de Janeiro
- Brasília
- Salvador
- Fortaleza
- Manaus
- Paraná River
- Tapajós River
- Amazon River
- Atlantic Ocean

Take It to the NET

Making a Poster Search the Internet for city maps of Brasília and Rio de Janeiro. Using the information you find, create sketch maps of the two cities, including major roads and any important buildings. Put both maps on a poster, along with a lengthy caption describing how you can tell that Brasília began as a planned city and that Rio de Janeiro developed as a port. Visit the World Geography section of **www.phschool.com** for help in completing this activity.

Applying Skills

16. The deforestation was neatly done in strips.

17. (a) Possible answer: forest fires (b) unlikely, given the precision of the deforestation

18. between 1974 and 1984

19. Possible answer: Agricultural employment has decreased.

Test Preparation

20. A

Activities

Using the Regional Atlas
Check students' maps and map keys for accuracy. Their presentations should demonstrate an understanding of the relationship between climate and elevation.

Mental Mapping
Review students' maps for relative and absolute location.

Take It to the Net
Students' work should reflect sound research. Poster captions should accurately describe the origins of both cities.

 MENTAL MAPPING

Games for Review See pages 58–63 of the Simulations, Games, and Lab Activities booklet for games to review place names in preparation for the Chapter 12 Map Test.

Chapter Map Test Students should use the completed outline maps and the Unit 3 Checklist in their Atlas Portfolios to prepare for the Chapter 12 Map Test. Point out to students that the test will cover only those place names on the Unit 3 Checklist relating to Brazil.

Alternative Assessment

Final Evaluation

Writing a Position Paper Use the Position Paper Evaluation Form on page 9 of the Alternative Assessment booklet in the Prentice Hall Assessment System to evaluate students' papers. Either teachers or students can complete the forms to indicate which level of work was achieved for each of the criteria. The evaluation should include specific examples and comments.

Chapter 13 Planning Guide

Resource Manager

	CORE INSTRUCTION	READING/SKILLS
Chapter-Level Resources	**Teaching Resources** **Unit 3**/Ch. 13 • Reviewing Main Ideas, p. 56 **Mental Mapping booklet** • Unit 3 Checklist, p. 34 **Simulations, Games, and Lab Activities** • Place Location Review Games, pp. 58–63 **TeacherExpress™ CD-ROM**, Ch. 13 **Companion Web site, www.phschool.com** • eTeach	**Teaching Resources** **Unit 3**/Ch. 13 • Map/Graph Skills, p. 58 **Mental Mapping booklet** • Outline Map 13, p. 48 **Book on CD**, Ch. 13 **Social Studies Skills Tutor CD-ROM**
1 The Northern Tropics 1. Describe how migration affected the population of the Guianas. 2. Identify the geographic influences on Venezuela's economy. 3. Discuss the problems of one-crop agriculture in Colombia.	**Teaching Resources** **Unit 3**/Ch. 13 • Guided Reading and Review, p. 50 **Prentice Hall Presentation Pro CD-ROM**, Ch. 13, Sec. 1	**Teaching Resources** **Guide to the Essentials (English/Spanish)** • Section Summary, Ch. 13, Sec. 1 **Guided Reading Audiotapes (English/Spanish)**, Ch. 13, Sec. 1 **Section Reading Support Transparencies**, Ch. 13, Sec. 1
2 The Andean Countries 1. Explain how the physical geography of the Andean countries has affected the people who live there. 2. Compare the economies of Ecuador and Peru. 3. Describe how climate affects the people of Bolivia and Chile.	**Teaching Resources** **Unit 3**/Ch. 13 • Guided Reading and Review, p. 52 **Prentice Hall Presentation Pro CD-ROM**, Ch. 13, Sec. 2	**Teaching Resources** **Guide to the Essentials (English/Spanish)** • Section Summary, Ch. 13, Sec. 2 **Social Studies Skills Handbook** • Reading a Bar Graph, p. 53 **Guided Reading Audiotapes (English/Spanish)**, Ch. 13, Sec. 2 **Section Reading Support Transparencies**, Ch. 13, Sec. 2
3 The Southern Grassland Countries 1. Describe the physical characteristics of the southern grassland countries. 2. Explain the recent changes in political conditions in Paraguay and Uruguay. 3. State how urbanization has affected life in Argentina.	**Teaching Resources** **Unit 3**/Ch. 13 • Guided Reading and Review, p. 54 **Creative Teaching Activities** • The Northern and Southern Hemispheres, p. 15 **Prentice Hall Presentation Pro CD-ROM**, Ch. 13, Sec. 3	**Teaching Resources** **Guide to the Essentials (English/Spanish)** • Section Summary, Ch. 13, Sec. 3 **Guided Reading Audiotapes (English/Spanish)**, Ch. 13, Sec. 3 **Section Reading Support Transparencies**, Ch. 13, Sec. 3

ENRICHMENT/HONORS/PREAP

📘 Teaching Resources

📗 **Unit 3**/Ch. 13
- Critical Thinking, p. 57

📖 **Mental Mapping booklet**
- Atlas Activity, p. 49

📖 **Social Studies Skills Handbook**
- Study and Research Skills, pp. 94–108

📺 **World Geography Map and Photo Transparencies**
- Latin America: Maps and Photos

📼 **World Geography Videos**
- Climates: Countries of South America, Tape 1

💻 **Companion Web site,**
www.phschool.com
- Chapter 13 Activities

💻 **Companion Web site,**
www.phschool.com
- Chapter 13 Activities

📘 Teaching Resources

📗 **Unit 3**/Ch. 13
- Geography and World Literature, p. 65

📖 **Social Studies Skills Handbook**
- Reading a Bar Graph, p. 53

💻 **Companion Web site,**
www.phschool.com
- Chapter 13 Activities

💻 **Companion Web site,**
www.phschool.com
- Chapter 13 Activities

ASSESSMENT

PRENTICE HALL
ASSESSMENT SYSTEM

Core Assessment

📖 ExamView Test Bank booklet, Ch. 13

💿 ExamView Test Bank CD-ROM, Ch. 13

💿 ExamView Test Bank CD-ROM, Unit 3

Standardized Test Preparation

Review and Reteach

📖 **Review Book for World Geography,** pp. 7–8

Practice and Assess

📖 **Test-taking Strategies With Transparencies for High School**

Test-taking Strategy Poster

📖 **Alternative Assessment booklet**

📖 **Test Prep Book for World Geography**

📘 Teaching Resources

📗 **Unit 3**/Ch. 13
- Section Quizzes, pp. 51, 53, 55
- Test Forms A and B, pp. 60–63

📖 **Guide to the Essentials (English/Spanish)**
- Chapter 13 Test

📖 **Spanish Resources,** Ch. 13
- Section Quizzes, pp. 30–32

📖 **Mental Mapping booklet**
- Chapter 13 Map Test, p. 50
- Unit 3 Map Test, p. 51

💻 **Companion Web site, www.phschool.com**
- Chapter 13 Self-Test

CUSTOMIZE FOR INDIVIDUAL NEEDS

Honors/PreAP
- Teacher's Edition, Customize for . . . , pp. 277, 279

Less Proficient Readers
- Guide to the Essentials (English), Ch. 13, Section Summaries
- Guided Reading Audiotapes (English), Ch. 13
- Section Reading Support Transparencies, Ch. 13
- Book on CD, Ch. 13
- Teacher's Edition, Reading Strategy, pp. 268, 274, 280
- Teacher's Edition, Activity: Vocabulary, pp. 270, 273, 279

Students Acquiring English/ESL
- Guide to the Essentials (English/Spanish), Ch. 13
- Guided Reading Audiotapes (English/Spanish), Ch. 13
- Section Reading Support Transparencies, Ch. 13
- Book on CD, Ch. 13
- Teacher's Edition, Customize for . . . , p. 269

Less Proficient Writers
- Social Studies Skills Handbook, p. 89
- Alternative Assessment, Writing Assignment Rubric, p. 6
- Teacher's Edition, Customize for . . . , p. 273

Introducing
CHAPTER
13
pp. 266–283

MENTAL MAPPING

Ask students to look at the map on this page, and point out that 10 South American countries surround the giant nation of Brazil. These countries are grouped into three regions: northern South America, the Andean countries, and southern South America.

Mapping the Region In assigning the activity described below, ask students to sketch their own maps of South America, or you may distribute the Chapter 13 Outline Map of the region on page 48 of the Mental Mapping booklet in the Teaching Resources. Ask students to lightly shade each country in a different color. Next, direct them to label the countries. Remind students to keep their maps in their Atlas Portfolios to prepare for the Chapter 13 Map Test.

Countries of South America

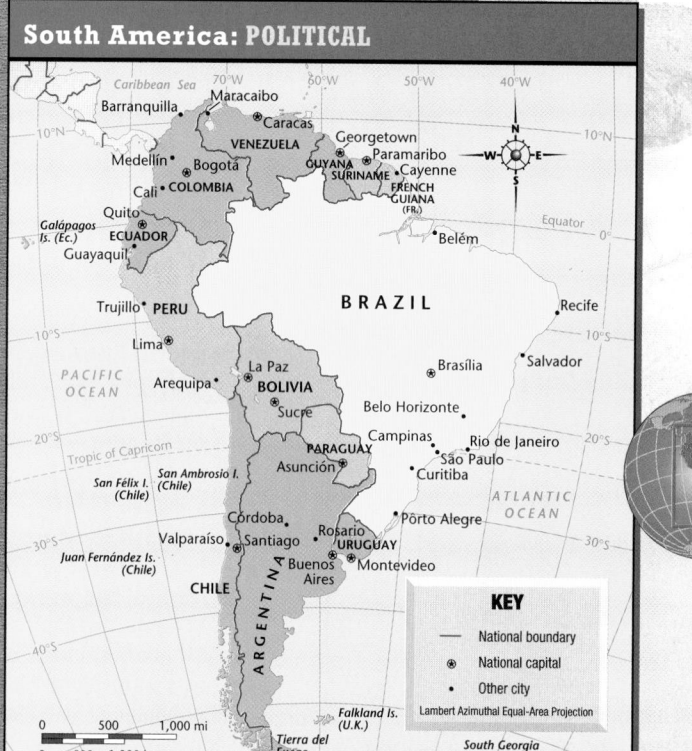

South America: POLITICAL

KEY
— National boundary
⊛ National capital
• Other city
Lambert Azimuthal Equal-Area Projection

266 Chapter 13

Go Online
PHSchool.com
For: More information about South America and access to the Take It to the Net activities
Visit: phschool.com
Web Code: mjk-0014

eTeach

Be sure to check out this month's online forum with a Master Teacher to join in an exchange of teaching ideas. **www.phschool.com**

RESOURCE DIRECTORY

Teaching Resources
Unit 3, Chapter 13
• Section 1 Guided Reading and Review, p. 50
Guide to the Essentials (English/Spanish)
• Section Summary, Chapter 13, Section 1
Mental Mapping booklet
• Outline Map 13, p. 48
• Atlas Activity, p. 49
• Unit 3 Checklist, p. 34

Technology
Guided Reading Audiotapes (English/Spanish),
Chapter 13, Section 1

Section Reading Support Transparencies,
Chapter 13, Section 1
World Geography Map and Photo Transparencies
• Latin America: Maps and Photos
Book on CD, Chapter 13
World Geography Videos
• Climates: Countries of South America, Tape 1
TeacherExpress™ CD-ROM, Chapter 13
Prentice Hall Presentation Pro CD-ROM, Chapter 13
Social Studies Skills Tutor CD-ROM
Companion Web site, www.phschool.com
• Chapter 13 Activities

1 The Northern Tropics

Reading Focus

- How has migration made the Guianas culturally distinct from the rest of the nations in South America?
- How do Venezuela's physical characteristics and climate regions influence the nation's economic activities?
- What are the problems of a one-crop agricultural system in Colombia?

Key Terms

mulatto

bauxite

llano

cordillera

campesino

Main Idea The countries along South America's northern coast have distinctive cultures, physical characteristics, and economies.

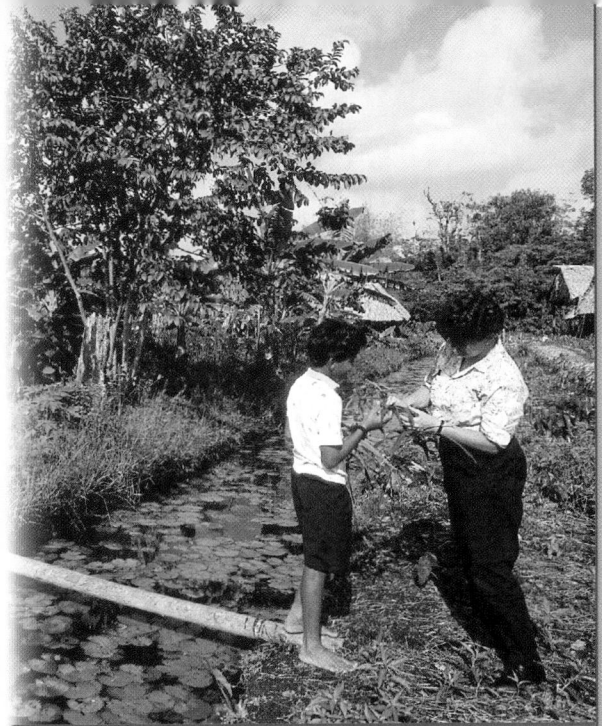
Ecosystems Rain forest covers much of the Guianas, although some land has been cleared for agriculture.

Grouped around Brazil, the twelve other countries of South America can be separated into three regions. The three regions are the northern tropics, the Andean countries, and the southern grassland countries. The countries of the northern tropics are located along the northern coast of South America. They share some characteristics, but they differ in their ethnic makeup, their economies, and their physical geography.

The Guianas

Guyana, Suriname (SUR ih nahm), and French Guiana together are known as the Guianas (gee AHN ahs). They share a tropical wet climate, vast stretches of rain forest, and a narrow coastal plain on the Atlantic Ocean; but their human characteristics give each a distinct personality. These differences reflect each country's history and pattern of colonization. They also set the Guianas apart culturally from most of the rest of

South America, where Spanish or Portuguese is spoken and where Roman Catholicism is the main religion.

Guyana's official language, for example, is English because it was once the English colony of British Guiana. Dutch is spoken in Suriname, a colony of the Netherlands until 1975. Many people in both countries are Muslim or Hindu. French is the official language of French Guiana, which is not an independent nation but an overseas department of France.

Effects of Migration Ethnic composition varies in the three Guianas and reflects patterns of migration. Europeans brought Africans to work as slaves on colonial sugar plantations. Asians from China, India, and Southeast Asia began migrating to the area as workers in the mid-1800s, after slavery was abolished. Today, most people in Guyana belong to those two major ethnic groups. People of Asian descent make up about half the population, many speaking

◀ Mt. Fitzroy in the Andes, Argentina *(photo left)*

Objectives

Upon completion of Section 1, students should be able to:

- ◆ describe how migration affected the population of the Guianas;
- ◆ identify the geographic influences on Venezuela's economy;
- ◆ discuss the problems of one-crop agriculture in Colombia.

National Geography Standards

The following National Geography Standards are highlighted in this section: 2, 4, 5, 10, 12, 15, 16, 18

Bellringer

Ask students to write one or two sentences describing their feelings about neighbors. Do students think that neighbors should work to get along with one another? Tell students that the nations of South America are neighbors of the United States.

LESSON PLAN

1. Focus Explain that rubber trees are an important natural resource of tropical rain forests. Ask students to list all the ways they use rubber in their daily lives. Point out that deforestation now threatens rubber trees.

2. Instruct Draw a chart on the board with the following headings: *Landforms, Culture, Economic Activities,* and *Challenges to Development.* Help students complete the chart for the Guianas, Venezuela, and Colombia.

3. Close/Reteach Divide the class into pairs. Assign one member of each pair the role of a government official and the other that of a reporter. Ask the reporter to prepare five questions on northern South America. Then, ask the official to answer the questions.

Pacing Suggestions

For 90-minute Blocks

You will want to vary activities.

- Extend the Creative Teaching Activity on page 15 in the Creative Teaching Activities booklet by asking students to prepare quiz questions about the Northern and Southern Hemispheres. Assign each group four cities. Ask them to research the average daily temperatures in June and December in their cities. Instruct them to quiz the rest of the class about when summer and winter occur in their cities.

Sidebar (left column)

BACKGROUND

Connecting With . . .

Science France operates the Guiana Space Center near the town of Kourou as its main base for launching space satellites.

READING STRATEGY

Visualizing

Ask students to prepare Venn diagrams to compare any two of the Guianas. Similarities include tropical wet climates, vast stretches of rain forest, and narrow coastal plains. Differences include languages, history, and patterns of colonization. Have students use the information from their Venn diagrams to write a paragraph summarizing the similarities and differences between the two countries.

Alternative Assessment

Introduce the Activity

Writing Assignment Ask students to select one country discussed in the chapter and write a vivid, expressive description of the regions and climate of that country. Distribute the Writing Assignment Rubric found on page 6 of the Alternative Assessment booklet in the Prentice Hall Assessment System for student reference during the project.

Answer to Graph Skills

Haiti

268 Chapter 13

Main content

Major Ethnic Groups in Selected Latin American Countries

GRAPH SKILLS

● **Migration** Latin American countries vary in ethnic composition because of differing patterns of migration.
- *In which Latin American country do people of African descent make up the majority of the population?*

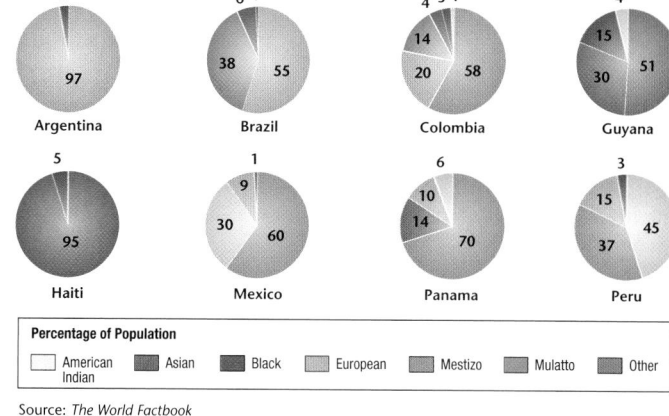

Source: *The World Factbook*

languages of India. Another 43 percent are of African ancestry.

Suriname's population has greater variety. Just over 50 percent are descended from the Asian workers who came in the 1800s, but only about 10 percent are of African descent. About 30 percent are **mulattoes,** people of mixed African and other ancestry. Most of the rest are indigenous Indians. The ethnic makeup of French Guiana is similar to that of Suriname, except that mulattoes are the largest group. People of European descent also live in French Guiana.

Economic Activities Although their populations are different, the three Guianas have similar primary economic activities because of their shared natural resources. Fishing boats harvest large quantities of fish and shrimp from the sea. In the lowlands, farmers grow sugar cane and rice. From the hills of Guyana and Suriname, miners extract **bauxite,** a mineral used in making aluminum. Guyana is one of the world's largest bauxite exporters.

Venezuela

Guyana's larger western neighbor, Venezuela, is a striking contrast. While fewer than 1 million people live in Guyana, Venezuela's population is almost 24 million. Guyana's per capita GNP of about $780 makes it the poorest nation in South America. Venezuela has an annual per capita GNP of more than $3,530. In Guyana, average life expectancy is 64 years, while average life expectancy in Venezuela is 73.1 years.

Venezuela's culture is more typical of the rest of South America than are those of the Guianas. Its official language is Spanish, and its people are mainly mestizos or of European descent. Nearly all are Roman Catholics.

The Andean Highlands Venezuela's landscapes are varied. In the northwest corner, the Andes tower over a narrow Caribbean coastal plain. A lower range of mountains, hills, and plateaus, the Andean Highlands, stretch across the rest of northern Venezuela. Most of Venezuela's people live in fertile mountain valleys. The capital city, Caracas, is located in this region.

Side by side with the sidewalk cafes, universities, and busy department stores of Caracas are scenes of poverty. As Brazil's cities have their *favelas,* Caracas has its *ranchitos,* or small shacks, where almost one third of the people live. In the last thirty years the government has used its oil wealth to launch massive programs to improve living conditions for the country's poor.

Waterfalls and Grasslands In southeastern Venezuela another mountain system, the Guiana Highlands, covers nearly half of the

---

RESOURCE DIRECTORY

Teaching Resources
Unit 3, Chapter 13
• Critical Thinking, p. 57

Prentice Hall Assessment System
Alternative Assessment booklet
• Writing Assignment Rubric, p. 6

country. Near the border with Brazil are dense tropical forests.

The world's highest waterfall, Angel Falls, is located in Canaima National Park in the Guiana Highlands. This thundering ribbon of water drops more than 3,200 feet (980 m) into the Churún River, a tributary of the Orinoco.

Between the two highland regions, the great Orinoco River flows through central Venezuela. Along both sides of the river stretches a wide tropical grassland, or savanna, region called the **llanos** (YAH nohs), which means "plains" in Spanish. (The United States has a parallel in the Llano Estacado, which stretches across Arizona, New Mexico, and Texas.) The llanos flood during the rainy season, from April to December. For the rest of the year, the hot sun of the dry season quickly burns the vegetation, and the soil becomes parched and cracked. Still, the region is important for grazing cattle.

Elevation and Climate Venezuela lies within the tropics, but its varied climates depend more on elevation than on distance from the Equator. As in many mountainous areas of Latin America, Spanish terms are commonly used for the different climate zones that occur as elevation increases. The diagram on page 270 shows these vertical climate zones.

Venezuelan farmers grow different crops at different elevations. Coffee trees, for example, are ideally suited for growing in the climate zone called *tierra templada*—"temperate country." At that middle elevation, temperatures are relatively mild.

An Oil-Rich Region Venezuela's wealth can be described in one word: oil. Four large beds of "liquid gold" lie in the eastern llanos, the Orinoco delta, the lowlands near Lake Maracaibo, and offshore. Petroleum dominates Venezuela's economy, making it one of the top ten oil producers in the world.

Experts have suggested that Venezuela could become the Western Hemisphere's biggest oil and gas producer in the twenty-first century. While it has huge oil reserves, they are finite. Venezuela therefore has reinvested a large share of its oil profits in other industries. It is developing bauxite and iron mines, building power plants, and setting up factories that will provide jobs when the oil wells run dry.

Angel Falls

Physical Characteristics Angel Falls, Venezuela, is about 20 times as high as Niagara Falls. This waterfall explodes out of caves in the cliff and plunges down to the Churún River.

Place *Why do you think the Venezuelan government created a national park around the falls?*

Colombia

Colombia—named after Christopher Columbus—is the only country in South America that borders both the Caribbean Sea and the Pacific Ocean. Its population of around 40 million makes it the second most populous country on the continent.

Physical Characteristics Like neighboring Venezuela, Colombia has three distinct physical regions—lowlands, mountains, and the llanos, or grassy plains. About 75 percent of the country's people live in fertile valleys between

BACKGROUND

Word Origin

Venezuela *Venezuela* means "Little Venice" in Spanish. The country was named by Spaniards who found Indians living in houses built on stilts. The elevated houses reminded them of buildings along the canals in Venice, Italy.

ACTIVITY

Group Work

Activity: Conducting a talk show

Purpose: Divide the class into groups of five. Assign each group a country from Section 1. After studying the economy and culture of the assigned country, each group should create four characters representing significant groups of people in that country.

Roles: Four characters and a talk show host

Result: Each group should conduct a "talk show" with these four characters as guests. The host should ask several questions to introduce relevant issues, and then open the discussion to questions from the class.

CUSTOMIZE FOR...

Students Acquiring English/ESL

A Country Tile Point out that in Spanish architecture, colorful ceramic tiles are often used to decorate buildings. Ask the students to study one of the five countries described in Section 1. Then give each student a large square of poster board on which to design a tile that shows the most significant aspects of his or her assigned country. Ask students to discuss why they chose to represent the countries in this way.

Answer to Photo Caption

Answers will vary, but students may suggest that the Venezuelan government wanted to preserve the natural beauty and wonder of the world's highest waterfall, rather than allow the resource to be exploited.

Chapter 13 ▪ **Section 1** **269**

Cultures

Pan American Games Athletes from North and South America compete in the Pan American Games, which are similar to the Olympic Games. The games, which began in 1951, take place every four years.

Vocabulary

Campesino Point out the list of Key Terms on page 267. Ask students to look up the word *campesino* in the Glossary. Then ask: **What problem do many campesinos face?** (Most profits go to the landowner.)

Reteach

Cause and Effect To illustrate why Colombian campesinos grow coca (which is used to manufacture cocaine) and marijuana, ask students to create cause-and-effect charts showing the relationships among the demand for illicit drugs, exorbitant rents for land, and the growing of cash crops of coca and marijuana. (Visual/Spatial)

Answers to Diagram Skills

tierra fría

coffee, corn, citrus fruit

GLOBAL CONNECTIONS

Global Trade Patterns
Production of the coffee bean began before 1000 A.D. in Ethiopia. The beans were not grown in South America until the eighteenth century. Today, Brazil and Colombia are two of the top coffee producers in the world.

three **cordilleras,** or parallel mountain ranges, of the Andes. Bogotá (bo guh TAH), Colombia's capital and largest city, lies on a high plateau of the Andes.

A Single Crop Although many different crops can grow in mountain climates, Colombia's farmers depend heavily on one crop. Surpassed only by Brazil, Colombia is famous for coffee, which is grown on more than 300,000 small farms. Most of the country's farmland is owned by a few wealthy families who rent small amounts of land to tenant farmers at high prices. Tenant farmers, or **campesinos,** are often barely able to grow enough food for their families because they focus their efforts on producing a cash crop of coffee.

A country that depends on one crop, such as coffee, is at risk if world demand for coffee drops, or if the coffee trees are destroyed. Officials are trying to reduce Colombia's dependence on a single cash crop by encouraging the export of other farm products.

The Drug Trade Although coffee is Colombia's major legal crop, two other products have proved to be extremely profitable for a small minority of Colombians. Huge quantities of marijuana and cocaine, a dangerous addictive drug made from the leaves of the coca plant, are exported illegally from Colombia. Authorities estimate that smuggling illegal drugs brings twice as much money into Colombia as coffee does. Those who control the illegal drug trade also hold considerable power. The governments of Colombia and the United States are working

Vertical Climate Zones in Latin America

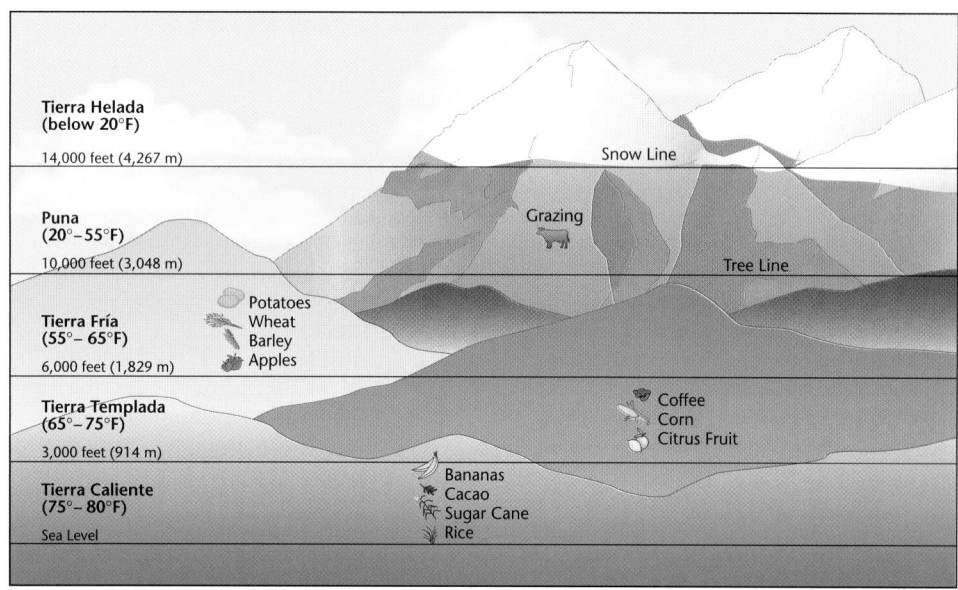

DIAGRAM SKILLS

Climates In mountainous areas, climate varies greatly with elevation.
- *What do Latin Americans call the region between 6,000 and 10,000 feet?*
- *Which crops are commonly grown in the* tierra templada?

Teaching Resources
Unit 3, Chapter 13
- Section 1 Quiz, p. 51

Spanish Resources
- Section 1 Quiz, p. 30

Growing Coffee

Economic Activities The Andes offer soil and climate perfect for growing coffee. Colombia is a world leader in coffee production, and coffee makes up half of all Colombian agricultural exports.

Human-Environment Interaction *What is the danger of a country's dependence on a single cash crop for income?*

together to stop the drug trade and the violence associated with it.

Cooperation and Conflict Colombia has had a stormy political history since the wars for independence from Spain ended in the 1820s. Continuing disputes between two major political parties reached a violent climax in the 1950s, when about 200,000 people were killed in a bloody civil war. In 1958, however, the two parties agreed to work together. Civil strife continues, however, as rebel groups compete for control of both the streets and the countryside.

Like many South American countries, Colombia struggles with the challenges that result from social inequality. A few people hold a majority of the country's wealth and power, while many suffer from extreme poverty.

SECTION 1 ASSESSMENT

1. **Key Terms** Define **(a)** mulatto, **(b)** bauxite, **(c)** llano, **(d)** cordillera, **(e)** campesino.

2. **Migration** What patterns of migration are reflected in the Guianas?

3. **Economic Activities** **(a)** What are the chief economic activities of Venezuela? **(b)** In which parts of the country do they take place?

4. **Global Trade Patterns** How do Colombia's chief exports differ from those of Venezuela and the Guianas?

5. **Critical Thinking Predicting Consequences** How might geographic factors such as natural hazards and changing climatic conditions affect an economy that is based on only one crop?

Activity

Writing a News Report Find periodical articles in the library or on the Internet on one of the following current events topics concerning a South American country of the northern tropics: government, natural resources, economic activities, conflict. Visit the World Geography section of **www.phschool.com** for help in completing the activity.

Answers to Section 1 Assessment

1. **(a)** mulatto, p. 268 **(b)** bauxite, p. 268 **(c)** llano, p. 269 **(d)** cordillera, p. 270 **(e)** campesino, p. 270

2. Migration has affected the ethnic composition of the Guianas. English, Dutch, and French settlers came from Europe. They brought Africans to South America as slaves to work on their plantations. Later, migrants from China, India, and Southeast Asia came to the region in search of work.

3. **(a–b)** The most profitable economic activity is oil and gas production in the eastern llanos, the Orinoco delta, the lowlands near Lake Maracaibo, and offshore. Cattle ranching, in the llanos, is another important activity, as is the growing of crops such as coffee in the tierra templada.

4. The exports of Venezuela and the Guianas are more diverse than those of Colombia. Colombia has one main export: coffee. Colombia also has a large illegal drug trade.

5. Answers will vary, but students should recognize that an economy dependent on a single crop is especially vulnerable to natural hazards or climatic conditions (such as flooding or drought) that could cause the crop to fail.

Activity Rubrics Share rubrics with students before they write their news reports.
Attempted The news report does not reflect sufficient research and is poorly written.
Minimal News report reflects some research but has few details.
Adequate The news report is well written with sufficient details.
Exemplary News report reflects thorough research and is informative, well organized, and well written.

TEST PREPARATION

Have students read the subsection Cooperation and Conflict on this page to answer the following question.

What is the source of civil strife in Colombia today?

   A Legalization of marijuana and cocaine use

   B Struggles between campesinos and the government

   Ⓒ Competition among rebel groups

   D War between the two major political groups

Answer to Photo Caption

If a crop fails or if demand decreases or prices drop, the country will face a loss of income. Also, devoting land to cash crops means that there is less land available to grow food.

Objectives

Upon completion of Section 2, students should be able to:

◆ explain how the physical geography of the Andean countries has affected the people who live there;

◆ compare the economies of Ecuador and Peru;

◆ describe how climate affects the people of Bolivia and Chile.

National Geography Standards

The following National Geography Standards are highlighted in this section: 1, 2, 4, 5, 8, 11, 13, 15, 16

Bellringer

Ask students to describe the effort required to hike long distances over rough terrain. Ask any students who have visited mountains over 10,000 feet high (3,048 m) to describe the physical sensations associated with high altitudes.

LESSON PLAN

1. Focus Ask students to locate the nations of Ecuador, Peru, Bolivia, and Chile on the map on page 207. Then ask them to speculate about similarities and differences among these nations.

2. Instruct Begin a chart on the board with two columns labeled *Similarities* and *Differences*. Then compare the landforms, climate, economic activities, and ethnic composition of the four Andean countries.

3. Close/Reteach Read the following descriptions to the class and ask students to name the jobs the people described might hold: an Ecuadorian mestizo living on the coastal plain; a descendant of a European family in Ecuador; a Peruvian family living in the mountains; a Bolivian mestizo living in a city.

2 The Andean Countries

Reading Focus

- **How have the physical characteristics of the Andean countries affected the people who live there?**
- **How are the economies of Ecuador and Peru similar and different?**
- **How do climatic conditions affect the people of Bolivia and Chile?**

Key Terms

altiplano

páramo

timber line

selva

Main Idea The physical characteristics of the Andes affect cultural patterns and economic activities in this region.

Physical Characteristics The towering peaks of the Andes dominate the west coast of South America.

The Andes form the backbone of Ecuador, Peru, Bolivia, and Chile. It is the longest unbroken mountain chain in the world, soaring higher than any range except the Himalayas in South Asia. Some of the Andes' snow-capped peaks tower more than 20,000 feet (6,000 m) above sea level. The Andes have shaped not only the physical geography of the Andean nations, but also the economies and lifestyles of the people who make their homes in this region.

Physical Characteristics

The Andes stretch some 5,500 miles (8,850 km) all the way from the Caribbean Sea to the southernmost tip of South America. At places in Peru and Bolivia the mountain range is nearly 500 miles (800 km) wide. Its rocky walls divide the Andean nations into three distinct environments: coastal plain, highlands, and forest.

Coastal Plain Between the mountains and the sea, a narrow plain stretches along the entire Pacific coast from Colombia to the southern end

of Chile. At some points it is no more than a sandy beach at the foot of the mountains; in other places it reaches inland for 100 miles (160 km).

The Atacama Desert, the driest and one of the most lifeless places on earth, occupies the coastal plain in northern Chile. Because ocean winds lose their moisture blowing across the cold waters of the Peru Current, only dry air ever reaches the land, creating a desolate wasteland. The Atacama is so dry that archaeologists have found perfectly preserved relics from ancient times. These include colored textiles woven hundreds of years ago, ancient mud-brick dwellings, and even human mummies. The desert is rich in minerals, however.

Coastal plains north and south of the Atacama get more rainfall. To the north, along the coast of Ecuador, lie oppressively hot and humid rain forests. To the south lies an area with a Mediterranean climate of hot, dry summers and mild, rainy winters.

Highlands Inland from the coastal plain, the peaks of the Andes rise skyward to incredible heights. Between the cordilleras lie highland valleys and plateaus. The high plateaus range from

RESOURCE DIRECTORY

Teaching Resources

Unit 3, Chapter 13
- Section 2 Guided Reading and Review, p. 52

Guide to the Essentials (English/Spanish)
- Section Summary, Chapter 13, Section 2

Mental Mapping booklet
- Unit 3 Checklist, p. 34

Technology

Guided Reading Audiotapes (English/Spanish), Chapter 13, Section 2

Section Reading Support Transparencies, Chapter 13, Section 2

World Geography Map and Photo Transparencies
- Latin America: Maps and Photos

Book on CD, Chapter 13

Social Studies Skills Tutor CD-ROM

Companion Web site, www.phschool.com
- Chapter 13 Activities

6,500 to 16,000 feet (1,980 to 4,900 m) above sea level. Plateau regions are known by different names in different countries: the *altiplano*, or "high plain," in Peru and Bolivia, and the *páramos* in Ecuador.

The climate in the Andes varies with elevation. At very high elevations, the vegetation is known as alpine tundra. Alpine tundra usually grows above the **timber line**, the boundary above which continuous forest vegetation cannot grow. Only plants that can survive cold temperatures, gusting winds, spotty precipitation, and short growing seasons grow in the alpine tundra.

The highest altitudes of the Andes are in the midsection of the mountain chain. Mountaintop areas here are snow-covered and cold all year long. Further north, however, the picture changes. Mountain temperatures there are warmer, rains more frequent, and rain forest growth thick and lush.

Tropical Forests   Inland, the eastern slopes of the Andes descend to forested tropical lowlands. A dramatic contrast exists between the cold, dry mountains and the steamy lowlands. In Ecuador, Peru, and Bolivia, these forested regions are called

the *selva.* The rain forests of the Amazon River basin begin in the selva. Jaguars, hummingbirds, monkeys, and toucans inhabit this ecosystem, but not many people do.

People and the Environment

People have always been drawn to the Andes because of the area's natural resources. The soil is mostly rich and suited for growing a variety of crops, depending on the elevation. The mountains contain a wealth of gold, silver, tin, copper, and other minerals. At the same time, the mountains often have served as barriers to trade among the Andean countries and with the outside world.

Economic Activities   One way in which the people of the Andes have adapted to mountain living is by "vertical trade." In a typical Andean market town, people from villages at different elevations meet to trade their crops. Because people grow crops suited to their own climate zone, here

273

Environmental Issues

Endangered Vicuñas Prior to Spanish contact, some million or more undomesticated vicuña (mammals related to the llama and alpaca) roamed the Andean highlands. The Spanish slaughtered the vicuña for their fine wool, and now the vicuña is an endangered species.

ACTIVITY

Group Work

Activity: Re-creating an Andean market day

Purpose: The class will re-create a typical market day in an Andean village. Each group will represent one of the vertical climate zones shown in the diagram on page 270. Ask students to find or make replicas of the following products to bring to market: foods, pottery, jewelry, clothing, or manufactured goods.

Roles: Assign a group leader. Each student is responsible for supplying at least one item for market day.

Result: On market day, ask students to barter the goods or sell them for play money.

READING STRATEGY

Asking Questions

Write the following questions on the board: *What ethnic groups live there? Where are they located? What do they do for a living?* Tell students that these are the types of questions geographers ask when studying a region. Instruct students to ask questions and jot down answers to the three questions as they read the subsection Ecuador.

---

they trade "up" and "down." Tropical foods such as bananas and sugar cane, grown in the *tierra caliente,* may be traded for the potatoes and cabbages that grow in the *tierra fría.* Village farmers, highland cheesemakers, coastal fishermen, and peddlers all meet in the Andean market town.

Physical Effects The original inhabitants of the highlands, before the Spanish arrived in the 1500s, were groups of Native Americans. Indians still make up between 25 and 55 percent of the populations of Bolivia, Ecuador, and Peru. Andean Indians, who have lived for centuries at altitudes up to 17,000 feet (5,200 m) have developed unusual physical characteristics, such as larger hearts and lungs, that let them live and work in the thin, oxygen-poor air.

Ecuador

Ecuador takes its name from the Equator, which cuts across the country. About one fourth of the 12.9 million Ecuadorians are of Indian descent. They speak Quechua (KECH wah), the language of the Incas. They follow a traditional lifestyle in the highlands, practicing subsistence agriculture. People of European background make up only about 10 percent of Ecuador's population. But, because they own the largest farms and factories, they have the most political influence.

Roughly half of Ecuador's population are mestizos, who speak Spanish and live mainly in highland cities and towns. Some mestizos work in urban factories, while others have moved to the coastal plain and work there as tenant farmers on plantations that grow bananas, cacao, and coffee for export.

Only a few decades ago, Ecuador's population was concentrated in the mountainous central highland. Today, due to internal migration, the population is about evenly divided between the highlands and the coastal lowlands. East of the mountains, the tropical forest region remains sparsely populated.

In the 1960s, Ecuadorians discovered oil in the *selva* lowlands. In spite of the challenges of transporting oil by pipeline from the *selva* to the coast, petroleum became one of Ecuador's most important exports. During the 1990s, however, fluctuating oil prices and government mismanagement hampered Ecuador's economic growth.

South America and the United States
Health Care Data

Country	Infant Mortality Rate (per 1,000 births)	Life Expectancy (years)	Population per Physician
Argentina	19	74.5	373
Bolivia	64	60.9	2,348
Brazil	37	64.4	705
Chile	10	75.2	938
Colombia	25	70.1	1,154
Ecuador	32	71.8	652
Guyana	49	62.3	8,946
Paraguay	57	72.2	3,583
Peru	43	70.0	969
Suriname	27	70.6	1,279
Uruguay	14	75.5	312
Venezuela	28	72.7	639
United States	6	76.1	400

Source: *Encarta World Atlas*

CHART SKILLS

● **Economic Activities** In which country is it probably most difficult to make an appointment to see a doctor? Explain.

● **Science and Technology** How do you think differences in medical technology affect life expectancy data? Explain.

Peru

Peru was the heart of the vast Inca Empire, which fell to the Spaniards in the early 1500s. The conquistadors destroyed the empire but the Incas remain. About 45 percent of Peru's population are Indians who speak Quechua or Aymara (EYE muh RAH). Most live by subsistence farming or herding llamas and alpacas in the highlands. Magnificent ruins, such as the fortress of Machu Picchu and the buildings of the Incan capital city of Cuzco, are fine examples of Incan architecture.

Most other Peruvians are mestizos who live in urban areas in or near the coastal plain. For the most part, they work for low wages in factories that produce fish meal for animal feed or on

---

RESOURCE DIRECTORY

Teaching Resources
Unit 3
• Geography and World Literature, The Younger Brother, p. 65

Answers to Chart Skills

Guyana; it has the greatest number of people per physician.

Access to better medical technology would likely increase the life expectancy rate.

plantations that export cotton, sugar cane, and rice. Poverty and unemployment are part of the character of this place.

In Peru, as in Ecuador, a minority of people of European descent control most of the country's wealth and are leaders in the government and in the army. More recently, many Asians have immigrated to Peru. In 1995, Alberto Fujimori, a Peruvian of Japanese ancestry, was elected to a second term as Peru's president. Fujimori made economic reforms and suppressed a terrorist movement, but his years in office were stained with scandal and abuse of power. Many claimed that he stole a third election in 2000. Facing outrage in the citizenry, Fujimori resigned. Peru struggled to abolish political abuses and establish a truly democratic government.

Bolivia

Because Bolivia is landlocked, it lacks the profitable coastal ports and factories of Ecuador and Peru. Lake Titicaca, the world's highest navigable lake, straddles the border between Bolivia and Peru. Bolivia has many minerals, but the best ores already have been removed. Most of Bolivia's people are Indians—mostly subsistence farmers who live in the highlands. Bolivian farm families grow potatoes, wheat, and barley. At higher elevations they herd alpacas and llamas. Children contribute to the family economy by helping herd the animals.

In Bolivia, the climate varies with the altitude—from humid and tropical to cold and semiarid. The cold, thin air of the high plateau makes physical activity difficult for nonnative-born people.

Chile

Chile, meaning "end of the land," was appropriately named by the Indians who once lived on this strip of land. Chile edges the west coast of South America like a long, narrow ribbon. The country is about 2,700 miles (4,300 km) long but only averages 100 miles (160 km) wide. About two thirds of

GLOBAL CONNECTIONS

Government and Citizenship Long, narrow countries, called elongated states, often suffer from poor internal communication. A region at one end of the country can be isolated from the capital, which is often centrally located. Chile, Italy, and Gambia are all elongated states.

Herding Llamas

Economic Activities Traditional economic activities, such as the herding of llamas and alpacas by the Tocco Indians, sustain the local economy of Peru.

Movement *Why do herders often have to move their livestock in order to find the best grazing land?*

275

Chilean Fishing Industry

Global Trade Patterns
The 7 million tons (6.5 million metric tons) of fish caught off the coast of Chile each year makes Chile a world leader in the fishing industry. Most of this catch is processed into fish meal and fish oil and sold to other countries.

Location *How does Chile's shape and location aid the fishing industry?*

the approximately 15 million people in Chile are mestizos. Another quarter of the population is of European descent—mostly Spanish, British, and German. Unlike the other Andean nations, Chile has relatively few Indians.

The barren Atacama Desert in the north is uninhabited. In contrast, about three fourths of the Chilean people live in the thickly populated Central Valley. It is a region of fertile river basins between the Andes and the coastal ranges. Fruit, vegetables, and wine grapes grow there in abundance. Because Chile's productive summer season comes during the Northern Hemisphere's winter, its products find good markets in the United States and Europe.

Most of Chile's cities and factories are also in the Central Valley. Santiago, the capital, is home to about one third of the country's population. Many people are newcomers from the country-side, unskilled and illiterate. As a result, Santiago has high unemployment and many poor, crowded communities. Although Chile's economy has grown rapidly, about 3 million of its people still live below the poverty line.

SECTION 2 ASSESSMENT

1. Key Terms Define **(a)** *altiplano*, **(b)** *páramo*, **(c)** timber line, **(d)** *selva*.

2. Physical Characteristics (a) How do physical characteristics divide the Andean nations into three environments? **(b)** How have the people of Andean countries adapted to the natural environment?

3. Economic Activities (a) How are the economies of Ecuador and Peru similar? **(b)** How are the economies of the two countries different?

4. Climates (a) How do climatic conditions affect economic activities in Bolivia? **(b)** Why does Chile find good markets for its agricultural produce in the United States?

5. Critical Thinking Analyzing Data Review the health care data on page 274. How do the data suggest which two countries provide the best health care for pregnant women?

Activity

USING THE **REGIONAL ATLAS**

Review the Regional Atlas for Latin America and this section. Then, plan a two-week educational tour of the Andean countries that will introduce high-school students to the physical characteristics, peoples, and economic activities of the region. Create an itinerary and write a brief description of each place on the tour.

Comparing and Contrasting Data

When you compare and contrast data, you determine what is similar and different. You can use this skill to make informed decisions as a consumer, such as when you buy new clothing and compare color, sizes, and costs. By comparing data in the graph below, you can draw conclusions about economic and political opportunities for women around the world.

Learn the Skill Use the following steps to learn how to compare and contrast data.

1 *Identify the categories of data being compared.* Statistics are usually grouped together by topic. To determine the topic, read all the key words that accompany the data. If there is a key, identify and understand the use of colors and any other symbolism. **(a)** *What is the one main topic of the data in the graph below?* **(b)** *Into what two categories is the one main topic divided?*

2 *Look for basic similarities.* It is important to look for relationships. First, analyze the data for similarities. **(a)** *In all the countries listed below, do women hold more than half or less than half of all government jobs?* **(b)** *Do women in those countries generally earn more than men or less than men?*

3 *Look for basic differences.* Study the data to see if there are any distinct differences or exceptions that stand out in contrast to the similarities. **(a)** *According to the graph below, in what country do women make more money than men?* **(b)** *In what country do women hold the most power in government?*

4 *Determine patterns and connections.* After establishing basic similarities and differences, one can try to find more complex patterns and connections. **(a)** *In the selected countries, how do opportunities for women compare to opportunities for men?* **(b)** *In general, do women in these countries have better economic or political opportunities? Explain.*

5 *Make recommendations.* Data is usually used not only to understand the past, but also to plan for the future. Based on the analysis of data, you can draw conclusions and make recommendations. **(a)** *Based on the graph, where is the best place for a woman to live if she wants to participate in government? Where is the worst place for her to live?* **(b)** *Would you recommend that women in the countries listed below devote the bulk of their efforts to seeking economic change or political change? Why?*

Do It Yourself

Practice the Skill In the library or on the Internet, find data on a particular topic for selected countries of South America. Compare and contrast the data by following each of the above steps. In a written report, be sure to make recommendations based on your analysis of the data.

Apply the Skill See Chapter 13 Review and Assessment.

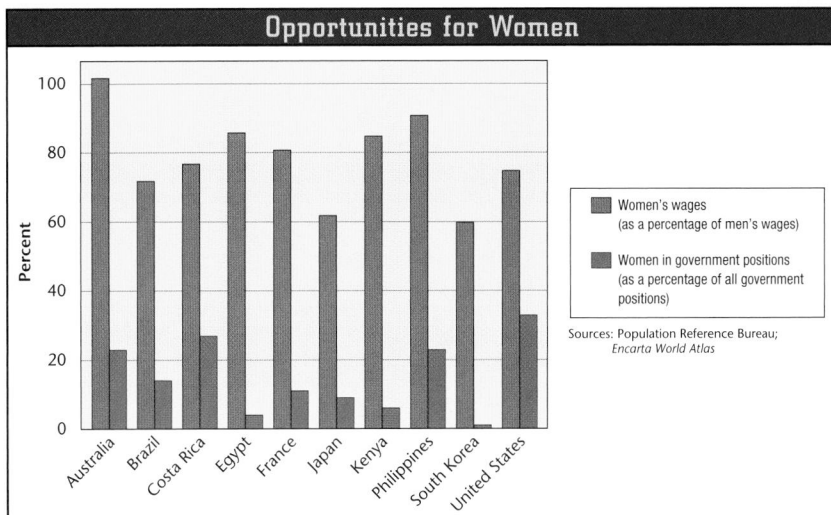

Sources: Population Reference Bureau; *Encarta World Atlas*

Chapter 13   **277**

Teaching the Skill
Read the introductory paragraph with the class. Discuss how the factors mentioned in the paragraph influence the students when they shop for clothing. Ask students: **Why do people compare these factors when shopping?** (Possible answer: They're looking for something that fits their needs, and they want to make an informed decision.) As you work through the steps on this page with the students, ask volunteers to draw parallels between the skills mentioned and comparison shopping.

Answers to Learn the Skill
1. (a) economic and political opportunities for women **(b)** women's wages as a percentage of men's wages; women in government positions as a percentage of all government positions
2. (a) less than half **(b)** Women earn less than men.
3. (a) Australia **(b)** the United States
4. (a) In general, women have fewer opportunities than men. **(b)** Women have better economic opportunities than political opportunities—their wages as a percentage of men's wages are higher in comparison to the percentages of women in government positions.
5. (a) the United States; South Korea **(b)** Possible answer: Students may recommend that women seek political change because there is more evident inequality between women and men in this area.

Answer to Practice the Skill
Have students document their data; check to see that the reports are properly prepared. Encourage students to share their generalizations or inferences and to explain how they arrived at those ideas.

CUSTOMIZE FOR...

Honors/PreAP
Writing Captions Have students use books, magazines, and the Internet to collect examples of graphs, charts, tables, or any other form of data about South America or any South American countries. Have students write captions expressing patterns, connections, and inferences based on the data in their selections and display them on a large poster.

Chapter 13   **277**

Section 3 pp. 278–281

Objectives
Upon completion of Section 3, students should be able to:

♦ describe the physical characteristics of the southern grassland countries;

♦ explain the recent changes in political conditions in Paraguay and Uruguay;

♦ state how urbanization has affected life in Argentina.

National Geography Standards
The following National Geography Standards are highlighted in this section: 1, 2, 5, 7, 8, 9, 11, 12, 13

Bellringer
Ask students to find Uruguay, Paraguay, and Argentina on the map on page 207 and compare their landforms and locations. Lead a discussion about how differences among these nations might affect society and the economy in these three nations.

LESSON PLAN

1. Focus Tell students that just as Colombia depends on coffee and Venezuela depends on oil, southern South America depends heavily on a single product. Tell one student that the product is livestock, and challenge the rest of the class to play "Twenty Questions" to figure out what the product is.

2. Instruct In a discussion, stress the physical features of the area by tracing on a map the rivers that link southern South America. Explain the contrasting features of western and eastern Argentina. Then point out that Paraguay has a geographic disadvantage—it is landlocked.

3. Close/Reteach Write the names of the three countries—*Uruguay, Paraguay,* and *Argentina*—on the board. Divide the class into three teams and challenge each team to describe the cities, climate, and economy of one of the three countries.

3 The Southern Grassland Countries

Reading Focus
- What are the physical characteristics of the southern grassland countries?
- How have political conditions in Paraguay and Uruguay changed in recent years?
- How has urbanization affected life in Argentina?

Key Terms
estuary

piedmont

pampas

gaucho

Main Idea Paraguay, Uruguay, and Argentina have developed prosperous economies despite histories of political troubles.

Economic Activities This commercial district serves people in the city of Buenos Aires, Argentina.

The three nations that make up southern South America—Uruguay, Paraguay, and Argentina—contrast sharply with the rest of the continent. Although they face economic problems, they are among the most prosperous South American nations. Ethnically, they have more in common with Europe than with their neighbors.

Physical Characteristics
Southern South America consists of several physical regions with varying characteristics. These regions are bound together by a great river system.

Great Rivers As the map on page 207 shows, several large rivers flow from the interior into the Río de la Plata. Although its name means "River of Silver," the Plata is an **estuary,** a broad river mouth formed where a flooded river valley meets the sea.

Four rivers in the Plata estuary system form national boundaries: the Uruguay, the Pilcomayo,

the Paraguay, and the Paraná. The capitals of Argentina and Uruguay—Buenos Aires and Montevideo—are both located on the Río de la Plata. This vast river system provides an inexpensive and efficient way for people in this functional region to ship goods.

Andean Region The highest peaks of the Andes are in western Argentina. They include the four highest mountains in the Western Hemisphere, including Mount Aconcagua (ah kuhn KAH gwah), which towers 22,834 feet (6,960 m) above sea level. From this great height, the Andes gradually give way to a gently rolling **piedmont,** or foothills, region.

Tropical Lowlands The Gran Chaco, or "hunting land," is an interior lowland region of savanna and dense shrub in parts of Paraguay, Argentina, and Bolivia. Temperatures in the Gran Chaco are mild and change little. Rainfall, however, is seasonal. Summer rains turn the area into mud. In winter the soil is dry and windblown.

278 Chapter 13 ▪ Countries of South America

RESOURCE DIRECTORY

Teaching Resources

Creative Teaching Activities, The Northern and Southern Hemispheres, p. 15

Unit 3, Chapter 13
- Section 3 Guided Reading and Review, p. 54

Guide to the Essentials (English/Spanish)
- Section Summary, Chapter 13, Section 3

Mental Mapping booklet
- Atlas Activity, p. 49
- Unit 3 Checklist, p. 34

Technology

Guided Reading Audiotapes (English/Spanish), Chapter 13, Section 3

Section Reading Support Transparencies, Chapter 13, Section 3

World Geography Map and Photo Transparencies
- Latin America: Maps and Photos

Book on CD, Chapter 13

Social Studies Skills Tutor CD-ROM

Companion Web site, www.phschool.com
- Chapter 13 Activities

Grasslands The **pampas** of Argentina and Uruguay are one of South America's best-known features. These temperate grasslands, which stretch for hundreds of miles, were formerly home to hundreds of **gauchos** (GOW chohs), the cowboys who herded cattle there. Fewer gauchos now work on Argentina's interior ranches. Today the pampas are Argentina's breadbasket, producing about 80 percent of the nation's grain and about 70 percent of its meat. The pampas have warm summers and cold winters. Occasional violent winter thunderstorms are known as "pamperos."

Patagonia South of the pampas lies the windswept plateau of Patagonia. This desolate, dry, cold, and sometimes foggy plain is well suited for raising sheep. Its natural resources also include rich deposits of oil and bauxite.

Paraguay

Although Paraguay is landlocked, the Plata River system provides an outlet to the sea. Almost all Paraguayans live in the highlands of the eastern part of their country, rather than the swampy Chaco. About half the people live in urban areas, especially the capital city of Asunción, on the Paraguay River. Most Paraguayans are mestizos, who speak Guarani, the local Indian language, as well as Spanish.

The Paraguayan economy is based on agriculture, mostly cotton, grains, and livestock. Paraguay and Brazil have cooperated in building the huge Itaipu Dam on the Paraná River, one of the world's largest hydroelectric projects. It began generating electricity in 1984. Paraguayans hope that inexpensive hydroelectric power will make up for the country's lack of minerals and other resources.

For 35 years, Paraguay was ruled by a military dictator, General Alfredo Stroessner. During this period, political freedoms were restricted, and critics were persecuted. In 1989, however, discontented military officers replaced him. The new leader, General Andres Rodriguez, made the government more responsive to people's needs. Since 1993, Paraguay has held free democratic elections. In 2000, power passed peacefully to an opposition party that had not held power for decades.

Uruguay

Uruguay takes its name from an Indian word meaning "river of the painted bird." The name probably comes from the brightly colored tropical birds found along the Río de la Plata. Because much of Uruguay is rolling grasslands, the country's primary economic activities are raising livestock, processing meat, and making products such as wool and leather. About 75 percent of the land

Hydroelectric Energy

Science and Technology The waters of the Paraná River power the Itaipu Dam's hydroelectric plant. One of the world's largest-capacity hydroelectric plants, the Itaipu has the potential to generate 12,600 megawatts of electricity. (A megawatt is one million watts, the basic unit for measuring electric power.)

Human-Environment Interaction *How does a dam affect the natural environment?*

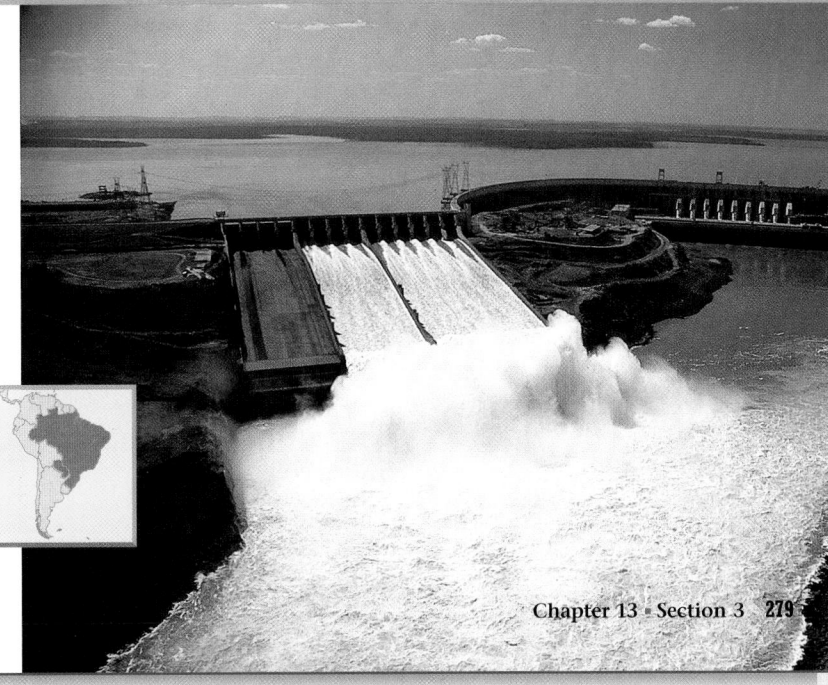

Answer to Photo Caption

A dam across a river usually creates a lake. The dam can disrupt the migration of fish and cause other ecological damage.

280 **Chapter 13**

is devoted to livestock grazing and another 10 percent to raising feed grains. Uruguay produces no fuel and few consumer goods, so it must import these expensive products.

Most Uruguayans are of European descent, mainly Italian and Spanish. The country has a large middle class, who live comfortably in urban areas with few slums. Politically, however, Uruguay has an unstable history. In 1973, the military took power, ruling for 12 years. Repression was widespread, and many people were imprisoned. Since 1985, Uruguay has held free elections. Today, it is one of the few countries in which people are required to vote and are fined if they do not.

Argentina

Like their neighbors in Uruguay, most of Argentina's nearly 37 million people have European ancestors, mostly Spanish and Italian. Eighty-eight percent of them live in cities. Some 13 million people live in sprawling Buenos Aires. Argentina is Latin America's wealthiest nation in terms of per capita GNP, although the nation's wealth is unevenly distributed.

Urbanization Buenos Aires is a vibrant capital city that looks to Europe for its fashions, art, food, and style. Busy factories produce goods for export, and the harbor is filled with freighters from all over the world. One result of all this activity is the heavy air pollution that blankets Buenos Aires. Still, Buenos Aires is like a magnet, pulling in rural people who seek jobs and a better way of life.

Political History From the mid-1940s until 1983, Argentina was ruled by a series of military dictators. The best known was Juan Domingo Perón, who was president from 1946 to 1955. Perón wanted to develop Argentina's industry and to distribute wealth more evenly. His first wife, Eva, became a heroine to Argentina's poor. Other dictators used government power to help the wealthy, ignoring the problems of the poor. But all of them censored newspapers, closed down universities, and imprisoned political opponents. They tried to give the appearance of progress by borrowing money from foreign banks to build dams, roads, and factories.

Conditions under military rule in the 1970s were particularly bad. So many people were

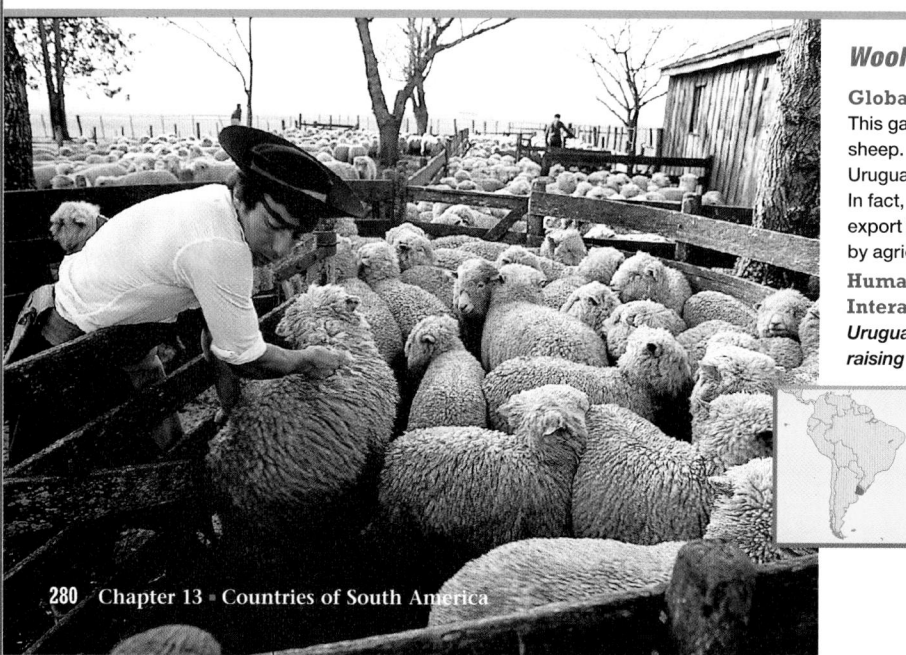

280 Chapter 13 ▪ Countries of South America

Wool for Export

Global Trade Patterns
This gaucho is vaccinating sheep. Wool is one of Uruguay's major exports. In fact, most of Uruguay's export income is generated by agriculture.

Human-Environment Interaction *Why is Uruguay well suited to raising livestock?*

Fertile Pampas

Ecosystems Moderate rainfall creates large areas of grassland. In Argentina, the temperate grasslands are called pampas. *Estancias,* or cattle ranches, like the one shown here, and farms of the vast, fertile pampas make Argentina a leading exporter of food.

Regions *The pampas of South America are similar to what region in the United States?*

kidnapped by the military and never seen again that the period became known as the "dirty wars." People regularly gathered at the presidential palace, demanding to know what had happened to missing family members.

In 1982, Argentina lost a war with Great Britain over control of the Falkland Islands off the country's southern Atlantic coast. Facing disgrace, the military allowed open elections. Political stability since then has been hampered by a volatile economy. The economy prospered in the mid-1990s. Since then, Argentina has dealt with periods of soaring inflation and enormous debt.

SECTION 3 ASSESSMENT

1. **Key Terms** Define **(a)** estuary, **(b)** piedmont, **(c)** pampas, **(d)** gaucho.

2. **Physical Characteristics** How do physical characteristics divide southern South America into several regions?

3. **Government and Citizenship** How have recent government reforms benefited the people of Paraguay and Uruguay?

4. **Urbanization** How do conditions in Buenos Aires, Argentina, demonstrate both the attractiveness and the problems of city life?

5. **Critical Thinking** **Analyzing Photographs** Study the photograph on page 278. How does the photograph provide evidence of cultural convergence between the United States and South America? Explain.

Activity

 Take It to the NET

Creating an Advertisement Use information from the Internet to make a magazine advertisement that might attract businesses in the United States to trade with businesses in Argentina. Visit the World Geography section of **www.phschool.com** for help in completing this activity.

Articles From NATIONAL GEOGRAPHIC

The following article may be used to extend the content in this section.

Putnam, John J., and Stuart Franklin, photographer. "Buenos Aires." *National Geographic,* Vol. 186, No. 6 (Dec. 1994), pp. 84–105.

After surviving a long history of violence, political unrest, and corruption, Buenos Aires experienced economic growth and political reform during the 1990s.

TEST PREPARATION

Have students read the subsection Political History beginning on the opposite page to answer the following question.
What caused Argentina's military to allow open elections in the 1980s?

A A new president was elected.

B People demonstrated at the presidential palace to support military rule.

C Rural people stopped moving to Buenos Aires.

(D) Argentina lost a war with Great Britain.

Answers to Section 3 Assessment

1. **(a)** estuary, p. 278 **(b)** piedmont, p. 278 **(c)** pampas, p. 279 **(d)** gaucho, p. 279

2. The Andean region is mountainous; the Gran Chaco is a tropical lowland; the pampas are temperate grasslands; Patagonia is a cold and dry plain.

3. Both countries have moved away from repressive governments and have held free elections.

4. The city is vibrant and sophisticated and attracts people seeking jobs and better lives. The harbor is filled with freighters from around the world. Like many cities, however, it suffers from heavy air pollution.

5. Possible answer: The city, with its high-rises, fast-food restaurants, and advertisements for North American and European products, resembles many cities in the United States and suggests that there has been an influence.

Activity Rubrics Share rubrics with students before they begin.
Attempted Students attempt the project but fail to complete the advertisement.
Minimal The advertisement is complete but shows little understanding of why United States businesses might want to trade with Argentine businesses.
Adequate The advertisement is neat, visually appealing, and shows an understanding of Argentina's economy and resources.
Exemplary The advertisement is original, well researched, persuasive, and eye-catching. Student's work shows a good understanding of Argentina's economy.

Answer to Photo Caption

The pampas are similar to the prairies found on the Great Plains of the United States.

Creating a Chapter Summary
As a reteaching opportunity, pair a more able student with a less able student to complete this chapter summary.

Students might add the following entries: **Northern Tropics** *Human Characteristics:* Descendants of African and Asian workers, Indians, People of European descent. *Physical Characteristics:* Tropical rain forest, Coastal plain, Highlands, Savanna, Lowlands, **Andean Countries** *Human Characteristics:* Indians, People of European descent, Mestizos. *Physical Characteristics:* Coastal plain, Highlands, Tropical forest (*selva*) **Southern Grassland Countries** *Human Characteristics:* Mestizos, People of European descent. *Physical Characteristics:* Mountains, Piedmont, Tropical lowlands (Gran Chaco), Pampas, Patagonia

Reviewing Key Terms
1–10. Students' sentences should demonstrate a clear understanding of the key terms.

Understanding Key Ideas
11. People in the Guianas speak English, French, and Dutch rather than Spanish or Portuguese. Many are of East Asian or South Asian ancestry and are Hindu or Muslim, not Roman Catholic.
12. Elevation influences agriculture and physical differences in humans. Andean peoples who live at higher altitudes have developed larger hearts and lungs to make working in the thinner air easier.
13. About 80 percent of Argentina's grain and about 70 percent of its meat are produced in the pampas.
14. (a) Uruguay, Paraguay, and Argentina **(b)** The river system provides an inexpensive and efficient way for people to ship goods.
15. People hope to get better jobs and earn higher wages in the cities.

Critical Thinking and Writing
16. Possible answer: A large farm needs many workers, who need housing and other basic necessities. Bringing supplies into and shipping

---

Creating a Chapter Summary

Copy this graphic organizer on a piece of paper. Fill in information about the human characteristics and physical characteristics of regions in South America. Some entries have been completed to serve as an example.

	NORTHERN TROPICS	ANDEAN COUNTRIES	SOUTHERN GRASSLAND COUNTRIES
HUMAN CHARACTERISTICS	• Mestizos • Mulattoes •		
PHYSICAL CHARACTERISTICS		• Coastal plain • Desert •	

Take It to the NET
Chapter Self-Test For practice test questions for Chapter 13, go to the World Geography section of **www.phschool.com**.

Reviewing Key Terms

Use each of the following key terms in a sentence that shows the term's meaning. You may use two terms in one sentence.

1. mulatto
2. bauxite
3. cordillera
4. campesino
5. *altiplano*
6. timber line
7. *selva*
8. estuary
9. piedmont
10. pampas

Understanding Key Ideas

11. **Cultures** How do the human characteristics of the Guianas differ from those of other Andean countries?
12. **Physical Characteristics** How does elevation influence life in the Andean countries?
13. **Economic Activities** Why are the pampas important to the economy of Argentina?
14. **Global Trade Patterns** (a) What countries depend on the Río de la Plata system

for trade and transportation? **(b)** Why do they depend on the river system?
15. **Migration** Why have many people in this region left their villages in the mountains and countryside and moved to cities?

Critical Thinking and Writing

16. **Analyzing Photographs** Study the photograph of the coffee plantation on page 271. Based on the photograph, what challenges do you think the owner of a large farm in the mountains must face?
17. **Drawing Conclusions** (a) Why are market towns important to Andean local economies? (b) What do you think is an ideal location for a market town? Why?
18. **Analyzing Causes and Effects** (a) How did a territorial dispute cause Argentina to engage in war in the 1980s? (b) What were the long-term effects of that war?
19. **Sequencing** Make a time line that identifies the major political changes that have occurred in southern South America since the 1940s.

---

produce out of a remote area may be difficult.
17. (a) Market towns allow for "vertical trade," in which people from various elevations can bring crops that they have grown or other items to trade for crops or other items that they need. **(b)** Answers may vary, but students should recognize that an important aspect of an ideal market town would be its accessibility to both coastal fishermen and farmers who come down from the Andean highlands.

18. (a) Argentina fought with Great Britain over the Falkland Islands off Argentina's southern Atlantic coast. **(b)** After losing the war, the Argentine military agreed to allow open elections.
19. Check students' time lines for accuracy. You may wish to have students work together on time lines.

Applying Skills

Comparing and Contrasting Data Refer to the bar graph on page 277 to answer these questions:

20. (a) In comparison to men, do women earn more in Kenya or in France? **(b)** Do women in Brazil have a good chance of assuming leading roles in government? Explain.

21. If a woman wanted to run for a government position, in which four countries would she probably have the greatest chance of success? Explain.

Reading a Chart Study the chart below, and answer the following questions:

22. In which country is life expectancy the longest?

23. Which set of statistics in the chart could be a factor that contributes to the infant mortality rate? Explain.

South America and the United States
Health Care Data

Country	Infant Mortality Rate (per 1,000 births)	Life Expectancy (years)	Population per Physician
Argentina	19	74.5	373
Bolivia	64	60.9	2,348
Brazil	37	64.4	705
Chile	10	75.2	938
Colombia	25	70.1	1,154
Ecuador	32	71.8	652
Guyana	49	62.3	8,946
Paraguay	57	72.2	3,583
Peru	43	70.0	969
Suriname	27	70.6	1,279
Uruguay	14	75.5	312
Venezuela	28	72.7	639
United States	6	76.1	400

Test Preparation

Read the question and choose the best answer.

24. One reason why most Chilean people live in the Central Valley is that —

A the soil there is fertile

B the barren Atacama Desert is there

C summer lasts all year there

D the Central Valley is close to the Andes

Activities

USING THE REGIONAL ATLAS

Review Chapter 13 and study the photographs in the Regional Atlas for Latin America. Then, make a two-column chart to show human-environment interaction in South America. In one column, list ways in which people change the environment. In the other column, list ways in which the natural environment affects people.

MENTAL MAPPING

Review a map of South America. On a separate piece of paper, draw a sketch map of South America from memory. Label the following places on your map:

- Andes
- Venezuela
- Colombia
- Río de la Plata
- Atacama Desert
- Peru
- Argentina
- Patagonia
- Uruguay
- Chile

Take It to the NET

Review what you learned about El Niño in the Regional Atlas for Latin America. Then, do research on the Internet to learn more about El Niño's effects on countries along the western coast of South America. Write a news report on the topic. Visit the World Geography section of **www.phschool.com** for help in completing this activity.

Applying Skills

20. (a) Kenya **(b)** Women in Brazil have limited opportunities to assume roles in government. The graph shows that women hold only about 17 percent of government positions in Brazil.

21. United States, Costa Rica, Philippines, Australia; these countries have the highest percentages of women in government positions.

22. United States

23. Population per physician; if there are not enough physicians, women are less likely to have good prenatal care, and their babies are more at risk.

Test Preparation
24. A

Activities

Using the Regional Atlas
Check students' charts for accuracy. Check that students' charts reflect an understanding of human-environment interaction in South America.

Mental Mapping
Review students' maps for relative and absolute location.

Take It to the Net
Students' work should reflect sound research. Check that their articles accurately describe El Niño's effects on the western coast of South America.

MENTAL MAPPING

Games for Review See pages 58–63 of the Simulations, Games, and Lab Activities booklet for games to review place names.

Chapter Map Test Students should use the completed outline maps and the Unit 3 Checklist in their Atlas Portfolios to prepare for the Chapter 13 Map Test.

Unit Map Test To prepare for the Unit 3 Map Test, students will need to study the location of the place names on the Unit 3 Checklist.

Alternative Assessment

Final Evaluation

Writing Assignment Use the Writing Assignment Evaluation Form on page 7 of the Alternative Assessment booklet in the Prentice Hall Assessment System to evaluate students' papers. Either teachers or students can complete the forms to indicate which level of work was achieved for each of the criteria. The evaluation should include specific examples and comments.

Use this sample exam to help your students prepare for standardized tests.

You might want to remind your students of the following:

Tips for Test Taking

1. Read the directions carefully.

2. Read each question carefully.

3. For multiple choice questions, try to answer the question before you look at the choices. Read all the choices. Then, eliminate those that are absolutely incorrect.

4. For short answer questions, be sure to answer the question completely if there is more than one part.

5. Answer the easy questions first. Then, go back to the ones that will take more time.

6. Pace yourself. Be sure to set aside enough time for the writing questions.

Write answers on a separate sheet of paper.

Multiple Choice

1 How have tectonic plate boundaries affected physical characteristics in Latin America?

A Plate movement created the Andes Mountains along the west coast of South America.

B Plate spreading increases the size of South America by 5 percent every 100 years.

C Many volcanoes lie along South America's east coast.

D Plate movement causes the Amazon Basin to sink, lowering the average elevation of the region.

2 In Mexico City, physical processes such as inversion and human activities such as reliance on cars and trucks contribute to —

A unequal distribution of income

B erosion

C overcrowding

D air pollution

3 Damage from earthquakes is greatest near the epicenter, which is the point on the surface —

A directly above the focus

B where a tsunami begins

C at which a landslide is triggered

D at which an avalanche is triggered

Use the chart and your knowledge of social studies to answer the following question.

Population, Wealth, and Literacy for Four Countries				
	Costa Rica	Cuba	Honduras	Panama
Population	3,300,000	11,200,000	5,500,000	2,600,000
Infant Mortality Rate (per 1,000 births)	13.7	9.4	50	28
Per Capita GNP	$2,160	$1,250	$580	$2,580
Literacy Rate	93%	96%	73%	88%

4 In which of these countries would a newborn child have the best chance of surviving?

A Costa Rica

B Cuba

C Honduras

D Panama

5 Why was Brazil's capital moved from Rio de Janeiro to Brasília in the mid-1950s?

A Brasília's climate is more appealing than that of Rio de Janeiro.

B Many people had already moved to Brasília in search of better job opportunities.

C The government wanted to draw people away from the coastal cities and develop the interior of the country.

D The government wanted the capital to be in a city with a port.

PRENTICE HALL
ASSESSMENT SYSTEM

Diagnose and Prescribe
- Profile student skills with Diagnostic Tests A&B.
- Address student needs with program materials identified in the test.

Review and Reteach
- Provide cumulative content review with the Review Book.

Practice and Assess
- Build test-taking skills with Test-Taking Strategies on Transparencies.

Use the map <u>and</u> your knowledge of social studies to answer the following question.

Brazil: Population Density

Per sq. km	Per sq. mi.
Under 1	Under 2
1–25	2–60
25–50	60–125
50–100	125–250
Over 100	Over 250

Cities
☐ Over 10,000,000
⊡ 5,000,000–10,000,000
○ 2,000,000–5,000,000
⊙ 1,000,000–2,000,000

6 What is the overall pattern of population density in Brazil?

A Density is greatest in cities on the Atlantic coast and in settlements along the Amazon River.

B Density is greatest in the northwestern region of the country, near tributaries of the Amazon River.

C Density is greatest in or around Brasília.

D Density is greatest in the Amazon Basin.

7 How have climate zones affected trade in the Andes?

A Many people prefer to work in the mining industry, which is less affected by climate.

B People trade items from different latitudes and longitudes.

C Andean Indians have, over centuries, developed larger hearts and lungs for living in thin air.

D Many people grow crops suited to their climate zone and rely on "vertical trade."

Use the quotation <u>and</u> your knowledge of social studies to answer the following question.

> Something I'm proud of is that I became good friends with the children of the smallholders and peasants. With them I shared my infancy, my playthings, my house and my food. From that time I began to understand our country's painful inequalities.
>
> –Vicente Fox, President of Mexico, quoted in *nytimes.com*, July 4, 2000

8 Based on the quotation, which statement best explains Vicente Fox's view on social conditions in Mexico?

A Poor farmers have the richest land in Mexico.

B Social equality is widespread throughout all of Mexico.

C Life has been difficult for lower-class people in Mexico.

D Peasants have the most power in Mexican society.

Writing Practice

9 **(a)** How have *maquiladoras* affected the Mexican economy? **(b)** What concerns have some people raised about *maquiladoras?*

10 How has migration affected the economies of Caribbean nations?

11 What consequences do you predict for continuing urbanization in Brazil?

12 Why is cattle ranching a major economic activity in Argentina but not in Peru?

Test Preparation Answers

Multiple Choice

1 A

2 D

3 A

4 B

5 C

6 A

7 D

8 C

Writing Practice

9 **(a)** *Maquiladoras* have provided employment for many people and brought new industries to the United States-Mexican border. **(b)** People have raised concerns about low pay, tedious tasks, health issues, and environmental damage.

10 Migration has brought income to Caribbean nations as people travel in search of work and send money home. As a result, some people remaining in these nations have been able to purchase more luxury goods and increase their standard of living.

11 Answers will vary. Students may predict an increase in poverty and the growth of *favelas*.

12 The grassy plains of Argentina's pampas are well suited to cattle ranching. Much of Peru is too mountainous.

Introducing

UNIT

....

4

......

pp. 286–369

estern
Europe

Activating Prior Knowledge

Have students share what countries come to mind when they think of Western Europe. Tell students to study the map on this page. Ask: **How does Western Europe's size compare with other regions of the world?** (It is relatively small.)

Photo Study

Paris, France

The first inhabitants of Paris settled on an island between two tributaries of the Seine River. Fishing and shipping brought prosperity to early Paris. Caesar took France for Rome in 52 B.C. The Romans called Paris *Lutetia* ("Midwater-Dwelling"), a name that highlights the city's most important asset—its proximity to the Seine. In the centuries that followed, Paris became a center for commerce, government, culture, and learning because the Seine provided a link to international markets and ideas. **Drawing Conclusions** Ask students: **Why were settlers who chose a spot because of its advantages for trade more interested in its relative location than its absolute location?** (To be in a good spot for trading, a settlement has to be located well in relation to other locations.)

Be sure to check out this month's online forum with a Master Teacher to join in an exchange of teaching ideas. **www.phschool.com**

Locating the Region

The continent of Europe is sometimes called "a peninsula of peninsulas" because a number of smaller peninsulas jut out to the north, west, and south. In the north is the Scandinavian Peninsula. On the southwest is the Iberian Peninsula, made up of Spain and Portugal. Stretching into the Mediterranean Sea is the Italian peninsula. It takes the shape of a boot with a "heel" pointing to Greece—which forms yet another peninsula.

Robinson Projection

RESOURCE DIRECTORY

Teaching Resources

Unit 4
• Geography and World Literature, The Eclipse, p. 60

Mental Mapping booklet
• Unit 4 Checklist, p. 52
• Unit 4 Map Test, p. 66

Simulations, Games, and Lab Activities
• Where on Earth? Games, pp. 70–71

Global Environmental Posters

Technology

TeacherExpress™ CD-ROM
World Geography: Building a Global Perspective Teaching Resources on CD-ROM offers lesson planning flexibility, test-generation capability, and resource manageability.

Prentice Hall Presentation Pro CD-ROM
This CD-ROM allows you to create custom lessons for instruction or review for every chapter.

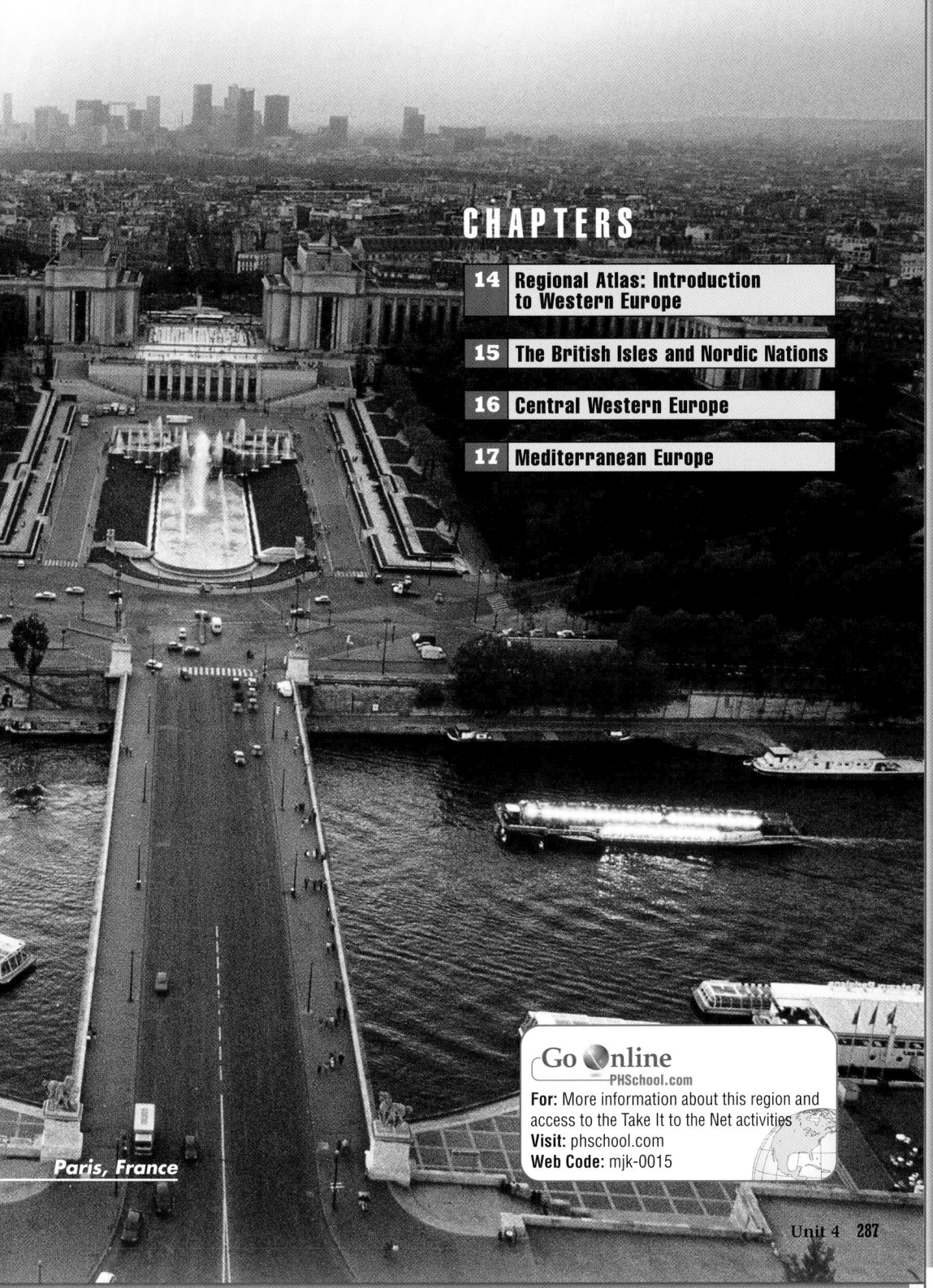

CHAPTERS

Go Online
PHSchool.com
For: More information about this region and access to the Take It to the Net activities
Visit: phschool.com
Web Code: mjk-0015

Paris, France

Unit 4 **287**

Unit 4 **287**

Resource Manager

	CORE INSTRUCTION	READING/SKILLS
Chapter-Level Resources	**Teaching Resources** **Unit 4/Ch. 14** • Regional Atlas Study Guide, p. 2 **Mental Mapping booklet** • Unit 4 Checklist, p. 52 **Simulations, Games, and Lab Activities** • Place Location Review Games, pp. 58–63 **TeacherExpress™ CD-ROM**, Ch. 14 **Companion Web site,** **www.phschool.com** • eTeach	**Teaching Resources** **Unit 4/Ch. 14** • Regional Atlas Review, p. 3 **Guide to the Essentials (English/Spanish)** • Chapter 14 Summary **Spanish Resources** • Regional Atlas Review, p. 33 **Guided Reading Audiotapes (English/Spanish)**, Ch. 14 **Section Reading Support Transparencies**, Ch. 14 **Book on CD**, Ch. 14 **Social Studies Skills Tutor CD-ROM**
Historical Overview Describe significant events and developments in the history of Western Europe.	**Teaching Resources** **Mental Mapping booklet** • Outline Map 14A, p. 53 **Prentice Hall Presentation Pro CD-ROM**, Ch. 14	**Teaching Resources** **Social Studies Skills Handbook** • Reading a Political Map, p. 19
Physical Characteristics Identify major physical characteristics of Western Europe.	**Teaching Resources** **Mental Mapping booklet** • Outline Map 14B, p. 54 **Prentice Hall Presentation Pro CD-ROM**, Ch. 14	**Teaching Resources** **Social Studies Skills Handbook** • Elevation on a Map, p. 20 • Four Types of Landforms, p. 21 • Relief on a Map, p. 22
Climates Compare climate regions in Western Europe.	**Prentice Hall Presentation Pro CD-ROM**, Ch. 14	**Teaching Resources** **Social Studies Skills Handbook** • Reading a Climate Map, p. 26 • Reading an Ocean Currents Map, p. 37 • Reading a Wind Map, p. 38
Ecosystems Describe characteristics of major ecosystems in Western Europe.	**Teaching Resources** **Creative Teaching Activities** • Endangered Wildlife in Western Europe, p. 16 **Prentice Hall Presentation Pro CD-ROM**, Ch. 14	**Teaching Resources** **Social Studies Skills Handbook** • Reading a Natural Vegetation Map, p. 25
People and Cultures Discuss elements of culture in Western Europe.	**Prentice Hall Presentation Pro CD-ROM**, Ch. 14	**Teaching Resources** **Social Studies Skills Handbook** • Using the Map Scale, p. 5 • Reading a Population Density Map, p. 31
Economics, Technology, and Environment Identify how the economy, technology, and the environment interact in Western Europe.	**Prentice Hall Presentation Pro CD-ROM**, Ch. 14	**Teaching Resources** **Social Studies Skills Handbook** • Reading an Economic Activity Map, p. 27 • Reading a Natural Resources Map, p. 34
Database • Define compulsory education. • Compare the educational systems of select Western European countries and the United States.	**Teaching Resources** **Unit 4/Ch. 14** • Regional Atlas Database Skills, p. 4 **Prentice Hall Presentation Pro CD-ROM**, Ch. 14	**Teaching Resources** **Unit 4/Ch. 14** • Regional Atlas Database Skills, p. 4 **Social Studies Skills Handbook** • Reading a Table, p. 62

ENRICHMENT/HONORS/PREAP

Teaching Resources

Mental Mapping booklet
- Atlas Activity, p. 55

Social Studies Skills Handbook
- Study and Research Skills, pp. 94–108

World Geography Map and Photo Transparencies
- Western Europe: Maps and Photos

World Geography Videos
- Regional Atlas: Western Europe, Tape 2

Companion Web site, www.phschool.com
- Chapter 14 Activities

World Geography Map and Photo Transparencies
- Western Europe: Political

World Geography Map and Photo Transparencies
- Western Europe: Physical

World Geography Map and Photo Transparencies
- World Climate Zones

World Geography Map and Photo Transparencies
- Western Europe: Natural Hazards

World Geography Map and Photo Transparencies
- Western Europe: Population Density

World Geography Map and Photo Transparencies
- Western Europe: Economic Activities

World Geography Map and Photo Transparencies
- Per Capita GDP: Literacy Rate

ASSESSMENT

PRENTICE HALL
ASSESSMENT SYSTEM

Core Assessment
- ExamView Test Bank booklet, Ch. 14
- ExamView Test Bank CD-ROM, Ch. 14

Standardized Test Preparation

Diagnose and Prescribe
- Diagnostic Tests for High School Social Studies Skills

Review and Reteach
- Review Book for World Geography, pp. 9–10

Practice and Assess
- Test-taking Strategies With Transparencies for High School

  Test-taking Strategy Poster
- Alternative Assessment booklet
- Test Prep Book for World Geography

Teaching Resources

Unit 4/Ch. 14
- Test Forms A and B, pp. 5–10

Guide to the Essentials (English/Spanish)
- Chapter 14 Test

Mental Mapping booklet
- Chapter 14 Map Test, p. 56

Companion Web site, www.phschool.com
- Chapter 14 Self-Test

CUSTOMIZE FOR INDIVIDUAL NEEDS

Less Proficient Readers
- Guide to the Essentials (English), Ch. 14
- Guided Reading Audiotapes (English), Ch. 14
- Section Reading Support Transparencies, Ch. 14
- Book on CD, Ch. 14

Students Acquiring English/ESL
- Guide to the Essentials (English/Spanish), Ch. 14
- Guided Reading Audiotapes (English/Spanish), Ch. 14
- Section Reading Support Transparencies, Ch. 14
- Book on CD, Ch. 14
- Teacher's Edition, Customize for . . . , p. 291

Less Proficient Writers
- Social Studies Skills Handbook, p. 90
- Alternative Assessment, Writing Assignment Rubric, p. 6

CHAPTER **14**

Introduction to WESTERN EUROPE

Objectives
Upon completion of the Regional Atlas, students should be able to:
◆ describe significant events and developments in the history of Western Europe;
◆ identify major physical characteristics of Western Europe;
◆ compare climate regions in Western Europe;
◆ describe characteristics of major ecosystems in Western Europe;
◆ discuss elements of culture in Western Europe;
◆ identify how the economy, technology, and the environment interact in Western Europe.

National Geography Standards
The following National Geography Standards are highlighted in this Regional Atlas: 1, 3, 4, 5, 7, 8, 9, 10, 11, 13, 14, 15, 16, 17

Bellringer
Tell students to choose a country in Western Europe and then to write down three things that come to mind when they think of that country.

Answers to Assessment
1. (a) cultural diffusion, p. 288
(b) Renaissance, p. 288 **(c)** Industrial Revolution, p. 288

2. Unlike other countries in Western Europe, the five main colonial powers all had coastlines on the Atlantic Ocean.

3. Their access to major bodies of water made sea travel and overseas conquests possible.

Historical Overview

By 35,000 B.C., people occupied most of Western Europe. Farming developed in Southwest Asia and began to spread into Western Europe by about 5400 B.C. Farming spread by means of migration and a process of **cultural diffusion,** in which peoples adopt the practices of their neighbors. Over the centuries, forests vanished as farmers cleared and cultivated land.

Ancient Civilizations Meanwhile, cities, powerful states, and writing developed in the Middle East and spread to ancient Greece. The ancient Greeks made important advances in art and science. They founded colonies along the Mediterranean coasts of Spain, France, and Italy, where they influenced new civilizations. The most important of these was Rome, which conquered an empire that stretched from England to Southwest Asia. Germanic tribes conquered the western Roman Empire by A.D. 500, and Europe passed through centuries of poverty, disease, political upheaval, and warfare.

Rebirth and Expansion By about 1400, Western Europeans began to rediscover the knowledge of the ancient Greeks and Romans. This contributed to new advances in science and technology during a period known as the **Renaissance,** meaning "rebirth." Powerful new states developed in England, France, Spain, Portugal, and the Netherlands. Using new technologies of sea travel and warfare, these new nations were able to explore and establish colonies in other parts of the world, including

Africa, Asia, and the Americas. These overseas colonies produced great riches for Western European merchants and kings. As nations grew stronger, many people questioned the power and practices of the Roman Catholic Church. The Protestant Reformation led to the formation of other churches, ending religious unity in Europe.

Industrialization and Democracy During the 1700s, new technological advances resulted in machines powered by water, steam, and fuel. Machine power could produce more goods than human power. The growing use of machines, known as the **Industrial Revolution,** began first in England and spread to the rest of Western Europe during the 1800s. Around the same time, increasing wealth and education encouraged citizens of Western European nations to demand more rights. At first, only wealthy men were allowed to vote in elections. By the mid-1900s, however, workers and women had won the right to vote across Western Europe.

Conflict and Cooperation After 1900, conflicts among the powerful nations of Western Europe caused two deadly world wars. In World War II, German Nazis killed millions of civilians, including six million Jews. After World War II, most of Western Europe and Eastern Europe were caught up in a tense rivalry called the Cold War, which lasted until 1989. Meanwhile, the nations of Western Europe pursued greater political and economic cooperation by forming organizations such as the European Union.

ASSESSMENT

1. **Key Terms** Define **(a)** cultural diffusion, **(b)** Renaissance, **(c)** Industrial Revolution.

2. **Map Skills** **Location** How does the location of the five main colonial powers differ from the location of other countries in Western Europe?

3. **Critical Thinking** **Developing a Hypothesis** How might the location of these nations be connected to their conquest of overseas empires?

REGIONAL ATLAS

Western Europe: POLITICAL

(Map of Western Europe showing countries, capitals, and cities)

- 30°W, 20°W, 10°W, 0°, 10°E, 20°E, 30°E, 40°E, 50°E
- 80°N, 70°N, 60°N, 50°N, 40°N

ARCTIC OCEAN

Jan Mayen (Nor.)

Reykjavik ⊛ ICELAND

Arctic Circle

Prime Meridian

0   250   500 mi
0   250   500 km

Faeroe Is. (Den.)

Shetland Is. (U.K.)

FINLAND

Gulf of Bothnia

SWEDEN

NORWAY   Helsinki ⊛

Oslo ⊛   Stockholm ⊛

ATLANTIC OCEAN

North Sea

Baltic Sea

UNITED KINGDOM

IRELAND
Dublin ⊛   • Manchester

DENMARK   Copenhagen ⊛

NETHERLANDS
The Hague ⊛ ⊛ Amsterdam   Berlin ⊛

London ⊛   Cologne •

English Channel   Brussels ⊛   GERMANY
BELGIUM   • Bonn
• Frankfurt

LUXEMBOURG ⊛ Luxembourg

⊛ Paris

Donube R.

Munich •   ⊛ Vienna
LIECHTENSTEIN

Bay of Biscay

FRANCE   ⊛ Bern   AUSTRIA
SWITZERLAND

• Milan

Black Sea

SAN MARINO

Marseille •

MONACO

PORTUGAL   ANDORRA   Corsica   ITALY
• Madrid   • Barcelona   VATICAN   ⊛ Rome
CITY

Lisbon ⊛   SPAIN   Sardinia   • Naples

GREECE   ASIA

Balearic Is.   Tyrrhenian Sea   Ionian Sea   ⊛ Athens

Strait of Gibraltar   Gibraltar (U.K.)

Mediterranean Sea   Sicily

MALTA   Crete

AFRICA

KEY

—— National boundary
⊛ National capital
• Other city

Lambert Azimuthal Equal-Area Projection

Chapter 14 ▪ Regional Atlas: Western Europe **289**

MENTAL MAPPING

Making a Political Map Study this political map and then draw your own sketch map of Western Europe. Label the countries and major cities of the region. Use various colors to outline and shade each country.

TEACHING TIP
From A Master Teacher

Diversity in Western Europe Western Europe is a region with enormous diversity. Multiple culture groups exist, each with its own languages, beliefs, institutions, and technologies, within relatively short distances. As students are studying Western Europe, ask them to consider how these differences might contribute to tensions between the forces encouraging large-scale, region-wide integration (such as the European Union) and the forces seeking to recognize smaller-scale, local identities.

LESSON PLAN

1. Focus Have students brainstorm a list of landforms in their state. Point out that some of these landforms exist in Western Europe.

2. Instruct Ask students to complete the Mental Mapping activities and the photo and assessment questions in each section of the Regional Atlas. Go over the answers as a class.

3. Close/Reteach Ask students what factors divide Western Europe and what factors unite it. Have them write a paragraph explaining why Western Europe should or should not be considered a single region.

Map Study Extension
Use the question below to develop an additional geographic theme.

Place A few of the nations in Western Europe are actually large islands. Ask: **Which is the largest Western European island nation?** (United Kingdom)

Unit Checklist Distribute the Unit 4 Checklist on page 52 of the Mental Mapping booklet in the Teaching Resources. This list includes all the place names students should learn in this unit. Ask students to store the Unit Checklist and maps in their Atlas Portfolios for use throughout the unit.

Making a Political Map Students can complete the mapping activity on this page either by sketching their own maps or by coloring and labeling the Chapter 14A Outline Map on page 53 of the Mental Mapping booklet. Ask students to label all of the countries and major cities listed in the Unit 4 Checklist.

Alternative Assessment

Introduce the Activity

Creating Maps You may wish to distribute the Map Rubric found on page 14 of the Alternative Assessment booklet in the Prentice Hall Assessment System.

WESTERN EUROPE
Physical Characteristics

Western Europe stretches from the Scandinavian Peninsula in the north to the Iberian Peninsula in the south. It is a relatively small region, yet it contains a great variety of physical features. The **summits,** or highest points, of the Alps contrast with the flat North European Plain. Oceans and seas surround much of Western Europe, and rivers wind their way through fertile valleys.

Coastal Erosion
Nearly every European nation has a coastline. Where waves hit the shore, the process of erosion chips away at stone and earth. In the British Isles, the Orkney Islands are marked by sea stacks like the one shown here. **PHYSICAL PROCESSES** *Over time, what may happen to this sea stack?*

North European Plain
The North European Plain stretches eastward from France to Northern Eurasia. Rivers such as the Rhine (RYN), shown here, have long provided travelers and merchants with access to interior lands. **ECONOMIC ACTIVITIES** *How does this photograph suggest that the North European Plain is an important agricultural region?*

High Mountains
The Alps, a mountain range separating Italy from countries to the north, run through Austria, Italy, Switzerland, Germany, and France. The highest peaks are snow-covered throughout the year. **PHYSICAL CHARACTERISTICS** *Name three other mountain ranges in Europe.*

ASSESSMENT

1. **Key Term** Define summit.

2. **Map Skills** **Location** Why is Finland's access to the Atlantic Ocean limited, in spite of its coastline?

3. **Critical Thinking** **Defending a Position** Agree or disagree with the following statement: Western Europe is a peninsula of peninsulas. Explain your position.

REGIONAL ATLAS

Western Europe: PHYSICAL

[Map of Western Europe — Physical]

Jan Mayen
ARCTIC OCEAN
Arctic Circle
Reykjavik · ICELAND
0   250   500 mi
0   250   500 km
Norwegian Sea
KJÖLEN MTS. LAPLAND
SCANDINAVIAN PENINSULA
·Oulu
FINLAND
Faeroe Is.
Prime Meridian
Gulf of Bothnia
Shetland Is.
NORWAY   SWEDEN
Oslo
Helsinki·
Gulf of Finland
Hebrides
·Stockholm
Skagerrak
North Sea
DENMARK
Baltic Sea
Galway Bay
British Isles
Dublin·
IRELAND   UNITED KINGDOM
NETHERLANDS
Amsterdam·
London·
Thames
English Channel
BELGIUM
LUXEMBOURG
·Paris
NORTH EUROPEAN PLAIN
·Berlin
Elbe R.
GERMANY
Black Forest
Rhine R.
Seine R.
Loire R.
ATLANTIC OCEAN
Bay of Biscay
FRANCE
Mont Blanc 15,771 ft. (4,807 m)
Danube R.
LIECHTENSTEIN
·S   AUSTRIA
SWITZERLAND
Vienna
·Rome
Po R.
ITALY
APENNINES
SAN MARINO
MONACO
Adriatic Sea
Garonne R.
MASSIF CENTRAL
PYRENEES
Corsica
VATICAN CITY
Black Sea
Douro R.
Ebro R.
ANDORRA
PORTUGAL
Tagus
MESETA
·Madrid
Cabo da Roca
·Lisbon   SPAIN
IBERIAN PENINSULA
Guadalquivir R.
SIERRA NEVADA   ·Cartagena
Strait of Gibraltar
AFRICA
Sardinia
Mt. Vesuvius 4,203 ft. (1,281 m)
Balearic Is.
Tyrrhenian Sea
Mediterranean Sea
Sicily
Mt. Etna 10,902 ft. (3,323 m)
MALTA
GREECE
Aegean Sea
PINDUS MTS.
·Athens
Ionian Sea
PELOPONNESE
Crete
ASIA

KEY
Elevation
Feet		Meters
14,000		4,270
7,000		2,135
1,500		457
700		213
(sea level) 0		0 (sea level)

· Major city
▲ Mountain
△ Volcano
Lambert Azimuthal Equal-Area Projection

Making a Physical Map Study this physical map and then draw your own sketch map of Western Europe. Label the major physical features, including rivers and other bodies of water.

Chapter 14 ▪ Regional Atlas: Western Europe   **291**

MENTAL MAPPING

Mapping Physical Features
Students can complete the mapping activity on this page either by adding labels to the political maps they have already completed or by coloring and labeling the Chapter 14B Outline Map on page 54 of the Mental Mapping booklet. Ask students to label all the bodies of water and landforms listed under Part II in the Unit 4 Checklist.

BACKGROUND

Word Origin

Peninsula The word *peninsula* has two Latin roots: *paene,* meaning "almost"; and *insula,* meaning "island." Thus, a peninsula is "almost an island."

ACTIVITY

Reteach

Making Charts Have each student make a chart listing the peninsulas, mountains, rivers, and plains of Western Europe. (Visual/Spatial)

CUSTOMIZE FOR...

Students Acquiring English/ESL
Erosion Instruct students to create two sketches. The first should show a sea stack or coastline in Western Europe, and the second should portray the same scene affected by erosion. Ask students to label their sketches or add a brief caption describing what is being illustrated.

WESTERN EUROPE
Climates

Climates in Western Europe tend to be milder than those of other world regions that are located at the same latitudes. These temperate climates are caused by the relative locations of oceans and land—no point in Western Europe is more than 300 miles (483 km) from the sea. Mountains also affect Western Europe's climates. The Alps in the south and the mountains along the Scandinavian Peninsula create drier climates by blocking the winds that ride on ocean currents.

Ocean Currents and Wind Patterns

The North Atlantic Drift carries tropical waters toward Europe. The winds that blow across this warm current are the **prevailing westerlies**—the constant flow of air from west to east in the temperate zones of the earth. On the west coasts of Scotland and Ireland, the tropical air permits the growth of palm trees in places that are normally cool. **PHYSICAL PROCESSES** *What current carries cold water away from Europe?*

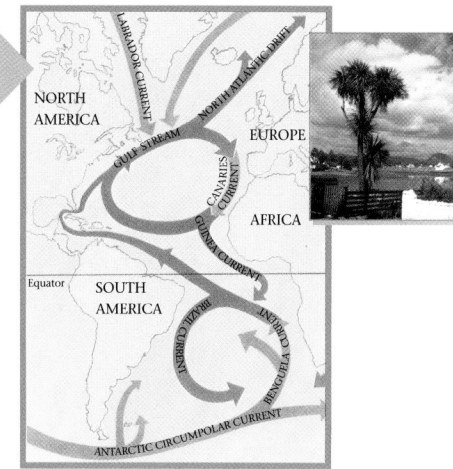

Mediterranean Climate

The Mediterranean climate of Andalusia, Spain, encourages olive cultivation. Warm summers and cool winters characterize this climate region. **CLIMATES** *Which country has a Mediterranean climate even though it is not on the Mediterranean?*

Subarctic Climate

Mountains along the Scandinavian Peninsula block winds from the Atlantic. The result is a very dry, cold, subarctic climate for much of the area. **PHYSICAL CHARACTERISTICS** *How does the distribution of climate zones in Scandinavia suggest the location of the mountains?*

ASSESSMENT

1. **Key Term** Define prevailing westerlies.

2. **Map Skills** **Regions** Which climate regions dominate Western Europe?

3. **Critical Thinking** **Drawing Conclusions** Why does Western Europe experience less extreme climate variation than other parts of the world at similar northern latitudes?

REGIONAL ATLAS

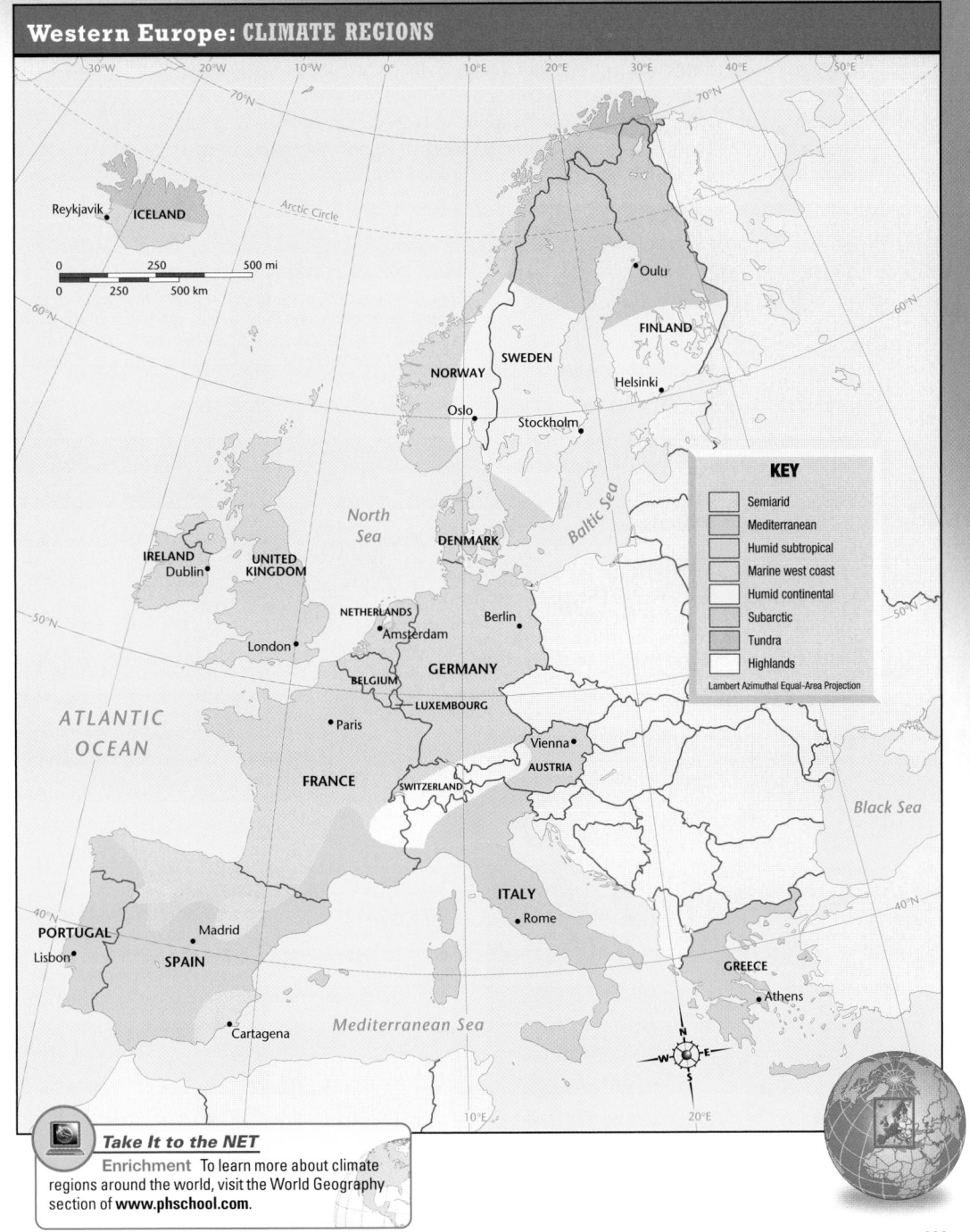

Western Europe: CLIMATE REGIONS

KEY

- Semiarid
- Mediterranean
- Humid subtropical
- Marine west coast
- Humid continental
- Subarctic
- Tundra
- Highlands

Lambert Azimuthal Equal-Area Projection

Take It to the NET
Enrichment To learn more about climate regions around the world, visit the World Geography section of **www.phschool.com**.

Chapter 14 ▪ Regional Atlas: Western Europe **293**

BACKGROUND

The Physical World

Fjords of Scandinavia Every year, tourists visit the coast of Norway in Scandinavia to see *fjords*—long, narrow passages of water that lead inland from the ocean and are surrounded by steep slopes or cliffs. Norway's Sognafjorden is its longest, at 127 miles (180 km).

ACTIVITY

Critical Thinking

Mountains and Climate Refer students to the diagram on the previous page that illustrates how the North Atlantic Drift and prevailing westerlies affect the climate of Western Europe. Then, use the following questions to help students analyze how mountains affect climate: **Why does southern Europe receive little rain in the summer?** (Southern mountains block moist air from the Atlantic.) **Why does rain fall on the North European Plain throughout the year?** (No mountains block the moist air carried by the prevailing westerlies.)

ACTIVITY

Group Work

Activity: Making climate comparisons

Purpose: Assign one of the following cities to each group: London, Paris, Munich, Helsinki, Rome. Then have each group identify a North American city that shares the same latitude. Encourage groups to hypothesize whether the climates of the two cities are similar or different. Remind students to think about how geographic features such as mountains or bodies of water influence climate. Have each group research its cities' climates to check its hypotheses.

Roles: Researchers and a group leader

Result: Each leader should first explain the group's original hypothesis and reasoning to the class and then explain how the group's research supported or disproved the hypothesis.

294 Chapter 14

Map Study Extension
Use the questions below to develop additional geographic themes.

1. Human-Environment Interaction Although many of Western Europe's forests have been cleared by humans, some forested areas remain. Ask: **Where are the largest remaining areas of coniferous forests in Western Europe?** (Sweden and Finland)

2. Place Tundra supports little vegetation other than grasses and mosses. Ask: **What European island consists entirely of tundra vegetation?** (Iceland)

Answers to Assessment
1. mostly mid-latitude deciduous forests and some mixed forests

2. (a) Vegetation and animal life are sparse above the tree line.
(b) Possible answer: Humans can alter a region's natural ecosystem by cutting and clearing forests and grasslands to make room for farms and buildings.

Answers to Photo Captions

Reforestation Animal populations would decrease without the food and shelter the forests provide.

Elevation and Ecosystems The bottom of the valley is used for farmland.

Wetlands National parks and preserves provide a protected sanctuary for wildlife and natural habitats.

WESTERN EUROPE
Ecosystems

As in other industrialized regions of the world, Western Europe's ecosystem has been altered by humans. Much of the original forests and grasslands were cut and cleared long ago to build farms, towns, and cities. Large wild animals, such as European bison, as well as many smaller animals that once roamed freely over Europe have lost their habitats. Many can now only be found in large preserves or in zoos. Yet, Western Europe's ecosystems today support a variety of wildlife, including birds, bears, foxes, badgers, and deer.

Reforestation
Over the centuries, most of Europe's forests vanished as people cleared the land. Today, new growth is taking place in a few protected forests such as the one shown here. **ECOSYSTEMS** *How might the disappearance of forests affect animal life?*

Ski resorts are built in the snowy peaks.

Conifer trees on higher slopes are cleared for farming.

The lower slopes are used as meadowland.

Vines and crops are in the valley bottom.

Elevation and Ecosystems
As this diagram shows, altitude affects the vegetation and animal life of a region. In the Alps, few plants and animals live above the tree line. Below the tree line, grassy meadows support cows, sheep, and other grazing animals. **ECOSYSTEMS** *Describe the ecosystem at the bottom of the valley.*

Wetlands
Wetlands, pine forests, and sand dunes dominate Doñana National Park in southern Spain. The park is a seasonal home to many species of native and migratory birds, including flamingos. **ENVIRONMENTAL CHANGE** *Why do countries set aside lands for national parks and preserves?*

ASSESSMENT

1. **Map Skills** **Place** What type of vegetation is found at 50°N latitude in Western Europe?

2. **Critical Thinking** **Identifying Relationships** (a) How does elevation affect a region's ecosystem? (b) How can human settlement affect a region's ecosystem?

RESOURCE DIRECTORY

Teaching Resources
Creative Teaching Activities, Endangered Wildlife in Western Europe, p. 16
Social Studies Skills Handbook
• Reading a Natural Vegetation Map, p. 25

Technology
World Geography Map and Photo Transparencies
• Western Europe: Maps and Photos

REGIONAL ATLAS

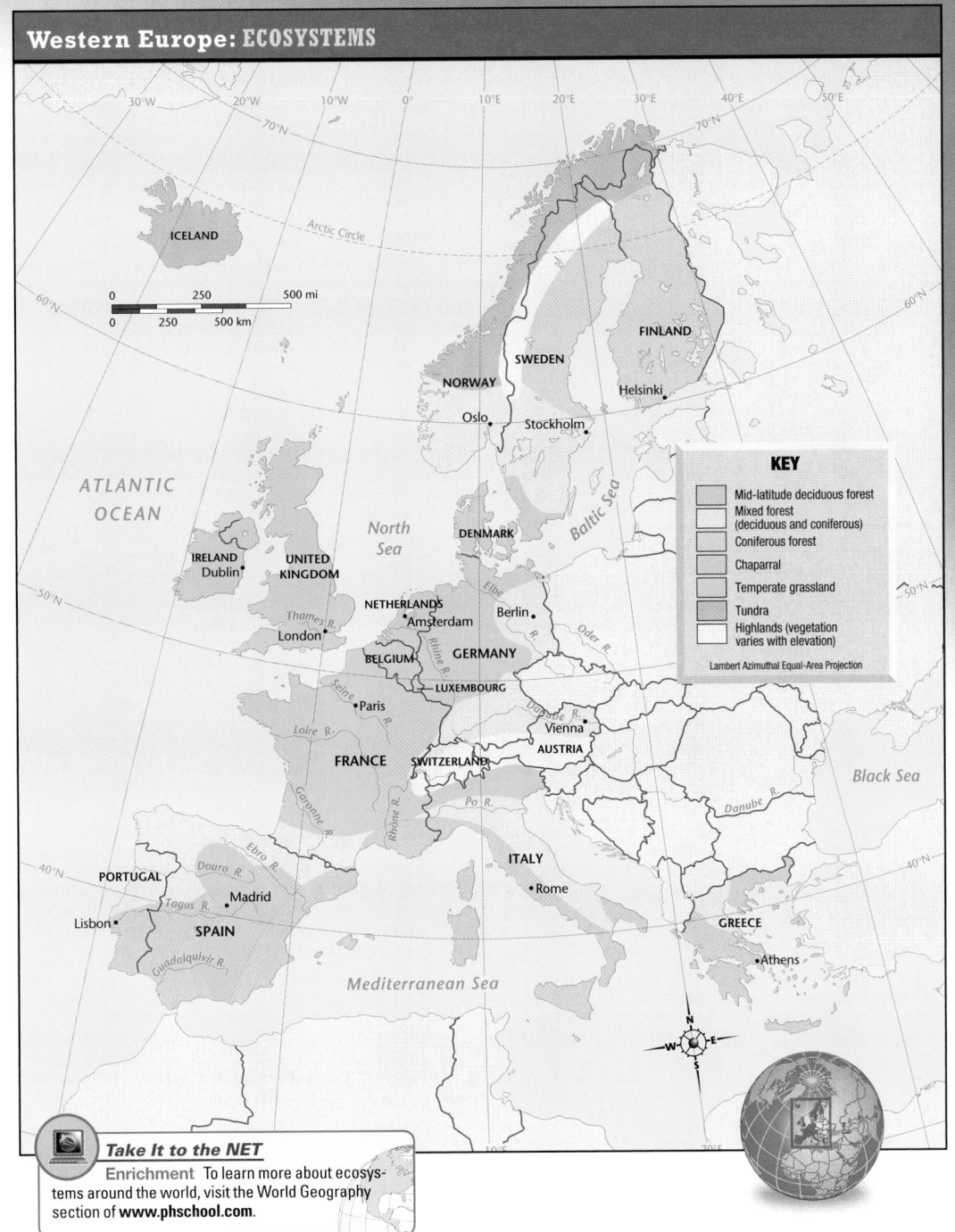

Western Europe: ECOSYSTEMS

KEY

- Mid-latitude deciduous forest
- Mixed forest (deciduous and coniferous)
- Coniferous forest
- Chaparral
- Temperate grassland
- Tundra
- Highlands (vegetation varies with elevation)

Lambert Azimuthal Equal-Area Projection

ICELAND

0   250   500 mi
0   250   500 km

Arctic Circle

FINLAND

SWEDEN

NORWAY

Helsinki

Oslo   Stockholm

ATLANTIC OCEAN

North Sea

Baltic Sea

DENMARK

IRELAND
Dublin

UNITED KINGDOM

NETHERLANDS
Amsterdam

Berlin

Thames R.

London

Elbe R.

Oder R.

BELGIUM

GERMANY

Rhine R.

LUXEMBOURG

Seine

Paris

Loire R.

Danube R.

Vienna

AUSTRIA

FRANCE   SWITZERLAND

Black Sea

Garonne R.

Rhône R.

Po R.

Danube R.

Ebro R.

Douro R.

PORTUGAL

ITALY

Rome

Tagus R.

Madrid

Lisbon

SPAIN

GREECE

Guadalquivir R.

Athens

Mediterranean Sea

Take It to the NET
Enrichment To learn more about ecosystems around the world, visit the World Geography section of **www.phschool.com**.

Chapter 14 ▪ Regional Atlas: Western Europe **295**

Enrichment

Western Europe's Animal Life
Instruct students to use the library and the Internet to find information on the fox, deer, bear, and European bison. Then draw four columns on the board. Label each column with the name of one of the animals. In the columns, have students list ways that each animal relies on its environment for food, shelter, and defense from predators. Then ask: **Why are smaller animals such as the fox, deer, and bear still living in the wild in Western Europe, while much larger animals, such as European bison, are not?** (Possible answer: Smaller animals do not need to eat as much vegetation as larger animals do. Also, smaller animals could still find shelter from hunters in tall grass, thickets, and remaining forests.) (Verbal/Linguistic)

B A C K G R O U N D

Word Origin

Chaparral The word *chaparral* comes from the Spanish word for evergreen oak, *chaparro*, which comes from the Basque word for thicket, *txapar*.

Map Study Extension

Use the questions below to develop additional geographic themes.

1. Location Two areas in Europe are especially densely populated. The first extends from central England into France, across the North European Plain, and into Eastern Europe. Have students compare the population density map on page 297 to the physical map on page 291. Ask: **Where is the other most densely populated area in Western Europe located?** (northern Italy and the coastlines of Italy)

2. Place A few of the languages spoken in Western Europe originated with the Celts, an early people who occupied parts of the region before the Romans arrived. Ask: **In which parts of Western Europe are Celtic languages spoken?** (in western parts of the British Isles and across the English Channel in northwestern France)

Answers to Assessment

1. (a) English, Gaelic, Welsh, and Irish **(b)** English is a Germanic language; Gaelic, Welsh, and Irish are Celtic languages.

2. A minority in the north of Spain speaks Basque, whereas Spanish is spoken throughout the rest of the country.

Western Europe is one of the world's smallest regions, occupying only about 3 percent of the world's landmass. Yet, it is one of the most densely populated regions in the world and is home to many cultures. The population, however, is not evenly distributed. The nations of Scandinavia are lightly populated, whereas the Netherlands is very densely populated.

Viennese Shopping District

The Graben, a busy shopping district in the heart of Vienna, Austria, shows the blend of old and new in European cities. **URBANIZATION** *How are elements of Austria's traditional culture preserved in this urban district?*

Chartres Cathedral

Beginning in the 1100s, architectural developments allowed leaders of the Roman Catholic Church to construct soaring cathedrals such as the one shown here, in Chartres, France. For centuries, cathedrals were the religious, social, and cultural centers of towns and cities across Western Europe. **CULTURES** *How does this photograph illustrate the importance of Christianity in Western European society?*

Migration to Europe

Economic growth has encouraged people to travel to Europe from all over the world in search of employment. The arrows on this map indicate the European nations most affected by migration from various other nations. **MIGRATION** *How would you expect migration to affect European cultures?*

ASSESSMENT

1. **Map Skills Place (a)** What are the major languages spoken in the United Kingdom? **(b)** To what group of languages does each language belong?

2. **Critical Thinking Drawing Conclusions** How does the language map of Western Europe suggest that there may be ethnic conflict in Spain?

Answers to Photo Captions

Viennese Shopping District Possible answer: The traditional architecture of the buildings and the use of horse and carriage help to preserve Austria's culture in this urban district.

Chartres Cathedral The cathedral is centrally located and is significantly larger than all of the other buildings in the town.

Migration to Europe Possible answer: Migration would introduce new traditions, languages, and religions to European cultures.

REGIONAL ATLAS

Western Europe: LANGUAGES

KEY

Indo-European languages
- Romance languages
- Germanic languages
- Slavic languages
- Celtic languages
- Hellenic

Non-Indo-European languages
- Finno-Ugric languages
- Basque

Lambert Azimuthal Equal-Area Projection

0   250   500 mi
0   250   500 km

ATLANTIC OCEAN

Arctic Circle

Icelandic
Faeroese
Gaelic
Irish
English
Welsh
Breton
Basque
Portuguese
Spanish
Catalan
French
Italian
Greek
German
Dutch
Danish
Norwegian
Swedish
Finnish
Lappish

Mediterranean Sea

Western Europe: POPULATION DENSITY

KEY

Persons per sq mi	Persons per sq km
520 and over	200 and over
260–519	100–199
130–259	50–99
25–129	10–49
1–24	1–9
Less than 1	Less than 1

Metropolitan areas
- ■ 5,000,000–9,999,999
- ○ 2,000,000–4,999,999
- ◉ 1,000,000–1,999,999
- • 250,000–999,999

Lambert Azimuthal Equal-Area Projection

0   250   500 mi
0   250   500 km

ICELAND
Norwegian Sea
Arctic Circle
SWEDEN
NORWAY
Oslo
Stockholm
FINLAND
Helsinki
North Sea
Glasgow
Edinburgh
Belfast
Liverpool
IRELAND
Dublin
Manchester
Birmingham
London
UNITED KINGDOM
NETH.
Amsterdam
Antwerp
BELG.
LUX.
Paris
FRANCE
Lyon
Zurich
SWITZ.
LIECHTENSTEIN
Turin
Milan
Genoa
SAN MARINO
Marseille
ANDORRA
Florence
DENMARK
Copenhagen
Hamburg
GERMANY
Berlin
Hannover
Rotterdam
Cologne
Frankfurt
Bonn
Munich
AUSTRIA
Vienna
SPAIN
Madrid
Barcelona
PORTUGAL
Lisbon
Valencia
Naples
Rome
ITALY
GREECE
Athens
ATLANTIC OCEAN
Bay of Biscay
Mediterranean Sea

GET THE FACTS . . .
Go to the Table of Countries at the back of this book for additional population data.

Articles From NATIONAL GEOGRAPHIC

The following article may be used to extend the content in this section.

Range, Peter Ross, and Joanna B. Pinneo, photographer. "Europe Faces an Immigrant Tide." *National Geographic,* Vol. 183, No. 5 (May 1993), pp. 94–126.

Recent immigrants to many Western European countries are often met with resentment and even violence.

Connecting With . . .

History Tell students that cooperation among the nations of Western Europe is a relatively new trend. For hundreds of years, nations used warfare to gain control over territory. In the twentieth century, European power struggles set off two world wars. Both resulted in new political boundaries for the region. Post–World War II settlements created many of Europe's current political boundaries. Have students use historical atlases to compare national boundaries before and after World War I and World War II.

Area Comparison

Using the Table of Countries Ask students to use the Table of Countries beginning on page 742 of their textbooks to compare the land areas and populations of the United States and Western Europe. **Connections: Math** Ask students: **Which region has the greater overall population density— the United States or Western Europe?** (While Western Europe's land area is less than one half that of the United States, its population is nearly 1.5 times greater than the population of the United States. Therefore, Western Europe has a much higher population density. In fact, it is nearly four times as densely populated as the United States.)

Daily Life

English Of the thousands of languages in the world today, English is the most widely used. About 470 million people speak English as their primary language. About 100 million additional people speak English as well as their own language, while an estimated 200 million more understand at least some English.

Map Study Extension

Use the questions below to develop additional geographic themes.

1. Place Rivers drop alluvium, or sediment, as they flow slowly into the sea. Compare the economic activity map on the next page to the physical map on page 291. Ask: **What economic activity takes place around the mouth of the Rhine River?** (commercial farming)

2. Location Oil has brought great economic benefits to some of Western Europe's countries. Ask: **In what sea is much of the region's petroleum found?** (North Sea)

Answers to Assessment

1. euro, p. 298

2. British Isles, northern France, northwest Germany, the Netherlands

3. Iceland, the British Isles, Belgium, Germany, France, and Italy seem to be more industrialized based on the presence of manufacturing and trade in these countries. Norway, Sweden, Finland, the Netherlands, Spain, Portugal, and Ireland seem to be less industrialized because their economies have little or no industrial activity and rely almost entirely on some form of agricultural activity.

Economics, Technology, and Environment

During the Industrial Revolution, products began to be made by machines in factories rather than by hand in homes. A wealth of natural resources helped transform Western Europe from an agricultural society to an industrial society. Today, Western Europe is one of the world's most heavily industrialized regions.

A Busy Port

Rotterdam, in the Netherlands, is the site of the busiest port in the world. Located at the mouth of the Rhine River, the vast port can handle 300 cargo ships at a time. **GLOBAL TRADE PATTERNS** *How does the photograph suggest that Rotterdam handles a great deal of petroleum?*

European Union

Beginning in the 1950s, six Western European nations formed a "common market" for their mutual economic benefit. As the organization expanded, it became known as the European Union (EU). In 1999, the EU introduced the **euro**, a single currency to be used by member nations. **ECONOMIC ACTIVITIES** *How might a single currency benefit EU members?*

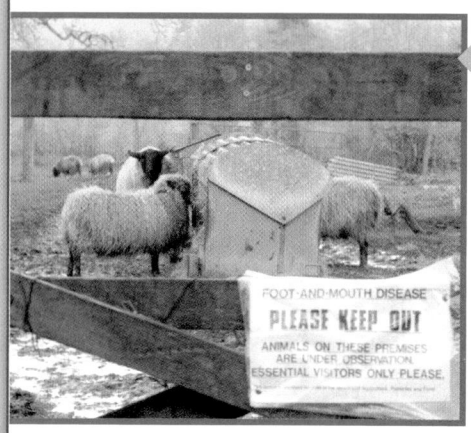

Foot-and-Mouth Disease

In 2001, the United Kingdom experienced an outbreak of foot-and-mouth disease. People cannot contract the disease, but can carry it to other animals by walking through contaminated areas. Despite precautions, the disease spread to other countries. **NATURAL HAZARDS** *How can the spread of contagious diseases be limited?*

ASSESSMENT

1. **Key Term** Define euro.

2. **Map Skills** **Location** Where are Western Europe's coal resources located?

3. **Critical Thinking** **Analyzing Information** Based on the map, which nations seem to be more industrialized? Which seem to be less industrialized? Explain.

Answers to Photo Caption

A Busy Port Possible answer: The photograph shows a large number of petroleum holding tanks.

European Union Possible answer: Nations of the EU can trade more easily with a single currency.

Foot-and-Mouth Disease Possible answer: The spread of contagious disease can be limited if infected individuals or animals are placed in quarantine.

RESOURCE DIRECTORY

Teaching Resources
Social Studies Skills Handbook
• Reading an Economic Activity Map, p. 27
• Reading a Natural Resources Map, p. 34

Technology
World Geography Map and Photo Transparencies
• Western Europe: Maps and Photos

REGIONAL ATLAS

Western Europe: ECONOMIC ACTIVITIES AND RESOURCES

KEY

- Nomadic herding
- Forestry
- Commercial farming
- Manufacturing and trade
- Commercial fishing
- Little or no activity
- Iron
- Copper
- Bauxite
- Coal
- Petroleum
- Hydroelectric power
- Lead

Lambert Azimuthal Equal-Area Projection

ATLANTIC OCEAN

Arctic Circle

Black Sea

Mediterranean Sea

Take It to the NET

Enrichment To learn more about the economic activities and resources of this region, visit the World Geography section of **www.phschool.com**.

Chapter 14 ■ Regional Atlas: Western Europe   **299**

Environmental Issues

Air Pollution The Industrial Revolution, which began around 1750, forever changed Europe. Before industrialization, most people were farmers. After the Industrial Revolution, cities formed near coal fields. Without air pollution controls, smokestacks belched huge quantities of pollutants. Thus began air pollution and the major source of acid rain.

Critical Thinking

A Common Currency For many years, different groups within Western Europe opposed the creation of the euro. Ask students to think about the designs and motifs of American currency and currency from other countries. Then ask: **Why would some Europeans resist the idea of a single European currency?** (Possible answer: Currency frequently depicts people, locations, ideas, or events that are points of national pride. Some might think this would be lost without a national currency.)

Culture

Literature The United States has been described as a "Eurocentric" culture, or a culture that draws its primary influences from Europe. One place where Europe's influence on the United States is evident is in popular children's stories and poems. Many nursery rhymes and fairy tales have European roots. "Cinderella," "Red Riding Hood," and "Sleeping Beauty" were first published in France. "Hansel and Gretel," "Snow White," and "Rapunzel" were collected and written down by the Grimm Brothers, who were German. "The Ugly Duckling" first appeared in a collection of stories by Hans Christian Andersen, a Danish writer.

Database:
Comparing Education

pp. 300–301

Objectives
Upon completion of this lesson, students should be able to:
◆ define compulsory education;
◆ compare the educational systems of select Western European countries and the United States.

National Geography Standards
The following National Geography Standards are highlighted in this feature: 1, 4

Bellringer
Tell students that the average student-teacher ratio in the United States is 15:1. Ask students to compare their school's ratio to this national average.

LESSON PLAN

1. Focus Read the introductory paragraph with the students. Ask: **How do tertiary schools differ from primary and secondary schools?** (Possible answers: In Western Europe and the United States, primary and secondary school are compulsory and tuition-free, but tertiary school is not. Unlike most primary and secondary schools, many tertiary schools prepare students for specific jobs.)

2. Instruct Ask students to examine the six categories of statistics given for each country before reading the rest of the feature. Discuss how each factor could affect a student's daily life and future. As you continue reading with the students, ask them to identify the countries with the highest and lowest statistics in each category.

3. Close/Reteach Ask students to write a brief essay comparing the United States and one of the other countries listed in terms of school environment and opportunities for a tertiary education. Request that they include statistics from the Regional Database to support their ideas.

WESTERN EUROPE
Database: Comparing Education

The idea of free nationwide education originated in Europe in the 1800s. Today, children in Western Europe and the United States are entitled to free primary and secondary education. Primary school is elementary school, including prekindergarten and kindergarten. Secondary school includes middle school, high school, and vocational school. After completing secondary school, students may attend a tertiary school, such as a university, technical college, or professional school. By studying the data below, you can compare education systems.

GET THE FACTS . . .

Go to the Table of Countries at the back of this book to view additional data for the countries of Western Europe.

Take It to the NET
Data Update For the most recent update of this database, visit the World Geography section of **www.phschool.com**.

Sources: *Dorling Kindersley World Desk Reference; Encarta World Atlas*

Key Term: **compulsory**

Finland

Education Expenditure as a Percentage of GNP	5.0
Literacy Rate (percentage)	99.5
Primary School Students per Teacher	15
Percentage of Students in Primary School	98
Percentage of Students in Secondary School	93
Percentage of Students in Tertiary School	74

Education is a top priority in Finland. As in all Western European nations, education is **compulsory,** or required, for a certain number of years. Every Finnish child from 7 to 16 years of age must attend school. Most attend college or university, giving Finland one of the highest rates of enrollment in tertiary education in the world.

France

Education Expenditure as a Percentage of GNP	5.8
Literacy Rate (percentage)	99.0
Primary School Students per Teacher	19
Percentage of Students in Primary School	100
Percentage of Students in Secondary School	95
Percentage of Students in Tertiary School	51

France's national government sets high standards for French students. The curriculum is set by the national government and is strictly followed by every school in the country. About 20 percent of French students attend Catholic schools, which receive some government funding. The most highly regarded tertiary schools in France are the more than 160 *grandes écoles* (grandz ay KOL).

RESOURCE DIRECTORY

Teaching Resources
Unit 4, Chapter 14
• Regional Atlas Review, p. 3
• Regional Atlas Database Skills, p. 4
• Test Forms A and B, pp. 5–10
Spanish Resources
• Regional Atlas Review, p. 33
Guide to the Essentials (English/Spanish)
• Chapter 14 Test
Mental Mapping booklet
• Chapter 14 Map Test, p. 56
Simulations, Games, and Lab Activities
• Place Location Review Games, pp. 58–63

Social Studies Skills Handbook
• Study and Research Skills, pp. 94–108

Prentice Hall Assessment System
Alternative Assessment booklet, Map Evaluation Form, p. 15

Technology
ExamView Test Bank CD-ROM, Chapter 14 Test
Companion Web site, www.phschool.com
• Chapter 14 Self-Test

Italy

Education Expenditure as a Percentage of GNP	4.6
Literacy Rate (percentage)	98.6
Primary School Students per Teacher	11
Percentage of Students in Primary School	100
Percentage of Students in Secondary School	95
Percentage of Students in Tertiary School	47

Although Italian students are required to attend school until they are 14 years old, Italy has a high dropout rate. The percentage of students in tertiary schools is only 47 percent. Italy has more than 50 universities where students study for several years to earn a degree. In northern Italy, the famous University of Bologna is more than 900 years old. Some believe it to be the world's oldest university.

United Kingdom

Education Expenditure as a Percentage of GNP	4.4
Literacy Rate (percentage)	99.0
Primary School Students per Teacher	19
Percentage of Students in Primary School	99
Percentage of Students in Secondary School	92
Percentage of Students in Tertiary School	52

In the United Kingdom, all children attend primary school. A large percentage go on to attend secondary school. A system of national examinations is a key part of the nation's education system. When students are 16, they take the first series of examinations in about ten subjects. When they are 18, they take Advanced (A) Level exams. These exams help determine whether students will be admitted to one of the United Kingdom's many universities.

ASSESSMENT

Use the data for Western Europe and the United States (at right) to answer the following questions.

1. **Key Term** Define compulsory.
2. **Government and Citizenship** Which nations do not have 100 percent of students enrolled in primary schools?
3. **Cultures** Which nation has the largest percentage of students in tertiary school?
4. **Critical Thinking** **Making Generalizations** Based on these data, make a generalization about education in Western Europe and the United States.

United States

Education Expenditure as a Percentage of GNP	5.0
Literacy Rate (percentage)	99.5
Primary School Students per Teacher	15
Percentage of Students in Primary School	95
Percentage of Students in Secondary School	90
Percentage of Students in Tertiary School	81

Games for Review See pages 58–63 of the Simulations, Games, and Lab Activities booklet in the Teaching Resources for games to review place names in preparation for the Chapter 14 Map Test.

Chapter Map Test Students should use the completed Chapter 14 Outline Map and the Unit 4 Checklist in their Atlas Portfolios to prepare for the Chapter 14 Map Test. Point out to students that the test will cover all of the countries, cities, bodies of water, and landforms listed on the Unit 4 Checklist.

Alternative Assessment

Final Evaluation

Creating Maps Use the Map Evaluation Form on page 15 of the Alternative Assessment booklet in the Prentice Hall Assessment System to evaluate students' maps.

Answers to Assessment

1. compulsory, p. 300

2. Finland, the United Kingdom, and the United States

3. the United States

4. Possible answer: Education is considered important in both Western Europe

TEST PREPARATION

Have students read the charts on this page and the opposite page to answer the following question.

Which of the following countries has less than 50 percent of its students attending tertiary school?

  A Finland
  B France
  C Italy
  D United Kingdom

Do-It-Yourself Skills

Objectives

Upon completion of this feature, students should be able to:

◆ explain the purpose of a climate graph;

◆ make a climate graph;

◆ analyze and compare climate graphs.

 National Geography Standards

The following National Geography Standards are highlighted in this feature: 1, 2, 4, 7, 15, 18

 Bellringer

Ask students where they have seen climate graphs in their daily life. (in newspapers or on television news programs) Ask them to suggest the types of news stories that might feature a climate graph. (drought, flooding, severe cold, record highs and lows)

....

LESSON PLAN

1. Focus Have students examine the climate graph of Paris, France, on this page. Ask: **Why is it helpful to see climate information presented in a graph?** (A graph makes it easy to tell which months are hottest, coldest, and rainiest.)

2. Instruct Review steps 1 and 2 of the instructions. Then ask a student to read step 3. Model this step on the board and encourage students to do it themselves on paper. Continue to model the graph-making process through step 7.

3. Close/Reteach When students have finished their graphs, help them make a list of questions their graph could help them answer. Use the questions in step 8 as an example. Then work together to answer the students' questions.

Do-It-Yourself Skills

Making and Analyzing Climate Graphs

What Is a Climate Graph?

A climate graph is a visual representation of average climate conditions at a certain location over a particular period of time. A great variety of climate data may be graphed, but the most common data sets are temperature and rainfall.

How Can I Use This Skill?

Displaying data in a graphic format is a valuable communications skill. The ability to analyze data is important for making decisions. No matter what work you do in the future, it is likely that you will need to make and analyze graphics based on data. The graphic format helps us to recognize patterns and trends on which we can base logical conclusions. For example, if you were planning a vacation or business trip to Paris, France, you could use the climate graph at right, to decide when would be the best time to go.

Step by Step

Follow these steps to make and analyze a climate graph. As you proceed, use the climate graph for Paris, France, at right, as a model.

Paris, France

Curved lines show temperatures in Fahrenheit degrees.
Bars show rainfall in inches.

Source: www.worldclimate.com

1 Select a place and the data that you will graph. For this lesson, you are going to graph average temperatures and rainfall for Rome, Italy.

2 Find and collect climate data from a reliable source, such as an almanac or atlas. For this lesson, we have provided the data for you. Our statistics for Rome were derived from data available through the Web site for the National Climatic Data Center.

3 Make a horizontal axis and mark 12 points, one for each month of the year. The space between each point should be exactly the same. Label each point with a month. Note how abbreviations are used in the Paris model above.

RESOURCE DIRECTORY

Teaching Resources

Social Studies Skills Handbook
• Reading a Climate Graph, p. 65
• Comparing Climate Graphs, p. 66

Social Studies Skills Tutor CD-ROM, Analyzing Graphic Data

Make two vertical axes, each rising from either end of the horizontal axis. On the left vertical axis, mark 6 points for temperature and label them as in the Paris model. On the right vertical axis, mark 6 points for rainfall and label them. Remember to indicate at the tops of the axes that we are measuring data in degrees Fahrenheit and inches.

Use the climate data for Rome in the table at right to plot points for average temperature in Rome. Plot a point at 45°F for January, at 47°F for February, and so on. Draw a line connecting the points for each month.

Use the data from the table to make vertical bars for rainfall. The bar for January will rise to the level for 3.1 inches, the bar for February will rise to the level for 2.8 inches, and so on.

Provide a title and key for your climate graph. The key should indicate that vertical bars represent rainfall and that the horizontal line above the bars represents temperature.

Average Temperatures and Rainfall for Rome, Italy

MONTH	TEMPERATURE (°F)	RAINFALL (inches)
January	45	3.1
February	47	2.8
March	51	2.7
April	57	2.6
May	64	2.0
June	71	1.3
July	76	0.6
August	75	1.0
September	70	2.7
October	62	4.5
November	53	4.4
December	47	3.8

Source: www.worldclimate.com

Analyze the climate graph you have made. Climate data influence decision making in agriculture, insurance, construction, tourism, and other areas. Here are some simple examples of ways in which the climate data for Paris and Rome can influence decisions.

- If you were planning a school trip to Rome, which two months would you avoid because of their excessive rainfall?

- If you were a Roman farmer and your crop needed to be harvested before average temperatures rose above 75°F, when would you harvest your crop?

- How would a French construction engineer use the climate graph for Paris to decide the best thickness of the insulation needed for a new home?

- Would you budget more money for heating a home in Paris or for heating a home in Rome? Explain.

TIP

Evaluating Data

Climate data from different sources for the same place can vary significantly. One reason is that the sources may use data from different time spans. Our data for Rome were based on records dating back to 1871. Another source might have higher or lower average temperatures because its records only date back ten years.

APPLY YOUR SKILL

Select another city in Western Europe or any other region. Create a climate graph for that city. Then, write some questions that illustrate how the graph might influence decision making in various fields of endeavor. Exchange questions with those of another student, and then write answers to the questions.

Group Work

Activity: Designing a local climate graph

Purpose: Encourage students to collect information about average rainfall and temperature in their area for a specific period of time ending in the current year. Assign each group a different period to investigate. Then have them graph their information.

Roles: Researchers, a graph designer, and a graph interpreter

Result: The graph interpreter explains the graph to classmates. Discuss with the class how averages differ depending on the period studied.

ACTIVITY

Critical Thinking

Landscape and Climate Ask students to examine a map of Italy, paying careful attention to features of the landscape. Ask: **Do you think Rome's average winter temperatures are characteristic of the rest of Italy?** Have them explain their answers. (No; for example, it is colder farther north, especially in the Alps.)

Answers to Apply Your Skills

Check students' climate graphs for accuracy. Questions and answers will vary based on the country students choose.

CUSTOMIZE FOR...

Less Proficient Writers

Transitions Point out to students that the instructions on pages 302 and 303 are divided into numbered steps. Remind them that sometimes how-to essays use transitions instead of numbers to link their steps in a logical manner. Review with students the following words used in transitions: *first, second, third,* and so on; *then, next, last, finally.* Have students rewrite several steps of the lesson using transition words instead of numbers.

Resource Manager

	CORE INSTRUCTION	READING/SKILLS
Chapter-Level Resources	**Teaching Resources** 📓 **Unit 4**/Ch. 15 • Reviewing Main Ideas, p. 19 📒 **Mental Mapping booklet** • Unit 4 Checklist, p. 52 📒 **Simulations, Games, and Lab Activities** • Place Location Review Games, pp. 58–63 📒 **Creative Teaching Activities** • What Is a Culture Hero?, p. 17 💿 **TeacherExpress™ CD-ROM**, Ch. 15 💻 **Companion Web site,** **www.phschool.com** • eTeach	**Teaching Resources** 📓 **Unit 4**/Ch. 15 • Map/Graph Skills, p. 21 💿 **Book on CD**, Ch. 15 💿 **Social Studies Skills Tutor CD-ROM**
1 England 1. Identify the major physical characteristics of England. 2. Explain why London became one of the world's greatest commercial and shipping centers. 3. Describe how the Industrial Revolution affected Britain's economic activities.	**Teaching Resources** 📓 **Unit 4**/Ch. 15 • Guided Reading and Review, p. 11 💿 **Prentice Hall Presentation Pro CD-ROM**, Ch. 15, Sec. 1	**Teaching Resources** 📒 **Guide to the Essentials (English/Spanish)** • Section Summary, Ch. 15, Sec. 1 📒 **Mental Mapping booklet** • Outline Map 15, p. 57 📼 **Guided Reading Audiotapes (English/Spanish)**, Ch. 15, Sec. 1 📖 **Section Reading Support Transparencies**, Ch. 15, Sec. 1
2 Scotland and Wales 1. Identify the major physical characteristics of Scotland. 2. Explain how Scotland and Wales have preserved their cultural identities. 3. Describe how technological changes have affected economic activities in Wales.	**Teaching Resources** 📓 **Unit 4**/Ch. 15 • Guided Reading and Review, p. 13 💿 **Prentice Hall Presentation Pro CD-ROM**, Ch. 15, Sec. 2	**Teaching Resources** 📒 **Guide to the Essentials (English/Spanish)** • Section Summary, Ch. 15, Sec. 2 📼 **Guided Reading Audiotapes (English/Spanish)**, Ch. 15, Sec. 2 📖 **Section Reading Support Transparencies**, Ch. 15, Sec. 2
3 The Two Irelands 1. Describe Ireland's physical characteristics. 2. Identify the geographic processes that have caused cooperation and conflict in Ireland. 3. Explain how the Republic of Ireland has tried to boost economic activity.	**Teaching Resources** 📓 **Unit 4**/Ch. 15 • Guided Reading and Review, p. 15 💿 **Prentice Hall Presentation Pro CD-ROM**, Ch. 15, Sec. 3	**Teaching Resources** 📒 **Guide to the Essentials (English/Spanish)** • Section Summary, Ch. 15, Sec. 3 📒 **Social Studies Skills Handbook** • Reading a Time Line, p. 61 📼 **Guided Reading Audiotapes (English/Spanish)**, Ch. 15, Sec. 3 📖 **Section Reading Support Transparencies**, Ch. 15, Sec. 3
4 The Nordic Nations 1. Describe the physical and cultural characteristics that define the Nordic nations. 2. Explain how the Nordic people have used natural resources to pursue a variety of economic activities.	**Teaching Resources** 📓 **Unit 4**/Ch. 15 • Guided Reading and Review, p. 17 💿 **Prentice Hall Presentation Pro CD-ROM**, Ch. 15, Sec. 4	**Teaching Resources** 📒 **Guide to the Essentials (English/Spanish)** • Section Summary, Ch. 15, Sec. 4 📒 **Mental Mapping booklet** • Outline Map 15, p. 57 📼 **Guided Reading Audiotapes (English/Spanish)**, Ch. 15, Sec. 4 📖 **Section Reading Support Transparencies**, Ch. 15, Sec. 4

ENRICHMENT/HONORS/PREAP

📗 **Teaching Resources**
📘 **Unit 4**/Ch. 15
  • Critical Thinking, p. 20
📖 **Mental Mapping booklet**
  • Atlas Activity, p. 58
📖 **Social Studies Skills Handbook**
  • Checking Consistency of Ideas, p. 44
  • Study and Research Skills, pp. 94–108
📙 **World Geography Map and Photo Transparencies**
  • Western Europe: Maps and Photos
📺 **World Geography Videos**
  • Understanding the Past: The British Isles and Nordic Nations, Tape 2
💻 **Companion Web site, www.phschool.com**
  • Chapter 15 Activities

💻 **Companion Web site, www.phschool.com**
  • Chapter 15 Activities

💻 **Companion Web site, www.phschool.com**
  • Chapter 15 Activities

💻 **Companion Web site, www.phschool.com**
  • Chapter 15 Activities

📗 **Teaching Resources**
📘 **Unit 4**/Ch. 15
  • Geography and World Literature, p. 60
💻 **Companion Web site, www.phschool.com**
  • Chapter 15 Activities

ASSESSMENT

PRENTICE HALL ASSESSMENT SYSTEM

Core Assessment
📖 ExamView Test Bank booklet, Ch. 15
💿 ExamView Test Bank CD-ROM, Ch. 15

Standardized Test Preparation
Review and Reteach
📖 Review Book for World Geography, pp. 9–10

Practice and Assess
📖 Test-taking Strategies With Transparencies for High School
📖 Test-taking Strategy Poster
📖 Alternative Assessment booklet
📖 Test Prep Book for World Geography

📗 **Teaching Resources**
📘 **Unit 4**/Ch. 15
  • Section Quizzes, pp. 12, 14, 16, 18
  • Test Forms A and B, pp. 22–27
📖 **Guide to the Essentials (English/Spanish)**
  • Chapter 15 Test
📖 **Spanish Resources**, Ch. 15
  • Section Quizzes, pp. 34–37
📖 **Mental Mapping booklet**
  • Chapter 15 Map Test, p. 59
💻 **Companion Web site, www.phschool.com**
  • Chapter 15 Self-Test

CUSTOMIZE FOR INDIVIDUAL NEEDS

Gifted and Talented
  • Teacher's Edition, Customize for . . . , p. 313
Honors/PreAP
  • Teacher's Edition, Customize for . . . , p. 321
Less Proficient Readers
  • Guide to the Essentials (English), Ch. 15, Section Summaries
  • Guided Reading Audiotapes (English), Ch. 15
  • Section Reading Support Transparencies, Ch. 15
  • Book on CD, Ch. 15
  • Teacher's Edition, Reading Strategy, pp. 308, 311, 316, 320
  • Teacher's Edition, Activity: Vocabulary, pp. 307, 311, 319
  • Teacher's Edition, Customize for . . . , pp. 307, 315
Students Acquiring English/ESL
  • Guide to the Essentials (English/Spanish), Ch. 15
  • Guided Reading Audiotapes (English/Spanish), Ch. 15
  • Section Reading Support Transparencies, Ch. 15
  • Book on CD, Ch. 15
Less Proficient Writers
  • Social Studies Skills Handbook, p. 91
  • Alternative Assessment, Writing Assignment Rubric, p. 6

Ⓜ️ ENTAL MAPPING

Point out that the British Isles and the Nordic nations are part of Western Europe. Ask: **What are the names of the Nordic nations?** (Denmark, Sweden, Finland, Norway, and Iceland) Then ask: **What are the bodies of water that surround the British Isles?** (Atlantic Ocean, English Channel, North Sea)

Mapping the Region Have students study the map on this page. Then instruct them to close their books and create a sketch map of the British Isles and the Nordic nations. You may also distribute the Chapter 15 Outline Map on page 57 of the Mental Mapping booklet in the Teaching Resources. Ask students to shade each country a different color and to label the countries and bodies of water.

C H A P T E R
15
The British Isles and Nordic Nations

SECTIONS

1. **England**
2. **Scotland and Wales**
3. **The Two Irelands**
4. **The Nordic Nations**

The British Isles and Nordic Nations: POLITICAL

KEY
— National boundary
⊛ National capital
• Other city

Lambert Azimuthal Equal-Area Projection

Go Online
PHSchool.com

For: More information about the British Isles and Nordic nations and access to the Take It to the Net activities
Visit: phschool.com
Web Code: mjk-0016

---

eTeach

Be sure to check out this month's online forum with a Master Teacher to join in an exchange of teaching ideas. **www.phschool.com**

RESOURCE DIRECTORY

Teaching Resources
Unit 4, Chapter 15
• Section 1 Guided Reading and Review, p. 11
Guide to the Essentials (English/Spanish)
• Section Summary, Chapter 15, Section 1
Mental Mapping booklet
• Atlas Activity, p. 58
• Unit 4 Checklist, p. 52
Technology
Guided Reading Audiotapes (English/Spanish),
Chapter 15, Section 1
Section Reading Support Transparencies,
Chapter 15, Section 1

World Geography Map and Photo Transparencies
• Western Europe: Maps and Photos
Book on CD, Chapter 15
World Geography Videos
• Understanding the Past: The British Isles and Nordic Nations, Tape 2
TeacherExpress™ CD-ROM, Chapter 15
Prentice Hall Presentation Pro CD-ROM, Chapter 15
Social Studies Skills Tutor CD-ROM
Companion Web site, www.phschool.com
• Chapter 15 Activities

1 England

Reading Focus

- **What major physical characteristics can be found in different regions of England, and how do they affect the economy?**
- **Why did London become one of the greatest commercial and shipping centers in the world?**
- **How did the Industrial Revolution change and expand economic activities in the United Kingdom?**

Key Terms

fertile

ore

tertiary economic activity

Main Idea Resources, trade, and industrial innovation helped the small nation of Britain to become a global economic power.

Physical Characteristics Rich soil and a moderate climate contribute to lush gardens in southwestern Great Britain.

The many islands clustered off the northwest coast of Europe are called the British Isles. The largest island in the British Isles—and in all of Europe—is Great Britain.

The island of Great Britain comprises three formerly independent countries: England, Scotland, and Wales. Together with Northern Ireland, they form the United Kingdom of Great Britain and Northern Ireland, or simply the United Kingdom.

The core of the United Kingdom is England. Notice from the population map on page 297 that England is the most densely populated area in the British Isles. Nearly 80 percent of the region's population live here.

England's Physical Characteristics

"Our England is a garden," declared English poet Rudyard Kipling in the late 1800s. Kipling was describing rural England with its green, rolling meadows, peaceful rivers, and neat farms. The English landscape is actually made up of three very different areas: the Highlands, Midlands, and Lowlands.

The Highlands are a band of hills running the length of England's west coast. Older and harder rock formations in this region have been worn down by centuries of weathering. Even so, some peaks rise to 3,000 feet (900 m), and the land is difficult to farm.

A short distance to the southeast are the Midlands. Here lie the thick veins of coal that fueled the country's Industrial Revolution. Factory towns such as Birmingham, Manchester, and Stoke-on-Trent still darken the air with fumes from their mills. Heavy industrial development means that some of England's highest population densities are in the Midlands.

To the south and east are the rolling Lowlands. The land slopes gently toward the English Channel, and elevations rarely top 1,000 feet (300 m). Younger, softer rocks lie beneath the land's surface. Because these rocks break up easily, soil in the Lowlands tends to be **fertile**—able to produce abundant crops.

◀ Royal Guards, London, England (photo left)

Chapter 15 ▪ Section 1 **305**

Objectives

Upon completion of Section 1, students should be able to:

◆ identify the major physical characteristics of England;

◆ explain why London became one of the world's greatest commercial and shipping centers;

◆ describe how the Industrial Revolution affected Britain's economic activities.

 National Geography Standards

The following National Geography Standards are highlighted in this section: 1, 3, 5, 8, 9, 11, 12, 14, 16, 17

 Bellringer

Ask students: **How do you think a small island nation such as Great Britain came to control a global empire that stretched from Africa to Asia and included Australia and territory in the Americas?** Lead a discussion of why Great Britain was able to control a worldwide empire.

LESSON PLAN

1. Focus Have students turn the subheadings in this section into questions using the words *what, where, how,* and *when.* Then, as they read the section, have them answer the questions.

2. Instruct Write these words on the board: *Atlantic Ocean, Thames River, Pennine Chain, Lowlands, Midlands.* Have students use the text to write one or two sentences explaining how each of these places is related to the economic development of England.

3. Close/Reteach Ask students to identify how Britain is combating its recent economic problems. As a class, brainstorm other ways that Britain could improve its economy.

TEACHING TIP
From A Master Teacher

Religion and Culture Religion is a significant driving force in creating patterns of conflict and cooperation among people. It influences peoples' beliefs, values, traditions, behavior, and worldview. In Europe, as in other parts of the world, many modern political tensions have their origins in historical events related to culture and religion—events shaped by geographic processes like diffusion and migration. The geography of religion provides insights into past events and can help us understand present conditions.

Pacing Suggestions

 For 90-minute Blocks

You will want to vary activities.

- Complete page 17 of the Creative Teaching Activities booklet in the Teaching Resources with the class. Explain that a culture hero reflects the values of the culture that created him or her. Tell students to hypothesize about the values of the societies that created the culture heroes in the lesson. Have students write paragraphs that summarize their ideas, and ask volunteers to share their paragraphs with the class.

Chapter 15 ▪ Section 1 **305**

BACKGROUND

Word Origin

Liverpool Liverpool was a tidal creek that existed where the city is now located. *Liverpool* means "pool of thick water."

GLOBAL CONNECTIONS

Understanding the Past

The British Empire From 1890 to 1920 when their empire was at its largest, Britons could brag that "the sun never sets on the British Empire": It encompassed a fifth to a quarter of the earth's land surface and considered more than a quarter of the world's population its subjects.

Alternative Assessment

Introduce the Activity

Participating in a Cooperative Learning Project Divide students into groups of four and ask each group to choose a country in the British Isles or a Nordic country and plan a walking tour of that country. Distribute the Cooperative Learning Project Rubrics found on pages 16 and 18 of the Alternative Assessment booklet in the Prentice Hall Assessment System for student reference during the project.

Answers to Map Caption

Grampian Mountains, Pennine Chain, Cambrian Mountains

The Lowlands are easier to farm because of the region's fertile soil and rolling flatlands.

306 Chapter 15

The British Isles: PHYSICAL-POLITICAL

KEY

Elevation

Feet	Meters
14,000	4,270
7,000	2,135
1,500	457
700	213
(sea level) 0	0 (sea level)

⊛ National capital
• Major city
▲ Mountain

Lambert Azimuthal Equal-Area Projection

0   50   100 mi
0   50 100 km

APPLYING THE GEOGRAPHIC THEMES

Regions The British Isles have clearly defined regions of highlands and lowlands.
- *Which mountain ranges are the dominant features of the Highlands?*
- *Would you expect farming to be more common in the Highlands or Lowlands? Explain.*

The Lowlands provide England with some of its most productive farms. Farmers grow wheat, vegetables, and other crops on small plots of land. They set aside larger parcels of land for pasture. The cool, moist weather of England's marine west coast climate is perfect for raising sheep and dairy and beef cattle. British goods are sold both in the United Kingdom and in other European Union nations.

Rise of London as a Trade Center

Even before industrialization, England's farms produced surplus goods for export. Trade within England and with other European nations fostered the growth of cities along rivers and the coast. Of these, London was the most important.

306 Chapter 15 ▪ The British Isles and Nordic Nations

RESOURCE DIRECTORY

Teaching Resources
Unit 4, Chapter 15
- Map/Graph Skills, p. 21

Mental Mapping booklet
- Outline Map, p. 57

Prentice Hall Assessment System
Alternative Assessment booklet
- Cooperative Learning Project Rubrics A and B, pp. 16 and 18

Technology
World Geography Map and Photo Transparencies
- Western Europe: Maps and Photos

Why did London, with its inland location, become one of the greatest commercial and shipping cities in the world? The answer can be found in one of the five geographic themes—location.

London's Relative Location The map on page 306 shows that although London is only about 70 miles (110 km) from the continent of Europe, the city of Dover is even closer to the mainland. So why isn't Dover the English capital of trade? London has a big advantage over Dover and other southern coastal ports. The hills along the English Channel drop sharply, forming steep cliffs that plunge straight down to the water. In contrast, London is located on the Thames (TEHMZ) River. Since the Thames Valley was formed, the level of the Atlantic Ocean has risen. The result is an estuary—a flooded valley at the wide mouth of a river. Thus, ships could sail directly up to the port of London.

As early as the 1500s, London was a bustling port. One writer described activity along the waterfront in this way:

66 A forest of masts. . . . Huge square-rigged ships lay side by side, surrounded by barges and small craft. . . . The . . . boats had to fight . . . to their landing places. 99

Global Trade Patterns The port of London grew rapidly in the 1500s because of changes in patterns of world settlement and trade. The influence of the Roman Empire meant that the Mediterranean Sea traditionally had been the center of trade. London remained on the far edge of European trade. In the late 1400s, however, improved ships and navigational devices allowed Europeans to push westward across the Atlantic Ocean. Great Britain's strategic, central location on the Atlantic was ideal for trade. So, as trade across the Atlantic increased, Britain's relative location improved.

Economic Activities

In the 1500s, Britain shipped mostly the products of its farms. But within its small area, the island nation had the resources to fuel the start of the Industrial Revolution.

British Isles, Nordic Nations, and the United States
Energy Data

Country	Electricity Consumption (per capita kilowatt-hours)	Petroleum Imports (thousand barrels per year)	Petroleum Exports (thousand barrels per year)
Denmark	5,508	42,879	40,223
Finland	12,846	68,071	0
Iceland	19,028	0	0
Ireland	4,837	16,870	0
Norway	23,977	8,944	1,082,290
Sweden	14,811	146,790	0
United Kingdom	5,376	323,654	530,646
United States	12,235	2,742,208	40,129

Source: *Encarta World Atlas*

CHART SKILLS

● **Economic Activities** *Which three nations consume the most electricity per person? How might climate and location contribute to high energy needs in those countries?*

● **Natural Resources** *Which nation has vast resources of fossil fuels?*

As shipowners and merchants earned profits from trade, they looked for new ways to invest their money. Wealthy business owners built factories to produce manufactured goods to sell to Britain's colonies. As ships plied the oceans loaded with British goods, Britain became known as the "workshop of the world."

The Rise of Heavy Industry Some of the earliest technological advances of the Industrial Revolution were used in factories that produced textiles, or cloth. British manufacturers first used water power to run spinning

GEOFacts

The Thames River was once so polluted that Britain's capitol building, the Parliament, had to be equipped with chemical-soaked curtains to keep out the odor. Now anti-pollution efforts have resulted in a river so clean it is again a home to salmon.

308 Chapter 15

machines but later switched to coal as a source of power for the steam engine.

Major coal fields lay along the edges of the Pennine mountain range, as well as in the northeast, near the city of Newcastle. Britain also possessed large reserves of iron **ore,** or rocky material containing a valuable mineral. Inventors improved methods of melting iron ore and using it in the production of steel. The towns of Birmingham, Sheffield, and Newcastle grew dramatically in size as nearby coal fields made them centers of manufacturing. Coal supplies were so plentiful that the phrase "carrying coals to Newcastle" developed to describe an unnecessary action.

The Industrial Revolution brought wealth to Britain, but the factories and mines also changed the English landscape. English poet William Blake condemned the "dark, Satanic mills" for spoiling "England's green and pleasant land." A visitor to Birmingham in the early 1800s reported that the noise there was "beyond description," and the filth was "sickening."

Challenges to British Industry

Britain's plentiful supply of raw materials and its position on major sea routes made it the world's industrial leader for years. But in the late 1800s, Britain was challenged by two new industrial powers—Germany and the United States. By 1900, both the United States and Germany were making as much steel as the United Kingdom.

In recent years, British industry has fallen upon hard times. Much of the area's coal supply was used up during the Industrial Revolution. Since the 1970s, Britain has turned to oil and gas deposits beneath the floor of the North Sea as a source for fuel.

Birmingham and Industry

Migration Birmingham became one of the world's leading industrial cities during the 1800s. With workers flooding into Birmingham, the city's population grew from 70,000 in 1801 to more than 400,000 at the end of the century.

Movement *How did this movement of people into cities change the landscape of Great Britain?*

The English Channel Tunnel

Folkestone Terminal — UNITED KINGDOM

English Channel

White-gray chalk

Coquelles Terminal

FRANCE

Crossover

Crossover | Faults

Not to scale

Chalk marl

Gault clay

Green sand

DIAGRAM SKILLS

● **Science and Technology** In 1994, France and England completed building a tunnel beneath the English Channel. The Chunnel, as it is nicknamed, connects the two nations with a 31-mile (50-km) underwater rail link.

• *How might the Channel Tunnel change the lives of people in England and France?*

Despite its problems, Britain's overall economy has been growing steadily. To offset the loss of heavy industry, the government has encouraged the growth of **tertiary economic activities,** or service industries, such as finance, insurance, and tourism. Inflation rates have been low, and unemployment has been decreasing. Though a member of the European Union, the United Kingdom has been reluctant to adopt the euro—the common currency system of the European Union.

SECTION 1 ASSESSMENT

1. **Key Terms** Define **(a)** fertile, **(b)** ore, **(c)** tertiary economic activity.

2. **Physical Characteristics** Describe the three different physical areas of the English landscape.

3. **Global Trade Patterns** What geographic factors affected London's level of development?

4. **Economic Activities (a)** What impact did technological innovations have on the British economy? **(b)** What impact did they have on Britain's physical landscape?

5. **Critical Thinking** **Analyzing Causes and Effects (a)** What was the effect of the Industrial Revolution on Britain's coal supply? **(b)** How has the British economy recovered from this loss?

Activity

USING THE REGIONAL ATLAS

Review the natural resources and political maps in the Regional Atlas for Western Europe and this section. Find the location of England's chief mineral deposits and the cities of Birmingham, Manchester, and Leeds. Write a paragraph explaining some of the reasons why these cities became major urban centers.

TEST PREPARATION

Have students use the diagram on this page to complete the following statement. A tourist traveling from England to France via the English Channel Tunnel would disembark at the —

A Crossover
B Folkestone Terminal
Ⓒ Coquelles Terminal
D Chalk marl

Answers to Section 1 Assessment

1. (a) fertile, p. 305 **(b)** ore, p. 308 **(c)** tertiary economic activity, p. 309

2. The Highlands are the band of hills running the length of England's west coast. To the southeast are the Midlands, which contain thick veins of coal. South and east of the Midlands are the rolling Lowlands, where the soil is fertile.

3. Before the 1500s, London was not a major port because it was far west of the major trade routes. As trade across the Atlantic increased, London's relative location changed and it experienced rapid growth as a port city.

4. (a) Technological advances made it possible to harness new sources of energy, such as water power and coal. Improved methods of melting iron ore and producing steel led to the rise of heavy industry. **(b)** Factories and mines polluted the countryside with dirt and noise.

5. (a) Much of Britain's coal supply was used up during the Industrial Revolution. **(b)** Britain has turned to other sources of fuel and encouraged the growth of service industries to offset the loss of heavy industry.

Activity Rubrics Share rubrics with students before they write their paragraph.

Attempted The paragraph gives very few valid reasons, contains factual errors, and is messy or difficult to read.

Minimal The paragraph gives several valid reasons but contains factual errors.

Adequate The paragraph gives a number of valid reasons, contains no factual errors, and is well thought out.

Exemplary The paragraph contains no factual errors, is perceptive, and reflects a clear understanding of how these cities became major urban centers.

Answer to Diagram Skills

Possible answer: The Chunnel might promote cultural diffusion as French and British people are able to work and travel abroad more easily.

Objectives

Upon completion of Section 2, students should be able to:

◆ identify the major physical characteristics of Scotland;

◆ explain how Scotland and Wales have preserved their cultural identities;

◆ describe how technological changes have affected economic activities in Wales.

National Geography Standards

The following National Geography Standards are highlighted in this section: 1, 3, 4, 5, 6, 8, 10, 13, 16, 17

Bellringer

Write the following sentence on the board: *Aberystwyth* [a buh RHIS twith], *Ebbw Vale* [EH boo vayl], *and Gwynedd* [GWI neth] *are places in Cymru* [KUHM ree] *on the British Isles.* Have students guess where Cymru is. (Wales) Explain that its language, Welsh, comes from an ancient Celtic language.

....

LESSON PLAN

1. Focus Discuss preconceived notions about the two nations. Ask: **What kinds of images come to mind when you think of Scotland and Wales?** (possible answers: bagpipes, sheep, wool, green rolling hills) Ask students to write a few lines to answer this question: **What do you think it would be like to live in either country?** As they read, have students alter their notes to reflect any new information.

2. Instruct Draw two large, overlapping circles on the board. Label one circle *Scotland* and the other *Wales*. Have students find distinctive features of each country. Write them in the areas of each circle that do not overlap. Then have students find similarities between the two countries, and write these in the overlapping area.

3. Close/Reteach Have students write a one-page magazine "profile" of either country. Instruct them to include information about its people and its physical geography.

---

2 Scotland and Wales

Reading Focus

• **What are the major physical characteristics of Scotland?**

• **How have Scotland and Wales prevented their cultural identities from being completely replaced by English culture?**

• **How have technological changes affected economic activities in Wales?**

Key Terms

moor

bog

glen

 Main Idea   Although united with England politically, Scotland and Wales have some distinctive physical and cultural characteristics.

Cultures   Bagpipes are an important feature in Scotland's cultural landscape.

An English writer once remarked, "[A Scot] is British, yes, and he will sing 'There will always be an England,' but he murmurs to himself, 'As long as Scotland is there.'" This story reveals something about how the Scots view England. The two nations have been tied together politically for almost three hundred years. Still, Scotland has always kept its own identity. The same can be said of Wales, which has been united with England since the late 1200s.

Scotland's Physical Characteristics

Scotland occupies nearly one third of the land area in the United Kingdom, but less than 10 percent of the nation's population live there. The landscape is rugged. It bears the marks of heavy glaciers that moved across the northern part of Great Britain during the last ice age.

The map on page 306 shows that the Cheviot Hills and the Tweed River are the physical features that separate Scotland from England. Scotland itself is divided into three formal regions—the northern Highlands, the central Lowlands, and the southern Uplands.

The Highlands The Highland region is a large, high plateau with many lakes, called lochs (LAHKHS), which were carved by retreating glaciers. The Grampian Mountains cut across the region with peaks reaching past 4,000 feet (1,200 m). Both coasts are etched deeply by the sea with inlets called firths.

Much of the Highlands are covered with **moors**—broad, treeless rolling plains. The moors, in turn, are dotted with **bogs**—areas of wet, spongy ground. Steady winds off the Atlantic Ocean bring abundant rainfall to the moors. The dampness of the soil limits plant growth to grasses and low shrubs such as purple heather.

The land, water, and climate of the Highlands are well suited to the region's economies of fishing and sheep herding. A few people produce a type of handwoven, woolen cloth known as tweed. This Scottish home industry has continued over hundreds of years, in sharp contrast to the factory production of textiles in England.

RESOURCE DIRECTORY

Teaching Resources

Unit 4, Chapter 15
• Section 2 Guided Reading and Review, p. 13

Guide to the Essentials (English/Spanish)
• Section Summary, Chapter 15, Section 2

Mental Mapping booklet
• Unit 4 Checklist, p. 52

Technology

Guided Reading Audiotapes (English/Spanish), Chapter 15, Section 2

Section Reading Support Transparencies, Chapter 15, Section 2

World Geography Map and Photo Transparencies
• Western Europe: Maps and Photos

Book on CD, Chapter 15

Social Studies Skills Tutor CD-ROM

Companion Web site, www.phschool.com
• Chapter 15 Activities

The Central Lowlands South of the Highlands runs a long lowland region. Nearly 75 percent of Scotland's people live in this region, stretching between Glasgow and Edinburgh (EHD ihn BUHR oh).

Industry came to the central Lowlands in the early 1800s. The Clyde River near Glasgow grew into a huge shipbuilding center. The Clyde shipbuilders played a major role in establishing the United Kingdom as the world's leading naval power. Explained one observer:

❝ Through all the transitions—wood to iron, iron to steel, paddle to . . . turbine engines—Clyde shipbuilders have been to the front with ships. ❞

Since the mid-1900s, however, heavy industries in Scotland have fallen on hard times. Old factory centers such as Glasgow have declined. The loss of jobs has caused more than one third of Glasgow's residents to leave since 1960.

The Southern Uplands Closest to the English border, the Southern Uplands is primarily a sheep-raising region. The Tweed River valley woolen mills are kept well supplied with wool by area farmers. The Cheviot Hills, the highest in the area, give way to rolling plateaus worn down by glaciers. Medieval abbeys and low, hilly landscapes draw many visitors to the region.

Scottish Culture

New industries are slowly taking the place of mining, steel making, and shipbuilding. Oil discoveries in the North Sea, off the northeastern shore of Scotland, have helped the economies of some cities such as Aberdeen. Computer and electronic businesses have also developed along the Clyde and Tweed rivers. Some people call the Clyde Valley the Silicon Glen, after the area in California known as Silicon Valley. A **glen** is a narrow valley.

Although politically united with England, Scotland has retained its own culture. When the Scottish and English parliaments were united through the Act of Union in 1707, Scotland kept important trading and political rights. Many Scots also remained members of the Presbyterian Church, rather than joining the Church of England. In 1997, Scottish voters approved the creation of a new Scottish parliament. A small minority of Scottish people even promote the idea of once

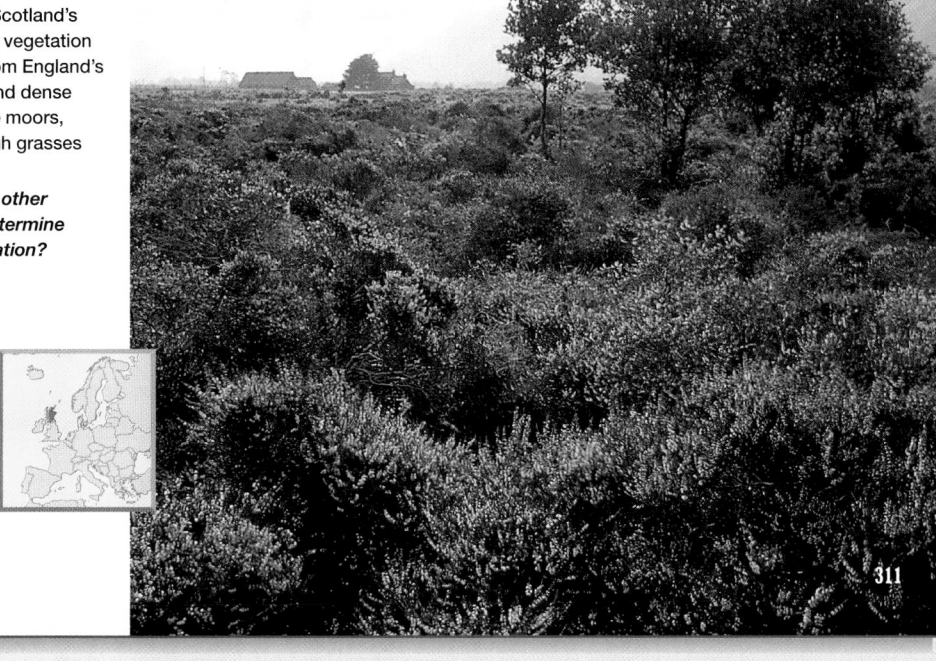

Heather on a Scottish Moor

Ecosystems Scotland's climate supports vegetation quite different from England's lush meadows and dense forests. On these moors, heather and tough grasses stretch for miles.

Regions *What other factors might determine a region's vegetation?*

Articles From
NATIONAL GEOGRAPHIC

The following article may be used to extend the content in this section.

Ward, Andrew, and Jim Richardson, photographer. "Scotland." *National Geographic,* Vol. 190, No. 3 (Sept. 1996), pp. 2–27.
Scotland proudly maintains its heritage and traditions, resisting England's cultural influences.

TEST PREPARATION

Have students read the subsection The Highlands on the opposite page to answer the following question.
The economy of the Highlands includes —
- **A** shipbuilding, fishing, and mining
- **B** fishing, heavy industry, and textile production
- **C** mining, animal herding, and shipbuilding
- **(D)** fishing, textile production, and sheep herding

---

312   Chapter 15

ACTIVITY

Connecting With . . .

History Three distinctive symbols of Scotland are the bagpipe, the kilt, and Edinburgh Castle. The Welsh flag with its red dragon is a well-known symbol of Wales. Have students research one of these symbols and prepare short, illustrated reports explaining why it has become a symbol of its country.

ACTIVITY

Group Work

Activity: Forming an opinion
Purpose: Assign each group Scotland or Wales. Tell each group that its job is to form an opinion about whether its assigned country should be part of the United Kingdom. Have each group research its assigned country and discuss the advantages and disadvantages of becoming an independent nation. Finally, groups should put this question to a vote: Which would be best for this country—to remain a member of the United Kingdom, or to become an independent country again?
Roles: All group members should participate in the research and discussion. One member should also act as scribe to record responses, and another should also act as ballot counter.
Result: Each ballot counter should read his or her group's decision to the class.

BACKGROUND

Connecting With . . .

Music Robert Burns, who was born in 1759, is Scotland's national poet. He wrote many poems to be sung to Scottish folk tunes that are etched in the hearts of his country's people. His best known song is probably "Auld Lang Syne." In the United States, this song is traditionally sung on New Year's Eve.

Answer to Photo Caption

No; this dense growth requires plenty of moisture and nutrient-rich soil.

again becoming a separate country. As Scottish patriot Gordon Wilson explained:

> ❝You can tell me that Scotland is a part of the United Kingdom, and I will tell you that that is the truth but not the whole truth. . . . You see, national boundaries are not simply a matter of geographical frontiers. It's culture we're talking about, a set of national characteristics. These Scotland has retained.❞

Wales

A similar spirit of pride and independence exists in Wales, which also has a culture pattern distinct from that of England. It has its own capital city, postage stamps, flag, and language. However, Wales is strongly influenced by its powerful neighbor, England, which conquered it in 1284.

Welsh Physical Characteristics

Wales is really a peninsula of the island of Great Britain. About the size of Massachusetts, it has a landscape similar to that of Scotland. On the map on page 306 you can find a highland area in northern Wales, lowlands running along the southern coast near Cardiff, and the Cambrian Mountains in central Wales.

Wales enjoys a marine west coast climate like the rest of Great Britain. However, the rain-carrying winds from the Atlantic pass over Wales before reaching England. So, Wales usually receives even more rain than southern England.

A Separate Language Since the 1500s, Welsh representatives have sat in Parliament. Some have risen to high office in the British government, including that of Prime Minister. Even so, the Welsh have fought for cultural independence.

One of the keys to preserving Welsh culture is language. Most of its 2.9 million people speak English, but nearly 20 percent still speak Welsh as their first language. Handed down from the Celtic peoples who lived in Wales for thousands of years, Welsh is spoken mainly in the mountains of northern Wales. In the 1980s, Welsh patriots fought for and won the right to broadcast television programs entirely in Welsh.

Economic Activities

The economic history of Wales is similar to that of England and Scotland. In the late 1800s and early 1900s, industry and coal mining changed the landscape and economy of southern Wales. Mines in the Rhondda Valley, just north of the

A Living Fence

Environmental Change With the right conditions, bushes planted in a row can grow so tightly together that livestock cannot pass through. Here, a dense double hedge separates two flocks of sheep.
Place *Could hedges this dense be grown in less fertile land? Explain your answer.*

RESOURCE DIRECTORY

Teaching Resources
Unit 4, Chapter 15
• Section 2 Quiz, p. 14
Spanish Resources
• Section 2 Quiz, p. 35

A History of Mining

Understanding the Past
The Welsh have a long history of mining: the Romans mined gold in the Welsh mountains as early as A.D. 250. Since then, the Welsh have mined coal, lead, and zinc, and have quarried both limestone and slate.

Human-Environment Interaction *What products do you use that are mined from the ground?*

capital city of Cardiff, became some of Britain's biggest coal producers.

By the mid-1900s, however, heavy industries in Wales had fallen behind in technology. A writer described the Welsh economy in 1945:

66[Miners] still picked coal by hand from two-foot seams. . . . In many places things like bread, milk and coal were still being delivered by horse and cart. 99

By the 1980s, most of the coal mines in the Rhondda Valley had closed. Unemployment rates soared, and many students leaving high school could not find jobs despite the arrival of new petroleum refineries.

In the 1990s, the situation improved as foreign investment in Wales, as in Scotland, provided new jobs in high-tech industries. Some people in Wales also promoted tourism for those interested in seeing the traditional Welsh way of life.

SECTION 2 ASSESSMENT

1. **Key Terms** Define **(a)** moor, **(b)** bog, **(c)** glen.

2. **Physical Characteristics** What are the major physical characteristics of Scotland?

3. **Cultures** **(a)** In what ways has Scotland preserved its cultural heritage? **(b)** How have the Welsh maintained their cultural identity?

4. **Economic Activities** What role has technology played in the economic changes that have occurred in Wales between the late 1800s and today?

5. **Critical Thinking** **Identifying Relationships** Analyze the survival of the Welsh language in modern Welsh society. What does it say about Welsh society's view of cultural change?

Activity

Analyzing Data Use statistical information from the library or the Internet to create and draw a bar graph on per capita income in the United Kingdom and in three other Western European countries. Which economy is most prosperous? Do additional research to determine some of the reasons for the prosperity that this country is experiencing.

CUSTOMIZE FOR...

Gifted and Talented
Mining in Wales Have students research the prosperous years of the Welsh mining industry, focusing on the workers, the conditions in the mines, and life in the mining communities. Have them create and present a dramatization of family life based on their research.

Answers to Section 2 Assessment

1. **(a)** moor, p. 310 **(b)** bog, p. 310 **(c)** glen, p. 311

2. Scotland's landscape is divided into three regions: the large, high plateau of the northern Highlands; the Lowlands to the south containing the Clyde River; and the low, hilly Southern Uplands.

3. **(a)** Scotland has its own parliament, and many Scots remain Presbyterian instead of adopting the religion of the Church of England. **(b)** Wales has its own language, as well as its own capital city, flag, and postage stamps.

4. In the late 1800s and early 1900s, Wales became involved in industry and mining, which changed the landscape and economy of the country. By the mid-1900s, however, the country had fallen behind in technology. By the 1980s, coal mines closed, and unemployment soared. In the 1990s, foreign investment led to new jobs in high-tech and tourism industries.

5. Possible answer: Some of the Welsh have fought to preserve their language rather than accept English completely. This may indicate that they oppose cultural change.

Activity Rubrics Share rubrics with students before they create their bar graphs.
Attempted The bar graph contains factual errors, does not include the information requested, and is messy or difficult to read.
Minimal The bar graph contains factual errors, but it includes some of the information requested and is legible.
Adequate The bar graph contains no factual errors, includes all of the information requested, is accurately drawn, and is easy to read.
Exemplary The bar graph contains no factual errors, includes all of the information requested, and is well organized, accurately drawn, and attractive.

Answer to Photo Caption
Possible answers: petroleum products, gold, silver, tin, lead

Teaching the Skill

Read the introductory paragraph on this page. Then, have each student write a brief description of the same recent school event. Encourage students to include their opinions. Arrange students in groups and ask them to compare their descriptions with those of their group members. Direct each group to write a new, group description that all of its members can agree on. Share and compare group descriptions. Discuss the kinds of changes that had to be made to the individual versions to create a group version. As you proceed through the steps in the lesson with the students, point out similarities between the lesson and the earlier exercise in point of view.

Answers to Learn the Skill

1. Catholics. It opposes the parade.
2. (a) to defend their faith and maintain their British citizenship (b) a message of support and solidarity
3. (a) Protestant parade (b) They are sealing off the parade route.
4. (a) "No one should be allowed to create a no-go area." (b) The parade is "a bigoted, sectarian display."
5. Answers will vary. Students' answers will reflect how they have interpreted the viewpoints.

Answers to Practice the Skill

Students' essays should reflect an understanding of the differing points of view on the issues they have chosen.

 Alternative Assessment

Mid-Point Monitoring

Participating in a Cooperative Learning Project You may wish to monitor students' progress on planning their walking tour.

Recognizing Points of View

When people describe an idea or event, they usually provide some facts and their own personal viewpoints. A person's point of view is shaped by subjective influences such as feelings, prejudices, and past experiences. You often encounter divergent viewpoints, as when two of your friends describe the same event differently. By identifying different viewpoints, you will be able to better understand issues and form your own ideas and opinions.

Learn the Skill Read the two points of view below. Then, follow these steps to learn how to recognize different points of view.

1 *Identify the authors.* It is important to always identify the author of a viewpoint. Recognizing the background of the author will help you understand the viewpoint. *Do you think Viewpoint B was authored by Protestants or Catholics? Why?*

2 *Make sure you understand the arguments being made.* Try to identify the main idea and supporting arguments in each viewpoint. **(a)** *Why are Orangemen and women being asked to march in the parade?* **(b)** *What message are the residents of Garvaghy Road sending to the people of Lower Ormeau Road?*

3 *Find common information.* If two viewpoints are on the same topic, there should be some points on which they agree. Often, these will be basic facts that can be proved. **(a)** *What central event*

is the topic of both points of view? **(b)** *What are government officials doing to try to prevent violence?*

4 *Find opinions.* Differentiate the opinions from the facts. The opinions represent the authors' points of view about the facts. They often reflect emotions. Opinions cannot be proved. **(a)** *Identify one opinion in Viewpoint A.* **(b)** *Identify one opinion in Viewpoint B.*

5 *Draw conclusions.* Draw conclusions about the viewpoints and the topic that they deal with. Analyze the opinions, and decide whether they are based on facts or reasonable arguments. *Do you agree with the idea that not allowing a parade to go through a certain neighborhood is like racial segregation? Explain.*

 ## Do It Yourself

Practice the Skill Identify a geographic issue in your local community or state on which people have differing points of view. Write a series of basic questions about the issue. Then, ask some older friends or family members to answer your questions. Record their responses. Then, follow the steps above to recognize and analyze their points of view. Express your results in a brief essay.

Apply the Skill See Chapter 15 Review and Assessment.

Two Viewpoints

Background There is a long history of conflict between the Protestant majority and Catholic minority in Northern Ireland. One source of division today is the issue of parades. Protestants hold parades to celebrate their culture and religion—and their past military victories over Catholics. These parades sometimes go through Catholic neighborhoods, often resulting in outbreaks of violence.

Viewpoint A	Viewpoint B
"The Orange Family . . . must hold its head high and not in any way be sidetracked from its primary objectives: the defense of our . . . faith and the maintenance of our cherished British citizenship. We expect, over the next few days and weeks, that our parades . . . will again be the focus of attack by those in the community who show intolerance and hostility toward Orange traditions and culture. . . . No one should be allowed to create a no-go area. Segregation did not work in South Africa or in the United States. It must not be allowed to work in the United Kingdom."	"Sunday morning, security forces moved into the Lower Ormeau Road, sealing it off completely . . . in preparation for Orange feet to parade down their street. . . . The Residents of the Garvaghy Road send their full support and solidarity to those on the Lower Ormeau. The Garvaghy Road community . . . knows the hardship and pain of being put under siege for the sake of a bigoted, sectarian display. May all the communities that are imprisoned this week . . . see a peaceful conclusion to the situation and justice and equality for the Nationalist people of Ireland."

314 Chapter 15 ▪ The British Isles and Nordic Nations

RESOURCE DIRECTORY

Teaching Resources

Unit 4, Chapter 15
- Section 3 Guided Reading and Review, p. 15

Guide to the Essentials (English/Spanish)
- Section Summary, Chapter 15, Section 3

Mental Mapping booklet
- Unit 4 Checklist, p. 52

Social Studies Skills Handbook
- Checking Consistency of Ideas, p. 44

Technology

Guided Reading Audiotapes (English/Spanish), Chapter 15, Section 3

Section Reading Support Transparencies, Chapter 15, Section 3

World Geography Map and Photo Transparencies
- Western Europe: Maps and Photos

Book on CD, Chapter 15

Social Studies Skills Tutor CD-ROM, Identifying Reference and Point of View

Companion Web site, www.phschool.com
- Chapter 15 Activities

3 The Two Irelands

Reading Focus

- How would you describe Ireland's physical characteristics?
- What geographic processes caused cooperation and conflict in Ireland?
- What initiatives has the Republic of Ireland pursued in order to encourage economic activity?

Key Terms

peat

cultural divergence

blight

Main Idea By ending civil conflict and attracting high-tech industry, Ireland hopes to escape a troubled past.

Climates Ireland's marine west coast climate keeps the fields green near this farmstead in County Donegal.

Objectives

Upon completion of Section 3, students should be able to:

◆ describe Ireland's physical characteristics;

◆ identify the geographic processes that have caused cooperation and conflict in Ireland;

◆ explain how the Republic of Ireland has tried to boost economic activity.

National Geography Standards

The following National Geography Standards are highlighted in this section: 2, 4, 5, 6, 7, 9, 10, 13, 17, 18

Bellringer

Ask students: **How might citizens be affected if two countries tried to claim the area in which they live?** (Possible answers: The people may be subjected to violence, their rights may not be upheld, and their social and civic institutions may lose stability.)

LESSON PLAN

1. Focus Bring these objects to class: a bowl, an emerald-like stone, and a potato. Ask students what they think each object might have to do with Ireland. After they have read the section, have students link the geography and history of Ireland to these items.

2. Instruct Write these dates and time periods on the board: *1066; 1500s; 1840s; 1916–1921; 1949; 1990s.* Have students copy them on a piece of paper. As they read the chapter, ask them to identify the significance of each date in the religious and political struggle that has characterized the history of the two Irelands.

3. Close/Reteach Write *Ireland is divided* on the board. Have students explain why this statement is true politically, religiously, and culturally. Then, have them identify ways in which the two Irelands are geographically alike.

Ireland is divided politically into two parts: Northern Ireland and the Republic of Ireland. Ireland is also divided in religion between Protestants and Catholics. Finally, Ireland is divided culturally between the descendants of native Celtic peoples and the descendants of English and Scottish immigrants.

Ireland's Physical Characteristics

The divisions in Ireland are not visible immediately. The island itself is shaped like a huge bowl. Hills ring most of the coastline, while the middle of the island is a plain that drains into the River Shannon. Ireland's moist marine west coast climate keeps vegetation a brilliant green for most of the year. To the eye, Ireland lives up to its nickname, the Emerald Isle.

About one sixth of the island is covered by **peat,** a spongy material containing waterlogged mosses and plants. Because Ireland has few forests, farmers cut and dry blocks of peat as fuel for cooking and heating. The Republic of Ireland recently developed a method for using peat in power plants, which now produce nearly one quarter of the nation's electricity.

Cooperation and Conflict

Ireland's history has been shaped by invasions and wars. Celtic tribes from Europe first settled Ireland around 300 B.C. They repeatedly defended themselves against Viking raids, which lasted roughly from A.D. 800 to 1014.

In 1066, Norman invaders from France conquered England. Some of the Normans also seized large tracts of land in Ireland, built castles to protect themselves, and tried to control the Celts. They forbade marriage between Normans and Celts, banned use of the Celtic language, known as Gaelic (GAY lik), and even outlawed Celtic harp music.

King Henry II of England declared himself Lord of Ireland in 1171 and tried unsuccessfully to force Norman lords to obey him. But English rulers who followed Henry held on to the title and began thinking of Ireland as a possession.

Religious Conflicts Until the 1500s, the Roman Catholic Church had directed religious affairs in much of Western Europe. In the early 1500s, groups in Europe tried to change some of the Church's practices and started a reform movement known as the Reformation. Many of the reformers,

Chapter 15 ▪ Section 3   **315**

CUSTOMIZE FOR...

Less Proficient Readers

Visualizing After students have read the first paragraph in the subsection Ireland's Physical Characteristics, ask them to sketch the physical characteristics of Ireland as the paragraph describes them. Have students compare their sketches to the physical-political map of the British Isles on page 306.

Word Origin

Ireland In the ancient Celtic language of Gaelic, Ireland is called Eire (pronounced AIR uh). The Gaelic phrase *Erin go bragh* means "Ireland forever."

Summarizing Main Ideas

Divide the class into three groups. Assign each group one of the subsections in Section 3. Have each group identify and write down its subsection's main idea with two supporting statements. Have each group share its main idea with the class.

Group Work

Activity: Problem solving

Purpose: Tell each group to research the conflict between Protestants and Catholics in Northern Ireland and to make a list of suggestions for resolving it.

Roles: Groups should include researchers, a scribe, and a leader.

Result: Each leader shares his or her group's suggestions with the class.

Answer to Photo Caption

Possible answer: The government could provide educational programs to train people for better-paying technical and professional jobs.

---

called Protestants, broke with the Roman Catholic Church and formed new Christian churches.

Most English people became Protestants. The Irish, for the most part, remained Catholics. This division led to bitter conflicts between Irish Catholics and landlords sent from England. Economics played a major part in the hostility. The Protestant minority controlled much of the wealth, and the Irish Catholics were poor. Conflict between Irish Protestants and Catholics led to **cultural divergence,** or deliberate efforts to keep the cultures separate.

The Potato Famine hit Ireland in the 1840s. A **blight,** or plant disease, destroyed the potato crop year after year. Most of the people in Ireland relied on potatoes as their major source of nutrition. As a result, about one million Irish died of starvation or disease. The crisis further inflamed anti-British feelings because many Irish Catholics blamed England for not providing enough aid.

The famine brought push-and-pull migration factors into play. Pushed from the island by famine, nearly two million Irish emigrated in just seven years. Pulled by the lure of jobs, most immigrated to the United States.

Government and Citizenship Many Irish continued to press for independence throughout the nineteenth century. Rebellions between 1916 and 1921 led officials in the United Kingdom and Ireland to divide the island into two parts. The six northeastern counties remained part of the United Kingdom, but the rest of Ireland became a free state under British supervision. This free state declared its total independence as the Republic of Ireland in 1949. Independence did not end political turmoil on the island.

Today, a little over half of Northern Ireland's people are Protestant. Most of the rest are Catholic. Most Catholics support the reunification of Ireland, whereas most Protestants oppose it.

Both Protestant and Catholic extremists have used violence to try to win control of Northern Ireland. Bombings, hunger strikes, and gun battles kept antagonism high. Peace talks began in 1994. Despite violent outbreaks that regularly erupt, an agreement signed in 1998 offered a solid chance for peace. As British Prime Minister Tony Blair said in 1999, "I accept that this . . . [is] an imperfect process and an imperfect peace, but it is better than no process and no peace at all."

Poverty in Northern Ireland

Planning for the Future In this Catholic community in Northern Ireland, children play on burnt cars surrounded by signs of poverty and neglect. Many Catholics in Northern Ireland complain that they do not share the same economic opportunities as the Protestant majority.

Place *How might the British government help to mend the gap between rich and poor in Northern Ireland?*

Teaching Resources

Unit 4, Chapter 15
• Section 3 Quiz, p. 16

Spanish Resources
• Section 3 Quiz, p. 36

Social Studies Skills Handbook
• Reading a Time Line, p. 61

Economic Growth

Economic Activities
Investment has brought new life to the economy of the Republic of Ireland. In Dublin, the International Financial Services Center provides a base for a number of commercial and banking businesses from around the world.
Regions *How did the government encourage foreign businesses to open offices in the Republic of Ireland?*

Economic Activities

In the 1990s, the Republic of Ireland took bold economic initiatives. The government invested in education and modern telecommunications. It offered tax incentives that persuaded foreign high-tech companies to locate administrative offices in Ireland. The plan was so successful that Irish economic growth was the highest in Europe between 1994 and 2000. Per capita income increased dramatically and unemployment fell to 3.8 percent,

one of Europe's lowest unemployment rates. The new economic climate pulled immigrants to Ireland. It also lured many Irish emigrants in the United States back to their homeland.

Change has not been without cost, however. In 1999, Ireland adopted the euro, the currency of the European Union. Inflation rose to 6.2 percent, triple the European average. Housing costs skyrocketed. Some people also worry about a growing income gap between workers in the new economy and those in traditional service industries.

SECTION 3 ASSESSMENT

1. **Key Terms** Define **(a)** peat, **(b)** cultural divergence, **(c)** blight.

2. **Physical Characteristics** Why is Ireland called the Emerald Isle?

3. **Cooperation and Conflict** Describe the geographic processes that led to the formation of two political units in Ireland.

4. **Economic Activities** How has the government of Ireland tried to improve the economy?

5. **Critical Thinking Distinguishing Fact From Opinion (a)** Determine whether or not the following statement is a fact or an opinion: "Protestants and Catholics in Northern Ireland

both feel threatened by the past and are reluctant to negotiate." **(b)** Do you agree or disagree with the statement? Explain.

Activity

Take It to the NET

Writing Biographical Essays Use Internet resources to read about Mairead Corrigan and Betty Williams, winners of the Nobel Peace Prize. Then, write a biography for each, emphasizing those achievements that earned international recognition. Visit the World Geography section of **www.phschool.com** for help in completing this activity.

Objectives

Upon completion of Section 4, students should be able to:

◆ describe the physical and cultural characteristics that define the Nordic nations;

◆ explain how the Nordic people have used natural resources to pursue a variety of economic activities.

National Geography Standards

The following National Geography Standards are highlighted in this section: 1, 4, 5, 7, 8, 10, 11, 13, 15, 17

Bellringer

Ask students how their lives would change if the sun shone for only two or three hours a day.

LESSON PLAN

1. Focus Divide the class into groups, assigning each group one of the Nordic nations. Tell them to use the physical-political map on the opposite page to answer the following question: **How might your country's physical geography, including its location, affect its economy?** As the students read the chapter, compare their answers to the text.

2. Instruct Make two double-column charts on the board. Title the first chart *Physical Ties,* and list the following categories in its first column: *Location, Landforms, Climate.* Title the second chart *Cultural Ties,* and list the following categories in its first column: *History, Government, Religion, Language, Economy.* Have students fill in the charts by describing the physical and cultural features that unite Norden as a region.

3. Close/Reteach Have students draw physical maps of Norden that include three intentional errors, such as the misplacement of a body of water or the movement of a mountain range. Have students exchange maps and identify the errors. Discuss how some of the students' changes might affect people living in Norden.

4 The Nordic Nations

Reading Focus

- **What physical characteristics define the Nordic nations as a region?**
- **What kind of historical, cultural, and economic bonds do the Nordic nations share?**
- **How have the people of the Nordic nations used natural resources to successfully pursue a variety of economic activities?**

Key Terms

fjord

geothermal energy

mixed economy

Main Idea Similar physical characteristics, climates, and cultures are shared by the Nordic nations of Norway, Sweden, Finland, Denmark, and Iceland.

Physical Processes Glacial valleys cut sharply into Norway's Atlantic coast.

The people of northern Europe call their land *Norden,* from an ancient word meaning "Northlands." Norden includes five independent nations: Norway, Sweden, Finland, Denmark, and Iceland. These nations, called the Nordic nations in English, are unified as a region by location and strong cultural bonds.

Physical Characteristics

Norden is identified as a region in part by its location in the northern latitudes. Parts of some Nordic nations reach past the Arctic Circle into the polar zone.

A Varied Landscape The region is a collection of peninsulas and islands separated by seas, gulfs, and oceans. The most continuous land masses are the Scandinavian and Jutland peninsulas. The terrain varies dramatically throughout the Nordic nations. Denmark is so flat that its highest point is less than 600 feet (183 m) high, whereas Norway is one of the most mountainous nations in Europe.

Environmental Change Much of the landscape on the Scandinavian Peninsula is the product of the last ice age. Glaciers carved out thousands of lakes across the peninsula. They also removed topsoil and other materials and deposited them in Denmark and other parts of Western Europe. As a result, much of the soil in Scandinavia today remains rocky and difficult to farm.

Notice the jagged coastlines along the Scandinavian Peninsula on the map on page 319. When the glaciers advanced, they carved out deep valleys along the coasts. When the glaciers melted, water filled the valleys, creating flooded glacial valleys known as **fjords** (fee YAWRDZ). Some fjords are so deep that oceangoing ships can sail into them. Most have such steep walls that even mountain climbers find them difficult to scale.

Natural Resources In Iceland, volcanoes and glaciers exist side by side. Icelanders call their island "a land of fire and ice." They have learned to take advantage of the island's geology

RESOURCE DIRECTORY

Teaching Resources

Creative Teaching Activities, What Is a Culture Hero?, p. 17

Unit 4, Chapter 15
- Section 4 Guided Reading and Review, p. 17
- Geography and World Literature, The Eclipse, p. 60

Guide to the Essentials (English/Spanish)
- Section Summary, Chapter 15, Section 4

Mental Mapping booklet
- Unit 4 Checklist, p. 52
- Outline Map 15, p. 57

Technology

Guided Reading Audiotapes (English/Spanish), Chapter 15, Section 4

Section Reading Support Transparencies, Chapter 15, Section 4

World Geography Map and Photo Transparencies
- Western Europe: Maps and Photos

Books on CD, Chapter 15

Social Studies Skills Tutor CD-ROM

Companion Web site, www.phschool.com
- Chapter 15 Activities

The Nordic Nations: PHYSICAL-POLITICAL

KEY

Elevation

Feet		Meters
14,000		4,270
7,000		2,135
1,500		457
700		213
(sea level) 0		0 (sea level)

⊛ National capital
• Major city
▲ Mountain

Lambert Azimuthal Equal-Area Projection

APPLYING THE GEOGRAPHIC THEMES

● **Location** *Nordic* means "north."
• *What island is at the most extreme northern latitude of the Nordic nations?*

---

to produce **geothermal energy,** or energy produced from the heat of the earth's interior. Today, geothermal energy accounts for a large share of the power used for heat and electricity in Iceland.

Long Winters, Short Summers

"Winter is the element for which we are born," declared a Finnish historian in the 1800s. Norden's location to the far north results in long winters and short summers. At midwinter the sun may shine only 2 or 3 hours a day. In midsummer, it shines for more than 20 hours.

Winter is when the greenish white and red lights of the aurora borealis, or northern lights,

shine most brightly in the Nordic nations. These lights appear when atomic particles from the sun, attracted by the magnetic fields of the North Pole, break through the northern atmosphere.

The start of summer is a public holiday in most Nordic nations, when people celebrate the return of the "midnight sun." In the northernmost territories, the sun never really sets for several weeks in midsummer. People call the long twilight hours of evening the "white nights."

The Ocean and the Climate
Despite the length of winter, the climate in much of Norden can be surprisingly mild. As is evident from the climate map on page 293, half of Iceland, all

---

Enrichment

Creating Collages Have students create a "Blue Meadow" or "Midnight Sun" collage using magazines or original drawings to illustrate these aspects of Nordic geography. (Visual/Spatial)

Group Work

Activity: Making a television show

Purpose: Tell each group to prepare a five-minute television show introducing one of the Nordic nations. Shows could include a greeting in the native language; descriptions of sports, foods, major cities, places of interest; "fun facts" about the country; and a description of travel arrangements to a major city in the assigned country.

Roles: Groups should include researchers, writers, narrators, and a director.

Result: Each group presents its show to the class.

Building Vocabulary

Before reading the subsection Shared Cultural Bonds, ask students to skim the section to find unfamiliar words. List the words on the board and have students read the words' definitions aloud from dictionaries. Ask volunteers to write two- or three-word definitions next to the words on the board. As the students read the subsection, remind them to use the list on the board for reference.

Answer to Photo Caption

The Nordic nations practice a mixture of free enterprise and socialism. Nordic governments guarantee certain goods and services to everyone and operate some industries.

320 Chapter 15

Glass Factory

Economic Activities Although Norway's economy relies most heavily on services, industry also plays an important role. Here, a Norwegian factory worker prepares to create a piece of glass.

Regions *How do mixed economies work among Nordic nations?*

Scandinavian Peninsula. The result is a cold, dry subarctic climate.

Shared Cultural Bonds

More than climate and location bind the Nordic nations into a region. They also have strong cultural ties.

Understanding the Past The Nordic nations have similar histories. From around A.D. 800 to 1050, Vikings sailed out of the fjords and inlets of southern Norden to raid much of Western Europe. The Vikings were more than warriors. They were traders, colonizers, and explorers who left their mark on world history.

The Nordic nations were also united at times. Queen Margrethe of Denmark joined the five lands under one crown in 1397. The union ended in 1523 when Sweden (which included Finland) withdrew. But Denmark, Norway, and Iceland remained united for several centuries more. Sweden and Finland were united until the early 1800s, when Sweden ceded Finland to Russia.

Religion, too, unites the Nordic people. Most Nordic peoples belong to the Lutheran Church, first established during the Reformation.

With the exception of Finnish, Nordic languages have common roots. Finland is bilingual, and most Finns have a working knowledge of Swedish, Finland's second language. In addition, Nordic schools require students to learn English, which helps bridge any linguistic differences.

Economic Systems Nordic countries share certain political and economic beliefs. All five of the Nordic nations are democracies, and their economic systems are **mixed economies,** or systems combining different degrees of government regulation. They practice a mixture of free enterprise and socialism.

Most businesses in the Nordic countries operate much as they do in the United States. But, the Nordic governments guarantee certain goods and services to everyone and operate some industries that are run privately in the United States. For example, Denmark and Sweden have state-run day-care centers and state-supported medical care.

As a rule, the Nordic nations are politically neutral in foreign affairs. That is, they do not take

of Denmark, the west coast of Norway, and southern Sweden have mild marine west coast climates. The warm currents of the North Atlantic Drift moderate the weather and keep the coast free of ice.

The coldest areas in Norden lie just east of a mountain chain that runs northeast to southwest through Norway. This range prevents the warm, moist ocean winds from reaching the rest of the

RESOURCE DIRECTORY

Teaching Resources
Unit 4, Chapter 15
- Section 4 Quiz, p. 18
- Reviewing Main Ideas, p. 19
- Critical Thinking, p. 20
- Test Forms A and B, pp. 22–27
Spanish Resources
- Section 4 Quiz, p. 37
Guide to the Essentials (English/Spanish)
- Chapter 15 Test
Mental Mapping booklet
- Chapter 15 Map Test, p. 59

Simulations, Games, and Lab Activities
- Place Location Review Games, pp. 58–63
Social Studies Skills Handbook
- Study and Research Skills, pp. 94–108

Technology
ExamView Test Bank CD-ROM, Chapter 15 Test
Companion Web site, www.phschool.com
- Chapter 15 Self-Test

Stockholm

Understanding the Past
Stockholm, Sweden's capital since 1523, is tied closely to the Baltic Sea. The city is built on a group of islands along Sweden's eastern shore. In the 1600s the city became the center of a thriving empire that dominated many parts of Europe.

Place *How can you tell from this photograph that Stockholm has a long, prosperous history?*

sides in international disputes. Currently, Norway refuses to open its excellent harbors for military use. It also forbids the storage of nuclear weapons on its territory. Denmark and Sweden actively promote peaceful solutions to international crises.

Economic Activities

Compared with other regions of the world, the Nordic nations have sound economies. They derive their wealth from varied sources. Denmark and southern Sweden have flat land and a mild climate suitable for agriculture. Denmark uses 60 percent of its land for farming and in recent years produced more than three times the amount of food needed to feed its people. Fishing is also an important economic activity. The Norwegians, in particular, look to the sea. They compare it to farmland and call their offshore waters the Blue Meadow. The region also profits from oil and gas production, high-grade ores, and vast expanses of forest.

SECTION 4 ASSESSMENT

1. **Key Terms** Define **(a)** fjord, **(b)** geothermal energy, **(c)** mixed economy.

2. **Physical Characteristics (a)** What physical processes are at work in the Nordic nations? **(b)** How does the North Atlantic Drift affect climatic conditions in Norden?

3. **Cultures** What cultural similarities define northern Europe as a region?

4. **Economic Activities** What are the various resources from which the Nordic nations derive their wealth?

5. **Critical Thinking Identifying Relationships** How do the economies of the Nordic nations show characteristics of both free enterprise and socialism?

> **Activity**
>
> **Identifying Nordic Customs** Use library resources to learn more about the Midnight Sun holiday in two or more Nordic nations. In a short paragraph, describe and compare the customs that make each holiday distinctive to its country. Then, create a poster advertising one nation's event. Identify traditional foods, arts, contests, and ceremonies of the event.

Articles From **NATIONAL GEOGRAPHIC**

The following article may be used to extend the content in this section.

Keillor, Garrison, and Sisse Brimberg, photographer. "Civilized Denmark." *National Geographic,* Vol. 194, No. 1 (July 1998), pp. 50–73.

The smallest of the Nordic nations, Denmark is among the countries with the lowest crime and poverty rates in the world.

CHAPTER
15 REVIEW AND ASSESSMENT

Creating a Chapter Summary
As a reteaching opportunity, pair a more able student with a less able student to complete this chapter summary.

Venn diagrams might include the following additional entries: **British Isles:** Evenly divided seasons, Large coal deposits, Tertiary economic activities, Cultural divergence, Religious conflict, Quaternary economic activities **Nordic Nations:** Volcanoes, Geothermal energy, Long winters and short summers, Cultural convergence, Religious unity, Primary economic activities **Both:** Located in Western Europe, Glaciers helped shape landscape, Fertile soil in south, Democracies, Oil and gas production

Reviewing Key Terms
1–10. Students' sentences should show a clear understanding of each term.

Understanding Key Ideas
11. Answers include highlands, midlands, uplands, lowlands, and coal deposits.
12. It led to population concentrations in the cities.
13. Scotland has its own parliament and religion. Wales has its own language, capital city, flag, and postage stamps.
14. (a) religious, economic, and political differences between Catholics and Protestants **(b)** Lasting peace has been difficult to achieve. The 1998 agreement offered some hope for peace.
15. (a) Many people left Ireland in search of employment and adequate food. **(b)** The lure of jobs pulled them to the United States.
16. Their location in the northern latitudes defines them as a region.

Critical Thinking and Writing
17. Possible answer: Britain may fear that it will lose the ability to control the value of its own currency.
18. Possible questions: How do the mountains affect patterns of settlement? How is the climate affected by the Atlantic Ocean?
19. Answers will vary but should take into account the long-standing political divisions between Catholics and Protestants.

(Continued on next page.)

322 Chapter 15

Creating a Chapter Summary

On a sheet of paper, draw a Venn diagram like the one below. In the left oval, write characteristics of the British Isles. In the right oval, write characteristics that apply to the Nordic nations. In the overlapping center area, write characteristics that apply to both regions.

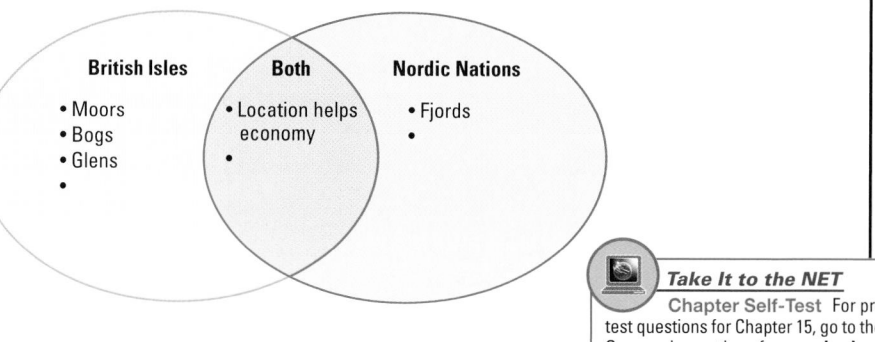

British Isles
• Moors
• Bogs
• Glens
•

Both
• Location helps economy
•

Nordic Nations
• Fjords
•

Take It to the NET
Chapter Self-Test For practice test questions for Chapter 15, go to the World Geography section of **www.phschool.com**.

Reviewing Key Terms

Write each of the following terms in a sentence that shows its meaning. You may use two terms in one sentence.

1. fertile
2. ore
3. moor
4. bog
5. glen
6. peat
7. blight
8. fjord
9. geothermal energy
10. mixed economy

Understanding Key Ideas

11. Physical Characteristics What are some major physical characteristics of the British Isles?

12. Patterns of Settlement How did the Industrial Revolution change patterns of settlement in the British Isles?

13. Cultures What are the ways in which Scotland and Wales have kept their cultural identities somewhat distinct from English culture?

14. Cooperation and Conflict (a) What are sources of conflict in Ireland? **(b)** Have peace efforts been successful? Explain.

15. Migration (a) How did the Potato Famine lead to migration away from Ireland? **(b)** Why did many Irish emigrants choose to relocate in the United States?

16. Physical Characteristics Describe the physical characteristics that define the Nordic nations as a region.

Critical Thinking and Writing

17. Analyzing Change Why might Britain be reluctant to adopt the euro as its currency?

18. Asking Geographic Questions Study the map on page 306. Write a series of questions about the physical characteristics of the British Isles and their effects on the British people.

19. Predicting Consequences Some demographers estimate that Catholics soon will outnumber Protestants in Northern Ireland. What might be the political result of such a trend?

20. Sequencing Create a flowchart that high-lights the most significant changes in the English economy from the 1500s to today.

Applying Skills

Recognizing Points of View Refer to the points of view on page 314 to answer these questions:

21. What is the central event or issue on which the two viewpoints are based?

22. Can you think of a compromise point of view that might offer a solution to the disagreement? Explain.

Analyzing Data Study the data below, and answer the following questions:

23. Based on the data and what you have learned about Iceland, why does Iceland not need to import petroleum?

24. Which country pays the greatest amount of money for imported oil?

British Isles, Nordic Nations, and the United States

Energy Data

Country	Electricity Consumption (per capita kilowatt-hours)	Petroleum Imports (thousand barrels per year)	Petroleum Exports (thousand barrels per year)
Denmark	5,508	42,879	40,223
Finland	12,846	68,071	0
Iceland	19,028	0	0
Ireland	4,837	16,870	0
Norway	23,977	8,944	1,082,290
Sweden	14,811	146,790	0
United Kingdom	5,376	323,654	530,646
United States	12,235	2,742,208	40,129

Test Preparation

Read the question and choose the best answer.

25. The climate of the British Isles and Nordic nations is milder than other countries of similar latitudes because of —

A the relationship between the earth and sun

B the effects of geothermal energy

C the nation's great distance from the Equator

D the warm currents of the North Atlantic Drift

Activities

USING THE REGIONAL ATLAS

Using information from Chapter 15 and the Regional Atlas for Western Europe, make a table identifying physical processes in the British Isles and Nordic nations. Make a table with two columns. In the first column, list physical processes, such as erosion, ocean currents, and glaciation. In the second column, describe the effects of each process on the physical and cultural characteristics of the region.

 MENTAL MAPPING

Study a map of the British Isles and the Nordic nations. On a separate piece of paper, draw a sketch map of the region from memory. Label the following places on your map:

- England
- Scotland
- Wales
- Republic of Ireland
- Northern Ireland
- Denmark
- Iceland
- Sweden
- Finland
- Norway
- Atlantic Ocean
- North Sea
- Baltic Sea

Take It to the NET

Analyzing Data Search the Internet for data about oil and natural gas exploration in the North Sea. Analyze the data to determine general trends regarding exports of oil and gas by the British Isles and Nordic nations. Create a report that includes graphs and tables, and prepare a written summary of your findings. Visit the World Geography section of **www.phschool.com** for help in completing this activity.

---

20. Flowcharts will vary but should show the transition from agrarian to industrial to service industries.

Applying Skills
21. Protestant parades in Northern Ireland
22. Answers will vary. Students might find it difficult to come up with a compromise because the positions on each side are so hardened.
23. Geothermal energy accounts for a large share of the power used for heat and electricity in Iceland.
24. the United States

Test Preparation
25. D

Activities

Using the Regional Atlas
Check students' tables for accuracy.

Mental Mapping
Review students' maps for relative and absolute location.

Take It to the Net
Students' work should reflect sound research. Graphs and tables should be based on information from reliable Web sites. Summaries should accurately interpret data and identify general trends.

 MENTAL MAPPING

Games for Review See pages 58–63 of the Simulations, Games, and Lab Activities booklet for games to review place names in preparation for the Chapter 15 Map Test.

Chapter Map Test Students should use their completed outline maps and the Unit 4 Checklist in their Atlas Portfolios to prepare for the Chapter 15 Map Test. The test will cover only those place names on the list relating to the region covered in Chapter 15.

Alternative Assessment

Final Evaluation
Participating in a Cooperative Learning Project Use the Cooperative Learning Project Evaluation Forms on pages 17 and 19 of the Alternative Assessment booklet in the Prentice Hall Assessment System to evaluate students' participation. Either teachers or students can complete the forms to indicate which level of work was achieved for each of the criteria. The evaluation should include specific comments.

Resource Manager

	CORE INSTRUCTION	READING/SKILLS
Chapter-Level Resources	**Teaching Resources** ■ **Unit 4**/Ch. 16 • Reviewing Main Ideas, p. 36 📖 **Mental Mapping booklet** • Unit 4 Checklist, p. 52 📖 **Simulations, Games, and Lab Activities** • Where to Put the Landfill, pp. 23–29 • Place Location Review Games, pp. 58–63 📖 **Creative Teaching Activities** • Traveling Through Central Western Europe, p. 18 💿 **TeacherExpress™ CD-ROM**, Ch. 16 💻 **Companion Web site,** **www.phschool.com** • eTeach	**Teaching Resources** ■ **Unit 4**/Ch. 16 • Map/Graph Skills, p. 38 📖 **Mental Mapping booklet** • Outline Map 16, p. 60 📖 **Social Studies Skills Handbook** • Distinguishing Fact from Opinion, p. 43 💿 **Book on CD**, Ch. 16 💿 **Social Studies Skills Tutor CD-ROM**
1 France 1. Identify the physical and economic regions of France. 2. Explain how changes in government have affected the extent of French territory. 3. Explain how language is related to culture in France. 4. Describe how economic and social uncertainties affect life in France.	**Teaching Resources** ■ **Unit 4**/Ch. 16 • Guided Reading and Review, p. 28 💿 **Prentice Hall Presentation Pro CD-ROM**, Ch. 16, Sec. 1	**Teaching Resources** 📖 **Guide to the Essentials (English/Spanish)** • Section Summary, Ch. 16, Sec. 1 📖 **Social Studies Skills Handbook** • Maps with Accurate Distances: Equidistant Maps, p. 17 📼 **Guided Reading Audiotapes (English/Spanish)**, Ch. 16, Sec. 1 🗔 **Section Reading Support Transparencies**, Ch. 16, Sec. 1
2 Germany 1. Describe how Germany achieved unification in the 1800s and 1900s. 2. Explain how physical characteristics affect Germany's economy and its patterns of settlement. 3. List the challenges that Germany faces today.	**Teaching Resources** ■ **Unit 4**/Ch. 16 • Guided Reading and Review, p. 30 💿 **Prentice Hall Presentation Pro CD-ROM**, Ch. 16, Sec. 2	**Teaching Resources** 📖 **Guide to the Essentials (English/Spanish)** • Section Summary, Ch. 16, Sec. 2 📼 **Guided Reading Audiotapes (English/Spanish)**, Ch. 16, Sec. 2 🗔 **Section Reading Support Transparencies**, Ch. 16, Sec. 2
3 The Benelux Countries 1. Identify the major way in which the Dutch have changed their physical environment. 2. Describe how language has affected culture in Belgium. 3. Explain how diversification has changed Luxembourg's economy.	**Teaching Resources** ■ **Unit 4**/Ch. 16 • Guided Reading and Review, p. 32 💿 **Prentice Hall Presentation Pro CD-ROM**, Ch. 16, Sec. 3	**Teaching Resources** 📖 **Guide to the Essentials (English/Spanish)** • Section Summary, Ch. 16, Sec. 3 📼 **Guided Reading Audiotapes (English/Spanish)**, Ch. 16, Sec. 3 🗔 **Section Reading Support Transparencies**, Ch. 16, Sec. 3
4 Switzerland and Austria 1. Describe how the character of Switzerland is shaped by its history, culture, and economy. 2. Explain how shifting political boundaries and patterns of settlement have affected life in Austria.	**Teaching Resources** ■ **Unit 4**/Ch. 16 • Guided Reading and Review, p. 34 💿 **Prentice Hall Presentation Pro CD-ROM**, Ch. 16, Sec. 4	**Teaching Resources** 📖 **Guide to the Essentials (English/Spanish)** • Section Summary, Ch. 16, Sec. 4 📼 **Guided Reading Audiotapes (English/Spanish)**, Ch. 16, Sec. 4 🗔 **Section Reading Support Transparencies**, Ch. 16, Sec. 4

ENRICHMENT/HONORS/PREAP

📕 Teaching Resources

📓 Unit 4/Ch. 16
- Critical Thinking, p. 37

📘 Mental Mapping booklet
- Atlas Activity, p. 61

📘 Social Studies Skills Handbook
- Study and Research Skills, pp. 94–108

📘 People and Geography
- Environmental Change, pp. 19–24

📖 World Geography Map and Photo Transparencies
- Western Europe: Maps and Photos

📼 World Geography Videos
- Global Trade Patterns: Central Western Europe, Tape 2

💻 Companion Web site, www.phschool.com
- Chapter 16 Activities

💻 Companion Web site, www.phschool.com
- Chapter 16 Activities

💻 Companion Web site, www.phschool.com
- Chapter 16 Activities

💻 Companion Web site, www.phschool.com
- Chapter 16 Activities

📕 Teaching Resources

📘 Social Studies Skills Handbook
- Expressing Problems Clearly, p. 40

💻 Companion Web site, www.phschool.com
- Chapter 16 Activities

ASSESSMENT

PRENTICE HALL ASSESSMENT SYSTEM

Core Assessment

📘 ExamView Test Bank booklet, Ch. 16
💿 ExamView Test Bank CD-ROM, Ch. 16

Standardized Test Preparation

Review and Reteach

📘 Review Book for World Geography, pp. 9–10

Practice and Assess

📘 Test-taking Strategies With Transparencies for High School

Test-taking Strategy Poster

📘 Alternative Assessment booklet

📘 Test Prep Book for World Geography

📕 Teaching Resources

📓 Unit 4/Ch. 16
- Section Quizzes, pp. 29, 31, 33, 35
- Test Forms A and B, pp. 39–44

📘 Guide to the Essentials (English/Spanish)
- Chapter 16 Test

📘 Spanish Resources, Ch. 16
- Section Quizzes, pp. 38–41

📘 Mental Mapping booklet
- Chapter 16 Map Test, p. 62

💻 Companion Web site, www.phschool.com
- Chapter 16 Self-Test

CUSTOMIZE FOR INDIVIDUAL NEEDS

Honors/PreAP
- Teacher's Edition, Customize for . . . , pp. 339, 341

Less Proficient Readers
- Guide to the Essentials (English), Ch. 16, Section Summaries
- Guided Reading Audiotapes (English), Ch. 16
- Section Reading Support Transparencies, Ch. 16
- Book on CD, Ch. 16
- Teacher's Edition, Reading Strategy, pp. 326, 334, 338, 343
- Teacher's Edition, Activity: Vocabulary, pp. 329, 332, 343
- Teacher's Edition, Customize for . . . , p. 331

Students Acquiring English/ESL
- Guide to the Essentials (English/Spanish), Ch. 16
- Guided Reading Audiotapes (English/Spanish), Ch. 16
- Section Reading Support Transparencies, Ch. 16
- Book on CD, Ch. 16
- Teacher's Edition, Customize for . . . , pp. 329, 343

Less Proficient Writers
- Social Studies Skills Handbook, p. 92
- Alternative Assessment, Writing Assignment Rubric, p. 6

MENTAL MAPPING

Referring to the map on this page, point out that Central Western Europe includes France, Germany, Belgium, Luxembourg, the Netherlands, Switzerland, and Austria. Have students name the countries that are landlocked. (Luxembourg, Switzerland, and Austria)

Mapping the Region Either ask students to sketch their own outline maps of Central Western Europe or distribute the Chapter 16 Outline Map on page 60 of the Mental Mapping booklet in the Teaching Resources. Ask students to lightly shade each country a different color. Then instruct them to add labels for the countries and bodies of water that are shown on the map on this page. Students should keep their maps in their Atlas Portfolios in order to prepare for the Chapter 16 Map Test.

eTeach

Be sure to check out this month's online forum with a Master Teacher to join in an exchange of teaching ideas. **www.phschool.com**

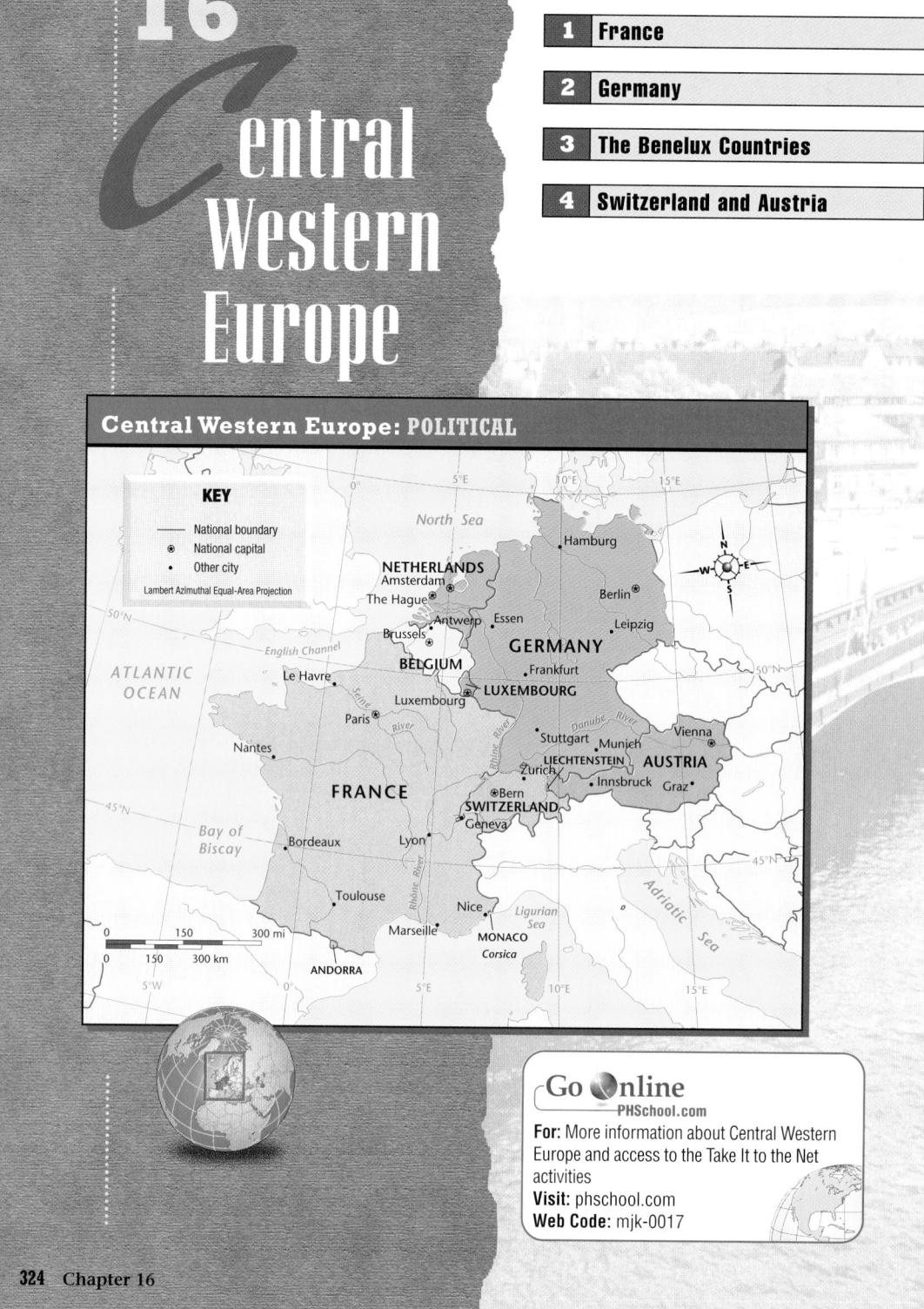

C H A P T E R

16

Central Western Europe

SECTIONS

1 **France**

2 **Germany**

3 **The Benelux Countries**

4 **Switzerland and Austria**

Central Western Europe: POLITICAL

KEY
— National boundary
⊛ National capital
• Other city
Lambert Azimuthal Equal-Area Projection

North Sea

Hamburg

NETHERLANDS
Amsterdam
The Hague ⊛
Antwerp • Essen
Brussels ⊛
BELGIUM
Le Havre •
Luxembourg
Paris ⊛
LUXEMBOURG

Berlin ⊛
Leipzig •

GERMANY
Frankfurt •

Nantes •

ATLANTIC
OCEAN

English Channel

50°N

Seine River

Stuttgart • Munich
Zurich • LIECHTENSTEIN
⊛ Bern
SWITZERLAND
Geneva •

Rhine River

Danube River

Vienna ⊛

AUSTRIA
Innsbruck • Graz •

FRANCE

Bay of
Biscay

45°N

Bordeaux • Lyon •

Rhône River

Toulouse •

Nice •
Ligurian
Sea

Marseille •

MONACO
Corsica

Adriatic Sea

45°N

0   150   300 mi
0   150   300 km

ANDORRA

5°W   0°   5°E   10°E   15°E

Go Online
PHSchool.com

For: More information about Central Western Europe and access to the Take It to the Net activities
Visit: phschool.com
Web Code: mjk-0017

324   Chapter 16

RESOURCE DIRECTORY

Teaching Resources
Unit 4, Chapter 16
• Section 1 Guided Reading and Review, p. 28
Guide to the Essentials (English/Spanish)
• Section Summary, Chapter 16, Section 1
Mental Mapping booklet
• Atlas Activity, p. 61
• Unit 4 Checklist, p. 52

Technology
Guided Reading Audiotapes (English/Spanish),
Chapter 16, Section 1

Section Reading Support Transparencies,
Chapter 16, Section 1
World Geography Map and Photo Transparencies
• Western Europe: Maps and Photos
Book on CD, Chapter 16
World Geography Videos
• Global Trade Patterns: Central Western Europe, Tape 2
TeacherExpress™ CD-ROM, Chapter 16
Prentice Hall Presentation Pro CD-ROM, Chapter 16
Social Studies Skills Tutor CD-ROM
Companion Web site, www.phschool.com
• Chapter 16 Activities

1 France

Reading Focus

- **What are the main physical and economic regions of France?**
- **How have changes in government affected the extent of French territory?**
- **How is language related to culture in France?**
- **What economic and social uncertainties are part of French life today?**

Key Terms

dialect

Impressionism

nationalize

recession

Main Idea Although France has varied physical characteristics, its shared history and language encourage national unity.

Economic Activities Natural resources and a large workforce provide a basis for industry in northern France.

The map of France on page 327 shows why the French sometimes call their country "The Hexagon." If you smooth out the zigs and zags of France's borders, you will see that the country is roughly six-sided. Water borders three of the sides. Mountains form forbidding barriers on two other sides. Only in the northeast do low hills and flat, wide plains provide easy passage into neighboring countries.

Over the centuries, the French have established a strong national identity. As journalist Flora Lewis observed, "The French have no problems of identity. They know who they are and can't imagine wanting to be like anybody else."

Regions and Economic Activities

Even while France maintains a strong national identity, historic cultural and economic regions exist within the nation. The people of each of France's regions proudly continue their own traditions and way of life. From rich farming areas to huge, urban manufacturing and commercial centers, the different regions contribute to France's varied market economy.

Northern France In the interior of northern France lies the Paris Basin, a part of the North European Plain. The Paris Basin is a large functional region drained by the Seine (SEHN) and other rivers.

In the center of the Paris Basin, on the banks of the Seine, lies Paris, the economic, political, and cultural capital of France. Paris and its surrounding area form France's chief center of commercial industry. Raw materials shipped here from other parts of France and from other countries are turned into finished products.

The city of Lille (LEEL), north of Paris, is another important industrial center. Since the late 1800s, the availability of coal for fuel in nearby Belgium has been a major pull factor, attracting many industries. Steel mills, textile factories, and chemical plants in and around Lille have provided jobs. Lille's location near northern European Union countries has helped it recover in recent years from economic problems and high unemployment.

Vineyards of the Southwest In the southern parts of France, the air is warmer and the soil drier. The grapes used to make French

◄ Rhine River, Konstanz, Germany (photo left)

Objectives

Upon completion of Section 1, students should be able to:

◆ identify the physical and economic regions of France;

◆ explain how changes in government have affected the extent of French territory;

◆ explain how language is related to culture in France;

◆ describe how economic and social uncertainties affect life in France.

National Geography Standards

The following National Geography Standards are highlighted in this section: 1, 2, 4, 5, 6, 8, 10, 11, 12, 13, 15, 17

Bellringer

Ask students to think of objects that symbolize France. Use students' responses to create a word web on the board.

LESSON PLAN

1. Focus Tell students to imagine that they are walking through a supermarket and then a department store. Have them name products from France that they might find in each.

2. Instruct Make a four-column by four-row chart on the board, labeling the columns *Northern France, Southwestern France, Mediterranean France,* and *Eastern France* and the rows *Cities, Landforms, Climate,* and *Economic Activities.* Ask students to use their text to complete the chart.

3. Close/Reteach Write this quotation on the board: *"The French have no problems of identity. They know who they are and can't imagine wanting to be like anybody else."* Ask students to write a brief definition of what it means to be French.

TEACHING TIP
From A Master Teacher

Economic Activity Use the study of Europe to reinforce students' understanding that centers of economic activity are often marked by prosperity and dense settlement. In Europe, the core of economic activity lies along a broad band from Manchester, England, to Milan, Italy, running through northern France, Belgium, the Netherlands, and western Germany and Switzerland. As one moves away from the core, Europe becomes more rural and agricultural, less prosperous, and less densely settled.

Pacing Suggestions

■ For 60-minute Blocks

You will want to vary activities.

- As the class nears the end of the chapter, work with students to complete the Critical Thinking Skills Activity, Expressing Problems Clearly, on page 40 of the Social Studies Skills Handbook. Then tell the students to clearly express the problems that Germany and the Netherlands now face, using the questions from the Critical Thinking Skills Activity as guides. Discuss student responses as a class.

The Physical World

Weather The mistral is an intense, strong, cold, and dry wind that blows from the north, down through the Rhône Valley across southern France. The mistral blows continually for days at a time at speeds that often exceed 60 miles (100 km) per hour. It is strongest and most frequent in the winter and spring, when it can damage crops. When there is a high-pressure center over central France and a low-pressure center over the northwestern Mediterranean Sea, a southward airflow results. The mistral's intensity is caused by the "jet effect"—the funneling of this southward airflow as it passes through the narrow Rhône Valley.

Visualizing

As students read the subsection Life in Southern France, help them visualize the landscape described in the subsection. Ask questions like the following: **What does the Massif Central look like?** (It is mountainous and rugged. The landscape includes sharp and flattened peaks. The soil is poor.) **On which side of the Rhône does it lie?** (west) **How are the Alps different from the Massif Central?** (Unlike the Massif Central, the Alps are snowcapped.) **On which side of the Rhône do the Alps lie?** (east) You might also encourage students to draw a map of the region based on what they have read.

Alternative Assessment

Introduce the Activity

Writing a Position Paper Ask students to conduct historical and current events research and write a position paper agreeing or disagreeing with the following statement: "Nationalism is dead in Central Western Europe." Distribute the Position Paper Rubric found on page 8 of the Alternative Assessment booklet in the Prentice Hall Assessment System for students' reference during this project.

Answer to Photo Caption

Climate and soil conditions are important factors for growing grapes.

---

wines thrive in these conditions. Wine grapes are grown in many parts of France. However, the region around the busy seaport of Bordeaux (bor DOH) in southwestern France has a reputation for producing the best wines. The town of Bordeaux has given its name to the whole wine crop of the region. How the region's physical characteristics help wine production is explained by Baron Geoffroy de Luze, who owns vineyards near Bordeaux.

> **❝**It's a combination of the sun, . . . just the right amount of rainfall and no frost, and . . . the miserable soil. . . . It's true. You'll notice how stony and poor the soil is here. . . . When the soil is rich, the production of grapes is large. So the individual grapes draw less concentration of the good things in the earth and from the sun. You'll find that the most refined wines come from the poorest soil. With fewer fruits and more sun, one arrives at unbelievably good grapes.**❞**

Life in Southern France East of Bordeaux lie two mountainous areas—the Massif Central (ma SEEF sahn TRAHL) and the Alps. Dividing these two rugged regions is the Rhône River. The Massif Central lies to the west of the Rhône and forms one sixth of France's land area. The landscape is a mixture of older peaks worn flat by time and newer, sharper peaks that are not yet eroded. Though much of the soil is poor, various crops are grown and there is some industry.

East of the Rhône are the Alps, a rugged barrier of mountains that provide spectacular scenery. Unlike the Massif Central, the Alps are a long range of towering, snowcapped mountains. Mont Blanc, the tallest peak in the Alps, rises 15,771 feet (4,807 m) above sea level.

For centuries, the Alps hindered movement between France and Italy. In 1787, Horace de Saussure, a naturalist and physicist, climbed to the top of Mont Blanc. He wrote, "Someday, a carriage road will be built under Mont Blanc, uniting the two valleys." His vision took 178 years to become reality. In 1965, engineers dug a highway tunnel through Mont Blanc, which straddles the border between France and Italy.

The Alps are known worldwide for their fashionable ski resorts and challenging skiing. During the summer, a magnificent array of

The Vineyards of the Rhône Valley

Physical Characteristics The Romans first recognized that the Rhône Valley was well suited for raising grapes over 2,000 years ago. Today, the Rhône Valley is still one of France's most important wine regions.

Regions *What geographic factors make a region valuable for growing grapes?*

Teaching Resources

Mental Mapping booklet
• Outline Map 16, p. 60

Social Studies Skills Handbook
• Maps with Accurate Distances: Equidistant Maps, p. 17

Prentice Hall Assessment System

Alternative Assessment booklet
• Position Paper Rubric, p. 8

Technology

World Geography Map and Photo Transparencies
• Western Europe: Maps and Photos

France: PHYSICAL-POLITICAL

KEY

Feet	Elevation	Meters
14,000		4,270
7,000		2,135
1,500		457
700		213
(sea level) 0		0 (sea level)

⊛ National capital
• Major city
▲ Mountain

Lambert Azimuthal Equal-Area Projection

APPLYING THE GEOGRAPHIC THEMES

● **Place** The six-sided country of France has coasts along the English Channel, the Bay of Biscay, and the Mediterranean Sea. Natural barriers form two of France's remaining three borders.
- *What landforms serve as France's natural borders?*
- *How have those borders helped France develop and maintain a strong national identity?*

alpine wildflowers covers the mountain slopes. Hikers come from around the world to enjoy the scenery.

Along the Mediterranean Nestled between the Alps and the Mediterranean Sea in southeastern France is a thin strip of low-lying coastal land. This area, known as the Riviera, attracts millions of tourists each year. The warm climate is ideal for sunbathing on the region's famous beaches and swimming in the sea. The French Riviera is also known as the Côte d'Azur— the Azure Coast—for the magnificent scenery formed by the sky, the sea, and the local flower, lavender. Many people like to visit the lively resort cities of Cannes (KAHN), Nice (NEES), and Saint-Tropez (SAN troh PAY). The city of Cannes

is also famous for its annual international film festival.

The port of Marseille (mar SAY) is the busiest seaport in France and the second most active in all of Western Europe. Tanker ships bring petroleum from Southwest Asia and North Africa to be unloaded at Marseille and processed at large oil refineries along the coast. Many French exports, including wine, electronic goods, and chemicals, are shipped from Marseille to other countries.

Industry in the East In the east of France lies the Rhine Valley. Here the Rhine River, Europe's busiest waterway, forms part of France's border with Germany. Alsace (al ZAS) and Lorraine, two Rhine Valley provinces with rich natural resources, have changed hands many

Making a Map Puzzle Ask students to make a map of France showing the country's various economic and geographical regions. Then instruct them to cut out their map as puzzle pieces and exchange them with another student to put together. (Visual/Spatial, Bodily/Kinesthetic)

ACTIVITY

Group Work

Activity: Designing souvenirs

Purpose: Explain to students that the word *souvenir* comes from the French verb "to remember." Tell each group that its job is to create designs for six souvenirs that visitors might buy as a memento of a visit to France. No more than three designs should represent places of interest to visit in Paris; the rest should represent aspects of cultural or economic life in other parts of France. Students may use sources from the school library to determine places of interest.

Roles: Each group should include a leader and souvenir designers/ researchers.

Result: The group leader should oversee the work of the designers/ researchers so that he or she can explain to the class what each souvenir recalls about France.

Articles From
NATIONAL GEOGRAPHIC

The following article may be used to extend the content in this section.

Bryson, Bill, and William Allard, photographer. "Essence of Provence." *National Geographic*, Vol. 188, No. 3 (Sept. 1995), pp. 52–77.

Provence, a region of France, prides itself on its simple and natural beauty.

TEST PREPARATION

Have students read the second paragraph of the subsection Along the Mediterranean and answer the following question.

Which statement best expresses the main idea of the paragraph?

A France's Mediterranean coast is a major oil refining region.

B Marseille is a center for petroleum imports.

C The port of Marseille is the busiest seaport in France.

D Marseille is a center for French exports.

Answers to Map Caption

The Pyrenees form a southern border; the Alps and Jura Mountains, an eastern border.

The borders have helped isolate and protect France, enabling it to develop a national identity with little outside influence.

GLOBAL CONNECTIONS

Cooperation and Conflict
In the 700s, Muslims conquered Spain but not France. The Pyrenees served as a natural barrier that helped defend France against invasion from the south.

times during conflict between France and Germany. Lorraine has France's largest deposits of iron ore. Nearby, coal is mined. Strasbourg, France's major port on the Rhine, is located in Alsace.

Understanding the Past

Referring to France's great diversity, former French President Charles de Gaulle once said, "How can you govern a country that has 246 varieties of cheese?" Despite having the kinds of cultural and economic differences that often have caused other countries to break apart, France is a highly unified country.

Cooperation and Conflict France was known as Gaul when the Romans conquered it in the first century B.C. For more than five

hundred years, the area prospered under the Romans. The Gauls, the native people of the area, were strongly influenced by this cultural convergence, adopting the Romans' Latin language and Christian religion.

As the Roman Empire declined, the Franks, who came from the area that is now Germany, conquered the region. The Franks gave France its name. One of the most famous conquerors of all time, Charlemagne (SHAR luh mayn), became king of the Franks in A.D. 768. By the time Charlemagne died in 814, he controlled a huge empire, known as the Holy Roman Empire, that included much of Western Europe.

Charlemagne set up an efficient government in his realm. He sent out missionaries to spread the teachings of Christianity throughout northern Europe. He also encouraged the arts and a revival of learning. Charlemagne's empire fell apart after his death. By the tenth century, most of the power lay in the hands of the nobles who controlled land in the kingdom. In 987, these nobles chose Hugh Capet (HUE ka PAY), the ruler of Paris and the lands around it, as their new king.

Walled City

Understanding the Past Many French cities and towns, such as Carcassonne, were founded hundreds of years ago. Craftspeople and merchants lived inside the towns, while farmers lived and worked in the surrounding regions.

Place *What reason might people have had for surrounding their towns with walls such as the one surrounding the oldest part of Carcassonne?*

Under Hugh Capet and his heirs, the monarchy grew strong. The lands ruled by the various nobles were united under one leader. Gradually the ruling monarchs of France expanded the kingdom's boundaries until, by 1589, they were almost the same as those of modern France. For the next two hundred years, French kings exercised absolute control over their lands. Then, in 1789, the monarchy came to a violent and bloody end during the French Revolution.

Since then, France has had several different forms of government, including a republic of the people, a constitutional monarchy, and empires under Napoleon Bonaparte and his nephew, Louis-Napoleon. Three times since 1870, German armies have swept across the flat northeastern plains and overrun northern France. The last two invasions, during World War I and World War II, were repelled with help from other countries, including the United States.

Language and Culture

Throughout their turbulent history, the people of France have maintained a strong sense of national identity. One reason for this is their belief in the historical unity of France. Language and culture have also played important roles in establishing a French character.

One Country, One Language Before the 1500s, the language that is now called French was spoken only in and around Paris. As the French kings expanded their control, they decreed that the language of Paris become the language of all the lands they ruled.

Several other languages, for example, Alsatian, German, Basque, and Breton, are still spoken in various parts of France. So are several **dialects**—variations of a language that are unique to a region or community. French, however, is the national language. New French words are published in official dictionaries only if they are approved by the French Academy. This body was established in 1635 to preserve the purity of the French language. It is a symbol of French cultural pride.

Cultural Identity The French also take enormous pride in their intellectual and artistic achievements. Among their greatest heroes are philosophers René Descartes (ruh NAY day CART),

Central Western Europe and the United States
Population Data

Country	Total Population	Population Density (persons per square mile)	Population Growth Rate (percentage)
Austria	8,188,207	253	0.22
Belgium	10,289,088	873	0.14
France	60,180,529	287	0.42
Germany	82,398,326	598	0.04
Liechtenstein	33,145	537	0.90
Luxembourg	454,157	455	1.23
Netherlands	16,150,511	1,007	0.50
Switzerland	7,318,638	459	0.21
United States	290,342,550	78	0.92

Source: Encarta World Atlas

CHART SKILLS

- **Population Growth** *Which country has the highest population growth rate?*
- **Planning for the Future** *What economic issues might face countries with high population growth rates?*

Jean-Paul Sartre (ZHAHN PAUL SART ruh), and Voltaire. Many of the world's most famous painters have been French, including Claude Monet (mo NAY) and Pierre Auguste Renoir (PYER aw GOOST ruhn WAHR). These artists were leaders in a style of painting known as **Impressionism.** This school of art sought to capture fleeting visual "impressions" made by color, light, and shadows. The French also take a lead role in setting clothing styles. Famous French designers create clothes that influence fashion all over the world.

For centuries Paris has been the cultural center of France. The city's atmosphere of freedom has attracted artists and intellectuals from many nations. Countless developments in the arts and literature can be traced to the studios of artists and writers living in Paris. Today the city's art galleries and museums, including the famous Louvre (LOOV ruh), celebrate the achievements of these artists. Paris is also known for its theaters, ballets, operas, orchestras, and cinemas.

France Today

Following World War II, the French government established national planning programs to modernize the economy and encourage more balanced growth among France's regions. It also reached out to its Western European neighbors to form new trade agreements. Because of these changes, France enjoyed a period of great prosperity and is today one of the leading exporters of goods in the world.

In recent decades, the French government has taken different approaches to stimulating its economy. It has **nationalized,** or brought under state control, some businesses considered vital to national interests. And it has privatized some government-owned companies to promote economic growth. Under pressure to meet standards set by the European Union, officials have enacted strict economic measures.

France is a wealthy nation, but it faced economic and political challenges in the 1990s and early 2000s. It struggled to recover from economic **recession**—an extended decline in business activity. Unemployment remained high, and workers and students waged frequent strikes against government reforms. France's opposition to military action against Iraq in 2003 disrupted its traditionally strong relationship with the United States.

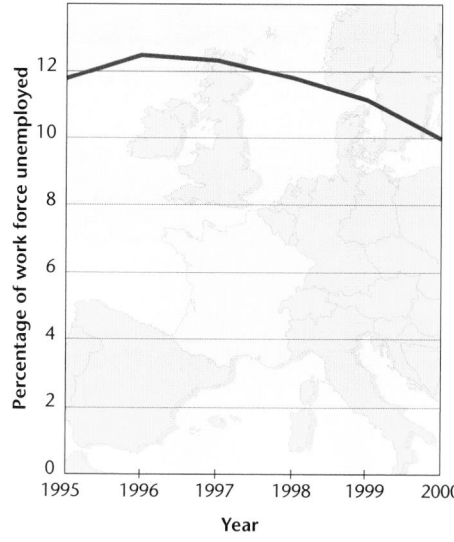

Unemployment in France 1995–2000

Sources: *Encarta World Atlas; The World Almanac and Book of Facts*

GRAPH SKILLS

● **Economic Activities** In the 1990s, France struggled with a variety of economic problems. One of these was a relatively high unemployment rate.
• *Were the French very successful in reducing the unemployment rate? Explain.*
• *How is a high unemployment rate a symptom of economic recession?*

SECTION 1 ASSESSMENT

1. Key Terms Define **(a)** dialect, **(b)** Impressionism, **(c)** nationalize, **(d)** recession.

2. Economic Activities Why is tourism a major industry in the French Alps?

3. Understanding the Past How did the Roman conquest of Gaul lead to cultural convergence?

4. Cultures (a) How has language helped unite France? **(b)** What efforts have been taken to ensure that France has one national language?

5. Cooperation and Conflict How have social and economic pressures caused conflict in France?

6. Critical Thinking Analyzing Causes and Effects How do you think that France's diverse physical characteristics have contributed to the nation's economic prosperity?

Activity

Take It to the NET
Preparing an Oral Report Use the Internet to locate some current events articles about an economic or social challenge facing France. In an oral report, summarize the issue. For help with this activity, visit the World Geography section of **www.phschool.com**.

2 Germany

Reading Focus

- How did Germany achieve unification in the 1800s and 1900s?
- How do physical characteristics affect economic activities and patterns of settlement in Germany?
- What challenges does Germany face in the world today?

Key Terms

confederation
reparation
inflation
lignite

 Main Idea After a long and difficult struggle to achieve national unity, Germany became a world economic power in the 1800s and 1900s.

Cultures Cultural events such as this festival provide Germans with a way to express their national heritage.

Objectives

Upon completion of Section 2, students should be able to:

◆ describe how Germany achieved unification in the 1800s and 1900s;

◆ explain how physical characteristics affect Germany's economy and its pattern of settlement;

◆ list the challenges that Germany faces today.

 ### National Geography Standards

The following National Geography Standards are highlighted in this section: 1, 3, 4, 5, 6, 10, 11, 12, 13, 14, 16, 17, 18

 ### Bellringer

Ask students to imagine that their state has been divided in half and that they are forbidden to cross to the other side or communicate with people living there. Ask: **How would your lives change?**

LESSON PLAN

1. Focus Display a map that shows East and West Germany before unification. Note the location of major waterways and canals, industrial cities, and resources. Ask students to brainstorm ways the unification of Germany could strengthen the German nation.

2. Instruct Write the following on the board as a list: *Protestant Reformation, formation of a Prussian state, German victory in the Franco-Prussian War, German defeat in World War II, fall of Communist government in East Germany.* Ask students to indicate next to each event whether its effect was to divide Germany *(D)* or to unify it *(U)*.

3. Close/Reteach Separate the class into groups. Ask each group to make up six questions: two questions about Germany's history, two questions about Germany's physical regions, and two questions about economic activities in Germany's regions. Collect questions and group them by category. Then have students take turns choosing categories and answering questions from each.

On Thursday night, November 9, 1989, thousands of East and West Berliners gathered along the Berlin Wall. Just hours earlier, the East German government had announced that the borders between East and West Germany would be opened. As reporter Serge Schmemann wrote:

> 66 They seemed to be drawn by the sense that . . . the barrier of concrete and steel that had figured so prominently in the history of this city and the world, might soon be relegated to history. Some came with hammers and chisels, others with guitars, most with cameras. 99

People all over the world were moved to tears of joy. The wall that had separated east from west finally was being torn down.

Germany's Struggle for Unity

The 103-mile-long wall was built in 1961 by the Communist East German government to keep its citizens from escaping to West Germany. Even in

earlier eras, however, before this century, Germany's history as a nation has been one of divisions and unifications.

Divided German States The area that is now Germany was once part of Charlemagne's great Holy Roman Empire. After Charlemagne's death, Germany broke up into many small, independent political units. Princes, dukes, counts, and bishops all ruled their own domains. Many cities were free states. Often there was bitter rivalry and fighting among these states.

During the 1500s, a movement called the Protestant Reformation divided the German states even further. The Protestants objected to many of the practices and teachings of the Roman Catholic Church. In the early 1600s, the Reformation sparked 30 years of warfare between Protestants and Catholics throughout Germany and other parts of Central Europe.

Starting in the late 1700s, the state of Prussia, in what is now eastern Germany, led a movement to merge many German states into a single **confederation,** or loose political union. After Germany defeated France in the Franco-Prussian War of 1870–1871, German states that until then

Chapter 16 ▪ Section 2 **331**

CUSTOMIZE FOR...

Less Proficient Readers

Identifying the Order of Events As students read the subsection Germany's Struggle for Unity that begins on this page, have them find words and phrases that signal time order. When they have finished, ask: **How is this subsection organized?** (It begins by talking about events that happened in 1961. Then it jumps back in time and moves forward in chronological order.) You might also have students organize the subsection by writing its facts on a time line.

Inflation Refer to the Key Terms list on page 331. Write the term *inflation* on the board. Ask: **What does it mean to *inflate* a tire?** (to fill it up with air so that it gets bigger) Ask a volunteer to look up *inflation* in the Glossary and read its definition aloud. Ask: **How does *inflation* relate to *inflate*?** (Prices, like tires, swell when they are inflated.)

Europe's Busiest Waterway Tell students that the Rhine River is Western Europe's busiest commercial waterway and is linked by canals with other major waterways of Europe. Starting at its source in the Swiss Alps, have students trace the course of the Rhine, naming the countries it flows through and its major tributaries as they go along. (Bodily/Kinesthetic)

Germany: PHYSICAL-POLITICAL

APPLYING THE GEOGRAPHIC THEMES

● **Location** Most of Germany's cities follow a pattern in their distribution: They lie along the country's waterways—some of which are natural, others of which are of human construction.
- *What German waterway links the North Sea and the Baltic Sea? Is it a natural waterway? Explain.*

had remained independent agreed to join the new German Empire.

United Germany's Defeats In 1882 Germany joined with Austria-Hungary and Italy to form a military alliance known as the Triple Alliance. Between 1914 and 1918, Germany, Austria-Hungary, and other countries fought against France, Russia, the United Kingdom, the United States, and other allies in World War I.

According to the terms of the treaty following the war, a defeated Germany had to pay the victors **reparations**—money for war damages. As a result, Germany suffered economically. The economy collapsed in the early 1920s when **inflation,** or sharply rising prices, ruined the value of Germany's currency. In 1929, a worldwide economic depression left millions of Germans without jobs.

In the early 1930s, Adolf Hitler and his Nazi party came to power in Germany. Hitler promised to restore Germany's past glory and to improve the economy. He blamed the Jews and other people whom he considered to be racially inferior for all of Germany's problems.

In 1939 Germany invaded Poland, and World War II began. During the war Hitler had millions of Jews, Poles, Gypsies, Slavs, and other people killed in concentration camps. Finally, in April 1945 Germany was defeated by the Allied countries—the United States, the United Kingdom, France, and the Soviet Union.

Answer to Map Caption

Kiel Canal; As a canal, it is of human construction.

One People, Two Countries Following the war, tensions grew between the Western Allies and the Soviet Union concerning Germany's future. In 1949, Western leaders established the democratic country of the Federal Republic of Germany—West Germany. The Soviet Union set up the Communist German Democratic Republic—East Germany. Although Berlin, the former German capital, was located within East Germany, American, British, and French forces remained in the western half of the city, which became part of West Germany.

For 40 years Germany remained divided between East and West. Then, in late 1989, a wave of demonstrations calling for democracy swept through Eastern Europe and overturned East Germany's Communist government. Soon the new East German government announced that it would open the country's borders. Celebrations in East and West Berlin were especially joyous. Within weeks large sections of the Berlin Wall, symbol of a divided Germany, were destroyed. On October 3, 1990, East and West Germany were officially reunited.

Physical Characteristics

The physical regions of Germany are varied, but the differences between regions are not as dramatic as they are in France. As journalist Flora Lewis observed:

❝It is a [mild] land, brisk but bright along the North Sea coast, heaving gently above green valleys to the majestic Bavarian Alps. The mighty Rhine, one of Europe's oldest, most traveled highways, is still a great commercial lifeline.❞

Germany's land can be divided into three bands that extend across the country. The high, craggy mountains of the south turn into hills, low peaks, and tall plateaus in central Germany before leveling off into the flat lands of the north.

Germany's generally mild climate is due largely to the influence of the North Sea. Away from the sea, in southern areas of the country, a humid continental climate prevails, causing colder winters and warmer summers. But even in January, temperatures are usually above freezing. However, cold winds from the east may bring sharp drops in temperatures for short periods.

Plains, Rivers, and Cities Northern Germany is covered by the North German Plain, which is a part of the North European Plain. For hundreds of miles flat, sandy plains spread out until they reach the North and Baltic seas. Wide rivers flow north out of the southern highlands across the plains to the sea.

Although much of the land in the plains is farmed, manufacturing and trade are also important economic activities. Hamburg, Germany's

Fall of the Berlin Wall

Government and Citizenship In 1989, Germans celebrated as they tore down the wall that had separated Communist East Berlin from democratic West Berlin. The Communist government of East Germany had built the wall to stop East Germans from escaping to the West.

Place *Why do you think many East Germans wanted to escape to West Germany?*

Articles From
NATIONAL GEOGRAPHIC

The following article may be used to extend the content in this section.

Vesilind, Priit J., and David Alan Harvey and Anthony Suau, photographers. "Berlin's Ode to Joy." *National Geographic*, Vol. 177, No. 4 (Apr. 1990), pp. 104–132.

A barrier dividing a city for nearly 30 years, the Berlin Wall no longer stands in the way of freedom for Germans.

BACKGROUND

U.S. and the World

Defense The North Atlantic Treaty Organization (NATO) was created in 1949 to defend Western Europe against possible Soviet expansion. West Germany became the main base for NATO's troops, a significant number of which were Americans. Today, with the breakup of the Soviet Union, fewer Americans are stationed in Germany but the American presence is still alive. In the 1990s, NATO forces were involved in peacekeeping missions in Bosnia-Herzegovina. In 1999, Poland, Hungary, and the Czech Republic joined NATO, bringing the number of member nations to 19.

ACTIVITY

Group Work

Activity: Writing a newspaper article

Purpose: Assign groups one of the following cities: Berlin, Dresden, Frankfurt, Leipzig. Tell each group that its job is to write a newspaper article on how residents think reunification has affected their city. Have each group research the changes that have taken place in Germany since 1990 and then write an article on these changes from the perspective of a resident of their assigned city.

Roles: Groups should include reporters, illustrators, and a news editor.

Result: Circulate finished articles for all groups to read. Discuss what students have learned about the effects of unification.

ACTIVITY

Reteach

Ask the Experts Tell students they are going to play a game called Ask the Experts. Select three students to act as "experts" on Germany. One student will be the history expert, a second the geography expert, and a third the economics/politics expert. Have the rest of the class ask the experts questions about Germany and assess the accuracy of their answers. (Verbal/Linguistic)

Answer to Photo Caption

to escape the economic, social, and political oppression of communism

Asking Questions

Have students formulate questions about the information in the subsection Natural Resources and Industry. Direct students to write at least three questions—one for each paragraph of the subsection. Then use students' questions as the basis for a quiz game.

ACTIVITY

Enrichment

Writing Captions Ask students to do outside research to find three photographs that show Germany's different physical regions and to write their own captions for these pictures. (Visual/Spatial)

BACKGROUND

Word Origin

Lignite The coal called *lignite* has the brown look of decayed wood. Hence, its name comes from the Latin *lignum,* meaning "wood."

---

largest port and second-largest city, is built around a harbor where the Elbe River flows into the North Sea. Since the end of the Middle Ages, Hamburg has been a leading center of trade. Most of Hamburg's old structures were destroyed in bombing raids during World War II and were rebuilt after the war.

Another German port, Rostock, is also a tribute to German achievement after World War II. When East Germany cut its connections with West Germany, it lost access to West German ports. Needing an outlet to the sea for shipping, the East Germans dug a new harbor at Rostock, creating a major port on the Baltic Sea.

Berlin, Germany's capital and its largest city, was badly damaged during World War II. Both East and West Germany spent a great deal of money to rebuild the parts of Berlin that they controlled. Today, Berlin is once again the prosperous capital of a united Germany.

Natural Resources and Industry
Two major rivers, the Rhine and the Elbe, flow through the central parts of Germany. This region of Germany is one of the most important industrial centers in the world. In the 1800s, huge coal deposits were found near the Ruhr (ROOR) River. With plenty of available fuel, the Ruhr Valley developed into Germany's first industrial center. Today, the Ruhr Valley produces most of Germany's iron and steel. It also has important chemical and textile industries. More than eight million people live in the large cities of Duisburg (DOOS boorg), Essen, Bochum (BO khuhm), and Dortmund and the smaller cities and towns in the area that form one huge metropolis.

In the eastern part of central Germany is another large industrial region. Steel, machinery, automobiles, and textiles are produced in cities such as Leipzig and Dresden and in the surrounding area. Power for the factories comes mostly from **lignite,** a soft, brown coal. Lignite is easy to mine, but it pollutes the air heavily.

Not everyone in central Germany lives

GLOBAL CONNECTIONS

Science and Technology
The Kiel Canal stretches from the Baltic Sea to the North Sea, and was built between 1887 and 1895 to reduce the need for ships to sail around Denmark.

Refugees to Western Europe

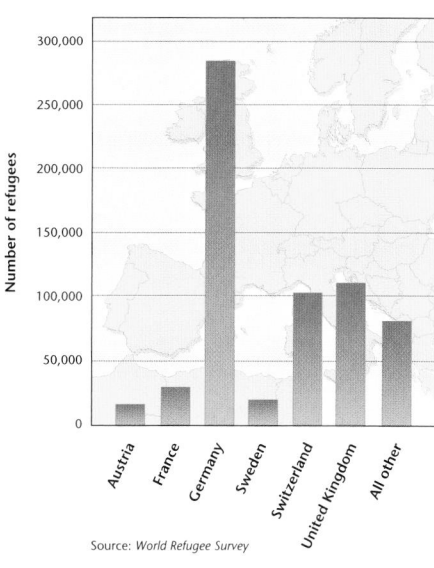

Source: *World Refugee Survey*

GRAPH SKILLS

Migration In recent years, refugees have poured into Western Europe to escape war, poverty, and oppression. Most come from Eastern Europe, North Africa, Turkey, and the republics of the former Soviet Union.

- *According to the graph above, which country received the most refugees?*
- *What problems might such a sudden rise in population cause a host country?*

---

in a big, industrial city. Many people live in cities such as Frankfurt, Germany's banking center, and Heidelberg (HY duhl berg), the site of a world-famous university. Others live on fertile farmland located in the southern part of central Germany.

Scenic Southern Germany Along Germany's southern border lie the Bavarian Alps. North of the Alps, the land is less mountainous. The Rhine and Danube rivers flow through this hilly land. Skiers and hikers enjoy the spectacular scenery of these mountains, rivers, hills, and thick evergreen forests.

The largest city in southern Germany is Munich (MYOO nikh). After World War II, Munich became Germany's cultural center. Theaters and museums that were destroyed during the war

---

RESOURCE DIRECTORY

Teaching Resources
Unit 4, Chapter 16
- Critical Thinking, p. 37
- Section 2 Quiz, p. 31

Spanish Resources
- Section 2 Quiz, p. 39

Answers to Graph Skills

Germany

The host country may not be able to provide jobs, housing, food supplies, and other resources.

Studying High-Tech Innovations

Science and Technology Germany has been an industrial leader for decades. Two Germans named Daimler and Benz were pioneers of the automobile industry in the 1880s. Today, Germany is the third-largest producer of cars in the world.

Human-Environment Interaction *What natural resources have helped make Germany a leading industrial nation?*

have been renovated. Damaged paintings and sculptures have been restored and are once again exhibited.

Germany in the World Today

Germany is the leading industrial nation in Europe. Its technologically powerful economy ranks fifth globally in terms of gross domestic product. Germany maintains strong economic ties with Russia and other nations in Central and Eastern Europe, and it is a leading member of the European Union. Germany, therefore, has access to increasing markets in which to sell its valuable products.

Despite its strengths, Germany faces several problems. Its aging population has pushed social security outlays to exceed contributions from workers. About $70 billion each year is spent to upgrade the economy of areas that were once under Communist control. Other challenges include high levels of unemployment, violence against foreign workers, and environmental pollution.

SECTION 2 ASSESSMENT

1. **Key Terms** Define **(a)** confederation, **(b)** reparation, **(c)** inflation, **(d)** lignite.

2. **Government and Citizenship (a)** How did religious differences delay the unification of Germany? **(b)** Why was Germany divided into two countries after World War II?

3. **Economic Activities** What geographic characteristics have helped to make industry an important part of the German economy?

4. **Global Trade Patterns** How has membership in the European Union benefited the German economy?

5. **Critical Thinking Drawing Conclusions** Based on Germany's history, why do you think some European countries might be uneasy now that Germany is united?

Activity

Making Maps Create a series of maps that show the changing boundaries of Germany in the 1800s and 1900s. Write a caption for each map explaining why the boundaries changed from the previous map. Use library or Internet resources to find the historical maps needed to complete this activity.

TEST PREPARATION

Have students read the subsections Natural Resources and Industry and Scenic Southern Germany on the opposite page to complete the following analogy.

Ruhr Valley is to industry as —

A Munich is to culture
B automobile is to Leipzig
C Bavarian Alps are to forests
D banks are to Frankfurt

Teaching the Skill

Have students write one fact and one opinion about their school. Draw two columns on the board, one for facts and one for opinions. Have the students read their answers and determine in which column they belong. Review the lists in each column with the students, noting any that might need to be reassigned. Ask students if they notice any similarities in the facts (possible answers: they are about location, size, etc.) and the opinions (possible answers: they are about likes and dislikes, they are judgments of quality). Read page 336 with the class, asking volunteers to answer the questions in the text. After students have evaluated the fact and opinion statements, ask: **Do you agree with the writer's opinions? Do the facts presented seem to justify the opinion?** Call on volunteers to state what conclusions they have reached about genetically engineered agriculture after reading the statements.

Answers to Learn the Skill

1. (a) C and E **(b)** any two: newspaper articles, journal articles, reference books
2. (a) A, B, and D **(b)** A—may; B—we believe, might be; D—might be
3. (a) resistance to insects, **(b)** possible adverse health effects and environmental damage

Answer to Practice the Skill

Check that students have gathered ten statements and have correctly distinguished the facts from the opinions.

Distinguishing Fact From Opinion

To determine the soundness of an author's ideas, you need to be able to distinguish between fact and opinion. This ability allows you to reach your own conclusions about issues and events.

Learn the Skill Use the following steps to learn how to distinguish fact from opinion.

1 *Determine which statements are based on facts.* A fact can be proven by checking other sources. Statements of fact do not include someone's own values or opinions. Read statements A through E below. **(a)** *Which statements about genetically engineered agriculture are based solely on facts?* **(b)** *List two sources you could use to check that these statements are true.*

2 *Determine which of the statements are opinions.* An opinion states a person's belief or feeling about a subject. It usually cannot be proven, even if it is a widely held opinion. Statements of opinion often contain words that stir an emotional response. Study statements A through E again. **(a)** *Which statements obviously include someone's opinion about genetically engineered agriculture?* **(b)** *Which words in each of those statements indicate that the statement is an opinion?*

3 *Draw conclusions.* Based on your answers to the preceding steps, you should be able to determine the soundness of the author's ideas about genetically engineered agriculture. **(a)** *What are the advantages to genetically engineering species of plants?* **(b)** *What are the disadvantages to genetically engineering agriculture?*

Practice the Skill Choose a news story from a newspaper or Internet news source. Take a survey of ten classmates, asking each classmate to make one statement about the topic discussed in the story. Record and study their responses. Which are facts and which are opinions? Explain.

Apply the Skill See Chapter 16 Review and Assessment.

Statements About Genetic Engineering

By moving genes from one organism into another, scientists quickly can give a species desirable traits such as greater resistance to insects, disease, or drought. In Western Europe and elsewhere, critics of this technology are concerned that the long-term effects of genetic engineering are not yet known. Several statements about the topic follow. Some statements are facts and some are opinions.

A. The creation of plants that have a greater resistance to insects is a technology that one day may reduce the use of chemical pesticides.

B. We believe that the bioengineering of crops goes against nature. It leads to the creation of Frankenfoods, whose long-term effects might be dangerous.

C. Genetic engineers working with plants sometimes add genes from nonplant organisms. For example, protein genes are used to make corn resistant to the European corn borer.

D. The producers of genetically engineered crops are creating a dangerous product and should have to pay fines for any environmental damage that might be caused by those crops.

E. In Germany, France, Belgium, and Switzerland, campaigns are being waged against genetically engineered foods. At the same time, genetically engineered crops are being grown in those same countries.

RESOURCE DIRECTORY

Teaching Resources

Unit 4, Chapter 16
• Section 3 Guided Reading and Review, p. 32

Guide to the Essentials (English/Spanish)
• Section Summary, Chapter 16, Section 3

Mental Mapping booklet
• Unit 4 Checklist, p. 52

Social Studies Skills Handbook
• Distinguishing Fact From Opinion, p. 43

Technology

Guided Reading Audiotapes (English/Spanish), Chapter 16, Section 3

Section Reading Support Transparencies, Chapter 16, Section 3

World Geography Map and Photo Transparencies
• Western Europe: Maps and Photos

Book on CD, Chapter 16

Social Studies Skills Tutor CD-ROM, Distinguishing Fact and Opinion

Companion Web site, www.phschool.com
• Chapter 16 Activities

3 The Benelux Countries

Reading Focus

- **In what major way have the Dutch changed their physical environment?**
- **How has language affected culture in Belgium?**
- **How have economic activities changed in Luxembourg?**

Key Terms

dike
polder
decentralize

 Main Idea The low-lying countries of the Netherlands, Belgium, and Luxembourg are a small but important part of central Western Europe.

Environmental Change In the Netherlands, windmills power pumps that drain water and create new farmland.

C rowded together in northwestern Europe are three small countries—Belgium, the Netherlands, and Luxembourg. From the first letters of their names, together these countries are known as the Benelux countries. The Benelux countries are also called the Low Countries because so much of their land is low and flat. Their combined land area is small, but their combined population of approximately 26.4 million people is almost as large as Canada's population. Belgium and the Netherlands are the most densely populated countries in Europe.

The Netherlands

"God made the world, but the Dutch made [the Netherlands]," commented French philosopher René Descartes. In few places is the result of human interaction with the environment more evident than in the Netherlands. The map on page 338 shows that the entire western side of the country is bordered by the North Sea. The Dutch have created one fifth of their country's land by reclaiming it

from sea, lakes, and swamps. A Netherlander stated the national goal of his country in one sentence: "It is to possess land where water wants to be."

Environmental Change Over two thousand years ago, people living in the area that is now the Netherlands began to build low mounds and surrounded them with stone walls to make dry islands on which to live and farm. When the Romans conquered the area, they constructed sophisticated **dikes,** or embankments of earth and rock, to hold back the water.

The Dutch became even more skillful at creating new land. They encircled a piece of land with dikes and then pumped the water out into canals. The Dutch call land reclaimed from the sea in this way a **polder.** Beginning in the 1200s, the Dutch used windmills to power the pumps that removed water from the land. Much of this new land is used for farming, but cities also have been built on some of the land.

Almost one third of the country is below sea level. Standing in a polder field, one often

Chapter 16 ▪ Section 3   **337**

TEST PREPARATION

Have students read the subsection Environmental Change beginning on this page to answer the following question. The quote "God made the world, but the Dutch made [the Netherlands]" accurately reflects how the Dutch —

   A use windmills as a renewable energy source
   B have a population that is almost as large as Canada's
   C learned to reclaim land from the sea
   D live in a small country

Objectives

Upon completion of Section 3, students should be able to:

◆ identify the major way in which the Dutch have changed their physical environment;

◆ describe how language has affected culture in Belgium;

◆ explain how diversification has changed Luxembourg's economy.

National Geography Standards

The following National Geography Standards are highlighted in this section: 1, 4, 5, 6, 9, 10, 11, 12, 13, 14, 15, 17

Bellringer

Ask students what comes to mind when they think of the Netherlands. List their responses on the board.

LESSON PLAN

1. Focus Ask students to describe ways nations throughout history have sought to increase their living area. (war and conquest; colonization; building, both underground and vertically) Explain that the Dutch found a uniquely peaceful solution to their crowding problems through a system of land reclamation.

2. Instruct Write these words on the board: *Benelux, polders, Walloons, Flemings, Randstad, Rotterdam.* Ask students to write statements to explain what these words mean.

3. Close/Reteach Ask each student to write in random order six fact statements and two opinion statements about the culture, the society, and the economy of the Benelux nations. Have pairs exchange papers, circle opinion statements, and return papers to their owners for checking.

looks up to see ships passing by in canals that run alongside the land.

Making Use of Land With more than 16 million people living on about 13,090 square miles (33,900 sq km) of land, the Netherlands has an extremely high population density. As a result, Dutch farmers cannot afford to waste any of the Netherlands' farmland. More than half of the land is used for agriculture, either to grow crops or as pasture. Farmers fertilize heavily and use modern agricultural methods.

Government leaders are devoting special attention to preserving the country's farmlands. The cities of The Hague (HAYG), Rotterdam, Amsterdam, and Utrecht (YOO trekht) form one huge arc-shaped metropolis that the Dutch call *Randstad*, or ring city. The government is trying to prevent this densely populated area from expanding into nearby rural areas. To preserve more of the natural environment, the Dutch are now flooding some of the land that they had previously reclaimed from the sea.

Advantages of Location The Dutch also have learned to make good use of their location on the North Sea. Rotterdam and Amsterdam are both important ports. Because it is situated near the mouth of Europe's largest inland waterway, Rotterdam serves as a link between much of Europe and the rest of the world.

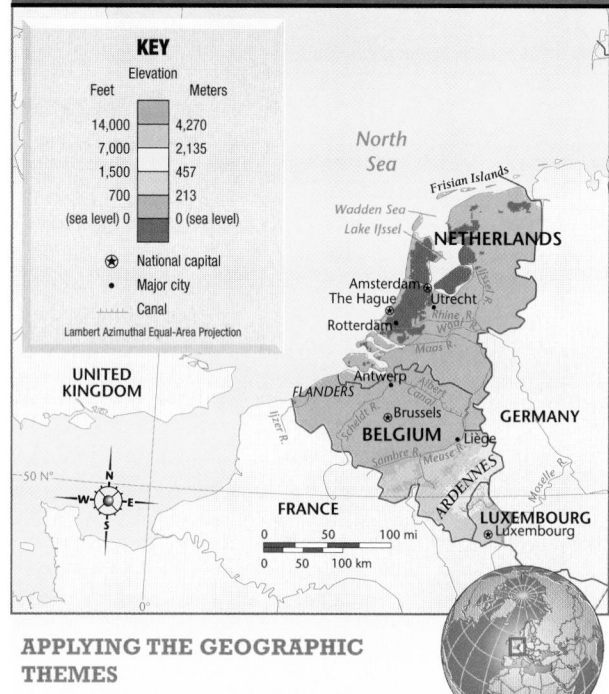

The Netherlands, Belgium, and Luxembourg: PHYSICAL–POLITICAL

APPLYING THE GEOGRAPHIC THEMES

● **Human-Environment Interaction** Three of the world's busiest ports lie within a space of about 80 miles (129 km): Rotterdam, Amsterdam, and Antwerp.

• *On which river is Antwerp located?*

• *Which cities appear to face the greatest threat of flooding? Explain.*

Belgium

The people who inhabit the modern country of Belgium show that cultural convergence sometimes creates an uneasy mix. About 30 percent of all Belgians speak French and call themselves Walloons. About 55 percent speak Flemish, a dialect of Dutch.

After Belgium gained independence from the Netherlands in 1830, relations between the Walloons and the Flemings grew tense. French was the country's only official language. Most government leaders spoke French, and all Belgian universities used French. As a result the Flemings, who spoke Dutch, could not hold government positions or enter professions in which a university education was needed.

Yet, the Flemings made up a large part of the population. They wanted the same cultural and economic rights that the Walloons enjoyed. To help resolve the conflict, the Belgian government made Flemish an official language in 1898. More recently, the Belgian Parliament passed laws to **decentralize** its

Crossroads at Luxembourg

Cultures Luxembourg shares borders with France, Germany, and Belgium. The nation's languages reflect these close ties. French and German are two of the major languages in the country. A third language, Luxembourgish, is unique to the nation.

Location *How does Luxembourg's economy benefit from these ties?*

government—that is, transfer power to smaller regions. These regions are Wallonia, Flanders, and Brussels.

Luxembourg

Luxembourg covers only 990 square miles (2,564 sq km), an area smaller than the state of Rhode Island. Despite its small size, Luxembourg has managed to endure for more than one thousand years. Although Luxembourg has close cultural ties to Germany, France, and Belgium, it has maintained an independent spirit. In Luxembourg three languages are spoken: French, German, and a German dialect called Luxembourgish.

Luxembourg has one of the highest standards of living in Europe. Economic activities, once dominated by the manufacture of steel, have become increasingly diversified. High-tech firms and service industries fill the gap left by reduced steel production. Luxembourg is a member of the European Union and trades most of its goods and services with other EU members.

 GEO Facts

Luxembourg was one of the six founders of the European Economic Community (EEC), now the European Union (EU).

SECTION 3 ASSESSMENT

1. **Key Terms** Define **(a)** dike, **(b)** polder, **(c)** decentralize.

2. **Natural Resources** How do the Dutch use most of the land that they reclaim from the sea?

3. **Cooperation and Conflict (a)** Why have the two main peoples of Belgium clashed in the past? **(b)** How have those conflicts been resolved?

4. **Economic Activities** What are Luxembourg's most important economic activities?

5. **Critical Thinking Developing a Hypothesis** Recall that some scientists are concerned that global warming could cause polar ice caps to melt and sea levels to rise. Which of the Benelux countries would be most affected by such an occurrence? Explain.

Activity

USING THE REGIONAL ATLAS

Review the Regional Atlas for Western Europe and this section. Think about a novel that could be set in the Benelux countries. Based on what you know about the region and its cultures, what plot would the novel have? Write three short paragraphs that could appear as a summary on the back of your novel.

Chapter 16 ▪ Section 3   339

CUSTOMIZE FOR...

Honors/PreAP

Economic Activities in Luxembourg Have students do research to find out what caused the decline in steel production in Luxembourg. Then ask them to investigate what new technologies or situations caused the surge in high-tech and service industries in Luxembourg. When they complete their research, ask students to present their findings to the class.

Objectives

Upon completion of this feature, students should be able to:

◆ explain why land reclamation is necessary in some parts of the world;

◆ summarize the history of land reclamation in the Netherlands;

◆ describe how global warming may affect the Netherlands in the future.

National Geography Standards

The following National Geography Standards are highlighted in this feature: 1, 3, 4, 6, 7, 9, 11, 12, 13, 14, 15, 16, 17, 18

Bellringer

Use a map of your town, city, or region to help students locate a nearby lake or river. Have students use the map to imagine how their lives would be different if the water level rose and the lake or river extended a mile farther in every direction.

LESSON PLAN

1. Focus Write *reclamation* on the board and have students define it. Ask: **Why would a country begin a reclamation project?** (population growth, insufficient arable land)

2. Instruct Make a two-column chart on the board. In the first column, list the problems that the sea has caused for Dutch citizens. In the second column, have students describe how the Dutch have responded to each of these problems.

3. Close/Reteach Ask: **Why is global warming a major concern for the Netherlands?** (Global warming raises the sea level, which would cause floods in populated areas.)

Answers to Photo Captions

People reclaim land for farming and other purposes.

Reeds are burned and ashes are plowed into the soil.

340   Chapter 16

People and Geography
Environmental Change and the Netherlands

The Issue

As the world's population continues to grow, so does its need for land on which to live and farm. Countries such as China, India, and the United States have used technology to change the environment through land reclamation. This process transforms wetland into dry land that can be used for farming and other purposes. The Netherlands has one of the oldest and most extensive land reclamation efforts in the world.

Dutch Tulip Farm
How does land reclamation benefit the Dutch economy?

Years 1-2
Earth dikes are built around an area of water, and the water is drained away.

Years 3-6
A mat of woven twigs is laid across the land. Planes sow seeds of reeds that grow through the mat.

Year 7
Reeds are burned, and ashes are plowed into the soil.

Year 8
Polder is used for farming and settlement.

Dikes and Polders

In response to the pressure of a growing population, the Netherlands began to reclaim marshy lowlands from the North Sea in the 1100s. This new dry land, called *polders,* was created with protective dikes and drainage ditches. The use of windmills made it easier to pump excess water off the land. A continuing problem, however, was the Zuider Zee, an arm of the North Sea. This body of water once protruded deep into the Netherlands and often flooded the surrounding land. Finally, in 1932, the Dutch completed a dike that stretched about 20 miles (32.2 km) across the water. On the inland side of the dike, the salt water gradually became a freshwater lake—Lake Ijssel.

Making a Polder
As a polder is being created, how is the land fertilized with organic matter?

RESOURCE DIRECTORY

Teaching Resources

People and Geography
• Environmental Change, pp. 19–24

Simulations, Games, and Lab Activities
• Where to Put the Landfill?, pp. 23–29

Technology

World Geography Map and Photo Transparencies
• Western Europe: Political

The Delta Plan

The sea continued its assault on the Netherlands even after the dike across the Zuider Zee was completed. The most vulnerable part of the country was the southwestern region where the Rhine and other rivers emptied into the North Sea and formed a low-lying delta. Disaster struck in 1953 when heavy storms flooded the region and caused nearly 2,000 deaths. To prevent such disastrous flooding from occurring again, the Delta Plan was undertaken. This network of dams took some 30 years to build and was completed in the mid-1980s.

Changing Perceptions

In recent years, however, perceptions have changed in the Netherlands. Many Dutch are concerned that too much of the natural environment has been lost. There are also concerns about farmers' widespread use of insecticides and fertilizers that contribute to contaminated drinking water, acid rain, and other environmental problems. In response, the Dutch have abandoned some plans for new polders. They have also flooded fields by tearing down dikes.

In the future, environmental change will continue to be a vital issue in the Netherlands. Scientists predict that sea levels could increase by 20 inches (50.8 cm) over the next 100 years because of global warming. More than 25 percent of the Netherlands is currently below sea level. Therefore, the Dutch government is pursuing an international environmental strategy to cut "greenhouse gases" thought to be responsible for global warming.

Holding Back the Sea
According to the map below, what portion of the Dutch coast is protected by dikes such as the one above?

ASSESSMENT: Making Decisions

1. **Identify the Issue** Why do people try to reclaim land?

2. **Gather Information** **(a)** Why did the Dutch pursue the Delta Plan? **(b)** Why do some Dutch people oppose land reclamation?

3. **Identify Options** **(a)** What can the Dutch do to gain farmland? **(b)** What can they do to reduce the ill effects of agriculture? **(c)** What can they do to reduce the threat of rising sea levels to the Netherlands?

4. **Make a Decision** Develop an environmental plan for the Dutch. Explain your reasoning.

5. **Plan for the Future** Do research to study another example of people changing the natural environment. **(a)** What have been the effects in this case? **(b)** What options can you determine? **(c)** What decision would you recommend and why?

Chapter 16 **341**

Chapter 16 **341**

Objectives

Upon completion of Section 4, students should be able to:

◆ describe how the character of Switzerland is shaped by its history, culture, and economy;

◆ explain how shifting political boundaries and patterns of settlement have affected life in Austria.

National Geography Standards

The following National Geography Standards are highlighted in this section: 4, 5, 6, 10, 11, 13, 15, 17

Bellringer

Ask students to imagine that they have won a trip to Switzerland. Ask each student to write a list of what she or he would like to do there.

LESSON PLAN

1. Focus Tell students to look at Switzerland on the map on page 343. Explain that the country is landlocked, mountainous, and resource poor. Ask: **How might these aspects of geography affect development?** (They would be expected to hinder it.) Tell students that, despite these limitations, Switzerland has one of the highest standards of living in the world. Have students speculate as to why this is so.

2. Instruct Ask students to fold a piece of paper in half. Tell them to write *Similar* at the top of one side of the folded sheet and *Different* at the top of the other side. Ask them to compare Switzerland and Austria by listing ways in which the two countries are similar and different.

3. Close/Reteach Ask students to read the Reading Focus questions at the top of this page and answer the questions based on what they read.

4 Switzerland and Austria

Reading Focus

- **How is the character of Switzerland shaped by its past, its cultural identity, its prosperous market economy, and its involvement in global trade?**
- **How have shifting political boundaries and patterns of settlement affected life in Austria?**

Key Terms

canton
neutral
perishable good
strip mining

Main Idea Although Switzerland and Austria share physical characteristics, their cultures and economies are distinct.

Physical Characteristics Switzerland, in the heart of the Alps, is Europe's most mountainous country.

The Alps tower above the two small, landlocked countries of Switzerland and Austria. They cover more than half of each country's land area. Both countries are politically neutral. Neither is a member of NATO. Despite these similarities, Switzerland and Austria are strikingly different.

Switzerland

Switzerland has three official languages—French, German, and Italian—and some of its people speak a dialect called Romansch. About 64 percent of the population speak German, and 19 percent speak French. Each Swiss ethnic group has its own name for Switzerland. The German-speaking Swiss call it Schweiz (SHVYTS). Suisse (SWEES) is the name used by those who speak French. Italian-speaking citizens call their country Svizzera (SVEE tay rah). Switzerland's official name is Confederation Helvetica. Others know it as the Swiss Confederation. A confederation is a loose organization of states united for a common good.

For more than 700 years, the Swiss have established cultural patterns by absorbing people from different cultural traditions. Even today, however, these various cultural groups have maintained their distinctive identities as well as much of their political autonomy.

Understanding the Past Switzerland was formed in 1291 when leaders of three **cantons,** or states, formed the Swiss Confederation to fight an Austrian emperor. They fought several wars against the Austrians. Attracted by the growing strength of the confederation, other cantons began to join. By 1513, thirteen cantons belonged to the confederation.

France fought Switzerland in Italy in 1515 and was defeated. Switzerland never again fought in a foreign war. In 1798 Napoleon's armies occupied Switzerland. When Napoleon's forces were defeated, the countries of Europe formally recognized Switzerland as a **neutral** country. Since that time, Switzerland has not taken sides in conflicts between other countries, and no other European country has invaded its borders.

Cultures and Citizenship Today, twenty-six cantons make up Switzerland. These cantons differ from one another greatly in language,

342 Chapter 16 ▪ Central Western Europe

RESOURCE DIRECTORY

Teaching Resources

Creative Teaching Activities, Traveling Through Central Western Europe, p. 18

Unit 4, Chapter 16
- Section 4 Guided Reading and Review, p. 34

Guide to the Essentials (English/Spanish)
- Section Summary, Chapter 16, Section 4

Mental Mapping booklet
- Unit 4 Checklist, p. 52
- Outline Map 16, p. 60

Technology

Guided Reading Audiotapes (English/Spanish), Chapter 16, Section 4

Section Reading Support Transparencies, Chapter 16, Section 4

World Geography Map and Photo Transparencies
- Western Europe: Maps and Photos

Book on CD, Chapter 16

Social Studies Skills Tutor CD-ROM

Companion Web site, www.phschool.com
- Chapter 16 Activities

religion, customs, and the ways in which people make a living. The people of each canton work hard to preserve their particular way of life.

The cantons have a great deal of control over their own affairs. In the early history of the Swiss Confederation, each canton governed itself as a separate country. Even today, any law passed by the national government must be ratified by popular vote if enough Swiss citizens so request. This practice gives Swiss citizens more direct control of their government.

A Prosperous Market Economy

The independent spirit of the cantons exists alongside a strong national unity. This, together with Switzerland's neutrality, has helped the country thrive. The Swiss enjoy one of the highest standards of living in the world. Although Switzerland has few natural resources within its borders, it has developed economic activities that are highly profitable.

Dairy farming is the most important form of agriculture, because there is little flat land on which to grow crops. Cattle are driven to high mountain pastures in the spring. In the fall they are brought down to the valleys to protect them from the harsh winter temperatures in the Alps. Since milk is a **perishable good,** meaning that it does not stay fresh for long, most of it is turned into processed products like chocolate and cheese for export. Switzerland is famous throughout the world for its high-quality chocolates.

Specializing for Global Trade

Switzerland has none of the mineral resources, such as iron ore, coal, or petroleum, needed for heavy industry. So the Swiss specialize in making products that require skilled labor, instead of many materials or costly transportation. For hundreds of years, Swiss jewelers have produced watches known the world over for their accuracy. Switzerland produces very high-quality

Switzerland and Austria: PHYSICAL–POLITICAL

KEY

Elevation	
Feet	Meters
14,000	4,270
7,000	2,135
1,500	457
700	213
(sea level) 0	0 (sea level)

⊛ National capital
• Major city
▲ Mountain
)(Mountain Pass

Lambert Azimuthal Equal-Area Projection

APPLYING THE GEOGRAPHIC THEMES

● **Location** The Brenner Pass is an important part of the border that Austria shares with Italy. The route has been used at least since Roman times.
• *Today, what Austrian city is closest to the Brenner Pass?*

CUSTOMIZE FOR...

Students Acquiring English/ESL
Analyzing a Photo Have students look at the photograph on the opposite page. Point to different features in the picture, such as the **mountains, snow,** and the **clock tower.** Say the names aloud as you point to the pictures. Then ask students what the photo tells them about Swiss culture. For instance, you might ask them to predict what kinds of sports are popular in Switzerland. (Skiing is tremendously popular with residents and tourists.)

Change Over Time

Climatic Change

Patterns of Settlement Zermatt, Switzerland, has changed greatly over the years. In 1880 (PAST), the glacier to the left side of the painting fed the stream that ran by the town. Over time, climate conditions changed (PRESENT). The glacier retreated, reducing the amount of water feeding the stream.

Human-Environment Interaction *What effects has the glacier's retreat had on the town of Zermatt?*

PRESENT

PAST

tools, including microscopes and measuring and cutting tools. Today, the Swiss also are world leaders in the development of new medicines.

Banking is an important service industry in Switzerland. Switzerland is seen as a safe place to keep money because of the country's neutrality. People from many countries deposit their money in banks in Zurich, Geneva, and other Swiss cities.

Tourism also is very important to Switzerland's economy. Many people come to ski at resorts such as Zermatt and Saint-Moritz in the snowy Alps. Others come to hike, climb mountains, or simply enjoy Switzerland's spectacular scenery.

Austria

Although Austria's present borders were created at the end of World War I, this country of German speakers has roots that reach

Economic Activities During the Holocaust, many Jews sent their money to Swiss banks. Later, bank officials said the accounts were lost or demanded nonexistent death certificates. In 1998, under international pressure, the banks agreed to pay $1.25 billion to survivors of the account holders.

back more than one thousand years. It grew from a small region with its own ruler in A.D. 976 to the large Austrian Empire by the early 1800s. After a defeat in 1866, Austria became part of the Austro-Hungarian Empire. In the late 1800s, this empire controlled parts of Italy and much of Eastern Europe. Austria-Hungary fought along with Germany during World War I. With their defeat in 1918, the empire collapsed. Austria and Hungary were separated into independent countries. Much of the land they had controlled was taken to form new Eastern European countries.

One of modern Austria's biggest challenges has been to rebuild itself within its new, smaller boundaries. Because mountains cover much of the country, Austria's population is concentrated in the eastern lowlands, where the terrain is mostly flat or gently sloping.

Austria has used Switzerland as a model for its economic renewal. Like Switzerland, Austria has created specialized industries. Much of its economic activity centers on manufacturing machine tools, chemicals, and textiles. Cattle breeding and dairy farming are important agricultural activities. However, unlike Switzerland, Austria has the added benefit of some mineral resources.

Austria's Iron Belt

Environmental Change This strip mine in Austria produces iron ore, an important natural resource in the eastern Alps. Here, Austria has used this resource to build its steel industry, a mainstay of the nation's economy.

Human-Environment Interaction *Why do you think that some people oppose strip mining?*

Deposits of iron ore are mined in the eastern Alps. Sometimes the chosen method is **strip mining,** whereby miners strip away the surface of the earth to lay bare the mineral deposits. Other mined resources include magnesite, aluminum, copper, and lead.

Vienna, the country's capital, also has had to adapt to its changing role in history. The political and cultural center of the Austrian Empire, Vienna had two million residents in 1910 and was one of the world's largest cities. Today, its population is only 1.5 million. One reason is that modern industries find Vienna too congested and prefer to locate in smaller cities like Graz, Linz, or Innsbruck. Tourists, however, are still drawn to Vienna with its many cultural and historical attractions.

SECTION 4 ASSESSMENT

1. **Key Terms** Define **(a)** canton, **(b)** neutral, **(c)** perishable good, **(d)** strip mining.

2. **Cultures** Explain how each of the following is a significant part of the culture of Switzerland: **(a)** citizenship, **(b)** neutrality, **(c)** a high standard of living, **(d)** tourism.

3. **Understanding the Past** **(a)** Why is Austria a much smaller country today than it was in the 1800s? **(b)** What is one reason why the population of Vienna is smaller today than it was in the past?

4. **Critical Thinking Making Comparisons** Compare the photograph of the strip mine on page 345 with the photograph of a shaft mine on page 273. **(a)** How is a shaft mine different from a strip mine? **(b)** What do you think are the advantages and disadvantages of a shaft mine? **(c)** What do you think are the advantages and disadvantages of a strip mine?

Activity

Creating a Brochure What would attract tourists to Switzerland and Austria? Review the information in this section and conduct additional research if you wish. Next, create a brochure inviting visitors to these two countries. Try to include informative descriptions, maps, and photographs. Include topics such as history, sports, and music.

TEST PREPARATION

Have students read the subsection Austria beginning on the opposite page to answer this question.
What geographic feature makes Austria's economy different from Switzerland's?
- **A** The Alps
- **B** Lowlands
- Ⓒ **C** Iron deposits
- **D** Large cities

Answers to Section 4 Assessment

1. (a) canton, p. 342 **(b)** neutral, p. 342 **(c)** perishable good, p. 343 **(d)** strip mining, p. 345

2. (a) Swiss citizens can call for a popular vote on national laws. **(b)** Since Napoleon's occupation, Switzerland has not taken sides in conflicts between other countries, and no other European country has invaded its borders. **(c)** Switzerland has developed highly profitable economic activities to make up for its lack of natural resources. **(d)** Tourism in the Swiss Alps is very important to Switzerland's economy.

3. (a) In the 1800s, Austria was part of the Austro-Hungarian Empire, but the empire collapsed after World War I, and the countries were separated. **(b)** Modern industries find Vienna too congested and prefer to locate elsewhere.

4. (a) Shaft mining is done inside the earth, while strip mining is done on the surface. **(b)** Advantage: Shaft mining does not mar the landscape. Disadvantage: Shaft mining creates dangerous working conditions. **(c)** Advantage: Strip mining provides better working conditions. Disadvantage: Strip mining mars the landscape.

Activity Rubrics Share rubrics with students before they create their brochures.
Attempted The brochure is incomplete.
Minimal The brochure is attempted but shows limited understanding of tourism in Switzerland and Austria.
Adequate The brochure is neatly designed, well researched, and demonstrates an understanding of the region.
Exemplary The brochure is well designed, shows thorough research, and contains appropriate images and text.

Answer to Photo Caption

Answers may vary but might suggest that strip mining damages the landscape.

Creating a Chapter Summary

As a reteaching opportunity, pair a more able student with a less able student to complete this chapter summary.

Possible answers: **France:** Five main regions, French language gave the French people a national identity **Germany:** Reunified in 1990, Land divided into three bands **Benelux Countries:** Land reclaimed from the sea, Land generally low and flat **Switzerland and Austria:** Mostly mountainous, Large Swiss dairy industry, Iron deposits in Austria

Reviewing Key Terms

1–10. Students' sentences should show a clear understanding of the meaning of each term.

Understanding Key Ideas

11. (a) France, Germany, Switzerland, Austria, Liechtenstein, and Italy **(b)** They hindered movement between countries.
12. Wine grapes grow best in a mild, frost-free climate, like that of southwestern France.
13. In France, a single language unifies people; in Belgium, Luxembourg, and Switzerland, languages connect people to individual ethnic groups.
14. Coal fueled the machinery that Germany needed to industrialize.
15. Germany's steel, machinery, automobile, textile, and chemical industries support one of the most technologically powerful economies in the world.
16. (a) Possible answer: After World War II, Germany was split in two. **(b)** Possible answer: Austria's boundaries were changed when the Austro-Hungarian Empire collapsed after World War I.
17. Switzerland has given power to individual cantons; it also allows citizens to call for a popular vote on national laws.

Creating a Chapter Summary

On a sheet of paper, copy this table. Make the boxes large enough to write in several facts. Fill in key geographic information for each country or region. Some items have been filled in to help you get started.

FRANCE
1. Five main regions.
2.
GERMANY
1.
2.
BENELUX COUNTRIES
1.
2. Land generally low and flat.
SWITZERLAND AND AUSTRIA
1.
2.

Take It to the NET
Chapter Self-Test For practice test questions for Chapter 16, go to the World Geography section of **www.phschool.com**.

Reviewing Key Terms

Write sentences, using the key terms listed below and leaving blanks where the terms should go. Exchange your sentences with those of another student, and fill in the blanks in each other's sentences.

1. dialect   **6.** reparation

2. Impressionism **7.** inflation

3. nationalize   **8.** polder

4. recession   **9.** decentralize

5. confederation **10.** canton

Understanding Key Ideas

11. Physical Characteristics (a) Through which countries do the Alps run? **(b)** How have the Alps served as a natural barrier to migration in the past?

12. Climates How does climate affect economic activities in southwestern France?

13. Cultures How does language play a different role in France than in Belgium, Luxembourg, or Switzerland?

14. Natural Resources How did coal deposits help make Germany an important industrial power?

15. Economic Activities What role does industry play in the German economy?

16. Cooperation and Conflict How have past conflicts changed the borders of **(a)** Germany, **(b)** Austria?

17. Government and Citizenship How has Switzerland given its citizens more direct control of their government?

Critical Thinking and Writing

18. Predicting Consequences How would the French economy be affected if climatic change in France was not favorable for the growing of grapes?

19. Analyzing Causes and Effects (a) At the end of World War I, why was Germany required to pay money to other countries? **(b)** How did these payments affect the German economy?

20. Analyzing Processes Write a paragraph that explains how technological developments

---

Critical Thinking and Writing

18. The French economy would suffer but not fail because it also draws income from commercial industries and tourism.
19. (a) Germany had to make reparations for wartime damage. **(b)** They ruined the German economy.
20. Beginning in the 1200s, the Dutch used windmill-powered pumps that removed water from the land.

(Continued on next page.)

made land reclamation more efficient in the Netherlands.

21. Identifying Relationships (a) Why do the Swiss specialize in making products that require skilled labor? (b) How has Swiss specialization been adapted to the Austrian economy?

Applying Skills

Distinguishing Fact From Opinion Refer to the statements on page 336 to complete the following activities:

22. Choose one opinion statement and rewrite it so that it clearly is a statement of fact.

23. Choose one fact statement and rewrite it so that it becomes a statement of opinion.

Reading a Graph Study the bar graph below, and answer the following questions:

24. Approximately how many refugees entered France?

25. Did more refugees enter Switzerland or the United Kingdom?

26. What are some possible reasons that could explain why Germany has the greatest number of refugees?

Refugees to Western Europe

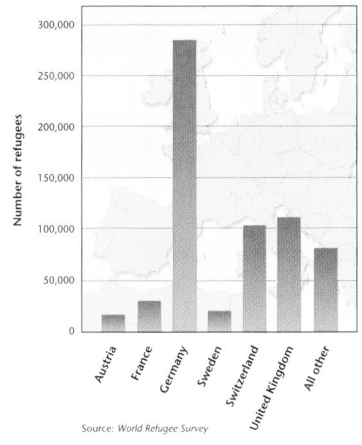

Source: *World Refugee Survey*

Test Preparation

Read the question and choose the best answer.

27. Ethnic tensions between Walloons and Flemings contributed to —

A the need for more land in the Netherlands

B the principle of Swiss neutrality

C the establishment of the Holy Roman Empire

D the adoption of two national languages in Belgium

Activities

USING THE **REGIONAL ATLAS**

Review the Regional Atlas for Western Europe and this chapter. Using the ecosystem and population density maps on pages 295 and 297 as a model, make a map for tourists who want to explore the ecosystems of central Western Europe. Recommend two of the areas shown on your map.

MENTAL MAPPING

Study a map of Europe. Then, on a separate piece of paper, draw a sketch map of central Western Europe from memory. Label the following places on your map:

- France
- Belgium
- Netherlands
- Germany
- Switzerland
- Austria
- Paris
- Berlin
- Amsterdam
- Vienna
- Seine River
- Rhine River
- Danube River
- Alps

Take It to the NET

Writing a Report Use the Internet to locate some current events articles about an environmental challenge facing Germany, Switzerland, or Austria today. Try to identify several perspectives on the issue. In a short written report, summarize the issue and the different viewpoints that you found. For help with this activity, visit the World Geography section of **www.phschool.com**.

Critical Thinking and Writing (cont.)

21. (a) Switzerland has none of the resources needed for heavy industry. Switzerland's highly skilled work force allows the nation's people to maintain a high standard of living. **(b)** Much of Austria's economic activity centers on specialized industries: manufacturing machine tools, chemicals, and textiles.

Applying Skills
22. Possible answer: B Bioengineering of crops is unnatural.
23. Possible answer: C Genetic engineers might add harmful genes to plant organisms.
24. About 30,000 refugees entered France.
25. More refugees entered the United Kingdom.
26. Possible answer: Germany's strong economy attracted them to the country.

Test Preparation
27. D

Activities

Using the Regional Atlas
Check students' maps for accuracy. Check that students have correctly identified the ecosystems of central Western Europe.

Mental Mapping
Review students' maps for relative and absolute location.

Take It to the Net
Students' work should reflect sound research. Check students' work for accuracy concerning environmental challenges faced by the country they chose.

MENTAL MAPPING

Games for Review See pages 58–63 of the Simulations, Games, and Lab Activities booklet for games to review place names in preparation for the Chapter 16 Map Test.

Chapter Map Test Students should use the completed outline maps and the Unit 4 Checklist in their Atlas Portfolios to prepare for the Chapter 16 Map Test. The test will cover only those place names on the list relating to the region covered in this chapter.

Alternative Assessment

Final Evaluation

Writing a Position Paper Use the Position Paper Evaluation Form on page 9 of the Alternative Assessment booklet in the Prentice Hall Assessment System to evaluate students' papers. Either teachers or students can complete the forms to indicate which level of work was achieved for each of the criteria. The evaluation should include specific examples and comments.

Resource Manager

Chapter-Level Resources	CORE INSTRUCTION	READING/SKILLS
	Teaching Resources **Unit 4**/Ch. 17 • Reviewing Main Ideas, p. 51 **Mental Mapping booklet** • Unit 4 Checklist, p. 52 **Simulations, Games, and Lab Activities** • Place Location Review Games, pp. 58–63 **Creative Teaching Activities** • Leonardo da Vinci, Renaissance Engineer, p. 19 **TeacherExpress™ CD-ROM**, Ch. 17 **Companion Web site,** **www.phschool.com** • eTeach	**Teaching Resources** **Unit 4**/Ch. 17 • Map/Graph Skills, p. 53 **Social Studies Skills Handbook** • Recognizing Cause and Effect, p. 49 **Book on CD**, Ch. 17 **Social Studies Skills Tutor CD-ROM**
1 Spain and Portugal 1. Describe how Spain differs physically, economically, and culturally from the rest of Europe. 2. Explain how political conditions and economic activities in Portugal have changed.	**Teaching Resources** **Unit 4**/Ch. 17 • Guided Reading and Review, p. 45 **Prentice Hall Presentation Pro CD-ROM**, Ch. 17, Sec. 1	**Teaching Resources** **Guide to the Essentials (English/Spanish)** • Section Summary, Ch. 17, Sec. 1 **Mental Mapping booklet** • Outline Map 17, p. 63 **Guided Reading Audiotapes (English/Spanish)**, Ch. 17, Sec. 1 **Section Reading Support Transparencies**, Ch. 17, Sec. 1
2 Italy 1. Discuss how Italians are adapting to their environment and expanding their economy as they plan for the future. 2. Describe how Italy's physical characteristics and economic activities divide the country into three large regions.	**Teaching Resources** **Unit 4**/Ch. 17 • Guided Reading and Review, p. 47 **Prentice Hall Presentation Pro CD-ROM**, Ch. 17, Sec. 2	**Teaching Resources** **Guide to the Essentials (English/Spanish)** • Section Summary, Ch. 17, Sec. 2 **Mental Mapping booklet** • Outline Map 17, p. 63 **Guided Reading Audiotapes (English/Spanish)**, Ch. 17, Sec. 2 **Section Reading Support Transparencies**, Ch. 17, Sec. 2
3 Greece 1. Describe how Greece's physical characteristics influence its economic activities 2. Summarize the mystery from Greece's past that scientists are trying to understand. 3. Explain why Greek culture is considered a mixture of Eastern and Western cultures.	**Teaching Resources** **Unit 4**/Ch. 17 • Guided Reading and Review, p. 49 **Prentice Hall Presentation Pro CD-ROM**, Ch. 17, Sec. 3	**Teaching Resources** **Guide to the Essentials (English/Spanish)** • Section Summary, Ch. 17, Sec. 3 **Guided Reading Audiotapes (English/Spanish)**, Ch. 17, Sec. 3 **Section Reading Support Transparencies**, Ch. 17, Sec. 3

ENRICHMENT/HONORS/PREAP

Teaching Resources
Unit 4/Ch. 17
- Critical Thinking, p. 52

Mental Mapping booklet
- Atlas Activity, p. 64

Social Studies Skills Handbook
- Study and Research Skills, pp. 94–108

World Geography Map and Photo Transparencies
- Western Europe: Maps and Photos

World Geography Videos
- Environmental Change: Mediterranean Europe, Tape 2

Companion Web site, www.phschool.com
- Chapter 17 Activities

Companion Web site, www.phschool.com
- Chapter 17 Activities

Companion Web site, www.phschool.com
- Chapter 17 Activities

Companion Web site, www.phschool.com
- Chapter 17 Activities

ASSESSMENT

PRENTICE HALL ASSESSMENT SYSTEM

Core Assessment
- ExamView Test Bank booklet, Ch. 17
- ExamView Test Bank CD-ROM, Ch. 17
- ExamView Test Bank CD-ROM, Unit 4

Standardized Test Preparation
Review and Reteach
- Review Book for World Geography, pp. 9–10

Practice and Assess
- Test-taking Strategies With Transparencies for High School
- Test-taking Strategy Poster
- Alternative Assessment booklet
- Test Prep Book for World Geography

Teaching Resources
Unit 4/Ch. 17
- Section Quizzes, pp. 46, 48, 50
- Test Forms A and B, pp. 54–59

Guide to the Essentials (English/Spanish)
- Chapter 17 Test

Spanish Resources, Ch. 17
- Section Quizzes, pp. 42–44

Mental Mapping booklet
- Chapter 17 Map Test, p. 65
- Unit 4 Map Test, p. 66

Companion Web site, www.phschool.com
- Chapter 17 Self-Test

CUSTOMIZE FOR INDIVIDUAL NEEDS

Gifted and Talented
- Teacher's Edition, Customize for . . . , pp. 351, 361

Less Proficient Readers
- Guide to the Essentials (English), Ch. 17, Section Summaries
- Guided Reading Audiotapes (English), Ch. 17
- Section Reading Support Transparencies, Ch. 17
- Book on CD, Ch. 17
- Teacher's Edition, Reading Strategy, pp. 351, 356, 364
- Teacher's Edition, Activity: Vocabulary, pp. 350, 357, 364
- Teacher's Edition, Customize for . . . , p. 355

Students Acquiring English/ESL
- Guide to the Essentials (English/Spanish), Ch. 17
- Guided Reading Audiotapes (English/Spanish), Ch. 17
- Section Reading Support Transparencies, Ch. 17
- Book on CD, Ch. 17
- Teacher's Edition, Customize for . . . , p. 359

Less Proficient Writers
- Social Studies Skills Handbook, p. 93
- Alternative Assessment, Writing Assignment Rubric, p. 6
- Teacher's Edition, Customize for . . . , p. 363

MENTAL MAPPING

Ask students to look at the map on this page, and point out the countries of Mediterranean Europe—Italy, Greece, Spain, and Portugal. Have students name the three Mediterranean countries that actually have coastlines on the Mediterranean Sea. (Italy, Greece, and Spain)

Mapping the Region Have students create a map like the one shown here. Ask them to sketch their own maps, or distribute the Chapter 17 Outline Map on page 63 of the Mental Mapping booklet in the Teaching Resources. Instruct students to lightly shade each country a different color. Then ask them to label the countries and bodies of water shown on this map. Students should keep their maps in their Atlas Portfolios in order to prepare for the Chapter 17 and Unit 4 map tests.

eTeach

Be sure to check out this month's online forum with a Master Teacher to join in an exchange of teaching ideas. www.phschool.com

---

CHAPTER

17

Mediterranean Europe

SECTIONS

1	Spain and Portugal
2	Italy
3	Greece

Mediterranean Europe: POLITICAL

KEY
- National boundary
- ⊛ National capital
- • Other city

Lambert Azimuthal Equal-Area Projection

ATLANTIC OCEAN
Bay of Biscay
PORTUGAL
SPAIN
Lisbon ⊛
⊛ Madrid
• Barcelona
Valencia •
Ebro River
Balearic Islands
Strait of Gibraltar
Gibraltar (U.K.)
Gulf of Lion
ANDORRA
Turin •
Milan • Venice
Po River
• Genoa
Florence •
SAN MARINO
Elba
Tiber R.
Rome •
ITALY
• Naples
Sardinia
Adriatic Sea
Tyrrhenian Sea
Sicily
Mediterranean Sea
Ionian Sea
Corfu
GREECE
Athens •
Thessaloniki
Aegean Sea
Rhodes
Crete
40°N
10°W 0° 10°E 20°E
0   150   300 mi
0   150   300 km

Go Online
PHSchool.com

For: More information about Mediterranean Europe and access to the Take It to the Net activities
Visit: phschool.com
Web Code: mjk-0018

RESOURCE DIRECTORY

Teaching Resources
Unit 4, Chapter 17
- Section 1, Guided Reading and Review, p. 45

Guide to the Essentials (English/Spanish)
- Section Summary, Chapter 17, Section 1

Mental Mapping booklet
- Atlas Activity, p. 64
- Unit 4 Checklist, p. 52

Technology
Guided Reading Audiotapes (English/Spanish), Chapter 17, Section 1

Section Reading Support Transparencies, Chapter 17, Section 1
World Geography Map and Photo Transparencies
- Western Europe: Maps and Photos

Book on CD, Chapter 17
World Geography Videos
- Environmental Change: Mediterranean Europe, Tape 2

TeacherExpress™ CD-ROM, Chapter 17
Prentice Hall Presentation Pro CD-ROM, Chapter 17
Social Studies Skills Tutor CD-ROM
Companion Web site, www.phschool.com
- Chapter 17 Activities

1 Spain and Portugal

Reading Focus

- How is Spain physically, economically, and culturally distinct from other nations of the European continent?
- How are political conditions and economic activities in Portugal different today from what they were in the past?

Key Terms

navigable
dry farming
sirocco
hub

Main Idea The history, culture, and location of Spain and Portugal help to distinguish them from other European nations.

Understanding the Past The Alcazar Castle sits on top of a high cliff in Segovia, Spain.

As the map on page 348 shows, the Iberian Peninsula dangles off the southwestern edge of Europe, separating the waters of the Mediterranean Sea from the Atlantic Ocean. Two countries dominate the peninsula, Spain and Portugal. Spain covers most of the peninsula; Portugal occupies about one sixth of the land.

Spain and Portugal seem closely tied to the rest of Europe, but location can be deceptive. The French emperor Napoleon once said, "Europe ends at the Pyrenees" (PIHR uh neez)—the mountains that divide the Iberian Peninsula from the rest of Europe. The reason people think of Spain and Portugal as isolated from the rest of Europe is revealed in the histories and in the distinct characters of the two places.

Spain

A castle appears on Spain's coat of arms. The castle is a symbol both of Spain's history and of its physical characteristics. Historically, the castle

represents Castile (cas TEEL) and the hundreds of years of war that are part of Spain's history. Castile was one of the Christian kingdoms of Spain that fought the Muslim Moors and finally expelled them in 1492, after being under their rule for more than 700 years.

Geographically, Spain is like a well-guarded castle. The Pyrenees Mountains block easy passage across the nation's only land border with the rest of Europe. Approaches by water are no easier. Steep cliffs rise directly from the water along large stretches of the coastline. Elsewhere coastal plains are very narrow.

Rising from the slender coastal plains are the high plateaus that form most of Spain. The plateau of central Spain is known as the *Meseta* (me SAY tuh), the Spanish word for "plateau." Several large rivers flow across the Meseta and between the few mountain ranges that divide the plateau. Of these rivers, only the Guadalquivir is **navigable;** that is, deep and wide enough to allow ships to pass. Dangerous rapids make all other rivers unnavigable.

 Temple of Poseidon, Greece *(photo left)*

Chapter 17 ▪ Section 1 **349**

Section 1 *pp. 349–353*

Objectives

Upon completion of Section 1, students should be able to:

- describe how Spain differs physically, economically, and culturally from the rest of Europe;
- explain how political conditions and economic activities in Portugal have changed.

National Geography Standards

The following National Geography Standards are highlighted in this section: 1, 2, 4, 5, 6, 7, 9, 10, 11, 13, 15, 17

Bellringer

Read aloud this passage from the introduction to *Iberia*, by James Michener: "Spain is a very special country, and one must approach it with respect and with his eyes open." Ask students what they think this statement means.

LESSON PLAN

1. Focus Have students look at the map of Spain and Portugal on page 350 and list three physical characteristics that would contribute to Spain's isolation from the rest of Europe. (the Pyrenees; Spain's location on a peninsula; sharp elevations that rise along much of the coast)

2. Instruct Have students construct a chart comparing Spain and Portugal in these categories: *Geography, Climate, Agriculture, Industries, Former Empires, Ethnic Groups.*

3. Close/Reteach Ask students to write sentences describing Spain and/or Portugal using the following terms: peninsula, Pyrenees, Meseta, Bilbao, Madrid, the Basques, cork, Lisbon, European Union. Choose volunteers to read their sentences aloud.

TEACHING TIP
From A Master Teacher

Regions A region is an area that is characterized by a common human or physical feature (a formal region), or linked in some way (a functional region). A place can be in many different kinds of regions. The nations in this chapter lie in a Mediterranean climate region. Have students locate other areas with a Mediterranean climate. Finding the differences and similarities among these places can provide insights into the ways different cultures interact in similar environments to produce dissimilar places.

Pacing Suggestions

For 90-minute Blocks

You will want to vary activities.

- Begin with the activity about Leonardo da Vinci on page 19 of the Creative Teaching Activities booklet. Have students research other scientific discoveries of the Renaissance. Then ask each student to create a poster showing one Renaissance discovery and identifying the scientist and the time and place of this discovery.

Chapter 17 ▪ Section 1 **349**

Vocabulary

Dry farming Refer to the Key Terms list on page 349. Write the term *dry farming* on the board. Ask a volunteer to look up the term in the Glossary and read its definition aloud. Then have another volunteer restate the definition in his or her own words. Ask: **In what type of environment is dry farming used?** (areas that receive very little rainfall)

The Global Economy

Communication A *lingua franca,* Italian for "Frankish tongue," developed in Mediterranean Europe during the Middle Ages. It was a mixture of Spanish, Italian, Greek, Arabic, and French. Travelers and traders spoke *lingua franca* so they had to learn only one language instead of five or six. Today the language is dead, but the term remains to describe a common language adopted by people of many different cultures.

Alternative Assessment

Introduce the Activity

Participating in a Classroom Discussion Tell students they will be participating in a classroom discussion at the end of this chapter on the role physical geography has played in the development of the unique cultures of Spain, Italy, and Greece. Distribute the Classroom Discussion Rubric found on page 22 of the Alternative Assessment booklet in the Prentice Hall Assessment System for students' reference.

Answer to Map Caption

the Pyrenees Mountains

Climates Almost all of Spain has a Mediterranean climate of mild, rainy winters and hot, dry summers. Spain's elevation has a strong influence on its climate. Moist, Atlantic winds rising over the Cantabrian (can TAH bree uhn) Mountains along the northern coast drop ample rain for farmers to raise corn and cattle there. The Meseta in the interior, however, is in the rain shadow of the mountains and is much drier. Farmers in the Meseta grow wheat or barley, using **dry farming** methods that leave land unplanted every few years in order to gather moisture. Sheep and goats graze on slopes too steep or dry for growing crops.

Parts of southeastern Spain are much drier than the rest of the country, making them semiarid.

Siroccos, or hot, dry winds from northern Africa, blow over this area. Irrigation provides water for economic activities such as growing citrus fruits and olive trees on the eastern coastal plains near Valencia and Barcelona.

Economic Activities Spain's economy has shifted from agriculture toward new industries in recent years. Its major export is transportation equipment. One major industrial center is in the north, around the city of Bilbao. Local iron ore provides material for producing steel and other products. Barcelona, the nation's largest port, is a center for the manufacture of textiles and plastics. Despite this economic shift, Spain often suffers from high unemployment rates.

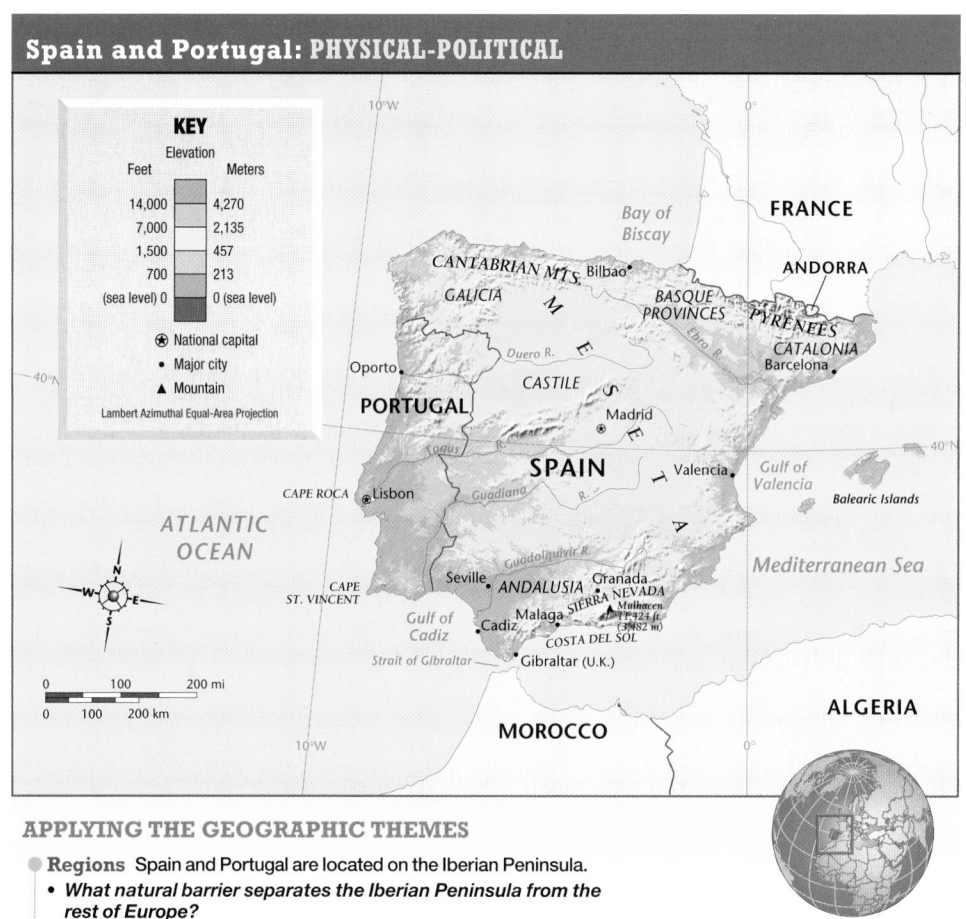

Spain and Portugal: PHYSICAL-POLITICAL

APPLYING THE GEOGRAPHIC THEMES

● **Regions** Spain and Portugal are located on the Iberian Peninsula.
- *What natural barrier separates the Iberian Peninsula from the rest of Europe?*

350 Chapter 17 ▪ Mediterranean Europe

RESOURCE DIRECTORY

Teaching Resources
Mental Mapping booklet
• Outline Map 17, p. 63

Prentice Hall Assessment System
Alternative Assessment booklet
• Classroom Discussion Rubric, p. 22

Technology
World Geography Map and Photo Transparencies
• Western Europe: Maps and Photos

Fishing Industry

Economic Activities
The northern region of Spain is dominated by the Basques, who have struggled to maintain their identity and independence. The Basques have a long history of seafaring, both as explorers and fishers.

Place *How has the geography of northern Spain helped the Basques retain their cultural identity?*

Patterns of Settlement Spain's largest city is its capital, Madrid. King Philip II made this city his capital in 1561. One story suggests that the king selected this site on the Meseta because its dry climate eased the pain of his gout, a disease that causes painful joints. Historical geographers give another reason for the capital's status: its central location. This factor allowed Philip and later rulers to control people and resources in all parts of the nation.

Over the years such central control grew easier as Madrid became the **hub**—a central point of concentrated activity and influence—of new transportation routes. The city prospered by tapping the wealth of other Spanish regions. An old Spanish saying suggests, "Everyone works for Madrid, and Madrid works for no one."

In recent decades, the Spanish have built newer industries in the area around Madrid. Migrants from poor farming areas have moved to the city and surrounding area. The metropolis now has more than 3 million residents. It also has problems associated with a large population, including heavy traffic and air pollution.

Cultural Divergence Despite nearly five hundred years of central control, Spain's regions hold on to their strong independent identities. Writer V. S. Pritchett said this about the Spanish people's strong regional ties:

> 66 They are rooted in their region, even nowadays. . . . They are Basques, Catalans, Galicians, Castilians . . . and so on, before they are Spaniards. 99

The most striking example of an independent identity may be the Basque (BASK) people of northern Spain. The Basques number fewer than one million people, yet they inhabit one of Spain's richest areas.

The Basque language is not related to any other European language and is difficult to learn. A Spanish story tells of a person who "spent seven years learning it and in the end knew only three words."

The Basques have a strong tradition of cultural divergence—a desire to protect their culture from outside influences. Although the region has been granted limited autonomy, some Basques demand total independence. A few of these separatists have engaged in violent acts against the central Spanish government.

Political tensions are less severe in Catalonia, the region surrounding Barcelona. However, pressures for greater use of the Catalan language—a mixture of French and Spanish—are evident in this region, too. Other parts of Spain are also asking for greater local control.

Portugal

English professor and novelist Frank Tuohy explained the differences he saw between Spain and Portugal this way:

> ❝Spain is like a novel with half a dozen chapters; Portugal is a short story. A compact country, with variety in a limited space, one small village church will commemorate six centuries of history and three golden ages of architecture.❞

Portugal is about the size of the state of Indiana but has more than one and a half times as many residents. The northeastern corner of the country is mountainous, but the land slopes gently toward the Atlantic. At least 20 inches (50 cm) of rain fall each year in much of the country.

The abundant rainfall favors farming. Grains such as wheat, corn, and barley grow on flat lands. Olive oil from the south is a major export, as is the port wine produced in northern valleys near the city of Oporto. Cork and cork products made from the bark of oak trees also are major exports.

Global Trade Patterns Portugal has had a large impact on world affairs. It emerged as an independent nation in 1143 when rulers of the area around Oporto defeated the Moors. Portugal quickly became a trading nation. Portugal's capital, Lisbon, became the leading port of the new nation.

In the fifteenth century, Portugal explored new sea routes to East Asia around Africa and established many trading colonies. When both Spain and Portugal expanded their colonial empires into

GEoFacts

To make cork, the bark of a cork oak is stripped from mature trunks and branches every nine years. Cork oak orchards make up about 21 percent of the forested land in Portugal. They also provide shelter for wildlife. Strict Portuguese laws ensure the trees' protection.

Mediterranean Europe and the United States
Trade Data

Country	Total Exports (billions of dollars)	Total Imports (billions of dollars)	Trade Balance (billions of dollars)
Greece	12.4	27.7	−15.3
Italy	242.6	206.9	35.7
Malta	1.8	2.7	−0.9
Portugal	25.0	34.9	−9.9
Spain	112.3	137.5	−25.2
United States	663.0	912.0	−249.0

Source: *The World Factbook*

CHART SKILLS

- **Geographic Tools** *How is a nation's trade balance calculated?*
- **Global Trade Patterns** *Which nation's economy profits most from trade?*

South America, conflicts arose over the division of land. In 1494, the two countries signed a treaty and Portugal gained control of large parts of Africa and Brazil. Spain claimed most of the rest of Latin America.

Migrations The empires of Portugal and Spain shrank in the early 1800s as many colonies gained their independence. Not until 1975 did the Portuguese grant independence to their largest African colonies. Since that time, nearly one million people from the former African colonies have immigrated to Portugal, seeking greater opportunities.

Banker Antonio Vasco de Mello observed about the old Portugal, "We didn't know if we were a small European country with big African holdings or a big African country with a foothold in Europe." When Portugal gave its colonies their freedom, the country turned back toward Europe. Like Spain, Portugal joined the European Union in 1986.

Planning for the Future Portugal's economy, once based heavily on agriculture, is

European Languages Around the World

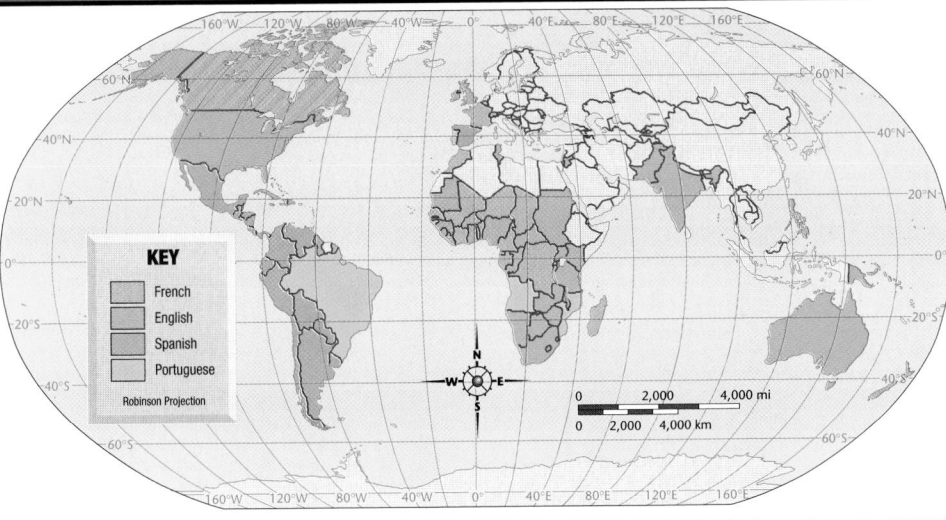

KEY
- French
- English
- Spanish
- Portuguese

Robinson Projection

APPLYING THE GEOGRAPHIC THEMES

● **Movement** Over the centuries, European languages have spread around the world as a result of colonialism and cultural diffusion. Each of these languages became a *lingua franca*, or language adopted by people of many different cultures.

- *According to this map, what* lingua franca *is used in South Asia?*

currently heading in new directions. As in Spain, industry now plays a major role in Portugal's economy. In the late 1990s, Ford and Volkswagen partnered in building a motor vehicle plant near Lisbon. Portuguese exports include cork,

textiles, clothing, and footwear. The nation is working to increase its literacy rate of about 87 percent. Industrial pollution is a growing problem. Portugal faces economic, environmental, and human challenges as it plans for the future.

SECTION 1 ASSESSMENT

1. **Key Terms** Define **(a)** navigable, **(b)** dry farming, **(c)** sirocco, **(d)** hub.

2. **Physical Characteristics (a)** How do Spain's physical characteristics affect climate conditions? **(b)** In what ways do physical characteristics influence economic activities? **(c)** In what ways might Spain's physical characteristics have influenced the location of its capital?

3. **Planning for the Future (a)** How did global trading help to establish Portugal as an economic power in the past? **(b)** What is the basis of Portugal's current economy?

4. **Critical Thinking Developing a Hypothesis** Why do you think that the central government of Spain granted the Basques limited autonomy?

Activity

USING THE **REGIONAL ATLAS**

Review the Regional Atlas for Europe and this section. Then, design and draw a chart of economic activities for Spain and Portugal. Label one column: Spain. Label a second column: Portugal. Create a row for each economic activity of the region. For each economic activity in which Spain or Portugal participates, place a check in the appropriate column.

Articles From NATIONAL GEOGRAPHIC

The following article may be used to extend the content in this section.

McCarry, John, and Medford Taylor, photographer. "Madeira Toasts the Future." *National Geographic*, Vol. 186, No. 5 (Nov. 1994), pp. 90–113.

Long steeped in tradition, the Portuguese Madeira Islands are now inviting change.

TEST PREPARATION

Ask students to read the subsection Global Trade Patterns on page 352 and then answer the following question:

Portugal's influence in world affairs throughout its early history could be attributed to its active and widespread involvement in what activity?

- **A** Ranching
- **B** Fishing
- **Ⓒ** Trade
- **D** Agriculture

Answers to Section 1 Assessment

1. (a) navigable, p. 349 **(b)** dry farming, p. 350 **(c)** sirocco, p. 350 **(d)** hub, p. 351

2. (a) Moist, Atlantic winds rising over the Cantabrian Mountains drop ample rain along the northern coast; the Meseta in the interior is much drier; the siroccos blow over parts of southeastern Spain, making them semiarid. **(b)** Corn and cattle are raised along the wet northern coast; wheat and barley are grown on the dry Meseta; irrigation along the eastern coastal plains provides water for growing citrus fruits and olive trees. **(c)** Madrid is located in the Meseta, which offers a dry climate and a central location.

3. (a) Portugal explored new sea routes to East Asia around Africa and established many trading colonies. **(b)** industry

4. Answers may vary, but students might suggest that the central government wanted to placate Basque demands for total independence.

Activity Rubrics Share rubrics with students before they create their charts.

Attempted The chart has very few entries or contains erroneous information.

Minimal The chart does not include all the important economic activities of the region.

Adequate The chart is neatly done and reflects a good understanding of the economic activities of Spain and Portugal.

Exemplary The chart is very well done and provides an accurate and complete overview of the economic activities of Spain and Portugal.

Answer to Map Caption

English

Objectives

Upon completion of Section 2, students should be able to:

◆ discuss how Italians are adapting to their environment and expanding their economy as they plan for the future;

◆ describe how Italy's physical characteristics and economic activities divide the country into three large regions.

National Geography Standards

The following National Geography Standards are highlighted in this section: 1, 2, 4, 5, 6, 7, 9, 10, 12, 14, 17, 18

Bellringer

Ask students: **What do all these people have in common: Julius Caesar, Christopher Columbus, Michelangelo, Sophia Loren?** (They all came from Italy.)

LESSON PLAN

1. Focus Have students think of some products they associate with Italy. List their responses on the board. (Examples: wine, pasta, olives, cars, clothing, shoes) Point out that the list represents agricultural and industrial products, and both are important to Italy's economy.

2. Instruct Write the following headings on the board: *Northern Italy, Central Italy,* and *Southern Italy.* Have students identify the geographic and economic characteristics of each region. List responses on the board under each heading.

3. Close/Reteach Have students work in pairs to decide whether they would prefer to visit northern, central, or southern Italy. Then, have each pair write reasons they would like to visit the area that they chose.

2 Italy

Reading Focus

• As they plan for their future, how do the people of Italy continue to adapt to their environment and expand their economy?

• How do Italy's physical characteristics and economic activities divide the country into three large regions?

Key Terms

seismic activity

subsidence

Renaissance

Main Idea Italy's physical characteristics and economic activities divide the nation into three distinct regions.

Environmental Change The vineyards at San Gimignano form part of Italy's distinctive landscape.

Italy has perhaps the best-known outline of any country in the world. Most people suggest that Italy looks like a giant boot ready to kick the triangular "rock" of Sicily across the Mediterranean Sea.

People and Environment

Italy's boot is formed around the Apennine Mountains. This mountain range begins in the northwest and arcs all the way down the Italian Peninsula. No peak in the Apennines is higher than 10,000 feet (3,000 m) above sea level. But they and other highlands cover much of the Italian peninsula, leaving the narrow coastal plains as the country's only flat land. This young range experiences **seismic activity**—that is, it has many earthquakes and volcanic eruptions. The Aeolian Islands off the southern toe of Italy and the island of Sicily have been sites of historic and recent volcanic eruptions. Sicily's Mount Etna violently erupted most recently in 2001.

Environmental Change The Alps run from east to west along the entire northern boundary of Italy. Their tall peaks block much

of the moisture that the prevailing westerlies carry from the North Atlantic into Western Europe. As a result, Italy's climate south of the Alps is Mediterranean—hot and dry in summer and mild and wet in winter.

Trees that once covered many hillsides have been cleared for space and fuel over the centuries. Only scrub vegetation remains. In addition, large volumes of soil have eroded through overgrazing by goats and sheep.

In spite of the dry climate and the scarcity of flat land, until recently Italy relied heavily on agriculture. As late as 1960, more than one third of the population lived and worked on farms. Today, however, only 10 percent of Italy's work force is agricultural.

Migration Italy has a population of about fifty-eight million. People cannot easily make their homes on the mountains that dominate much of Italy's landscape, so the populated areas are very crowded.

In the early 1900s, many Italians were forced to move because the small amount of farmland could not support the population. Unemployment in rural areas is still high, especially in southern

RESOURCE DIRECTORY

Teaching Resources

Unit 4, Chapter 17
• Section 2 Guided Reading and Review, p. 47
• Map/Graph Skills, p. 53

Guide to the Essentials (English/Spanish)
• Section Summary, Chapter 17, Section 2

Mental Mapping booklet
• Outline Map 17, p. 63
• Unit 4 Checklist, p. 52

Technology

Guided Reading Audiotapes (English/Spanish), Chapter 17, Section 2

Section Reading Support Transparencies, Chapter 17, Section 2

World Geography Map and Photo Transparencies
• Western Europe: Maps and Photos

Book on CD, Chapter 17

Social Studies Skills Tutor CD-ROM

Companion Web site, www.phschool.com
• Chapter 17 Activities

Italy. Since World War II, many workers have migrated from the poor southern regions to the northern provinces of Lombardy and Piedmont to find jobs in factories.

Economic Activities The Italian government has encouraged the development of new factories and services in recent years. Automobiles, home appliances, and other metal goods have been the most successful products. These commercial industries have boosted Italy's steel industry and helped the growth of many smaller factories that supply parts and machines.

Italy has turned its geographic disadvantages into opportunities. Until the 1950s, Italy was largely agricultural and relatively poor, but it worked hard to help form the organization now called the European Union. Italy could then reach a much larger and richer market. Because Italy was poor, its workers were willing to work for low wages. Italian goods could be sold at lower prices, and Italian industries boomed.

Creativity also played a role in the industrial boom. Italian businesses developed new styles, designs, and methods for making their products. These innovations made Italian products, such as sleek home furnishings and high-fashion clothes, more attractive to foreign markets.

The Regions of Italy

After the Roman Empire collapsed in the fifth century, the Italian peninsula became a changing patchwork of separate political units. Over the next thirteen hundred years, many Italian cities operated as independent states. Kingdoms grew and declined. As the influence of Christianity spread, the Roman Catholic Church gained control over large amounts of land.

It was not until 1861 that states in the northern part of the peninsula

joined together to form the country of Italy. Within a decade, the entire peninsula was united. During the twentieth century, a united Italy has survived two world wars and changes in national government.

Italy's survival as a unified nation is impressive because of the striking differences that exist among its many regions. Although each of its smaller regions has a distinct local character, Italy may be divided roughly into three large regions:

Italy: PHYSICAL-POLITICAL

KEY

Elevation	
Feet	Meters
14,000	4,270
7,000	2,135
1,500	457
700	213
(sea level) 0	0 (sea level)

⊛ National capital
• Major city
▲ Mountain
△ Volcano

Lambert Azimuthal Equal-Area Projection

APPLYING THE GEOGRAPHIC THEMES

● **Human-Environment Interaction** Italy's mountainous terrain has limited the amount of land available for agriculture.

• *How have people changed the environment in Italy?*

GEOFacts

Italian citizens who are voting and speaking out against crime and corruption in their country have had an impact in recent years. Change is apparent in new legislation regarding the direct election of legislators, stronger anticrime laws, and a more vigorous stance against crime by the Italian courts.

northern, central, and southern Italy.

Northern Italy The country's northern region is often called European Italy. The provinces in this region are located close to the rest of Europe, and they resemble Central European countries more than other Italian provinces do.

The heart of northern Italy is the lush Po River valley, a broad plain between the Alps and the Apennines. Since drainage was improved in the Middle Ages, the valley has been Italy's most productive agricultural area. Wheat and rice are important crops.

The Po Valley is now an important center of commercial industry. About two thirds of Italy's factory products are made there. Early industrial development focused on the cities of Milan and Turin, which are located near sources of raw materials. Today hydroelectricity from rivers in the Alps powers many factories. The industrial growth of the Po Valley has made Genoa a thriving port city.

Other parts of the northern region also are prosperous. Ski resorts in the Alps and the area's splendid lakes attract visitors all year round. Dairy farms are very productive and profitable.

Frequent flooding in the area around Venice has stunted its agricultural and industrial growth. Venice itself faces problems of pollution and **subsidence,** a geological phenomenon in which the ground in an area sinks. Still, Venice remains popular with tourists for its intricate network of canals that serve as streets and the ornate palaces built by Venetian traders in the late Middle Ages.

Central Italy Central Italy consists of Rome and the surrounding regions, which were once controlled by the Roman Catholic Church. Rome was chosen as the capital in the late 1800s for two reasons. First, its location was central. Second, it had been the capital of the Roman Empire,

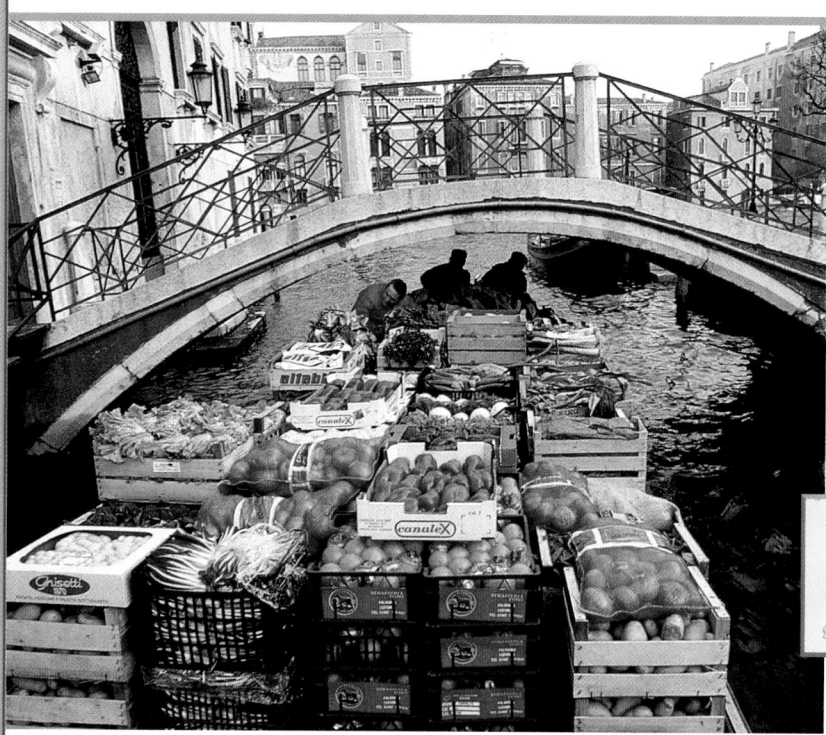

The Canals of Venice

Environmental Change The city of Venice has close ties to the sea. It is built on a series of small islands 2.5 miles (4 km) off the Italian mainland. The city is cut by some 180 canals, which are used as streets. Boats called gondolas carry people and goods through the city.

Location *What problems does Venice face because of its location?*

and its history symbolized the glory that the Italians hoped to restore to their new nation. Still standing there are the ruins of the Colosseum—ancient Rome's largest stadium—and the Forum, a public meeting place.

American novelist Michael Mewshaw described the flurry of activity one sees in Rome:

66 Many streets are as narrow as hallways, as steep as staircases, as dim and cool as cellars. Yet even where these cramped passages open into broad avenues and roomlike piazzas [open squares] full of people, Romans maintain their inalienable right to do outdoors anything they might do at home. . . . Romans simply like to do things together; they enjoy sharing with the world the endless wonder they take in themselves and in one another. 99

Within the city of Rome is an area measuring less than 1 square mile (2.6 sq km) known as Vatican City. This small tract serves as the world headquarters of the Roman Catholic Church. Fewer than one thousand people live in Vatican City, but the district swells daily with visitors to its two main structures, St. Peter's Basilica and the Vatican Museums.

Rome is not the only major city in central Italy. Bologna is a leading agricultural center known for its wonderful variety of foods. Florence is a cultural center made famous by Michelangelo and other Italian painters during the **Renaissance.** This was a great period of art and learning that

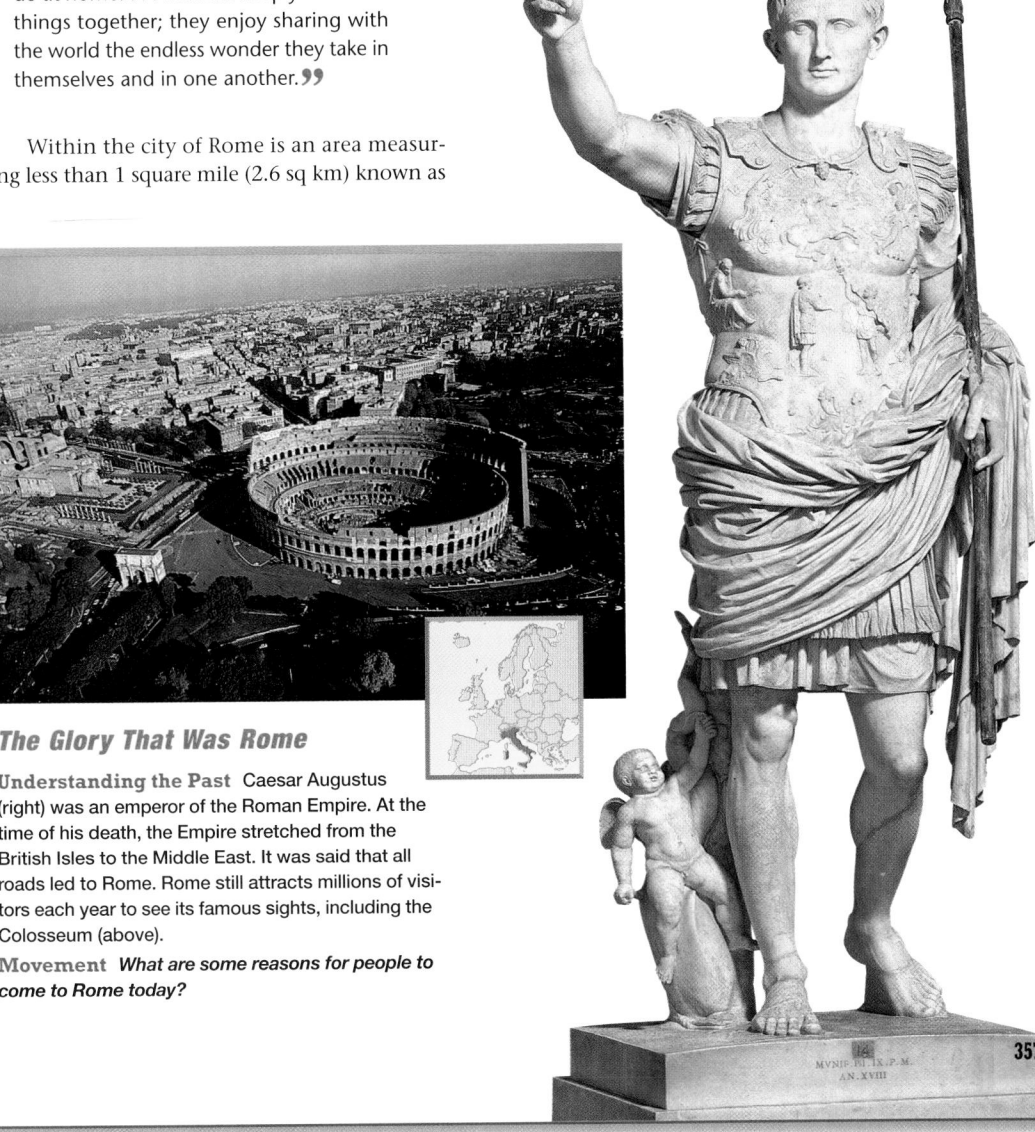

The Glory That Was Rome

Understanding the Past Caesar Augustus (right) was an emperor of the Roman Empire. At the time of his death, the Empire stretched from the British Isles to the Middle East. It was said that all roads led to Rome. Rome still attracts millions of visitors each year to see its famous sights, including the Colosseum (above).

Movement *What are some reasons for people to come to Rome today?*

Articles From ·········
NATIONAL GEOGRAPHIC

The following article may be used to extend the content in this section.

Zwingle, Erla, and Sam Abell, photographer. "Venice." *National Geographic*, Vol. 187, No. 2 (Feb. 1995), pp. 70–99.

Stressed by sinking classical structures, a rising ocean, and an economy that depends on tourism, Venice must find a way to preserve its 1,500-year-old beauty.

TEST PREPARATION

Have students read the subsection Central Italy beginning on page 356 and then complete the following sentence.

Rome was chosen as the capital of Italy in the late 1800s because —

(A) it is centrally located
B it was a new city
C it has few historical monuments
D it is in the lush Po River valley

Alternative Assessment

Participating in a Classroom Discussion Check to see that students are preparing for the classroom discussion.

Answers to Section 2 Assessment

1. (a) seismic activity, p. 354
(b) subsidence, p. 356
(c) Renaissance, p. 357
2. (a) Trees that once covered many hillsides have been cleared for space and fuel; overgrazing by goats and sheep has caused heavy soil erosion. **(b)** Many workers have migrated from the poor southern regions to the northern provinces to find jobs in factories. **(c)** The Italian government has encouraged the development of new factories and services; in addition, creative design innovations have made Italian products successful.
3. Central Italy is home to the major cultural centers of Rome, Bologna, and Florence. It is in Florence that Michelangelo and other Italian artists worked during the Renaissance.
4. Possible answers: **(a)** Many diverse cultures could stimulate the economy and attract tourists. **(b)** A disadvantage would be the difficulty of maintaining a unified nation.

Activity Rubrics Share rubrics with students before they write their journal entries.

Attempted The journal entry reveals little research, is poorly written, and contains many mechanical errors.
Minimal The journal entry reveals some research but is poorly written and contains many mechanical errors.
Adequate The journal entry reveals ample research, is well written and engaging, and contains few mechanical errors.
Exemplary The journal entry reveals extensive research, is insightful and very well written, and contains no mechanical errors.

Answer to Photo Caption

Sicily does not have large-scale agriculture because the soil is poor.

The Sicilian Landscape

Physical Characteristics Caltabellota and the surrounding land are typical of Sicily's hilly landscape, with rocky outcroppings in many places. The soil, while fertile, is often thin and poor for farming. Still, Sicilian culture has survived for thousands of years.
Human-Environment Interaction *Does Sicily's land make it suitable for large-scale agriculture? Explain.*

started in Italy in the 1300s and was diffused throughout Europe.

Southern Italy The southern region of Italy is known as the *Mezzogiorno* (MET soh ZHOR noh) and includes the islands of Sicily and Sardinia. The name means "midday" and points out one of the region's most noted features: its intense noontime sun. Poor roads once made travel difficult in this area. New freeways now bring this region closer to the rest of the nation. Agriculture is not highly profitable here because of poor soil and outdated farming techniques. Some heavy industries located here after World War II but have suffered in recent decades. As a result, many southerners have migrated to northern Italy.

Other southern Italians have moved to Naples, the largest city in the region. This port city suffers from some of the worst poverty in Europe. The number of available jobs cannot keep pace with the number of people who wish to work. The people hope that as Italy's economy develops within the European Union, their standard of living will improve.

SECTION 2 ASSESSMENT

1. **Key Terms** Define **(a)** seismic activity, **(b)** subsidence, **(c)** Renaissance.

2. **Economic Activities** **(a)** How have economic activities altered the natural environment of Italy? **(b)** What have been the economic causes of migration in Italy? **(c)** Why has Italy's economy grown over recent years?

3. **Cultures** How has the region of central Italy played an important cultural role in Italy's history?

4. **Critical Thinking** **Analyzing Information** **(a)** What are some of the advantages to Italy of having such diverse regions? **(b)** What are some disadvantages?

Activity

Take It to the NET
Writing a Journal Take a virtual tour of Vatican City in Rome. Explore the Sistine Chapel, the Basilica of St. Peter, and other famous sites. Write a journal entry about the history of the sites you visited and your reactions. Visit the World Geography section of **www.phschool.com** for help in completing this activity.

Recognizing Causes and Effects

People often try to figure out the causes and effects of things. For example, government officials conduct an investigation after an accident. Their goals are to identify the causes of the mishap and then to use that knowledge to prevent future accidents. By recognizing causes and effects and by taking appropriate action based on what is learned, you can gain greater control over events and conditions that affect your life.

Learn the Skill Read the passage below and use the following steps to learn how to recognize causes and effects.

1 *Identify the central event.* Identify the central condition or event whose causes or effects you wish to study. Disregard information that has little or nothing to do with the central event. **(a)** *In the passage below, what is the central event or issue for which causes and effects are identified?* **(b)** *What is one fact that is probably neither a cause nor an effect of that event?*

2 *Identify possible causes.* Causes precede the central event. They are the reasons that the central event or development occurred. Key terms such as *because of, due to,* and *since* often signal causes. **(a)** *What are two causes of the damage found in Venice?* **(b)** *What key terms helped you to identify the causes?*

3 *Identify possible effects.* Effects come after the central event. They occur as a result of the central event. Key terms such as *so, thus, therefore,* and *as a result* often indicate effects. ***What laws were made in Venice in response to public concern about environmental damage?***

4 *Make generalizations and recommendations.* After people find the causes and effects of a specific event, they try to apply what they have learned to other events. For example, after investigators find the causes of an automobile accident, they generalize and consider how they can use their knowledge to prevent other automobile accidents. By understanding causes and effects, you can recommend actions or make predictions based on what you have learned. ***How can governments around the world reduce the deterioration of buildings? Explain.***

Do It Yourself

Practice the Skill Gather information about another community that is attempting to control or reduce environmental damage. Share what you have learned by creating a flowchart that lists the central event, the causes of the central event, and the effects of the central event.

Apply the Skill See Chapter 17 Review and Assessment.

An Environmental Issue in Venice

Venice is a beautiful and historic city that suffers from flooding. After a flood, a lot of time and money are invested in repairs. Therefore, the Venetian government studied the problem. Scientists learned that several factors were responsible for environmental damage in Venice.

Scientists found soil subsidence, or ground sinking, due to the rising and falling of water. As a result, there was wear and tear on the wood piles that support the city's buildings. The buildings' bricks and mortar were weakened because of salt and chemicals dissolved in the water.

In addition, Venice has suffered from its close proximity to the Mestre-Marghera industrial region. Smoke from the industrial region, mixed with acid and humidity, resulted in damage to art treasures inside buildings, as well as damage to the buildings themselves.

The people of Venice wanted to limit further damage. Therefore, several plans were put into place. Today, laws limit industrial pollution and protect the area from oil spills. People are required to use cleaner fuels, and automobiles are banned from the center of Venice.

Teaching the Skill

Have students read Steps 1 and 2 and then answer the questions and explain their answers. To prepare for Step 3, have students identify terms in the passage (such as *therefore* and *as a result*) that indicate effects. During the lesson, emphasize that cause and effect is a two-step relationship. Cause comes before effect in time, but a writer may present the effect before discussing the cause. Stress that there can be multiple causes and multiple effects, and that effects can turn into new causes with new results.

Answers to Learn the Skill

1. (a) environmental damage in Venice **(b)** Venice is a beautiful and historic city.

2. Answers will vary but may include **(a)** salt and chemicals dissolved in the water; smoke from the industrial region **(b)** *because of; resulted in*

3. Laws limit industrial pollution and protect the area from oil spills. People are required to use cleaner fuels, and automobiles are banned from the center of Venice.

4. Answers will vary, but students may suggest that governments should work to reduce automobile and industrial pollution.

Answer to Practice the Skill

Students' flowcharts should accurately reflect the causes and effects of the central event.

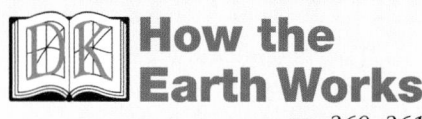
Objectives

Upon completion of this feature, students should be able to:

◆ explain what a volcano is;

◆ describe the immediate effects of a volcanic eruption;

◆ identify some long-term effects of a volcanic eruption.

 National Geography Standards

The following National Geography Standards are highlighted in this feature: 4, 7, 8, 15, 17, 18

 Bellringer

Have students list ten effects of a volcanic eruption. Examples may include clouds of smoke, lava trails, and a scorched landscape.

LESSON PLAN

1. Focus Ask students to read the captions on this page and the next. Have them make a list of places in the United States and in other countries where volcanoes are or have been active.

2. Instruct Draw a four-column chart on the board. Label the columns as follows: *Volcanic Effect, Definition of Effect, Immediate or Long-Term Effect,* and *Local or Worldwide Effect.* Have students use information on these pages to complete the chart.

3. Close/Reteach Have students review the information in the charts they have created. Ask: **What are some positive effects of volcanoes?** (They create islands, fertilize soil, and create beautiful rock formations.)

Effects of Volcanoes

A **volcano** is an opening in the earth's crust from which **lava,** or molten rock, escapes to the surface. The impact of powerful volcanic eruptions is both immediate and long-lasting. Burning rocks are flung out in all directions. Huge clouds of scorching ash and fiery gases billow high into the sky. As a result, the landscape and even the weather can be changed. Soil may become more fertile when enriched with nutrients from volcanic ash. Islands, mountains, and other landforms may be created from the material emitted by volcanoes.

The Giant's Causeway in Northern Ireland

DRAMATIC ROCK FORMATIONS
Lava flows can form amazing rock formations. **Columnar rocks** are volcanic rocks that split into columns as the lava cools. The Devil's Tower in Wyoming (below) is one example of a columnar rock. Another example is the Giant's Causeway (left). This rock formation in Northern Ireland is the result of a lava flow that erupted millions of years ago.

The Devil's Tower in Wyoming

DUST AND GAS
Explosive volcanoes, like Mount St. Helens in Washington (right), spit clouds of ash and fumes into the sky. The debris can completely cover human communities. Another hazard is that volcanic gases are deadly poisons.

ERUPTING LAVA
Red-hot lava is hurled into the air during an eruption of a volcano on Stromboli, an island off the coast of southern Italy. The Stromboli volcano is one of only a few volcanoes to display continuous eruptive activity over a period of more than a few years.

360

RESOURCE DIRECTORY

Technology
World Geography Map and Photo Transparencies
• How the Earth Works, Unit 4
Companion Web site, www.phschool.com
• Chapter 17 Activities

AFFECTING THE WORLD'S WEATHER

Powerful eruptions emit gas and dust that can rise high into the atmosphere and travel around the world. Volcanic material can reduce average temperatures in parts of the world by filtering out some of the sunlight that warms the earth.

A satellite image shows the global spread of emissions from the 1991 eruptions of Mount Pinatubo in the Philippines.

A STRING OF ISLANDS

The Hawaiian Islands are the tops of volcanic mountains. They have developed over millions of years as a **plume,** or a very hot spot in the earth's mantle, erupted great amounts of lava. As the Pacific Plate moves over the stationary plume, it carries older islands in the chain to the northwest. Today, active volcanoes are found on the island of Hawaii and the newly forming island of Loihi.

Kauai Oahu Maui Hawaii

Volcanic pipe

Stationary plume

Magma chamber

Plate moving across plume

A crater lake in Iceland

A CRATER LAKE

A **crater lake** is a body of water that occupies a bowl-shaped depression around the opening of an extinct or dormant volcano. An eruption can hurl the water out of the crater. The water can then mix with hot rock and debris and race downhill in a deadly mudslide.

LIFE RETURNS TO THE LAVA

In time, plant life grows on lava. Lichen and moss often appear first. Grass and larger plants slowly follow. The upper surface of the rock is gradually weathered, and the roots of plants help break down the rock to form soil. After many generations, the land may become lush and fertile again.

A few lichens find a home on the lava.

Plants take root in the beginnings of topsoil.

ASSESSMENT

1. **Key Terms** Define **(a)** volcano, **(b)** lava, **(c)** columnar rock, **(d)** plume, **(e)** crater lake.

2. **Natural Resources** How can soil become more fertile as a result of volcanic eruptions?

3. **Environmental Change (a)** How can volcanic activity create new landforms? **(b)** How can explosive volcanic eruptions affect the atmosphere and weather around the world?

4. **Natural Hazards** What are some of the ways in which a volcanic eruption can devastate nearby human settlements?

5. **Critical Thinking Sequencing** Study the diagram of the Hawaiian Islands and the caption that accompanies it. **(a)** Which island on the diagram is probably the oldest? Why do you think so? **(b)** What will happen to the volcanoes on the island of Hawaii as a result of plate movement?

Chapter 17   **361**

Objectives

Upon completion of Section 3, students should be able to:

◆ describe how Greece's physical characteristics influence its economic activities;

◆ summarize the mystery from Greece's past that scientists are trying to understand;

◆ explain why Greek culture is considered a mixture of Eastern and Western cultures.

 National Geography Standards

The following National Geography Standards are highlighted in this section: 1, 4, 5, 6, 7, 8, 11, 12, 13, 14, 17

 Bellringer

Ask students: **Why does Greece get to go first in the parade of nations at the opening for the Olympic games?** (because the games started in Greece)

LESSON PLAN

1. Focus Have students locate Greece on the map on page 363 and again on the World Political map in the Atlas. Ask students why they think Greece has been an important trading nation since ancient times. (It is situated at the "crossroads" of the Middle East, North Africa, and Europe.) Tell students that Greek merchants transported ideas and goods throughout the Mediterranean.

2. Instruct Write the following chart title on the board: *Greece.* Under the title, make three columns labeled *Land, Economy,* and *Foreign Influences.* Have students fill in details to complete the columns.

3. Close/Reteach Write the following statement on the board: *The physical geography of Greece was the most important factor in shaping Greek culture.* Have students debate this statement in a class discussion.

3 Greece

Reading Focus

• How do Greece's physical characteristics influence its economic activities and trade patterns?

• What mystery from Greece's past are scientists trying to understand?

• Why is Greek culture considered a mixture of Eastern and Western cultures?

Key Terms

graben

inhabitable

tsunami

 Main Idea Throughout its long history, Greece has benefited from agriculture, trade, and cultural exchange.

Patterns of Settlement Athens is the economic cultural center of Greece.

reece does not fit neatly into any single regional group. There are several reasons to consider Greece to be part of Mediterranean Europe. First, Greece has strong geographical and historical ties to the Mediterranean. Second, Greece is now a member of both the EU and NATO. Third, Greece is the birthplace of a culture that reached full expression in Western Europe.

Greece bears the imprint of other regions, too. As the map on the next page shows, Greece shares its northern border with the region of Eastern Europe occupied by Albania, Bulgaria, and the former Yugoslav republic of Macedonia. On the east it meets the Southwest Asian nation of Turkey.

People and Environment

The land area of Greece includes some 2,000 islands. Its northern mountains are extensions of the Dinaric Alps, which form the mountainous backbone of the Balkan nations. Southern Greece is the product of tectonic forces—it is where the Eurasian tectonic plate meets the African Plate. Major faults here thrust some lands higher and

caused others to sink. **Grabens,** areas of land that have dropped down between faults, were flooded. The Aegean Sea to the east of the Greek mainland occupies one such graben.

Another graben was flooded to form the Gulf of Corinth. As shown on the map on the next page, this thin inlet separates most of Greece from the Peloponnese (pel uh puh NEES), a large peninsula of rugged mountains.

Economic Activities Greece is a country covered by mountains and rocky soil. Its tallest peak, Mount Olympus, rises 9,570 feet (2,900 m), and many areas have elevations over 3,000 feet (900 m). Parallel ranges make travel difficult in many places. Narrow coastal plains, however, provide flat areas on which wheat and other grains are grown. Here, olive and citrus groves also abound. Agriculture is an important economic activity for Greece, despite problems such as poor soil, sparse rainfall, and outdated farming methods. With financial assistance from their government and from the European Union, Greek farmers are growing new products for export.

On the more rugged slopes, farmers graze sheep and goats. As in other Mediterranean

362 Chapter 17 ▪ Mediterranean Europe

RESOURCE DIRECTORY

Teaching Resources

Unit 4, Chapter 17
• Section 3 Guided Reading and Review, p. 49
• Critical Thinking, p. 52

Guide to the Essentials (English/Spanish)
• Section Summary, Chapter 17, Section 3

Mental Mapping booklet
• Outline Map 17, p. 63
• Unit 4 Checklist, p. 52

Technology

Guided Reading Audiotapes (English/Spanish), Chapter 17, Section 3

Section Reading Support Transparencies, Chapter 17, Section 3

World Geography Map and Photo Transparencies
• Western Europe: Maps and Photos

Book on CD, Chapter 17

Social Studies Skills Tutor CD-ROM

Companion Web site, www.phschool.com
• Chapter 17 Activities

nations, however, these animals have destroyed natural forests, leaving a scrubby vegetation that does little to prevent soil erosion.

Athens Greece's capital, Athens, is located in a part of Greece known as Sterea Hellas. Modern Athens has matured mainly within the last hundred years. It is one of the youngest capital cities in Europe. But the monuments of Athens have stood on the hill known as the Acropolis for thousands of years.

Over one third of Greece's 10.5 million inhabitants live in and around this crowded city. Modern apartments and houses line crowded city streets, as do new office buildings and an array of stores, taverns, and restaurants. One hallmark of this modern city is its daily traffic jams. The downtown streets are so choked by traffic that walking is faster than driving. As one visitor noted, "There is only one proven solution to Athens' traffic problems: live television coverage of an important international soccer match. Whenever that happens, the streets are deserted."

Shipping Just 5 miles (8 km) to the south, Athens merges with Greece's largest port, Piraeus (py REE us). The harbor there grew steadily in importance during the twentieth century. As one might expect in a nation where no point is more than 85 miles (137 km) from the sea, Greece relies heavily on trade over water. It has one of the world's largest commercial shipping fleets, and shipbuilding is an important industry. Other industries also have located near the docks of Piraeus. In this way, they can take advantage of low transportation costs for imported raw materials and exported manufactured goods.

The sea also enables Greece to maintain contact with its many islands. Many of these are in

GE⊕Facts

Greece is finding solutions to its severe pollution problems. To combat air pollution in Athens, car and truck traffic is restricted. Greece has more solar collectors than any other country in Europe, and power stations run by wind as well as photovoltaics (electricity generated by sunlight) now provide some of Greece's electricity.

Greece: PHYSICAL-POLITICAL

KEY

Elevation

Feet	Meters
14,000	4,270
7,000	2,135
1,500	457
700	213
(sea level) 0	0 (sea level)

⊛ National capital
• Major city
▲ Mountain

Lambert Azimuthal Equal-Area Projection

0   100   200 mi
0 100 200 km

APPLYING THE GEOGRAPHIC THEMES

● **Place** Greece is a mountainous land composed of many peninsulas and islands.
  • *What are some advantages and disadvantages of living on a mountainous peninsula?*

Cultures

Democracy Athens is called the birthplace of Western civilization because so many of the ideas fundamental to Western culture originated there, including the form of government known as democracy. There are major differences, however, between ancient Greek democracy and democracy in other countries today. For example, in the United States, government protects the individual against the state, which is seen as a threat to personal liberty. In ancient Greece, the good of the state and the good of the individual were seen as one; therefore, there was no reason for a government that would protect the individual against the state. Women and enslaved laborers were not allowed to participate in government in any way, including voting.

The Physical World

Volcanoes The island of Thera, or Santorini as some call it, is actually the rim of an exploded volcano. In antiquity, the island was called Calliste ("Most Beautiful"). About 1500 B.C., the volcano erupted and all life on the island was destroyed. Today the bow-shaped island has an area of 29 square miles (76 sq km). Along with two other islands that are the remnants of the volcano, Thera forms a lagoon. In the center of the lagoon are two active volcanic islets, Néa Kaméni ("New Burnt Island") and Palaía Kaméni ("Old Burnt Island").

CUSTOMIZE FOR...

Less Proficient Writers

Supporting the Main Idea Direct students to the Main Idea on page 362. Point out that Section 3 contains detailed information to support this main idea. After students have read the section, ask them to write at least three sentences supporting the main idea. Ask several students to read their sentences aloud.

Answer to Map Caption

Possible answer: Advantage: access to the sea; disadvantage: minimal flat land for agriculture

Vocabulary

Tsunami Refer students to the Key Terms list on page 362. Write the following sentence on the board: *Tsunamis as high as 300 feet (91 m) may have crashed over Crete during the 1500s B.C., destroying its lovely palaces.* Ask students to define *tsunamis* based on its context in the sentence. Then have students compare their contextual definitions to the definition for *tsunami* in the Glossary.

ACTIVITY

Group Work

Activity: Poetry writing

Purpose: Tell each group it should work together to write a poem about the geography of Greece or the contributions of ancient Greece. Groups may do library research to prepare their poems.

Roles: Groups should include a scribe and an orator.

Result: Each orator should read the group's poem to the class.

READING STRATEGY

Summarizing Main Ideas

Have students read the subsection Understanding the Past on this page. After they finish, ask them to write two or three sentences explaining why the fall of Minoan civilization is a mystery. Then have them describe the theories scientists and historians have proposed to explain the fall.

Answer to Photo Caption

The picture suggests little development because the road is unpaved and the man is traveling by horse.

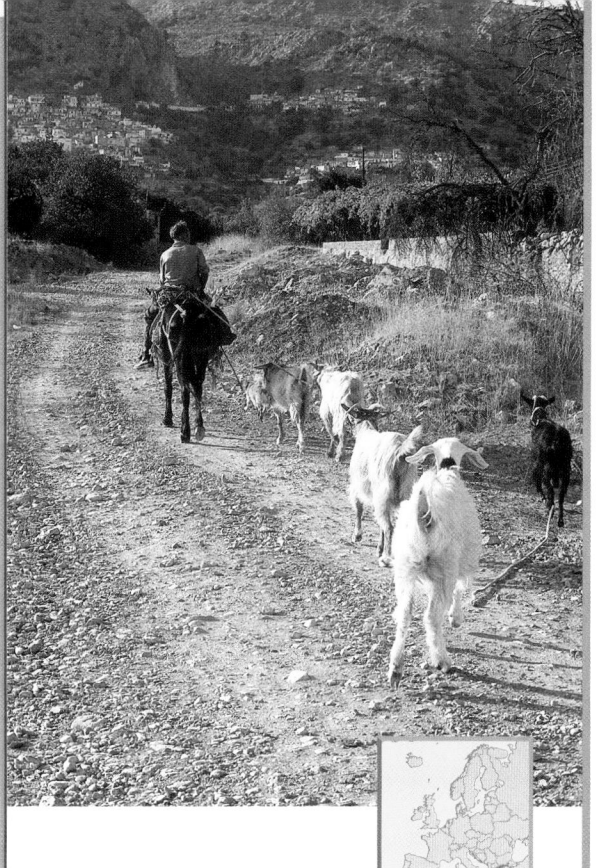

Goat Herder in Crete

Economic Activities A local man leads his goats toward a hillside village on the Greek island of Crete.

Place *What does this picture suggest about the level of development on Crete? Explain.*

the Aegean Sea, although the largest, Crete, is south of the mainland in the Mediterranean Sea. Fewer than two hundred of these islands are **inhabitable**—that is, able to support permanent residents. Many people make a living from fishing, but tourism continues to grow as a major economic activity. Visitors from around the world seek the sun, sparkling water, and gleaming beaches of the Greek islands.

Understanding the Past

Part of Greece's appeal to visitors lies in its rich history. One historical mystery surrounding the island of Crete puzzles archaeologists to this day.

About thirty-five hundred years ago, the Mediterranean island of Crete was the center of Greece's flourishing Bronze Age culture. This culture is called Minoan after Minos, a legendary king of Crete. Expert shipbuilders, the Minoans traveled and traded throughout the Aegean and Mediterranean seas.

Then, around 1500 B.C., Minoan culture fell into a rapid decline. Some scholars believed that people from the Greek mainland attacked and destroyed Crete. Others thought that an earthquake demolished the island. But Greek archaeologist Spyridon Marinatos believed these explanations were incomplete.

Excavating near an ancient port in Crete, Marinatos discovered a piece of pumice from Thera, an island located 70 miles (113 km) from Crete. From that rock and others, he proposed a theory. He described destruction caused by a blanket of ash from a volcanic eruption, giant sea waves called **tsunamis** (tsoo NAH mees), and earthquakes that caused oil lamps to overturn and set fires.

Investigations by other scientists appear to show that Marinatos's theory was incorrect. Evidence gathered elsewhere from ice-core samples and tree rings of ancient trees dates the eruption on Thera to more than one hundred years before the collapse of the Minoan civilization. The fate of the Minoan civilization has again been cast into doubt. Archaeologists must reconsider the evidence to determine what happened to this once vital civilization.

Cultural Influences

Discussing the in-between cultural area to which some say Greece belongs, geographer T.R.B. Dicks observed:

❝Many would argue that the Greeks are a curious mixture of eastern and western. . . . It is in the towns and cities that western influence is most marked, but even in Athens the colors of the Orient are strongly represented.❞

Cultural Convergence Greece may be considered a Western nation, in part, because Western culture has so many of its roots in ancient

The Cyclades

Environmental Change The Cyclades are a group of Greek islands in the Aegean Sea. Their rugged beauty and dry, mild climate have encouraged the development of tourism. As a result, pollution and water shortages have occurred.

Human-Environment Interaction *What can be done to deal with the environmental problems in the Cyclades?*

Greece. Some Western ideas about democratic government, for example, are based on Greek ideals. The *Iliad* and the *Odyssey,* Homer's epic poems about the Trojan War and the fall of Troy, remain popular centuries after they were composed. To ancient Greeks the poems provided a guide for moral behavior and were the cornerstone of a proper education.

Cooperation and Conflict While the influence of ancient Greek culture spread through Western Europe, other cultures put their stamp on Greece, usually through military conquest.

From the second century B.C. to the fifth century A.D., Greece was part of the Roman Empire. As the Roman Empire declined, Greece became an important part of the Byzantine Empire. For the next thousand years, Greece was invaded from all directions, over land and water. Slavs, Albanians, and Bulgarians came from the north. Arabs swept in from the south. Normans and Venetians attacked from the west. In 1453, Turks conquered Constantinople, now the city of Istanbul, and ruled Greece for almost four centuries. Finally, after a ten-year rebellion, the modern state of Greece gained its independence from Turkey in 1829.

SECTION 3 ASSESSMENT

1. **Key Terms** Define **(a)** graben, **(b)** inhabitable, **(c)** tsunami.

2. **Physical Characteristics** Explain how Greece's rugged terrain and proximity to the sea have affected its economic activities.

3. **Understanding the Past (a)** What mystery about ancient Crete remains unsolved? **(b)** Why might the solution be important to archaeologists and historians?

4. **Cultures** What other cultures have influenced Greece throughout history?

5. **Critical Thinking** **Drawing Conclusions** Do you think that centuries of foreign rule weakened or strengthened the Greek national identity? Give reasons for your answer.

Activity

Synthesizing Information Many ideas from ancient Greece have influenced government in the United States. For example, the word *democracy* is derived from the Greek language. Do research in the library or on the Internet to learn about the government of ancient Athens. Then, make a list of the political ideas that the United States borrowed from the ancient Athenians.

Literature Obtain a taped recording of Homer's *Iliad* or *Odyssey,* epic poems based on the Trojan War, and play portions of it in class.

Answers to Section 3 Assessment

1. **(a)** graben, p. 362 **(b)** inhabitable, p. 364 **(c)** tsunami, p. 364
2. Greece's proximity to the sea has enabled it to develop successful tourism, fishing, shipping, and shipbuilding industries. Because of the generally rugged terrain, most farming takes place on narrow coastal plains.
3. **(a)** the decline of the Minoan culture **(b)** Crete was once the center of Greece's flourishing Bronze Age culture.
4. Greece was once part of the Roman and Byzantine empires and has been invaded by Slavs, Albanians, Bulgarians, Arabs, Normans, Venetians, and Turks.
5. Answers will vary. Students might suggest that foreign rule weakened Greece's national identity because of the mixing of Eastern and Western cultures. Others may feel that it strengthened the national identity by creating a desire for independence.

Activity Rubrics Share rubrics with students before they make their lists.
Attempted The list is incomplete or contains erroneous information.
Minimal The list includes only a few political ideas borrowed from the ancient Athenians.
Adequate The list reveals sufficient research, contains no factual errors, and is neatly done.
Exemplary The list reveals extensive research and provides a comprehensive compilation of political ideas borrowed from the ancient Athenians.

TEST PREPARATION

Have students read the subsection Cultural Influences on pages 364–365 and complete the following sentence.
Greece's culture was molded and shaped by outside influences because of —
    A poetry
    B the Trojan War
    C democracy
    (D) military conquest

Answer to Photo Caption

Possible answer: The Greek government can impose water rationing and limit further development on the islands. Hotels on the islands can educate visitors and staff about the problems.

Creating a Chapter Summary

As a reteaching opportunity, pair a more able student with a less able student to complete this chapter summary.

Possible entries: **Spain:** On the Iberian Peninsula, Mediterranean climate, Regions have distinct independent identities **Portugal:** On the Atlantic coast of the Iberian Peninsula; Agricultural products include wheat, corn, barley, olives, and grapes; Abundant rainfall **Italy:** Population: about 58 million, Mediterranean climate south of the Alps, Scarcity of flat land **Greece:** Includes some 2,000 islands, Covered by mountains and rocky soil, Population: about 10.5 million

Reviewing Key Terms

1–8. Possible answers: Physical Characteristics: navigable, sirocco, subsidence, graben. Cultures: hub, Renaissance. Natural Hazards: seismic activity, tsunami. Students' sentences should explain how each term relates to the particular concept.

Understanding Key Ideas

9. Moist, Atlantic winds rising over the Cantabrian Mountains drop ample rain along the northern coast; the Meseta, in the rain shadow of the mountains, is much drier; siroccos blow over parts of southeastern Spain, making them semiarid.
10. (a) Because of its central location, Madrid became a transportation hub and center of industry. **(b)** Answers include heavy traffic, air pollution, and other problems associated with a large population.
11. Portugal was a colonial power that used the sea as its trading passport to the world, exporting its language and culture worldwide.
12. (a) Southern Italy has poor soil, while northern Italy contains the fertile Po River valley. **(b)** Northern Italy is prosperous; southern Italy contains regions of severe poverty.
13. Greece relies heavily on trade over water.
14. Some Western ideas about democratic government are based on Greek ideals.

Creating a Chapter Summary

On a sheet of paper, draw a graphic organizer like this one. For each country, fill in key geographic characteristics. Some information has been filled in to help you get started.

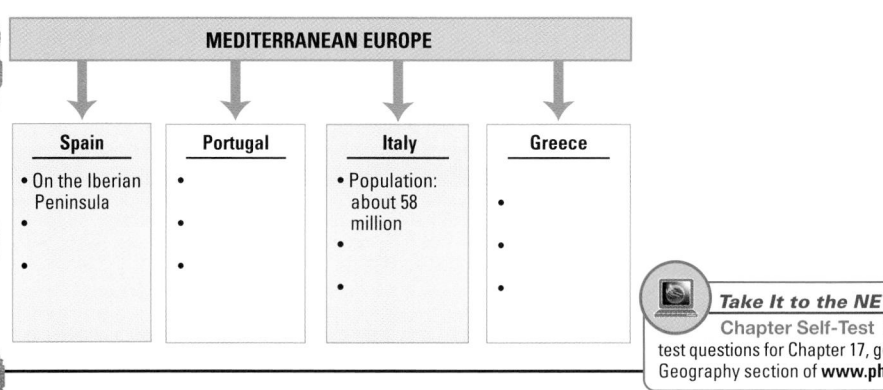

MEDITERRANEAN EUROPE

Spain
• On the Iberian Peninsula
•
•

Portugal
•
•
•

Italy
• Population: about 58 million
•
•

Greece
•
•
•

Take It to the NET
Chapter Self-Test For practice test questions for Chapter 17, go to the World Geography section of **www.phschool.com**.

Reviewing Key Terms

Classify each of the terms below under one of the following concepts: Physical Characteristics, Cultures, or Natural Hazards. Then, write a sentence explaining how the term relates to the concept.

1. navigable   **5.** subsidence

2. sirocco   **6.** Renaissance

3. hub   **7.** graben

4. seismic activity   **8.** tsunami

Understanding Key Ideas

9. Climates How do physical characteristics of the Iberian Peninsula affect the climate of Spain?

10. Patterns of Settlement (a) What factors have contributed to the growth of Madrid? **(b)** What challenges does Madrid face?

11. Global Trade Patterns How has Portugal influenced people and cultures in other parts of the world?

12. Physical Characteristics (a) How do the physical characteristics of southern Italy differ from those of northern Italy? **(b)** How do these differences affect the economies of the two regions?

13. Economic Activities How does Greece's location continue to shape its economic activities?

14. Cultures How has Greek culture influenced the cultures of modern Western nations?

Critical Thinking and Writing

15. Analyzing Primary Sources Refer to the quote on page 352. What do you think the novelist Frank Tuohy is saying about the differences between Spain and Portugal when he writes, "Spain is like a novel with half a dozen chapters; Portugal is a short story"?

16. Interpreting Maps Refer to the map on page 353. **(a)** On what continents did Portugal once have colonies? **(b)** How might your life be different today if North America had been colonized by Asians rather than by Western Europeans?

Critical Thinking and Writing

15. Possible answer: Spain is larger than Portugal and has several distinct cultures with their own histories and identities; Portugal is a compact country with a single culture, history, and identity.
16. (a) South America and Africa **(b)** Possible answers include different language, customs, form of government, and religion.

(Continued on next page.)

17. Distinguishing Fact From Opinion Consider the following statement: "Because of the climate, the best olives and olive oil in the world are from Greece." **(a)** Is this statement a fact or an opinion? **(b)** What are the reasons for your response?

Applying Skills

Recognizing Causes and Effects Refer to the article on page 359 to answer these questions:

18. What causes the deterioration of wooden piles in Venice?

19. What laws were created to help preserve Venice's art and buildings?

20. In a reading passage, what key words are signals that effects are being discussed?

Analyzing a Photograph Study the photograph below, and answer the following questions:

21. Do you think that automobiles are common in this part of Crete? Explain your answer.

22. Do you think that agriculture is very profitable in this part of Crete? Why or why not?

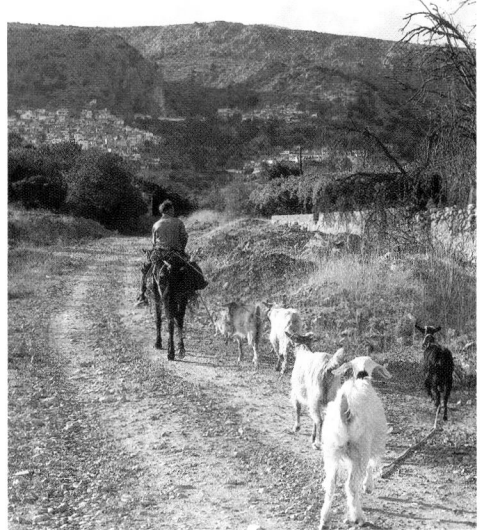

Test Preparation

Read the question and choose the best answer.

23. The nations of Mediterranean Europe all share the following physical characteristic—

A a flat, landlocked terrain

B a cold climate with long winters

C location on a peninsula

D a hot, tropical climate

Activities

USING THE **REGIONAL ATLAS**

Review the Regional Atlas for Western Europe and Chapter 17. Prepare a set of questions that compare and contrast Mediterranean Europe with other parts of the continent. Exchange questions with a partner. Then, answer each other's questions.

 MENTAL MAPPING

Review a map of Europe. On a separate piece of paper, draw a sketch map of Mediterranean Europe from memory. Label the following places on your map:

- Italy
- Aegean Sea
- Spain
- Greece
- Crete
- Portugal
- Rome
- Pyrenees
- Madrid
- Mediterranean Sea

Take It to the NET

How's today's traffic in Madrid? What's the weather like in Rome? Webcams can give you up-to-the-minute information about these questions and others. Visit a Webcam of a place that you have read about in Chapter 17. Take notes on what you see. Use your notes and information from the chapter to make generalizations about the place. Visit the World Geography section of **www.phschool.com** for help in completing this activity.

Critical Thinking and Writing (cont.)

17. **(a)** opinion **(b)** It expresses a personal preference ("the best") rather than giving objective information.

Applying Skills
18. subsidence
19. Laws limit industrial pollution. People are required to use cleaner fuels and automobiles are banned from the center of Venice.
20. *so, thus, therefore,* and *as a result*
21. Possible answer: The unpaved road may indicate that automobiles are not widely used in this part of Crete.
22. Possible answer: The soil appears rocky and the terrain rugged, conditions not particularly conducive to agriculture.

Test Preparation
23. C

Activities

Using the Regional Atlas
Check students' questions for accuracy. Check that students have made valid comparisons between Mediterranean Europe and other parts of the continent.

Mental Mapping
Review students' maps for relative and absolute location.

Take It to the Net
Students' work should reflect sound research. Check that students have made reasonable generalizations about the place they have selected.

 MENTAL MAPPING

Games for Review See pages 58–63 of the Simulations, Games, and Lab Activities booklet for games to review place names.
Chapter Map Test Students should use the completed outline maps and the Unit 4 Checklist in their Atlas Portfolios to prepare for the Chapter 17 Map Test.
Unit Map Test To prepare for the Unit 4 Map Test, students will need to study the location of all the place names on the Unit 4 Checklist.

Alternative Assessment

Final Evaluation

Participating in a Classroom Discussion
Use the Classroom Discussion Evaluation Form on page 23 of the Alternative Assessment booklet in the Prentice Hall Assessment System to evaluate students' participation. Either teachers or students can complete the forms to indicate which level of work was achieved for each of the criteria. The evaluation should provide specific examples and comments.

Use this sample exam to help your students prepare for standardized tests.

You might want to remind your students of the following:

Tips for Test Taking

1. Read the directions carefully.
2. Read each question carefully.
3. For multiple choice questions, try to answer the question before you look at the choices. Read all the choices. Then, eliminate those that are absolutely incorrect.
4. For short answer questions, be sure to answer the question completely if there is more than one part.
5. Answer the easy questions first. Then, go back to the ones that will take more time.
6. Pace yourself. Be sure to set aside enough time for the writing questions.

Write answers on a separate sheet of paper.

Multiple Choice

1 Which of the following geographic factors helped both Spain and Portugal to establish global trade networks with the Americas?

A The Pyrenees separate Spain and Portugal from the rest of Europe.

B Spain and Portugal are located on a peninsula jutting into the Atlantic Ocean.

C Muslims ruled over much of the Iberian Peninsula.

D The cultures of Spain and Portugal are closely related because they were both part of the ancient Roman Empire.

2 Which of the following statements best explains why the production of wine is a major economic activity in France but not in the British Isles?

A France has a much larger land area and population than the British Isles.

B The tropical climate of France is much more suitable for wine production than is the arid climate of Britain.

C The acid rain that falls in France improves the flavor of the grapes and other fruits that are used to make wine.

D The soils and climates of southern France are much more suitable for the growing of grapes than the soils and climates of the British Isles.

3 In general, how do wind and ocean currents across the Atlantic affect the climate of the British Isles and other lands of northwestern Europe?

A Most of the region's natural vegetation is a mix of temperate grassland and coniferous forest.

B Temperatures are moderated by the warm currents that flow from the Gulf of Mexico to northwestern Europe.

C Hurricanes commonly strike the northwestern coast of Europe from about June through October.

D The British Isles experience harsh winters with extremely cold temperatures and frequent blizzards.

Use the chart and your knowledge of social studies to answer the following question.

Comparing Education			
Country	Percentage of Students in Primary School	Percentage of Students in Secondary School	Secondary School Students per Teacher
Finland	99	93	13
France	100	94	13
Italy	98	88	10
U.K.	100	92	14

Sources: *Dorling Kindersley World Desk Reference; Encarta World Atlas*

4 Based on the information presented in the table, what is one possible reason Italy has the lowest number of secondary school students per teacher?

A The lower percentage of students enrolled means that class sizes are smaller.

B Italian schools hire more teachers than schools in other countries.

C Leaders in other countries prefer to have classrooms with more students per teacher.

D Percentages of students enrolled in primary school do not differ greatly.

5 How have the people of the Netherlands used technology to overcome the problem of flooding in their country?

A They have built a network of dams and reservoirs for containing the waters that melt off snow-covered mountains.

B They have built canals that divert excessive rainwater away from the Netherlands toward France and Belgium.

C They have used windmills to blow moisture-laden air away from the Dutch coast.

D They have built dikes to hold back seawater, and they have formed polders by draining water off the land.

PRENTICE HALL
ASSESSMENT SYSTEM

Diagnose and Prescribe
- Profile student skills with Diagnostic Tests A&B.
- Address student needs with program materials identified in the test.

Review and Reteach
- Provide cumulative content review with the Review Book.

Practice and Assess
- Build test-taking skills with Test-Taking Strategies on Transparencies.

6 Why is farming a main economic activity in only a small part of Scandinavia?

   A Volcanoes and earthquakes make the area unsafe for agricultural development.

   B Rainfall in much of the region is inadequate for farming.

   C Long ago, glaciers swept much of the topsoil from the peninsula.

   D Scandinavian governments have set aside only a small portion of land for farming.

7 The eruption of a volcano in one part of the world can affect weather conditions in other parts of the world because —

   A the flow of lava into the ocean causes worldwide ocean temperatures to rise

   B volcanic smoke and ash can be carried around the world by wind, blocking some of the sun's rays

   C after a volcanic eruption, geothermal energy causes global air temperatures to rise

   D trees and other plants quickly grow on fertile volcanic rock, and they add large amounts of cooling oxygen to the earth's atmosphere

8 Which of the following developments occurred in England as a result of the Industrial Revolution?

   A England's economy was transformed from a market economy to a command economy.

   B England began to develop more subsistence agriculture and cottage industries.

   C England no longer had a significant interest in acquiring raw materials from overseas colonies.

   D England experienced increased levels of population growth and urbanization.

Use the quotation <u>and</u> your knowledge of social studies to answer the following question.

> Laura Lesley remembers the day the war hit closest to home. It was October 7, 1996. Hot fragments from a bomb's blast rained down on her school's playground in Lisburn. . . . Laura ran inside in fear. The attack was a sign that the latest attempt to bring peace to her country had failed. "It was frightening. I'd never been close to a bomb before," Laura [explained]. . . .
>
> —Time for Kids (Web site), April 24, 1998

9 This excerpt refers to conflict in Northern Ireland between —

   A Catholics and Protestants

   B Serbs and Croats

   C supporters of democracy and supporters of communism

   D those who want union with England and those who want union with Scotland

10 A major difference between the agricultural regions of the North European Plain and the Meseta in the Iberian Peninsula is that the —

   A North European Plain is landlocked

   B North European Plain has a higher elevation

   C Meseta has a warmer, drier climate

   D Meseta is more densely populated

Writing Practice

11 **(a)** How did World War II result in the division of Germany into two countries? **(b)** What led the two countries to reunite?

12 How do the Alps affect economic activities in Switzerland?

13 Would you expect Europeans who hold strong nationalist positions to favor or to oppose membership in the European Union? Explain.

Test Preparation Answers

Multiple Choice

  1 B

  2 D

  3 B

  4 A

  5 D

  6 C

  7 B

  8 D

  9 A

10 C

Writing Practice

11 Germany's defeat in the war put its future into the hands of the victors. The Western Allies and the Soviet Union had sided together during the war, but they disagreed about how to deal with Germany afterward. Ultimately they agreed to divide Germany. In the eastern portion, the Soviet Union established the German Democratic Republic, a Communist state; in the other portion, Western leaders established the Federal Republic of Germany, a democracy.

12 On the positive side, students may suggest that the leaders would want to develop manufacturing and service industries, as did Italy. Italy also was instrumental in the formation of the European Union; another country in Italy's position also might seek an economic alliance with neighboring countries for the benefit of all. On the negative side, students may suggest that since Italy's industrialization and urbanization led to overcrowded cities, the leaders of the hypothetical country might want to plan ahead to deal with that challenge.

13 Students may suggest that they would appeal to what the countries share—for example, a past of cultural richness that influenced most of the rest of the world, or hopes for the future, as symbolized by the European Union.

Central Europe and Northern Eurasia

Activating Prior Knowledge

Tell students to look through the chapters in Unit 5, paying close attention to photographs, maps, and other visual elements. Ask students if any of the illustrations in the unit either confirm or conflict with what they already know about Central Europe and Northern Eurasia.

Photo Study

Prague, Czech Republic

Prague is a major commercial and industrial center located on both banks of the Vltava (or, in German, Moldau) River. The city was occupied by the Germans between 1939 and 1945 and by the Soviet Union and the Warsaw Pact military forces in 1968 to put down political protests. **Predicting Consequences** Ask students to guess what changes Prague has undergone since the fall of communism in Central Europe. (Possible answers: increased trade due to economic reforms, increased tourism due to the historic beauty of the city)

eTeach

Be sure to check out this month's online forum with a Master Teacher to join in an exchange of teaching ideas. **www.phschool.com**

Central Europe and Northern Eurasia

Locating the Region

Central Europe and Northern Eurasia cover a vast area, sprawling across two continents and covering nearly half the Northern Hemisphere. Although the region historically has been dominated by Russia, it is home to many peoples with different languages, religions, and ways of life.

Robinson Projection

RESOURCE DIRECTORY

Teaching Resources

Unit 5
• Geography and World Literature, The Steppe, p. 43

Mental Mapping booklet
• Unit 5 Checklist, p. 67
• Unit 5 Map Test, p. 78

Simulations, Games, and Lab Activities
• Where on Earth? Games, pp. 72–73

Global Environmental Posters

Technology

TeacherExpress™ CD-ROM
World Geography: Building a Global Perspective
Teaching Resources on CD-ROM offers lesson planning flexibility, test-generation capability, and resource manageability.

Prentice Hall Presentation Pro CD-ROM
This CD-ROM allows you to create custom lessons for instruction or review for every chapter.

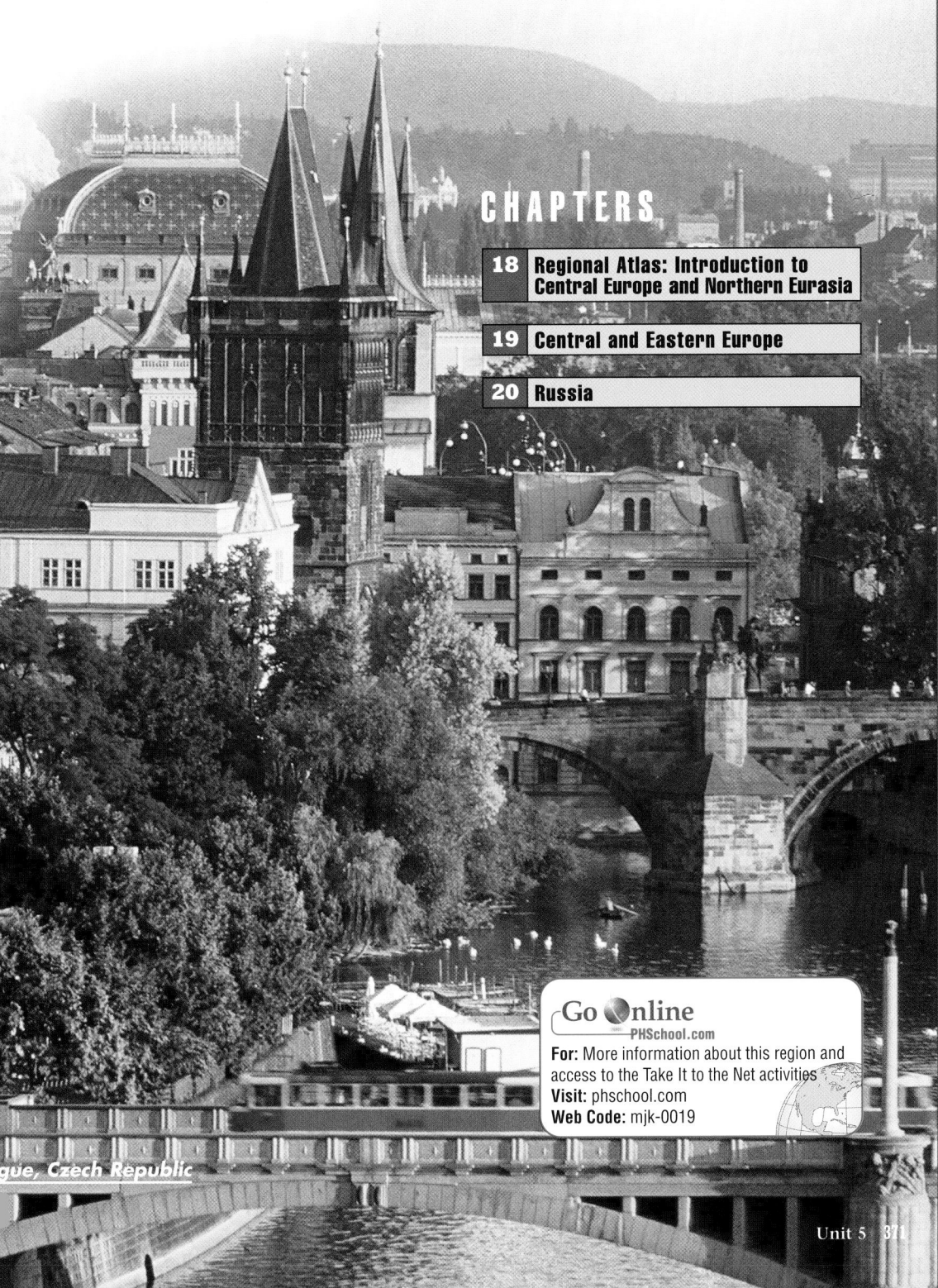

CHAPTERS

Go Online
PHSchool.com

For: More information about this region and access to the Take It to the Net activities
Visit: phschool.com
Web Code: mjk-0019

gue, Czech Republic

Unit 5 371

Promoting Geographic Understanding

Introduce the unit by using the themes below.

1. Place Direct students' attention to the map on page 373 and point out that Central Europe and Northern Eurasia have been the focus of worldwide attention because of the fall of communism and ensuing political conflicts. As students read this unit, they will learn how conflicts among ethnic groups have affected a number of nations.

2. Movement Point out that Central Europe has acted as a corridor for armies marching east and west. As a result, its boundaries have been changed several times. One geographer has labeled Central Europe the "zone of political change." Ask students to use their knowledge of history to name some groups that have conquered this region. (Romans, Byzantines, Huns, Vikings, Goths, Ottoman Turks, Austrians, Prussians, Germans, Russians, Soviets)

3. Region Point out that Central Europe is more of a political region than a distinct physical region. For many years it stood between the democratic countries to the west (Western Europe and the United States) and the Communist countries to the east (most of Northern Eurasia). After the fall of communism, most nations in Central Europe and Northern Eurasia were in turmoil. Although some nations have restored order, a number continue to struggle to achieve stability.

4. Movement Ask students how the size of Northern Eurasia might affect the movement of people and goods. (The vast distances might affect how much time it would take to transport people and goods.)

RESOURCE DIRECTORY

World Geography Map and Photo Transparencies
The World Geography Map and Photo Transparencies provide thematic maps and photos to help students understand key geographic concepts.

World Geography Videos
These chapter-level videos help students understand the key concepts and themes of geography through case studies.

ExamView Test Bank CD-ROM
The test bank CD-ROM allows you to create, edit, and print out chapter-level tests.

Social Studies Skills Tutor CD-ROM
This interactive CD-ROM provides students with the opportunity to learn and practice critical social studies skills.

Take It to the NET
Prentice Hall's Web site offers Internet activities and links that supplement *World Geography: Building a Global Perspective.* Visit us in the Social Studies area at **www.phschool.com.**

Resource Manager

Chapter-Level Resources	CORE INSTRUCTION	READING/SKILLS
	Teaching Resources **Unit 5**/Ch. 18 • Regional Atlas Study Guide, p. 2 **Mental Mapping booklet** • Unit 5 Checklist, p. 67 **Simulations, Games, and Lab Activities** • Place Location Review Games, pp. 58–63 **TeacherExpress™ CD-ROM**, Ch. 18 **Companion Web site,** **www.phschool.com** • eTeach	**Teaching Resources** **Unit 5**/Ch. 18 • Regional Atlas Review, p. 3 **Guide to the Essentials (English/Spanish)** • Chapter 18 Summary **Spanish Resources** • Regional Atlas Review, p. 45 **Guided Reading Audiotapes (English/Spanish)**, Ch. 18 **Section Reading Support Transparencies**, Ch. 18 **Book on CD**, Ch. 18 **Social Studies Skills Tutor CD-ROM**
Historical Overview Describe significant events and developments in the history of Central Europe and Northern Eurasia.	**Teaching Resources** **Mental Mapping booklet** • Outline Map 18A, p. 68 **Creative Teaching Activities** • The Changing Structure of Europe, p. 20 **Prentice Hall Presentation Pro CD-ROM**, Ch. 18	**Teaching Resources** **Social Studies Skills Handbook** • Reading a Political Map, p. 19
Physical Characteristics Identify major physical characteristics of Central Europe and Northern Eurasia.	**Teaching Resources** **Mental Mapping booklet** • Outline Map 18B, p. 69 **Prentice Hall Presentation Pro CD-ROM**, Ch. 18	**Teaching Resources** **Social Studies Skills Handbook** • Elevation on a Map, p. 20 • Four Types of Landforms, p. 21 • Relief on a Map, p. 22
Climates Compare climate regions in Central Europe and Northern Eurasia.	**Prentice Hall Presentation Pro CD-ROM**, Ch. 18	**Teaching Resources** **Social Studies Skills Handbook** • Reading a Climate Map, p. 26 • Reading a Climate Graph, p. 65 • Comparing Climate Graphs, p. 66
Ecosystems Describe characteristics of major ecosystems in Central Europe and Northern Eurasia.	**Prentice Hall Presentation Pro CD-ROM**, Ch. 18	**Teaching Resources** **Social Studies Skills Handbook** • Reading a Natural Vegetation Map, p. 25
People and Cultures Discuss elements of culture in Central Europe and Northern Eurasia.	**Prentice Hall Presentation Pro CD-ROM**, Ch. 18	**Teaching Resources** **Social Studies Skills Handbook** • Reading a Population Density Map, p. 31
Economics, Technology, and Environment Identify how the economy, technology, and the environment interact in Central Europe and Northern Eurasia.	**Prentice Hall Presentation Pro CD-ROM**, Ch. 18	**Teaching Resources** **Social Studies Skills Handbook** • Reading an Economic Activity Map, p. 27 • Reading a Natural Resources Map, p. 34
Database • Compare the state of health care in Poland, Romania, Russia, Ukraine, and the United States. • Discuss how economic systems can affect health care systems.	**Teaching Resources** **Unit 5**/Ch. 18 • Regional Atlas Database Skills, p. 4 **Prentice Hall Presentation Pro CD-ROM**, Ch. 18	**Teaching Resources** **Unit 5**/Ch. 18 • Regional Atlas Database Skills, p. 4 **Social Studies Skills Handbook** • Reading a Table, p. 62

ENRICHMENT/HONORS/PREAP

Teaching Resources
- **Mental Mapping booklet**
  - Atlas Activity, p. 70
- **Social Studies Skills Handbook**
  - Study and Research Skills, pp. 94–108
- **World Geography Map and Photo Transparencies**
  - Central Europe and Northern Eurasia: Maps and Photos
- **World Geography Videos**
  - Regional Atlas: Central Europe and Northern Eurasia
- **Companion Web site, www.phschool.com**
  - Chapter 18 Activities

Teaching Resources
- **Simulations, Games, and Lab Activities**
  - Where on Earth? Games, pp. 72–73
- **World Geography Map and Photo Transparencies**
  - Central Europe and Northern Eurasia: Political

- **World Geography Map and Photo Transparencies**
  - Central Europe and Northern Eurasia: Physical

Teaching Resources
- **Unit 5**/Ch. 18
  - Geography and World Literature, p. 43
- **World Geography Map and Photo Transparencies**
  - World Climate Zones

- **World Geography Map and Photo Transparencies**
  - Central Europe and Northern Eurasia: Natural Hazards

- **World Geography Map and Photo Transparencies**
  - Central Europe and Northern Eurasia: Population Density

- **World Geography Map and Photo Transparencies**
  - Central Europe and Northern Eurasia: Economic Activities

- **World Geography Map and Photo Transparencies**
  - Per Capita GDP: Life Expectancy

ASSESSMENT

PRENTICE HALL ASSESSMENT SYSTEM

Core Assessment
- **ExamView Test Bank booklet**, Ch. 18
- **ExamView Test Bank CD-ROM**, Ch. 18

Standardized Test Preparation

Diagnose and Prescribe
- **Diagnostic Tests for High School Social Studies Skills**

Review and Reteach
- **Review Book for World Geography**, pp. 11–12

Practice and Assess
- **Test-taking Strategies With Transparencies for High School**
- **Test-taking Strategy Poster**
- **Alternative Assessment booklet**
- **Test Prep Book for World Geography**

Teaching Resources
- **Unit 5**/Ch. 18
  - Test Forms A and B, pp. 5–10
- **Guide to the Essentials (English/Spanish)**
  - Chapter 18 Test
- **Mental Mapping booklet**
  - Chapter 18 Map Test, p. 71
- **Companion Web site, www.phschool.com**
  - Chapter 18 Self-Test

CUSTOMIZE FOR INDIVIDUAL NEEDS

Less Proficient Readers
- Guide to the Essentials (English), Ch. 18
- Guided Reading Audiotapes (English), Ch. 18
- Section Reading Support Transparencies, Ch. 18
- Book on CD, Ch. 18
- Teacher's Edition, Background: Vocabulary, p. 379

Students Acquiring English/ESL
- Guide to the Essentials (English/Spanish), Ch. 18
- Guided Reading Audiotapes (English/Spanish), Ch. 18
- Section Reading Support Transparencies, Ch. 18
- Book on CD, Ch. 18

Less Proficient Writers
- Alternative Assessment, Writing Assignment Rubric, p. 6
- Teacher's Edition, Customize for . . . , pp. 377, 387

Introducing

CHAPTER

18

pp. 372–387

Objectives

Upon completion of the Regional Atlas, students should be able to:

◆ describe significant events and developments in the history of Central Europe and Northern Eurasia;

◆ identify major physical characteristics of Central Europe and Northern Eurasia;

◆ compare climate regions in Central Europe and Northern Eurasia;

◆ describe characteristics of major ecosystems in Central Europe and Northern Eurasia;

◆ discuss elements of culture in Central Europe and Northern Eurasia;

◆ identify how the economy, technology, and the environment interact in Central Europe and Northern Eurasia.

National Geography Standards

The following National Geography Standards are highlighted in this Regional Atlas: 1, 4, 5, 8, 9, 10, 12, 13, 14, 16, 17

Bellringer

Explain that the map of Central Europe and Northern Eurasia has been redrawn many times. Ask students what factors have changed the area's political boundaries. (fall of communism, ethnic strife, civil wars)

Answers to Assessment

1. (a) domestication, p. 372
(b) communism, p. 372

2. Nearly all of the countries of the region were invaded at one time or another, including Poland, Hungary, Czech Republic, and Slovakia.

3. The Soviet Union's political and economic control over the Central European countries left many of them in states of economic decline after the Soviet Union collapsed. However, Poland and Hungary, which were independent from the Soviet Union between 1918 and 1945, have prospered.

372   Chapter 18

CHAPTER 18

Introduction to CENTRAL EUROPE AND NORTHERN EURASIA

Historical Overview

By 4000 B.C., peoples living on the steppes of present-day southern Russia and Ukraine first trained and bred horses for use by humans, in a process called **domestication.** These people were probably early Indo-Europeans, the first of a series of invaders to sweep westward from the steppes of Russia and Ukraine.

Migrations and Religious Diversity

Between A.D. 375 and 600, the Huns and Avars invaded from the east. In response, the Slavs moved into Eastern Europe. The Bulgars then conquered Bulgaria, and the Magyars took control of present-day Hungary.

Byzantine missionaries won converts, mainly in present-day Russia and southeastern Europe. Roman Catholicism predominated in Poland, the Czech lands, Hungary, and Croatia. When the Roman Catholic and Eastern Orthodox churches finally separated in 1054, Eastern Europe was divided between them.

Meanwhile, by 644 Arab invaders had brought Islam to the northeastern Caucasus. Mongols, or Tatars, conquered most of Russia in 1245. During the following century, the Tatars of Russia converted to Islam.

The Growth of Empires   Over time, new empires spread across the region. Poland and Lithuania, united in 1386 as Europe's largest kingdom, expanded southeast across Ukraine by 1500. Soon, the Turkish Ottoman Empire conquered southeastern Europe. In 1526, the Austrian Hapsburg emperors gained control of Hungary, the Czech lands, and Slovakia.

By the 1500s, the princes of Moscow had ended Tatar domination and emerged as the leaders of Russia. Over the next few centuries, Russia established an empire stretching from the Baltic and Black seas to the Pacific Ocean. Meanwhile, Poland disappeared from the map, as its territory was seized by Russia and other powers. Russian monarchs tended to be more autocratic than Western monarchs, and many economic and political developments bypassed Russia.

Political Change   In the late 1800s, Romania, Serbia, and Bulgaria declared independence from the Ottomans. The formation of nation-states accelerated after World War I when Poland, Czechoslovakia, and Hungary gained independence. The Russian Revolution of 1917 led to the establishment of the Soviet Union. This new nation adopted **communism,** a system in which the government controlled almost all aspects of political and economic life.

After World War II, the Soviet Union gained control over Eastern Europe, which also became Communist. Soviet domination lasted until 1989, when countries began adopting democracy and market economies. Communist industrial and military practices caused severe environmental problems in some regions.

The Soviet Union dissolved in 1991, breaking up into Russia and smaller national states such as Ukraine and Belarus. Since then, ethnic conflicts have erupted. While Russia and parts of Eastern Europe have declined economically, countries such as Hungary and Poland have prospered.

ASSESSMENT

1. **Key Terms** Define **(a)** domestication, **(b)** communism.

2. **Map Skills Movement** Which present-day Eastern European countries were invaded in past centuries?

3. **Critical Thinking Identifying Relationships** How have the different histories of the region's countries influenced their present-day economic well-being?

372   Chapter 18 ▪ Regional Atlas: Central Europe and Northern Eurasia

---

RESOURCE DIRECTORY

Teaching Resources
Creative Teaching Activities, The Changing Structure of Europe, p. 20
Unit 5, Chapter 18
• Regional Atlas Study Guide, p. 2
Guide to the Essentials (English/Spanish)
• Chapter 18 Summary
Mental Mapping booklet
• Unit 5 Checklist, p. 67
• Outline Map 18A, p. 68
Social Studies Skills Handbook
• Reading a Political Map, p. 19

Technology
Guided Reading Audiotapes (English/Spanish), Chapter 18
Section Reading Support Transparencies, Chapter 18
World Geography Map and Photo Transparencies
• Central Europe and Northern Eurasia: Maps and Photos
Book on CD, Chapter 18
World Geography Videos
• Regional Atlas: Central Europe and Northern Eurasia

REGIONAL ATLAS

Central Europe and Northern Eurasia: POLITICAL

Inset 1: Baltic States

Inset 2: Central Europe

KEY

— National boundary

⊛ National capital

• Major city

Robinson Projection

MENTAL MAPPING

Making a Political Map Study this political map and then draw your own sketch map of Central Europe and Northern Eurasia. Label the countries and major cities of the region. Use various colors to outline and shade each country.

LESSON PLAN

1. Focus Tell students to briefly review the introductory paragraphs and maps within each subsection of the Regional Atlas. Ask volunteers to summarize each section aloud. Tell students to write down the most important points to use as a study aid.

2. Instruct Have students complete the Mental Mapping activities and answer the caption questions in each section. Go over the answers as a class.

3. Close/Reteach Divide the class into small groups. Have each group make a brief list of the physical and cultural characteristics of one assigned region of Central Europe or Northern Eurasia.

Map Study Extension

Use the questions below to develop additional geographic themes.

Human-Environment Interaction Ask: **Where are most of Northern Eurasia's cities?** (toward the west) **Why might they be located there?** (In the west, the land is flatter and the climate is more temperate.) **Why do you think major cities in Central Europe grew on the banks of the Danube?** (It provides easy transportation of people and goods.)

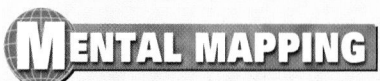

Unit Checklist Distribute the Unit 5 Checklist on page 67 of the Mental Mapping booklet. It includes all the place names, bodies of water, and physical features that students should learn in this unit.

Making a Political Map Students can complete the mapping activity on this page by sketching their own maps or coloring and labeling the Chapter 18A Outline Map on page 68 of the Mental Mapping booklet.

Alternative Assessment

Introduce the Activity

Creating a Map You may wish to distribute the Map Rubric found on page 14 of the Alternative Assessment booklet in the Prentice Hall Assessment System.

TEACHING TIP
From A Master Teacher

A Diverse Region Have students picture themselves traveling from west to east across Central Europe and Northern Eurasia. In the west, the standard of living is higher and the economy more advanced. As one moves east, the standard of living declines. The climate is warmer in the west, and colder and with greater climate extremes eastward. To the west, the cultures are more attuned to Western Europe and people are connected to other regions of the world. In the east, the people are more isolated and uniquely Russian.

Map Study Extension

Use the questions below to develop additional geographic themes.

1. Region Point out the numerous mountain ranges in Central Europe and Northern Eurasia. Ask: **Which mountain ranges form the southern border of Poland?** (the Sudetic Mountains and the Carpathian Mountains)

2. Place The North European Plain stretches from the Atlantic Ocean in the west to the Ural Mountains in the east. Ask: **What nations cover most of the North European Plain in Central Europe and Northern Eurasia?** (Poland, Ukraine, and Russia)

3. Human-Environment Interaction Ask: **Which areas in Central Europe and Northern Eurasia would you expect to focus on farming?** (Hungarian Basin, North European Plain, plains drained by rivers) **Why?** (Flat areas are easy to farm, and basins have sources of water.)

4. Movement Ask: **How would elevation affect the building of an east-west highway across Northern Eurasia?** (The fairly uniform elevations would present few obstacles in central Northern Eurasia. The mountains in the west and east would make work more difficult.)

Answers to Assessment

1. Eurasia, p. 374

2. Czech Republic, Slovakia, Hungary, Bosnia and Herzegovina, Macedonia, Belarus, Moldova

3. Mountains block Siberia from China and Mongolia to the south, making trade difficult. In the north, the Arctic Ocean is icy and difficult to travel.

Answers to Photo Captions

The Danube River Any two: Bulgaria, Romania, and Yugoslavia

Lake Baikal Possible answers: commercial fishing, tourism

Broad Plains There are no mountains or large oceans to cross. People can move easily through this part of the region.

Central Europe and Northern Eurasia form a huge region composed of many nations. One of these is Russia, the world's largest nation. Some geographers contend that the Ural Mountains in Russia mark the border between Europe and Asia. Others suggest that Europe and Asia should be viewed as a large single continent called **Eurasia.**

The physical landscape of this large region follows a general pattern. The land is flat in the west and rises higher toward the east and south. The map on the opposite page illustrates this trend.

The Danube River

The Danube is the second-longest river in Europe. It flows eastward from its source in Germany for about 1,770 miles (2,850 km) before emptying into the Black Sea. Here, the Danube moves through a narrow gorge called the Iron Gates. **PHYSICAL CHARACTERISTICS** *Name two nations whose borders are at least partially formed by the Danube.*

Lake Baikal

Located in southeastern Siberia, Lake Baikal is the world's deepest lake and the largest freshwater lake, holding some 20 percent of the world's fresh water. Logging and chemical industries have polluted the lake in recent years. **ENVIRONMENTAL CHANGE** *What types of economic activities might benefit from reducing the pollution in Lake Baikal?*

Broad Plains

Much of the land of Central Europe and Northern Eurasia is covered in broad plains and gently rolling hills. As a result, movement in the region has been fairly easy throughout history. **PHYSICAL CHARACTERISTICS** *How would a lack of natural barriers make movement easier?*

ASSESSMENT

1. **Key Term** Define Eurasia.

2. **Map Skills Place** Which nations in this region lack seacoasts?

3. **Critical Thinking Interpreting Maps** How do physical characteristics affect Siberia's ability to trade with other regions?

RESOURCE DIRECTORY

Teaching Resources

Mental Mapping booklet
• Outline Map 18B, p. 69

Social Studies Skills Handbook
• Elevation on a Map, p. 20
• Four Types of Landforms, p. 21
• Relief on a Map, p. 22

Technology

World Geography Map and Photo Transparencies
• Central Europe and Northern Eurasia: Maps and Photos

TeacherExpress™ CD-ROM, Chapter 18

Prentice Hall Presentation Pro CD-ROM, Chapter 18

Social Studies Skills Tutor CD-ROM

Companion Web site, www.phschool.com
• Chapter 18 Activities

REGIONAL ATLAS

Central Europe and Northern Eurasia: PHYSICAL

Arctic Ocean
Barents Sea
Novaya Zemlya
Kara Sea
Laptev Sea
Arctic Ocean
80° N
Arctic Circle
NORTHERN SIBERIAN LOWLAND
WESTERN SIBERIAN LOWLAND
CENTRAL SIBERIAN PLATEAU
VERKHOYANSKI RANGE
CHERSKOGO RANGE
KOLYMA MOUNTAINS
KAMCHATKA PENINSULA
Arctic Circle
60° N
St. Petersburg
URAL MOUNTAINS
Ob R.
Irtysh
Lena
Klyuchevsk
△15,585 ft.
(4,750 m)
Moscow
Volga R.
R U S S I A
Inset 2
Irkutsk
YABLONOV MOUNTAINS
STANOVOI RANGE
Amur R.
Sea of Okhotsk
UKRAINE
KAZAKHSTAN
MONGOLIA
Sakhalin I.
Kuril Is.
CRIMEA
Black Sea
CAUCASUS MOUNTAINS
Caspian Sea
UZBEKISTAN
GEORGIA
ARMENIA
TURKMENISTAN
KYRGYZSTAN
C H I N A
AZERBAIJAN
TAJIKISTAN
Tropic of Cancer
20° N

KEY

Elevation	
Feet	Meters
14,000	4,270
7,000	2,135
1,500	457
700	213
(sea level) 0	0 (sea level)

• Major city
△ Volcano

Robinson Projection

0 500 1,000 mi
0 500 1,000 km

Inset 1: Baltic States

Baltic Sea
Tallinn
ESTONIA
L. Peipus
RUSSIA
Gulf of Riga
LATVIA
Gaizina Kalns
▲ 1,020 ft.
(311 m)
Riga
W. Dvina R.
NORTH EUROPEAN PLAIN
LITHUANIA
RUSSIA
Vilnius
BELARUS
POLAND
20° E

0 50 100 mi
0 50 100 km

Inset 2: Central Europe

ESTONIA
LATVIA
W. Dvina R.
LITHUANIA
Baltic Sea
RUSSIA
NORTH EUROPEAN PLAIN
RUSSIA
Warta R.
Vistula R.
Minsk
Warsaw
BELARUS
GERMANY
Prague
ODRA PLAIN
BOHEMIA
POLAND
Kiev
Dnieper R.
CZECH REPUBLIC
MORAVA
SLOVAKIA
CARPATHIAN MOUNTAINS
UKRAINE
Kiev
Bratislava
Budapest
MOLDOVA
Chisinau
SLOVENIA
L. Balaton
HUNGARY
GREAT ALFOLD
ROMANIA
CRIMEA
Ljubljana
Zagreb
TRANSYLVANIAN ALPS
CROATIA
Belgrade
Bucharest
Black Sea
BOSNIA AND HERZEGOVINA
DINARIC ALPS
WALLACHIAN PLAIN
Sarajevo
BALKAN PENINSULA
SERBIA AND MONTENEGRO
BULGARIA
Danube R.
Podgorica
Sofia
BALKAN MTS.
Skopje
MACEDONIA
Tirane
ALBANIA
TURKEY
GREECE

20° E 30° E 40° E

0 150 300 mi
0 150 300 km

MENTAL MAPPING

Making a Physical Map Study this physical map and then draw your own sketch map of Central Europe and Northern Eurasia. Label the major physical features, including rivers and other bodies of water.

MENTAL MAPPING

Mapping Physical Features

Students can complete the mapping activity on this page either by adding labels to the political maps they have completed or by coloring and labeling the Chapter 18B Outline Map on page 69 of the Mental Mapping booklet in the Teaching Resources. Ask students to label all of the bodies of water and landforms listed under Part II of the Unit 5 Checklist.

BACKGROUND

Word Origin

Balkan The word *balkan* is Turkish for "mountain." The mountain ranges of the Balkan Peninsula include the Dinaric Alps, the Pindus Mountains, the Balkan Mountains, and the Transylvanian Alps.

ACTIVITY

Connecting With . . .

Music Explain that one of the world's most famous musical compositions is "The Blue Danube," a waltz by Johann Strauss. Assign students to do research and present a short oral report on Strauss, this waltz, and the historical circumstances at the time it was written.

BACKGROUND

Word Origin

Arctic The origin of the word *arctic* can be traced to ancient Greek. According to Greek myth, the constellation Ursa Major, or Great Bear, is actually a nymph who was turned into a bear by one of the gods. Unfortunately, she was mistaken for a real bear and was killed by a hunter. Zeus, who was in love with the nymph, added her to the heavens in the form of a constellation. The Greek word for "bear" is *arktos,* so the Greeks called the northern region containing the Great Bear *arktikos.*

Map Study Extension
Use the questions below to develop additional geographic themes.

1. Regions Refer to the Central Europe and Northern Eurasia climate map on page 377. Ask: **Which Central European and Northern Eurasian countries have a single predominant climate?** (Czech Republic, Slovenia, Estonia, Latvia, Lithuania, and Belarus)

2. Location Central Europe and Northern Eurasia have a variety of climates. While much of the region has a tundra or subarctic climate, other parts of the region are humid, arid, or even Mediterranean. Ask: **What nations have a Mediterranean climate in at least part of their territory?** (Croatia, Bosnia-Herzegovina, Yugoslavia, Albania, Macedonia, and Bulgaria)

Answers to Assessment
1. inland sea, p. 376

2. marine west coast and humid continental

3. (a) Budapest, about 40°; Irkutsk, about 70° **(b)** Irkutsk

Climates

Several major climates dominate the vast region of Central Europe and Northern Eurasia. The map at right shows that much of the region lies in the cooler climate regions. Subarctic, tundra, and humid continental climate regions cover much of Russia. A smaller portion of the region enjoys milder weather.

Winter on the Neva
The Neva River runs through St. Petersburg, Russia. During winter, the river freezes over. Here, local residents cut holes in the ice to fish. **CLIMATES** *In what climate zone does St. Petersburg lie?*

Black Sea Resort
The Black Sea is an **inland sea,** or a sea that is almost completely surrounded by land. During the winter, cold northerly winds bring strong storms. Warm summers, however, have encouraged the development of beach resorts such as this one in Sozopol, Bulgaria. **ECONOMIC ACTIVITIES** *Why might Black Sea resorts be particularly popular with people from northern cities in this region?*

Source: www.worldclimate.com
Curved lines show temperatures in Fahrenheit degrees.
Bars show rainfall in inches.

Comparing Climate Zones
The climates of Central Europe and Northern Eurasia range from mild Mediterranean to frigid tundra. Irkutsk, Russia, is in Siberia and endures the coldest winters of any place in the world except Antarctica. Budapest, Hungary, enjoys much milder weather. **CLIMATES** *In what month is Irkutsk warmest?*

ASSESSMENT

1. **Key Term** Define inland sea.

2. **Map Skills** **Regions** What climates are found in Poland?

3. **Critical Thinking** **Analyzing Data** Study the climate graphs for Irkutsk and Budapest.
   (a) What is the difference between the lowest and highest temperatures in each city?
   (b) Which city experiences the greater difference between high and low temperatures?

Answers to Photo Captions

Winter on the Neva humid continental

Black Sea Resort People from northern cities endure long, cold winters and many crave the mild weather of the Black Sea region.

Comparing Climate Zones July

REGIONAL ATLAS

Central Europe and Northern Eurasia: CLIMATE REGIONS

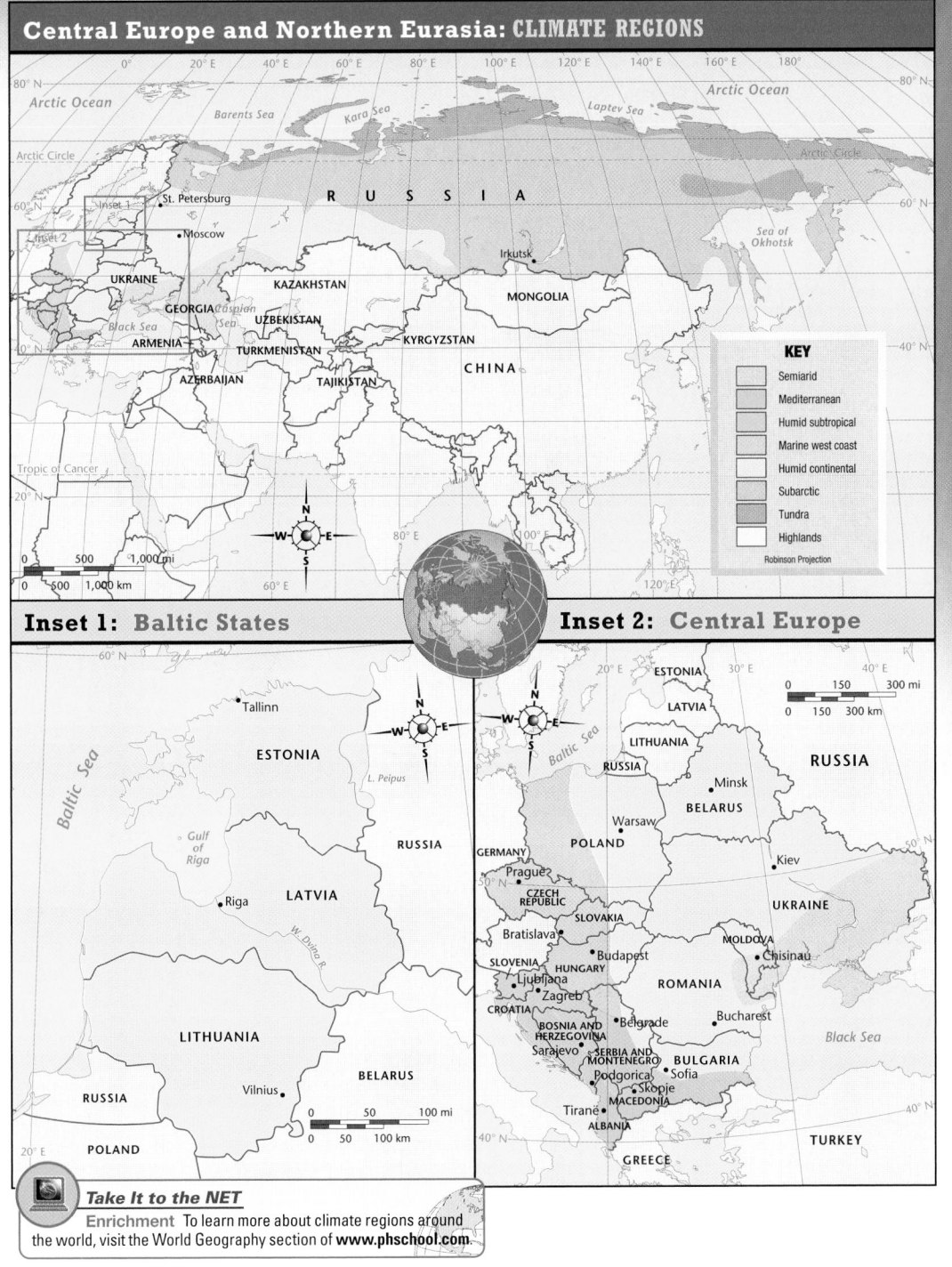

KEY
- Semiarid
- Mediterranean
- Humid subtropical
- Marine west coast
- Humid continental
- Subarctic
- Tundra
- Highlands

Robinson Projection

Inset 1: Baltic States

Inset 2: Central Europe

Take It to the NET
Enrichment To learn more about climate regions around the world, visit the World Geography section of **www.phschool.com**.

Chapter 18 ■ Regional Atlas: Central Europe and Northern Eurasia **377**

ACTIVITY

Enrichment

Comparing Regions On the board, create a two-column chart titled *Comparing the Geography of the U.S. to Central Europe and Northern Eurasia.* Label the columns *Similarities* and *Differences.* After students read page 376 and examine the map on page 377, have them complete the chart and compare the landforms and climates of both regions. (Visual/Spatial)

BACKGROUND

Connecting With . . .

History Russia's harsh winters provided a defense against invasion in two different wars. In 1812, blizzards, deep snow, and bitter cold helped defeat French emperor Napoleon as he and his military attempted to return to France after capturing Moscow. In 1941, a Nazi attempt to capture Moscow was thwarted by the coldest winter Russia had seen in decades. Nazi dictator Adolf Hitler lost about 1 million soldiers when temperatures on the Russian front dropped far below zero.

CUSTOMIZE FOR...

Less Proficient Writers

Climates Provide students with index cards or slips of paper. On one side of each card, have students write the name of a city from each of the climate zones shown on the map on this page. On the other side of the card, have them show the dictionary pronunciation of the city. Then have them write an original sentence noting the climate of the city. Encourage students to add information about the cities and climate regions as they work through the chapters in this unit.

378 Chapter 18

Map Study Extension
Use the questions below to develop additional geographic themes.

1. Place Much of Central Europe and Northern Eurasia is forested. The largest forest region in the world covers nearly half of Northern Eurasia, south of the tundra. Ask: **What three types of forest can be found in Central Europe and Northern Eurasia?** (coniferous, mixed deciduous and coniferous, and mid-latitude deciduous)

2. Human-Environment Interaction The Danube River flows through central Hungary. East of this river is Hungary's Great Plain region, an area of temperate grassland. Agriculture has taken over much of this region. Ask: **What makes this region suitable for farming?** (This grassland region is relatively flat, contains fertile soil, and maintains a climate favorable for agriculture.)

Answers to Assessment
1. (a) tundra, p. 378 **(b)** taiga, p. 378 **(c)** steppe, p. 378

2. (a) coniferous forest **(b)** temperate grassland

3. Possible answer: The most populated areas are mixed forest and temperate grassland regions, while the least populated are coniferous forest, desert scrub, and tundra regions. The latter regions have harsh climates and physical environments.

Answers to Photo Captions
Forest Ecosystem mixed forest (deciduous and coniferous)

Grassland Ecosystem Possible answer: Land has been converted to farmland.

Tundra The tundra extends from east to west from about 30°E to 170°W. Mostly, it lies north of the Arctic Circle.

CENTRAL EUROPE AND NORTHERN EURASIA
Ecosystems

A region as large as Central Europe and Northern Eurasia is bound to have a variety of ecosystems. The **tundra,** a treeless plain in arctic areas where short grasses and mosses grow, is found where the region touches the Arctic Ocean. South of the tundra are coniferous forests called **taiga,** as well as the expansive grasslands known as the **steppe.**

Forest Ecosystem
Bialowieza National Park in Poland contains one of the last surviving areas of forests that covered much of Europe in 8000 B.C. The park is home to European bison, elk, deer, wolves, and wild horses. **ECOSYSTEMS** *What is the predominant ecosystem in Poland today?*

Grassland Ecosystem
The steppe, which covers much of Ukraine and southern Russia, provides fertile soil for agriculture. **ENVIRONMENTAL CHANGE** *What types of environmental change are visible in this photograph?*

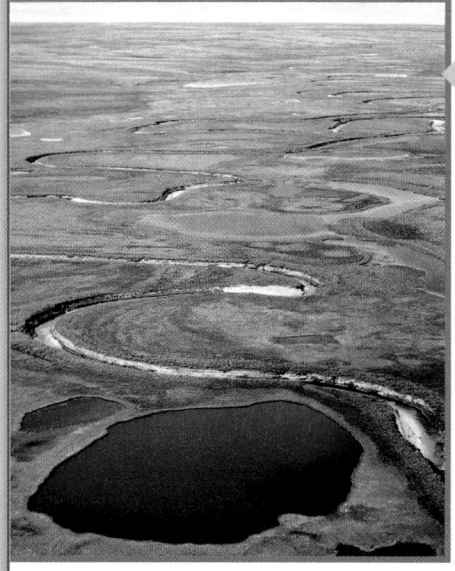

Tundra
Tundra and lakes are distinguishing characteristics of Northern Eurasia. The polar conditions in northern Russia discourage all but the toughest grasses, mosses, and lichens, which grow during the short summer. **GEOGRAPHIC TOOLS** *Use latitude and longitude to determine the general extent of the ecosystem represented by this photograph of the Yamal Peninsula.*

ASSESSMENT

1. **Key Terms** Define **(a)** tundra, **(b)** taiga, **(c)** steppe.

2. **Map Skills** **Regions** What ecosystem covers most of **(a)** Russia, **(b)** Ukraine

3. **Critical Thinking** **Identifying Relationships** Based on what you have learned about the ecosystems of this region, where do you think are the most populated areas? Where do you think are the least populated areas? Explain.

REGIONAL ATLAS

Central Europe and Northern Eurasia: ECOSYSTEMS

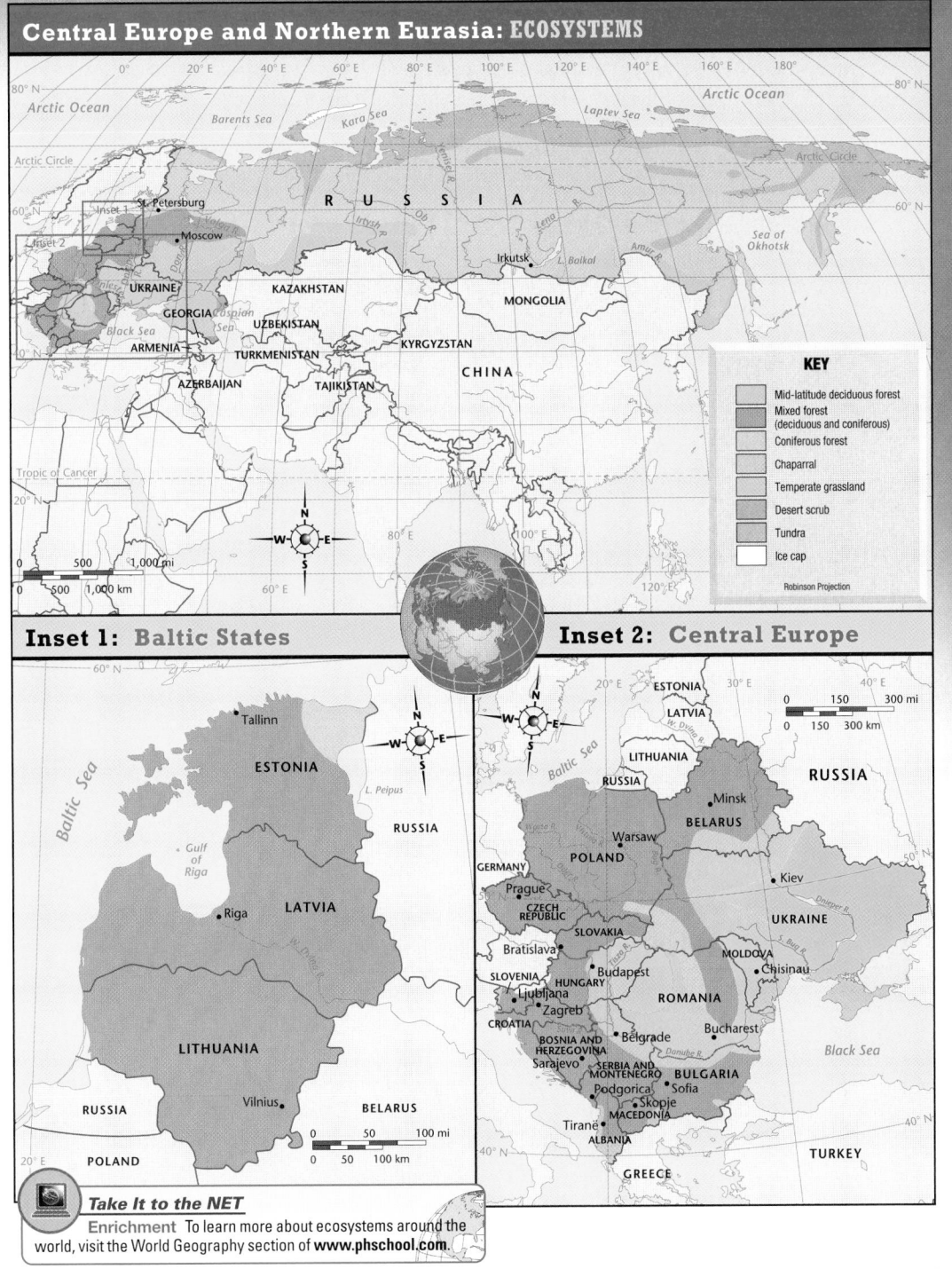

KEY
- Mid-latitude deciduous forest
- Mixed forest (deciduous and coniferous)
- Coniferous forest
- Chaparral
- Temperate grassland
- Desert scrub
- Tundra
- Ice cap

Robinson Projection

Inset 1: Baltic States

Inset 2: Central Europe

Take It to the NET
Enrichment To learn more about ecosystems around the world, visit the World Geography section of **www.phschool.com**.

Chapter 18 ▪ Regional Atlas: Central Europe and Northern Eurasia **379**

Vocabulary

Taiga Refer students to the term *taiga* on the opposite page. Taiga (pronounced TY guh) comes from the Russian word for "little sticks."

Enrichment

Creating a Bulletin Board As a class project, have students use books, magazines, the Internet, and other references to collect photographs or photocopies of scenes showing the variety of natural environments in Central Europe and Northern Eurasia. Have them sort the collected pictures according to ecosystems shown on the map on this page, use colored markers or paper to key the illustrations to the map colors, and arrange the pictures in a bulletin board display. Ask students to give their display an appropriate title. (Visual/Spatial)

Ecosystems

Steppes and Steppe Peoples
Extensive grasslands called steppes are found in many places throughout the world, including Central Europe and Northern Eurasia, North America, South America, and Australia. The first steppe people were nomads and hunters. For example, the people of the Eurasian steppes were nomadic herders. Each season they moved their livestock to new grazing lands. Indians living on the grasslands in central North America survived by hunting the migrating buffalo herds. In modern times, however, people have used the rich soils of such grasslands for agriculture. Wheat and alfalfa are grown on the grasslands of South America, while parts of the Eurasian steppes—especially in Ukraine—have become leading grain producers.

Map Study Extension

Use the questions below to develop additional geographic themes.

1. Human-Environment Interaction Look at the population density map on page 381. Note the areas with the highest population densities. Ask: **What types of economic activity might you expect to find in these areas?** (High population density often indicates urban land use activities such as manufacturing rather than farming or mining.)

2. Regions Ask: **What parts of Central Europe and Northern Eurasia are sparsely populated?** (much of eastern Northern Eurasia and the southern border of Central Europe) **Why?** (The harsh climates in Siberia as well as the higher elevations of southern Central Europe make living in those regions very difficult.)

Answers to Assessment

1. (a) multiethnic, p. 380 **(b)** ethnic group, p. 380

2. in the west

3. nomadic herding, hunting and gathering, commercial farming, subsistence farming, livestock raising, coal, gold, natural gas, bauxite, iron, tin, lead

Answers to Photo Captions

Orthodox Christianity Possible answer: Religious traditions mean a great deal to many people, and they are willing to put themselves at risk to practice their faith.

Estonian Culture Possible answer: Traditions have been passed down through generations, defining individuals' identities.

Urban Life Possible answer: Traditional architecture is maintained on streets with modern roads and automobiles.

380 Chapter 18

CENTRAL EUROPE AND NORTHERN EURASIA
People and Cultures

History and geography have influenced culture in Central Europe and Northern Eurasia. Movement has been easy, with few physical barriers, such as mountains or wide oceans. People settled in the region to gain control of natural resources and territory, to flee religious or political persecution, or to find a better life. Migration has made most nations of the region **multiethnic,** containing many ethnic groups.

Orthodox Christianity

Orthodox Christianity has been important in Central Europe for centuries. Although Communist governments restricted religious activities, democracy has given people more opportunity to practice traditional faiths. **UNDERSTANDING THE PAST** *Why might people choose to maintain their traditions in spite of oppression?*

Estonian Culture

Central Europe and Northern Eurasia are home to dozens of ethnic groups. An **ethnic group** is composed of people who share such things as culture, language, and religion. Here, an Estonian couple performs a traditional dance. **CULTURES** *Why do you think it is important to the people of this region to maintain their traditions?*

Urban Life

Like other cities in the region, Prague can boast a mixture of traditional architecture and modern businesses. **GLOBAL TRADE PATTERNS** *How does this photograph indicate cultural convergence in the Czech Republic?*

ASSESSMENT

1. **Key Terms** Define **(a)** multiethnic, **(b)** ethnic group.

2. **Map Skills Human-Environment Interaction** Where do most people in Central Europe and Northern Eurasia live?

3. **Critical Thinking Synthesizing Information** Compare this map with the map on page 383. What economic activities are prevalent in areas with the fewest people?

380 Chapter 18 ▪ Regional Atlas: Central Europe and Northern Eurasia

RESOURCE DIRECTORY

Teaching Resources
Social Studies Skills Handbook
• Reading a Population Density Map, p. 31

Technology
World Geography Map and Photo Transparencies
• Central Europe and Northern Eurasia: Maps and Photos

REGIONAL ATLAS

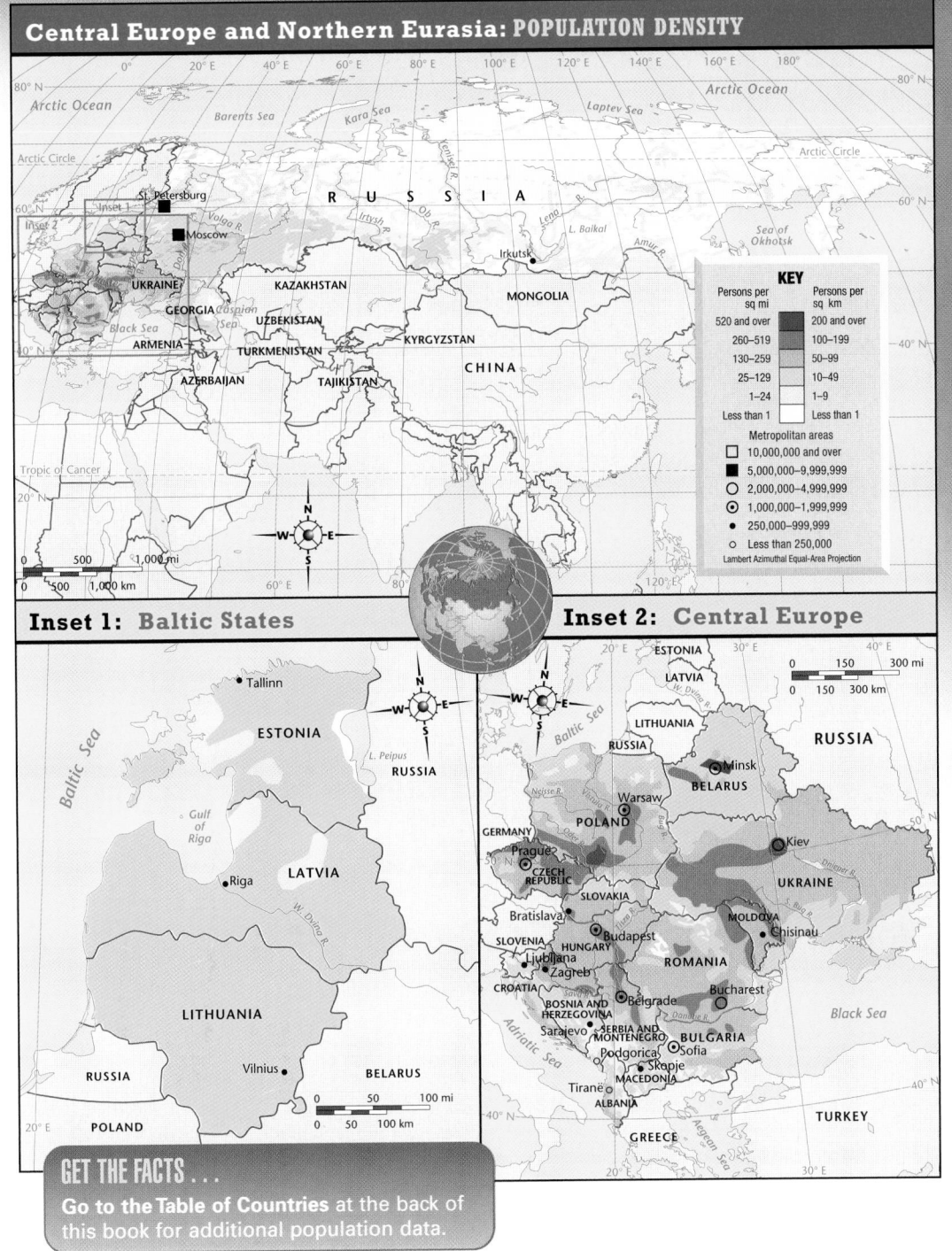

Central Europe and Northern Eurasia: POPULATION DENSITY

KEY

Persons per sq mi	Persons per sq km
520 and over	200 and over
260–519	100–199
130–259	50–99
25–129	10–49
1–24	1–9
Less than 1	Less than 1

Metropolitan areas
- ☐ 10,000,000 and over
- ■ 5,000,000–9,999,999
- ○ 2,000,000–4,999,999
- ◉ 1,000,000–1,999,999
- • 250,000–999,999
- ○ Less than 250,000

Lambert Azimuthal Equal-Area Projection

Inset 1: Baltic States

Inset 2: Central Europe

GET THE FACTS . . .

Go to the Table of Countries at the back of this book for additional population data.

Group Work

Activity: Creating a dialogue

Purpose: Arrange the class in pairs. Instruct each pair to select two towns or cities in Central Europe or Northern Eurasia that are at least 800 miles (1,300 km) apart. Then, tell students to work individually to research the climate, population, predominant languages, and major economic activities of one of their pair's locations. Ask students to work with their partners and imagine what would happen if a person from one community were to meet a person from the other community. Record the conversation in a dialogue between the two fictional characters.

Roles: All students should act as both researchers and writers.

Result: Have students perform their dialogues for the class.

ACTIVITY

Area Comparison

Using the Table of Countries Ask students to use the Table of Countries beginning on page 742 of their textbooks to compare the land areas and populations of the United States, Russia, and Poland.

Connections: Math Compare the per capita GDPs of Russia and Poland to that of the United States. **How many times greater is the figure for the United States compared to those of the other two countries?** (The GDP of the United States is more than four times greater than Poland's GDP and ten times greater than Russia's GDP.)

Map Study Extension

Use the questions below to develop additional geographic themes.

1. Location Point out the areas in southern Poland, western Russia, Ukraine, and the Czech Republic where manufacturing and trade are concentrated. Ask: **What obstacles do these areas face in transporting goods to markets?** (Most of these areas lack a seaport; transportation must be overland or on rivers, which may be closed by ice in the winter.)

2. Movement Ask: **Where do you think Russia sells the timber it produces in the southeast?** (to Japan, to countries to the east, across the Pacific)

3. Place Ask: **Do you notice any serious scarcity of critical natural resources in Northern Eurasia?** (No; the most essential natural resources are present.)

Answers to Assessment

1. acid rain, p. 382

2. (a) in Macedonia, Bulgaria, Romania, Czech Republic, Slovakia, Ukraine, and Russia **(b)** Volga, Yenisei, and Danube rivers

3. (a) Moldova, Belarus, and Latvia have no resources. Estonia, Lithuania, Macedonia, Bosnia-Herzegovina, Slovenia, and Czech Republic have very few resources. **(b)** Possible answer: It weakens the economy because the nation does not have plentiful resources for industry and trade.

Economics, Technology, and Environment

Since the late 1980s, the economies of Central Europe and Northern Eurasia have generally moved from communism to some form of capitalism. In a Communist economy, the government controls the means of production and distribution of goods and services. In a capitalist economy, producers and consumers control business, with some government regulation.

Women in the Work Force

A large percentage of Russia's men lost their lives in World War II. Since then, women have made up more than 50 percent of Russia's work force. Women workers can be found in nearly every profession, from bus driving to medicine. **UNDERSTANDING THE PAST** *Why might there be a larger percentage of women in Russia's work force than in the United States work force?*

Baltic Port

The Russian port of Vyborg lies on the Gulf of Finland. For centuries, Russian leaders have sought ports that can be open to shipping throughout the year. **ECONOMIC ACTIVITIES** *How would winter conditions affect the Russian shipping industry?*

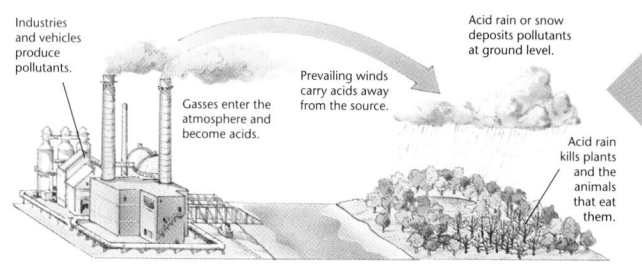

Industries and vehicles produce pollutants.

Gasses enter the atmosphere and become acids.

Prevailing winds carry acids away from the source.

Acid rain or snow deposits pollutants at ground level.

Acid rain kills plants and the animals that eat them.

Acid Rain

Industrial activities in Central Europe and Northern Eurasia have resulted in **acid rain,** a form of pollution in which toxic chemicals in the air come back to the earth as rain, snow, or hail. **ENVIRONMENTAL CHANGE** *What role do factories play in the development of acid rain?*

ASSESSMENT

1. **Key Term** Define acid rain.

2. **Map Skills** **Human-Environment Interaction** **(a)** Where are the region's hydroelectric power sources located? **(b)** Study the physical map on page 375, and name at least two rivers that provide water power.

3. **Critical Thinking** **Analyzing Information** **(a)** Which nations seem to have few natural resources? **(b)** How do you think having few natural resources affects the economy of a nation?

Answers to Photo Captions

Women in the Work Force Possible answer: Many Russian men died during World War II and women had to work to support families and to fill jobs.

Baltic Port Winter conditions could hinder or even halt the shipping industry in much of Russia.

Acid Rain Factories release pollution that can create acid rain.

REGIONAL ATLAS

Central Europe and Northern Eurasia: ECONOMIC ACTIVITY AND RESOURCES

KEY

Nomadic herding	Manufacturing and trade	Bauxite	Hydroelectric power
Hunting and gathering	Commercial fishing	Gold	Nickel
Forestry	Little or no activity	Silver	Tungsten
Livestock raising	Coal	Natural gas	Diamonds
Commercial farming	Petroleum	Lead	Phosphates
Subsistence farming	Copper	Iron	Uranium
		Tin	

Robinson Projection

Inset 1: Baltic States

Inset 2: Central Europe

Take It to the NET
Enrichment To learn more about the economic activities and resources of this region, visit the World Geography section of **www.phschool.com**.

Chapter 18 ▪ Regional Atlas: Central Europe and Northern Eurasia   **383**

Database:
Comparing Health Care
pp. 384–385

Objectives
Upon completion of this lesson, students should be able to:

◆ compare the state of health care in Poland, Romania, Russia, Ukraine, and the United States;

◆ discuss how economic systems can affect health care systems.

National Geography Standards
The following National Geography Standards are highlighted in this feature: 4, 16, 18

Bellringer
Explain that from 1957 to 1997, life expectancy in the United States increased from 69.5 years to 76.5 years. Ask: **What might these figures indicate about health care in the United States?** (Possible answer: Life expectancy is increasing because health care is improving.)

....

LESSON PLAN

1. Focus Read the introductory paragraph with the students. Remind students that when the Soviet Union collapsed, the economies of many nations in Central Europe and Northern Eurasia declined. Ask: **Why would a declining economy affect a nation's health care system?** (The nation would not have the funding to offer safe and modern health care facilities and services.)

2. Instruct After students read the database, have them create a bar graph showing the life expectancy of females and males in each of the nations in the database. Ask: **In which country do women have the highest life expectancy?** (Poland) **Where do men have the lowest life expectancy?** (Russia)

3. Close/Reteach Have students use the statistics and accompanying information to write a paragraph comparing one of the health care systems in this feature with that of the United States.

By comparing the data below, you will learn about the state of health care in several nations in Central Europe and Northern Eurasia. The fall of communism in this region greatly affected health care. Under communism, central governments provided health care to nearly all their citizens. Today, the nations of the region are struggling to build new health care systems. When you compare the data for these nations with the United States data on page 385, you will notice some great differences.

Sources: *Encarta World Atlas; World Health Organization*

Key Terms: **infant mortality, maternal mortality, life expectancy**

Poland

Poland	
Infant Mortality Rate (deaths per 1,000 live births)	9
Maternal Mortality Rate (deaths per 100,000 live births)	12
Life Expectancy at Birth	73.9
Female	78.3
Male	69.8
Population per Physician	435
Population per Hospital Bed	196

In Poland, medical care is free for most people and is of relatively high quality. Birth-related mortality rates are low. **Infant mortality** is the number of children per 1,000 live births who die within the first year. **Maternal mortality** is the number of women who die due to pregnancy and childbirth complications, per 100,000 live births. **Life expectancy,** the number of years an individual is expected to live as determined by statistics, is fairly high in Poland.

Romania

Romania	
Infant Mortality Rate (deaths per 1,000 live births)	18
Maternal Mortality Rate (deaths per 100,000 live births)	60
Life Expectancy at Birth	70.6
Female	74.6
Male	66.9
Population per Physician	537
Population per Hospital Bed	132

Compared to most other European nations, Romania has a low life expectancy and a weak health care system. High pollution levels in some parts of the country contribute to health problems and an even lower life expectancy. For example, in parts of Transylvania, life expectancy is only 61 years. The health care system has suffered major problems. A strike staged by health care workers in 1998 signaled that the system was on the verge of collapse. Romanians hope that the future will bring improved health care.

384 Chapter 18 ▪ Regional Atlas: Central Europe and Northern Eurasia

Russia

Infant Mortality Rate (deaths per 1,000 live births)	20
Maternal Mortality Rate (deaths per 100,000 live births)	75
Life Expectancy at Birth	67.7
Female	73.1
Male	62.5
Population per Physician	243
Population per Hospital Bed	83

Until the collapse of communism, state-run enterprises in the Soviet Union provided extensive health care for employees. After the fall of communism, a Medical Insurance Fund was set up, and employers are supposed to make payments into the fund for their employees. However, the Russian system is in crisis and is underfunded. Infant and maternal mortality are relatively high. Medicine and medical equipment are often in short supply. Bribing medical staff to obtain treatment is common.

Ukraine

Infant Mortality Rate (deaths per 1,000 live births)	21
Maternal Mortality Rate (deaths per 100,000 live births)	45
Life Expectancy at Birth	66.5
Female	72.2
Male	61.1
Population per Physician	334
Population per Hospital Bed	101

Although Ukraine has a high number of physicians per person, its health care system faces serious problems. The nuclear accident that took place at Chernobyl in 1986 continues to pose one of the most serious health threats to Ukrainians. The United Nations runs a program that provides $2 million per year for treatment and preventive care for 350,000 people who were affected by the Chernobyl disaster. Over 3 million people live on radioactively contaminated land.

ASSESSMENT

Use the data for Central Europe and Northern Eurasia and the United States (at right) to answer the following questions.

1. **Key Terms** Define **(a)** infant mortality, **(b)** maternal mortality, **(c)** life expectancy.

2. **Economic Systems** How did the end of communism change health care in Russia?

3. **Population Growth** Which of these nations has the highest infant mortality rate?

4. **Critical Thinking Making Comparisons** Compare life expectancy data for the United States and the other nations shown here.

United States

Infant Mortality Rate (deaths per 1,000 live births)	7
Maternal Mortality Rate (deaths per 100,000 live births)	12
Life Expectancy at Birth	77.1
Female	80.0
Male	74.4
Population per Physician	465
Population per Hospital Bed	278

Chapter 18 ▪ Regional Atlas: Central Europe and Northern Eurasia **385**

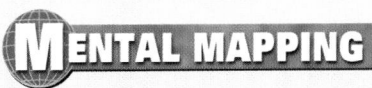

MENTAL MAPPING

Games for Review See pages 58–63 of the Simulations, Games, and Lab Activities booklet in the Teaching Resources for suggested games to review place names in preparation for the Chapter 18 Map Test.

Chapter Map Test Students should use the completed Chapter 18 outline maps and the Unit 5 Checklist to prepare for the Chapter 18 Map Test. Point out that the test will cover all of the countries, cities, bodies of water, and landforms listed on the Unit 5 Checklist.

Alternative Assessment

Final Evaluation

Creating a Map Use the Map Evaluation Form on page 15 of the Alternative Assessment booklet in the Prentice Hall Assessment System to evaluate students' maps. Either teachers or students can complete the forms to indicate which level of work was achieved for each of the criteria.

Answers to Assessment

1. (a) infant mortality, p. 384
(b) maternal mortality, p. 384
(c) life expectancy, p. 384

2. Under communism, state-run businesses provided health care to nearly all citizens. Today, the nations of the region are struggling to build new health care systems. For example, after the fall of communism, Russia set up an insurance fund, but the system is not funded adequately and the quality of health care is in decline.

3. Ukraine

4. The United States has a higher life expectancy than the countries shown here.

Do-It-Yourself Skills

pp. 386–387

Objectives

Upon completion of this feature, students should be able to:

◆ explain the goal of a research project;

◆ describe each step in the process of completing a research project.

National Geography Standards

The following National Geography Standards are highlighted in this feature: 1, 3, 4, 15, 17

Bellringer

Ask students to define *research*. Explain that there are many different sources that they can use to research a geographic topic or any topic. Ask students to list sources they have used to complete research reports in the past. Discuss whether they would be useful sources for a geography research project. Then have students suggest additional sources that might be helpful.

LESSON PLAN

1. Focus Write the word *research* in the center of the board. Draw lines, like bicycle spokes, around it. Ask students to label each spoke with a career or a professional task that involves research.

2. Instruct Teach students to target useful information as they read. Write the topic question from Step 1 on the board: *Why is life expectancy in Russia so poor compared with life expectancy in countries forming the European Union?* Then help students make a list of research questions to help them streamline their search for information. Tell them to consider what they know about their topics when writing their questions.

3. Close/Reteach After students complete research on their topics, encourage them to draw conclusions. They can adapt the concept map on page 387 to organize their ideas clearly and to find answers to their overall geographic questions. Ask volunteers to share their conclusions with the class.

D.I.Y. Do-It-Yourself Skills

Completing a Research Project

What Is a Research Project?

A research project involves many skills. You begin by asking questions, focusing on a topic, and creating ideas. Next, you acquire, analyze, and organize information. Finally, you answer questions and present your perspectives, usually in a written or an oral presentation. In a research project, you do not just report information from various sources. You use the information to develop your own ideas and perspectives.

How Can I Use This Skill?

Completing a research project is one of the most complex and valuable skills that you will ever develop. It involves a variety of critical thinking and communication skills. Legal briefs, credit reports, and proposals for new products are just a few of the professional tasks that are closely related to research projects.

Step by Step

Follow this series of steps to learn how to complete a research project. As you proceed through this lesson, be sure to refer to the graphic organizer and special tip on the next page.

1 Decide on a topic by asking geographic questions. In school or at a workplace, a research project often begins with a general subject that is assigned to you. However, you are expected to focus on a more specific topic within that subject area. You can do this by studying the general subject and asking logical questions. For this lesson, consider the line graph at right. The data presented in the graph should lead you to an obvious question: Why is life expectancy in Russia so low compared with life expectancy in countries forming the European Union?

Male Life Expectancy in Russia and the European Union

RESOURCE DIRECTORY

Teaching Resources

Social Studies Skills Handbook
• Study and Research Skills, pp. 94–104

Technology

Social Studies Skills Tutor CD-ROM, Identifying Cause and Effect, Using Reliable Information

2 Acquire geographic information. Now that you have a topic, it is time to do research using library resources and the Internet. Consider the kinds of resources that are most likely to contain the information you need. For a current events topic, such as this one, you will probably do best with articles from newspapers, newsmagazines, and scholarly journals. As you gather information, take notes or make copies or printouts. Remember that you will need to make a bibliography citing all your sources.

3 Analyze the information. Remember that the goal of a research project is to offer perspectives or hypotheses based on the information. You should develop a main idea and show how the information you gathered supports this idea. For example, your research might suggest that there are economic, environmental, and cultural reasons for the relatively low life expectancy in Russia.

4 Organize your ideas by making an outline or a concept map like the one below. Each main idea should be supported by specific facts and details. Be careful to place information under the appropriate categories.

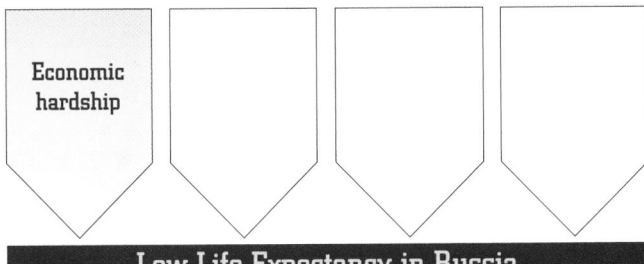

Economic hardship

Low Life Expectancy in Russia

5 Answer geographic questions. After organizing your ideas and information, you can begin to formulate clear answers to the geographic question or questions that initiated your research. As you answer the question of why life expectancy is so low in Russia, form viewpoints that are clear, logical, and based on facts.

6 Communicate the results. Write a first draft for your written or oral presentation. Then, revise your work to express your ideas more logically and clearly. Make sure that you use geographic terminology correctly. Be sure to use standard grammar, spelling, sentence structure, and punctuation. Revise your work repeatedly until you achieve satisfactory results.

> **TIP**
>
> **Skills of Geography**
> - Ask geographic questions.
> - Acquire information.
> - Analyze information.
> - Organize ideas.
> - Answer geographic questions.
> - Communicate results.

APPLY YOUR SKILL

Review the Regional Atlas for Central Europe and Northern Eurasia. Then, choose another topic on which you can complete a research project. Follow each of the steps that you have learned, and communicate your results in a written or an oral presentation.

ACTIVITY

Reteach

Drawing Conclusions To help students draw conclusions from their research, have them complete the following sentence stem: I think _____ because _____. The first part of the sentence should state their conclusion. The second part should present facts that helped them reach that conclusion. (Verbal/Linguistic)

ACTIVITY

Group Work

Activity: Evaluating sources
Purpose: Have students work in groups to evaluate the sources they consulted for their research. Group members should explain how easy each source was to use, how much information it provided, and whether the information was helpful.
Roles: Each group should have two television anchors to present the evaluations.
Result: Anchors present the evaluations to the class as if they were movie or television critics.

Answers to Apply Your Skill

Check students' research reports for evidence of logical ideas and questions and careful research.

CUSTOMIZE FOR...

Less Proficient Writers
Peer Critiques Pair students and have them read drafts of each other's research projects two times. The first time, have them look for errors in spelling, grammar, and mechanics and underline them. Then have them read again and circle ideas that need more development or explanation. Have them return the draft to the writer to make corrections.

Resource Manager

	CORE INSTRUCTION	READING/SKILLS
Chapter-Level Resources	**Teaching Resources** **Unit 5**/Ch. 19 • Reviewing Main Ideas, p. 19 **Mental Mapping booklet** • Unit 5 Checklist, p. 67 **Simulations, Games, and Lab Activities** • Resolving a Land Dispute, pp. 49–57 • Place Location Review Games, pp. 58–63 **TeacherExpress™ CD-ROM**, Ch. 19 **Companion Web site, www.phschool.com** • eTeach	**Teaching Resources** **Unit 5**/Ch. 19 • Map/Graph Skills, p. 21 **Mental Mapping booklet** • Outline Map 19, p. 72 **Book on CD**, Ch. 19 **Social Studies Skills Tutor CD-ROM**
1 Poland 1. List some major physical characteristics of Poland. 2. Explain how World War II affected Polish culture. 3. Describe how the fall of communism affected nationalism and the economy in Poland.	**Teaching Resources** **Unit 5**/Ch. 19 • Guided Reading and Review, p. 11 **Prentice Hall Presentation Pro CD-ROM**, Ch. 19, Sec. 1	**Teaching Resources** **Guide to the Essentials (English/Spanish)** • Section Summary, Ch. 19, Sec. 1 **Guided Reading Audiotapes (English/Spanish)**, Ch. 19, Sec. 1 **Section Reading Support Transparencies**, Ch. 19, Sec. 1
2 The Czech and Slovak Republics, and Hungary 1. Discuss changes in political and economic conditions in the Czech Republic since the 1980s. 2. List the challenges facing the regions of Bohemia and Moravia. 3. Explain the economic issues Slovakia faces. 4. Describe how privatization has affected Hungary's economy.	**Teaching Resources** **Unit 5**/Ch. 19 • Guided Reading and Review, p. 13 **Prentice Hall Presentation Pro CD-ROM**, Ch. 19, Sec. 2	**Teaching Resources** **Guide to the Essentials (English/Spanish)** • Section Summary, Ch. 19, Sec. 2 **Guided Reading Audiotapes (English/Spanish)**, Ch. 19, Sec. 2 **Section Reading Support Transparencies**, Ch. 19, Sec. 2
3 The Balkan Peninsula 1. Summarize how Romania's economy has changed since the end of Communist rule. 2. Identify the signs of Bulgaria's economic growth. 3. Describe the effects of foreign investment on Albania. 4. Explain why internal tensions challenge the people of the Balkan nations.	**Teaching Resources** **Unit 5**/Ch. 19 • Guided Reading and Review, p. 15 **Creative Teaching Activities** • Practicing Conflict Resolution Skills, p. 21 **Prentice Hall Presentation Pro CD-ROM**, Ch. 19, Sec. 3	**Teaching Resources** **Guide to the Essentials (English/Spanish)** • Section Summary, Ch. 19, Sec. 3 **Guided Reading Audiotapes (English/Spanish)**, Ch. 19, Sec. 3 **Section Reading Support Transparencies**, Ch. 19, Sec. 3
4 Baltic States and Border Nations 1. Describe how location has affected the history and economics of the Baltic states. 2. Explain why many Ukrainians were eager to break free of foreign domination. 3. Describe the link between Belarus and Russia and the link between Moldova and Romania.	**Teaching Resources** **Unit 5**/Ch. 19 • Guided Reading and Review, p. 17 **Prentice Hall Presentation Pro CD-ROM**, Ch. 19, Sec. 4	**Teaching Resources** **Guide to the Essentials (English/Spanish)** • Section Summary, Ch. 19, Sec. 4 **Guided Reading Audiotapes (English/Spanish)**, Ch. 19, Sec. 4 **Section Reading Support Transparencies**, Ch. 19, Sec. 4

ENRICHMENT/HONORS/PREAP

Teaching Resources
- **Unit 5**/Ch. 19
  - Critical Thinking, p. 20
- **Mental Mapping booklet**
  - Atlas Activity, p. 73
- **Social Studies Skills Handbook**
  - Study and Research Skills, pp. 94–108
- **People and Geography**
  - Conflict, pp. 25–29
- **World Geography Map and Photo Transparencies**
  - Central Europe and Northern Eurasia: Maps and Photos
- **World Geography Videos**
  - Urbanization: Central and Eastern Europe
- **Companion Web site, www.phschool.com**
  - Chapter 19 Activities

- **Companion Web site, www.phschool.com**
  - Chapter 19 Activities

Teaching Resources
- **Social Studies Skills Handbook**
  - Identifying Assumptions, p. 46
- **Companion Web site, www.phschool.com**
  - Chapter 19 Activities

- **Companion Web site, www.phschool.com**
  - Chapter 19 Activities

- **Companion Web site, www.phschool.com**
  - Chapter 19 Activities

ASSESSMENT

PRENTICE HALL
ASSESSMENT SYSTEM

Core Assessment
- ExamView Test Bank booklet, Ch. 19
- ExamView Test Bank CD-ROM, Ch. 19

Standardized Test Preparation

Review and Reteach
- Review Book for World Geography, pp. 11–12

Practice and Assess
- Test-taking Strategies With Transparencies for High School
- Test-taking Strategy Poster
- Alternative Assessment booklet
- Test Prep Book for World Geography

Teaching Resources
- **Unit 5**/Ch. 19
  - Section Quizzes, pp. 12, 14, 16, 18
  - Test Forms A and B, pp. 22–27
- **Guide to the Essentials (English/Spanish)**
  - Chapter 19 Test
- **Spanish Resources**, Ch. 19
  - Section Quizzes, pp. 46–49
- **Mental Mapping booklet**
  - Chapter 19 Map Test, p. 74
- **Companion Web site, www.phschool.com**
  - Chapter 19 Self-Test

CUSTOMIZE FOR INDIVIDUAL NEEDS

Gifted and Talented
- Teacher's Edition, Customize for . . . , p. 397

Honors/PreAP
- Teacher's Edition, Customize for . . . , p. 411

Less Proficient Readers
- Guide to the Essentials (English), Ch. 19, Section Summaries
- Guided Reading Audiotapes (English), Ch. 19
- Section Reading Support Transparencies, Ch. 19
- Book on CD, Ch. 19
- Teacher's Edition, Reading Strategy, pp. 390, 394, 399, 407
- Teacher's Edition, Activity: Vocabulary, pp. 390, 395, 399, 408
- Teacher's Edition, Customize for . . . , p. 391

Students Acquiring English/ESL
- Guide to the Essentials (English/Spanish), Ch. 19
- Guided Reading Audiotapes (English/Spanish), Ch. 19
- Section Reading Support Transparencies, Ch. 19
- Book on CD, Ch. 19
- Teacher's Edition, Customize for . . . , pp. 403, 405

Less Proficient Writers
- Alternative Assessment, Writing Assignment Rubric, p. 6

MENTAL MAPPING

Ask students to study the map on this page. Point out that there are 18 nations in Central and Eastern Europe. The region stretches from the Baltic Sea in the north to Greece and Turkey in the south. Russia lies to the east of the region, while the nations of Germany, Austria, and Italy lie to the west.

Mapping the Region Ask students to sketch their own outline maps like the one on this page, or distribute the Chapter 19 Outline Map on page 72 of the Mental Mapping booklet in the Teaching Resources. Instruct students to lightly shade each country a different color. Then ask them to label the countries and bodies of water shown on this map. Students should keep their maps in their Atlas Portfolios to prepare for the Chapter 19 Map Test.

eTeach

Be sure to check out this month's online forum with a Master Teacher to join in an exchange of teaching ideas. www.phschool.com

---

C H A P T E R

19

Central and Eastern Europe

SECTIONS

1	Poland
2	The Czech and Slovak Republics, and Hungary
3	The Balkan Peninsula
4	Baltic States and Border Nations

Central and Eastern Europe: POLITICAL

KEY

— National boundary
⊛ National capital
• Other city

Lambert Azimuthal Equal-Area Projection

ESTONIA — Tallinn
LATVIA — Riga
LITHUANIA — Vilnius
Gdańsk
POLAND — Warsaw
Łódź
Prague — Katowice — Kraków
CZECH REPUBLIC — Brno
SLOVAKIA — Bratislava
Budapest
SLOVENIA — HUNGARY
Ljubljana — Zagreb
CROATIA
BOSNIA AND HERZEGOVINA — Belgrade
Sarajevo
SERBIA AND MONTENEGRO
Podgorica — Skopje
Tiranë — MACEDONIA
ALBANIA
BELARUS — Minsk
Kiev
UKRAINE
MOLDOVA — Chişinău — Odessa
Cluj-Napoca
ROMANIA — Bucharest
Danube R.
BULGARIA — Sofia
Black Sea
Baltic Sea
Adriatic Sea
Danube R.

0   150   300 mi
0   150 300 km

Go Online
PHSchool.com

For: More information about Central and Eastern Europe and access to the Take It to the Net activities
Visit: phschool.com
Web Code: mjk-0020

388   Chapter 19

RESOURCE DIRECTORY

Teaching Resources
Unit 5, Chapter 19
• Section 1, Guided Reading and Review, p. 11
Guide to the Essentials (English/Spanish)
• Section Summary, Chapter 19, Section 1
Mental Mapping booklet
• Atlas Activity, p. 73
• Unit 5 Checklist, p. 67

Technology
Guided Reading Audiotapes (English/Spanish),
Chapter 19, Section 1

Section Reading Support Transparencies,
Chapter 19, Section 1
World Geography Map and Photo Transparencies
• Central Europe and Northern Eurasia: Maps and Photos
Book on CD, Chapter 19
World Geography Videos
• Urbanization: Central and Eastern Europe
TeacherExpress™ CD-ROM, Chapter 19
Prentice Hall Presentation Pro CD-ROM, Chapter 19
Social Studies Skills Tutor CD-ROM
Companion Web site, www.phschool.com

1 Poland

Reading Focus

- **What are some major physical characteristics of Poland?**
- **How did World War II affect Poland's cultural patterns?**
- **How did the Polish people maintain their national identity and achieve economic prosperity after communism?**

Key Terms

national identity
ghetto
Holocaust

Main Idea Despite political hardships in the past, the Polish people have maintained their national identity.

Economic Activities Poland's economy is service-oriented, but most of the land is used for farming.

Objectives

Upon completion of Section 1, students should be able to:

♦ list some major physical characteristics of Poland;

♦ explain how World War II affected Polish culture;

♦ describe how the fall of communism affected national identity and the economy in Poland.

 National Geography Standards

The following National Geography Standards are highlighted in this section: 1, 4, 5, 8, 9, 10, 11, 13, 14, 17, 18

Bellringer

Using the map on page 375, have students trace the Danube River from its source to its mouth.

LESSON PLAN

1. Focus Ask: **How has Poland's geography contributed to its history of foreign domination?** (no natural barriers to invasion from east or west; abundance of valuable farmland and mineral resources attract invaders)

2. Instruct State that most people who live in Poland are Roman Catholic. Discuss how life in this society might be different from life in a pluralistic society like that of the United States.

3. Close/Reteach Explain that Lech Walesa was voted out of office for mainly economic reasons. Discuss how recent changes in Poland's economy have affected the Polish people.

 "If you cannot prevent your enemies from swallowing you, at least prevent them from digesting you." This was the advice that French philosopher Jean-Jacques Rousseau offered to the Poles in the late 1700s.

For more than two centuries, Poles have followed Rousseau's advice. Although they have seen their nation "swallowed" many times, the Poles have refused to allow foreign nations to "digest" the Polish **national identity,** or sense of what characteristics make them a nation. For example, even though the former Soviet Union controlled Poland in the years following World War II, the Polish people never forgot their cultural heritage or gave up hope for reclaiming independence. During the 1980s they launched an independence movement to reclaim their national identity.

Physical Characteristics

One factor that has helped the Poles and many other nationalities retain their identity as a people is their attachment to the land. Most of Poland is covered by the North European Plain. Thick forests once covered the flat lands, but most of the trees were cut down long ago to create farmland.

Today, more than two thirds of Poland is open field.

Although much of Poland's soil is fertile, it tends to become poor and sandy and thus less suited for farming in the east and northeast. In the northeast, around the Baltic Sea, thousands of lakes break up the landscape. Poland has severe winters, and its mild summers are often rainy.

Poland has valuable industrial resources, too. In the Carpathian Mountain region of the south, large deposits of coal, sulfur, and copper have been found. However, Poland must depend upon other countries for two vital minerals—iron ore and petroleum.

World War II

Nearly ninety-five out of every one hundred people who live in Poland are Roman Catholic. But this was not always the case. Before World War II, Poland was a multiethnic nation. However, Nazi occupation and Soviet control changed this ethnic diversity.

The Holocaust Today, no more than 9,000 Jews live in all of Poland—a nation once home

◄ **Kraków, Poland** *(photo left)*

Chapter 19 ■ Section 1 **389**

TEACHING TIP
From a Master Teacher

Economic Issues When the Soviet Union controlled Central and Eastern Europe, it planned the region's economic development for its own benefit. Transportation and trade networks were oriented east. After the fall of communism, each nation struggled to create a market-focused economy with a reorientation westward, toward the European Union. Nations closest to the core of the European Union—Poland, the Czech Republic, Slovakia, Hungary, and Slovenia—have been more successful than those farther away.

Pacing Suggestions

 For 90-minute Blocks

You will want to vary activities.

- Separate the class into four groups, and assign each group one of these countries or regions: Poland; Czech and Slovak Republics and Hungary; Balkan Peninsula; Baltic States and Border Nations. Ask students to monitor the media for one week for stories involving the assigned region. Then ask each group to present a news update on its region to the class.

Vocabulary

Ghetto Ask students to look up the term *ghetto* in the Glossary and paraphrase the definition. Ask: **How did ghettos form in the United States?** (Ethnic minorities clustered in ghettos, often because they were unable to obtain housing elsewhere due to discrimination or high costs.)

Group Work

Activity: Comparing viewpoints

Purpose: Have each group research the 1980 Gdańsk shipyard strike and write a speech summarizing the viewpoint of one of the following: Solidarity leaders, shipyard managers, government officials, citizens, and reporters.

Roles: Group leader, researchers, speech writers

Result: Have groups read their speeches and compare viewpoints.

Asking Questions

Ask students to read the bold headings in the subsection Communist No More and to turn each of the headings into a question. Remind students that considering each heading in terms of *who, what, when, where, why,* and *how* can be helpful in forming questions. Then have them read the subsection to discover the answers to their questions.

Alternative Assessment

Introduce the Activity

Class Discussion Ask students to conduct research and prepare for a class discussion of which country in Central and Eastern Europe has the greatest potential for economic growth in the next 20 years, and which faces the greatest obstacles. Distribute the Class Discussion Rubric found on page 22 of the Alternative Assessment booklet for students' reference.

Answer to Map Caption

The Carpathian Mountain region has large deposits of coal, sulfur, and copper, which can help support industry.

Poland: PHYSICAL-POLITICAL

KEY

Elevation

Feet	Meters
14,000	4,270
7,000	2,135
1,500	457
700	213
(sea level) 0	0 (sea level)

★ National capital
• Major city

Lambert Azimuthal Equal-Area Projection

APPLYING THE GEOGRAPHIC THEMES

● **Movement** Despite the fact that much of Poland is flat and fertile, only 5 percent of its gross domestic product comes from agriculture. The rest of Poland's GDP comes from industry and services.

• *What part of Poland is most likely to support industrial activities?*

to more than 3 million Jews. Almost all of Poland's Jews were killed by the Nazis during World War II. The Nazis sealed off Jewish **ghettos** in Polish cities such as Warsaw. A ghetto is an area of a city where a minority is forced to live. When Jews in the Warsaw ghetto rebelled, the Nazis retaliated and slaughtered all the people remaining in the ghetto, then burned it to the ground.

The Nazis also built six of their infamous concentration camps, or prison camps, in Poland. Here, people from many nations suffered horribly or were brutally murdered;

GLOBAL CONNECTIONS

Global Trade Patterns Poland, one of the most polluted industrialized countries in the world, has devised a unique approach to the problem. Instead of repaying its foreign debt, an arrangement with lending countries allows Poland to spend the money on environmental cleanup.

but the majority of those who lost their lives were Poles. By the war's end, roughly 6 million Poles had been killed in concentration camps, about half of them Jews. In all, the Nazis massacred more than 6 million Jews from across Europe. This destruction of human life is known as the **Holocaust.** The word derives from a Greek word that means "a fire that burns something completely."

Fleeing Soviet Control

After the war, the former Soviet Union took over lands in eastern Poland. The Soviets then expanded Poland's western border into what had once been Germany. Millions of Poles fled from lands seized by the former Soviet Union. Germans living in lands given to Poland also fled. As a result, nearly everyone living in Poland today is Polish.

Communist No More

A Communist government backed by the Soviet Union took control in Poland in the late 1940s and banned opposition parties. The Communists never enjoyed widespread support of the Polish people despite their efforts to develop industry within the nation.

The Catholic Church Although the government tried to stamp out religion, the Roman Catholic Church continued to play an important role in the everyday lives of most people. It unified the Poles as it always had, even when there was no Polish nation. Catholic leaders worked out an uneasy compromise with the Communist government leaders that allowed churches to remain open.

Solidarity Solidarity is an independent Polish workers' labor union. It gained worldwide recognition in 1980 when its members staged a strike by shipyard workers in the Baltic port of Gdánsk. Led by Lech Walesa (LEK vah LEN sah), Solidarity pressed for economic and democratic reform.

RESOURCE DIRECTORY

Teaching Resources

Unit 5, Chapter 19
• Section 1 Quiz, p. 12
• Critical Thinking, p. 20
• Map/Graph Skills, p. 21

Spanish Resources
• Section 1 Quiz, p. 46

Mental Mapping booklet
• Outline Map 19, p. 72

Prentice Hall Assessment System

Alternative Assessment booklet
• Class Discussion Rubric, p. 22

Technology

World Geography Map and Photo Transparencies
• Central Europe and Northern Eurasia: Maps and Photos

Cultural Convergence

Economic Systems
Poland has worked hard to attract foreign investors as it moves from a command economy to a market economy. Often, this investment brings increased contact between cultures.

Human-Environment Interaction *How does this photograph show evidence of cultural convergence?*

Solidarity was outlawed by the government in 1981, but the movement did not die. In 1989, public opinion forced the first free elections in Poland in more than 40 years, and Solidarity candidates won a large majority of the votes. By the end of 1990, Walesa had been elected the nation's president.

A Troubled Economy The end of communism did not bring instant prosperity to Poland. Changing from a command economy to a market economy was difficult. It was also difficult to attract much-needed capital from foreign investors. With diminished government control, prices for food and consumer products rose rapidly at first, and many people became unemployed. By the mid-1990s, however, economic growth was up, and the rise in unemployment had slowed.

All the same, the Polish people were uncertain about the future. Electoral swings removed Walesa from office in 1995. Today, Poland's economy is still growing. However, there is a need for agricultural production to increase and for mining and heavy industry to become more competitive.

SECTION 1 ASSESSMENT

1. **Key Terms** Define **(a)** national identity, **(b)** ghetto, **(c)** Holocaust.

2. **Physical Characteristics (a)** Which physical characteristics of Poland encourage agriculture? **(b)** Which physical characteristics promote industry?

3. **Cultures** How did World War II change the ethnic diversity of Poland?

4. **Economic Systems** How has changing from a command economy under communism to a market economy under democracy affected Poland?

5. **Critical Thinking Identifying Main Ideas** What major part of their national identity have the Poles lost in the twentieth century?

Activity

Creating a Time Line Review the information in this section about the Solidarity movement. On your own, do some additional research. Then, create a time line to trace the rise and achievements of this historic movement. As you present your time line, explain how the Solidarity movement embodies the Polish national character.

TEST PREPARATION

Have students read the subsection A Troubled Economy on this page and then answer the question below.
When Poland adopted a market economy, consumers were affected by a —
  A rise in the price of food and the rate of unemployment
  B drop in the price of food and the rate of unemployment
  C dramatic increase in agricultural production
  D dramatic decrease in heavy industry

Answers to Section 1 Assessment

1. **(a)** national identity, p. 389 **(b)** ghetto, p. 390 **(c)** Holocaust, p. 390
2. **(a)** Poland's fertile plains encourage agriculture. **(b)** Its industrial resources such as coal, sulfur, and copper encourage industry.
3. During the war, the Nazis killed most of Poland's 3 million Jews.
4. After a period of adjustment, unemployment has slowed and the economy has grown.
5. They have lost Poland's Jewish population and culture.

Answer to Photo Caption

The sign advertises coke, a soft drink made by a company in the United States.

Teaching the Skill

Have students read the introductory paragraph. Ask them to think about instances when they have had to follow a specific process to accomplish a task, such as when cooking a particular dish or assembling an item from a store. Have volunteers share their experiences aloud. Ask: **What steps did you take to achieve your goal? What would have happened if you had done some of the steps out of order?** (You might not have achieved what you were trying to accomplish, or you might have come up with a very different result than you wanted.) Finally, complete the steps on this page with the students.

Answers to Learn the Skill

1. (a) the nuclear reactor **(b)** underground waste tanks
2. (a) dispersion to air, leaks to ground, direct irradiation, and deposited materials leached to groundwater or surface water **(b)** Crops become contaminated when contaminated rainwater falls on them.
3. (a) Deposited materials leach to groundwater, water irrigates grass, cows eat grass, and the milk supply becomes contaminated. **(b)** Deposited materials leach to surface water, fish live in polluted water, and people eat the fish. **(c)** No, a person may eat or drink contaminated food, milk, or water.

Answer to Practice the Skill

Check students' instructions for clarity and logic. Students' paragraphs or diagrams should be easy to read and should follow the steps outlined here.

Analyzing Processes

A process is the set of steps or stages that lead to some result. The instructions on the back of a cake mix outline the process for making the cake. The steps by which your body gets oxygen from the air and into the cells of your body is a process. A process can follow a direct path, or it can branch off in more than one direction. The diagram below shows a process by which nuclear contamination, or radiation, is spread throughout the environment.

Learn the Skill Use the following steps to learn how to analyze the steps in a process.

1 *Identify the process and look for clues to its beginning.* In the illustration below, rising steam and arrows lead away from the sources of nuclear contamination. Follow them back to where they originate. **(a)** *What is the source of the evaporated or solid material in suspension?* **(b)** *What is the source of groundwater contamination?*

2 *Determine the path, or order, of the process.* Follow the trail of contamination by following the direction in which the arrows are sweeping and where they are ending. **(a)** *What are four paths of contamination from underground waste tanks?* **(b)** *How do crops become contaminated?*

3 *Summarize the steps of the process in the order in which they occur.* Because a process can branch off into more than one path, follow each path independently. **(a)** *What are the steps it takes for nuclear contamination to get from a source into the milk supply?* **(b)** *How could nuclear contamination get into the fish that someone eats?* **(c)** *Would a person have to come in direct contact with nuclear waste in order to become contaminated? Explain.*

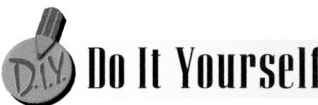

Practice the Skill You can use the steps of analyzing a process to provide step-by-step instructions on how to do something or to give information about how something happens. Choose something you know how to do or some process with which you are familiar, and then write a paragraph or create a diagram detailing the process.

Apply the Skill See Chapter 19 Review and Assessment.

Pathways of Contamination

2 The Czech and Slovak Republics, and Hungary

Reading Focus

- **How have political and economic conditions in the Czech Republic changed since the 1980s?**
- **What challenges face the two regions of Bohemia and Moravia?**
- **Why has Slovakia's economic transition been difficult?**
- **What effect did privatization have on Hungary's economy?**

Key Terms

velvet revolution   collective farm

privatization

Main Idea Formerly under Communist control, the Czech and Slovak Republics and Hungary face new challenges.

Cultures Street musicians in Prague celebrate the division of Czechoslovakia into two republics.

Objectives

Upon completion of Section 2, students should be able to:

- ◆ discuss changes in political and economic conditions in the Czech Republic since the 1980s;
- ◆ list the challenges facing the regions of Bohemia and Moravia;
- ◆ explain the economic issues Slovakia faces;
- ◆ describe how privatization has affected Hungary's economy.

 National Geography Standards

The following National Geography Standards are highlighted in this section: 1, 5, 6, 8, 9, 10, 11, 13, 14, 16, 17

 Bellringer

Explain that Czechoslovakia experienced a "velvet revolution" during the 1980s and 1990s. Ask students to explain what they think this term means. Explain that it refers to the occurrence of major political changes without bloodshed.

LESSON PLAN

1. Focus Direct students to look at the map on page 394 and ask them to describe the physical features of the Czech Republic, Slovakia, and Hungary.

2. Instruct Point out that many ethnic groups live in this region, including Czechs, Croats, and Slovaks. Although Communist governments after 1945 tried to restrain ethnic conflicts in the area, bitterness among these groups remained. Discuss what happened after the fall of communism when new groups vied for power.

3. Close/Reteach Draw a chart on the board with three columns: *Czech Republic, Slovakia,* and *Hungary.* Ask students to find comparisons among the three countries within the section.

I f you asked residents of the Czech Republic, Slovakia, and Hungary what region they live in, they would answer that they were part of Europe. But for more than forty years after the end of World War II, they were controlled by the former Soviet Union. As Communist control ended in the late 1980s, Czechs, Slovaks, and Hungarians reaffirmed their historical links with the West.

Although they share Western outlooks and ways, the three countries have crucial differences. Those differences will require them to use distinct approaches to address the problems they face as former Communist nations.

The Czech Republic

More than 10 million people live in the Czech Republic, a land about the size of South Carolina. It has few flat areas, except the plains that lie beside the Elbe River. The landscape is dominated by plateaus and mountains, and high ridges define its boundaries. Although the Czech people

in this rugged and mountainous land have been recognized as a separate ethnic group for almost a century, the nation known as the Czech Republic did not exist as an independent nation until 1993.

Path to Nationhood The Czech kings ruled an independent kingdom within the Holy Roman Empire into the fourteenth century. Then came nearly 400 years of rule by the Austrian Hapsburg monarchs. In 1918, during the final weeks of World War I, the victorious allies approved plans to create a new nation—Czechoslovakia. Brought together were Czech lands and Slovakia, which had been controlled by Hungary. Despite the multiethnic character of the new nation, over the next two decades it developed one of the most stable, democratic governments in the region.

Hitler used the fact that many Germans lived in northwestern Czechoslovakia as an excuse to invade the republic in the late 1930s. After Soviet forces expelled the Germans in 1945, they

Chapter 19 ▪ Section 2   **393**

Activity: Holding a multiethnic fair

Purpose: Separate the class into thirds and assign each third one of the following cultures: Hungarian, Czech, or Slovak. Tell each group to research the following three topics: (1) language and folk tales, (2) customs and clothing, (3) arts and foods. Each group should create a display booth for a multiethnic fair that includes information about all three topics for its country. Displays may include pictures, sample items, storytelling, demonstrations of arts and crafts, taped folk music, and so on.

Roles: Each group should have a leader for each topic. All of the group members should do research and contribute to the booth.

Results: When all the booths are finished, invite other classes to the fair.

Have students note the subsection head Economic Systems. Then ask them to note the term *privatization* in this subsection. As a class, discuss how the concept of privatization might be linked to the Czech Republic's economic system. Then have students read the section to see if their predictions were accurate.

Answer to Map Caption

Hungary is relatively flat and at a low elevation; the Czech Republic and Slovakia are more mountainous.

directed a Communist takeover. From 1948 to 1989, Communists controlled the nation.

The declining influence of the Soviet Union in the late 1980s spurred a **velvet revolution**—a revolution without bloodshed. It resulted in the election of a democratic parliament. Under the leadership of President Vaclav Havel (VAH tsluhv HAH vuhl), Czechoslovakia began a transition to a free society and a market-based economy.

Despite the new government's attempts at fairness and equality, Slovaks increasingly felt that the Czech-dominated government did not serve their interests adequately. As a result, Czech and Slovak leaders worked together on a velvet divorce, creating two separate countries in 1993—the Czech and Slovak republics.

Economic Systems The Czechs pursued their strategies for economic reforms. **Privatization** of many parts of the Czech economy began in the 1990s and continues today. Privatization is the process of selling government-owned industries and businesses to private owners who can run them more efficiently. The Czechs have sought membership in the European Union (EU), but this path has not been smooth. Activation in 2000 of the Temelin nuclear power plant near Austria and Germany led to border blockades by Austrian environmentalists. Whether or not it joins the EU, a strong industrial base and a skilled work force make continued Czech progress likely.

Two Regions

The western half of the Czech Republic is a region known as Bohemia. This region contains many of the nation's mines and industries. Coal, iron ore, copper, and lead are mined in the mountains of the north. Bohemia also has deposits of quartz, a substance used to make glass. The Czech capital city of Prague lies in central Bohemia. More than 100 church steeples rise above the rooftops—a visual reminder of the region's Roman Catholic heritage.

The eastern region of the Czech Republic is known as Moravia. Its industry dates back to the

Czech and Slovak Republics, and Hungary: PHYSICAL-POLITICAL

KEY

Elevation	
Feet	Meters
14,000	4,270
7,000	2,135
1,500	457
700	213
(sea level) 0	0 (sea level)

⊛ National capital
• Major city
▲ Mountain

Lambert Azimuthal Equal-Area Projection

APPLYING THE GEOGRAPHIC THEMES

● **Regions** Mountains and major plains and waterways make this part of Central Europe an attractive region, filled with economic opportunity.
• *How does Hungary differ from the Czech and Slovak republics?*

Teaching Resources
Mental Mapping booklet
• Outline Map 19, p. 72
Social Studies Skills Handbook
• Identifying Assumptions, p. 46

Technology
World Geography Map and Photo Transparencies
• Central Europe and Northern Eurasia: Maps and Photos

Slovakian Slopes

Physical Characteristics
The northern portion of Slovakia boasts a resort region in a part of the Carpathians known as the High Tatras. Much of the land is under the protection of national park status, but the region offers world-class skiing and other mountain recreations. It was even under consideration as the site for the 2002 Winter Olympics.
Regions *How might hosting the Olympics have helped Slovakia's economy?*

Industrial Revolution. Moravia's old coal and steel industries now face an uncertain future, because they are too inefficient to compete in the world market.

Among the gravest challenges facing Moravian industries, as well as those in Bohemia, is ending air and water pollution. Experts estimate that 56 percent of the nation's forests had been destroyed by acid rain and industrial pollution by 1993. And trees were not the only victims. One scientist observed: "If you go to the doctor with a sore throat, cough, or a headache, the [doctor] . . . will tell you, 'You must have opened a window last night.'"

Slovakia

Slovakia, also called the Slovak Republic, became an independent nation in 1993 when Czechoslovakia was peacefully divided. More than 5 million people live cradled within the arch formed by the Carpathian Mountains. Slovakia unfolds from rugged peaks in the north to the plains of the Danube in the south. Unlike the Czech Republic, Slovakia has a mixed economy of farming and manufacturing.

Farms Slovakia traditionally was an agricultural region. Fruits, vegetables, and grains are still grown near the Danube. Oats and potatoes are raised farther north in higher elevations.

The Communists ended private ownership of farms in 1948 and set up government-owned **collective farms.** On collective farms, workers were paid by the government and they shared the profits from their products. In Slovakia, as elsewhere in Eastern Europe, a major task of the present-day government is to find ways of returning land to private ownership.

Factories Manufacturing did not become important until the Communists assumed power after World War II. They built many new plants in the region. Because wages in factories were better than they were in rural areas, many Slovaks left the farms and migrated to cities like the capital, Bratislava.

Since independence, Slovaks have struggled to improve their economy. Some industries made successful transitions. A large arms factory that once made tanks now produces earth-moving equipment in cooperation with a German company. Smaller and mid-size firms have had more

Articles From
NATIONAL GEOGRAPHIC

The following article may be used to extend the content in this section.

Abercrombie, Thomas J., and James L. Stanfield, photographer. "Czechoslovakia: The Velvet Divorce." *National Geographic,* Vol. 184, No. 3 (Sept. 1993), pp. 2–37.

Czechs and Slovaks adjust to their new independence with hope and a strong desire for economic growth.

Budapest

Urbanization Straddling the Danube River is Hungary's capital city, Budapest. Budapest was once three separate cities: Obuda and Buda on the west bank and Pest on the east bank. Merged in the late 19th century, Budapest is now the largest city of Hungary and its industrial and commercial center. About one fifth of Hungary's people live there.

Place *To which ethnic group do most Hungarians belong?*

difficulty, however, especially in the poorer, eastern part of the country. Relations between Slovakia and Hungary have been strained because of concerns about the treatment of Hungarians living in Slovakia and Slovaks living in Hungary.

Hungary

Like Poland, Hungary's population is dominated by one ethnic group. About 90 percent of Hungarians are descended from the Magyars who settled the area in the late 800s.

The Roman Catholic faith and fierce patriotism have guided Hungarians throughout their history. They date the birth of their nation from the year 1000, the year the Pope crowned King Stephen. Several times since then the Hungarians have had to throw off foreign rulers. They even tried to oust a Soviet-backed Communist government in 1956, but their revolt was crushed. Not until 1990 were Hungarian voters able to freely elect their first non-Communist government in over forty years. But they considered this just one more step in their long history. A member of the new parliament declared, "The Magyar nation has been preserved!"

Hungary's Landscape Today, Hungary is about the size of the state of Indiana. The Danube River divides it into two parts. The eastern half consists of a broad plain known as the Great Alföld. This region's fertile soil has given Hungary the nickname the "breadbasket" of Europe.

The western half of Hungary has more hills. Because this region lies west of the Danube, it is known as Transdanubia, or "land across the Danube." The region is an area of plateaus, hills, and valleys. It contains large deposits of bauxite, coal, and iron ore that support Hungary's aluminum and steel industries.

Free Enterprise Like other nations in Eastern Europe, Hungary faced many difficulties

Environmental Change
Hundreds of Hungarians responded when an international tree-planting organization known as Global ReLeaf called for proposals to plant trees in Hungary. Grants were awarded for trees to be planted near a contested dam on the Danube River, at an apartment complex, in a children's park, and elsewhere.

Free Enterprise in Hungary

Economic Activities
Rather than raising his flock on a collective farm, this Hungarian goose farmer rents his barn and land and buys his geese from a cooperative. He raises the geese at his own expense, with the help of workers he pays, and then sells the meat and feathers back to the cooperative.

Place *How is this arrangement an example of free enterprise?*

in converting from Communist control to an economic system based on a free market. As old, inefficient industries that had been supported by the government struggled or failed outright, production dropped sharply. Unemployment was high, the government was badly in debt, and most people were getting poorer, not richer. To counter these problems, the government began an ambitious privatization program. Steady growth, declining inflation, and increased foreign investment all resulted. In 2000, the prime minister announced that average salaries and economic productivity had returned to 1990 levels.

As in Poland, former Communists have taken a hand in the new government. But Hungary's new government system appears to be stable and long-lasting. It should be well able to guide the nation of the Magyars into the twenty-first century.

SECTION 2 ASSESSMENT

1. **Key Terms** Define **(a)** velvet revolution, **(b)** privatization, **(c)** collective farm.

2. **Understanding the Past** How has the Czech Republic demonstrated a tradition of stability?

3. **Economic Systems** Give evidence that the two regions of the Czech Republic have been successful in changing to a free market economy.

4. **Economic Activities** How has farming in Slovakia changed since World War II?

5. **Government and Citizenship** What has the Hungarian government done to bring about an economic upturn?

6. **Critical Thinking Making Comparisons** How do the economies of the Czech Republic and Slovakia differ?

Activity

USING THE REGIONAL ATLAS

Review the Regional Atlas for Central Europe and Northern Eurasia and this section. Plan a series of summer work projects for American teenagers visiting Central Europe. Write one project for each country in the region. Base your project on what you know about the physical characteristics and economies of these nations.

CUSTOMIZE FOR...

Gifted and Talented

Creating a Chart Have students do research on unemployment rates and salary levels in Hungary since 1990, when the country began converting to a free enterprise system. Ask them to create a chart showing how salary levels and unemployment rates have changed. Have students share completed charts and a summary of their findings with the class.

BACKGROUND

Global Economy

Economic Transitions The change to a free market economy has not been easy for any of the Central and Eastern European countries. When Vaclav Havel became the first president of the Czech Republic, he observed, "Whole sectors of industry are producing things in which no one is interested. Our outdated economy is squandering energy, of which we are in short supply." Since then, changes have improved both the focus of the economy and its efficiency.

Answers to Section 2 Assessment

1. **(a)** velvet revolution, p. 394 **(b)** privatization, p. 394 **(c)** collective farm, p. 395

2. After World War I, Czechoslovakia developed a stable, democratic government. In the late 1980s, it cast off communism in a velvet revolution. In 1993, Czech and Slovak leaders peacefully separated the area into two countries.

3. Many businesses and industries have been privatized.

4. Under Soviet rule, private farms were replaced with collective farms. Since the breakup of the Soviet Union, Slovakia's government has been working to return farmland to private ownership.

5. It has begun an ambitious program of privatization.

6. The economy of the Czech Republic is based on industry, while the economy of Slovakia is based on farming and manufacturing.

Activity Rubrics Share rubrics with students before they begin.
Attempted The plan is not attempted.
Minimal The plan addresses some physical characteristics and economic issues, but it includes mechanical and factual errors.
Adequate The plan incorporates physical characteristics and economic issues from each country and is well organized.
Exemplary The plan is well conceived and shows a thorough understanding of the region.

Answer to Photo Caption

The farmer invests his own money and sells his product.

Objectives

Upon completion of Section 3, students should be able to:

◆ summarize how Romania's economy has changed since the end of Communist rule;

◆ identify the signs of Bulgaria's economic growth;

◆ describe the effects of foreign investment on Albania;

◆ explain why internal tensions challenge the people of the Balkan nations.

 National Geography Standards

The following National Geography Standards are highlighted in this section: 1, 4, 5, 8, 9, 10, 11, 13, 16, 17

 Bellringer

Note that the roots of many of the ethnic conflicts in the Balkans today are more than 100 years old. Ask: **What events and patterns within the United States have created ongoing ethnic conflict?** (Civil War, slavery, reactions to immigration) Compare these conflicts with the conflicts in the Balkans.

LESSON PLAN

1. Focus Ask students to imagine that they are members of a minority group in a newly independent nation. The official language is not their native language. Members of their ethnic group who live in a different region attack the nation. Explain that this happened in Yugoslavia.

2. Instruct Ask students to turn to the list of Reading Focus questions at the beginning of the section. As they read the section, have them write answers to each question.

3. Close/Reteach Ask: **How has the physical geography of the Balkans contributed to the region's ethnic diversity?** (Mountains isolated communities; ethnic groups from other regions met in its central location.)

3 The Balkan Peninsula

Reading Focus

- **How have Romania's economic activities changed since the end of Communist rule?**
- **What signs of economic growth can be seen in Bulgaria?**
- **How have foreign nations been involved in Albanian development?**
- **Why do internal tensions continue to challenge the people of the Balkan nations?**

Key Terms

balkanize

entrepreneur

multiplier effect

Main Idea	The geography of the Balkans has isolated its people into small and often hostile political and ethnic groups.

Economic Activities These Romanian workers are part of the nation's economic growth.

I n 1918, a new term crept into the English language: **balkanize.** The word *balkanize* means "to break up into small, mutually hostile political units." It is what took place in the Balkans after World War I. The term grew out of the complex cultural patterns and political geography of the Balkan Peninsula.

Perhaps the one thing that the Balkan nations share is their historical experience. The peoples of this region have all known the ordeal of foreign domination. For 500 years they were ruled by the Turks, whose influence can be seen there to this day.

Today, the Balkan Peninsula is divided into many small nations. Most of them fell under Communist control after 1948, but anti-Communist revolutions overturned the governments of those states in the late 1980s and early 1990s. Internal strife and conflict between nations have nevertheless continued to affect the region.

Romania

Nearly 23 million people live in Romania. Most belong to the Romanian ethnic group. They speak a language derived from Latin, and most people practice the Eastern Orthodox faith.

Romania possesses broad plains with fertile soils along the Danube River. Farther north, the foothills of the Carpathian Mountains hold many minerals. Despite these natural resources, the Romanian people have been impoverished in recent decades.

Romania's first Communist leader oversaw a Soviet-style industrialization. The second leader, Nicolae Ceausescu (NIH kah lie chow CHESS koo), gradually led the nation to economic chaos. Energy was so scarce that television aired only two hours each night. In 1989 Ceausescu was forced from office and executed. Ineffective governments in the 1990s led the economy to deteriorate even

---

RESOURCE DIRECTORY

Teaching Resources

Unit 5, Chapter 19
- Section 3 Guided Reading and Review, p. 15

Guide to the Essentials (English/Spanish)
- Section Summary, Chapter 19, Section 3

Mental Mapping booklet
- Outline Map 19, p. 72
- Unit 5 Checklist, p. 67

Technology

Guided Reading Audiotapes (English/Spanish), Chapter 19, Section 3

Section Reading Support Transparencies, Chapter 19, Section 3

World Geography Map and Photo Transparencies
- Central Europe and Northern Eurasia: Maps and Photos

Book on CD, Chapter 19

Social Studies Skills Tutor CD-ROM

Companion Web site, www.phschool.com
- Chapter 19 Activities

more, despite promises of economic reform. Experts predicted that it would be 2025 before Romania could again see an economy even as good as the terrible economy of 1989.

One ray of hope shone in Romania's economic nightmare, however. An American soft drink maker spent $150 million in Romania to build up its operations there. Its investment helped about 25,000 small shops start or stay in business, selling soft drinks. Some **entrepreneurs**—go-getter individuals who start and build businesses—have made small fortunes selling soft drinks in Romania. Through the **multiplier effect,** eleven new jobs have been added to Romania's economy for each job that the soft drink company created. The multiplier effect is the effect an investment has in multiplying related jobs throughout an economy. For instance, Romanian plastics makers have added jobs to handle the new demand for soft drink bottles, and printers have added jobs to print labels. Observers hope that Western investment, and the multiplier effect, will bring dramatic changes not just to Romania, but to all of Eastern Europe.

Bulgaria

Bulgaria is located south of the Danube from Romania. It enjoys the fertile soils of the Danube Plains and the plains south of the Balkan Mountains. Summers are warm, and winters along the Black Sea coast are mild. Because of these physical characteristics, Bulgaria is known as the garden of Eastern Europe.

The Bulgarians are a Slavic people. The Russians, also largely a Slavic people, have long been strong supporters of native Bulgarians. Because of this fact, many Bulgarians welcomed Soviet control after World War II.

Bulgaria turned away from strict communism in the early 1990s. It now has a democratic government, although some former Communists still are politically active. Like other nations in the region, Bulgaria's economy went into a tailspin in the first years of freedom. However, by the late 1990s, it found new markets for its goods in Western countries. Foreign companies made investments. Millions of tourists came to the Black Sea resorts, bringing with them desperately

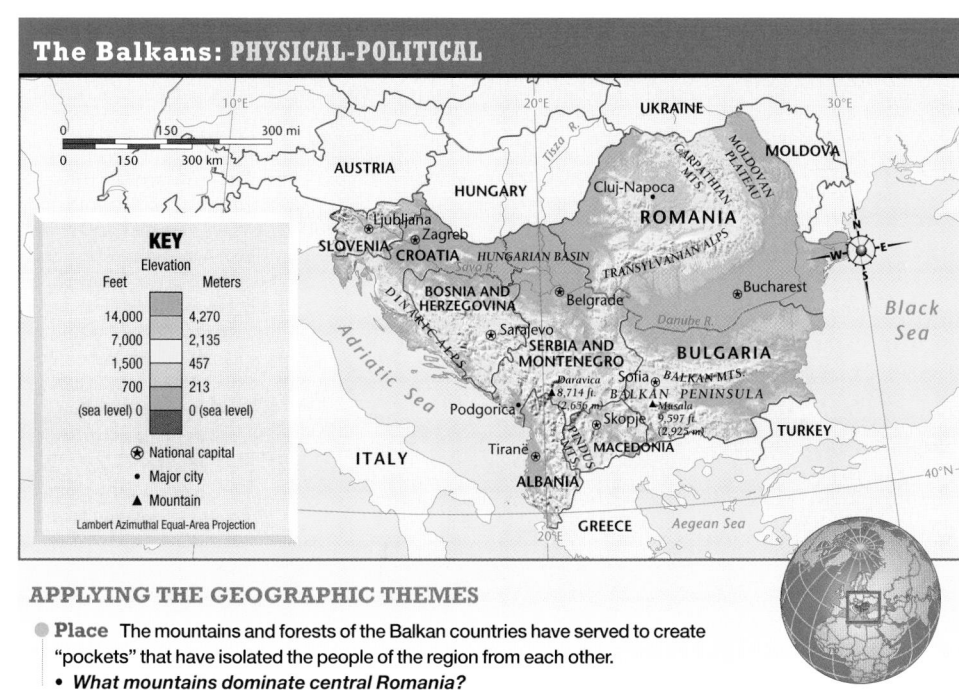

The Balkans: PHYSICAL-POLITICAL

APPLYING THE GEOGRAPHIC THEMES

● **Place** The mountains and forests of the Balkan countries have served to create "pockets" that have isolated the people of the region from each other.
• *What mountains dominate central Romania?*

BACKGROUND

Word Origin

Albania Albania takes its name from the Albanos, a group of people who originally inhabited the region. Albanians, however, prefer to call their country Shqipëri (shkyee-puh-REE), or "Country of the Eagle," a name the country has had since the 1500s.

needed foreign currency. Inflation levels dropped as the country's currency was stabilized.

Albania

Tucked beside the Adriatic Sea in the southwestern part of the Balkan Peninsula is Albania. About 3.5 million people live in this mountainous nation. Known for decades as "Europe's hermit," Albania is now rebuilding links with a number of other nations.

As a people living in a small nation with a distinctive culture, Albanians have often felt threatened by their neighbors. This fear continued after World War II, when its Communist leaders turned away from both the former Soviet Union and China. This isolation left Albania one of the poorest nations in Europe.

Since the end of communism in the 1990s, Albania has received billions of dollars from foreign nations and from Albanians who have relocated to live in other countries. Because most Albanians earn less than $100 a month, Italian and Greek manufacturers have built factories in Albania in order to take advantage of the low wages. Internal political conflicts slowed growth, however, as did the influx of refugees from neighboring Kosovo in 1999.

Other Balkan Nations

The most complex new nation created at the end of World War I was Yugoslavia. The name meant "the land of the southern Slavs." But a common Slavic heritage did not produce unity. Six separate republics made up the unsteady nation, which after World War II was held together only by strict Communist rule. Within these republics, some two dozen independent ethnic groups lived, either intermixed or in jigsaw-puzzle ethnic regions.

After Communist control ended in the late 1980s, internal tensions increased. First, Slovenia grew restless. It was the most wealthy republic and was afraid the other Yugoslavian republics would drag it down into poverty. Soon Croatia, too, grew nervous about its future, fearing that the wealth it gained from the tourist business on its long Mediterranean coastline would be eaten up by other regions. Both Slovenia and Croatia declared themselves independent in 1991. They were quickly followed by Macedonia, and then, in 1992, by Bosnia-Herzegovina (sometimes called simply Bosnia). All that was left of Yugoslavia were the republics of Serbia and Montenegro.

Conflicts flared within and between the new nations. In Bosnia-Herzegovina, the Muslims,

Bread Distribution

Economic Activities The collapse of communism in Albania created near-chaos in one of Europe's poorest countries. The bread in this photograph is distributed from behind bars in an attempt to maintain order. Some Albanians have been killed in bread riots that erupt as hungry crowds clamor for food.

Movement *How might an end to isolation help Albania's economy?*

400   Chapter 19 ▪ Central and Eastern Europe

Civil War in the Balkans

Cooperation and Conflict As Yugoslavia broke into separate republics, warfare destroyed vast quantities of property and cost hundreds of thousands of lives. These homes in Dubrovnik were destroyed during the war.

Human-Environment Interaction *How did economic concerns contribute to civil war in the Balkans?*

ACTIVITY
Group Work

Activity: Making a poster

Purpose: Arrange the class in groups of three. Assign each group one of these countries: Slovenia, Croatia, Serbia and Montenegro, Bosnia and Herzegovina, Macedonia, Albania, Bulgaria, Romania.

Roles: One member of each group should research its region's interesting cultural and physical characteristics, one its daily life and local holidays, and another the historical or current events in the region.

Result: Ask each group to display the results of its research on a poster including drawings, time lines, and photographs.

ethnic Croats, and ethnic Serbs battled for power for four years. As a result, an estimated 250,000 people lost their lives and 2 million were driven from their homes. At the same time, "ethnic cleansing" entered the world's vocabulary. Serbs used the term to label the process of driving other ethnic groups out of regions captured by Serbs. In practice, it meant mass murder and terror.

In 1995, a peace treaty enforced by NATO troops divided Bosnia along ethnic lines. Another round of ethnic cleansing began in 1999, however, when Serbia tried to force ethnic Albanians out of Kosovo. NATO forces intervened with an airborne bombing campaign that devastated much of Serbia.

Serbia and Montenegro After the other republics broke away and formed independent nations, Serbia and Montenegro kept the name Yugoslavia for their own union. In 2003, the government was changed into a loose federation and the Yugoslav name was dropped. In 2006, residents in each republic are expected to be able to vote on full independence.

The physical geography of this area includes the rugged peaks of Montenegro and the fertile plains of the Danube valley in Serbia. About 6.5 million of the 10.6 million people in these republics are Serbs. Another 2 million Serbs live in neighboring republics.

The breakup of Yugoslavia and the wars that followed resulted in economic disaster for Serbia and Montenegro. By 2000, the gross domestic product was only half as high as it had been in 1990. Unemployment soared to more than 50 percent. The economy slowly recovered in the early 2000s, but by 2002, unemployment was still nearly 30 percent.

Croatia More than three quarters of the nearly 5 million people who live in Croatia are ethnic Croats. Croats descended from the same early Slavic people as the Serbs, and the spoken languages of the two groups are nearly identical. Serbs practice Eastern Orthodoxy and use the Cyrillic alphabet, whereas most Croats are Roman Catholics and use the

GLOBAL CONNECTIONS

Cooperation and Conflict By the beginning of 2000, about 830,000 Bosnians still were displaced within their own country. In addition, the nation was hosting approximately 40,000 ethnic Serbs from Croatia and 20,000 refugees from Yugoslavia. About 300,000 Bosnians remained refugees in other countries.

BACKGROUND
Daily Life

A Taste of Croatia Travelers visiting Croatia may sample the country's distinct cuisine, which has Austrian and Hungarian influences. A variety of local specialties are offered in Croatia, including fried cheese, chicken à la Backa (a dish made with tomatoes, paprika, and onions), Zagreb veal cutlet, and *gibanica,* a layered cheese pastry.

BACKGROUND
History

Written Language In the A.D. 860s, a Christian missionary named Cyril and his brother Methodius preached among the Slavs. In order to translate the Bible into a language the Slavs could understand, they created an alphabet based on Greek and Hebrew characters. The alphabet became known as the Cyrillic alphabet, versions of which are still used in Belarus, Bulgaria, Russia, and Ukraine.

Answer to Photo Caption

Slovenia and Croatia, the two wealthiest Yugoslav republics, feared the other republics would drag down their economies and declared themselves independent in 1991. Soon after, other republics broke away.

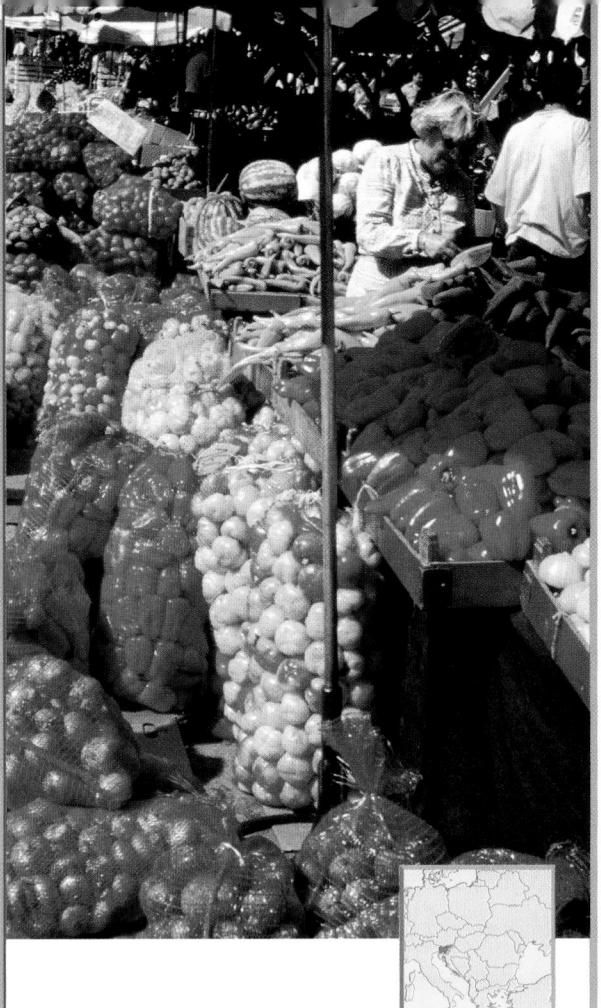

Slovenian Market

Economic Activities Shoppers examine produce at an open-air market in Ljubljana, Slovenia. A solid industrial base has helped the Slovenian economy recover from civil war.

Human-Environment Interaction *How does this photograph suggest that Slovenia's economy continues to grow?*

Latin alphabet. These differences have been heightened by frequent conflicts between Serbs and Croats.

After Croatia declared its independence, Serbs within its borders fought to gain their own independence or to link themselves with Serbia. Although fighting has tapered off, political and economic uncertainty continues.

Slovenia Most of the 2 million residents of Slovenia are Slovenes, one of the Slavic peoples. This nation in the Julian Alps has long maintained close ties with Western European nations. Industrial development took place earlier in Slovenia than in other parts of the Balkan Peninsula. Because of its solid industrial base, Slovenia was expected to recover quickly from the problems brought by war and independence.

Bosnia and Herzegovina The former Yugoslav republic of Bosnia and Herzegovina declared itself independent in 1991, but its initial prospects were not bright. Its population was a complex mix. Of every six residents, two were Serbs, one was a Croat, and the other three called themselves Bosniaks and practiced Islam.

Long-standing hostilities among different groups in Bosnia and Herzegovina erupted into war when Communist control ended. After vicious fighting and many failed efforts to end the strife, a 1995 peace treaty divided the nation into two roughly equal parts: one controlled by Bosniaks and Croats and the other controlled by Bosnian Serbs.

Civil war made the impoverished nation even poorer. Many industrial plants were destroyed during the war, and although production has started to rebound, the nation's gross domestic product is still far below its 1990 level.

Bosnia and Herzegovina has abundant mineral resources, including iron ore and lead. Considerable time and investments, however, are still needed to rebuild these industries.

Macedonia While other former Yugoslav republics were erupting into conflict, Macedonia remained relatively quiet. Still, tensions with neighboring Greece and Albania complicated trade patterns and hampered the Macedonian economy. In 2001, conflict flared among ethnic groups within Macedonia. Issues of culture and national identity, particularly language, were at the center of the dispute. International mediators proposed that Macedonian be one official language, as well as any language spoken by at least 20 percent of the population. While ethnic Albanians in Macedonia believed that this would provide them with greater political power and equality, Macedonians felt that a single official language would better ensure national unity.

402   Chapter 19 ▪ Central and Eastern Europe

Keeping the Peace

Government and Citizenship In 1993 the United Nations sent a peace-keeping force to Macedonia in order to shield it from its warring neighbors.

Movement *Which Balkan nations might be a threat to Macedonian independence?*

Kosovo Although Kosovo is officially a province of Serbia, more than three out of four residents of Kosovo were Albanian when Yugoslavia dissolved in 1991. However, Serbia was unwilling to grant Kosovo independence, and its armed forces began a campaign to drive Albanians from the region.

In response, the Kosovo Liberation Army waged guerrilla war against the Serbs. NATO forces finally launched a powerful air campaign to drive Serbian forces from the region. Despite massive aid, recovery was slow, and a 2002 study reported that more than half of all Kosovans still lived in poverty.

SECTION 3 ASSESSMENT

1. **Key Terms** Define **(a)** balkanize, **(b)** entrepreneur, **(c)** multiplier effect.

2. **Economic Systems** How did Communist rule change Romania's economy?

3. **Global Trade Patterns** How have foreign trade and investment affected the Bulgarian economy? Provide examples from the text.

4. **Economic Activities (a)** What nations have established factories in Albania? **(b)** How might location have been a factor in this development?

5. **Cooperation and Conflict** How has the concept of "ethnic cleansing" created challenges for some Balkan nations?

6. **Critical Thinking Making Generalizations** How do you think people in the Balkan nations feel about the change from Communist rule? Give three facts to support your answer.

Activity

Take It to the NET

Writing an Oral Report Use Internet resources to research current information about a country or an ethnic group discussed in this section. Share your findings in a brief oral presentation. Visit the World Geography section of **www.phschool.com** for help in completing this activity.

Chapter 19 ▪ Section 3   403

Articles From
NATIONAL GEOGRAPHIC

The following article may be used to extend the content in this section.

Vesilind, Priit J., and Sarah Leen, photographer. "Macedonia: Caught in the Middle." *National Geographic*, Vol. 189, No. 3 (Mar. 1996), pp. 118–139.

The former Yugoslav republic of Macedonia struggles for national unity.

Answers to Section 3 Assessment

1. (a) balkanize, p. 398 **(b)** entrepreneur, p. 399 **(c)** multiplier effect, p. 399

2. Under Communist leaders, Soviet-style industrialization was imposed, and economic chaos gradually set in.

3. Foreign nations have provided Bulgaria with investment money and with markets for goods. Foreign tourists bring currency into the country.

4. (a) Greece and Italy **(b)** The countries are neighbors. Albania shares a border with Greece and is a short distance across the Adriatic Sea from Italy.

5. The term applies most directly to the situation in Bosnia and Herzegovina, where Serbs have tried to drive away non-Serbs, and in Kosovo, where Serbs have tried to drive away ethnic Albanians. The diverse cultural pattern in the Balkans provides fuel for ethnic strife throughout the region.

6. Answers may vary. Students may cite the existence of new social freedoms and new democratic and economic opportunities on the one hand, and new economic difficulties on the other in support of their answers.

Activity Rubrics Share rubrics with students before they make their oral presentations.

Attempted The presentation is incomplete.

Minimal The presentation contains factual errors, includes little current information, and is poorly delivered.

Adequate The presentation contains no factual errors, includes all of the most important current information, and is well delivered.

Exemplary The presentation contains no factual errors and is comprehensive, detailed, well organized, and well delivered.

Answer to Photo Caption

Possible answers: Greece, Albania, and Serbia

Chapter 19 ▪ Section 3   403

People and Geography

pp. 404–405

Objectives

Upon completion of this feature, students should be able to:

◆ identify factors that can lead to conflicts over territorial borders;

◆ identify religious and cultural groups in the Balkan Peninsula;

◆ explain why boundaries changed in the Balkans;

◆ describe the effects of changing boundaries.

National Geography Standards

The following National Geography Standards are highlighted in this feature: 1, 3, 4, 5, 6, 9, 10, 12, 13, 17

Bellringer

Have students think about the history of the United States. Ask: **When has there been competition in the United States over control of territory?** (French and Indian War; American Revolution; War of 1812; wars with Indians; Mexican War) **Why do students think that it has often resulted in war?** (People want to hold on to what they have.)

··

LESSON PLAN

1. Focus Have students read Religious and Ethnic Divisions on this page. Ask: **How did divisions in early Christianity affect the development of the Balkan Peninsula?** (The western part became Roman Catholic; the eastern part became Orthodox. As other groups arrived, they adopted one religion or the other.) **What other ethnic and religious groups came to the Balkans?** (Over time, Bulgars, Slavs, and Magyars arrived. In the 600s, Muslim groups also came.)

2. Instruct As students read the text, have them create an annotated time line of events in the Balkans. When they have completed it, have them write a generalization about the history of the region.

Answer to Map Caption

Slavs (Croats, Serbs), Bulgars, Magyars

404 Chapter 19

People and Geography

Changing Boundaries and the Balkan Peninsula

Competition for Territory

Some types of regions are defined by their physical characteristics. Others are defined by people or groups who seek to control an area and define its boundaries. These attempts at control can lead to competition. Sometimes this competition is solved peacefully, but often territorial disputes lead to violent conflict.

People find many motives for this conflict. Valuable resources or vital trade routes can lead people to fight for economic control of a region. Different political philosophies may lead groups to compete for power. Religious or ethnic differences also can bring cultures into conflict. Migration and changes in patterns of settlement often play a role as well. The Balkan Peninsula in southeastern Europe is one region where most, if not all, of these factors have led to conflict over territorial borders. For thousands of years the peninsula has been an unstable region of divided loyalties, frequent conflict, and changing boundaries.

Balkan Peninsula, c. 1370

An Ethnic Patchwork
What different nationalities established small states in the Balkan Peninsula?

Religious and Ethnic Divisions

The Balkan Peninsula was once part of the ancient Roman Empire. Before the Empire fell, it split into two halves. One part of the Balkan Peninsula was in the Eastern Empire, later called the Byzantine Empire for its capital in Byzantium. The other part of the peninsula was part of the Western Empire, where Rome remained the imperial capital.

Christianity, the official religion of the later Roman Empire, was also divided. The Greek-speaking Orthodox Church developed in the east while the Latin-speaking Roman Catholic Church dominated the west.

Over several centuries, Slavs, Bulgars, Magyars, and other ethnic groups moved into southeastern Europe. They established a number of states and adopted different religions. For example, Croats became Roman Catholic whereas Serbs became Orthodox. Following the rise of Islam in the 600s, Muslim groups also moved into the Balkan Peninsula and gained control of territory.

RESOURCE DIRECTORY

Teaching Resources

Simulations, Games, and Lab Activities
• Resolving a Land Dispute, pp. 49–57

Technology

World Geography Map and Photo Transparencies
• Central Europe and Northern Eurasia: Political

Rise and Fall of Empires

By the late 1400s, Muslim Turks of the Ottoman Empire ruled the Balkan Peninsula. To the north was the Austro-Hungarian Empire and the Russian Empire. For hundreds of years the borders between these three empires shifted back and forth. Meanwhile, ethnic and religious differences led to hatred and conflict. By the late 1800s, all three empires showed signs of struggle and decline. Serbs, Greeks, Romanians, and Bulgars all gained independence. In the early 1900s, several small wars broke out in the Balkan Peninsula. The peninsula's explosiveness earned the region a nickname: "the powder keg of Europe." In 1914, a Serb assassinated Archduke Francis Ferdinand of Austria-Hungary, starting a chain of events that led to World War I and the fall of all three empires.

Imperial Rivalry
In the 1800s, what three empires competed for power in the Balkan Peninsula?

Balkan Peninsula, 1885

Violent Conflict Continues

After the war, the victorious Allied nations established new countries in Europe. One of these was the Kingdom of the Serbs, Croats, and Slovenes, later called Yugoslavia. The monarch of the new multinational country was the king of Serbia. In the 1920s, King Alexander tried to unite the nationalities by forcing them all to use one language, Serbo-Croatian. He also created new political boundaries that ignored the ethnic groups' historical territories. Alexander's actions worsened relations between the groups. In 1934, the king was assassinated by a Macedonian from Bulgaria who was supported by Croatian revolutionaries. As you have learned, conflict and changing boundaries are still a part of life in the Balkans today.

Multinational State
How did the creation of Yugoslavia lead to conflict in the Balkan Peninsula?

Balkan Peninsula, 1920

ASSESSMENT: Analyzing Causes and Effects

1. **Identify the Issue** What is the central issue whose causes and effects can be determined?

2. **Identify Possible Causes** Why have boundaries changed so often in southeastern Europe?

3. **Identify Possible Effects** What are some of the effects of these changing boundaries?

4. **Make Generalizations** In general, what forces usually break multinational states or empires into smaller states?

5. **Make Recommendations** (a) What are some ways that nations or individuals might approach problems created by national or ethnic tensions? (b) What are the advantages or disadvantages of these possible approaches?

3. Close/Reteach Review the maps on this page and the previous page. Then have students look at a current map of the region and identify how it is different from the Balkans in 1920. (Slovania, Croatia, and Bosnia-Herzegovina are broken away from Yugoslavia.) Have students describe why they think these changes have continued to occur.

ACTIVITY

Enrichment

Recent Balkan Conflicts Have students research recent conflicts in the Balkan Peninsula and explain how and why the boundaries have changed since 1980. Encourage them to use what they learned about the region to predict whether the boundaries could change again. Have them explain their answer. (Visual/Spatial; Verbal/Linguistic)

Answers to Assessment

1. the changing boundaries of the Balkan Peninsula

2. desire for resources and trade routes, different political philosophies, religious and ethnic differences, migration and changing patterns of settlement

3. divided loyalties, frequent conflict, and changing boundaries

4. rivalry for power

5. Possible answers: **(a)** promote tolerance, treat each group fairly, provide economic opportunities **(b)** Each of these approaches would lower tension, but they require a lot of cooperation, which is hard to achieve.

Answers to Map Captions

Ottoman Empire, Austro-Hungarian Empire, and Russian Empire

The leader created new political boundaries that ignored ethnic groups' historical boundaries. He tried to force everyone to use one language.

Objectives

Upon completion of Section 4, students should be able to:

◆ describe how location has affected the history and economies of the Baltic states;

◆ explain why many Ukrainians were eager to break free of foreign domination;

◆ describe the link between Belarus and Russia and the link between Moldova and Romania.

National Geography Standards

The following National Geography Standards are highlighted in this section: 1, 4, 5, 6, 8, 9, 10, 11, 13, 14, 16, 17, 18

Bellringer

Ask students to think about the advantages and disadvantages that would result if their state decided to become an independent, separate nation. Have students share their ideas with the class. Point out that the nations included in this section broke away from the former Soviet Union in 1991.

LESSON PLAN

1. Focus Ask students to locate the Baltic states, Ukraine, Belarus, and Moldova on the map on the opposite page. Ask students to speculate about similarities and differences among these nations.

2. Instruct Begin a chart on the board with the following headings: *Baltic States* and *Border Nations.* Ask volunteers to write the names of the republics under the appropriate headings. Based on this chapter, ask students to add information about each of the republics, including location and concerns for the future.

3. Close/Reteach Ask each student to list the republics in the order of his or her preference for visiting them. Ask volunteers to explain their lists.

---

4 Baltic States and Border Nations

Reading Focus

• How has location affected the history and economies of the Baltic states of Latvia, Lithuania, and Estonia?

• Why were many Ukrainians eager to break free of foreign domination?

• How is Belarus closely linked with Russia, and how is Moldova closely linked with Romania?

Key Terms

annex

diversify

Main Idea The Baltic states and border nations have established new international relations in the years since the fall of the Soviet Union.

Understanding the Past Riga, the capital of Latvia, has been an important port since the 1100s.

So far in this chapter, you have learned about countries of Central and Eastern Europe that were dominated by the Soviet Union from the late 1940s through the 1980s. Technically, however, these countries were independent. In contrast, to their east lay European states that officially were republics within the Soviet Union until that nation broke apart in 1991. Three of these states are the Baltic Sea nations of Lithuania, Latvia, and Estonia. To the south of these three countries are Belarus, Ukraine, and Moldova, which together form a border region between European Russia and the rest of Europe.

The Baltic States

The small nations of Lithuania, Latvia, and Estonia are tucked along the eastern edge of the Baltic Sea. The three Baltic states share a similar flat terrain, covered with marshy lowlands and fertile low plains. In Estonia, the average elevation is only 164 feet (50 m). The region's humid continental climate is influenced by the air that comes off the Baltic Sea. Generally, the region experiences wet, moderate winters and summers.

The combined populations of the three Baltic states total only about 8 million. Lithuanians and Latvians speak similar languages. Estonians, however, speak a distinctive non–Indo-European tongue closely related to Finnish. Most Estonians and Latvians are Lutheran, whereas the majority of Lithuanians are Roman Catholic. Russians make up a significant percentage of the populations of both Latvia and Estonia.

Effects of Location Historically, location has had an important effect on all three Baltic nations. They have benefited from their access to the sea and their location along major

---

trade routes. However, at various times, they have suffered from their location between powerful states such as Sweden, Austria, Germany, and Russia. For centuries, invading armies battled for control of the region. As a result, the Baltic states have been subject to frequent conquests by other powers.

The former Soviet Union was the most recent foreign power to rule the Baltic states. Lithuania, Latvia, and Estonia had gained their independence after World War I. However, Soviet forces invaded the three states in 1939; and those states were soon **annexed,** or formally added, to the Soviet Union.

Soviet Republics Under Soviet rule, life in the Baltic republics was harsh. The Soviet Union

took advantage of their strategic location on the Baltic Sea by establishing naval bases in all three Baltic nations. Tens of thousands of people were expelled from their homelands. Nationalist symbols were removed from public view. Resistance, whether violent or not, was forcefully put down.

The breakup of the Soviet Union brought independence to the Baltic nations in 1991. A number of challenges and opportunities came with that independence.

Challenges and Opportunities
Ethnic diversity is one of the key challenges for the Baltic states. In Estonia and Latvia there are large Russian minorities. In fact, Latvians constitute little more than half the population of Latvia. As

Baltic States and Border Nations: PHYSICAL-POLITICAL

KEY

Elevation

Feet		Meters
14,000		4,270
7,000		2,135
1,500		457
700		213
(sea level) 0		0 (sea level)

✴ National capital
• Major city
▲ Mountain
Marshlands

Lambert Azimuthal Equal-Area Projection

APPLYING THE GEOGRAPHIC THEMES

● **Location** The Baltic states and border nations stretch from the Baltic Sea to the Black Sea.
• *What advantage does Ukraine have over Moldova and Belarus in terms of trade?*

Enrichment

Radio Tour Ask students to choose one nation from this section. Have them use tape recorders to prepare a three-minute radio segment describing the government, economy, particular problems, and daily lives of citizens in that nation. Programs should include "interviews" with officials and ordinary citizens. Programs may also include music and sound effects. (Verbal/Linguistic)

READING STRATEGY

Summarizing Main Ideas

Tell students to read the subsection Soviet Republics. As they read, have them list three important facts from the text. Then ask students to use their lists to help determine the main idea of this section. Call on volunteers to read their lists and main ideas to the class. If main ideas vary, lead a class discussion to identify the correct main idea.

Answer to Map Caption

Ukraine has access to the Black Sea, while Moldova and Belarus are landlocked.

a result, many Latvians favor measures that would limit the extent of Russian influence in the country. Such measures include policies that would restrict the use of the Russian language and make it difficult for Russians to become citizens of Latvia.

All three Baltic states have transformed their economies since achieving independence from the Soviet Union. They have worked to privatize industries that were formerly operated by the government. They have invited foreign investment and have sought increased trade with nations other than Russia. Lithuania, Latvia, and Estonia each applied for membership in the European Union.

Despite their small size and limited natural resources, the Baltic states have taken successful steps to expand and **diversify,** or increase the variety of, their industries. In Estonia, the majority of the people are involved in services and industries such as mining, shipbuilding, and manufacturing. Primarily agricultural before 1940, Lithuania has developed considerable industry, including food processing, shipbuilding, and the manufacture of machinery. Latvia's industries are extremely diversified. They include the production of motor vehicles, pharmaceuticals, and electrical equipment.

Ukraine

According to an old proverb, "Moscow is the heart of Russia; St. Petersburg, its head; but Kiev, its mother." Kiev, the current capital of Ukraine (yoo KRAYN), was where the first Russian state began more than 1,000 years ago. Kievan traders carried fur, honey, and farm products to the busy markets of Constantinople, the capital of the Byzantine Empire.

Foreign Domination By the 1200s, Russian power moved northeast to Moscow and foreign powers fought for control of the region. For nearly five centuries, the region was controlled by foreign powers—the Mongols, then Lithuania, then Poland. The Poles tried to establish Roman Catholicism, but Ukrainians remained Orthodox.

By the 1700s, Russian rulers established authority over the region. The Russians called the region *Ukraine*, meaning "the border." Attempts to impose the Russian language on Ukrainians were unsuccessful, but nearly four centuries of Russian rule developed strong links between the nations. Historically, Ukrainians sometimes called their country *Malaya Russiya*, or "Little Russia."

Aftermath of Chernobyl

Environmental Change Radioactive material from the Chernobyl nuclear reactor can be detected in people as well as in the environment. These children are being tested for radioactivity.

Human-Environment Interaction *What are the possible long-term effects of radiation exposure?*

Even so, Ukrainian nationalism remained strong. After a Communist revolution broke out in Russia in 1917, the Ukrainians unsuccessfully attempted to establish their own independent country.

Under Soviet Rule After Russia became the Communist Soviet Union, Ukrainians often suffered from harsh government policies. Beginning in the 1920s, Soviet rulers forced farmers to give up their land and work on large state-run collective farms. Many people resisted by burning crops. In response, the government seized all grain, leaving the people to starve. Between five and eight million Ukrainians died in the resulting famine. During World War II, many Ukrainians welcomed the invading Germans as liberators and collaborated with them against the Soviet Union.

Parts of Ukraine suffered serious environmental damage in 1986 when an accidental explosion destroyed a nuclear reactor at Chernobyl (CHAYR noh bul), sending a cloud of radiation into the air. At least 26 people were killed, hundreds more injured, and millions exposed to radiation. Some 12.3 million acres (5 million hectares) of land were polluted by radiation from the damaged plant. Ukrainians still must deal with the long-term effects of Chernobyl, including water pollution, birth defects, and various kinds of cancer. The land surrounding Chernobyl is not likely to be fit for human occupation for a long time.

Since Independence Since the breakup of the Soviet Union in 1991, Ukraine has reaffirmed itself as an independent nation. With more than 50 million people, vast fertile plains, and huge coal resources, Ukraine has great potential for development.

Slightly smaller than the state of Texas, Ukraine long has been a "breadbasket" of Eastern Europe. On the fertile steppe, farmers produce food that is exported to Russia and other nearby nations. Ukrainian farmers grow many crops, especially wheat, rye, barley, and potatoes. Agriculture is so productive because the country lies in a region with warm weather and adequate precipitation. Also important for farm productivity are rich, black-earth soils called chernozem that formed beneath the lush grasses that once covered the steppe.

Central Europe, Eastern Europe, and the United States
Economic Data

Country	GDP per Capita (U.S. dollars)	GDP Growth Rate (percentage)	Unemployment (percentage)
Albania	3,800	7.3	17.0
Belarus	8,200	4.1	2.1
Bosnia and Herzegovina	1,800	6.0	40.0
Bulgaria	6,200	4.0	17.5
Croatia	8,300	4.0	23.0
Czech Republic	14,400	3.4	8.5
Estonia	10,000	4.7	12.4
Hungary	12,000	3.9	6.5
Latvia	7,800	6.3	7.6
Lithuania	7,600	4.8	12.5
Macedonia	4,400	−4.0	39.0
Moldova	2,550	6.1	1.9
Poland	8,800	1.5	16.7
Romania	6,800	4.8	9.1
Serbia and Montenegro	2,250	5.0	30.0
Slovakia	11,500	3.0	19.8
Slovenia	16,000	4.0	11.5
Ukraine	4,200	9.0	3.6
United States	36,300	0.3	5.0

Source: *The World Factbook*

CHART SKILLS

● **Economic Activities** *Which nation has a negative GDP growth rate?*

● **Planning for the Future** *How would you expect a decrease in the unemployment rate to affect GDP per capita in this nation?*

Ukraine's industries face several difficulties. One of these is that Ukraine must import large quantities of oil and natural gas. Another problem is that much of its machinery is old and obsolete. Because the government has been slow to implement laws, regulations, and policies

Articles From ....
NATIONAL GEOGRAPHIC

The following article may be used to extend the content in this section.

Suchy, Lida, and Miso Suchy, photographer. "Portrait of a Village: The Hutsuls of Ukraine." *National Geographic*, Vol. 192, No. 5 (Nov. 1997), pp. 78–93.

The Hutsul people of Ukraine's Carpathian Mountains revive a traditional culture that had been suppressed by the former Soviet Union.

TEST PREPARATION

Have students read the subsection Under Soviet Rule on this page and complete the following sentence.

The Ukrainians suffered a human-made famine during the early 1900s because they protested against —

A World War II
B the Germans
C Chernobyl
Ⓓ Soviet rule

Widespread Faith Orthodox Christianity is named for the Greek word *orthodox,* meaning "right-believing." Followers of this faith believe that its teachings were handed down directly from the disciples of Jesus. This religion is not only common among the Slavic people of Belarus but among many other nations as well. The Orthodox Church has over 174 million followers, with practicing communities in Western Europe, the Americas, Africa, and Asia.

Fuel in Belarus Now that it has to buy expensive oil from Russia, Belarus has worked to build up its own energy reserves. In western Belarus, geothermal plants use heated underground water to drive generators. Most Belarussian industries run on peat (densely compressed vegetation), which is burned for fuel.

Answer to Photo Caption

Belarus and Russia signed a pact in 1996 that strengthened economic ties between the two nations. They have also agreed to develop a single currency.

to encourage private ownership of industries, investors have been reluctant to invest in Ukrainian businesses.

Belarus and Moldova

Together with Ukraine, Belarus and Moldova form the border region between Russia and the rest of Europe. Belarus and Moldova share another characteristic. The two countries are similar in that they both have very close ties with larger nations.

Belarus Belarus (byel ah ROOS), which lies to the north of Ukraine, is a nation of more than 10 million people in an area about the size of Kansas. Like Russians and Ukrainians, the people of Belarus are mainly Slavic and have practiced Orthodox Christianity. Unlike people in most of the other new nations that formed when the Soviet Union dissolved, many Belarussians favored reestablishing close political and economic ties with Russia.

In 1996, Belarus and Russia signed a pact to form a "union state" that would strengthen political, cultural, and economic ties. In subsequent years, additional treaties called for the development of a single currency, a joint defense policy, and other measures to integrate the two nations. However, real integration progressed slowly.

Today, Belarus's economy depends mainly on industry and services. The nation, however, must import most of the raw materials needed to produce the finished goods. Belarus has oil reserves as well as large deposits of potash, which is used to make fertilizer.

Belarus suffered severely from the Chernobyl disaster. Winds blew the radioactive cloud northward from Ukraine. More than one fifth of the country's farmland was contaminated. As a result, people had to stop using this land to produce food.

Moldova Landlocked between the states of Ukraine and Romania, Moldova is the second

Agricultural Workers

Economic Systems The economy of Belarus combines elements of market and socialist economies. Nearly one quarter of the nation's GDP comes from agriculture.

Regions *How have Belarus and Russia worked to strengthen economic ties?*

Gravel Quarry

Natural Resources Both agriculture and industry are vital to the Moldovan economy. Here, a gravel quarry lies next to a plowed field.

Human-Environment Interaction *Does this photograph show primary, secondary, or tertiary economic activities?*

smallest of the former Soviet republics. It also is the most densely populated, with more than 4 million people living in an area about the same size as the states of Maryland and Delaware, combined.

Moldova was once a Romanian principality, and most of its residents are of Romanian descent. With the end of the Soviet Union, Romanian again became the language used in schools. Despite these strong ties, however, Moldova's

residents rejected a proposal to unify this new nation with Romania in 1994.

Moldova's hilly terrain slopes gradually in a southerly direction toward the Black Sea. Its location and inviting terrain have made it a historic route between Asia and Southern Europe. It has also been subject to frequent invasions. Although Soviet planners built up Moldova's factories, the economy still depends on exports of wine, sugar beets, and seed oils.

SECTION 4 ASSESSMENT

1. **Key Terms** Define **(a)** annex, **(b)** diversify.

2. **Understanding the Past** Why did the Soviet Union establish naval bases in the Baltic states?

3. **Natural Resources (a)** How do natural resources benefit Ukrainian agriculture? **(b)** How does the lack of certain natural resources limit industrial growth in Ukraine?

4. **Planning for the Future** What steps has the government of Belarus taken to promote closer ties with Russia?

5. **Critical Thinking Making Comparisons** Would you expect to find a higher standard of living in the Baltic states or in the border nations? Explain.

Activity

Making a Map Draw a sketch map of the Baltic states and border nations. Using symbols and shading, indicate how different types of environmental change have affected this region. Include human and natural alterations to the environment.

CUSTOMIZE FOR...

Honors/PreAP

Writing a Story Ask students to conduct research on the country of Moldova. Based on their findings, have them write a fictional first-person account of a typical day in the life of a Moldovan student. Ask volunteers to share their stories with the class.

REVIEW AND ASSESSMENT

pp. 412–413

Creating a Chapter Summary

As a reteaching opportunity, pair a more able student with a less able student to complete this chapter summary.

Completed charts may include the following entries: **Under Foreign Influence:** *Poland* Widespread opposition by the Polish people to Soviet policies *The Czech and Slovak Republics and Hungary* Czech Republic united with Slovakia, Failed Hungarian revolt against Soviet rule *The Balkan Peninsula* Economic ruin and poverty *Baltic States and Border Nations* Soviet naval bases established **After Independence:** *Poland* Somewhat painful economic growth *The Czech and Slovak Republics and Hungary* Actively pursuing privatization *The Balkan Peninsula* Aid from foreign nations helps economy recover *Baltic States and Border Nations* Combating Soviet pollution

Reviewing Key Terms

1–8. Students' quiz items should show a clear understanding of each term.

Understanding Key Ideas

9. The Poles never gave up their cultural heritage nor their hope for independence.
10. Moravia's industries are old and inefficient. Industrial pollution and acid rain have fouled the air and water and destroyed more than half the country's forests.
11. Hungary has fertile soil and deposits of coal, iron ore, and bauxite.
12. Conflict in Macedonia centered on language. Macedonians wanted their language to be the only official language. Other ethnic groups wanted their languages to have official status.
13. (a) Latvians and Lithuanians speak similar languages. **(b)** Most Latvians and Estonians are Lutheran.

Critical Thinking and Writing

14. Possible answer: Countries struggle at first as they move from a government-controlled economy to a market economy. Ethnic conflicts no longer stifled by Communist control often cause internal trouble.

Creating a Chapter Summary

On a sheet of paper, draw a chart like this one. Fill in each box with a key development in the nation or region indicated. Some information has been filled in to help you get started.

INDEPENDENCE AND RECOVERY IN CENTRAL AND EASTERN EUROPE

UNDER FOREIGN INFLUENCE		AFTER INDEPENDENCE
• Widespread opposition by the Polish people to Soviet policies	POLAND	•
•	THE CZECH AND SLOVAK REPUBLICS, AND HUNGARY	•
•	THE BALKAN PENINSULA	• Aid from foreign nations helps economy to recover
•	BALTIC STATES AND BORDER NATIONS	•

Take It to the NET
Chapter Self-Test For practice test questions for Chapter 19, go to the World Geography section of **www.phschool.com**.

Reviewing Key Terms

Use the key terms listed below to create a matching quiz. Exchange quizzes with a classmate. Complete the quiz, and then check each other's answers.

1. national identity
2. ghetto
3. privatization
4. collective farm
5. balkanize
6. entrepreneur
7. multiplier effect
8. velvet revolution

Understanding Key Ideas

9. Understanding the Past Why did communism never gain widespread support in Poland?
10. Science and Technology How has industrial technology created problems for Moravia?
11. Natural Resources What natural resources have given Hungary an advantage in establishing itself as an independent nation?
12. Cooperation and Conflict How did tensions in Macedonia show the influence of cultural beliefs on government and citizenship?
13. Cultures (a) How are the people of Latvia and Lithuania similar? **(b)** How are the people of Latvia and Estonia similar?

Critical Thinking and Writing

14. Recognizing Patterns Based on what you have read, what pattern of events seems common for countries emerging from Communist control? Explain.
15. Identifying Relationships How does the location of Poland explain why its government was closely tied to that of the former Soviet Union?
16. Analyzing Change Describe how Czechoslovakia became two separate countries and why this development was unusual.
17. Analyzing Photographs How does the photograph on page 400 illustrate the fact that Albania is one of Europe's poorest countries?
18. Analyzing Causes and Effects Why has Belarus's economy become dependent upon industry only recently?

---

15. Answers should show an understanding of the importance of Poland's location between the Soviet Union and Western Europe.
16. Slovaks felt poorly represented in the Czech-dominated system. The Slovaks and the Czechs agreed to separate. The process was unusual because it was peaceful.

17. The photograph suggests that Albania is struggling even to provide bread for its people.
18. Belarus's economy was based on agriculture until the disaster at Chernobyl in 1986 contaminated much of the nation's farmland.

Applying Skills

Analyzing Processes Refer to the Skills for Life lesson on page 392 to answer this question.

19. Why is analyzing a process important?

Analyzing Data Study the data below, and answer the following question:

20. Which country appears to have the slowest-growing economy?

Central Europe, Eastern Europe, and the United States
Economic Data

Country	GDP per Capita (U.S. dollars)	GDP Growth Rate (percentage)	Unemployment (percentage)
Albania	3,800	7.3	17.0
Belarus	8,200	4.1	2.1
Bosnia and Herzegovina	1,800	6.0	40.0
Bulgaria	6,200	4.0	17.5
Croatia	8,300	4.0	23.0
Czech Republic	14,400	3.4	8.5
Estonia	10,000	4.7	12.4
Hungary	12,000	3.9	6.5
Latvia	7,800	6.3	7.6
Lithuania	7,600	4.8	12.5
Macedonia	4,400	−4.0	39.0
Moldova	2,550	6.1	1.9
Poland	8,800	1.5	16.7
Romania	6,800	4.8	9.1
Serbia and Montenegro	2,250	5.0	30.0
Slovakia	11,500	3.0	19.8
Slovenia	16,000	4.0	11.5
Ukraine	4,200	9.0	3.6
United States	36,300	0.3	5.0

Test Preparation

Read the question and choose the best answer.

21. After communism, many of the economies of the nations of Central and Eastern Europe became —

A command economies

B market economies

C traditional economies

D mixed economies

Activities

USING THE REGIONAL ATLAS

Review the Regional Atlas for Central Europe and Northern Eurasia and Chapter 19. Then, create a graph that shows the relative economic health of several countries of Eastern Europe. Support your data with facts from the text.

MENTAL MAPPING

Study a map of Europe. Then, on a separate piece of paper, draw a sketch map of Eastern Europe from memory. Label the following places on your map:

- Poland
- Belarus
- Budapest
- Black Sea
- Bosnia and Herzegovina
- Ukraine
- Carpathian Mountains
- Romania
- Prague
- Adriatic Sea

Take It to the NET

Writing an Article As you have read, much of Central and Eastern Europe face environmental challenges. Go online to research and compare how two of the nations in this region are dealing with an environmental problem, such as acid rain or pollution. Share your findings in a short article. Visit the World Geography section of **www.phschool.com** for help in completing this activity.

Applying Skills
19. Possible answer: Analyzing a process allows one to understand and work through complex problems or instructions.
20. The U.S. economy is actually growing the slowest. Poland has the slowest-growing economy of the Central and Eastern European countries. Macedonia has a shrinking economy with negative growth.

Test Preparation
21. B

Activities

Using the Regional Atlas
Students' graphs should show clear and supportable differences among the countries depicted.

Mental Mapping
Review students' maps for relative and absolute location.

Take It to the Net
Students' work should reflect sound research. Check that their articles accurately reflect the environmental problems of two nations.

MENTAL MAPPING

Games for Review See pages 58–63 of the Simulations, Games, and Lab Activities booklet for games to help students review for the Chapter 19 Map Test.

Chapter Map Test Students should use the completed outline maps and the Unit 5 Checklist in their Atlas Portfolios to prepare for the Chapter 19 Map Test.

Alternative Assessment

Final Evaluation

Class Discussion Use the Class Discussion Evaluation Form on page 23 of the Alternative Assessment booklet in the Prentice Hall Assessment System to evaluate students' participation. Teachers or students can complete the forms to indicate which level of work was achieved. Evaluations should include specific comments.

Resource Manager

	CORE INSTRUCTION	READING/SKILLS

Chapter-Level Resources	▣ Teaching Resources
	▫ **Unit 5**/Ch. 20
	  • Reviewing Main Ideas, p. 34
	▤ **Mental Mapping booklet**
	  • Unit 5 Checklist, p. 67
	▤ **Simulations, Games, and Lab Activities**
	  • Place Location Review Games, pp. 58–63
	▤ **Creative Teaching Activities**
	  • Architecture and Social Change, p. 22
	◉ **TeacherExpress™ CD-ROM**, Ch. 20
	▣ **Companion Web site,**
	www.phschool.com
	  • eTeach
		▣ Teaching Resources
		▫ **Unit 5**/Ch. 20
		  • Map/Graph Skills, p. 36
		▤ **Social Studies Skills Handbook**
		  • Drawing Conclusions, p. 52
		◉ **Book on CD**, Ch. 20
		◉ **Social Studies Skills Tutor CD-ROM**

1 Regions of Russia
1. Identify the main physical characteristics of Russia.
2. Describe how location and climate affect ecosystems in Russia.
3. Explain how Siberia offers opportunities and poses unique challenges.
	▣ Teaching Resources
	▫ **Unit 5**/Ch. 20
	  • Guided Reading and Review, p. 28
	◉ **Prentice Hall Presentation Pro CD-ROM**, Ch. 20, Sec. 1
		▣ Teaching Resources
		▤ **Guide to the Essentials (English/Spanish)**
		  • Section Summary, Ch. 20, Sec. 1
		▤ **Mental Mapping booklet**
		  • Outline Map 20, p. 75
		▣ **Guided Reading Audiotapes (English/Spanish)**, Ch. 20, Sec. 1
		▥ **Section Reading Support Transparencies**, Ch. 20, Sec. 1

2 Emergence of Russia
1. Explain how Russian territory expanded under the czars.
2. Identify the economic and political conditions that marked the Communist era.
3. Discuss how the end of Communist rule led to changes in Russia.
	▣ Teaching Resources
	▫ **Unit 5**/Ch. 20
	  • Guided Reading and Review, p. 30
	◉ **Prentice Hall Presentation Pro CD-ROM**, Ch. 20, Sec. 2
		▣ Teaching Resources
		▤ **Guide to the Essentials (English/Spanish)**
		  • Section Summary, Ch. 20, Sec. 2
		▣ **Guided Reading Audiotapes (English/Spanish)**, Ch. 20, Sec. 2
		▥ **Section Reading Support Transparencies**, Ch. 20, Sec. 2

3 Geographic Issues in Russia
1. Identify some of the defining characteristics of life in Russia today.
2. Explain how ethnic turmoil challenges Russia.
3. List the common methods of transportation in Russia.
4. Summarize the economic and environmental problems facing Russia.
	▣ Teaching Resources
	▫ **Unit 5**/Ch. 20
	  • Guided Reading and Review, p. 32
	◉ **Prentice Hall Presentation Pro CD-ROM**, Ch. 20, Sec. 3
		▣ Teaching Resources
		▤ **Guide to the Essentials (English/Spanish)**
		  • Section Summary, Ch. 20, Sec. 3
		▣ **Guided Reading Audiotapes (English/Spanish)**, Ch. 20, Sec. 3
		▥ **Section Reading Support Transparencies**, Ch. 20, Sec. 3

ENRICHMENT/HONORS/PREAP

Teaching Resources
- **Unit 5/Ch. 20**
  - Critical Thinking, p. 20
- **Mental Mapping booklet**
  - Atlas Activity, p. 76
- **Social Studies Skills Handbook**
  - Study and Research Skills, pp. 94–108
- **World Geography Map and Photo Transparencies**
  - Central Europe and Northern Eurasia: Maps and Photos
  - How the Earth Works, Unit 5
- **World Geography Videos**
  - Cultures: Russia
- **Companion Web site, www.phschool.com**
  - Chapter 20 Activities

Teaching Resources
- **Unit 5/Ch. 20**
  - Geography and World Literature, p. 43
- **Companion Web site, www.phschool.com**
  - Chapter 20 Activities

Companion Web site, www.phschool.com
- Chapter 20 Activities

ASSESSMENT

PRENTICE HALL ASSESSMENT SYSTEM

Core Assessment
- ExamView Test Bank booklet, Ch. 20
- ExamView Test Bank CD-ROM, Ch. 20
- ExamView Test Bank CD-ROM, Unit 5

Standardized Test Preparation

Review and Reteach
- Review Book for World Geography, pp. 11–12

Practice and Assess
- Test-taking Strategies With Transparencies for High School
- Test-taking Strategy Poster
- Alternative Assessment booklet
- Test Prep Book for World Geography

Teaching Resources
- **Unit 5/Ch. 20**
  - Section Quizzes, pp. 29, 31, 33
  - Test Forms A and B, pp. 37–42
- **Guide to the Essentials (English/Spanish)**
  - Chapter 20 Test
- **Spanish Resources, Ch. 20**
  - Section Quizzes, pp. 50–52
- **Mental Mapping booklet**
  - Chapter 20 Map Test, p. 77
  - Unit 5 Map Test, p. 78
- **Companion Web site, www.phschool.com**
  - Chapter 20 Self-Test

CUSTOMIZE FOR INDIVIDUAL NEEDS

Gifted and Talented
- Teacher's Edition, Customize for . . . , p. 429

Honors/PreAP
- Teacher's Edition, Customize for . . . , p. 417

Less Proficient Readers
- Guide to the Essentials (English), Ch. 20, Section Summaries
- Guided Reading Audiotapes (English), Ch. 20
- Section Reading Support Transparencies, Ch. 20
- Book on CD, Ch. 20
- Teacher's Edition, Reading Strategy, pp. 417, 424, 428
- Teacher's Edition, Customize for . . . , pp. 419, 421

Students Acquiring English/ESL
- Guide to the Essentials (English/Spanish), Ch. 20
- Guided Reading Audiotapes (English/Spanish), Ch. 20
- Section Reading Support Transparencies, Ch. 20
- Book on CD, Ch. 20
- Teacher's Edition, Customize for . . . , pp. 421, 425

Less Proficient Writers
- Alternative Assessment, Writing Assignment Rubric, p. 6

Introducing
CHAPTER
20
pp. 414–433

MENTAL MAPPING

Ask students to look at the map on this page. Point out the absolute location of Russia—its latitude and longitude and its nearness to the North Pole. Ask students how Russia's absolute location might affect its climate. (Its climate is mostly tundra and subarctic.)

Mapping the Region Have students study the map. Then instruct them to close their books and create a sketch map of Russia, or distribute the Chapter 20 Outline Map on page 75 of the Mental Mapping booklet in the Teaching Resources. Ask students to add labels for major cities and bodies of water on their maps. Students should keep their maps in their Atlas Portfolios in order to prepare for the Chapter 20 Map Test.

eTeach

Be sure to check out this month's online forum with a Master Teacher to join in an exchange of teaching ideas. **www.phschool.com**

414 Chapter 20

CHAPTER
20
Russia

Russia: POLITICAL

[Map of Russia showing: North Pole, ARCTIC OCEAN, NORWAY, LATVIA, FINLAND, LITHUANIA, ESTONIA, BELARUS, St. Petersburg, Moscow, Nizhniy Novgorod, UKRAINE, Nizhniy Tagil, Samara, Yekaterinburg, Magnitogorsk, GEORGIA, Omsk, AZERBAIJAN, KAZAKHSTAN, Novosibirsk, Bratsk, Irkutsk, L. Baikal, MONGOLIA, CHINA, Vladivostok, JAPAN, Verkhoyansk, Sea of Okhotsk, Sakhalin Island, Bering Strait, Bering Sea, Barents Sea, Novaya Zemlya, White Sea, Kara Sea, Laptev Sea, RUSSIA, Volga R., Don R., Ob R., Irtysh R., Yenisey R., Lena R., Amur R., Caspian Sea, Arctic Circle]

Scale: 0 500 1,000 mi / 0 500 1,000 km

KEY
— National boundary
⊛ National capital
• Other city
Two-Point Equidistant Projection

Go Online
PHSchool.com
For: More information about Russia and access to the Take It to the Net activities
Visit: phschool.com
Web Code: mjk-0021

414 Chapter 20

RESOURCE DIRECTORY

Teaching Resources
Unit 5, Chapter 20
• Section 1 Guided Reading and Review, p. 28
Guide to the Essentials (English/Spanish)
• Section Summary, Chapter 20, Section 1
Mental Mapping booklet
• Atlas Activity, p. 76
• Unit 5 Checklist, p. 67

Technology
Guided Reading Audiotapes (English/Spanish), Chapter 20, Section 1

Section Reading Support Transparencies, Chapter 20, Section 1
World Geography Map and Photo Transparencies
• Central Europe and Northern Eurasia: Maps and Photos
Book on CD, Chapter 20
World Geography Videos
• Cultures: Russia
TeacherExpress™ CD-ROM, Chapter 20
Prentice Hall Presentation Pro CD-ROM, Chapter 20
Social Studies Skills Tutor CD-ROM
Companion Web site, www.phschool.com

1 Regions of Russia

Reading Focus

- What are the main physical characteristics of Russia?
- How do location and climate affect ecosystems in Russia?
- How does Siberia offer opportunities and pose unique challenges?

Key Terms

tundra

taiga

steppe

chernozem

permafrost

Main Idea Russia's varied regions provide the nation with many resources, but access to these resources is not always easily available.

Physical Characteristics The flat lands surrounding Nizhniy Novgorod are one of Russia's dominant features.

Russia is the world's largest country in terms of land area. Look at a globe, and notice how it sprawls more than three quarters of the way across the northern part of the Eurasian continent. Compare Russia with the world's next largest countries: Canada, the United States, China, and Brazil. Russia's land area is nearly twice the size of any two of these other large nations. From west to east, Russia stretches across eleven time zones. Before people in St. Petersburg have gone to bed on Tuesday evening, it is already Wednesday morning on the Kamchatka Peninsula.

Physical Characteristics

Russia has varied terrain, although the landscape generally has specific characteristics in different regions. Its highest points lie along its southern and eastern borders. The highest mountain range is the Caucasus, which stretches from the Black Sea to the Caspian Sea. The rugged peaks of this range reach as high as 18,000 feet (5,486 m). Mountains that reach more than 10,000 feet

(3,048 m) also rise near the Mongolian border in central Asia and in the far northeast.

Plains While mountains ring parts of Russia in the south and east, most of the land is fairly flat. Gently rolling plains cover nearly all of the nation west of the Yenisei River. East of the Yenisei, higher plateaus provide slightly more varied terrain.

Ural Mountains Extending from north to south across the plains and dividing Europe from Asia are the Ural Mountains. Because the mountains are a dividing line between continents, many people assume that the Urals are a mighty range. In reality, they are low and unimposing. Their average elevation is only about 2,000 feet (610 m), and even the tallest peak reaches up only 6,200 feet (1,890 m). A number of low passes through the Urals have permitted migration through the range for centuries. Although erosion has worn down the peaks, the Urals still have great importance for Russia, because they contain many valuable minerals.

◄ Cathedral in Pushkin, Russia *(photo left)*

Chapter 20 ▪ Section 1 **415**

Objectives

Upon completion of Section 1, students should be able to:

◆ identify the main physical characteristics of Russia;

◆ describe how location and climate affect ecosystems in Russia;

◆ explain how Siberia offers opportunities and poses unique challenges.

National Geography Standards

The following National Geography Standards are highlighted in this section: 1, 3, 4, 5, 7, 8, 9, 12, 16

Bellringer

Ask students to list the clothes they would pack for a journey through Russia from north to south.

LESSON PLAN

1. Focus Have students use the map and scale on page 429 to calculate how many hours it would take to travel through Russia from Moscow to Khabarovsk on a nonstop train traveling 60 miles per hour. (about 73 hours)

2. Instruct Arrange students in small groups. Distribute the Chapter 20 Outline Map to each group and have students draw the Ural Mountains on their maps. Ask students to sketch the bands of major ecosystems described in the subsection Ecosystems beginning on page 416. Then have them add drawings or symbols to represent the physical characteristics of each ecosystem. Compare completed maps.

3. Close/Reteach Ask volunteers to explain which of Russia's physical characteristics and ecosystems seem similar to those of the United States.

Pacing Suggestions

For 90-minute Blocks

You will want to vary activities.

- Ask student pairs to do research on the Winter Palace in St. Petersburg, Russia. Tell them that they will design posters to attract tourists to the palace. Posters should advertise the building's rich history, its spectacular architecture, and its famous collection of artwork and royal treasure. Display completed posters around the room.

The Physical World

Time Zones There are a total of 24 time zones for the entire world. The contiguous United States fall within four time zones. Russia, by comparison, stretches across ten of the world's time zones.

The Physical World

Lake of Extremes Lake Baikal, Russia, is the oldest and deepest lake in the world. Over 20 million years old, the lake reaches depths of more than a mile (1.6 km). Its waters are home to more than 1,500 plant and animal species, most of which are found nowhere else on earth. Over 350 bird species inhabit the area. Lake Baikal holds about one fifth of the world's fresh water, more than all the Great Lakes of North America combined.

GEOFacts

The Volga River is Russia's main waterway, carrying one half of the nation's total river freight. On the Volga, many commodities are shipped upstream, such as grain, building materials, salt, and caviar. Lumber is the primary consumer good shipped downstream.

Rivers The extensive plains and plateaus of Russia are drained by some of the world's mightiest rivers. Waters from much of the land west of the Urals ultimately pass into the Volga River, which is Europe's longest river. The Volga drains into the Caspian Sea, a landlocked lake with no outlet. The Caspian, which lies below sea level, is the world's largest lake. East of the Urals, several rivers flow north into the Arctic Ocean. Near their mouths, the Ob, Yenisei, and Lena are so wide that a person on one bank can have trouble seeing the other shore.

Ecosystems

The dominant plant and animal life in different parts of Russia is closely related to location and climate. At the heart of the world's largest landmass, most parts of Russia are far removed from any bodies of water. Even the Arctic Ocean, to the north, is frozen for many months of the year.

As a result, the climate in most parts of Russia is subarctic or continental. Winters are long and bitterly cold. The coldest temperature ever recorded outside of Antarctica was in far eastern Russia—a metal-shattering –94°F (–70°C). Summers are shorter, but daytime temperatures still can exceed 80°F (27°C). Spring and fall tend to be brief periods of transition between the freezing winters and warm summers. Climatic conditions become more severe as one moves toward the north. As a result, the major ecosystems of Russia lie in bands that stretch across much of the nation.

Tundra Far to the north, in a band that parallels the Arctic shoreline, is a zone of **tundra**. This largely treeless zone is dominated by very small plants and animals that have adapted to the polar conditions of the region. Only the tiniest plants, which are not exposed to biting winds, can survive. These plants must be able to retain what little moisture they can gather in these desert-like conditions. Reindeer, rabbits, foxes, and polar bears are among the animals that live in tundra regions.

Taiga Extending across Russia to the south of the tundra is a broad forested zone called the **taiga** (TAI guh). The term *taiga* means "land of little sticks," a reference to the fact that trees do not grow to great size under the harsh conditions. But what the trees lack in size, they make up for in number. In colder areas, dense stands of conifers,

Logging Industry

Economic Activities
Logging trucks near the city of Archangel, in Russia's northern reaches, use plank roads to avoid becoming stuck in the mud.

Place *What does this photograph suggest about climates and ecosystems in Russia?*

RESOURCE DIRECTORY

Teaching Resources

Unit 5
• Geography and World Literature, The Steppe, p. 43

Mental Mapping booklet
• Outline Map 20, p. 75

Technology

World Geography Map and Photo Transparencies, Central Europe and Northern Eurasia: Maps and Photos

---

Answer to Photo Caption

Possible answer: Russia's harsh climate and ecosystems can make transportation challenging.

Russia: PHYSICAL

APPLYING THE GEOGRAPHIC THEMES

● **Region** Because of Russia's vast size, the country includes many types of physical features.
  • *In what elevation range do most of Russia's cities lie?*

KEY

Elevation

Feet		Meters
14,000		4,270
7,000		2,135
1,500		457
700		213
(sea level) 0		0 (sea level)

⊛ National capital
• Major city
△ Volcano

Two-Point Equidistant Projection

such as pines, firs, larches, and cedars, are common. More protected areas have an abundance of deciduous trees such as aspen, birches, oaks, maples, and poplars. Altogether, forests blanket almost half of Russia's land, covering 4 million square miles (10 million sq km). The taiga is so large and sparsely inhabited that forest fires can rage unnoticed for weeks.

In addition to being a great source of paper and other forest products, the taiga is home to many different animals. In the east, the sable's luxurious fur has made it a trapper's prize for centuries, while wolves, hares, and other mammals are found throughout the region. Also common in the taiga is the brown bear, which long has been a national symbol of Russia. For many centuries, the bear's ancient name was never spoken for fear of provoking its anger. Even today, the Russian term for this animal is *medved* (mid VYED), which means "one who knows where the honey is."

Steppes South of the forests are broad open stretches that the Russians call the **steppes.** In European Russia, the steppes were once a grassland. As occurred in the prairies of the central United States and Canada, the Pampas of South America, and other natural grasslands, the deep roots of the grasses formed a very rich soil. In the Russian steppes, the soil is known as **chernozem,** which means "black earth." Few natural grasses remain today, but the chernozems provide nutrients for Russia's most productive agricultural area.

Siberia

The Asian expanse of Russia is known as Siberia. Although considerable effort has been made to link this area with the rest of the nation, it

---

**Answers to
Section 1 Assessment**

1. (a) tundra, p. 416 **(b)** taiga, p. 416
(c) steppe, p. 417 **(d)** chernozem,
p. 417 **(e)** permafrost, p. 418
2. Passes through the mountains
have permitted migrations over the
centuries. The Urals also contain
many valuable mineral resources.
3. (a) taiga **(b)** steppes
4. High-rise buildings are built 6 feet
off the ground on special pilings to
allow frigid air to circulate beneath
them and diffuse the heat that buildings generate.
5. Siberia has huge deposits of oil,
natural gas, and minerals beneath the
permafrost. However, the region is far
removed from the more populated
areas of Russia.

Activity Rubrics Share rubrics
with students before they write their
journal entries.
Attempted Journal entries do not
include the required descriptions.
Minimal Journal entries meet basic
requirements but are poorly written
and include few details.
Adequate Journal entries are complete, include important details, and
show understanding of the topic.
Exemplary Journal entries demonstrate extensive research and are detailed, creative, and informative.

Omsk

Cultures The city center of
Omsk is a popular gathering
place. Although Siberia is
known for its harsh climate,
local residents look forward
to spring and summer.

Location *How does geographic location affect the
climate of Omsk?*

continues to be a remote area with relatively few
human residents.

Much of Siberia is cool and swampy, with a
layer of permanently frozen soil, or **permafrost.**
In some places, permafrost extends 5,000 feet
(1,524 m) below the ground. Modern high-rise
buildings in Siberia stand 6 feet (1.8 m) off the
ground on special pilings, or posts. This allows
the frigid air to circulate beneath them and diffuse the heat that buildings generate. Engineers
learned this tactic after the first tall buildings

erected on permafrost collapsed when their heat
thawed the soil around their foundations.

The geology of Siberia is complex, and it has
rich reserves of many valuable materials. Gold,
silver, platinum, and zinc all are extracted from
Siberia, as is petroleum and natural gas. These
reserves offer great wealth to people who can
develop them. However, the harsh climate and
terrain of the region often make it difficult and
very expensive to reach areas with abundant
natural resources.

SECTION 1 ASSESSMENT

1. Key Terms Define **(a)** tundra, **(b)** taiga,
(c) steppe, **(d)** chernozem, **(e)** permafrost.

2. Physical Characteristics How have the Ural
Mountains affected Russia?

3. Ecosystems **(a)** Which ecosystem provides a
great source of paper and other forest products?
(b) Which ecosystem provides most of Russia's
agricultural production?

4. Science and Technology How does permafrost affect construction in Siberia?

5. Critical Thinking Interpreting Maps Study
the map on page 417. How does this map suggest that many of Siberia's natural resources are
undeveloped?

Activity

Writing a Journal Suppose that you have been hired
to work for a company that is based in Siberia. Write
three journal entries. The first should describe your
feelings before leaving for Siberia, and the second
should describe your impressions upon arrival. The
third should focus on how life in Siberia affects your
work. You may wish to do additional research to complete this activity.

RESOURCE DIRECTORY

Teaching Resources
Unit 5, Chapter 20
• Section 1 Quiz, p. 29
Spanish Resources
• Section 1 Quiz, p. 50
Social Studies Skills Handbook
• Drawing Conclusions, p. 52

Technology
Social Studies Skills Tutor CD-ROM, Making
 Inferences/Drawing Conclusions

Answer to Photo Caption

Possible answer: Its winters are long
and bitterly cold.

Evaluating Conclusions

You draw conclusions every day. Not all conclusions, though, are valid. A valid conclusion is based on factual evidence, and connects that evidence in a logical manner. An invalid conclusion, on the other hand, is based on incorrect information, or connects factual evidence in a way that the evidence does not support.

Learn the Skill Use the following steps to learn how to evaluate conclusions.

1 *Identify the topic.* Whether you are evaluating conclusions about a photograph, chart, or written text, you will need to identify the topic of the material presented. *What is the topic of the passage below?*

2 *Look for relationships and patterns.* Examine the evidence provided, and pay attention to relationships between pieces of evidence. *In the paragraph below, what relationship can be seen between floods and living conditions?*

3 *Identify valid conclusions.* A valid conclusion is based on evidence. Read conclusions A through D, and determine if any rely on evidence. Identify conclusions that are not based on the evidence, and consider them invalid.

Which conclusion below is not based on the evidence presented?

4 *Explain why other conclusions are valid or invalid.* A conclusion that contradicts the available evidence is also invalid. Similarly, a conclusion is invalid if it cannot be confirmed or refuted by the available facts. *Which conclusion is invalid based on one of these characteristics?*

5 *Identify valid conclusions.* A valid conclusion is based on facts and has a logical structure. *Which conclusions are valid?*

 ## Do It Yourself

Practice the Skill Choose an article from a newspaper or current events magazine. Write a list of four conclusions that can be drawn from the information in the article. Exchange articles and conclusions with another student, and use the steps above to evaluate his or her conclusions.

Apply the Skill See Chapter 20 Review and Assessment.

Flooding in Siberia

One of the coldest winters on record left large quantities of snow and ice blocking the rivers in northern Siberia. A sudden temperature increase caused rapid melting of snow and ice, which raised the level of the Ob River to more than 20 feet (6.1 m). As a result, the river overflowed its banks and flooded more than 500 homes in the city of Barnaul alone. In parts of Siberia, floods forced the evacuation of more than 17,000 people. Warplanes and helicopter gunships had to be called in to destroy the ice floes that blocked the rivers.

Possible Conclusions

A Floods occurred because of little snowfall in a mild winter.

B Severe winters can lead to flooding in spring.

C Floods on the Lena River were more destructive than floods on the Ob River.

D Officials expected that breaking up the ice floes would cause the flood waters to recede.

Teaching the Skill

Read the introductory paragraph with the students. Then write this sentence on the board: *Russia is potentially a wealthy nation.* Call on volunteers to suggest evidence from Section 1 that would support this statement. List their suggestions under the statement on the board. Then erase the original statement and tell students to suppose they had started with the list of suggestions. Ask: **Was the original statement a valid conclusion? Could you reach other valid conclusions from this evidence?** Complete Learn the Skill with the students.

Answers to Learn the Skill

1. flooding in Siberia
2. Flooding has forced the evacuation of thousands of people from their homes.
3. C
4. A
5. B and D

Answers to Practice the Skill

Make sure that students have chosen appropriate articles from which to draw conclusions. Have them follow the steps outlined in the lesson to evaluate each other's conclusions.

CUSTOMIZE FOR...

Less Proficient Readers

Drawing Conclusions From Visuals Ask students to collect a variety of photos of plants and animals found in a particular part of Russia. Have each student choose two pictures and draw a separate conclusion about the climate in that part of Russia from each picture. Then tell students to group several related photos and draw a conclusion about climate from the grouping. Have students take turns evaluating one another's conclusions.

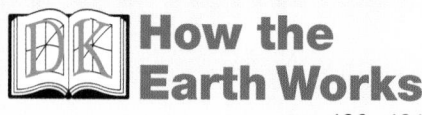

Objectives

Upon completion of this feature, students should be able to:

◆ describe how soil is formed;

◆ identify the qualities of different kinds of soil;

◆ explain how soil supports various kinds of life.

National Geography Standards

The following National Geography Standards are highlighted in this feature: 7, 8

Bellringer

Ask students to describe in as many ways as they can how the sand at the beach is different from the soil in which plants grow in a flowerpot. (Possible answers: Sand is lighter in color; it washes away easily; it does not make things as dirty; water runs right through it.) Tell students that as they read this lesson, they will learn some of the reasons for the differences.

LESSON PLAN

1. Focus Have students study the diagram that shows how soil is formed. Ask them to define *regolith.* (weathered rock) Then ask: **What is the difference between mature soil and immature soil?** (Mature soil has more humus and supports a wide variety of plants and animals.)

2. Instruct Make a two-column chart and label it *Ways Soil Can Be Different.* In the left column, write: *Soil is different at different depths.* In the right column, have students add facts from the feature to support the statement. Then have them complete the chart by showing how the texture and pH of soil can vary.

3. Close/Reteach Have students draw a circular flowchart that illustrates the mutually beneficial relationship between the soil and the creatures that live in it. Then ask: **How do people rely on the soil? What changes do they make to it?** Have students use information from the feature to support their answers.

How the Earth Works

Soil

On the surface of the earth, **soil** is the thin layer of loose material in which plants grow. Soil consists partly of mineral particles, and partly of **organic matter** derived from living plants and animals and their remains. Other key components of soil are water and air. Complex natural processes build soil over many thousands of years. The process begins when rock is broken down by weathering. Next, plants take root in the weathered rock. Then, organic material in the soil, called **humus,** is formed from decaying vegetation and animals. Different types of soil occur because of variations in climate, types of vegetation, and types of rock. In large countries like Russia, there is a wide variety of soil types.

SOIL FORMATION
Typically, the first step in soil building is the development of **regolith**, or weathered rock. Next, immature soil is formed as organic material begins to decay. Finally, mature soil supports abundant life both above and below the surface.

1. Regolith

Moss and lichen

Rock fragments

Bedrock

2. Immature soil

A layer of organic material begins to form

3. Mature soil

Decaying plants and animals form humus

Worms improve the soil texture

Root system

Grasses and small plants

Burrowing animals break up the soil

O horizon
Humus

A horizon
Topsoil

B horizon
Subsoil

C horizon
Rock fragments

R horizon
Bedrock

SOIL HORIZONS
As soil develops, distinct layers, called **soil horizons**, appear. Beneath a thin layer of humus, or O horizon, is the A horizon, or topsoil that is rich in minerals and organic matter. The B horizon is poorer in humus but rich in minerals washed down from above. Further below lie the C horizon of weathered rock and the R horizon of unweathered bedrock.

SOIL CREEP
In a process called **soil creep,** soil moves gradually and constantly downhill because of gravity. Trees on a slope often show the effects of this process. Terrace farming is an agricultural method used to slow the process of soil creep.

420   Chapter 20 ● Russia

RESOURCE DIRECTORY

Technology

World Geography Map and Photo Transparencies
• How the Earth Works, Unit 5

Companion Web site, www.phschool.com
• Chapter 20 Activities

SOIL pH
The pH scale measures acidity or alkalinity on a scale of 0 to 14. When a chemical solution called an indicator is added to a soil sample, the indicator changes color, showing the soil's pH. Most plants thrive only in soils with a pH between 5 and 9.

Highly alkaline

Highly acidic

Neutral

Clay soil

Silty soil

SOIL TEXTURE
Soil texture depends on the size and nature of soil particles. Clay soils have the smallest grains, silty soils have medium-sized grains, and sandy soils have the largest grains. **Loam,** a mixture of clay, silt, and sand, is the best soil for agriculture.

Sandy soil

Wildflowers *Grass* *Snail*

Slug

Decomposing leaf

Roots

LIFE IN THE SOIL
Soil is home to a vast array of life, including microorganisms, ants, termites, worms, and rodents. Fungi and bacteria convert dead plant and animal matter into chemicals that enrich the soil. Burrowing creatures improve the soil by mixing it.

Spodosol is a sandy soil found in northern coniferous forests.

Aridisols, found in deserts, have high concentrations of salts

SOIL CLASSIFICATION
Some experts recognize thousands of different soil types. The U.S. Department of Agriculture has devised a comprehensive soil classification system for categorizing soils. Each type of soil can be identified by the sequence and characteristics of its horizons.

ASSESSMENT

1. **Key Terms** Define (a) soil, (b) organic matter, (c) humus, (d) regolith, (e) soil horizon, (f) soil creep, (g) loam.

2. **Physical Processes** Describe the three stages of soil formation.

3. **Physical Characteristics** How do various types of soil differ from one another?

4. **Natural Resources** What soil characteristics are most beneficial for agriculture?

5. **Critical Thinking Making Comparisons** Study the cross-sections of spodosol and aridisol. (a) How are they alike? (b) How do they differ? (c) Do research to learn more about their different characteristics.

Chapter 20   **421**

Objectives

Upon completion of Section 2, students should be able to:

◆ explain how Russian territory expanded under the czars;

◆ identify the economic and political conditions that marked the Communist era;

◆ discuss how the end of Communist rule led to changes in Russia.

National Geography Standards

The following National Geography Standards are highlighted in this section: 1, 3, 4, 6, 9, 11, 12, 13, 17

Bellringer

Ask students to write headlines for any news items about Russia they have heard or seen recently.

LESSON PLAN

1. Focus Ask students what their lives would be like if they had to wait in an hour-long line to buy a loaf of bread, another hour-long line to buy a gallon of milk, and yet another to buy chicken for dinner. Comment that had they lived in the Soviet Union, such lines would have been part of daily life.

2. Instruct Draw four columns headed *Early, Czarist, Communist,* and *Post-Communist* on the board. Ask volunteers to supply the time spans and political, social, and economic facts appropriate to each period in Russian history. When the chart is complete, ask students to suggest possible advantages and disadvantages of life under each regime.

3. Close/Reteach Have students create journal entries for a person living in each of the four periods of Russian history. Entries should reflect daily life and some major events or conditions of the time.

2 Emergence of Russia

Reading Focus

- **How did Russian territory expand under the czars?**
- **What economic and political conditions marked the Communist era?**
- **How did the end of Communist rule lead to changes in Russia?**

Key Terms

czar	command economy
abdicate	glasnost
soviet	perestroika

Main Idea Russia has a history of authoritarian rule, but more recent democratic reforms offer hope to many people.

Cultures The onion domes of this cathedral reflec influence of the Byzantine Empire on Russia's history.

Much of northern Eurasia consists of gently rolling plains. As a result, many different peoples have ranged across this land. Modern Russia began in the 800s when Slavic people living in eastern Europe confronted Norsemen, or Vikings, who were sailing along the region's rivers in search of trade routes between Scandinavia and the Black Sea. Tired of fighting enemies and themselves, the Slavs allowed the Vikings to establish a state. From the 800s through the 1200s, Russian princes ruled a sizable area in and around the current Ukrainian capital of Kiev. During this time, Russian rulers adopted Orthodox Christianity. The Russian Orthodox Church was a pillar of state power for centuries.

Russia Under the Czars

Mongol warriors from east central Asia overran the Kievan state in 1237. For more than 150 years, Mongol forces known both as the Tatars and the Golden Horde dominated the region. But starting in the late 1300s, Russian princes in Moscow began two centuries of fighting to repel the Mongols.

Expansion Once the Mongol threat was ended, Russia began nearly three centuries of

growth. No sizable or powerful groups of people stood up against them, and few natural barriers limited the steady expansion of the nation.

A series of monarchs called **czars** (a variant on the title "caesar") oversaw this expansion. Peter the Great, who governed in the late 1600s and early 1700s, expanded control to the Pacific in the east and to the Baltic in the west, where he built a new capital city, St. Petersburg. Later in the 1700s, Catherine the Great extended Russian control farther to the west and gained control of parts of Poland, Belarus, and Ukraine.

Russian power was challenged in 1812, when French emperor Napoleon led an invasion with approximately 600,000 soldiers. Late in the year, Napoleon captured Moscow. As they fled the city, departing residents set the city on fire, depriving the French troops of badly needed food and materials. In the following months, Russia's geography became its best defender. The bitterly cold weather and the vast distances separating the French troops from their own supplies forced Napoleon to make a long, harrowing retreat. Of the 100,000 who left Moscow with him, fewer than 30,000 returned safely to France.

In the century that followed, Russian czars consolidated their power across northern Eurasia, taking control of Finland, the Crimean Peninsula on the Black Sea, and far eastern Siberia. The czars conquered and annexed the homelands of more than one hundred different ethnic groups. By the beginning of the twentieth century, Russia controlled nearly all of Northern Eurasia.

Social Structure Despite the enormous size of its empire, Russia remained more backward than the nations of Western Europe. Remnants of feudalism remained through the 1800s. Many peasants were forced to work on the land of wealthy property owners through the system of serfdom. Controlled virtually as slaves, serfs even needed the landowner's permission in order to marry.

Serfdom finally was abolished in 1861, four years before slavery was ended in the United States. Although some former serfs found work in cities, tens of millions of people were forced to remain on the same estates and pay high prices for what little land they were given. This left them as poor and dissatisfied as they had been before they were freed.

The Rise of Communism

Dissatisfaction with the czarist governments increased. A series of Russian defeats in World War I and severe food shortages led to riots in St. Petersburg in February 1917. When government troops joined the rioters, the czar **abdicated,** or gave up his crown.

The Russian Revolution in 1917 established a government that was based on the ideas of Karl Marx, a German economist. Marx and his followers believed that to achieve social equality, land and businesses should be owned by people in common, hence the word communism. When the Union of Soviet Socialist Republics was established, it comprised Russia and the homelands of the largest ethnic groups. Each republic had its own **soviet,** or governing council. The Supreme Soviet in Moscow made national laws. In 1940, the Soviet Union forcibly annexed the Baltic nations of Lithuania, Latvia, and Estonia.

The Soviet System Leaders such as V. I. Lenin and Joseph Stalin established a Communist dictatorship. The Soviet Union had a **command economy,** one in which a central authority decides what goods will be produced. Officials in Moscow set production goals for the managers of state-run farms, mines, and factories.

Millions of Russians believed that communism would improve their lives. They found instead that the Communists had become their new masters. The standard of living remained poor, and people had no freedom to make personal decisions or express their opinions. Millions who resisted were sent to prisons or forced-labor camps in Siberia or elsewhere. Vast numbers of people

Russian Revolution

Cooperation and Conflict The Russian Revolution led to a Communist government for the nation. To show the break with the past, the name of the country was changed to the Soviet Union, and St. Petersburg, shown here, became known as Leningrad.

Place *Why did the Russian people start a revolution in 1917?*

Introduce the Activity
Making a Time Line Ask students to create a time line showing 20 major events in Russian history. Distribute the Time Line Rubric found on page 12 of the Alternative Assessment booklet in the Prentice Hall Assessment System for student reference during the project.

Articles From
NATIONAL GEOGRAPHIC

The following article may be used to extend the content of this section.

Raymer, Steve, text and photographs. "St. Petersburg, Capital of the Tsars." *National Geographic,* Vol. 184, No. 6 (Dec. 1993), pp. 96–121.

St. Petersburg remains the center of Russian culture.

TEST PREPARATION

Have students read the subsection Russia Under the Czars beginning on the opposite page to answer this question. Which of the following is the main idea of this subsection?

A Russia expanded under the czars, but many Russians were oppressed.

B Catherine the Great extended Russian control to the west.

C Serfdom was abolished in Russia in 1861.

D The French invasion of Russia was thwarted.

Answer to Photo Caption

A series of Russian defeats in World War I and severe food shortages intensified the Russian people's dissatisfaction with czarist rule.

Chapter 20 ■ Section 2   **423**

Using Prior Knowledge

Ask students to write down what they think the term *Cold War* means and any facts they recall hearing about the Cold War. As they read the subsection Cold War, have them check the accuracy of their prior knowledge.

SOVIET UNION
No. 8   OCTOBER 1950

Soviet Magazine

Understanding the Past Under Soviet rule, economic decisions were made by the central government.

Human-Environment Interaction *Based on this magazine cover, what was one priority of the Soviet Union?*

were executed. Leaders of the Russian Orthodox Church were often targeted, and religious worship was suppressed. Still, many continued to practice their beliefs in secret.

Agriculture and Industry Under Soviet rule, farmland was reorganized into state farms and collective farms. Farmers were forced to work on them. State farmworkers, like factory workers, received wages. On collectives, workers shared any surpluses that remained after products were sold and costs were paid.

Because few incentives existed to encourage farmers to work hard, Soviet agricultural production

and distribution remained low. Despite strict central control, many Soviet farmers were permitted to cultivate gardens on small plots of land. These gardens became major sources of fruits and vegetables.

Soviet policies also emphasized the development of heavy industry—the production of goods that are used in other industries, such as machines or steel.

International Conflicts In June 1941, German troops attacked the Soviet Union. In just six months, German forces were on the outskirts of Moscow and Leningrad (as St. Petersburg had been renamed). Soviet troops and people fought back fiercely. Like the French a century earlier, German troops learned how hard it was to maintain lengthy supply lines and deal with the harsh Russian climate. German forces slowly were swept from Soviet land.

In May 1945, Soviet troops controlled the German capital, Berlin. The victory came at great cost, however. More than 20 million Soviet troops and civilians died during what became known as the Great Patriotic War.

Cold War The period after World War II was a high point for Soviet power. Nuclear weapons, advanced tanks, jet planes, and submarines made the Soviet Union a major world power. From the late 1940s into the 1980s, Soviet rulers in Moscow controlled Communist governments in Eastern Europe.

However, in a struggle called the Cold War, the Soviet Union competed for power with the United States. Although the two nations never fought directly, both states spent enormous sums of money on military weapons.

The End of Communist Rule

Parades often highlighted Soviet military strength, but the spending on troops and equipment weighed heavily on the economy. Most Soviet citizens thought only of the long lines for limited supplies of food and other products.

Economic Reorganization In the late 1980s, a new leader, Mikhail Gorbachev

Answer to Photo Caption

Possible answer: modern urban construction

Growth of Russia

KEY

Principality of Moscow, 1300
Territory added, 1300–1462
Territory added, 1462–1505
Territory added, 1505–1584
Territory added, 1584–1800
Territory added, 1800–1855
Territory added, 1855–1955
Soviet Union
Present-day Russia

Two-Point Equidistant Projection

APPLYING THE GEOGRAPHIC THEMES

• **Region** Under the czars, Russian territory was expanded to stretch across Asia to the Pacific Ocean.
• *During which era did Russian territory first extend north of the Arctic Circle?*

(gor buh CHAWF), began radical reforms. He instituted the policy of **glasnost** (GLAHZ nost), or "openness," which allowed citizens and news media to say what they wished without fear of government persecution.

Gorbachev also offered a plan for **perestroika** (per uh STROY kuh), or economic restructuring, which called for a gradual change from a command system to private ownership. Under perestroika, factory managers rather than central planners decided what kinds and quality of goods to produce and how much to charge. Farmers were granted long-term leases on land in hopes of increasing food production. For the first time in decades, independent businesses were established.

Political Change Given new freedoms, many people called for an end to communism and central government domination. The Baltic republics declared their independence. Early in 1991, Russians voted in their first democratic election, selecting Boris Yeltsin as president of the Russian Republic. Some Communist officials tried to use military force to reclaim control, but Yeltsin defeated this threat. In the months that followed, newly elected national leaders declared their republics independent of the Soviet Union.

At the end of the year, Gorbachev resigned, announcing the end of the Soviet Union. "We live in a new world," he said. Some of the republics joined with Russia in a loose association, the Commonwealth of Independent States (CIS). As they established their own governments, however, these new nations emphasized their own independence rather than cooperation.

Planning for the Future With only a brief experience in democracy, Russia faces

Chapter 20 ▪ Section 2   **425**

Chapter 20 ▪ Section 2   **425**

Improving Relations

Cooperation and Conflict After years of communism and Cold War tension, Russia is trying to establish a new democratic identity in the international community. Russian presidents like Vladimir Putin (left) have initiated closer economic and diplomatic ties with the United States.

Region How did the Cold War affect Russian relations with the United States?

many challenges. In the years immediately after the fall of the Soviet Union, many leaders were committed to democratic reforms, but the constitution allowed the president to rule by decree and ignore the elected parliament. Except for the Communist party, there were no major political organizations operating nationwide.

The problems and hardships associated with economic change placed Russian citizens in a difficult position. Many yearned for the prosperity they associated with free-market economies in Western nations. At the same time, they missed the secure jobs, benefits, and pensions of the old Communist system.

Russia's second democratic presidential election in 1996 saw a spirited campaign and high voter turnout as reformer Boris Yeltsin defeated a Communist candidate. When Yeltsin resigned in 1999, Vladimir Putin became acting president. His position was later affirmed in the 2000 election. Putin's administration has been characterized by a range of different activities to build alliances with a range of groups, including the Russian Communist party, other former Soviet republics, and Western nations, including the United States. Russia has sought a closer diplomatic relationship with the United States as it has taken a more active role in world affairs.

SECTION 2 ASSESSMENT

1. Key Terms Define **(a)** czar, **(b)** abdicate, **(c)** soviet, **(d)** command economy, **(e)** glasnost, **(f)** perestroika.

2. Understanding the Past Which ruler expanded Russian territory from the Baltic to the Pacific?

3. Economic Systems How did centrally planned spending affect the economy of the Soviet Union?

4. Government and Citizenship How did reforms introduced by Mikhail Gorbachev affect political organization?

5. Critical Thinking Making Comparisons Compare and contrast serfdom under the czars with state farms and collective farms under Communist rule.

3 Geographic Issues in Russia

Reading Focus

- **What are some defining characteristics of life in Russia today?**
- **How does ethnic turmoil challenge Russia?**
- **What methods of transportation are common in Russia?**
- **What economic and environmental problems does Russia face?**

Key Terms

ruble

black market

Main Idea Although Russia has a rich and diverse culture, many problems face the nation and its people.

Cultures Russians enjoy a wide variety of leisure activities, including basketball.

Objectives
Upon completion of Section 3, students should be able to:

◆ identify some of the defining characteristics of life in Russia today;

◆ explain how ethnic turmoil challenges Russia;

◆ list the common methods of transportation in Russia;

◆ summarize the economic and environmental problems facing Russia.

 National Geography Standards
The following National Geography Standards are highlighted in this section: 1, 3, 4, 5, 6, 9, 10, 11, 13, 14, 15, 16, 18

 Bellringer
Ask students to suggest why it might be more expensive to purchase raw materials from far away than to purchase the same materials found locally.

LESSON PLAN

1. Focus Write the following four subjects on the board: *Ethnic Turmoil, Transportation, Economic Problems,* and *Environmental Problems.* Ask: **What role do you think government should play in addressing each of these issues?**

2. Instruct Arrange students in pairs and assign each pair one of the four issues on the board. Ask each pair to create a concept map illustrating how its assigned issue is affecting Russia, based on the information in the corresponding subsection of the text. Then gather the class to discuss the issues as a group and create a class concept map on the board for each subject.

3. Close/Reteach Have students write a question they would like to ask a Russian leader about each of the four topics in the concept maps. Have volunteers share their questions with the class. Discuss possible answers for these questions.

ithin the vast country of Russia, ways of life vary greatly. More than 80 percent of Russia's residents consider themselves to be Russians, descendants of the Slavic peoples who first moved to the region more than 1,200 years ago. Ethnic minorities comprise the rest of the population. As a nation striving to govern an enormous area and as a nation in economic and social transition, Russia faces distinctive challenges. Many of these have important geographic dimensions.

Urban and Rural Life

Almost three fourths of Russia's people live in large cities, while traditional ways of life continue in villages and rural areas. During Soviet rule, housing shortages in cities became common. The government built huge apartment blocks, but several families often had to share an apartment. To escape crowded conditions, people look forward to spending weekends and vacations in the country.

Russians love the beauty of their countryside and enjoy hiking or camping in the mountains and forests. The Black Sea coast is a favorite vacation spot. Soccer and other sports are popular, as are movies and television. With the end of Soviet censorship, young Russians are free to enjoy and play rock, pop, and jazz.

Russia has a long, rich tradition of artistic creativity, although in the past, writers and composers were persecuted and silenced by Soviet authorities. Despite economic problems, many Russians enjoy concerts, opera, and ballet performances. They fill famous theaters such as the Bolshoi in Moscow and the Mariinsky (Kirov) in St. Petersburg.

Ethnic Turmoil

About 25 million residents of Russia belong to non-Russian ethnic groups. A sizable group of citizens are Ukrainians, Belarussians, and closely related Slavic groups. Many of the residents of Siberia descend from people who lived in the area for centuries before the Russians asserted control. Other groups migrated into European Russia.

The most complicated and unsettled collection of ethnic groups is in the Caucasus region of far southern Russia. The Russian federation that

Chapter 20 ▪ Section 3 **427**

Russia and the United States
Education Data

Country	Education Expenditure (as percentage of GNP)	Literacy Rate (percentage)	Students in Secondary School (percentage of age group)
Russia	4.1	99.5	85.5
United States	5.3	99.5	97.3

Source: *Encarta World Atlas*

CHART SKILLS

● **Economic Activities** *Which country spends a greater percentage of funds on education?*

● **Planning for the Future** *Based on the chart, which country is likely to have a higher percentage of students enrolled in college?*

emerged after the end of the Soviet Union consisted of 21 separate states, six of which are in the northern Caucasus. From 1992 through 2001, armed conflict had occurred in five of those six, as different groups fought ethnic Russians and each other.

Chechnya The most intense resistance to Russian control has been in Chechnya. Chechens had fought czarist expansion into the Caucasus region in the nineteenth century and Soviet control throughout much of the twentieth century. A region the size of New Jersey with about 1.2 million residents, Chechnya declared its independence in 1991 when the Soviet Union disintegrated. From 1994 to 1997, Russian troops tried to regain control of the region. They held the capital city of Grozny, but Chechen guerrilla forces dominated much of the mountainous countryside.

GLOBAL CONNECTIONS

Global Trade Patterns In 2001, Russia agreed to construct an oil pipeline from its Black Sea coast to Ankara, Turkey. The pipeline would be the world's deepest, about 7,000 feet below the water's surface. Some world leaders expressed concern that the pipeline would give Russia too much control over the regional oil market.

In the late 1990s, Islamic militants asserted themselves in Chechnya and nearby Dagestan. Chechen bombings in Moscow and other Russian cities have killed scores of civilians. Russia bombed and invaded Chechnya again starting in 1999, but the second invasion proved to be no more successful than the first, as Russian forces dominated in cities and towns while Chechens controlled the countryside. Both Russians and Chechens have been accused of terrorism and brutality. Peace does not seem possible in the short run, because Chechens want full independence, while Russia is unwilling to grant total autonomy to people it believes will spread violent opposition to Russia into other parts of the region.

Transportation

Russia's great size and harsh climates make it especially difficult to maintain good transportation routes. In many places, travel by road is often not practical. More than three quarters of all raw materials come from Siberia, where winter frosts buckle and pulverize concrete, and summer thaws turn roadways into mushy swamps. Siberian roads often are covered only with gravel. Although there is no speed limit, the roads themselves limit how fast one can travel. Air travel is expensive and unsuitable for transporting materials like oil and natural gas. These resources are brought to the western areas where they are needed through a maze of pipelines that crisscross the frozen wilderness.

Rivers Rivers historically have been important trade routes even though most Russian rivers are frozen for many months of the year. One journalist described how even frozen rivers can be useful transportation:

66 Throughout Siberia, boats ply rivers only in the summer; winter turns artery into bone. On the frozen surface, transportation is far easier. Trucks drive along the part-time pavement of the rivers and on the zimniki, as Siberians call their icy winter roads, a system far more reliable than the same quagmire routes during the brief summertime. 99

APPLYING THE GEOGRAPHIC THEMES

● **Human-Environment Interaction** Construction on the Trans-Siberian Railroad began in 1891. Today, it stretches east from Moscow with one line ending in Vladivostok and another in the port station of Nakhodka.

 • *Name three major cities located along the Trans-Siberian Railroad.*

One danger of this part-time road system comes in the spring when the ice begins to thaw and shift. Truckers must be careful to gauge the thickness of the ice, or they risk losing their cargoes in the rivers.

Railroads With about 93,000 miles (150,000 km) of track in the system, railroads are the greatest movers of people and goods in Russia. They are a practical alternative to pipelines for shipping oil. Because rail transport is inexpensive, Russian rail lines carry nearly half of all the railroad freight in the world.

The great Trans-Siberian Railroad, completed in 1904, runs across the country some 5,700 miles (9,300 km) from Moscow to Vladivostok on the Sea of Japan. Another major rail line runs about 1,900 miles (3,100 km) between Lake Baikal and the Amur River, near the Pacific coast. The Baikal-Amur Mainline opened in 1984. Its route crosses some 3,700 bodies of water and seven mountain ranges, passing through tunnels as much as 9 miles (14 km) long.

Economic Problems

The transition from the old Soviet command economy to a market economy has been difficult. Some Russians have prospered by starting their own businesses. However, others have lost secure government jobs, benefits, and pensions. Consumer goods have been scarce, and many people cannot afford them.

Inflation Soon after the Soviet Union fell apart, Russian leaders ended government price

---

Articles From
NATIONAL GEOGRAPHIC

The following article may be used to extend the content in this section.

Montaigne, Fen, and Gerd Ludwig, photographer. "Russia's Iron Road." *National Geographic*, Vol. 193, No. 6 (June 1998), pp. 2–33.

The Trans-Siberian Railroad—the world's longest—stands as a symbol of past imperialism as well as modernity.

Fast Food Comes to Moscow With the opening of the Soviet society and economy, U.S. companies found new markets and opportunities. The first McDonald's restaurant opened in Moscow in 1990, and Muscovites stood in line for hours to sample hamburgers and French fries. By the end of the year 2000, McDonald's had served 250 million Russians—that is, almost the whole population of Russia twice. Other American chains, such as Pizza Hut, have tried to imitate the success experienced by McDonald's in Russia, only to pull out after poor sales.

Making Judgments Have students discuss the following question: **What is the most crucial problem facing Russia's economy—geographical challenges or ideological challenges?** As the discussion progresses, ask for volunteers to write short summaries of student ideas on the board under the headings *Geographical Challenges* and *Ideological Challenges*. Ask for volunteers to summarize the discussion.

Answer to Photo Caption

Possible answer: The vehicles are a foreign brand.

Change Over Time

Economic Change

Economic Systems In the Soviet Union, a key economic priority was military spending (PAST). Today, more companies focus on producing consumer goods such as these sport utility vehicles (PRESENT).

Region *How does this photograph suggest the importance of foreign investment in Russia?*

PRESENT

PAST

controls. Prices skyrocketed. Within just a few years, the **ruble,** which had been officially set as equal to U.S. $1.75, fell to be worth less than one U.S. penny. Government controls and timely loans from international bankers helped bring inflation under control.

However, the financial instability led many Russians to resort to trading goods and services through barter. A **black market** through which goods and services move unofficially without formal record keeping also has grown. Some Russian economic observers argue that informal transfers now exceed formal economic transactions in value.

Privatization A central part of post-Communist economic restructuring was the conversion of state-run industries into private firms. This process was successful in a few industries, but faltered in others. Not all collective farms were divided into individual farms. Most farmers formed new cooperative arrangements that left farm management largely unchanged. Farmers seemed to prefer the familiarity of the Soviet-style arrangements despite their inefficiencies.

Other attempts to privatize state-held industries failed because of corruption. New owners

sold physical assets of the operations and deposited the profits in foreign bank accounts.

In other cases, industries were too old or inefficient to attract new buyers. A number of steel plants, coal mines, shipyards, and arms plants continued to be run by the government, but with no market for their products, workers were told to work only part-time or were laid off altogether.

As a result of rising inflation and unemployment, the standard of living for many dropped. Early in 1999, a state agency determined that nearly 4 in 10 Russians were trying to survive on incomes less than the official level for subsistence.

Health Problems The quality of health care declined during the 1990s. Death rates rose to a level of 14 deaths for every 1,000 people per year (compared with a rate of only 8.7 per 1,000 in the United States), and the average life expectancy for men fell to 61 years (compared with 74.24 in the United States).

Increases in alcoholism, drug abuse, divorce, and suicide also told of increased stresses on the Russian people. The economic uncertainty together with social pressures led to a decrease in the birthrate to a level of only 9 births for every

1,000 people per year. With far fewer native Russians being born than are dying, the nation's population has declined by more than 3 million people over the last decade.

Environmental Problems

At the same time that the Russian people and their leaders are wrestling with major economic problems, they have become aware of major environmental challenges. Many decisions made by Soviet central planners were wasteful and inefficient. Intense industrialization depleted resources and hurt the environment.

With its rich storehouse of natural resources, Siberia was particularly hard hit. Many Siberian cities rank among Russia's most polluted urban centers. In some areas, lung cancer levels and respiratory infections among children occur at an alarming rate. Oil spills and industrial pollution threaten to harm bodies of water beyond repair. The Volga River is so polluted and choked by dams that many fish species are now extinct. In the Barents Sea, a part of the Arctic Ocean north of European Russia, the navy dumped more than 17,000 containers filled with nuclear materials.

Many Russians have become increasingly concerned about environmental problems. Technical expertise is often lacking, however, to prevent further environmental damage and clean up past problems. An even greater problem is the shortage of money. As has been true in other nations undergoing the difficult transition from communism,

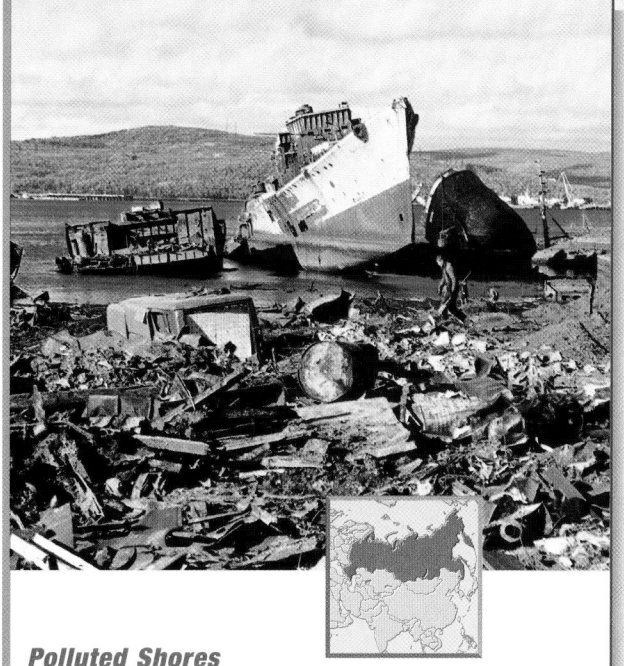

Polluted Shores

Environmental Change Abandoned oil tankers lie offshore from the Kola Peninsula, near the city of Murmansk. Oil drums and other debris litter the shore.
Human-Environment Interaction *What kinds of environmental issues does Russia face?*

clean air and water are admirable goals, but they are lower priorities behind immediate problems of keeping a job and obtaining adequate food and housing.

SECTION 3 ASSESSMENT

1. **Key Terms** Define **(a)** ruble, **(b)** black market.

2. **Cultures** How did living conditions in the Soviet Union influence the ways in which Russians spent their free time?

3. **Cooperation and Conflict** Why has Russia been unable to end fighting in Chechnya?

4. **Physical Characteristics** How do landscape and climate affect transportation in Russia?

5. **Economic Systems** How has the move away from communism affected the Russian economy and environment?

6. **Critical Thinking** **Defending a Position** Which of the problems facing Russia is the most significant? Explain.

Activity

Take It to the NET

Reporting the News Search the Internet for recent information about events and issues in Russia. Prepare a brief news report to deliver to the class. Visit the World Geography section of **www.phschool.com** for help in completing this activity.

Chapter 20 ▪ Section 3 **431**

TEST PREPARATION

Have students read the subsection Environmental Problems and the photo caption on this page to answer the following question.
Which of Russia's environmental problems does this photo suggest?
  A Air pollution
  B Nuclear waste
  C Resource depletion
  (D) Water pollution

Creating a Chapter Summary

As a reteaching opportunity, pair a more able student with a less able student to complete this chapter summary.

Regions Siberia, Plains, Ural Mountains, Tundra, Taiga, Steppes **History** Czars, Communism, Democratic reforms **Geographic Issues** Transportation, Ethnic turmoil, Environmental issues, Economic problems

Reviewing Key Terms

1–10. Students' sentences should show a clear understanding of each term.

Understanding Key Ideas

11. The Urals contain many valuable minerals.
12. The tundra is treeless and dominated by tiny plants, while taiga is covered by dense stands of small coniferous and deciduous trees.
13. The harsh climate and terrain of Siberia make it difficult to access the area.
14. Once the Mongol threat was ended, no sizable or powerful groups of people stood up against Russian expansion.
15. The economic policies of Communist Russia kept the standard of living very low. People had no freedom to make personal decisions or express their opinions.
16. Ethnic turmoil has decreased political stability. In several of the republics that make up the Russian federation, armed conflict has occurred as various ethnic groups fight Russians and each other.
17. Many decisions made by Soviet planners were wasteful and inefficient. Intense industrialization depleted resources and contributed to high levels of pollution. Oil spills and the dumping of nuclear waste have polluted water in and around Russia.

Critical Thinking and Writing

18. Climatic conditions become more severe as one moves toward the north. As a result, the major ecosystems of Russia lie in bands across the nation. The plants and animals in

each ecosystem have adapted to survive in their climates.
19. The czars oversaw the expansion of Russia, from the Pacific on the east to the Baltic on the west.
20. Answers will vary, but students should recognize that there were hardships under both systems: People were forced to work; they were not allowed to make personal decisions or express their opinions; and standards of living were poor.

21. (a) Russia's size and climates make it especially difficult to maintain good transportation routes.
(b) Economic development has been hindered. Although Russia is rich in resources, it has been difficult to develop them.
22. They see unemployment and poverty as more immediate, pressing problems.

Creating a Chapter Summary

Copy this concept web on a piece of paper. Add supporting details about each topic shown. You may need to add more circles. Some entries have been completed to serve as an example.

Take It to the NET
Chapter Self-Test For practice test questions for Chapter 20, go to the World Geography section of **www.phschool.com**.

Reviewing Key Terms

Write each of the following terms in a sentence that shows its meaning. You may use two terms in one sentence.

1. tundra
2. taiga
3. permafrost
4. czar
5. soviet

6. command economy
7. glasnost
8. perestroika
9. ruble
10. black market

Understanding Key Ideas

11. Physical Characteristics Why are the Ural Mountains important in Russia?
12. Ecosystems What type of vegetation distinguishes tundra from taiga?
13. Economic Activities What factors limit development in Siberia?
14. Understanding the Past Why was Russia able to expand in territory after the Mongols were driven from power?

15. Economic Systems How did economic policies of the Soviet Union affect daily life?
16. Cooperation and Conflict How do ethnic groups in some parts of Russia affect political stability?
17. Environmental Change How did Soviet policies and programs affect the environment?

Critical Thinking and Writing

18. Identifying Relationships How do climates affect ecosystems in Russia?
19. Identifying Main Ideas How did the czars affect the geography of Russia?
20. Making Generalizations Did people experience more hardships under the czars or under Communist rule? Explain.
21. Drawing Conclusions (a) How does Russia's size and climates affect transportation routes? (b) How might this affect the Russian economy?
22. Recognizing Points of View Why is environmental improvement a low priority for many Russians?

Applying Skills

Evaluating Conclusions Refer to the Skills for Life lesson on page 419 to answer these questions:

23. If you are looking at a photograph, chart, or written text, what is the first step in evaluating conclusions?

24. What are the characteristics of invalid conclusions?

25. What are the characteristics of valid conclusions?

Reading a Magazine Cover Study the magazine cover below, and answer the following questions:

26. What is the main message of the magazine cover?

27. Does the cover show a positive or negative image of the former Soviet Union? Explain.

28. Based on what you read in the chapter, does the cover contradict or confirm what urban life was like under Soviet control? Explain.

Test Preparation

29. Which geographic concept best identifies a major element in defeating the armies of Napoleon and Hitler?

A Population growth

B Migration

C Natural resources

D Climate

Activities

USING THE REGIONAL ATLAS

Review the Regional Atlas for Central Europe and Northern Eurasia and this chapter. Compare the Economic Activity and Resources map on page 383 with the map on page 417. Which natural resources in Siberia are most accessible? Which are most difficult to use?

MENTAL MAPPING

Study a map of Central Europe and Northern Eurasia. Then, on a separate piece of paper, draw a sketch map of Russia from memory. Label the following places on your map:

- Moscow
- St. Petersburg
- Nizhniy Novgorod
- Vladivostok
- Sakhalin Island
- Arctic Ocean
- Black Sea
- Caspian Sea
- Aral Sea
- Sea of Japan
- Bering Strait
- Lake Baikal

Take It to the NET

Making a Presentation Search the Internet for information about Murmansk convoys during World War II. Using maps and diagrams, explain to the class why Murmansk was important to the war, and what hardships were faced by convoys. Visit the World Geography section of **www.phschool.com** for help in completing this activity.

Applying Skills

23. identifying the topic

24. An invalid conclusion contradicts the available evidence or cannot be confirmed by the facts available.

25. A valid conclusion is based on facts and has a logical structure.

26. Possible answer: The Soviet Union is building a strong, modern society.

27. Positive. The city looks clean and modern.

28. Possible answer: Contradicts; during Soviet rule, city dwellers faced crowded conditions. Housing shortages were common.

Test Preparation
29. D

Activities

Using the Regional Atlas
Check students' work for accuracy. Students should present evidence to support their answers.

Mental Mapping
To check their work, have students compare their maps to those in the Regional Atlas.

Take It to the Net
Check maps and diagrams for accuracy and neatness. Presentations should reflect ample research.

MENTAL MAPPING

Games for Review See pages 58–63 of the Simulations, Games, and Lab Activities booklet for games to review place names.

Chapter Map Test Students should use the completed outline maps and the Unit 5 Checklist in their Atlas Portfolios to prepare for the Chapter 20 Map Test.

Unit Map Test To prepare for the Unit 5 Map Test, students will need to study the location of the place names on the Unit 5 Checklist.

Alternative Assessment

Final Evaluation

Making a Time Line Use the Time Line Evaluation Form on page 13 of the Alternative Assessment booklet in the Prentice Hall Assessment System to evaluate students' time lines. Either teachers or students can complete the forms to indicate which level of work was achieved for each of the criteria. The person evaluating the paper should provide specific examples and comments.

TEST PREPARATION

Use this sample exam to help your students prepare for standardized tests.

You might want to remind your students of the following:

Tips for Test Taking

1. Read the directions carefully.

2. Read each question carefully.

3. For multiple choice questions, try to answer the question before you look at the choices. Read all the choices. Then, eliminate those that are absolutely incorrect.

4. For short answer questions, be sure to answer the question completely if there is more than one part.

5. Answer the easy questions first. Then, go back to the ones that will take more time.

6. Pace yourself. Be sure to set aside enough time for the writing questions.

TEST PREPARATION

Write answers on a separate sheet of paper.

Multiple Choice

1 Merchant ships can reach the countries of Poland, Lithuania, Estonia, and Latvia by traveling into the —

   A   Black Sea

   B   Baltic Sea

   C   Mediterranean Sea

   D   Aral Sea

2 Siberia is most valuable to Russia because the region has —

   A   an abundance of natural resources

   B   a very high population density

   C   seaports that are free of ice all year

   D   fertile soil and a mild climate that are ideal for agriculture

3 Which of the following occurred in Poland as a result of World War II?

   A   Poland became an independent nation.

   B   The economy of Poland became more agricultural.

   C   Jews and other minorities in Poland were either killed or forced to leave the country.

   D   Poland was divided into two countries, one that had a democratic government and one that had a Communist government.

4 Which of the following generalizations about Communist economic policies in Central Europe, Eastern Europe, and Northern Eurasia is most accurate?

   A   Communist governments often encouraged industrial development with little concern for the environment.

   B   Communist governments urged farmers to buy more property so that the farmers' individual profits could increase.

   C   Communist governments encouraged people to form unions so that workers could win higher wages.

   D   Communist governments built high-quality nuclear reactors that experienced no major accidents.

5 Which of the following physical processes is typically the first step in soil formation?

   A   Climate change

   B   Weathering

   C   Precipitation

   D   Subduction

6 Which of these concepts best explains how human processes contributed to changes in political boundaries in Central Europe and Northern Eurasia during the 1980s and 1990s?

   A   Population growth

   B   Economic activities

   C   Migration

   D   Urbanization

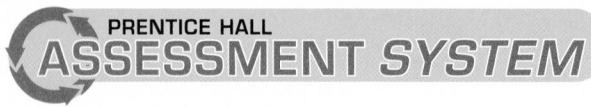

PRENTICE HALL
ASSESSMENT SYSTEM

Diagnose and Prescribe
  • Profile student skills with Diagnostic Tests A&B.
  • Address student needs with program materials identified in the test.

Review and Reteach
  • Provide cumulative content review with the Review Book.

Practice and Assess
  • Build test-taking skills with Test-Taking Strategies on Transparencies.

7 What factors contributed to changes in Russian boundaries between the 1500s and 1800s?

   A Few powerful groups of people and few natural barriers

   B Harsh winters and flooding during spring

   C Conquest by French troops

   D Seizure of territory by Mongols

Use the chart <u>and</u> your knowledge of social studies to answer the following question.

Country	Rate per 100,000 Population		
	Physicians	Nurses	Dentists
Poland	236	527	45.6
Romania	184	409	23.9
Russia	421	821	32.2
Ukraine	299	736	39.0

Source: World Health Organization, Estimates of Health Personnel

8 In which two countries is it probably most difficult for a person to get adequate medical care?

   A Poland and Ukraine

   B Romania and Russia

   C Russia and Ukraine

   D Romania and Poland

9 If Quebec were to become an independent nation and then follow the example of Belarus and Ukraine after the collapse of the Soviet Union, Quebec would probably —

   A establish close ties with the United States

   B abandon the French language and Roman Catholic religion

   C retain close ties with Canada

   D turn back from an industry-based economy to an agriculture-based economy

10 How have people used technology to adapt to climate conditions in Siberia?

   A The challenges of road construction have made air travel less expensive.

   B High-rise buildings are constructed on posts to keep them from collapsing when heat causes permafrost to thaw.

   C Extremely high temperatures cause heavy reliance on air conditioning.

   D Harsh winters have led people to conduct all transactions over the Internet, rather than by driving to stores and businesses.

Writing Practice

11 **(a)** How was the country of Yugoslavia formed in the years after World War I? **(b)** How did the country remain unified through much of the 1900s? **(c)** Why did the country fall apart by the end of the 1900s?

12 What are some of the political, social, and economic difficulties that Russia has faced since the collapse of the Soviet Union?

13 **(a)** Describe the importance of the Danube River to the people and nations of Central Europe. **(b)** How can the Danube River be a source of international disputes in the region?

Test Preparation Answers

Multiple Choice

  1 B

  2 A

  3 C

  4 A

  5 B

  6 B

  7 A

  8 D

  9 C

  10 B

Writing Practice

11 (a) After World War I, the victorious Allied nations established the Kingdom of the Serbs, Croats, and Slovenes, later called Yugoslavia. **(b)** Strong government rule kept Yugoslavia together. In the 1920s, King Alexander tried to force all Yugoslavs to use one language, Serbo-Croatian. He also created political boundaries that ignored ethnic claims. After World War II, a strict Communist government held the country together until the late 1980s. **(c)** After Communist rule ended, ethnic tensions grew and Yugoslavia broke up into several smaller countries.

12 One political problem is conflict arising from ethnic rivalries, such as in Chechnya. Another political problem is that government leaders find it hard to maintain popular support because many people are dissatisfied with the government's handling of new economic and social problems. Some social problems are increases in alcoholism, drug abuse, divorce, and suicide. Economic problems include inflation and corruption.

13 (a) The Danube flows through many countries of Central Europe. People rely on water from the Danube for drinking, farming, and industry. **(b)** Countries that pollute the Danube adversely affect the quality of the water for countries that lie downstream. This causes international disputes.

Central and South-west Asia

Activating Prior Knowledge
Have students share what they know about Central and Southwest Asia. Ask students to name any countries they know of that lie within the region. Have them describe the landscape of the region. Finally, ask if students have heard or read anything in the news about Central and Southwest Asia.

Photo Study

Shibam, Yemen
The old walled city of Shibam, Yemen, is located within a fertile valley along the Wadi Hadramaut. This east-central region has been inhabited since ancient times and still contains many ruins as evidence of its past. Within Shibam are some of the first multistoried buildings ever created, constructed approximately 500 years ago. **Drawing Conclusions** Ask: **From the above information and by looking at the photo, what conclusions can you draw about the physical terrain and cultural geography of this place?** (The terrain is rugged and dry. There is some vegetation around the perimeter of the urban area. The region has been settled for a long period of time.)

eTeach

Be sure to check out this month's online forum with a Master Teacher to join in an exchange of teaching ideas. **www.phschool.com**

Central and Southwest Asia

Locating the Region
For centuries, Central and Southwest Asia has been a crossroads of trade and cultures. Europe, Asia, and Africa meet in this region, and migration has spread both goods and ideas to the far corners of the world. At the same time, empires and philosophies have come into conflict over the region. As you read this unit, watch for evidence of movement and conflict at this intersection.

Robinson Projection

RESOURCE DIRECTORY

Teaching Resources

Unit 6
- Geography and World Literature, Memed, My Hawk, p. 43

Mental Mapping booklet
- Unit 6 Checklist, p. 79
- Unit 6 Map Test, p. 90

Simulations, Games, and Lab Activities
- Where on Earth? Games, pp. 74–75

Global Environmental Posters

Technology

TeacherExpress™ CD-ROM
World Geography: Building a Global Perspective Teaching Resources on CD-ROM offers lesson planning flexibility, test-generation capability, and resource manageability.

Prentice Hall Presentation Pro CD-ROM
This CD-ROM allows you to create custom lessons for instruction or review for every chapter.

CHAPTERS

21	**Regional Atlas: Introduction to Central and Southwest Asia**
22	**The Caucasus and Central Asia**
23	**The Countries of Southwest Asia**

Shibam, Yemen

Go Online
PHSchool.com

For: More information about this region and access to the Take It to the Net activities
Visit: phschool.com
Web Code: mjk-0022

Unit 6   **437**

Promoting Geographic Understanding

Introduce the unit by using the themes below.

1. Location Help students identify Central and Southwest Asia's location as an intersection by referring them to the Robinson projection map on page 436. Ask students to describe the locations of Africa, Europe, and Asia in relation to the region.

2. Location Point out to students that several countries in Central and Southwest Asia are bordered by seas and gulfs. Ask: **What benefit do countries in Southwest and Central Asia receive from being bordered by bodies of water?** (Possible answer: Water allows goods, people, and ideas to be transported in and out of the region.)

RESOURCE DIRECTORY

World Geography Map and Photo Transparencies
The World Geography Map and Photo Transparencies provide thematic maps and photos to help students understand key geographic concepts.

World Geography Videos
These chapter-level videos help students understand the key concepts and themes of geography through case studies.

ExamView Test Bank CD-ROM
The test bank CD-ROM allows you to create, edit, and print out chapter-level tests.

Social Studies Skills Tutor CD-ROM
This interactive CD-ROM provides students with the opportunity to learn and practice critical social studies skills.

Take It to the NET
Prentice Hall's Web site offers Internet activities and links that supplement *World Geography: Building a Global Perspective.* Visit us in the Social Studies area at **www.phschool.com**.

Chapter 21 Planning Guide

Resource Manager

	CORE INSTRUCTION	READING/SKILLS
Chapter-Level Resources	**Teaching Resources** ■ **Unit 6**/Ch. 21 • Regional Atlas Study Guide, p. 2 ■ **Mental Mapping booklet** • Unit 6 Checklist, p. 79 ■ **Simulations, Games, and Lab Activities** • Place Location Review Games, pp. 58–63 ● **TeacherExpress™ CD-ROM**, Ch. 21 ■ **Companion Web site,** **www.phschool.com** • eTeach	**Teaching Resources** ■ **Unit 6**/Ch. 21 • Regional Atlas Review, p. 3 ■ **Guide to the Essentials (English/Spanish)** • Chapter 21 Summary ■ **Spanish Resources** • Regional Atlas Review, p. 53 ▦ **Guided Reading Audiotapes (English/Spanish)**, Ch. 21 ▨ **Section Reading Support Transparencies**, Ch. 21 ● **Book on CD**, Ch. 21 ● **Social Studies Skills Tutor CD-ROM**
Historical Overview Describe significant events and developments in the history of Central and Southwest Asia.	**Teaching Resources** ■ **Mental Mapping booklet** • Outline Map 21A, p. 80 ● **Prentice Hall Presentation Pro CD-ROM**, Ch. 21	**Teaching Resources** ■ **Social Studies Skills Handbook** • Reading a Political Map, p. 19
Physical Characteristics Identify major physical characteristics of Central and Southwest Asia.	**Teaching Resources** ■ **Mental Mapping booklet** • Outline Map 21B, p. 81 ● **Prentice Hall Presentation Pro CD-ROM**, Ch. 21	**Teaching Resources** ■ **Social Studies Skills Handbook** • Elevation on a Map, p. 20 • Four Types of Landforms, p. 21 • Relief on a Map, p. 22
Climates Compare climate regions in Central and Southwest Asia.	● **Prentice Hall Presentation Pro CD-ROM**, Ch. 21	**Teaching Resources** ■ **Social Studies Skills Handbook** • Reading a Climate Map, p. 26 • Reading a Climate Graph, p. 65 • Comparing Climate Graphs, p. 66
Ecosystems Describe characteristics of major ecosystems in Central and Southwest Asia.	● **Prentice Hall Presentation Pro CD-ROM**, Ch. 21	**Teaching Resources** ■ **Social Studies Skills Handbook** • Reading a Natural Vegetation Map, p. 25
People and Cultures Discuss elements of culture in Central and Southwest Asia.	● **Prentice Hall Presentation Pro CD-ROM**, Ch. 21	**Teaching Resources** ■ **Social Studies Skills Handbook** • Reading a Population Density Map, p. 31
Economics, Technology, and Environment Identify how the economy, technology, and the environment interact in Central and Southwest Asia.	**Teaching Resources** ■ **Creative Teaching Activities** • Economic Activities and Mineral Resources, p. 23 ● **Prentice Hall Presentation Pro CD-ROM**, Ch. 21	**Teaching Resources** ■ **Social Studies Skills Handbook** • Reading an Economic Activity Map, p. 27 • Reading a Natural Resources Map, p. 34
Database • Define *trade deficit* and *trade surplus.* • Compare the trading systems of select Central and Southwest Asian countries to those of the United States.	**Teaching Resources** ■ **Unit 6**/Ch. 21 • Regional Atlas Database Skills, p. 4 ● **Prentice Hall Presentation Pro CD-ROM**, Ch. 21	Teaching Resources ■ **Unit 6**/Ch. 21 • Regional Atlas Database Skills, p. 4 ■ **Social Studies Skills Handbook** • Reading a Table, p. 62

ENRICHMENT/HONORS/PREAP

📦 **Teaching Resources**

📘 **Mental Mapping booklet**
- Atlas Activity, p. 82

📘 **Social Studies Skills Handbook**
- Study and Research Skills, pp. 94–108

📘 **Simulations, Games, and Lab Activities**
- Where on Earth? Games, pp. 74–75

📙 **World Geography Map and Photo Transparencies**
- Central and Southwest Asia: Maps and Photos

📺 **World Geography Videos**
- Regional Atlas: Central and Southwest Asia, Tape 3

💻 **Companion Web site, www.phschool.com**
- Chapter 21 Activities

📙 **World Geography Map and Photo Transparencies**
- Central and Southwest Asia: Political

📙 **World Geography Map and Photo Transparencies**
- Central and Southwest Asia: Physical

📙 **World Geography Map and Photo Transparencies**
- World Climate Zones

📙 **World Geography Map and Photo Transparencies**
- Central and Southwest Asia: Natural Hazards

📙 **World Geography Map and Photo Transparencies**
- Central and Southwest Asia: Population Density

📙 **World Geography Map and Photo Transparencies**
- Central and Southwest Asia: Economic Activities

📙 **World Geography Map and Photo Transparencies**
- World Trade Cartogram

ASSESSMENT

PRENTICE HALL ASSESSMENT SYSTEM

Core Assessment

📘 ExamView Test Bank booklet, Ch. 21

💿 ExamView Test Bank CD-ROM, Ch. 21

Standardized Test Preparation

Diagnose and Prescribe

📘 Diagnostic Tests for High School Social Studies Skills

Review and Reteach

📘 Review Book for World Geography, pp. 13–14

Practice and Assess

📘 Test-taking Strategies With Transparencies for High School

📘 Test-taking Strategy Poster

📘 Alternative Assessment booklet

📘 Test Prep Book for World Geography

📦 **Teaching Resources**

📘 **Unit 6**/Ch. 21
- Test Forms A and B, pp. 5–10

📘 **Guide to the Essentials (English/Spanish)**
- Chapter 21 Test

📘 **Mental Mapping booklet**
- Chapter 21 Map Test, p. 83

💻 **Companion Web site, www.phschool.com**
- Chapter 21 Self-Test

CUSTOMIZE FOR INDIVIDUAL NEEDS

Gifted and Talented
- Teacher's Edition, Customize for . . . , p. 453

Less Proficient Readers
- Guide to the Essentials (English), Ch. 21
- Guided Reading Audiotapes (English), Ch. 21
- Section Reading Support Transparencies, Ch. 21
- Book on CD, Ch. 21
- Teacher's Edition, Activity: Vocabulary, p. 449

Students Acquiring English/ESL
- Guide to the Essentials (English/Spanish), Ch. 21
- Guided Reading Audiotapes (English/Spanish), Ch. 21
- Section Reading Support Transparencies, Ch. 21
- Book on CD, Ch. 21

Less Proficient Writers
- Alternative Assessment, Writing Assignment Rubric, p. 6
- Teacher's Edition, Customize for . . . , p. 443

Introducing

C H A P T E R

21

pp. 438–453

Objectives

Upon completion of this Regional Atlas, students should be able to:

◆ describe significant events and developments in the history of Central and Southwest Asia;

◆ identify major physical characteristics of Central and Southwest Asia;

◆ compare climate regions in Central and Southwest Asia;

◆ describe characteristics of major ecosystems in Central and Southwest Asia;

◆ discuss elements of culture in Central and Southwest Asia;

◆ identify how the economy, technology, and the environment interact in Central and Southwest Asia.

National Geography Standards

The following National Geography Standards are highlighted in this Regional Atlas: 1, 3, 4, 5, 7, 8, 9, 10, 11, 12, 13, 14, 15, 16, 17

Bellringer

Explain that most people in Central and Southwest Asia are part of the Arabic culture. Have students guess the answer to the following riddle: **Every day we use something that comes from Arabic culture. What is it?** (Arabic numerals)

Answers to Assessment

1. (a) agricultural revolution, p. 438 **(b)** civilization, p. 438 **(c)** monotheism, p. 438 **(d)** protectorate, p. 438

2. Judaism: principally Israel

Christianity: large portions of the Americas, Europe, Russia, and Australia

Islam: Central and Southwest Asia, North and West Africa, and parts of South and Southeast Asia

3. The emergence and spread of three of the world's most influential religions have greatly shaped the history and culture of the region.

CHAPTER 21

Introduction to Central and Southwest Asia

Historical Overview

The Fertile Crescent, stretching from modern Iraq to Israel, was the birthplace of both agriculture and civilization. Here, hunters and gatherers first began to raise plants and animals for food about 8000 B.C. in a process known as the **agricultural revolution.**

Civilizations and Religions By 3000 B.C., the Sumerians of Mesopotamia developed writing, complex societies, and states—all elements of **civilization.** Around 2000 B.C., a new religion called Judaism emerged. It was the first major religion based on **monotheism,** or the belief in only one god. Its followers founded a kingdom called Israel around 1000 B.C. The second of these religions, Christianity, emerged in the same region about 2,000 years after Judaism did. Christianity is based on the teachings of Jesus.

Migrations and the Spread of Islam Although the region was often dominated by empires, invasion by nomadic tribes was a constant threat. The Arabic-speaking tribes of the Arabian Peninsula adopted Islam, another monotheistic religion, and founded an Islamic empire. Between A.D. 632 and 714, they gained control of most of Central and Southwest Asia. Most of the region's inhabitants adopted the new religion. Other nomadic peoples occupied Central Asia and invaded Southwestern Asia between 1038 and 1400. By the late thirteenth century, the powerful Ottoman Empire had emerged.

European Imperialism Over the following centuries, European states sought power over the region. After the Ottoman Empire's defeat in World War I, European powers divided it into a number of nations and **protectorates,** or areas that have their own government but are controlled by an outside power. Palestine, a former Ottoman territory, had begun attracting Jewish migrants from other parts of the world seeking to form a new society in their ancient homeland.

Independence and Conflict By 1945, the former Ottoman territories of Lebanon, Syria, and Iraq had gained independence, and the last of the British protectorates gained full independence in 1971. War broke out between Palestinian Arabs and Jews over control of Palestine, and the victorious Jews founded the state of Israel in 1948. Most Palestinian Arabs fled to neighboring countries or to the West Bank. This was the first of several Arab-Israeli conflicts.

Residents of Muslim countries are divided between supporters of Western-style democracy and supporters of Islamic rule. The Iranian revolution of 1979 established Islamic rule in that nation. Meanwhile, in 1991, when the Soviet Union dissolved, independent republics arose in Central Asia and the Caucasus region. Following the ouster of Saddam Hussein by American and British troops in 2003, Iraq also edged unsteadily toward democracy.

Despite political uncertainties, many nations in the region are prospering economically. Turkey, Israel, and other nations have developed modern industries. Also, oil production has brought wealth to the Persian Gulf countries.

ASSESSMENT

1. **Key Terms** Define **(a)** agricultural revolution, **(b)** civilization, **(c)** monotheism, **(d)** protectorate.

2. **Map Skills Movement** Examine the map on pages 94–95. Where are Judaism, Christianity, and Islam most common today?

3. **Critical Thinking Analyzing Change** How has movement contributed to cultural change in Central and Southwest Asia?

438   Chapter 21 ▪ Regional Atlas: Central and Southwest Asia

---

RESOURCE DIRECTORY

Teaching Resources

Unit 6, Chapter 21
• Regional Atlas Study Guide, p. 2

Guide to the Essentials (English/Spanish)
• Chapter 21 Summary

Mental Mapping booklet
• Unit 6 Checklist, p. 79
• Outline Map 21A, p. 80

Social Studies Skills Handbook
• Reading a Political Map, p. 19

Technology

Guided Reading Audiotapes (English/Spanish), Chapter 21

Section Reading Support Transparencies, Chapter 21

World Geography Map and Photo Transparencies
• Central and Southwest Asia: Maps and Photos

Book on CD, Chapter 21

World Geography Videos
• Regional Atlas: Central and Southwest Asia, Tape 3

438   Chapter 21

Central and Southwest Asia: POLITICAL

Map labels:
Petropavlovsk, RUSSIA, Astana, Qaraghandy, KAZAKHSTAN, L. Balkhash, Aral Sea, Syr Darya R., Irtysh R., Bishkek, Almaty, KYRGYZSTAN, Tashkent, UZBEKISTAN, Amu Darya R., Samarqand, TAJIKISTAN, Dushanbe, CHINA, TURKMENISTAN, Ashgabat, BULGARIA, Black Sea, Caspian Sea, GREECE, Istanbul, Samsun, GEORGIA, Tbilisi, Baku, Izmir, Ankara, Erzurum, Yerevan, TURKEY, Kayseri, ARMENIA, Rasht, Aegean Sea, Antalya, Konya, AZERBAIJAN, Tabriz, Adana, CYPRUS, Nicosia, Aleppo, Mosul, Tehran, AFGHANISTAN, Mediterranean Sea, LEBANON, SYRIA, Damascus, Baghdad, Isfahan, Euphrates R., Tigris R., Beirut, ISRAEL, GOLAN HEIGHTS, Tel Aviv, WEST BANK, IRAQ, IRAN, GAZA, Jerusalem, Amman, Dead Sea, Ahvāz, JORDAN, Basra, Shīrāz, PAKISTAN, KUWAIT, Kuwait, EGYPT, Ad Dammam, BAHRAIN, Manama, Doha, Medina, Persian Gulf, Strait of Hormuz, Riyadh, QATAR, Abu Dhabi, Gulf of Oman, SAUDI ARABIA, Jiddah, Mecca, UNITED ARAB EMIRATES, OMAN, Muscat, Arabian Sea, Red Sea, Tropic of Cancer, Sanaa, YEMEN, Aden, Socotra (Yemen), Gulf of Aden, INDIAN OCEAN

Scale: 0 250 500 mi / 0 250 500 km

KEY

- National boundary
- ⊛ National capital
- • Major city
- ▦ Area occupied by Israel after 1967

Lambert Azimuthal Equal-Area Projection

MENTAL MAPPING

Making a Political Map Study this political map and then draw your own sketch map of Central and Southwest Asia. Label the countries and major cities of the region. Use various colors to outline and shade each country.

TEACHING TIP
From A Master Teacher

A Culture Hearth The connections between history and geography provide a useful framework for the study of Central and Southwest Asia. This area encompasses a hearth of early civilization, the Tigris-Euphrates Valley. While other areas were plagued by barbarians, this region was the center of science and learning. Later, the Silk Road snaked across the lands to link East Asia with the Mediterranean. Starting in the 600s, Islam spread from the Arabian Peninsula throughout Central and Southwest Asia.

LESSON PLAN

1. Focus Ask students to look through the Regional Atlas for evidence that supports or contradicts the following statement: "Oil and water are as valuable as gold in Central and Southwest Asia."

2. Instruct Ask students to complete the Mental Mapping activities and the assessment and photo caption questions in the Regional Atlas. Review answers as a class.

3. Close/Reteach Have students plan a trip from Astana, Kazakhstan, to Tel Aviv, Israel. Have them use the maps on pages 441 and 443 to write five entries in a travel diary describing the changes in the landforms and climate they encounter.

MENTAL MAPPING

Unit Checklist Distribute the Unit 6 Checklist on page 79 of the Mental Mapping booklet in the Teaching Resources. This list includes all the place names students should learn in this unit. Ask students to store the Unit Checklist and maps in their Atlas Portfolios for use throughout the unit.

Making a Political Map Students can complete the mapping activity on this page either by sketching their own maps or by coloring and labeling the Chapter 21A Outline Map on page 80 of the Mental Mapping booklet in the Teaching Resources. Ask students to label all of the countries and major cities listed under Part I in the Unit 6 Checklist.

Alternative Assessment

Introduce the Activity

Making Maps You may wish to distribute the Map Rubric found on page 14 of the Alternative Assessment booklet in the Prentice Hall Assessment System.

Map Study Extension
Use the questions below to develop additional geographic themes.

1. Location The cities of Aden in Yemen and Muscat in Oman sit near the entrance to two strategic waterways. Ask: **These cities are located near the entrance of what two waterways?** (Red Sea and Persian Gulf)

2. Movement Point out that two narrow straits exist in northwest Turkey between Asia and Europe—Bosporus and Dardanelles—providing a pathway for ships. Ask: **What two seas do the Bosporus and the Dardanelles straits connect?** (Black Sea and Aegean Sea)

3. Region Some of the most fertile land in Southwest Asia is located between the Tigris and Euphrates rivers. Ask: **What country in Central and Southwest Asia includes the largest area of this fertile river valley?** (Iraq)

Answers to Assessment
1. the Caspian Depression
2. The rivers originate in the mountainous regions of Central and Southwest Asia, particularly the Zagros Mountains.

Physical Characteristics

Towering mountains and vast, arid plains cover much of Central and Southwest Asia. Large plateaus in Turkey and Iran are framed by mountains that experience frequent earthquakes. In Southwestern Asia, deserts cover much of the plains except where rivers provide water for irrigation. In Central Asia, two of the world's great deserts, the Kara Kum and Kyzyl Kum cover the low plains of the southwest, while rolling grasslands cover the northern plains.

Aral Sea
Soviet engineers diverted water from the rivers that feed the Aral Sea, a landlocked salt lake, to irrigate farmland in Central Asia. The sea has shrunk dramatically, and salt flats now cover the exposed lake bed. **ENVIRONMENTAL CHANGE** *How do you think that conditions in the Aral Sea region might affect future irrigation projects?*

Tigris River
In arid regions, rivers such as the Tigris provide a vital but limited source of water. As expanding populations and agriculture increase demands for water, shortages may result. **NATURAL RESOURCES** *Why are rivers so important in this region?*

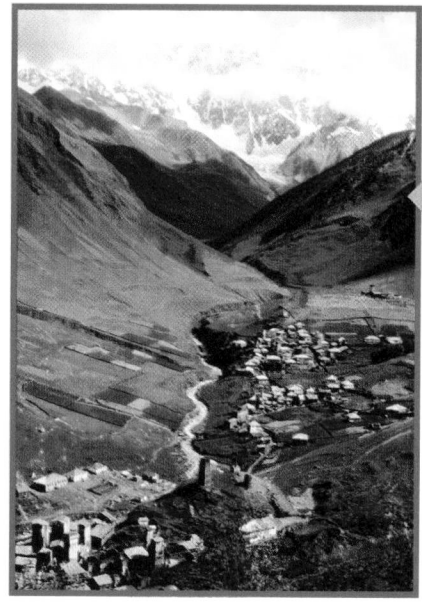

Caucasus Mountains
Forces from beneath the earth's surface have created the rugged mountain ranges that crisscross this region. **PHYSICAL CHARACTERISTICS** *Based on the map, what are the highest mountain ranges in this region?*

ASSESSMENT

1. **Map Skills Location** The Dead Sea, at about 1,312 feet (400 m) below sea level, is the lowest point on the earth's surface. What other parts of this region lie below sea level?

2. **Critical Thinking Interpreting Maps** Based on the map, what parts of this region provide most of the water for the rivers that cross the dry lowlands?

Answers to Photo Captions

Aral Sea There might be a shortage of water for future irrigation projects.

Tigris River Since the area is arid and receives very little rain, the river is the region's only source of water.

Caucasus Mountains Pamirs, Kirgiz Range, and Caucasus Mountains

RESOURCE DIRECTORY

Teaching Resources
Mental Mapping booklet
- Outline Map 21B, p. 81
- Unit 6 Checklist, p. 79

Social Studies Skills Handbook
- Elevation on a Map, p. 20
- Four Types of Landforms, p. 21
- Relief on a Map, p. 22

Technology
World Geography Map and Photo Transparencies
- Central and Southwest Asia: Maps and Photos

TeacherExpress™ CD-ROM, Chapter 21
Prentice Hall Presentation Pro CD-ROM, Chapter 21
Social Studies Skills Tutor CD-ROM
Companion Web site, www.phschool.com
- Chapter 21 Activities

Central and Southwest Asia: PHYSICAL

KEY

Elevation

Feet		Meters
14,000		4,270
7,000		2,135
1,500		457
700		213
(sea level) 0		0 (sea level)

• Major city
▲ Mountain
— Dam

Lambert Azimuthal Equal-Area Projection

Map labels:

RUSSIA · Astana · KIRGIZ STEPPE · L. Balkhash · KAZAKHSTAN · Aral Sea · Irtysh R. · Issyk-Kul · CASPIAN DEPRESSION · Shkhara Mountain 17,064 ft. (5,201 m) · BULGARIA · Black Sea · Bosporus · Inguri Dam · CAUCASUS MTS. · Caspian Sea · KYZYL KUM · Syr Darya R. · KIRGIZ RANGE · KYRGYZSTAN · Ismail Samani Peak 24,590 ft. (7,495 m) · GREECE · Istanbul · Dardanelles · GEORGIA · Tbilisi · UZBEKISTAN · Tashkent · TURKEY · PONTIC MTS. · ARMENIA · Samarqand · TAJIKISTAN · CHINA · PLATEAU OF ANATOLIA · Mt. Ararat 16,854 ft. · Atatürk (3,137 m) Dam · AZERBAIJAN · Tabriz · TURKMENISTAN · KARA KUM · Ashgabat · Amu Darya R. · Nurek Dam · PAMIRS · Aegean Sea · TAURUS MTS. · Urmia · ELBURZ MTS. · CYPRUS · Mediterranean Sea · LEBANON · SYRIA · Tehran · DASHT-E-KAVIR (GREAT SALT DESERT) · AFGHANISTAN · GOLAN HEIGHTS · SYRIAN DESERT · ISRAEL · GAZA · WEST BANK · Jordan R. · Euphrates R. · Baghdad · PLATEAU OF IRAN · Jerusalem · Dead Sea · IRAQ · Tigris R. · ZAGROS MTS. · IRAN · JORDAN · AN NAFUD · KUWAIT · Persian Gulf · PAKISTAN · EGYPT · ARABIAN PENINSULA · BAHRAIN · Strait of Hormuz · QATAR · Gulf of Oman · Riyadh · Muscat · SAUDI ARABIA · OMAN · Mecca · UNITED ARAB EMIRATES · Arabian Sea · Red Sea · RUB'AL-KHALI (EMPTY QUARTER) · YEMEN · Jabal an Nabi Shu'ayb 12,337 ft. (3,760 m) · Socotra · Gulf of Aden · INDIAN OCEAN

0 · 250 · 500 mi
0 · 250 · 500 km

MENTAL MAPPING

Making a Physical Map Students can complete the mapping activity on this page either by adding labels to the political maps they have already completed or by coloring and labeling the Chapter 21B Outline Map on page 81 of the Mental Mapping booklet in the Teaching Resources. Ask students to label all the bodies of water and landforms listed under Part II in the Unit 6 Checklist.

BACKGROUND

The Physical World

The Arabian Plate Three of the world's major continental plates meet in this region at the Arabian Plate. The Arabian Peninsula is a remnant of the ancient landmass called Gondwana, which many scientists think existed about 135 million years ago. Frequent earthquakes occur along the plate boundaries, especially in Turkey and Iran.

MENTAL MAPPING

Making a Physical Map Study this physical map and then draw your own sketch map of Central and Southwest Asia. Label the major physical features, including rivers and other bodies of water.

TEST PREPARATION

Have students use the information on the opposite page and the physical map on this page to answer the following question. Which area in Central and Southwest Asia would most likely be affected by earthquakes?

  A the Caspian Depression
  (B) the Zagros Mountains
  C the Persian Gulf
  D the Pampirs Mountains

Map Study Extension

Use the questions below to develop additional geographic themes.

1. Location While most of Central and Southwest Asia is arid, semiarid, or Mediterranean, small sections of the region are not. Ask: **What other climates are shown in Kyrgyzstan, Tajikistan, Azerbaijan, and Georgia?** (Parts of Kyrgyzstan, Tajikistan, Azerbaijan, and Georgia have a highlands climate; Georgia also has a humid subtropical climate.) **Why might these nations have different climates?** (The Pampirs Mountains in Kyrgyzstan and Tajikistan and the Caucasus Mountains in Georgia and Azerbaijan have created the highlands climates in those countries; Georgia's humid subtropical climate is due to its location on the Black Sea.)

2. Human-Environment Interaction The Karakum Canal was built in the 1950s and 1960s between the Amu Darya and the Caspian Sea. Ask students: **How do you suppose the canal changed life in what is now Turkmenistan?** (Irrigation allowed people to cultivate crops and raise livestock, and fishing developed.)

Answers to Assessment

1. the northeast corner

2. generally, the higher the elevation, the cooler and wetter the climate

Climates

Most of this region has an arid climate, with very little precipitation, or a semiarid climate, which receives limited seasonal precipitation. Mountainous and coastal parts of this region have cool, wet winters and warm, dry summers. Parts of Georgia are relatively warm and moist, whereas northern Kazakhstan experiences cold, snowy winters and hot, rainy summers.

Arid Climates

Large parts of both Southwest Asia and Central Asia have arid climates. Few plants can survive in these climates, and sandy deserts often develop. **CLIMATES** *Which countries lie mainly or completely within the arid-climate region?*

Source: www.weather.com

Curved lines show temperatures in Fahrenheit degrees.
Bars show rainfall in inches.

Comparing Climates

These graphs show average precipitation and average temperature for the cities of Beirut and Tashkent. Both get most of their precipitation in the winter. Beirut's seaside location gives it relatively steady temperatures. Tashkent has the cold winters and hot summers typical of inland regions. **CLIMATES** *Which city receives more precipitation?*

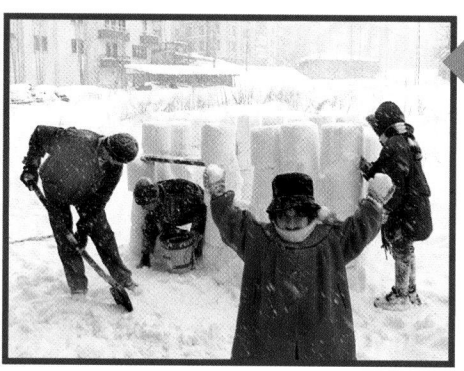

Cold Winters

Parts of this region have cold winters. A combination of heavy winter precipitation and cold temperatures produces snowfall in Turkey, Iran, Central Asia, and the mountains of the Caucasus and Iraq. **CLIMATES** *Would you expect higher snowfalls in seaside or inland locations in this region?*

ASSESSMENT

1. **Map Skills Place** Based on the map, which part of Iraq has the highest level of precipitation?

2. **Critical Thinking Recognizing Patterns** Compare this map to the physical map on page 441. What relationship do you see between elevation and climate?

442 Chapter 21 ▪ Regional Atlas: Central and Southwest Asia

Answers to Photo Captions

Arid Climates Syria, Iraq, Kuwait, Saudi Arabia, Bahrain, Qatar, United Arab Emirates, Oman, Yemen, Jordan, Israel, Uzbekistan, Kazakhstan

Comparing Climates Beirut

Cold Winters inland locations

RESOURCE DIRECTORY

Teaching Resources
Social Studies Skills Handbook
• Reading a Climate Map, p. 26
• Reading a Climate Graph, p. 65
• Comparing Climate Graphs, p. 66

Technology
World Geography Map and Photo Transparencies
• Central and Southwest Asia: Maps and Photos

REGIONAL ATLAS

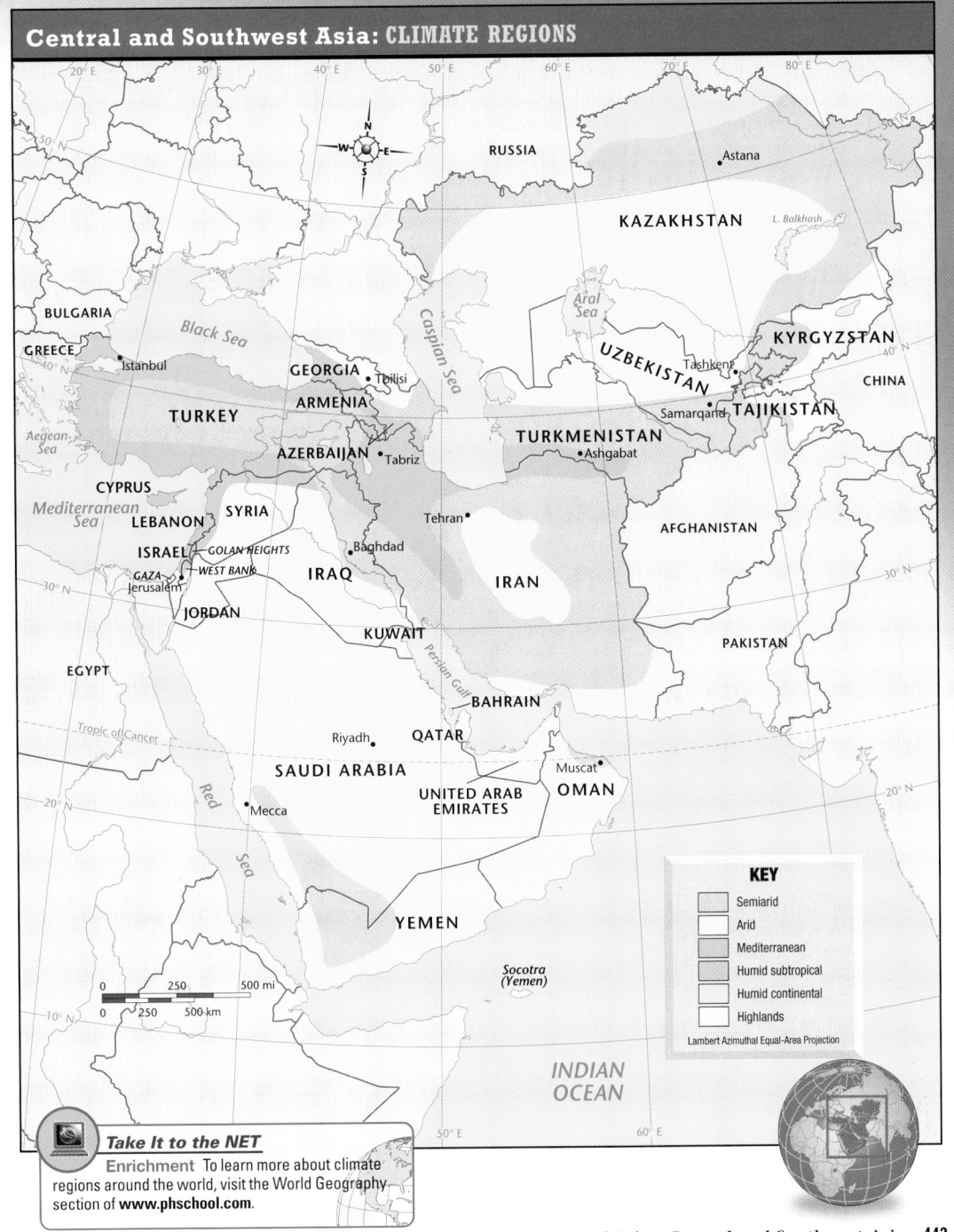

Central and Southwest Asia: CLIMATE REGIONS

RUSSIA

KAZAKHSTAN
• Astana

L. Balkhash

Aral Sea

BULGARIA

Black Sea

Caspian Sea

GREECE
• Istanbul

UZBEKISTAN
Tashkent •

KYRGYZSTAN

GEORGIA
• Tbilisi

CHINA

TURKEY

ARMENIA

Samarqand • TAJIKISTAN

AZERBAIJAN • Tabriz

TURKMENISTAN
• Ashgabat

Aegean Sea

CYPRUS

Mediterranean Sea

SYRIA

LEBANON

Tehran •

AFGHANISTAN

ISRAEL — GOLAN HEIGHTS
• Baghdad

GAZA — WEST BANK

Jerusalem •

IRAQ

IRAN

JORDAN

KUWAIT

PAKISTAN

EGYPT

BAHRAIN

Persian Gulf

Tropic of Cancer

QATAR

Riyadh •

SAUDI ARABIA

Muscat •

UNITED ARAB EMIRATES

OMAN

Red Sea

• Mecca

YEMEN

Socotra (Yemen)

INDIAN OCEAN

Scale
0   250   500 mi
0   250   500 km

KEY
	Semiarid
	Arid
	Mediterranean
	Humid subtropical
	Humid continental
	Highlands

Lambert Azimuthal Equal-Area Projection

Take It to the NET
Enrichment To learn more about climate regions around the world, visit the World Geography section of **www.phschool.com**.

BACKGROUND

Environmental Issues

Lack of Water In Central and Southwest Asia, where water scarcity is a major concern, groundwater is being pumped more quickly than the hydrologic cycle can replenish it. Fossil aquifers, underground reservoirs that have held water for millions of years, are being depleted in these water-stressed countries in order to meet greater demands to irrigate crops and provide for the needs of an ever-increasing population.

ACTIVITY

Reteach

Asking Questions Ask each student to write five questions and answers about climate in Central and Southwest Asia on index cards. Have students work in pairs, using their questions to quiz each other. (Verbal/Linguistic)

CUSTOMIZE FOR...

Less Proficient Writers

Comparing Climates Tell each student to choose two cities on the map on this page that have different climates. Have students create a two-column chart that compares the cities' climates. Finally, ask them to use their charts to write a paragraph that compares the climates of both cities.

Map Study Extension

Use the questions below to develop additional geographic themes.

1. Human-Environment Interaction Instruct students to look at the ecosystem map. Ask: **Where would you most likely find timber harvesting?** (in parts of Turkey, Georgia, Azerbaijan, Iraq, Iran, Turkmenistan, Uzbekistan, Kazakhstan, Kyrgyzstan, and Tajikistan)

2. Human-Environment Interaction Have students compare the desert regions and coastal regions on the map. Ask: **Before the age of modern technology, which parts of the region were least likely to support agriculture?** (the desert regions)

Answers to Assessment

1. (a) chaparral, p. 444 **(b)** poaching, p. 444

2. Turkey and Iran

3. Answers will vary, but students may suggest that the regions along the Persian Gulf and the Red Sea have arid climates.

Ecosystems

Desert ecosystems cover large parts of this region. Areas with slightly higher rainfall support temperate grasslands. Many of the most important domestic plants and animals, including wheat, cattle, and horses, originated in the grasslands of this region. Forests grow in the region's mountains and river valleys; **chaparral,** an ecosystem based on drought-resistant herbs and bushes, is dominant near the coasts of the Black and Mediterranean seas.

Deserts

Drought-resistant scrub covers parts of this region's vast deserts, but some desert areas are too dry to support much vegetation. The animals of these deserts, including camels, survive on very little water. **ECOSYSTEMS** *How can you tell that this ecosystem receives some precipitation?*

Tien Shan Forest

Much of this region is too dry for trees, but mountains such as the Tien Shan of Kazakhstan get enough rain and snow to support forests. The Tien Shan is home to a number of animals, including the golden eagle, a national symbol of Kazakhstan. **PHYSICAL CHARACTERISTICS** *Why might mountains receive more rainfall than neighboring flatlands?*

Caspian Sea

The Caspian Sea, the world's largest inland body of water, supports a rich variety of plant and animal life. These Caspian seals are threatened by pollution and **poaching,** or illegal hunting. **ECOSYSTEMS** *Why is the area around the Caspian Sea more likely to support many types of life than a desert?*

ASSESSMENT

1. **Key Terms** Define **(a)** chaparral, **(b)** poaching.

2. **Map Skills Location** Which countries have the largest forested areas?

3. **Critical Thinking Drawing Conclusions** What reasons might there be for the lack of chaparral along the Persian Gulf and Red Sea?

Answers to Photo Captions

Deserts There is some vegetation.

Tien Shan Forest Answers will vary. Students may suggest that mountains have more rainfall because of their cooler climates or higher elevations.

Caspian Sea The cooler climate and the water supplied by the Caspian Sea enable the region to support a variety of plant and animal life.

RESOURCE DIRECTORY

Teaching Resources
Social Studies Skills Handbook
• Reading a Natural Vegetation Map, p. 25

Technology
World Geography Map and Photo Transparencies
• Central and Southwest Asia: Maps and Photos

REGIONAL ATLAS

Central and Southwest Asia: ECOSYSTEMS

RUSSIA

• Astana

KAZAKHSTAN

L. Balkhash

Aral Sea

Syr Darya R.

BULGARIA

Black Sea

Caspian Sea

KYRGYZSTAN

GREECE

• Istanbul

GEORGIA

• Tbilisi

UZBEKISTAN

Tashkent•

CHINA

ARMENIA

Amu Darya R.

TURKEY

Samarqand• TAJIKISTAN

AZERBAIJAN

• Tabriz

TURKMENISTAN

• Ashgabat

Aegean Sea

CYPRUS

Mediterranean Sea

LEBANON

SYRIA

Tehran•

AFGHANISTAN

ISRAEL

GOLAN HEIGHTS

Baghdad•

GAZA

WEST BANK

IRAQ

IRAN

Jerusalem

Jordan R.

JORDAN

KUWAIT

PAKISTAN

EGYPT

Persian Gulf

BAHRAIN

Tropic of Cancer

Riyadh•

QATAR

SAUDI ARABIA

Muscat•

UNITED ARAB EMIRATES

OMAN

Red Sea

• Mecca

YEMEN

Socotra (Yemen)

INDIAN OCEAN

KEY

- Mid-latitude deciduous forest
- Mixed forest (deciduous and coniferous)
- Coniferous forest
- Chaparral
- Temperate grassland
- Desert scrub
- Desert (little or no vegetation)

Lambert Azimuthal Equal-Area Projection

0   250   500 mi
0   250   500 km

Take It to the NET

Enrichment To learn more about ecosystems around the world, visit the World Geography section of **www.phschool.com**.

Map Study Extension

Use the questions below to develop additional geographic themes.

1. Place Instruct students to compare the location of uninhabited areas on this map to the physical map on page 441 and the climate and ecosystem maps on pages 443 and 445. Ask: **How would these uninhabited areas look to a traveler?** (forbidding, incapable of cultivation)

2. Human-Environment Interaction Tell students that Istanbul, Turkey, was once Constantinople, the capital of the Roman Empire. Ask students: **Why do you think that the Romans chose this location for their capital?** (Its location on the Bosporus strait and its proximity to both Europe and Asia made it a convenient location for trade and transportation.) **Why do you think that Istanbul is now Turkey's most densely populated city?** (Its location and history allowed it to grow into a center of culture and commerce.)

Answers to Assessment

1. (a) mosque, p. 446 **(b)** muezzin, p. 446 **(c)** minaret, p. 446

2. Possible answers: Turkey, Lebanon, Israel, Azerbaijan, Georgia, Armenia, Bahrain, Syria

3. These areas have more water and are more fertile; oceans and rivers promote trade and settlement.

Answers to Photo Captions

Traditional Culture Their income would increase.

Islamic Worship Yes; most people in Central and Southwest Asia are Muslims.

A Holy City Different religious groups struggle for control of Jerusalem because each considers the city to be a sacred site.

446 Chapter 21

People and Cultures

Water is a scarce resource across much of this region, and the population is concentrated in fertile river valleys and the rainier coastal areas along the Black and Mediterranean seas. The arid deserts of the region have very few inhabitants. Despite its forbidding environment, the region has a rich cultural history. Judaism, Christianity, and Islam all developed in the region. Although each religion has many local followers, most people in Central and Southwest Asia are Muslims.

Traditional Culture

For centuries, the region's nomadic livestock herders have lived in movable tents called yurts. These herders have made additional money by producing fine carpets and rugs. Although these products used to be sold mainly within the region, they are now sold throughout the world. **GLOBAL TRADE PATTERNS** *How might a worldwide market for carpets affect the income of nomadic herders?*

Islamic Worship

Some of the most visible signs of Islamic heritage are the **mosques**—Islamic places of worship. Five times each day, a **muezzin** (myoo EZ in), or crier, climbs the **minaret,** the tower attached to the mosque, to call the people to prayer. **CULTURES** *Would you expect to find many mosques in Central and Southwest Asian cities? Explain.*

A Holy City

Jerusalem, shown here, is sacred to members of three religions. Jews consider it to be the site of the ancient kingdom of Israel. To Christians, it is the place where Jesus was crucified. Muslims believe that Muhammad visited heaven from Jerusalem. **COOPERATION AND CONFLICT** *Why might Jerusalem's religious importance contribute to conflict between different groups?*

ASSESSMENT

1. **Key Terms** Define **(a)** mosque, **(b)** muezzin, **(c)** minaret.
2. **Map Skills Place** Which countries in this region have the highest population densities?
3. **Critical Thinking Drawing Conclusions** Why do you think that the region's largest cities lie in river valleys or along the coast?

RESOURCE DIRECTORY

Teaching Resources
Social Studies Skills Handbook
• Reading a Population Density Map, p. 31

Technology
World Geography Map and Photo Transparencies
• Central and Southwest Asia: Maps and Photos

REGIONAL ATLAS

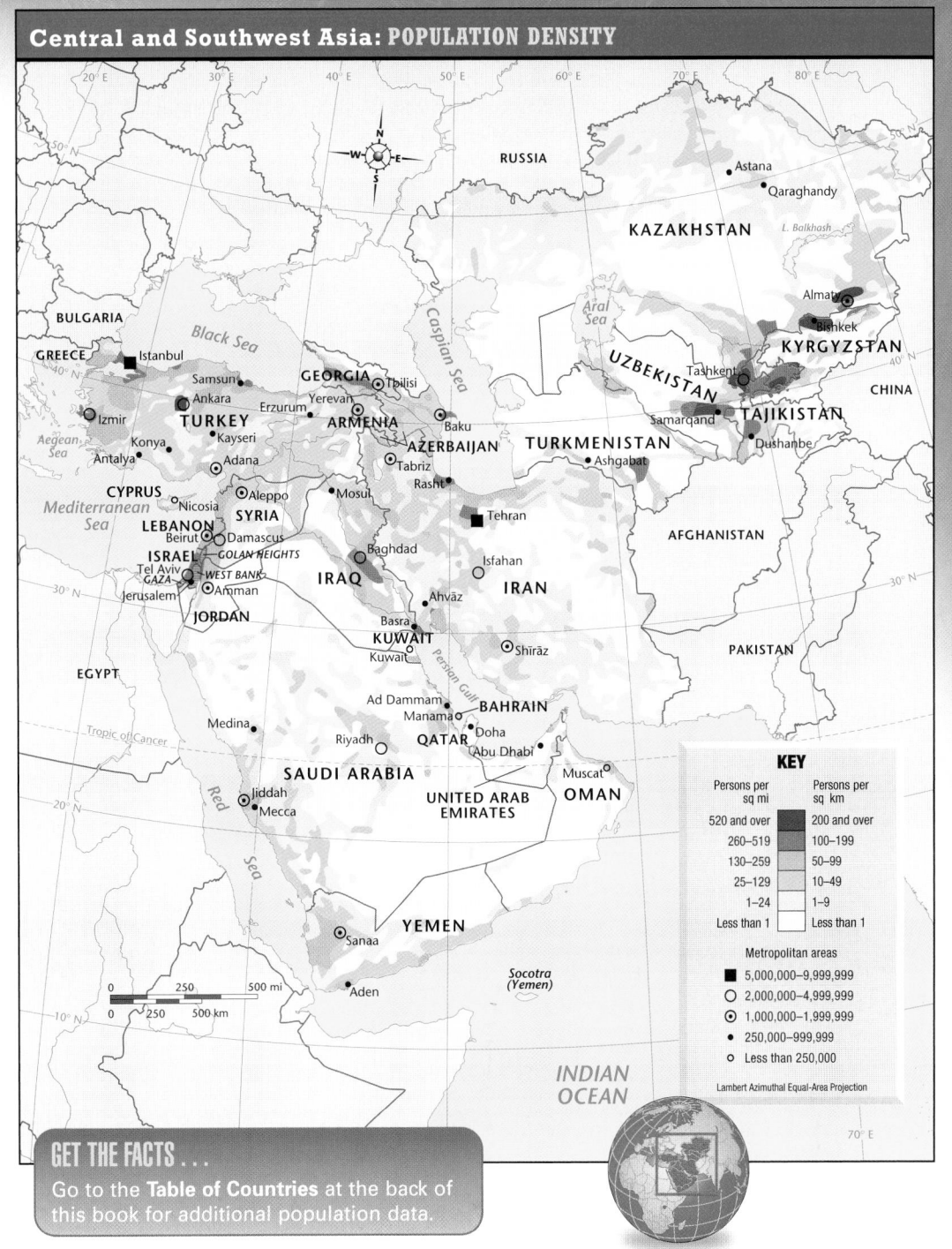

Central and Southwest Asia: POPULATION DENSITY

KEY

Persons per sq mi	Persons per sq km
520 and over	200 and over
260–519	100–199
130–259	50–99
25–129	10–49
1–24	1–9
Less than 1	Less than 1

Metropolitan areas

■ 5,000,000–9,999,999
O 2,000,000–4,999,999
◉ 1,000,000–1,999,999
• 250,000–999,999
o Less than 250,000

Lambert Azimuthal Equal-Area Projection

GET THE FACTS . . .
Go to the **Table of Countries** at the back of this book for additional population data.

Chapter 21 ▪ Regional Atlas: Central and Southwest Asia **447**

ACTIVITY

Area Comparison

Using the Table of Countries Ask students to use the Table of Countries beginning on page 742 of their textbooks to compare the land areas and populations of the United States and Saudi Arabia. **Connections: Math** Ask: **If the borders of the United States and Saudi Arabia do not change, which country is expected to have the greater population density in 2025?** (United States; students should divide the countries' projected populations by their land areas to find that Saudi Arabia is expected to have a population density of about 61 people per square mile, whereas the United States is expected to have a population density of about 90 people per square mile.)

BACKGROUND

Daily Life

Religion Although Southwest Asia was the birthplace of three major religions, all have spread far beyond their place of origin. Many Jews left the region around 2,000 years ago in the diaspora, settling in different parts of the world. Christianity became the official religion of the Roman Empire, spreading across Europe. Explorers and missionaries then carried Christianity to many other areas of the world. Merchants and soldiers helped to spread Islam through conquest and trade. The religion was adopted by people around the world, particularly in Africa and Asia. These religions continue to spread today, as immigrants bring elements of their cultures to many nations around the world.

Economics, Technology, and Environment

Although most of the land of this region is used for livestock raising and nomadic herding, the majority of its people live in urban areas, where services and industry are the main economic activities. In areas with fertile soils and water supplies, subsistence and commercial farming are important. There is very little economic activity in some of the region's deserts. Petroleum and natural gas deposits are among the region's main sources of wealth.

Atatürk Dam
Atatürk Dam provides Turkey with water for irrigation and hydroelectric power. Water is a scarce resource in this dry region, and Turkey's use of water from the Euphrates River has caused disputes with Syria and Iraq downstream. **ECONOMIC ACTIVITIES** *What economic activities benefit from dams like this one?*

Water From the Sea
Some countries with water shortages have built **desalination plants,** such as this one in Saudi Arabia. These plants evaporate seawater to obtain fresh water. **SCIENCE AND TECHNOLOGY** *Which countries have seacoasts, which would permit desalination, and which lack them?*

Nomadic Herding
Like other groups across Southwest Asia, these Bedouin shepherds are livestock-herding **nomads,** people who travel from place to place. Most nomadic herders move seasonally, often between winter and summer pastures. **ECONOMIC ACTIVITIES** *Which countries have the largest areas devoted to nomadic herding?*

ASSESSMENT

1. **Key Terms** Define **(a)** desalination plant, **(b)** nomad.

2. **Map Skills** **Location** Which countries have supplies of petroleum or natural gas?

3. **Critical Thinking** **Identifying Relationships** Why might water be a source of conflict in this region?

REGIONAL ATLAS

Central and Southwest Asia: ECONOMIC ACTIVITIES AND RESOURCES

KEY

- Nomadic herding
- Livestock raising
- Commercial farming
- Subsistence farming
- Manufacturing and trade
- Commercial fishing
- Little or no activity
- Coal
- Petroleum
- Natural Gas
- Hydroelectric power
- Iron
- Copper
- Bauxite
- Gold
- Silver
- Phosphates
- Uranium
- Tin
- Lead
- Nickel
- Tungsten

Lambert Azimuthal Equal-Area Projection

Take It to the NET
Enrichment To learn more about the economic activities and resources of this region, visit the World Geography section of **www.phschool.com**

GLOBAL CONNECTIONS

Global Trade Patterns

The Silk Road In ancient times, the Silk Road passed through parts of Central and Southwest Asia. The Silk Road was a trade route that connected China with cities on the Mediterranean Sea, from which goods could be shipped to Rome and sold throughout Europe. They traveled by caravan through the areas that are now Uzbekistan, Afghanistan, Iran, Iraq, Syria, Turkey, and Lebanon. Traders brought silks to the west and wool and precious metals to the east. In addition to enabling trade, the route facilitated the spread of Buddhism and Nestorian Christianity into China.

Articles From
NATIONAL GEOGRAPHIC

The following articles may be used to extend the content in this section.

Vesilind, Pritt J., and Ed Kashi, photographer. "Middle East Water—Critical Resource." *National Geographic*, Vol. 183, No. 5 (May 1993), pp. 38–72.

Cooperation is the key ingredient to making the most efficient use of water—a dwindling resource in the Middle East.

Cullen, Robert, and Reza, photographer. "The Rise and Fall of the Caspian Sea." *National Geographic*, Vol. 195, No. 5 (May 1999), pp. 2–35.

Once considered part of the Soviet Empire, the five nations surrounding the Caspian Sea struggle to resurrect their economies and start anew.

Database:
Comparing Trade
pp. 450–451

Objectives
Upon completion of this lesson, students should be able to:
◆ define *trade deficit* and *trade surplus;*
◆ compare the trading systems of select Central and Southwest Asian countries to those of the United States.

National Geography Standards
The following National Geography Standards are highlighted in this feature: 4, 11, 18

Bellringer
Ask students to define the words *export* and *import*. Have volunteers examine manufactured goods in the classroom to see how many of them are imports. Instruct the volunteers to state where the goods were made.

. . . .

LESSON PLAN

1. Focus Explain how a country comes to have a *trade surplus* (by exporting more than it imports) and a *trade deficit* (by importing more than it exports). Have students explain which they think is preferable and why.

2. Instruct Draw a rough world map on the board that includes the countries in the database, and draw lines from each country to its trading partners. Ask students to analyze the map and identify the distance between trading partners. Ask: **What kind of relationship would you expect Azerbaijan and Kazakhstan to have?** (They could have a competitive relationship, since they might compete for business from Russia. However, they could have a trade relationship with each other, since Azerbaijan exports machinery and Kazakhstan imports it.)

3. Close/Reteach Review with students the data on this page and the next. Then ask them to explain how each country would be affected by the following events: an oil shortage, a massive strike by factory workers, and an increased demand for natural gas.

450 Chapter 21

Database: Comparing Trade

As in other parts of the world, the countries in this region rely on trade to maintain their prosperity. They import goods that they cannot produce competitively themselves, and they export products that can compete on the world market. Conditions differ widely among the countries of this region and so do their trade relations. The data and explanations below help explain these differences. The data for the United States will allow you to compare that nation with countries in this region.

Source: *The World Factbook*

Key Terms: trade surplus, trade deficit

GET THE FACTS . . .
Go to the **Table of Countries** at the back of this book to view additional data for the countries of Central and Southwest Asia.

Take It to the NET
Data Update For the most recent update of this database, visit the World Geography section of **www.phschool.com**.

Azerbaijan

Exports, Total Value	$2.0 billion
Imports, Total Value	$1.6 billion
Trade Balance	$400 million
Leading Imports	Machinery and equipment, foodstuffs
Leading Exports	Oil and gas, machinery
Leading Trade Partners	Russia, Italy

Azerbaijan was formerly part of the Soviet Union, and Russia and other Soviet republics once accounted for most of its trade. After the Soviet Union dissolved in 1991, Azerbaijan expanded trade with its neighbors and with a few European nations. Today, Russia and Italy are its leading trade partners. Azerbaijan imports manufactured goods and food, and it exports oil and machinery. In recent years, it has increased exports by expanding oil production.

Kazakhstan

Exports, Total Value	$10.5 billion
Imports, Total Value	$8.2 billion
Trade Balance	$2.3 billion
Leading Imports	Machinery and parts, energy
Leading Exports	Oil, metals
Leading Trade Partners	Russia, China

Kazakhstan, another former Soviet republic, exports more than it imports, so it has a positive trade balance, or a **trade surplus.** Russia remains one of its most important trade partners, but trade with Germany and other European Union (EU) countries has increased. Trade with neighboring Uzbekistan and China is also important. Kazakhstan's main exports are oil and metals, and its main imports are manufactured goods.

RESOURCE DIRECTORY

Teaching Resources
Unit 6, Chapter 21
• Regional Atlas Review, p. 3
• Regional Atlas Database Skills, p. 4
• Test Forms A and B, pp. 5–10
Spanish Resources
• Regional Atlas Review, p. 53
Guide to the Essentials (English/Spanish)
• Chapter 21 Test
Mental Mapping booklet
• Chapter 21 Map Test, p. 83
Simulations, Games, and Lab Activities
• Place Location Review Games, pp. 58–63

Social Studies Skills Handbook
• Study and Research Skills, pp. 94–108

Prentice Hall Assessment System
Alternative Assessment booklet
• Map Evaluation Form, p. 15

Technology
ExamView Test Bank CD-ROM, Chapter 21 Test
Companion Web site, www.phschool.com
• Chapter 21 Self-Test

REGIONAL ATLAS

Saudi Arabia

Exports, Total Value	$66.9 billion
Imports, Total Value	$29.7 billion
Trade Balance	$37.2 billion
Leading Imports	Machinery and equipment, foodstuffs
Leading Exports	Petroleum and petroleum products
Leading Trade Partners	United States, Japan

Saudi Arabia is the world's largest exporter of petroleum, and petroleum products make up the vast majority of its exports. Its economy is centered on oil production and refining, and its desert climate does not allow it to produce enough food for its people. Even though Saudi Arabia has to import food and manufactured goods, its massive petroleum exports give it a huge trade surplus. Its main trade partners are the United States and Japan, and it trades heavily with EU countries, South Korea, and Singapore.

Israel

Exports, Total Value	$26.5 billion
Imports, Total Value	$30.6 billion
Trade Balance	–$4.1 billion
Leading Imports	Raw materials, military equipment
Leading Exports	Machinery and equipment, software, cut diamonds
Leading Trade Partners	United States, Belgium

Israel has a more technologically advanced economy than other countries in the region. However, it has a **trade deficit,** or a negative trade balance, meaning that it imports more than it exports. The deficit stems from Israel's need to import most of its raw materials, and also because it imports expensive military equipment. Israel's main trade partners are the United States as well as Belgium and other EU countries. Belgium is a major trade partner because Israel is a diamond-processing center and Antwerp, Belgium, is the world's leading diamond market.

ASSESSMENT

1. **Key Terms** Define **(a)** trade surplus, **(b)** trade deficit.
2. **Economic Activities** For which countries is oil, or petroleum, a major export?
3. **Global Trade Patterns** **(a)** Which countries in the region trade mainly with their neighbors? **(b)** Which trade mainly with the United States and other distant partners?
4. **Critical Thinking** **Drawing Conclusions** Which of the Central and Southwest Asian nations shown here would be most damaged by an oil shortage? Explain.

United States

Exports, Total Value	$723 billion
Imports, Total Value	$1.15 trillion
Trade Balance	–$425 billion
Leading Imports	Petroleum and petroleum products
Leading Exports	Capital goods, automobiles
Leading Trade Partners	Canada, Mexico

Games for Review See pages 58–63 of the Simulations, Games, and Lab Activities booklet in the Teaching Resources for games to review place names in preparation for the Chapter 21 Map Test.

Chapter Map Test Students should use the completed Chapter 21 Outline Maps and the Unit 6 Checklist in their Atlas Portfolios to prepare for the Chapter 21 Map Test. Point out to students that the test will cover all of the countries, cities, bodies of water, and landforms listed on the Unit 6 Checklist.

 Alternative Assessment

Final Evaluation

Making Maps Use the Map Evaluation Form on page 15 of the Alternative Assessment booklet in the Prentice Hall Assessment System to evaluate students' maps.

Answers to Assessment

1. (a) trade deficit, p. 450 **(b)** trade surplus, p. 450

2. Azerbaijan, Kazakhstan, and Saudi Arabia

3. (a) Azerbaijan and Kazakhstan **(b)** Saudi Arabia and Israel

4. Saudi Arabia; its export economy is entirely based on petroleum and petroleum products.

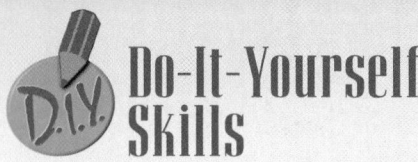

Do-It-Yourself Skills

pp. 452–453

Objectives

Upon completion of this feature, students should be able to:

◆ explain the purpose of a thematic map;

◆ follow a step-by-step process to make and analyze a thematic map.

 National Geography Standards

The following National Geography Standards are highlighted in this feature: 1, 2, 4, 9, 11

 Bellringer

Have students brainstorm about the kinds of information found in their textbook maps. (Answers include climate, population density, economic activities, physical characteristics, political boundaries, natural resources.) Ask students why this information is spread out on more than one map. (It is easier to see and to compare.)

....

LESSON PLAN

1. Focus Have students study the map of industry in the Persian Gulf region. Ask: **Which industries are most common in the region?** (oil and gas, oil refining, textile manufacturing) **Based on the map, what conclusions can you draw about natural resources in the Persian Gulf?** (Major resources are nonrenewable.)

2. Instruct Have students make their own charts with three columns—for Georgia, Armenia, and Azerbaijan. As students read the box about industry in the Caucasus, have them fill in each nation's major industries and their locations. Students should use this information to complete their thematic maps.

3. Close/Reteach Discuss with students the other types of thematic maps they might compare with the industry map of the Caucasus nations. Ask: **What kinds of questions would these maps help you answer?** Have students explain their responses.

Do-It-Yourself Skills

Making and Analyzing Thematic Maps

What Is a Thematic Map?

A thematic map shows very specific information. It may use shading or symbols to communicate data about a particular topic. One example of this type of map is an economics map, such as the map below. An economics map shows how people in an area make their living.

How Can I Use This Skill?

Thematic maps often appear in textbooks and periodicals. They are used to analyze current events and trends. This map (right) illustrates the industrial activities of the nations of the Persian Gulf region. Symbols are used to represent major industries, and each symbol is placed where the industry that it represents is most concentrated. For example, cities that are centers of finance receive a dollar sign symbol. By studying the map, you can recognize patterns. You can then draw conclusions by comparing the patterns with additional data and thematic maps, available from encyclopedias, almanacs, and other reference works.

Industry in Persian Gulf Nations

INDUSTRY
- Cement manufacturing
- Food processing
- Iron and steel
- Oil refining
- Textiles
- Oil and gas
- Finance
- Major industrial center / area
- Major road

Step by Step

Follow these steps to make and analyze a thematic map showing economic activities. As you proceed, use the map of industry in the Persian Gulf region (above) as a model.

1 Select a region. You can find economic activity data for regions, states, counties, and districts. For this lesson, you will map the major centers of industry for each country in the Caucasus region.

2 Research the data. The data for industry in the Caucasus nations, provided in the box on the opposite page, were derived from the *Encyclopædia Britannica Online*. Other reference works, such as almanacs, have similar information.

RESOURCE DIRECTORY

Teaching Resources
Social Studies Skills Handbook
• Using the Map Key, p. 3
• Reading an Economic Activity Map, p. 27

Technology
Social Studies Skills Tutor CD-ROM, Analyzing and Interpreting Special-Purpose Maps

Organize the data. In the box (right), notice that each country has several major industries. Create a table listing each country's major industries and the location of those industries. Remember to list only the economic activities that relate to industry.

Draw an outline map. On a separate piece of paper, make a map of the Caucasus nations, like the one below. Your map should include an outline of the region, country boundaries, national capitals, and major cities.

Create symbols, a key, and a title. Create symbols to represent each major industry of the Caucasus nations. Keep each symbol simple and easy to associate with its economic activity. As shown on the map of industry in the Persian Gulf region, you could use a symbol of a shirt to represent textiles. When you have created a symbol for each major industry, place the symbols in a key. Add a title to your map that summarizes the information presented.

Place the symbols. Reread your list of the Caucasus nations. For each major industry on your list, place the appropriate symbol in the correct location. Some locations may have more than one symbol, depending on the number of major industries there.

Analyze the data. Find patterns and compare them with other demographic data. For example, by comparing your industry map with a population density map of the Caucasus nations, you would learn that major centers of industry often are densely populated.

TIP

Analyzing Trends

Thematic maps usually correspond to surrounding text. Therefore, when you look for trends on a map, think of key points from the accompanying text. As a useful study aid, write a statement that summarizes the trends that the map illustrates.

APPLY YOUR SKILL

Make another thematic map for a nation of your choice. You might map farming and land use in one of the Caucasus nations you worked on above. Or you could map the major industries in your own state. Compare your map with thematic data available from an encyclopedia or almanac. Then, draw conclusions.

Industry in the Caucasus Nations

In the Caucasus nations of Georgia, Armenia, and Azerbaijan, industry holds an important place in the economy of the region. In Georgia, the coal industry is one of the oldest industries in the nation. Mines in Tqibuli produce high yields. Near the capital of Georgia in Rustavi, steel is a common industry.

Chemical industry and machine-tool manufacturing are important to Armenia's economy. The capital city of Yerevan is the main industrial center, accounting for more than half the total industrial output for the country. It is a machine-building city, as are Gyumri and Vanadzor. Yerevan is also a center of the chemical industry, as is Vanadzor.

In Azerbaijan, the city of Sumqayit is known as the center of production for industrial oils. In the cities of Baku, Gäncä, and Mingäçevir, the manufacturing of electrical equipment is a major industry. Baku and Mingäçevir also are centers of light industrial manufacturing, such as cotton and wool textiles. Baku is an important seaport as well.

Group Work

Activity: Analyzing thematic maps

Purpose: Have students find additional thematic maps for the Caucasus region in encyclopedias or atlases. Encourage them to use those maps and the industry map to provide additional data about the area. Have each group assemble its data and post the information on the bulletin board.

Roles: Each group should have researchers to find additional thematic maps, a scribe to create the list, and a reporter to present the list to the class.

Result: Reporters present data to the class and explain how the maps support their findings.

Answers to Apply Your Skill

Check students' thematic maps for accuracy. Conclusions will vary based on the map topic students choose.

CUSTOMIZE FOR...

Gifted and Talented

Analyzing Data When students have finished creating thematic maps for a nation of their choice, have them analyze the maps and draw conclusions about the probable level of economic development and standard of living of the people in that country. Then have students compare their estimates with the statistics in the Table of Countries in the back of their textbook. Have students explain how they arrived at their conclusions and do further research if the conclusions they drew were incorrect.

Resource Manager

Chapter-Level Resources	Core Instruction	Reading/Skills
	Teaching Resources 📕 **Unit 6**/Ch. 22 • Reviewing Main Ideas, p. 15 📖 **Mental Mapping booklet** • Unit 6 Checklist, p. 79 📖 **Simulations, Games, and Lab Activities** • Place Location Review Games, pp. 58–63 📖 **Creative Teaching Activities** • Ethnic Tensions in the Caucasus and Central Asia, p. 24 💿 **TeacherExpress™ CD-ROM**, Ch. 22 💻 **Companion Web site,** **www.phschool.com** • eTeach	**Teaching Resources** 📕 **Unit 6**/Ch. 22 • Map/Graph Skills, p. 17 💿 **Book on CD**, Ch. 22 💿 **Social Studies Skills Tutor CD-ROM**
1 The Caucasus Nations 1. Describe how climate and politics have shaped Georgia's economy. 2. Explain how political and religious differences with its neighbors have affected Armenia. 3. Identify conflicts over economic recovery and environmental issues in Azerbaijan.	**Teaching Resources** 📕 **Unit 6**/Ch. 22 • Guided Reading and Review, p. 11 💿 **Prentice Hall Presentation Pro CD-ROM**, Ch. 22, Sec. 1	**Teaching Resources** 📖 **Guide to the Essentials (English/Spanish)** • Section Summary, Ch. 22, Sec. 1 📖 **Mental Mapping booklet** • Outline Map 22, p. 84 📼 **Guided Reading Audiotapes (English/Spanish)**, Ch. 22, Sec. 1 📑 **Section Reading Support Transparencies**, Ch. 22, Sec. 1
2 The Central Asian Nations 1. Describe the physical features of the Central Asian nations. 2. Relate the effects of Islam on the peoples of Central Asia. 3. Explain how the economies of Kazakhstan and Uzbekistan changed under Soviet control. 4. Recognize the impact of irrigation, pesticides, and fertilizers on the region's environment.	**Teaching Resources** 📕 **Unit 6**/Ch. 22 • Guided Reading and Review, p. 13 💿 **Prentice Hall Presentation Pro CD-ROM**, Ch. 22, Sec. 2	**Teaching Resources** 📖 **Guide to the Essentials** (English/Spanish) • Section Summary, Ch. 22, Sec. 2 📖 **Mental Mapping booklet** • Outline Map 22, p. 84 📼 **Guided Reading Audiotapes (English/Spanish)**, Ch. 22, Sec. 2 📑 **Section Reading Support Transparencies**, Ch. 22, Sec. 2

ENRICHMENT/HONORS/PREAP

Teaching Resources

Unit 6/Ch. 22
- Critical Thinking, p. 16

Mental Mapping booklet
- Atlas Activity, p. 85

Social Studies Skills Handbook
- Study and Research Skills, pp. 94–108
- Expressing Problems Clearly, p. 40
- Identifying Central Issues, p. 42

World Geography Map and Photo Transparencies
- Central and Southwest Asia: Maps and Photos
- How the Earth Works, Unit 6

World Geography Videos
- Cooperation and Conflict: The Caucasus and Central Asia, Tape 3

Companion Web site, www.phschool.com
- Chapter 22 Activities

Companion Web site, www.phschool.com
- Chapter 22 Activities

Companion Web site, www.phschool.com
- Chapter 22 Activities

ASSESSMENT

PRENTICE HALL ASSESSMENT SYSTEM

Core Assessment
- ExamView Test Bank booklet, Ch. 22
- ExamView Test Bank CD-ROM, Ch. 22

Standardized Test Preparation

Review and Reteach
- Review Book for World Geography, pp. 13–14

Practice and Assess
- Test-taking Strategies With Transparencies for High School

  Test-taking Strategy Poster

- Alternative Assessment booklet
- Test Prep Book for World Geography

Teaching Resources

Unit 6/Ch. 22
- Section Quizzes, pp. 12, 14
- Test Forms A and B, pp. 18–23

Guide to the Essentials (English/Spanish)
- Chapter 22 Test

Spanish Resources, Ch. 22
- Section Quizzes, pp. 54–55

Mental Mapping booklet
- Chapter 22 Map Test, p. 86

Companion Web site, www.phschool.com
- Chapter 22 Self-Test

CUSTOMIZE FOR INDIVIDUAL NEEDS

Gifted and Talented
- Teacher's Edition, Customize for . . . , p. 457

Honors/PreAP
- Teacher's Edition, Customize for . . . , p. 459

Less Proficient Readers
- Guide to the Essentials (English), Ch. 22, Section Summaries
- Guided Reading Audiotapes (English), Ch. 22
- Section Reading Support Transparencies, Ch. 22
- Book on CD, Ch. 22
- Teacher's Edition, Reading Strategy, pp. 456, 461
- Teacher's Edition, Activity: Vocabulary, pp. 457, 461

Students Acquiring English/ESL
- Guide to the Essentials (English/Spanish), Ch. 22
- Guided Reading Audiotapes (English/Spanish), Ch. 22
- Section Reading Support Transparencies, Ch. 22
- Book on CD, Ch. 22
- Teacher's Edition, Customize for . . . , p. 465

Less Proficient Writers
- Alternative Assessment, Writing Assignment Rubric, p. 6
- Teacher's Edition, Customize for . . . , p. 461

Introducing
CHAPTER
22
pp. 454–467

MENTAL MAPPING

Ask students to look at the map on this page, and point out that the countries of the Caucasus and Central Asia lie to the south of Russia, with the Caspian Sea between the two regions. The nations of Central Asia stretch across to the western border of China.

Mapping the Region Have students create a map like the one on this page. Ask them to sketch their own outline maps, or distribute the Chapter 22 Outline Map on page 84 of the Mental Mapping booklet in the Teaching Resources. Instruct students to lightly shade each country a different color and label the countries and bodies of water. Students should keep their maps in their Atlas Portfolios in order to prepare for the Chapter 22 Map Test.

eTeach

Be sure to check out this month's online forum with a Master Teacher to join in an exchange of teaching ideas. **www.phschool.com**

454 Chapter 22

CHAPTER
22

The Caucasus and Central Asia

SECTIONS

1 The Caucasus Nations

2 The Central Asian Nations

The Caucasus and Central Asia: POLITICAL

KEY
— National boundary
⊛ National capital
• Major city
▦ Disputed territory

Lambert Azimuthal Equal-Area Projection

Go Online
PHSchool.com

For: More information about the Caucasus and Central Asia and access to the Take It to the Net activities
Visit: phschool.com
Web Code: mjk-0023

454 Chapter 22

RESOURCE DIRECTORY

Teaching Resources
Unit 6, Chapter 22
• Section 1 Guided Reading and Review, p. 11
Guide to the Essentials (English/Spanish)
• Section Summary, Chapter 22, Section 1
Mental Mapping booklet
• Atlas Activity, p. 85
• Unit 6 Checklist, p. 79

Technology
Guided Reading Audiotapes (English/Spanish),
Chapter 22, Section 1

Section Reading Support Transparencies,
Chapter 22, Section 1
World Geography Map and Photo Transparencies
• Central and Southwest Asia: Maps and Photos
Book on CD, Chapter 22
World Geography Videos
• Cooperation and Conflict: The Caucasus and Central Asia, Tape 3
TeacherExpress™ CD-ROM, Chapter 22
Prentice Hall Presentation Pro CD-ROM, Chapter 22
Social Studies Skills Tutor CD-ROM
Companion Web site, www.phschool.com
• Chapter 22 Activities

1 The Caucasus Nations

Reading Focus

- **What climatic and political conditions have influenced economic activities in Georgia?**
- **How have political and religious differences with neighboring nations affected the people of Armenia?**
- **How do demands for economic recovery conflict with environmental issues in Azerbaijan?**

Key Terms

autonomy

genocide

nationalism

Main Idea The Caucasus nations are rich in natural resources and are home to many ethnic groups.

Cultures Tbilisi, Georgia's capital, is a multicultural city with many different centers of worship.

Objectives

Upon completion of Section 1, students should be able to:

- ◆ describe how climate and politics have shaped Georgia's economy;
- ◆ explain how political and religious differences with its neighbors have affected Armenia;
- ◆ identify how economic recovery conflicts with environmental issues in Azerbaijan.

 National Geography Standards

The following National Geography Standards are highlighted in this section: 2, 4, 5, 6, 8, 9, 10, 11, 12, 13, 14, 16, 17

 Bellringer

Ask students to consider how the people of a country are affected by an economic setback. Point out that the American economy declined in 2001. Have students describe how that downturn affected people in the United States.

LESSON PLAN

1. Focus Point to Georgia, Armenia, and Azerbaijan on a map or globe. Ask students whether the location, size, and terrain of these countries offer advantages or disadvantages.

2. Instruct Draw a chart on the board with two columns headed *Causes* and *Effects*. Have students complete the chart with causes and effects of conflicts between the Armenians and people of other countries.

3. Close/Reteach Have students list the major economic activities and challenges of each Caucasus nation. Discuss which country faces the most significant challenges. Encourage students to support their views with information from the text.

Since ancient times, the lands of the Caucasus Mountains between the Black and Caspian seas have been home to many different ethnic groups. These groups have spoken a variety of languages and held various religious beliefs. The modern nations of Georgia, Armenia, and Azerbaijan (ah zur by ZHAHN) maintain their traditions, occupying lands their ancestors have fought for and defended for many centuries.

For much of the last century, all three nations existed as republics in the former Soviet Union. Their populations still contain many Russians and Ukrainians. Likewise, their economies are still closely tied to Russia and other former Soviet nations. Many of their problems today are rooted in past Soviet actions.

Georgia

Nestled between the Greater Caucasus Mountains on the north and the Lesser Caucasus to the south, the nation of Georgia sits on the eastern shore of the Black Sea. Slightly larger than the state of West Virginia, Georgia is mostly mountainous. River valleys in the west and east have fertile soils that support agriculture.

Climates and Economic Activities

The climate near the Black Sea is subtropical, with warm winters and heavy rainfall. These conditions support the production of grapes, citrus fruits, tobacco, tea, peaches, and silk. Georgia is well known for the fine wines and cognacs produced from grapes in this region. The pleasant climate also attracts many tourists from Russia and other Eastern European nations.

In the eastern part of the country, the climate is more continental, with hot summers, cold winters, and less moisture. Farm production in this part of Georgia consists mainly of grains and vegetables.

Economic Decline and Growth

Georgia's economy suffered severe setbacks after the fall of communism. The gross domestic product dropped by nearly three quarters, and inflation reached nearly 1,500 percent in one year.

◀ Turgen River in mountainous Kazakhstan *(photo left)*

Pacing Suggestions

For 60-minute Blocks

You will want to vary activities.

- Ask students to research the religions practiced in the Caucasus and Central Asia, including the percentage of the population in each country that belongs to each faith. Then have them prepare a bar graph based on their data and write a brief statement summarizing their findings.

The Physical World

Caucasus Mountains Stretching for hundreds of miles between the Black and Caspian seas, the Caucasus Mountains are often considered the boundary between Europe and Asia. They extend into Georgia, Armenia, Azerbaijan, and Russia, with many peaks more than 15,000 feet (5,000 m) high.

Building Vocabulary

Remind students that they can often determine the meaning of an unfamiliar word from its context. Have them read the subsection on this page entitled Cultures and note the word *incursions*. Then ask them to reread the sentence in which the word appears, looking for clues to its meaning. Discuss the clues they find. Then have a volunteer look up the word in a dictionary and read the definition to the class.

Alternative Assessment

Introduce the Activity

Writing a Report Ask each student to choose a country of the Caucasus or Central Asia and write a report about its physical geography and economy. As a group, decide on topics to be covered, such as climate, physical features, natural resources, agriculture, industries, transportation routes, imports, and exports. Distribute the Writing Assignment Rubric found on page 6 of the Alternative Assessment booklet in the Prentice Hall Assessment System for students' reference.

Answer to Map Caption

Answers will vary, but students may suggest that the mountains provide protection.

APPLYING THE GEOGRAPHIC THEMES

● **Human-Environment Interaction** The Caucasus Mountains run between the Black and Caspian seas. They form a natural barrier from Russia in the north.

- *How do you think that people in the region can use the mountains to their advantage?*

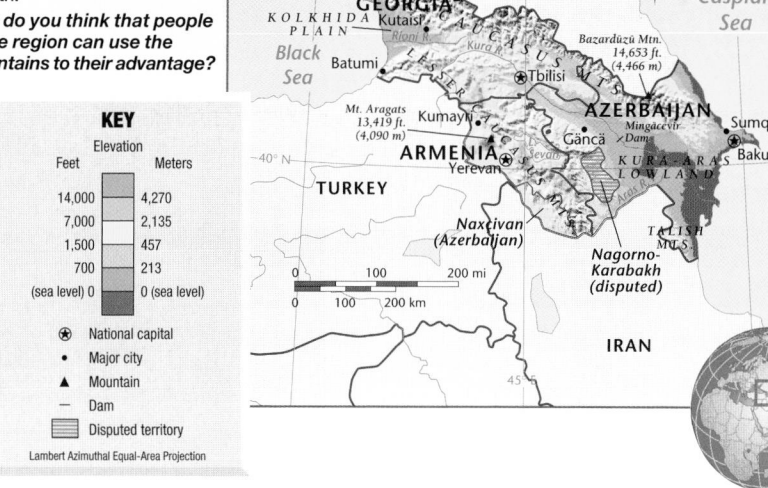

The Caucasus: PHYSICAL-POLITICAL

KEY

Elevation

Feet		Meters
14,000		4,270
7,000		2,135
1,500		457
700		213
(sea level) 0		0 (sea level)

✪ National capital
• Major city
▲ Mountain
— Dam
▨ Disputed territory

Lambert Azimuthal Equal-Area Projection

Since the mid-1990s, however, the economy has improved. Agriculture and machinery manufacturing have been key factors in the progression. Georgia is also a major supplier of manganese, a metallic chemical element; and it is developing its energy industries by increasing extraction of coal, petroleum, and natural gas. In the late 1990s, the construction of an oil pipeline from the Caspian Sea through the country's interior promised greater foreign investment.

Cultures Approximately 5 million people live in Georgia, and about 70 percent of those people are descendants of ethnic Georgians who have occupied the area for more than 2,500 years. Ethnic Georgians have maintained a distinctive language and culture despite frequent incursions into the area by peoples from what are now Iran, Turkey, and Russia.

Other ethnic groups found in Georgia— including Armenians, Azeris, and Russians—each total less than 8 percent of the population. The Abkhars and the Ossentians, two less-populous groups that each number fewer than 250,000

people, have pressed for more **autonomy,** or independence, in northern Georgia.

Georgia's president, H. E. Eduard Shevardnadze, has said the following about his country's long and difficult road to political and economic recovery:

❝Georgia's road of transformation has been fraught with ordeals. . . . [Today] Georgia has irreversibly embarked on the road of democracy [and a] market economy . . . [while] promoting respect for human rights and individual liberties.❞

Armenia

Landlocked Armenia is a small nation about the size of the state of Maryland. Most of this country's terrain is rocky, although farmers grow a variety of crops in southern valleys. Rug making is a traditional craft in both Armenia and neighboring Azerbaijan. Small factories manufacture goods, especially in the capital, Yerevan.

RESOURCE DIRECTORY

Teaching Resources
Creative Teaching Activities, Ethnic Tensions, p. 24
Unit 6, Chapter 22
- Critical Thinking, p.16
Mental Mapping booklet
- Outline Map 22, p. 84

Prentice Hall Assessment System
Alternative Assessment booklet
- Writing Assignment Rubric, p. 6

Technology
World Geography Map and Photo Transparencies
- Central and Southwest Asia: Maps and Photos

Understanding the Past The Armenians are an ancient Indo-European people. They have occupied lands of the southern Caucasus for more than 2,000 years. The country's rulers adopted Christianity in about A.D. 300, and the majority of Armenians continue to support their own national Orthodox church.

The fate of the Armenians often has been in the hands of other people, however. Mount Ararat, the peak where Noah's ark is said to have settled, has been a traditional symbol of Armenia. Although that mountain can be seen from many parts of Armenia, it lies within the boundaries of neighboring Turkey.

Armenian relations with Turkey have long been bitter. At the outbreak of World War I, the Turks attempted to deport the entire Armenian population. About one third of Armenia's total population died en route or were massacred by the Turks in an act of **genocide,** the systematic killing or intentional destruction of a people.

Recent Conflicts More recently, Armenians have fought with the Azeri people of Azerbaijan. Much of this tension is based on religion, as the Azeris are predominantly Islamic. Feelings of **nationalism,** the desire of a cultural group to rule themselves as a separate nation, are strong in both groups.

Policies of the former Soviet Union intensified tensions. The Soviets placed some areas settled primarily by Armenians under the control of Azerbaijan, including the region of Nagorno-Karabakh. Soon after Armenia and Azerbaijan became independent in 1991, Armenians invaded western Azerbaijan. By 1994, they had taken control of the disputed region.

Diplomats from the United States and other countries have tried to help these nations settle their dispute. In the meantime, the conflict has caused an estimated 350,000 Armenians to leave Azerbaijan and return to Armenia. About 190,000 Azeris fled Armenia to return to their homeland.

Azerbaijan

Located on the western shore of the Caspian Sea, Azerbaijan has rich deposits of petroleum, the country's main source of wealth. Almost half of the nation's inhabitants live in rural areas, where some people herd goats, sheep, and cattle on the mountain slopes. Farming occurs mostly in the valleys of the Kura and Aras rivers, which flow into the Caspian Sea. Farmers in the irrigated lowlands produce fruit, cotton, tea, and silk in the mild and dry climate.

Nearly 8 million people live in Azerbaijan. More than 90 percent of the population are ethnic Azeris. Many Armenians, Russians, Jewish people, and other minorities have left the area because of growing Azeri nationalism and ethnic conflicts.

Economic Problems The conflict with Armenia led to severe economic problems. As a plan of recovery, Azerbaijan hopes to continue development of its vast oil reserves near the Caspian Sea. Foreign investors are interested in these oil reserves but also hesitant—the area is prone to earthquakes.

The Caucasus, Central Asia, and the United States
Transportation Data

Country	Total Railroad Track Length (miles)	Total Airports	Motor Vehicles (per 1,000 people)
Armenia	512	11	2
Azerbaijan	1,318	69	47
Georgia	981	28	86
Kazakhstan	8,928	10	84
Kyrgyzstan	229	54	32
Tajikistan	298	59	1
Turkmenistan	1,356	64	NA
Uzbekistan	2,096	3	NA
United States	148,800	14,572	773

Sources: *Encarta World Atlas; The World Factbook*   NA = information not available.

CHART SKILLS

- **Science and Technology** *What Caucasus nation has the most vehicles per 1,000 people? What does this tell you about the level of development of this nation?*
- **Geographic Tools** *Tajikistan is the poorest Central Asian nation. Which statistics in this chart support this statement? Explain.*

GEOFacts

The conflict with Azerbaijan disrupted energy supplies in Armenia. As a result, deforestation occurred when citizens used wood for fuel.

TEST PREPARATION

Have students read the subsection Understanding the Past on this page to answer the following question.
Which statement best expresses the main idea of the subsection Understanding the Past?
   A The Turks practiced genocide.
   B The majority of Armenians support the national Orthodox church.
   C Armenian relations with Turkey have long been bitter.
   D Armenians are an ancient people whose fate often has been in others' hands.

Answers to
Section 1 Assessment

1. (a) autonomy, p. 456 **(b)** geno-cide, p. 457 **(c)** nationalism, p. 457
2. agriculture and tourism
3. (a) The Turks attempted to deport the entire Armenian population at the outbreak of World War I. About one third died en route or were mas-sacred by the Turks. **(b)** The conflict is largely based on religion: The Ar-menians are Christian and the Azeri are Islamic.
4. (a) by continuing development of its vast oil reserves **(b)** Azerbaijan's attempts to build an oil pipeline to access the Black or Mediterranean seas have been thwarted by earth-quakes and by resistance from Russia.
5. In an attempt to rebuild the econo-my, Azerbaijan hopes to develop its oil reserves. However, petroleum and related chemical industries have al-ready created severe environmental problems for the nation.

Activity Rubrics Share rubrics with students before they plan their itineraries.
Attempted The itinerary is incomplete.
Minimal The itinerary is complete, but it lacks important details and is poorly written.
Adequate The itinerary reveals suf-ficient research and is well written.
Exemplary The itinerary reveals extensive research, includes impor-tant details, and is creative and very well written.

Russia presents a second obstacle in getting oil to world markets. Azerbaijan is a country with-out direct access to the Black Sea or the Mediter-ranean Sea. Attempts to build an oil pipeline to one of these outlets have met with political re-sistance from Russia, which is wary of competi-tion. Therefore, Russia tries to make Azerbaijan use an existing oil pipeline that runs through Russian ports. Some consider this to be an attempt by the Russians to control events in Azerbaijan, despite the fact that Azerbaijan is no longer un-der Russian control.

Environmental Change Petroleum and related chemical industries have created severe environmental problems for Azerbaijan. The waters of the Caspian Sea have been badly polluted by sewage and petroleum wastes for decades. Dams along the major rivers flowing into the sea have reduced the influx of fresh wa-ter. As a result, far fewer fish are surviving in the sea's waters. Some scientists consider the Ap-sheron Peninsula, which is near Azerbaijan's capital city of Baku, to be one of the most ecolog-ically damaged regions in the world.

Other forms of pollution include air pollu-tion and overuse of pesticides and fertilizers in the nation's agricultural areas. Although many of these problems were kept hidden in the past, Azeris now are aware of the problems they face. Nevertheless, the demand for economic recov-ery often conflicts with the desire to clean up the environment.

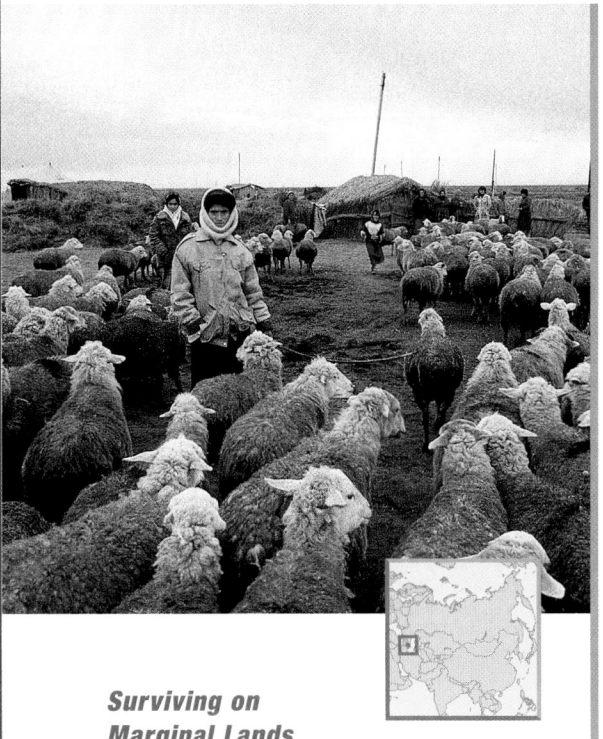

Surviving on Marginal Lands

Ecosystems Sheep can thrive where other live-stock fail. This chilly plateau in Azerbaijan is too dry to support rich pastures or intensively farmed crops. Still, sheep survive here and provide meat and valu-able wool.

Region *What environmental danger is posed when livestock graze in a dry, fragile ecosystem?*

SECTION 1 ASSESSMENT

1. **Key Terms** Define **(a)** autonomy, **(b)** genocide, **(c)** nationalism.

2. **Climates** What kinds of economic activities are benefited by the subtropical climate found in Georgia?

3. **Cooperation and Conflict (a)** Why have Armenian relations with Turkey been hostile? **(b)** Why have Armenians fought with the Azeri people of Azerbaijan?

4. **Economic Activities (a)** How does Azerbaijan hope to improve its economy? **(b)** What obsta-cles stand in the way of this plan?

5. **Critical Thinking Developing a Hypothesis** Why would the demands for economic recovery in Azerbaijan conflict with desires to clean up the environment?

Activity

Take It to the NET

Plan a Vacation A large tourist industry thrives along the Black Sea coast. Plan a vaca-tion itinerary to a coastal town along the Black Sea, including information about the sights, sounds, and tastes of the place. Visit the World Geography section of **www.phschool.com** for help in completing this activity.

RESOURCE DIRECTORY

Teaching Resources
Unit 6, Chapter 22
• Section 1 Quiz, p. 12
Spanish Resources
• Section 1 Quiz, p. 54
Social Studies Skills Handbook
• Expressing Problems Clearly, p. 40
• Identifying Central Issues, p. 42

Technology
Social Studies Skills Tutor CD-ROM, Making Inferences/Drawing Conclusions

Answer to Photo Caption

In areas of sparse vegetation, large flocks of sheep and other livestock can strip the land of plant life. This can lead to erosion by wind or water and other ecological problems.

Defending a Hypothesis

A hypothesis is a statement that provides a possible explanation for a set of facts. When you form a hypothesis, your idea should be based on information you have. However, a hypothesis is usually not limited to the information available. It often goes beyond that, and it therefore must be defended and tested.

Learn the Skill Study the photograph below and the hypothesis that is based on it. Then, use the following steps to learn how to defend a hypothesis.

1 *Make sure that the hypothesis is based on evidence.* Whether a hypothesis is based on text, statistics, or photographs, it should effectively explain the available facts or evidence. *What evidence in the photograph supports the hypothesis that oil is Azerbaijan's most profitable export?*

2 *Make sure that the hypothesis is based on common sense.* Based on the photograph alone, one might hypothesize that wool is Azerbaijan's most valuable export. However, you must refer to your general knowledge about the market value of wool and petroleum. *Which product, wool or oil, is more valuable in world markets?*

3 *Test the hypothesis.* After establishing that your hypothesis is based on the evidence and is consistent with other general knowledge, the next step is to test the hypothesis by doing research. You can use standard print and Internet sources for this step. If your research supports your hypothesis, you have successfully defended the hypothesis. *According to the database on pages 450–451 in the Regional Atlas for this unit, what are Azerbaijan's leading exports?*

4 *If necessary, begin again.* If the research disproves the hypothesis, you should form another hypothesis that incorporates the new information revealed by your research. *How should the original hypothesis be changed to make it more accurate?*

Do It Yourself

Practice the Skill Select another photograph from this chapter. Form a hypothesis about the information presented in the photograph. Use the steps in this lesson to defend your hypothesis. When you have completed the process, do a class presentation in which you present and defend your hypothesis.

Apply the Skill See Chapter 22 Review and Assessment.

Economic Activities in Azerbaijan

Hypothesis: Petroleum is Azerbaijan's most profitable export.

Teaching the Skill
To draw an accurate hypothesis from a photograph, students need to consider all the evidence in the picture. To make sure they do not overlook important details, have them list everything they see in the photo on this page. Then have them place a check beside the items that relate to economic activities. Encourage them to use the same technique when they complete the Practice the Skill activity.

Answers to Learn the Skill
1. There are numerous oil rigs in the photograph.
2. oil
3. oil and gas, machinery
4. Petroleum and machinery are Azerbaijan's most profitable exports.

Answer to Practice the Skill
Students' hypotheses will differ but should incorporate the steps on how to defend a hypothesis.

CUSTOMIZE FOR...

Honors/PreAP
Slide Show Encourage students to collect ten photos from a Caucasus nation. Have them draw hypotheses from the pictures and do research to make sure their conclusions are supported by facts. Then ask them to present the photos, their hypotheses, and the supporting facts as a slide show. Instead of actually making slides, they may use a picture album or presentation software.

Objectives

Upon completion of Section 2, students should be able to:

◆ describe the physical features of the Central Asian nations;

◆ relate the effect of Islam on the peoples of Central Asia;

◆ explain how the economies of Kazakhstan and Uzbekistan changed under Soviet control;

◆ recognize the impact of irrigation, pesticides, and fertilizers on the region's environment.

National Geography Standards

The following National Geography Standards are highlighted in this section: 2, 3, 4, 5, 6, 8, 9, 10, 11, 13, 14, 16, 17

Bellringer

Have students locate the Central Asian nations on a map or globe. Ask them to list the major physical features of the region. Then discuss the physical similarities and differences among the nations.

LESSON PLAN

1. Focus Remind students that Islam is the primary religion in Central Asia. Point out that during the period of Communist rule, Soviet officials discouraged the practice of religion. Have students debate how the Soviet policy might have affected the practice of Islam in the region.

2. Instruct Draw a two-column chart on the board and label the columns *Cause* and *Effect.* Under *Cause* write *Creation of government farms, Construction of irrigation systems,* and *Industrialization.* Have students complete the *Effect* column with information from Section 2.

3. Close/Reteach Ask students which of Central Asia's environmental problems poses the greatest threat to the region's future. Have them use information from the text and prior knowledge to support their answers. Then ask them what might be done to eliminate the threat.

460 Chapter 22

---

2 The Central Asian Nations

Reading Focus

• **What are some major physical characteristics of the Central Asian nations?**

• **How does Islam affect the peoples of Central Asia?**

• **How did the economic activities of Kazakhstan and Uzbekistan change under the control of the former Soviet Union?**

• **How has excessive irrigation and the overuse of pesticides and fertilizers changed the region's environment?**

Key Terms

chernozem   yurt

fundamentalism   desertification

> **Main Idea** After the breakup of the Soviet Union, five new independent nations emerged in Central Asia.

Cultures Islam is followed widely in Central Asia, as evidenced by this mosque in Samarqand, Uzbekistan.

Stretching from the Caspian Sea east to the towering mountain ranges along China's western border are five nations that emerged as new independent nations from the breakup of the Soviet Union. These five nations are Kazakhstan (kah zak STAN), Turkmenistan (turk MEN ih STAN), Uzbekistan (ooz BEK ih STAN), Kyrgyzstan (kihr geez STAN), and Tajikistan (tah jihk ih STAN). Together, these nations make up an area about half the size of the United States.

You might have noticed that each of the nations has a similar name. The *stan* that forms the last syllable of each name means "the land of," and the first part of each name is the name of an ethnic group whose people are the largest group in the nation. Kazakhstan, therefore, is the land of the Kazakhs, whereas Kyrgyzstan is the land of the Krygyz people. The names are somewhat deceptive, however, because each nation has a sizable number of minorities of at least one other ethnic group. For example, all five nations have significant numbers of inhabitants who are of Russian descent.

Physical Characteristics

The terrain of the Central Asian nations varies considerably. The Tien Shan and Pamir-Alai mountain ranges are in the southeastern part of the region. Here, some peaks rise to elevations greater than 24,000 feet (7,315 m) in eastern Kyrgyzstan. In Tajikistan, the Fedchenko Glacier extends for more than 40 miles (64 km), making it one of the largest alpine glaciers in the world. Farther to the west, the elevation drops and the land flattens considerably. Two large rivers, the Syr Darya and the Amu Darya, spill out of the mountains and flow down through the lowlands to the Aral Sea.

Climate The climate of these nations is mostly arid or semiarid. The nearest oceans are more than 500 miles (800 km) away. In northernmost Kazakhstan and near the highest southern mountains, precipitation totals more than 10 inches (25 cm) per year. To the east of the Caspian Sea are two of Asia's largest deserts: the Kara Kum in Turkmenistan and the Kyzyl Kum in Uzbekistan. Some locations in the Kara Kum

---

RESOURCE DIRECTORY

Teaching Resources

Unit 6, Chapter 22

• Section 2 Guided Reading and Review, p. 13

Guide to the Essentials (English/Spanish)

• Section Summary, Chapter 22, Section 2

Mental Mapping booklet

• Outline Map 22, p. 84

• Unit 6 Checklist, p. 79

Technology

Guided Reading Audiotapes (English/Spanish), Chapter 22, Section 2

Section Reading Support Transparencies, Chapter 22, Section 2

World Geography Map and Photo Transparencies

• Central and Southwest Asia: Maps and Photos

Book on CD, Chapter 22

Social Studies Skills Tutor CD-ROM

Companion Web site, www.phschool.com

• Chapter 22 Activities

APPLYING THE GEOGRAPHIC THEMES

● **Movement** The Central Asian nations lie on the route of the ancient Silk Road between Asia and Europe. The historic cities of Samarqand, Tashkent, Bishkek, and Bukhara were stops along this route.

- *Which of the above historic stops are national capitals now? Why do you think that they developed into capitals?*

Central Asia: PHYSICAL-POLITICAL

KEY

Elevation		
Feet		Meters
14,000		4,270
7,000		2,135
1,500		457
700		213
(sea level) 0		0 (sea level)

⊗ National capital
• Major city
▲ Mountain
— Dam

Lambert Azimuthal Equal-Area Projection

receive less than 3 inches (8 cm) of rain each year. Southern Kazakhstan also tends to be dry.

Natural Resources In northern Kazakhstan, there are steppes where grasslands create a rich topsoil called **chernozem.** Chernozem provides a sound base for agriculture. Parts of the region also have large reserves of oil and natural gas, as well as other valuable minerals.

People and Cultures

Although each country of Central Asia is named after a single ethnic group, all are home to a mixture of peoples. For instance, Uzbeks constitute almost one quarter of the population of Tajikistan. Furthermore, as long ago as the mid-1800s, the czar's government encouraged Russian and Ukrainian peasants to settle in Tajikistan and turn grazing lands into wheat fields. Russians are now a large ethnic minority in several of these five countries. They form, for example, more than one third of the population of Kazakhstan. As a result, some ethnic tensions have simmered in these nations but at much lower levels than in the Caucasus region.

Languages Four major groups—Kazakhs, Turkmen, Uzbeks, and Kyrgyz—speak related Turkic languages. The Tajiks speak a language related to modern Farsi, the language of Iran. Many people also speak Russian, once the official language.

Islamic Religion Most of the people living in the Central Asian nations adhere to the Islamic faith. The links between these people and the Arabian core of Islam have been traditionally weak, however. Their separation intensified further after the area was incorporated into the Soviet Union in the 1920s and 1930s. During the period when Communist officials discouraged the open practice of religion, many people native to the area quietly practiced Islam in the privacy of their own homes.

Following independence from the former Soviet Union in the early 1990s, some national leaders called for a more open adoption of Islamic rules as the basis for new governments. Religion is practiced more openly now, but popular support for Islamic fundamentalism as practiced in Iran and Afghanistan has not been widespread. **Fundamentalism** is a set of religious beliefs based on a strict interpretation of a sacred text, such as the Koran.

Chapter 22 ▪ Section 2 **461**

READING STRATEGY

Summarizing Main Ideas

Have students create a chart with a column for each Central Asian nation. As they read the subsection People and Cultures, have them write important facts about population, languages, and religion in the appropriate columns. When they finish reading, ask them to use their charts to summarize what they have learned about each nation.

ACTIVITY

Vocabulary

Fundamentalism Point out the Key Terms list on page 460. Have students look up *fundamentalism* in the Glossary and paraphrase the definition. Then ask a volunteer to use the term in a sentence.

Alternative Assessment

Mid-Point Monitoring

Writing a Report You may wish to monitor students' progress on writing their reports. Confer with students to see if they will soon complete their research and create a first draft of their reports.

CUSTOMIZE FOR...

Less Proficient Writers

Letters from Central Asia Ask students to imagine that they are on a journey through Central Asia and that they are writing to a friend about the trip. Have them write a letter describing the countries they have visited and the people they encountered there. Encourage them to mention historical events that have helped to shape the region's culture.

Answer to Map Caption

Tashkent and Bishkek; they were important centers for trade long before the nations became independent.

Chapter 22 ▪ Section 2 **461**

Activity: Holding a regional meeting

Purpose: Divide students into groups that will each represent a different nation of the Caucasus and Central Asia. Groups will research the problems and needs of their nation and develop a proposal to deal with those needs.

Roles: Each group must select a representative and may also choose a research leader and a proposal leader. Assign one student the role of president to conduct the meeting.

Result: Each representative presents the group's proposal to the rest of the class. The president calls a vote to determine whether it should be enacted.

Connecting With . . .

Language Arts Have students imagine that they are nomads from Central Asia and the Soviet government has forced them to leave their herds and work in a factory. Ask them to write a poem about their first day at the new job, using descriptive language to express their thoughts and feelings.

Answer to Photo Caption

Migration introduces new beliefs and traditions to the region, which might influence or alter existing religious beliefs.

Two Holidays in Kazakhstan

Cultures A Kazakh man prays (left) with other Muslims during the Islamic celebration of Eid-Ul-Adha. Eid-Ul-Adha is the holiday of the hajj, or pilgrimage. Also in Kazakhstan, a woman celebrates Navruz (below), an ancient traditional celebration of the New Year.

Movement *How can migration affect religious beliefs in a region?*

Economic Activities

Many people in Central Asia, especially in Kazakhstan and Kyrgyzstan, traditionally were nomadic herders. Sheep, goats, and yaks grazed in mountain valleys. Herders lived in **yurts,** which are large, portable, round tents made of wooden frames covered with felt or skins. Farmers worked small fields in some parts of the region.

Under the Soviet Union When the region came under the control of the former Soviet Union, people's lives changed dramatically. The Soviet government forced nomadic peoples to settle in villages and work on massive government farms. They grew wheat and other dryland crops in Kazakhstan. Massive irrigation systems diverted waters from the Syr Darya and Amu Darya to grow cotton in the warmer southern region. The Soviet government also encouraged industrial development in the cities of Central Asia.

Since Independence Industrialization continued in Central Asia after the breakup of the Soviet Union. Many Kazakh industries process the products of farms or the nation's rich range of mineral resources. Uzbekistan also has some significant industries, including the region's only significant aviation factory.

Industrial development spurred the growth of many cities. For example, about 60 percent of the residents of Kazakhstan now live in cities. A larger share of the region's population, however, continues to live in rural areas, where agriculture and herding predominate.

Tourism is beginning to become an important economic activity in the region. This is most notable in cities of eastern Uzbekistan along the ancient Silk Road. The modern cities of Samarqand, Tashkent, Bishkek, and Bukhara all were major stops on the Silk Road. From the second century B.C. to the sixteenth century A.D., traders moved fine silks along this route from China across Central Asia. Today, tourists from around the world visit the region so they themselves can travel the Silk Road.

Environmental Change

As in other parts of the former Soviet Union, rapid economic development has resulted in many critical environmental problems for the

RESOURCE DIRECTORY

Teaching Resources
Unit 6, Chapter 22
• Map/Graph Skills, p. 17
• Section 2 Quiz, p. 14
• Reviewing Main Ideas, p. 15
• Test Forms A and B, pp. 18–23
Spanish Resources
• Section 2 Quiz, p. 55
Guide to the Essentials (English/Spanish)
• Chapter 22 Test
Mental Mapping booklet
• Chapter 22 Map Test, p. 86

Simulations, Games, and Lab Activities
• Place Location Review Games, pp. 58–63
Social Studies Skills Handbook
• Study and Research Skills, pp. 94–108

Prentice Hall Assessment System
Alternative Assessment booklet
• Writing Assignment Evaluation Form, p. 7

Technology
ExamView Test Bank CD-ROM, Chapter 22 Test
Companion Web site, www.phschool.com
• Chapter 22 Self-Test

Central Asian nations. Perhaps the harshest example of environmental change is the salty Aral Sea on the border between Kazakhstan and Uzbekistan.

Irrigation and Desertification The Aral Sea began to suffer decades ago when Soviet planners developed a complex set of canals to water fields in the arid region around the sea. Fresh water from the Amu Darya and Syr Darya rivers, which flow into the Aral Sea, was diverted to irrigate nearby cotton fields.

Although the region became a leading cotton producer, the irrigation project devastated the Aral Sea region. With less fresh water flowing in, the sea shrank steadily and grew saltier, losing about two thirds of its volume. The town of Muynak, which once was a major fishing port on the southern shore of the sea, is now more than 20 miles (32 km) from the shoreline. The local fishing industry died out, and fishing boats now stand isolated on desert sands.

Clouds of sand and chemicals blew from the dry, exposed seabed, further contributing to the desertification of the surrounding area. **Desertification** is the extension of the desert landscape through the activities of people and livestock as well as climatic changes. Although Kazakhstan and Uzbekistan began to work actively in the 1990s to protect and restore the Aral Sea, many scientists believe that this activity may be too late. Some experts predict that the entire Aral Sea will disappear by 2030.

Irrigation: Promise and Costs

Environmental Change Irrigation allowed farmers in Central Asia to double their cotton production between 1960 and 1990. However, heavy irrigation has left many fields poisoned with salts and agricultural chemicals.
Human-Environment Interaction *How does irrigation affect rivers and other bodies of water?*

Pollution Other parts of Central Asia have been equally devastated by pollution. Excessive use of pesticides and fertilizers has left soil, running water, and groundwater highly contaminated. Another problem is that heavy doses of chemical fertilizers and pesticides used in the production of cotton created serious health risks for workers. The drive to develop oil, natural gas, and mineral resources of the Central Asian nations may also increase stress on sensitive ecosystems.

SECTION 2 ASSESSMENT

1. **Key Terms** Define **(a)** chernozem, **(b)** fundamentalism, **(c)** yurt, **(d)** desertification.

2. **Physical Characteristics** **(a)** Describe the physical characteristics of the Central Asian nations. **(b)** What are the climate conditions in these nations?

3. **Cultures** How did the breakup of the Soviet Union affect the role of religion in Central Asia?

4. **Economic Activities** What effect did the transformation of Kazakhstan's and Uzbekistan's economic activities have on patterns of settlement?

5. **Environmental Change** What kinds of environmental problems has the rapid economic development of Central Asia caused?

6. **Critical Thinking Recognizing Patterns** What similar challenges do the Central Asian nations face?

Activity
USING THE **REGIONAL ATLAS**

Review the Regional Atlas for Central Asia and this section. Suppose that you are an environmental scientist studying the Apsheron Peninsula in Azerbaijan, one of the most ecologically damaged regions in the world. Develop a plan that encourages economic development and reduces environmental damage.

---

1. (a) chernozem, p. 461 **(b)** fundamentalism, p. 461 **(c)** yurt, p. 462 **(d)** desertification, p. 463

2. (a) Mountain ranges are in the southeastern part of the region. Farther west, the elevation drops and the land flattens considerably. Two large rivers run through the lowlands to the Aral Sea. **(b)** The climate of these nations is mostly arid or semiarid.

3. After the breakup of the Soviet Union, some national leaders called for a more open adoption of Islamic rules as the basis for new governments; religion is practiced more openly now.

4. The industrial growth in Kazakhstan and Uzbekistan has spurred the growth of many cities.

5. Rapid economic development has led to desertification, pollution of soil and water, and the shrinking size and increasing saltiness of the Aral Sea.

6. The nations of Central Asia face similar economic and environmental challenges.

Activity Rubrics Share rubrics with students before they develop their plans.

Attempted The plan is incomplete.
Minimal The plan is poorly developed or only vaguely addresses the issues.
Adequate The plan is well developed and outlines a strategy for economic growth and reduction of environmental damage.
Exemplary The plan is extremely well developed and demonstrates a thorough understanding of the issues.

Articles From ·········
NATIONAL GEOGRAPHIC

The following article may be used to extend the content in this section.

Edwards, Mike, and Gerd Ludwig, photographer. "Kazakhstan: Facing the Nightmare." *National Geographic,* Vol. 183, No. 3 (Mar. 1993), pp. 22–37.

As the people of Kazakhstan begin to build their economy, they must cope with the legacy of decades of Soviet rule.

TEST PREPARATION

Have students read the subsection Irrigation and Desertification on this page to answer the following question.
Ironically, the irrigation systems that diverted waters from the Syr Darya and Amu Darya resulted in the _____ of the land they were designed to _____.
  A irrigation; expose
  (B) desertification; irrigate
  C irrigation; dry
  D isolation; irrigate

Answer to Photo Caption

Irrigation depletes water supplies. Diverting fresh water from the sea increases the sea's saltiness.

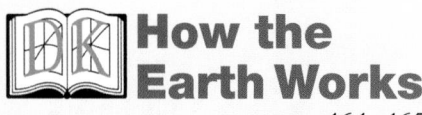

Objectives

Upon completion of this feature, students should be able to:

◆ define erosion and identify its agents;

◆ describe the effects of erosion on different landforms.

 National Geography Standards

The following National Geography Standards are highlighted in this feature: 1, 4, 7

 Bellringer

Ask students if they have ever collected rocks from a river or ocean. Ask them to describe the texture of those rocks. (Most of them are smooth.) Ask: **What would account for the smoothness of these stones?** (The constant motion of the water on the rocks wears down rough points and makes the surface smooth.) Discuss how running water affects hard objects and land over time.

LESSON PLAN

1. Focus Write the word *erosion* on the board. Have students define it. Have students brainstorm a list of places that show the effects of erosion in your region. Remind them of beaches, canyons, and other appropriate places.

2. Instruct Draw a two-column chart on the board. Label the columns *Eroding Agent* and *Effects*. Have students use information from the text to describe how streams, waves, glaciers, and other eroding agents change the landscape.

3. Close/Reteach Have students study the pictures and diagrams on this page and the next. Ask: **Are the effects of erosion obvious from year to year? Why or why not?** (In most cases, the effects are not obvious because erosion is a gradual process. In the case of erosion due to desert storms, the effects are more immediately obvious.)

How the Earth Works

Erosion

After rocks are broken down by weathering, the resulting loose material may be transported by the process of **erosion.** Rock material can be moved by streams and rivers, by waves, by glacial ice, or by wind. The number of fragments that are moved and the distance that they travel are affected by factors such as the size and weight of the particles and the speed at which the eroding agent is moving. The eroded material is carried to another site where it is deposited as **sediment.** Erosion affects the landscapes of Central Asia, the Caucasus, and all regions of the world.

WATER FLOWING
As water flows from highlands to the sea, sharp descents result in rapids and waterfalls. Flowing water is an important agent of erosion.

SAND DUNES
A dune begins to form where a plant or other obstacle slows the wind, which drops its load of sand. As the sand piles up, it creates an ever-growing barrier to the wind, causing more sand to be dropped. Eventually the dune crest may collapse like an ocean wave.

Sand dunes

Rock arch

Wadi

Rock fragme collect in wa

EROSION IN ARID LANDS
When rare torrential rain comes to arid areas in Central Asia and elsewhere, entire mountainsides may be swept clean of boulders, rock fragments, sand, and clay. Flash floods wash eroded material down **wadis**—the valleys of streams that are usually dry.

SEAS OF SAND
The huge amounts of sand that comprise some deserts started out as rock that was weathered to form fine particles. The finer the particle, the farther it can be transported by agents of erosion.

464 Chapter 22 ▪ The Caucasus and Central Asia

RESOURCE DIRECTORY

Technology
World Geography Map and Photo Transparencies
• How the Earth Works, Unit 6
Companion Web site, www.phschool.com
• Chapter 22 Activities

EROSION BY GLACIAL ICE

Huge masses of moving ice are called **glaciers.** Over thousands or millions of years, they can scour mountainsides and dramatically change the shapes of valleys.

1. Before glaciation
A narrow, V-shaped river valley is surrounded by rounded mountains.

2. During glaciation
moving ice erodes mountaintops and carves wider valleys.

3. After glaciation
The result is a U-shaped valley with rugged, sharp peaks above.

STREAM EROSION
Streams erode their banks and beds, continually widening and deepening them. In some cases, a canyon may result. A **canyon,** such as this one in Utah, is a deep valley with vertical sides that have been eroded by river water.

WAVE ACTION
Coastlines are constantly eroded by waves that are formed by winds blowing over water. Cracked and soft rocks are eroded away first, leading to the creation of arches. If the arch roof collapses, a **sea stack** results.

1. Waves curve around headland. *2. An arch forms.* *3. A sea stack results.*

Sea stack off the British Isles

ASSESSMENT

1. Key Terms Define **(a)** erosion, **(b)** sediment, **(c)** wadi, **(d)** glacier, **(e)** canyon, **(f)** sea stack.

2. Environmental Change How does water gradually reshape the land?

3. Physical Characteristics What are some major physical characteristics of an arid landscape eroded by wind and rain?

4. Physical Processes Analyze the three diagrams of glacial erosion. How can glaciers change the shapes of mountain valleys?

5. Critical Thinking Analyzing Causes and Effects How can erosion on farmlands cause a reduction in agricultural production?

Creating a Chapter Summary

As a reteaching opportunity, pair a more able student with a less able student to complete this chapter summary.

Completed diagrams may include the following entries: **Caucasus Nations** Located between the Black and Caspian seas, Ethnic tensions, Mountainous region **Both** Formerly under Soviet control, Vast oil reserves, Working to rebuild their economies, Environmental problems **Central Asian Nations** Population has a Muslim majority, Climate mostly arid or semiarid, Rapid industrialization and urbanization

Reviewing Key Terms

1–6. Puzzles and answers should show a complete understanding of each of the key terms.

Understanding Key Ideas

7. The Caucasus nations are still dealing with economic and environmental problems that are rooted in past Soviet actions.
8. Georgia has developed its agriculture, machinery manufacturing, and energy industries.
9. Nogorno-Karabakh was settled primarily by Armenians, but the Soviets placed the area under the control of the Azeris.
10. Central Asia's resources include the chernozem in northern Kazakhstan, oil, natural gas, and minerals.
11. Most of the people living in Central Asia practice Islam; after the breakup of the Soviet Union, some national leaders called for a more open adoption of Islamic rules as the basis for new governments.
12. Soviet planners developed an irrigation system that diverted rivers away from the Aral Sea; with less fresh water flowing in, the sea is steadily drying up.

Critical Thinking and Writing

13. The subtropical climate near the Black Sea supports the production of grapes, citrus fruits, tobacco, tea, peaches, silk, and wine and cognac, and it attracts many tourists.

Creating a Chapter Summary

Copy this diagram on a sheet of paper. Add information from the chapter to compare the Caucasus and Central Asian nations. Some information has been provided to help you get started.

Caucasus Nations
• Located between the Black and Caspian seas
•
•

• Formerly under Soviet control
•
•

Central Asian Nations
• Population has a Muslim majority
•
•

Take It to the NET
Chapter Self-Test For practice test questions for Chapter 22, go to the World Geography section of **www.phschool.com**.

Reviewing Key Terms

Use the chapter key terms listed below to create a crossword puzzle. Exchange puzzles with a classmate. Complete the puzzles and check each other's answers.

1. autonomy
2. genocide
3. nationalism
4. chernozem
5. fundamentalism
6. desertification

Understanding Key Ideas

7. **Understanding the Past** How are the Caucasus nations still affected by the fact that they were once part of the former Soviet Union?
8. **Economic Activities** How has Georgia improved its economy since becoming an independent nation?
9. **Cooperation and Conflict** Why is the region of Nogorno-Karabakh a site of contention between Armenian and Azeri peoples?

10. **Natural Resources** Describe three natural resources of the Central Asian nations.
11. **Cultures** How does Islam affect the peoples of Central Asia?
12. **Environmental Change** Why is the Aral Sea drying up?

Critical Thinking and Writing

13. **Asking Geographic Questions** How does nearness to the Black Sea affect the economy of Georgia?
14. **Distinguishing Fact From Opinion** Many people's image of Central Asia consists of a frozen landscape and bundled-up people trying to keep warm. Explain why this image is not accurate for the entire region.
15. **Defending a Position** Write an editorial discussing whether economic development in Azerbaijan has benefited or harmed the interests of the people.
16. **Identifying Relationships** What characteristics do the nations of Central Asia share?

14. The climate of Central Asia is mostly arid or semiarid.
15. Students may choose to support or oppose economic development, but they must be able to support their positions with facts.
16. The majority of people in Central Asia are Muslims. They live in generally semiarid, arid, or even desert climates. Many were once nomadic herders; many people have moved to cities.

Applying Skills

Defending a Hypothesis Refer to the Skills for Life lesson on page 459 to answer these questions:

17. What is a hypothesis?

18. Why is it important to test a hypothesis by doing research?

19. What should you do if your research disproves your hypothesis?

20. (a) Based on the photograph, create a hypothesis about the level of development in Azerbaijan. (b) Support your hypothesis with evidence from the chapter.

Reading a Chart Study the chart below, and answer the following questions:

21. What Caucasus nation has the most airports?

22. Vehicles are rare in what Caucasus nation?

23. What Central Asian nation has the most railroad track and the most motor vehicles per 1,000 people?

24. In what Central Asian nation would it be easiest to find an airport?

The Caucasus, Central Asia, and the United States
Transportation Data

Country	Total Railroad Track Length (miles)	Total Airports	Motor Vehicles (per 1,000 people)
Armenia	512	11	2
Azerbaijan	1,318	69	47
Georgia	981	28	86
Kazakhstan	8,928	10	84
Krygyzstan	229	54	32
Tajikistan	298	59	1
Turkmenistan	1,356	64	NA
Uzbekistan	2,096	3	NA
United States	148,800	14,572	773

Test Preparation

Read the question and choose the best answer.

25. What major characteristic do the Caucasus and Central Asian nations have in common?

A Tourism is a main economic activity.

B Pressure from Russia is an obstacle to oil development.

C They were formerly under Soviet control.

D The climate of these nations is mostly arid.

Activities

USING THE 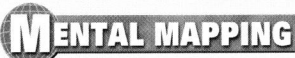 REGIONAL ATLAS

Review the Regional Atlas for Central Asia and Chapter 22. Study the distribution of population and natural resources in the Caucasus and Central Asian nations, and note what resources are available near the most densely populated areas. Create a table that lists each of these resources and explains why it is important in the region.

ENTAL MAPPING

Study a map of the Caucasus and Central Asian nations. On a separate piece of paper, draw a sketch map of the region from memory. Label the following places on your map:

- Armenia
- Azerbaijan
- Georgia
- Kazakhstan
- Kyrgyzstan
- Tajikistan
- Turkmenistan
- Uzbekistan
- Black Sea
- Caspian Sea

Take It to the NET

Creating a Chart Search the Internet for information about the history of ethnic diversity in Kazakhstan. Then, create a chart that identifies the major ethnic groups in Kazakhstan today, why they migrated to the area, and how they influenced the culture once they arrived. Visit the World Geography section of **www.phschool.com** for help in completing this activity.

Applying Skills

17. A hypothesis is a statement that provides a possible explanation for a set of facts.

18. Research will indicate whether or not your hypothesis is correct.

19. Form another hypothesis that incorporates the new information revealed by your research.

20. Hypotheses will vary. Students should support them with evidence from the chapter.

21. Azerbaijan

22. Armenia

23. Kazakhstan

24. Turkmenistan

Test Preparation

25. C

Activities

Using the Regional Atlas
Students' tables should be clear and accurate. Explanations should be well thought out and supportable.

Mental Mapping
To check their work, have students compare their maps to those in the Regional Atlas.

Take It to the Net
Students' work should reflect sound research and demonstrate an understanding of the origins of ethnic diversity in Kazakhstan.

ENTAL MAPPING

Games for Review See pages 58–63 of the Simulations, Games, and Lab Activities booklet in the Teaching Resources for games to review place names.

Chapter Map Test Students should use the completed outline maps and the Unit 6 Checklist in their Atlas Portfolios to prepare for the Chapter 22 Map Test. The test will cover only those place names on the Unit 6 Checklist that relate to this chapter.

Alternative Assessment

Final Evaluation

Writing a Report Use the Writing Assignment Evaluation Form on page 7 of the Alternative Assessment booklet in the Prentice Hall Assessment System to evaluate students' reports. Either teachers or students can complete the forms to indicate which level of work was achieved for each of the criteria. The evaluation should include specific examples and comments.

Chapter 23 Planning Guide

Resource Manager

	CORE INSTRUCTION	READING/SKILLS
Chapter-Level Resources	**Teaching Resources** 📖 **Unit 6**/Ch. 23 • Reviewing Main Ideas, p. 34 📓 **Mental Mapping booklet** • Unit 6 Checklist, p. 79 📓 **Simulations, Games, and Lab Activities** • Place Location Review Games, pp. 58–63 💿 **TeacherExpress™ CD-ROM**, Ch. 23 💻 **Companion Web site, www.phschool.com** • eTeach	**Teaching Resources** 📖 **Unit 6**/Ch. 23 • Map/Graph Skills, p. 36 📓 **Mental Mapping booklet** • Outline Map 23, p. 87 📓 **People and Geography** • Energy and Resources, pp. 30–35 💿 **Book on CD**, Ch. 23 💿 **Social Studies Skills Tutor CD-ROM**
1 Creating the Modern Middle East 1. Explain how the Ottoman Turks tried to unite the peoples of the Middle East. 2. Explain why European powers took control of the nations of Southwest Asia after World War I. 3. Describe how the creation of Israel affected relations between Arabs and Jews.	**Teaching Resources** 📖 **Unit 6**/Ch. 23 • Guided Reading and Review, p. 24 💿 **Prentice Hall Presentation Pro CD-ROM**, Ch. 23, Sec. 1	**Teaching Resources** 📓 **Guide to the Essentials (English/Spanish)** • Section Summary, Ch. 23, Sec. 1 📼 **Guided Reading Audiotapes (English/Spanish)**, Ch. 23, Sec. 1 🖥 **Section Reading Support Transparencies**, Ch. 23, Sec. 1
2 Israel 1. Discuss how Israel has changed its environment to make its land more productive and to increase prosperity. 2. Identify the major cultural groups in Israel and the roles they have played in the nation's history. 3. List the steps that Israel and its Arab neighbors have taken to prevent conflict.	**Teaching Resources** 📖 **Unit 6**/Ch. 23 • Guided Reading and Review, p. 26 📓 **Creative Teaching Activities** • A Personal View of History, p. 25 💿 **Prentice Hall Presentation Pro CD-ROM**, Ch. 23, Sec. 2	**Teaching Resources** 📓 **Guide to the Essentials (English/Spanish)** • Section Summary, Ch. 23, Sec. 2 📼 **Guided Reading Audiotapes (English/Spanish)**, Ch. 23, Sec. 2 🖥 **Section Reading Support Transparencies**, Ch. 23, Sec. 2
3 Jordan, Lebanon, Syria, and Iraq 1. Summarize how political conditions have changed society in Jordan. 2. Describe how Lebanon has recovered from civil war. 3. List the geographic factors and economic activities that make Syria a prosperous land. 4. Explain why there has been a series of conflicts in Iraq.	**Teaching Resources** 📖 **Unit 6**/Ch. 23 • Guided Reading and Review, p. 28 💿 **Prentice Hall Presentation Pro CD-ROM**, Ch. 23, Sec. 3	**Teaching Resources** 📓 **Guide to the Essentials (English/Spanish)** • Section Summary, Ch. 23, Sec. 3 📼 **Guided Reading Audiotapes (English/Spanish)**, Ch. 23, Sec. 3 🖥 **Section Reading Support Transparencies**, Ch. 23, Sec. 3
4 Arabian Peninsula 1. Explain how the discovery of oil changed the Arabian Peninsula. 2. Describe how Saudi Arabia has tried to balance modern-day changes and economic growth with respect for tradition. 3. Explain why Oman and Yemen are considered the least developed countries in the region.	**Teaching Resources** 📖 **Unit 6**/Ch. 23 • Guided Reading and Review, p. 30 💿 **Prentice Hall Presentation Pro CD-ROM**, Ch. 23, Sec. 4	**Teaching Resources** 📓 **Guide to the Essentials (English/Spanish)** • Section Summary, Ch. 23, Sec. 4 📼 **Guided Reading Audiotapes (English/Spanish)**, Ch. 23, Sec. 4 🖥 **Section Reading Support Transparencies**, Ch. 23, Sec. 4
5 Turkey, Iran, and Cyprus 1. Explain how Turkey became a modern nation after World War I. 2. List the effects that an Islamic revolution had on the level of development of Iran. 3. Summarize the major issue that divides the people of Cyprus.	**Teaching Resources** 📖 **Unit 6**/Ch. 23 • Guided Reading and Review, p. 32 💿 **Prentice Hall Presentation Pro CD-ROM**, Ch. 23, Sec. 5	**Teaching Resources** 📓 **Guide to the Essentials (English/Spanish)** • Section Summary, Ch. 23, Sec. 5 📼 **Guided Reading Audiotapes (English/Spanish)**, Ch. 23, Sec. 5 🖥 **Section Reading Support Transparencies**, Ch. 23, Sec. 5

ENRICHMENT/HONORS/PREAP

Teaching Resources
- **Unit 6**/Ch. 23
  - Critical Thinking, p. 35
- **Mental Mapping booklet**
  - Atlas Activity, p. 88
- **Social Studies Skills Handbook**
  - Study and Research Skills, pp. 94–108
- **World Geography Map and Photo Transparencies**
  - Central and Southwest Asia: Maps and Photos
- **World Geography Videos**
  - Natural Resources: The Countries of Southwest Asia, Tape 3

Teaching Resources
- **Social Studies Skills Handbook**
  - Comparing Maps of Different Scales, p. 6
- **Companion Web site, www.phschool.com**
  - Chapter 23 Activities

Companion Web site, www.phschool.com
- Chapter 23 Activities

Companion Web site, www.phschool.com
- Chapter 23 Activities

Companion Web site, www.phschool.com
- Chapter 23 Activities

Teaching Resources
- **Unit 6**/Ch. 23
  - Geography and World Literature, p. 43
- **Companion Web site, www.phschool.com**
  - Chapter 23 Activities

ASSESSMENT

PRENTICE HALL ASSESSMENT SYSTEM

Core Assessment
- ExamView Test Bank booklet, Ch. 23
- ExamView Test Bank CD-ROM, Ch. 23
- ExamView Test Bank CD-ROM, Unit 6

Standardized Test Preparation

Review and Reteach
- Review Book for World Geography, pp. 13–14

Practice and Assess
- Test-taking Strategies With Transparencies for High School
- Test-taking Strategy Poster
- Alternative Assessment booklet
- Test Prep Book for World Geography

Teaching Resources
- **Unit 6**/Ch. 23
  - Section Quizzes, pp. 25, 27, 29, 31, 33
  - Test Forms A and B, pp. 37–42
- **Guide to the Essentials (English/Spanish)**
  - Chapter 23 Test
- **Spanish Resources**, Ch. 23
  - Section Quizzes, pp. 56–60
- **Mental Mapping booklet**
  - Chapter 23 Map Test, p. 89
  - Unit 6 Map Test, p. 90
- **Companion Web site, www.phschool.com**
  - Chapter 23 Self-Test

CUSTOMIZE FOR INDIVIDUAL NEEDS

Gifted and Talented
- Teacher's Edition, Customize for . . . , p. 475

Honors/PreAP
- Teacher's Edition, Customize for . . . , pp. 483, 493

Less Proficient Readers
- Guide to the Essentials (English), Ch. 23, Section Summaries
- Guided Reading Audiotapes (English), Ch. 23
- Section Reading Support Transparencies, Ch. 23
- Book on CD, Ch. 23
- Teacher's Edition, Reading Strategy, pp. 471, 477, 486, 489, 498
- Teacher's Edition, Activity: Vocabulary, pp. 471, 484, 489, 498
- Teacher's Edition, Customize for . . . , pp. 489, 495

Students Acquiring English/ESL
- Guide to the Essentials (English/Spanish), Ch. 23
- Guided Reading Audiotapes (English/Spanish), Ch. 23
- Section Reading Support Transparencies, Ch. 23
- Book on CD, Ch. 23
- Teacher's Edition, Customize for . . . , p. 471

Less Proficient Writers
- Alternative Assessment, Writing Assignment Rubric, p. 6
- Teacher's Edition, Customize for . . . , p. 499

Introducing

CHAPTER

23

pp. 468–501

MENTAL MAPPING

Ask students to look at the map on this page. Point out that Southwest Asia lies in the Eastern Hemisphere, southeast of Europe. Have students refer to the political map of Asia in the Atlas and describe this region's location relative to the rest of Asia. Then ask students to name the countries that make up Southwest Asia. (Israel, Jordan, Lebanon, Syria, Iraq, Saudi Arabia, Kuwait, Bahrain, Qatar, Oman, United Arab Emirates, Yemen, Turkey, Cyprus, and Iran)

Mapping the Region Have students study the map on this page. Then instruct them to close their books and create a sketch map of the countries of Southwest Asia, or distribute the Chapter 23 Outline Map on page 87 of the Mental Mapping booklet in the Teaching Resources. Instruct students to lightly shade each country a different color. Then ask them to label the countries and bodies of water shown on this map. Students should keep their maps in their Atlas Portfolios in order to prepare for the Chapter 23 Map Test.

eTeach

Be sure to check out this month's online forum with a Master Teacher to join in an exchange of teaching ideas. **www.phschool.com**

468   Chapter 23

CHAPTER
23
The Countries of Southwest Asia

SECTIONS

1   Creating the Modern Middle East

2   Israel

3   Jordan, Lebanon, Syria, and Iraq

4   Arabian Peninsula

5   Turkey, Iran, and Cyprus

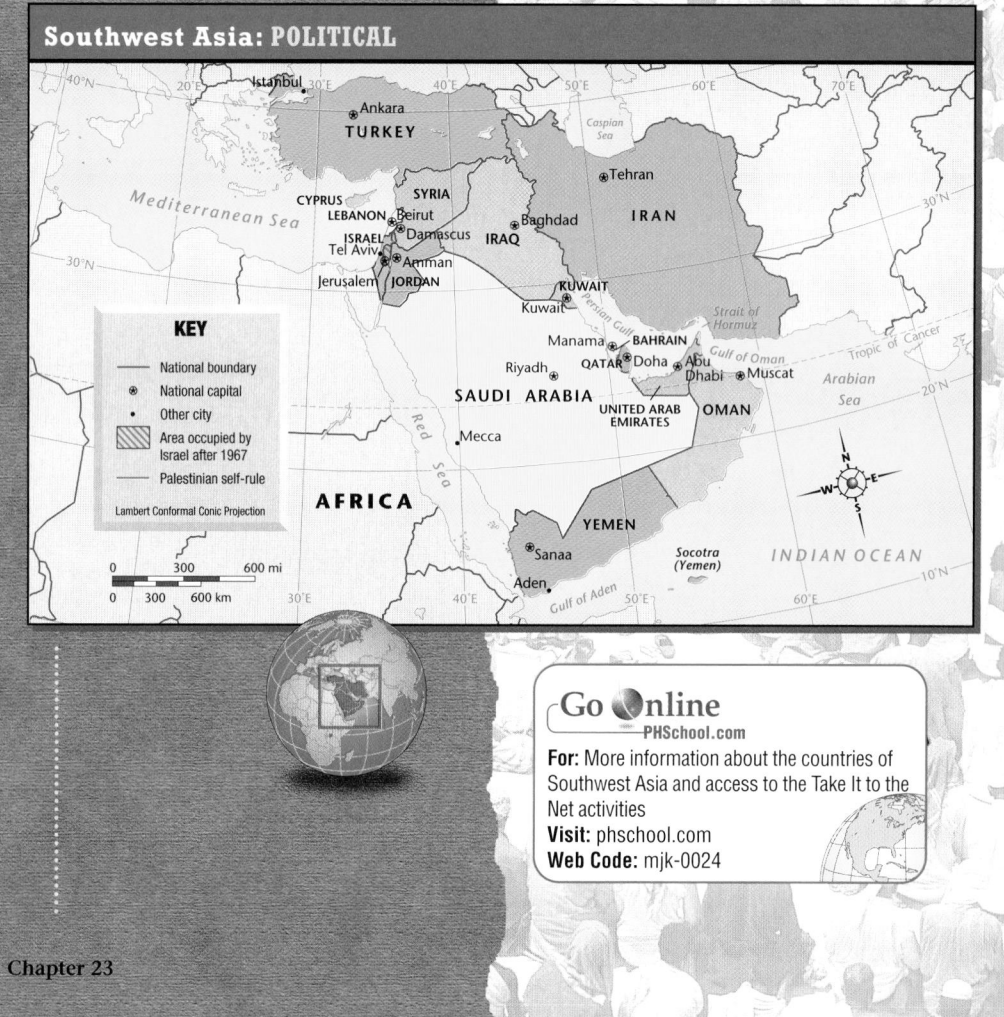

Southwest Asia: POLITICAL

KEY
— National boundary
⊛ National capital
• Other city
▨ Area occupied by Israel after 1967
— Palestinian self-rule
Lambert Conformal Conic Projection

0   300   600 mi
0   300   600 km

Go Online
PHSchool.com

For: More information about the countries of Southwest Asia and access to the Take It to the Net activities
Visit: phschool.com
Web Code: mjk-0024

468   Chapter 23

RESOURCE DIRECTORY

Teaching Resources
Unit 6, Chapter 23
• Section 1 Guided Reading and Review, p. 24
Guide to the Essentials (English/Spanish)
• Section Summary, Chapter 23, Section 1
Mental Mapping booklet
• Atlas Activity, p. 88
• Unit 6 Checklist, p. 79

Technology
Guided Reading Audiotapes (English/Spanish),
   Chapter 23, Section 1

Section Reading Support Transparencies,
   Chapter 23, Section 1
World Geography Map and Photo Transparencies
• Central and Southwest Asia: Maps and Photos
Book on CD, Chapter 23
World Geography Videos
• Natural Resources: The Countries of Southwest Asia, Tape 3
TeacherExpress™ CD-ROM, Chapter 23
Prentice Hall Presentation Pro CD-ROM, Chapter 23
Social Studies Skills Tutor CD-ROM
Companion Web site, www.phschool.com
• Chapter 23 Activities

1 Creating the Modern Middle East

Reading Focus

- How successful were the Ottoman Turks in uniting the diverse peoples of the Middle East?
- Why did several European powers take control of the nations of Southwest Asia after World War I?
- How did the creation of Israel affect relations between Arabs and Jews?

Key Terms

mandate

Zionist

self-determination

Main Idea Throughout recorded history, the Middle East has been a desirable and hotly contested region.

Global Trade Patterns The port city of Aden in Yemen is a busy center of international commerce.

The Middle East—as Southwest Asia has long been known—has a long and turbulent history. More than three thousand years ago, the region's great wealth and location at the center of trading routes between Europe, Africa, and Asia made it an important source of power. This area was conquered repeatedly by groups from within and without. The movement of conquering peoples across the Middle East gave the region a unique cultural pattern. It became a tangle of diverse ethnic groups and religious beliefs.

Diverse Peoples

When the followers of Muhammad swept out of the Arabian Peninsula into the ancient lands of Mesopotamia, Palestine, and Persia in the mid-600s, they encountered a mosaic of cultures. Most of the conquered people adopted the Islamic religion and the Arabic language. Others, mainly Christians and Jews, continued to practice their religions. The Persians, Kurds,

and Armenians maintained their own strong cultural identities.

For over 150 years Islam was successful in governing these different peoples as one political region. But beginning in the tenth century, the Arabs could no longer control their huge empire in the Middle East. Within a short time, large numbers of Turks, led by the Seljuks (SEL jooks), conquered almost all of the Middle East. They adopted the Islamic religion and ruled the Middle East for more than four hundred years before losing control to the region's last great empire builders—the Ottoman Turks.

Under the Ottomans, the people of the region continued to practice their religions. The Ottomans did not impose Islamic law on non-Muslims. Christians and Jews were allowed to govern important aspects of their lives, such as marriage and death, according to their beliefs.

Beginning in the late 1700s, discontent and rivalry developed among the different ethnic and religious groups under Ottoman control.

 Muslims at prayer in Mecca *(photo left)*

Chapter 23 ▪ Section 1   **469**

Objectives

Upon completion of Section 1, students should be able to:

- ◆ explain how the Ottoman Turks tried to unite the peoples of the Middle East;
- ◆ explain why European powers took control of the nations of Southwest Asia after World War I;
- ◆ describe how the creation of Israel affected relations between Arabs and Jews.

 ## National Geography Standards

The following National Geography Standards are highlighted in this section: 1, 5, 6, 9, 10, 11, 12, 13, 17

 ## Bellringer

Ask students: **Why is Southwest Asia often referred to as the Middle East?** (From a European perspective, the Middle East is the land that lies between Europe and the distant parts of Asia.)

LESSON PLAN

1. Focus Tell students to imagine they are members of the United Nations in 1947. Both Arabs and Jews are claiming Palestine as their homeland. The British, who control Palestine, have turned the problem over to the United Nations. Ask students to solve the dilemma.

2. Instruct Make a four-column chart on the board entitled *The Palestinian Dilemma*. Label the columns *Arab Viewpoint, Jewish Viewpoint, United Nations Solution*, and *Results*. Have students complete the chart.

3. Close/Reteach Based on what students have read in Section 1, ask them to write answers to the Reading Focus questions on this page.

Pacing Suggestions

For 90-minute Blocks

You will want to vary activities.

- Ask students to scan recent issues of periodicals that cover international events, looking for news about Iraq, Saudi Arabia, Oman, Yemen, Turkey, Iran, or Cyprus. For each story, tell students to record the name of the nation covered, the date of the news piece, and the source. Ask them to write a summary of each story and share it with the class. Then have the class discuss how each story relates to physical or human geography.

Chapter 23 ▪ Section 1   **469**

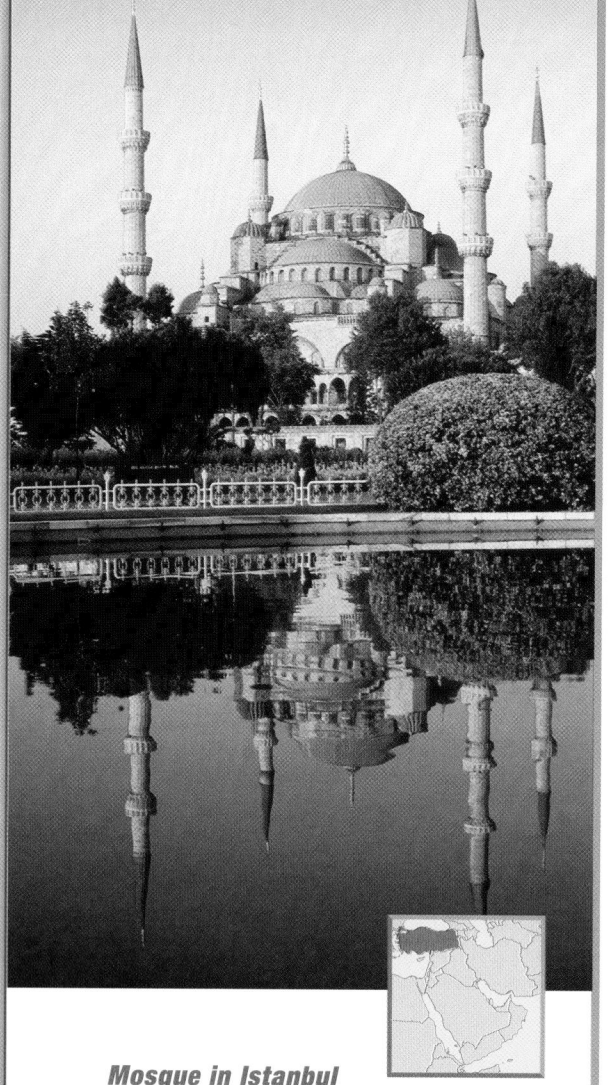

Mosque in Istanbul

Understanding the Past The Blue Mosque was built in the 1600s in Istanbul, the capital of the Ottoman Empire. By the start of World War I, the once-powerful empire was near collapse.

Place *How did rulers of the Ottoman Empire deal with cultural diversity in their empire?*

Many of these groups were eager to establish independent homelands. The Ottoman leadership was no longer powerful enough to hold its empire together.

At the same time, European nations were eager to exert political influence in the Middle

East and gain new markets for their products. By the mid-1800s, the Ottoman Empire was being called "the sick man of Europe." And Great Britain, France, and Russia were waiting for it to die.

World War I

In 1914 World War I broke out. Great Britain, France, and Russia, known as the Allies, were on one side. On the other side were Germany and Austria-Hungary, known as the Central Powers. The Ottoman Empire joined in alliance with the Central Powers. Although World War I was fought mainly in Europe, it greatly affected the course of modern Middle Eastern history.

Secret Negotiations Soon after the war started, the Allies began secret negotiations to decide how to divide the Ottoman Empire when it was defeated. They agreed that, except for the Arabian Peninsula, each of them would control different parts of the empire. The Arabs on the Arabian Peninsula would be given their independence when the war ended. Great Britain, eager to exert its power in the area, entered into other, separate agreements as well.

In 1915, Sir Henry McMahon, a representative of the British government, began to correspond with Husayn ibn 'Ali. Husayn was the Arab ruler of the sacred cities of Mecca and Medina on the Arabian Peninsula. He was an important leader among the Muslim Arabs who wanted to break away from the Ottoman Empire and establish an independent Arab homeland. In his letters, McMahon hoped to convince the Arabs to support Great Britain in its fight against the Ottomans. Letters discussing possible arrangements went back and forth between the two men for almost a year.

Finally, Husayn agreed to revolt against the Ottomans in exchange for British support of a homeland for all Arabs, including Christians. From the letters that had passed between him and McMahon, Husayn believed that almost all of the area from southern Turkey to southern Arabia, and from the Mediterranean Sea east to the borders of Iran, would be one vast Arab country.

A Broken Promise Unknown to Husayn, however, Great Britain and France were secretly working out another agreement for dividing the Ottoman Empire. This agreement, known as the Sykes-Picot Agreement, was signed on January 3, 1916. It limited the independent Arab state to the area that is now Saudi Arabia and Yemen. It gave the French control of Syria and allotted Iraq to Great Britain. Palestine was placed under joint control. When the Arabs discovered this, they felt Great Britain had broken its promise to them.

At the peace conference following the Allies' victory, the once-great empire of the Ottomans was reduced to a single independent country—Turkey. The Arab state the British promised to Husayn was limited to the area that is now Saudi Arabia and Yemen. France and Great Britain divided the rest of the Ottoman Empire between them. France took Syria—including the area that would become the country of Lebanon—as a mandate. A **mandate** referred to land to be governed by an outside power on behalf of the League of Nations until it was ready for independence. Great Britain was given Palestine, Trans-Jordan, and Iraq as mandates.

Arabs and Jews

By the mid-1940s, Iraq, Jordan, Syria, and Lebanon had been established as independent countries. The political future of what remained of Palestine after the creation of Jordan was still to be decided, however.

The issue of independence for Palestine created a dilemma for Great Britain. Two groups claimed Palestine as their homeland—the Arabs and the Jews. The Arabs had lived for centuries in Palestine. Many of them traced their ancestry back to the area's earliest settlers. But the Jews also had ancient historical ties to Palestine. Their ancestors had migrated to this region beginning around 1900 B.C. to 1700 B.C. By 1000 B.C. these people were known as the Hebrews. The Hebrews established a kingdom, which later split into two kingdoms and then was defeated in a succession of military conquests. After their defeat and exile by the Babylonians in 586 B.C., however, the Jews began to migrate to other lands. Over the centuries most Jews settled in other places, but some remained in Palestine.

APPLYING THE GEOGRAPHIC THEMES

- **Regions** The land that was Palestine and Trans-Jordan is now Israel and Jordan.
  - *According to the map, what was Palestine's status prior to and following World War I?*

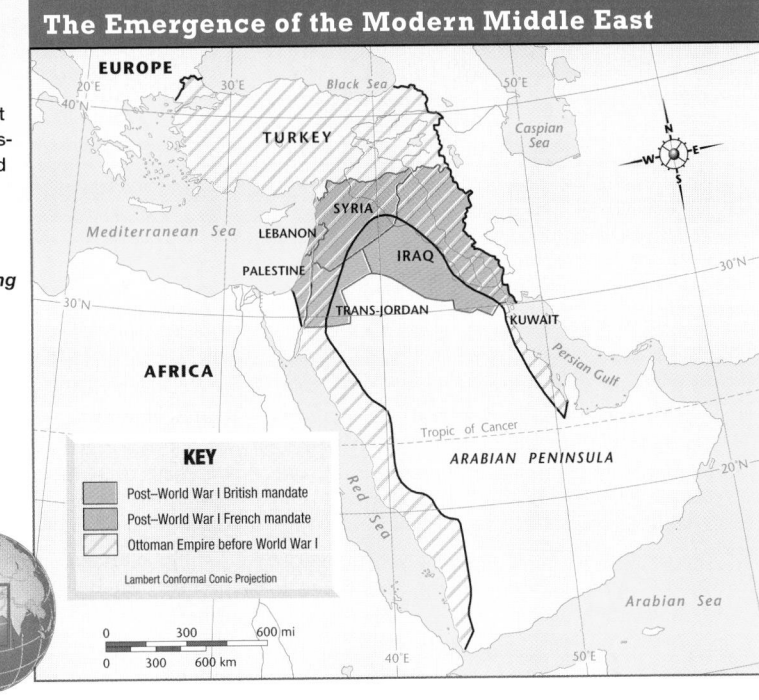

The Emergence of the Modern Middle East

KEY
- Post–World War I British mandate
- Post–World War I French mandate
- Ottoman Empire before World War I

Lambert Conformal Conic Projection

0   300   600 mi
0   300   600 km

Vocabulary

Mandate Ask a volunteer to look up the term *mandate* in the Glossary and read its definition aloud. Ask students why they think the League of Nations might have decided France and Great Britain should temporarily govern parts of Southwest Asia. (in order to give the newly freed regions time to establish a framework for government and set up other institutions before they became independent)

ACTIVITY

Reteach

Changing Regions Ask students to compare the map on page 468 to the one on this page. Ask them to determine which countries or parts of countries were part of the British mandate, which were part of the French mandate, and which were part of neither. (Visual/Spatial)

ACTIVITY

Reteach

Cause and Effect Ask students to use the material in their texts to make a list of the ways World War I changed Southwest Asia. Have volunteers read their lists to the class. (Verbal/Linguistic)

READING STRATEGY

Visualizing

Ask students to set up a time line that begins at 2000 B.C. and ends at A.D. 2000, marked off in even increments of 500 years. Then ask them to read the section Arabs and Jews on pages 471–474. As they read, have students look for dates and note the dated events in the correct places on their time lines.

CUSTOMIZE FOR...

Students Acquiring English/ESL

Making a Collage Pair fluent speakers with students acquiring English to create a collage about the religions practiced in the early Ottoman Empire. The collage can include photos and symbols representing each of the various religions. Ask students to share their collages with the class, explaining the images they selected.

Answer to Map Caption

Palestine was part of the Ottoman Empire prior to World War I and part of the British mandate after World War I.

Zionists The word *Zionist* comes from *Zion*, in Hebrew *Tsiyon*, the name of a hill in ancient Jerusalem where one of the first Jewish temples was located.

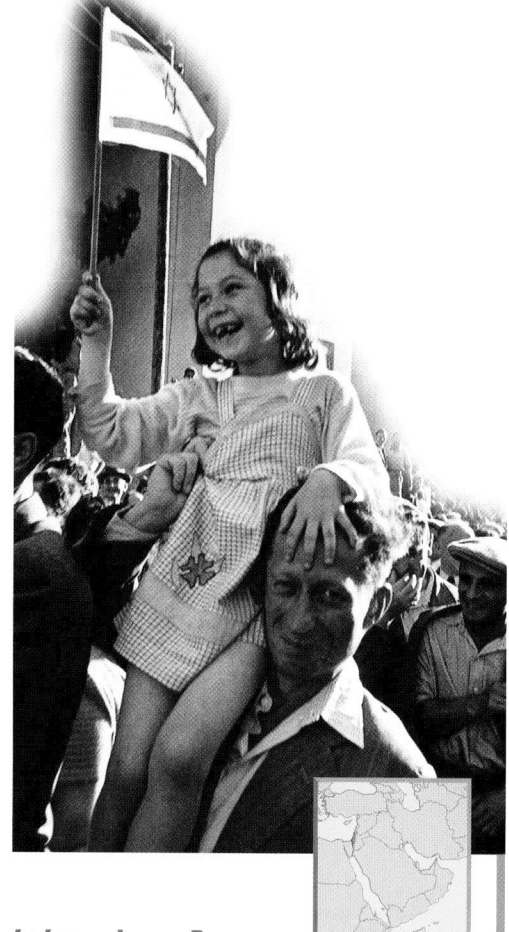

Independence Day

Understanding the Past The creation of the state of Israel was a joyous moment for many people.

Place *How did the creation of a Jewish national homeland in Palestine conflict with Arab self-determination?*

By the late 1800s, there were about ten million Jews scattered throughout the world. In many of the places they lived, they were discriminated against and cruelly persecuted. In Eastern Europe and Russia, where more than half of the world's Jews lived, they faced increasing oppression. Afraid of what lay ahead, many Jews began to emigrate. Some called themselves **Zionists,** after the hill in Jerusalem to which Jews had always prayed to return. They believed that the only way to solve the problem of oppression was by returning to the place they perceived as their homeland—Palestine—and creating their own country with their own government.

In 1882 the first group of Zionists immigrated to Palestine. Their numbers had reached almost 85,000 by 1914. As Jewish immigration increased, the Arabs who were living in Palestine under Ottoman rule grew more and more fearful of losing their land.

Two Peoples, One Homeland The Zionists put increasing pressure on Great Britain and other European nations to support their plan for an independent homeland. In 1917, in the midst of World War I, the British government issued the Balfour Declaration. It stated Britain's support for the creation of a Jewish national home in Palestine without violating the rights of Arabs living there:

> ❝His Majesty's Government view with favour the establishment in Palestine of a national home for the Jewish people, and will use their best endeavours to facilitate the achievement of this object, it being clearly understood that nothing shall be done which may prejudice the civil and religious rights of existing non-Jewish communities in Palestine, or the rights and political status enjoyed by Jews in any other country.❞

The Arabs were shocked and dismayed by the content of the declaration. They had been led by the British to believe that all Arabs would be granted the right of **self-determination,** or the right to decide their own political future. They believed that Palestine would become part of a larger, independent Arab country. The British sent representatives to Arab leaders to assure them that Great Britain's goal was still self-determination for the Arabs. As both groups pressured Great Britain to fulfill its promises to them, it became clear that the goals of Jews and Arabs were at odds.

While Britain searched for a way to solve the problem, the struggle between Jews and Arabs in Palestine became increasingly violent. As Jewish immigration grew, so did Arab feelings that their political future as an independent Arab country

Answer to Photo Caption

Arabs believed that they would be allowed to decide their own political future and that Palestine would become part of a larger Arab country.

Arab Refugees

Migration Conflict over the creation of Israel forced hundreds of thousands to migrate. Jews moved from Arab lands into Israel, while Palestinian Arabs moved to nearby Arab states. These Palestinian refugees are building a road.

Movement *How did events in Europe contribute to Jewish migration?*

was threatened. Finally, the Arabs revolted by boycotting Jewish businesses and burning bridges and crops. The Jews retaliated. People on both sides were killed.

Meanwhile, Hitler came to power in Germany in 1933. As Nazi Germany began to persecute Jews, thousands fled to Palestine. By 1939, the number of Jews living in Palestine had increased from 85,000 to 445,000.

Tensions between Great Britain, the Palestinians, and the Jews mounted. Britain decided to limit Jewish immigration to the area, leaving Jews stranded in Germany and other parts of Europe. In response, some Jews in Palestine began a campaign of guerrilla warfare against the British.

The Creation of Israel Nearly six million Jews had perished in Nazi concentration camps by the time World War II ended in 1945. Thousands of survivors had no place to go. When the world learned of the Holocaust, there was an outpouring of support for a Jewish homeland in Palestine. The Jewish Agency, an international organization, demanded that Britain end restrictions on Jewish immigration to Palestine.

At that time, however, the Arabs made up 70 percent of Palestine's population. They were bitterly opposed to the creation of a Jewish state in

Palestine. Why, they wondered, should they give up their land because of what the Nazis had done? In response to the call for a Jewish homeland, the nations of Egypt, Syria, Lebanon, Trans-Jordan, Iraq, Saudi Arabia, and Yemen formed the Arab League and announced their support for Arabs in Palestine.

In 1947, realizing that it could not find an acceptable solution, the British government announced that it was withdrawing from Palestine and turning the problem over to the United Nations. Immediately the United Nations formed a special committee to find a solution to the problem. After months of debate, the committee recommended that Palestine be partitioned into two states—one Arab and one Jewish. The city of Jerusalem, sacred to Jews, Christians, and Muslims, would be designated an international city.

The Jews accepted the United Nations plan. However, the Arabs were furious.

Cooperation and Conflict
Many of the world's regional conflicts are related to geographic boundaries and disputes over territory. The Golan Heights, the West Bank, and Gaza, shown on the map on page 476, are all examples of such disputed territories.

Chapter 23 ▪ Section 1 **473**

Answers to Section 1 Assessment

1. (a) mandate, p. 471 **(b)** Zionist, p. 472 **(c)** self-determination, p. 472

2. Beginning in the late 1700s, rivalries among different religious and ethnic groups led to rebellions. Weak Ottoman leaders could not maintain order.

3. World War I brought about the end of the Ottoman Empire. Decisions about how to rule and divide the conquered empire were left to the victors. Great Britain and France won authority over much of the region.

4. (a) The United Nations created a plan to divide Palestine into two states to ease the violent struggle. More than half of Palestine was declared the Jewish nation of Israel. **(b)** The Palestinians joined their Arab neighbors in an unsuccessful war against Israel. After the war, Jordan and Egypt claimed the remaining portions of Palestine, and the Palestinians were left with no country.

5. (a) Palestinians lost their homeland. **(b)** Israel controlled almost three fourths of Palestine; Jordan and Egypt divided the rest of Palestine.

Activity Rubrics Share rubrics with students before they write their hypotheses.

Attempted The hypothesis is unclear and is inconsistent with the information on the maps.

Minimal The hypothesis is plausible and provides an explanation for densely populated areas, but it contains many mechanical errors.

Adequate The hypothesis is well conceived and well supported and contains no mechanical errors.

Exemplary The hypothesis is insightful, well supported, and well written.

Answer to Photo Caption

By the end of the war, Israel controlled almost three fourths of Palestine. Jordan and Egypt divided the rest of Palestine between them.

Arab-Israeli Conflict

Cooperation and Conflict Troops from Jordan, shown here patrolling the Palestinian border, and other Arab League nations attacked the newly created nation of Israel in 1948.

Place *What was the outcome of this Arab-Israeli war?*

According to the plan, the Jewish state would include more than half the total land of Palestine, though less than one third of the population was Jewish. Much of the coast fell within the Jewish state, leaving largely upland and desert areas within Arab lands.

Arab leaders warned that dividing Palestine would result in war. One Arab leader stated, "We Arabs shall not be losers. We shall be fighting on our ground and shall be supported . . . by 70 million Arabs around us."

Nevertheless, the United Nations voted to approve the partition of Palestine. In May 1948, David Ben-Gurion, leader of the Palestinian Jews, announced the independent, new state of Israel. In a matter of hours, neighboring Arab countries attacked Israel. By the end of the 1948 war, Israel controlled almost three fourths of Palestine, including land in the Negev Desert and half of Jerusalem. Jordan and Egypt divided the rest of Palestine between them. The Palestinians were left with no country at all.

SECTION 1 ASSESSMENT

1. **Key Terms** Define **(a)** mandate, **(b)** Zionist, **(c)** self-determination.

2. **Understanding the Past** How did the diversity of the peoples of the Middle East contribute to the fall of the Ottoman Empire?

3. **Government and Citizenship** What effect did World War I have on the Middle East?

4. **Cooperation and Conflict (a)** How did the struggle between Arabs and Jews over Palestine lead to the creation of Israel? **(b)** What happened to the Palestinians after the state of Israel was created?

5. **Critical Thinking Identifying Main Ideas** Reread the last paragraph on this page. **(a)** What is the main idea of this paragraph? **(b)** What are two details that support the main idea?

Activity
USING THE **REGIONAL ATLAS**

Review the maps in the Regional Atlas for Central and Southwest Asia and this section. Locate the areas that are the most densely populated. Write a hypothesis that explains why these areas are so densely populated.

RESOURCE DIRECTORY

Teaching Resources

Unit 6, Chapter 23
- Section 1 Quiz, p. 25
- Section 2 Guided Reading and Review, p. 26

Spanish Resources
- Section 1 Quiz, p. 56

Guide to the Essentials (English/Spanish)
- Section Summary, Chapter 23, Section 2

Mental Mapping booklet
- Unit 6 Checklist, p. 79

Technology

Guided Reading Audiotapes (English/Spanish), Chapter 23, Section 2

Section Reading Support Transparencies, Chapter 23, Section 2

World Geography Map and Photo Transparencies
- Central and Southwest Asia: Maps and Photos

Book on CD, Chapter 23

Social Studies Skills Tutor CD-ROM

Companion Web site, www.phschool.com
- Chapter 23 Activities

2 Israel

Reading Focus

- How has Israel changed its environment in order to make its land more productive and increase prosperity?
- Who are the major cultural groups in Israel, and what roles have they played in the nation's history?
- What cooperative steps have Israel and its Arab neighbors taken to try to prevent conflicts from erupting?

Key Terms

drip irrigation

potash

Main Idea Israel struggles to maintain peace among its diverse population and with its Arab neighbors.

Economic Systems In a kibbutz, or collective community, all property is shared.

Objectives

Upon completion of Section 2, students should be able to:

- ◆ discuss how Israel has changed its environment to make its land more productive and to increase prosperity;
- ◆ identify the major cultural groups in Israel and the roles they have played in the nation's history;
- ◆ list the steps that Israel and its Arab neighbors have taken to prevent conflict.

 National Geography Standards

The following National Geography Standards are highlighted in this section: 1, 4, 5, 10, 11, 12, 13, 14, 15, 16

 Bellringer

Ask students to think of at least three challenges they would face if they decided to move to the frontier region of a country. (Challenges may include loneliness, lack of modern conveniences, and lack of services such as schools and hospitals.)

LESSON PLAN

1. Focus Tell students that, in an attempt to develop Israel's deserts, the Israeli government encouraged its citizens to move to desert areas by offering special incentives. Ask the students what incentives might convince them to move to the desert.

2. Instruct Write the following sentence on the board: *Technology is one of Israel's greatest allies.* Ask students to write five facts from the text that support this statement. Then have students share their facts with the class.

3. Close/Reteach Write the title *Israel* on the board. Ask students to develop an outline of Section 2, using the subsection titles as main headings.

---

66 There was nothing but desert and swamp; they had to clear it and build. . . . They never stopped to say, 'Should we clear a potato patch here, . . . or raise sheep over there?'. . . No, our founders said with breathtaking simplicity: 'Let there be a potato patch. . . . Anywhere, everywhere, and right away.' [Today] we do not say, 'Let there be a potato patch, and scratch it into the nearest soil.' We must say, 'Should there be a potato patch? And, if so, where is the best place to put it? . . . How much irrigation will it need? . . . Or do we need more cotton, more tools, or is there a more nutrient, efficient food than potatoes?' 99

Gideon Samet, a young Israeli journalist, used these words to describe the changing character of Israel. Today, Israel is a very different place from when its founders first cleared, irrigated, and farmed the land. Its landscape is different. Its diverse economy is different. Even the character of its people has changed. Since gaining independence, Israel has raced along a path of urgent and rapid development to become one of the most technologically advanced countries in the world.

Environmental Change

When the first Zionist settlers arrived in Palestine, people were already living along the fertile coastal plains and in the rich valleys of the highland regions. Much of the land available to the immigrants was either mosquito-infested swamp or barren stretches of desert. In the 1880s settlers began the long, slow process of reclaiming the land. Acre by acre they drained the swamps. Patiently they coaxed water into the desert.

Since 1948, when Israel became independent, the Israeli government has viewed the desert as one of the main challenges to its existence. David Ben-Gurion, Israel's first prime minister, said, "If the state does not put an end to the desert, the desert is likely to put an end to the state." Then and now, an important part of Israel's national policy has been directed at turning the unwelcoming desert into productive land that can be used for agriculture, industry, and settlement.

Chapter 23 ▪ Section 2 **475**

CUSTOMIZE FOR...

Gifted and Talented

Comparing Viewpoints Have each student do library or Internet research to find an account of the early days of Israel's independence. Ask students to highlight sentences in the accounts that seem to show either pro-Israeli or pro-Palestinian sentiments. Instruct students to write a brief report that first summarizes the account and then uses examples from the account to explain whether it is pro-Israeli, pro-Palestinian, or neutral.

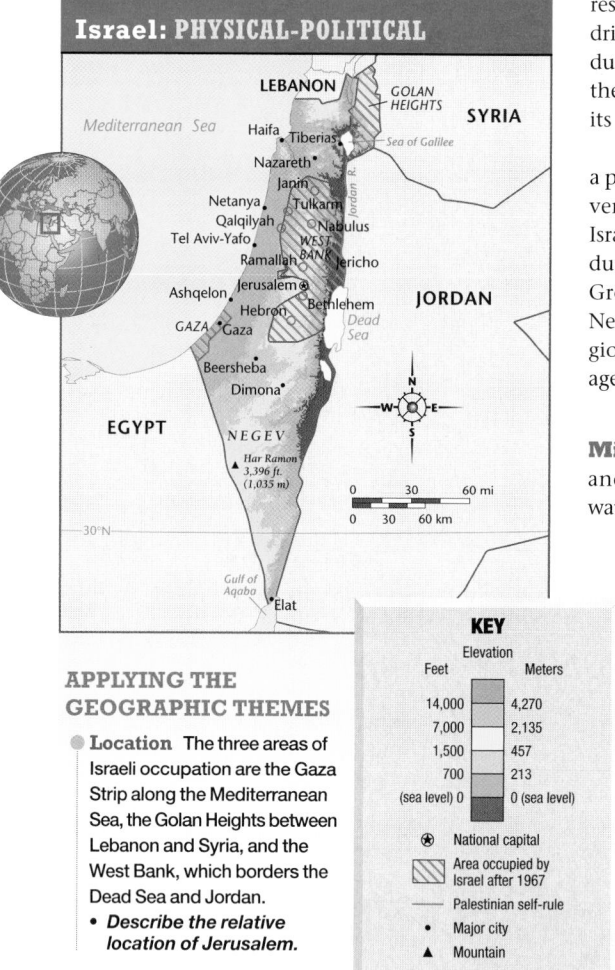

Israel: PHYSICAL-POLITICAL

APPLYING THE GEOGRAPHIC THEMES

● **Location** The three areas of Israeli occupation are the Gaza Strip along the Mediterranean Sea, the Golan Heights between Lebanon and Syria, and the West Bank, which borders the Dead Sea and Jordan.
• *Describe the relative location of Jerusalem.*

KEY

Elevation

Feet	Meters
14,000	4,270
7,000	2,135
1,500	457
700	213
(sea level) 0	0 (sea level)

⊛ National capital
▨ Area occupied by Israel after 1967
— Palestinian self-rule
• Major city
▲ Mountain

Lambert Conformal Conic Projection

Technology Transforms the Desert

The Negev Desert is Israel's driest region. It covers over half of the country. Here the Israelis have built a system of pipelines, canals, and tunnels almost 100 miles (160 km) long called the National Water Carrier. Water from the Sea of Galilee is pumped southward through the system to irrigate parts of the Negev. A region that was once barren stretches of sand is now striped with huge tracts of fertile green land.

The Israelis have also invented other scientific methods for increasing land use. A process called **drip irrigation** preserves precious water resources by letting precise amounts of water drip onto plants from pipes. Agricultural production in Israel has increased greatly over the years. Today Israel produces almost all of its own food.

However, Israel's agricultural success has a price. Increased demands for water have severely strained limited supplies. Therefore, Israel has investigated ways to save water. Industrial wastewater is treated and reused. Groundwater runoff is stored in reservoirs. Nevertheless, like other countries in the region, Israel could face a serious water shortage in the near future.

Mining the Dead Sea Between Israel and Jordan lies the Dead Sea, a huge saltwater lake. Because of the quantity of minerals in the sea, fish or other animals cannot live in it. Even the surrounding land is a dry, lifeless wilderness. The Israelis have built processing plants to extract **potash**—which is used in explosives and fertilizer—table salt, bromine, and other minerals from the Dead Sea. Israel exports these minerals worldwide.

Encouraging Migration to the Desert Despite the Israeli government's drive to develop the Negev and other desert areas, it was difficult to attract people to these places to work. Few people wanted to live and raise families away from the conveniences of modern life and in such an isolated area. New towns, such as Arad, had to be built. Workers had to be offered high pay and extra time off.

Still, feelings about living in the desert are mixed. One Israeli couple, Zvi and Rebecca Rubin, had differing views about their life in Arad.

❝I [Zvi] came to Arad because I was offered a high salary, a good flat, and low taxes. . . . This is a good place to live, work, and put money aside. . . . For him [Zvi] it is a good place to work and live. For me [Rebecca] it is the desert. . . . I wish he could find a job back in Haifa.❞

Economic Activities Israel has successfully developed its few natural resources. However, its agricultural and chemical industries alone could not produce enough employment opportunities to support the nation's rapidly growing population. It had to develop new economic activities.

Israel looked in part to high technology to help its struggling economy. With the help of grants and loans from other countries, Israel's well-educated and highly trained scientists and engineers applied their skills to make Israel a world leader in medical laser technology, sophisticated weaponry, aerospace equipment, and electronics.

Israel also developed service industries to support its growing population. Today more than three quarters of all Israelis work in areas such as education, housing, and tourism.

Diverse Cultures

Israel's citizens come from a great variety of backgrounds. About 80 percent are Jewish. But at any public gathering you will recognize that great differences exist even among the Jews of Israel. To strengthen the nation, the Israeli government has encouraged Jews to immigrate from around the world. If you listen, you will hear Hebrew spoken with a variety of accents—Russian, American, Turkish, and German.

Israel's Jews Until recently, two groups of Jews—Ashkenazi Jews and Sephardic Jews—formed a sharp division in Israeli society. Almost all the Jews who immigrated to Israel before 1948 were Ashkenazi Jews from Europe. As a result, when Israel was established it had a modern, Westernized character. After 1948, more than half of the Jews immigrating to Israel were Sephardic Jews from countries in Southwest Asia, North Africa, and Asia. These Sephardic Jews were generally poorer and less educated than the rest of Israel's citizens. Most of them worked as unskilled laborers. They earned less money and had a lower standard of living than that of the European Jews. They also had less influence in the government. In recent years, however, the gap between the two groups has begun to close.

Most recent immigrants to Israel come from Ethiopia and the former Soviet Union. In the

Change Over Time

Political Change

Migration In the 1940s, British officials in Palestine enforced restrictive immigration policies. Jewish refugees from Europe violated British regulations and risked their lives to enter Palestine (PAST). Today, Jewish immigrants from Africa and other parts of the world are welcomed to Israel (PRESENT).

Movement *Why do you think people risk their lives to emigrate to another country?*

PAST

PRESENT

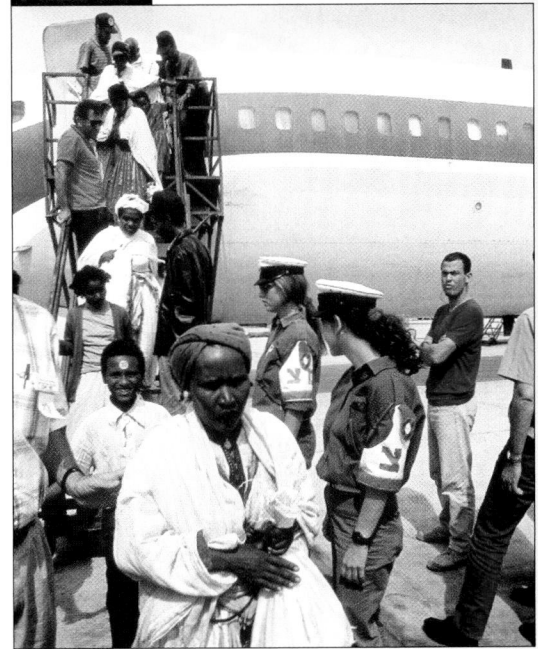

mid-1980s and early 1990s, thousands of Ethiopian Jews moved to Israel. Hundreds of thousands of Soviet Jews immigrated to the Jewish state when the Soviet Union relaxed its emigration policies in the 1980s.

Along with cultural differences among Jews in Israeli society, there are also wide political divisions. Representatives in the Knesset, Israel's democratically elected parliament, range from ultra-Orthodox Jews to the nonreligious. Ultra-Orthodox Jews adhere strictly to Jewish religious tradition and believe that Israel should be governed accordingly. The nonreligious believe that religion should not dictate the running of the state and interfere with people's daily lives. In between these two groups are a number of other groups. Divergent beliefs and goals have led to serious political conflicts in complicated, coalition governments. It is always difficult, and often impossible, for the government to reach any kind of agreement on important issues.

Israel's Arabs Almost 20 percent of Israel's population is Arab. This diverse population includes Christians, Muslims, and Druzes (independent people who broke from Islam in the eleventh century and live in villages in northern

Israel). As a minority, the Arabs hold a very different place from that of the Jews in Israel.

Israeli Arabs are citizens of Israel. As such, they have full political rights. Arabs serve in the Knesset, enjoy the benefits of a free press, and in most cases are allowed to form political parties. Nevertheless, many Israeli Arabs believe that they are discriminated against in education, employment, and other areas. In recent years, Arabs in Israel have begun to demand a greater voice in Israeli society.

Cooperation and Conflict

Along with building a strong economy and maintaining harmony among its diverse population, Israel faces another major challenge. It must build a lasting peace with the Palestinians and its other Arab neighbors. In recent years, Israel and the Arab nations have gone to war four times.

Palestinian Refugees The source of the conflict between the Israelis and the Palestinians goes back to 1947. That was the year when the United Nations voted to partition the British mandate of Palestine into two states—one Arab,

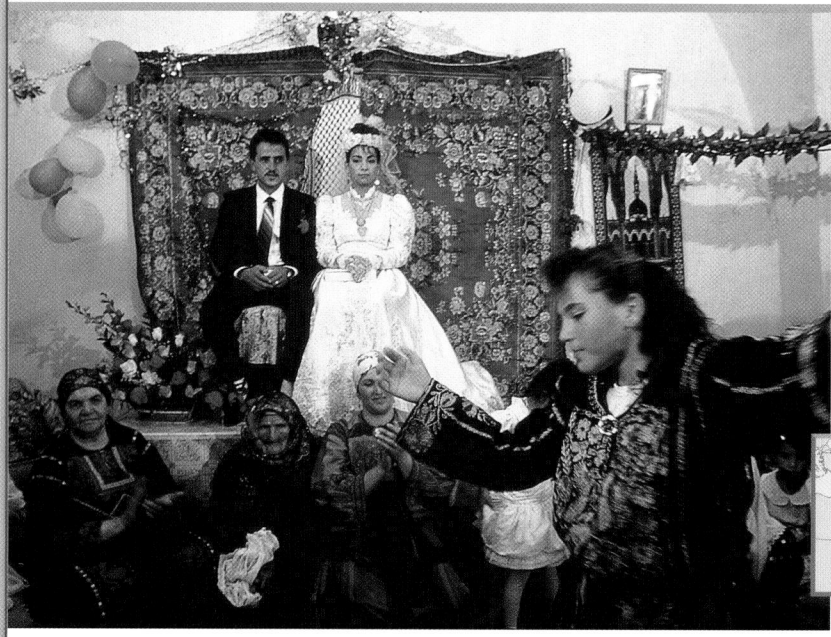

Palestinian Wedding Feast

Cultures The bride pictured here was born in the United States but met and married her husband in the West Bank.

Place *How is this wedding similar to and different from weddings in your community?*

478   Chapter 23 ▪ The Countries of Southwest Asia

478   Chapter 23

A Living Memorial

Cooperation and Conflict Conflicts between Jews and Palestinians over land have plagued Israel since its creation in 1948. The Palestinians in this photograph plant a tree in observance of Land Day, a day Palestinians set aside to commemorate their losses.

Place *What other sources of conflict are there between the Arabs and Jews of Israel?*

BACKGROUND

History

Gaza Strip This narrow strip of land along the Mediterranean Sea was taken by Israel from Egypt in the 1967 war. An area often rife with conflict, the region is now home to more than 750,000 Palestinian refugees and a small percentage of Jews as well.

ACTIVITY

Enrichment

Current Events Ask students to listen to the evening news for stories about the Israeli-Arab peace process. Then have them report back to the class about what they have heard. (Verbal/Linguistic)

GLOBAL CONNECTIONS

Cooperation and Conflict

Terrorism Terrorism and guerrilla warfare tactics have been used around the world to influence political decisions and to attract global attention. Like the PLO, the Irish Republican Army (IRA) has killed civilians in its attempts to overthrow the ruling government that it considers to have stolen its homeland. In French-controlled Algeria, terrorism was used not only by the Algerians who were seeking independence, but also by some of the French settlers who were trying to maintain control. In the United States, terrorism was used by the Ku Klux Klan to defy Reconstruction following the Civil War. More recently, American Timothy McVeigh bombed a federal building in Oklahoma City, killing nearly 170 people, to protest actions of the U.S. government. On September 11, 2001, terrorists flew planes into the World Trade Center towers in New York and the Pentagon near Washington, D.C. Thousands of civilians died in the attacks.

one Jewish. Arab leaders refused to accept that decision. As a result, when Israel declared independence in May 1948, a war between the new state of Israel and its Arab neighbors broke out as the British left.

By the end of the war in 1949, most of the Palestinians had lost their homes and property. As many as 500,000 people had fled to neighboring Arab countries. At the same time, an even larger number of Jews were expelled from Arab countries, most of whom were resettled in Israel. Societies across the Middle East were shattered.

The Palestinians took refuge in the Gaza Strip (ruled by Egypt), Jordan, Syria, and Lebanon. A conflict between these Arab countries and Israel erupted in 1967. Israeli troops took control of the West Bank in Jordan and the Gaza Strip. About 200,000 Palestinians fled from the West Bank to East Jordan. Fewer than one million Palestinians remained in the West Bank under Israeli military rule, but many Palestinians who had fled were not allowed to return to their homes.

By this time more than one million Palestinians were living permanently as refugees outside the area that was once Palestine. Some of these refugees eventually found jobs and housing in other Arab countries and resumed fairly normal lives. Others remained in crowded refugee camps in Lebanon, Syria, and Jordan. Palestinians everywhere dreamed of returning to their homeland someday and establishing an independent Palestinian state.

More Conflict In the mid-1960s, many of these refugee camps became bases for the Palestinian Liberation Organization (PLO)—the Palestinians' government in exile. The PLO refused to recognize Israel as a country. It demanded that Palestine be liberated and the refugees be allowed to return to their homes. PLO extremists gained worldwide attention for their cause by hijacking planes, kidnapping and killing Israeli civilians, and conducting raids on Israeli communities.

Most Israelis viewed the PLO as terrorists whose goal was to destroy not only Israel but also Israeli Jews. Israel began to conduct raids on PLO bases in neighboring Arab countries. By the mid-1970s, most PLO activity was being conducted from Lebanon. The Israelis

Global Trade Patterns The world depends on oil from Southwest Asia. In the past, fighting between Israel and its Arab neighbors has severely disrupted the world's oil supply.

TEST PREPARATION

Have students read the subsection More Conflict beginning on this page and then answer the following question.

What prompted many Palestinian fighters to leave Lebanon?

  A Plane hijackings and kidnappings
  (B) Israel's invasion of Lebanon
  C Frequent demonstrations, strikes, and violence
  D The settling of Israelis in occupied territories

Answer to Photo Caption

Possible answer: Many Arabs in Israel feel that they are discriminated against in education, employment, and other areas.

Chapter 23 ▪ Section 2 **479**

launched heavy attacks against Palestinian refugee camps situated near the Lebanese border that they suspected of supporting PLO guerrillas. In 1982, Israel invaded Lebanon in a final attempt to crush the PLO. After a long siege and a heavy bombardment, many Palestinian fighters left Lebanon.

Meanwhile, more and more Israelis were settling in the occupied territories—the West Bank and Gaza Strip. As Palestinians there increasingly despaired of ever gaining a homeland, support for the PLO grew. There were frequent demonstrations, strikes, and violence. In response, Israel tightened its control of the occupied territories, imprisoning or exiling thousands of suspected PLO supporters.

The Struggle for a Solution During the 1970s and 1980s, thousands of Palestinians and Israelis lost their lives in the fighting. Various solutions to the conflict were proposed, but Palestinians seemed unwilling to acknowledge the right of Israel to exist, and Israel seemed unwilling to permit creation of a Palestinian homeland. In 1987, Palestinians began hurling rocks at Israeli soldiers in Gaza and the West Bank. The uprising escalated into a movement called an *intifada* (in-tee-FAH-dah), a term that means "shaking off" in Arabic. Palestinian demonstrations, boycotts, and violent resistance were met with Israeli military force.

Southwest Asia and the United States
Communications Data

Country	Television Receivers (per 1,000 people)	Newspaper Circulation (daily, per 1,000 people)	Personal Computers (per 1,000 people)
Iran	64	24	32.7
Iraq	82	20	NA
Israel	291	291	186.1
Jordan	86	45	7.2
Kuwait	510	376	71.4
Lebanon	373	141	24.4
Oman	660	27	10.9
Saudi Arabia	260	59	43.6
Syria	69	20	1.4
Turkey	333	111	20.7
Yemen	29	15	NA
United States	805	212	406.7

Sources: *Encarta World Atlas*   NA = information not available.

CHART SKILLS

● **Cultures** *Which Middle Eastern countries have greater newspaper circulation than the United States?*

● **Economic Systems** *Which Middle Eastern countries seem to have low levels of development compared to other countries in the region? Explain.*

Interns for Peace

Planning for the Future Jewish children playfully welcome the newest arrival at a summer peace camp— a Palestinian Israeli citizen. Happily surprised at their own ability to work together, these young Interns for Peace offer Israel's future the possibility of peace.

Place *What other moves toward peace have Israelis made in recent years?*

Civil Strife in Israel

Cooperation and Conflict In the early 2000s, the peace process between Jews and Palestinians in Israel broke down. On the streets of many communities, the sounds of gunfire and the cries of human suffering became all too common.
Place *Why do you think violence is difficult to stop once it gets started?*

Peace talks resumed in 1991 and proceeded fitfully until Israel and the PLO agreed to terms in Oslo, Norway, in 1993. Israel agreed to withdraw from Gaza and parts of the West Bank, while the Palestinians assumed authority for self-governance in the vacated areas. However, the expansion of West Bank Israeli settlements angered the Palestinians, while periodic violent actions by some Palestinian groups threatened Israel's security.

Starting in 1995, various Israeli governments negotiated with the Palestinians, but each differed on what price Israel would pay for peace. U.S. President Bill Clinton facilitated peace talks in 2000, but Palestinian and Israeli leaders could not agree on terms. A new *intifada* erupted as violent Palestinian resistance—including suicide bombings by some terror groups—was again met with Israeli military force. Peace seemed out of reach as the cycle of violence continued.

SECTION 2 ASSESSMENT

1. **Key Terms** Define **(a)** drip irrigation, **(b)** potash.

2. **Environmental Change** How has Israel made use of technology in developing its land?

3. **Cultures** What are the main cultural, ethnic, and religious groups in Israel today?

4. **Cooperation and Conflict (a)** What is the source of conflict between the Israelis and the Palestinians? **(b)** How have both sides cooperated in an attempt to resolve the conflict?

5. **Critical Thinking** **Solving Problems** What are three factors to be taken into consideration when designing a peace treaty that addresses the demands of the Israeli Jews and the Palestinian Arabs?

Activity

Take It to the NET

Writing a Journal Since the early 1900s, kibbutzim, or communal farms, have played a major role in the agriculture and national identity of Israel. Use Internet resources to find out more about this topic. Then, create a journal to chronicle a typical week of activities on a kibbutz. Visit the World Geography section of **www.phschool.com** for help in completing this activity.

Objectives

Upon completion of Section 3, students should be able to:

◆ summarize how political conditions have changed society in Jordan;

◆ describe how Lebanon has recovered from civil war;

◆ list the geographic factors and economic activities that make Syria a prosperous land;

◆ explain why there has been a series of conflicts in Iraq.

National Geography Standards

The following National Geography Standards are highlighted in this section: 1, 5, 6, 8, 9, 10, 11, 12, 13, 14, 16, 17

Bellringer

Ask students to suggest ways that they would be affected if a war were being fought in the United States. Point out to students that war has been part of life for many people in Jordan, Lebanon, Syria, and Iraq.

LESSON PLAN

1. Focus Ask students to skim the section and read the headings and subheadings. Then have them formulate one question for each of the countries covered in this section.

2. Instruct Write the headings *Syria* and *Iraq* on the board. Ask students to volunteer facts about each country's economy. Write each fact under the appropriate heading.

3. Close/Reteach List the following events on the board: *Israel gains control of the West Bank; Palestinian refugees flee to Jordan; civil war erupts in Lebanon; Iraq invades Kuwait.* Ask students to copy the list and to write an effect or consequence of the event next to each entry. Have students discuss what they have written.

3 Jordan, Lebanon, Syria, and Iraq

Reading Focus

• **How have political conditions changed society in Jordan?**

• **How has Lebanon recovered from civil war?**

• **What geographic factors and economic activities make Syria a prosperous land?**

• **Why has there been a series of conflicts in Iraq?**

Key Terms

Fertile Crescent

militia

anarchy

embargo

Main Idea Jordan, Lebanon, Syria, and Iraq share a similar past and a variety of new challenges for the future.

Physical Characteristics Barren mountains rise above Aqaba, Jordan's port city on the Red Sea.

Along with Israel, the land that is now the modern countries of Jordan, Lebanon, Syria, and Iraq made up the center of the ancient Middle East. An arc of rich land known as the **Fertile Crescent** ran through this area, where farming and the first civilizations developed. These countries remain at the center of Southwest Asia today and often are the focus of political, economic, and social challenges that affect the entire region.

Jordan: Political and Social Change

Notice on the map on page 483 that Jordan is bordered by Israel, Syria, Iraq, and Saudi Arabia. Its position between Israel and neighboring Arab countries puts it in the middle of political struggles in the region. Since 1948, Jordan has been greatly affected by conflicts in the area.

Changing Boundaries When Jordan was given its independence in 1946, almost all of its land was dry, rocky desert. However, after the 1948 war between the Arab countries and Israel,

Jordan annexed the West Bank. The addition of the West Bank to Jordan's territory supplied it with fertile land for growing crops. Workers built irrigation canals and farmers learned modern methods of growing vegetables, fruit, and wheat. Herders raised large flocks of sheep and goats. Jordan also opened industries in the area. By the mid-1960s, about one third of Jordan's gross national product came from the West Bank. Then, in 1967 Jordan, Egypt, and Syria attacked Israel. Israel gained control of the West Bank. Jordan lost its second-largest city, East Jerusalem. The impact on Jordan's economy was devastating. Jordan lost a huge part of its agricultural production, its banking business, its tourism, and its industry.

Migrations The Arab-Israeli wars of 1948 and 1967 also had a significant effect on Jordan's population. After each of these wars, many Palestinian refugees fled to Jordan. Today about half of Jordan's population are Palestinian Arabs. Unlike other Arab countries, Jordan encouraged Palestinians to become part of its society. Most became Jordanian citizens. The Palestinians are a strong political force in Jordan. In the past, they

482 Chapter 23 ▪ The Countries of Southwest Asia

have challenged Jordan's government, which is a constitutional monarchy. Palestinian political groups threatened to overthrow King Hussein if he did not support them in their struggle for a homeland.

A Modern Country Despite the challenges of the last decades, Jordan has established itself as a modern country. Since the early 1990s, its economy has been improving. In 1989, King Hussein began a process of political reform. Since his death in 1999, his son, King Abdullah, has continued on that same path—to unite an Islamic heritage with modern political freedoms.

Lebanon: Civil War and Recovery

The tiny country of Lebanon was looked upon for many years with a mixture of awe and envy by people from other Southwest Asian countries.

Lebanon had a mild climate, beautiful beaches, and an open social and political atmosphere. It also had a thriving economy. Lebanon's capital, Beirut, was a center of international tourism, banking, and trade. A glamorous and free-spirited city, Beirut was often referred to as the "Paris of the Middle East." In recent years, however, a bloody civil war left the country in ruins. Today Lebanon struggles to rebuild itself.

The Beginning of the War The chaos in Lebanon grew out of a breakdown in the political system. Since Lebanon became independent of France in 1943, its many religious groups shared responsibility for governing the country. Power was divided among the Maronite Christians, Sunni Muslims, Shiite Muslims, Greek Orthodox Christians, and Druze based on the size of their populations. The Maronites, who were the largest group according to a census taken in 1932, held the most power.

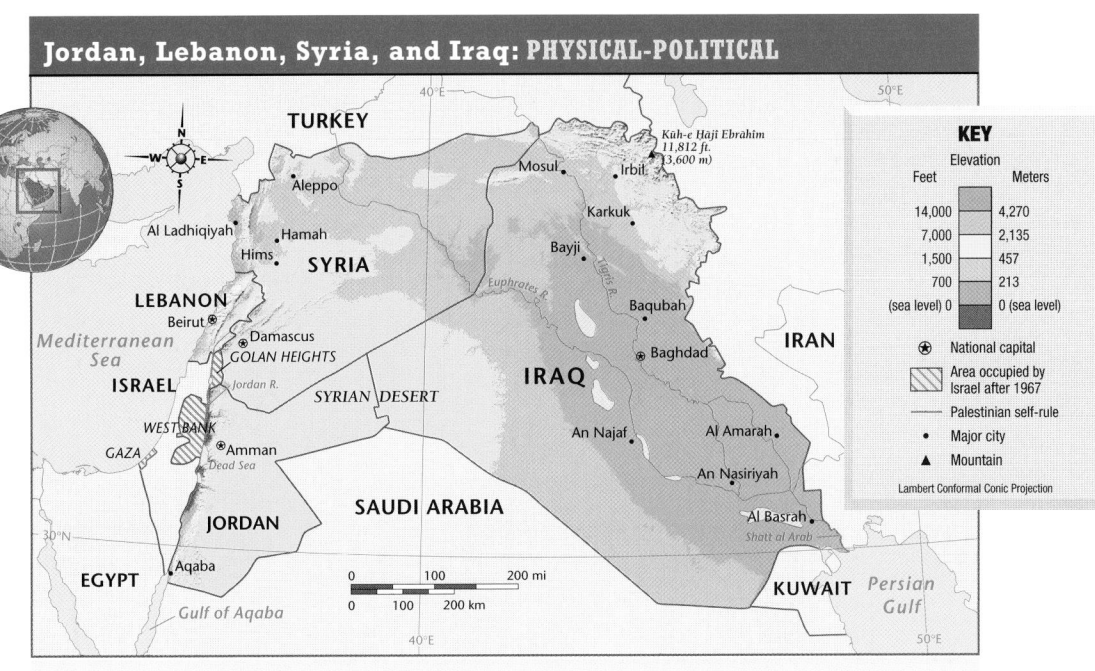

Jordan, Lebanon, Syria, and Iraq: PHYSICAL-POLITICAL

APPLYING THE GEOGRAPHIC THEMES

● **Location** The Tigris and Euphrates rivers provide water for the people, animals, and vegetation of this region. This is why the area is often referred to as the Fertile Crescent.
• *How do the Tigris and Euphrates rivers affect patterns of settlement in Iraq? Explain.*

ACTIVITY

Vocabulary

Militia Refer to the Key Terms list on page 482. Write the term *militia* on the board. Ask students to look up the word in the Glossary and paraphrase the definition. Ask several volunteers to use *militia* in a sentence.

ACTIVITY

Connecting With ...

Literature Tell students that the Lebanese poet and artist Kahlil Gibran is admired worldwide. His poetry taught universal peace and tolerance for all religions based on a spirit of love. Ask students to find a poem by Gibran and bring it to class to read aloud.

For many years this system of government worked well. But as the Muslim population grew, Muslims began to demand a greater share of power in the country's government. At the same time, growing economic inequality between groups in different parts of the country created disturbing social and political tensions. In southern Lebanon the Shiite Muslims felt that government policies particularly discriminated against them. A civil war erupted in 1958. Although a compromise was reached, the political system remained unchanged. In 1975 civil war broke out again.

A Kaleidoscope of Terror The situation had grown far more complicated by 1975. Thousands of Palestinian refugees had made their homes in Lebanon. The Palestinian Liberation Organization, or PLO, set up military bases in Lebanon from which it conducted raids across the border to Israel. The Israelis, in turn, struck back at PLO forces in Lebanon.

Because of the conflict between Israel and the PLO, other countries, including Syria, Iran, and the United States, became involved in Lebanon's civil war. In 1982 Israel invaded Lebanon to drive out the PLO. After destroying the PLO bases in southern Lebanon, the Israelis advanced to Beirut. They bombed the city heavily for weeks.

An international peacekeeping force, including several thousand United States Marines, was sent in to establish peace in Beirut. In early 1983, guerrillas from the radical Shiite group Hezbollah blew up the American embassy in Beirut, killing more than 60 people. The group struck again later that year when an explosive-filled truck crashed through the gates of a Marine barracks and exploded, killing 241 Americans. By February 1984, all American troops had been withdrawn from Lebanon. Muslim and Christian groups split into different factions. Each faction had its own **militia,** or citizen army.

By the mid-1980s, Lebanon was in a state of **anarchy,** or lawlessness. No government, army, or police force could maintain order. Bands of militia roamed the streets kidnapping members of other groups and foreign citizens whom they held hostage. In the middle of the day, fights broke out between militias on crowded streets. Families installed steel doors on their houses and apartments and bought machine guns to protect themselves.

Calm Returns After 16 years of civil war, Lebanese political groups agreed to share power once again. A formal agreement established a more equitable political system in 1991. Muslims gained more influence in the political process,

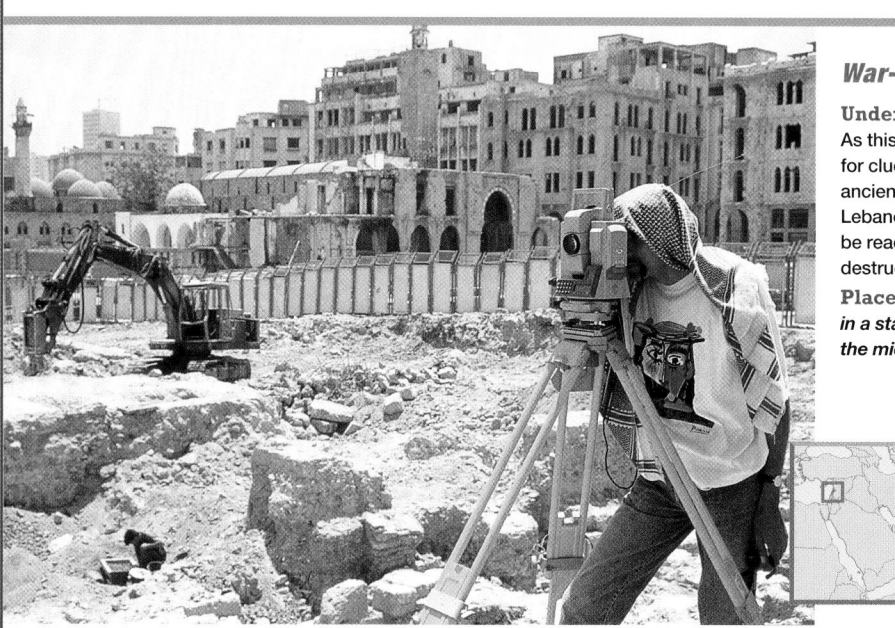

War-Torn Beirut

Understanding the Past As this archaeologist looks for clues to Lebanon's ancient Phoenician culture, Lebanon's recent history can be read in the surrounding destruction.

Place *Why was Lebanon in a state of anarchy during the mid-1980s?*

Answer to Photo Caption

A civil war was raging. No government, army, or police force could maintain order as militias fought each other.

while sectarian divisions in the government were solidified. The militias stopped fighting each other, and the economy slowly started to rebound. Banking services were restored, and both manufacturing and tourism increased. Israel removed its troops from southern Lebanon in 2000, but Syrian troops remain in the east and Hezbollah guerrillas operating in the south continue to threaten regional stability.

Syria: Challenges and Reforms

Since the time of its earliest settlers, Syria has been a prosperous land. Its location on the eastern edge of the Mediterranean between Europe, Africa, and Asia has made cities like Damascus, the capital, and Aleppo busy centers of trade. For thousands of years, Syria's people have taken advantage of its rich farmlands and its thriving cities to make a living. They grow cotton, wheat, fruit, and vegetables on the fertile land.

In recent decades, more and more Syrians have left their farms to work in the cities. Although Syria is fortunate to have fertile farmland, many farming methods are out-of-date. Few farmers have modern machinery and only about one third of the farms are irrigated. Most of Syria's farmers depend on rainfall to water their crops. However, rainfall is unreliable. When droughts occur, farmers are unable to make a living.

The Syrian government is trying to improve farming methods in the hope of encouraging farmers to stay on their land. It has given money to farmers to help them buy modern machinery. In the last decade, Syria has also been focusing more attention on research to improve crop output. The government has built dams in the north to irrigate more acres of land.

Changes upstream along the Euphrates may affect Syria's future. Turkey is building dams on the river that control the amount of water flowing downstream into Syria and Iraq. As a consequence, Syria claims to have less water available for agriculture and the production of electricity. Turkey claims that Syria wastes water through inefficient irrigation. No agreement has been reached between Turkey and Syria thus far, and drought conditions are likely to continue.

In 1970, General Hafez al-Assad took power in Syria. Assad made all of the country's political

Damascus Marketplace

Economic Activities At Damascus's center is a souk, or marketplace. Stalls, selling a range of produce, line the streets. Behind the stalls, craftsmen make their wares in workshops.
Place *How does this souk reflect the Syrian spirit of nationalism?*

and economic decisions. He allowed little political freedom. When Assad died in 2000, his son, Bashar Assad, became president. Rather than continuing his father's policies, Bashar Assad launched a series of economic and political reforms. New policies began to convert Syria's state-controlled economy into a marketing economy. Banks were privatized, and political prisoners were freed. However, in 2003, the United States and Great Britian suspected it of harboring terrorists as well as supporters of deposed Iraqi dictator Saddam Hussein.

BACKGROUND

Connecting With . . .

History In 1967, Israel seized the Golan Heights from Syria after Syria launched rocket attacks from the area on Israeli settlements. Today the resolution of the status of this strategic region, which is situated at the meeting point of Israel, Syria, Lebanon, and Jordan, is considered a key to establishing peace in Southwest Asia.

ACTIVITY

Enrichment

Making a Collage Ask students to do outside research on the city of Damascus, Syria. Tell them to use magazines, drawings, or other illustrations to make a collage about the city. Collages may include images representing the city's economic activities, attractions, architecture, art, culture, and inhabitants. (Visual/Spatial)

TEST PREPARATION

Have students read the subsection Syria: Challenges and Reforms on this page to answer the following question.

The most serious obstacle to making a living faced by Syrian farmers is the lack of —

  A fertile farmland
  B a market economy
  C water for irrigation
  D oil and natural gas

Answer to Photo Caption

Possible answer: Syria's flags are strung across the marketplace.

Activity: Fact-finding

Purpose: Each group selects five facts about each of the countries discussed in Section 3. Group members should write each fact on one side of an index card and identify the country on the other.

Roles: Each group should have fact-finders, a scribe, and a spokesperson.

Result: Shuffle the cards together. Have group spokespersons take turns reading facts. The rest of the class should determine which country is being described.

READING STRATEGY

Using Prior Knowledge

Have students read the headings and subheadings in the subsection Iraq: A Series of Conflicts beginning on this page. Ask them to make a few notes regarding anything they may have heard previously about these topics. Ask volunteers to share their remembrances aloud. Then have students read the section and compare the text with their notes.

Iraq: A Series of Conflicts

Iraq has a special location. A large part of the country lies on the well-watered plain between the Tigris and Euphrates rivers. Grains, fruits, and vegetables grow easily. For thousands of years, farming was the most important activity in this land.

GEOFacts

Before 1990, Iraq exported more than $12 billion worth of crude oil each year, which accounted for nearly 95 percent of the country's revenues.

Conditions changed dramatically after large quantities of oil were discovered in the late 1920s. Iraq spent billions of dollars of oil money to develop the country. It built roads, airports, and hospitals. It opened new schools and universities. Dams and irrigation systems were constructed to increase agricultural output. Iraq also rebuilt its capital, the ancient city of Baghdad.

War With Iran Since 1980, however, a series of wars has brought misfortune to Iraq. When Iran erupted in turmoil in 1980, Iraqi dictator Saddam Hussein occupied a disputed border area and then pushed deeper into Iran. Iran counterattacked. Iraq used its superior weapons, tanks, airplanes, and even poison gas to stop Iranian soldiers. When both sides attacked tankers and oil fields, the United States sent warships to protect Persian Gulf shipping lanes. By 1988, despite enormous human and economic losses, neither Iraq nor Iran emerged victorious. Exhausted, both sides accepted a UN cease-fire. The war severely damaged the economies of both countries and left Iraq heavily in debt.

The Persian Gulf War In 1990, Iraq invaded its neighbor Kuwait. Saddam Hussein, still in power as Iraq's president, declared Kuwait a historical province of Iraq, thereby gaining control of a large percentage of the world's oil. Many nations joined a coalition led by the United States and attacked and liberated Kuwait in 1991.

Iraq suffered huge losses during this Persian Gulf War. More than 85,000 soldiers and thousands of civilians were killed. Baghdad was badly damaged. Despite such a devastating defeat, Saddam Hussein retained power and suppressed efforts by Kurds and Shiite Muslims in Iraq to obtain more autonomy.

The Persian Gulf War ended after Iraq agreed to the terms of a UN cease-fire. When Iraq failed to comply with the agreement, the UN imposed an **embargo,** or a severe restriction on trade with other countries. The goal of the embargo,

Baghdad

Urbanization In the 1970s, Iraq used oil profits to build highways and water lines in Baghdad. Such improvements, however, were curtailed by the war with Iran in the 1980s and the Gulf Wars of the 1990s and early 2000s.

Location *How does Baghdad's location help it thrive as an economic and population center?*

486

RESOURCE DIRECTORY

Teaching Resources
Unit 6, Chapter 23
• Section 3 Quiz, p. 29
Spanish Resources
• Section 3 Quiz, p. 58

Answer to Photo Caption

Because Baghdad is located on a fertile plain along the Tigris River, it has rich farmland and access to the river for transportation of goods and people.

Regime Change

Cooperation and Conflict As American and British troops invaded Iraq to topple Saddam Hussein, Iraqi civilians suffered casualties and endured disruptions of basic services. Here, British soldiers hand out food and fresh water in an Iraqi village. **Region** *Why did the United States and Great Britain take action against Saddam Hussein?*

which prohibited Iraq from selling its oil on the international market, was to force Saddam Hussein to cease his chemical and nuclear weapons programs. The resulting loss of export income caused great suffering for the Iraqi people, and in 1996, the UN allowed limited Iraqi oil exports to pay for food and medicine.

The Ouster of Saddam Hussein

Despite economic controls, many suspected that Saddam Hussein continued to build weapons of mass destruction. After the September 11, 2001, terrorist attacks on the United States, the U.S. and Great Britain determined that Saddam Hussein was a threat to international security. Despite objections from other world powers that this threat should be investigated further, American and British troops invaded Iraq in 2003. Within a month, they had removed Saddam Hussein from power, but establishing an effective new government and reestablishing basic services proved to be much more difficult.

SECTION 3 ASSESSMENT

1. **Key Terms** Define **(a)** Fertile Crescent, **(b)** militia, **(c)** anarchy, **(d)** embargo.

2. **Migrations** How did Palestinian migrations influence politics in Jordan?

3. **Cooperation and Conflict (a)** What were the causes of Lebanon's civil war? **(b)** How did the people of Lebanon restore calm after the war?

4. **Government and Citizenship** How have recent government changes in Syria affected life there?

5. **Natural Resources** How did conflict with the United States affect Iraq's economy?

6. **Critical Thinking Predicting Consequences** How might Turkey's control of the waters of the Euphrates affect its political relationship with Syria?

Activity

Creating a Catalog Create a catalog of handmade crafts that are likely to be sold in the souks of the countries of Southwest Asia. Include photographs or drawings of the items in your catalog and a description as to how they were made. You might wish to do additional research in the library or on the Internet for help in completing this activity.

Articles From ········
NATIONAL GEOGRAPHIC

The following article may be used to extend the content in this section.

Severy, Merle, and Lynn Abercrombie, et. al., photographers. "Iraq: Crucible of Civilization." *National Geographic*, Vol. 179, No. 5 (May 1991), pp. 102–115.

Known as the birthplace of civilization, modern Iraq is brimming with history and artifacts.

Answers to Section 3 Assessment

1. **(a)** Fertile Crescent, p. 482 **(b)** militia, p. 484 **(c)** anarchy, p. 484 **(d)** embargo, p. 486
2. Palestinian immigrants challenged the government and threatened to overthrow King Hussein if he did not support them in their struggle for their homeland.
3. **(a)** disagreement among various religious groups over who should hold power; growing economic inequalities between regions **(b)** An agreement among political groups in Lebanon has enabled them to share power.
4. Bashar Assad, who rose to power in 2000, made a number of economic and political reforms and allowed Syrians some personal freedom.
5. Economic sanctions imposed after the first war harmed Iraq's economy by prohibiting the international sale of Iraqi oil. After the American and British invasion, Iraq's economy foundered amidst civil unrest.
6. The relationship between Syria and Turkey could become hostile and violent if Turkey were to cut off the flow of the Euphrates to Syria.

Activity Rubrics Share rubrics with students before they create their catalogs.
Attempted The catalog is incomplete.
Minimal The catalog includes descriptions and illustrations for several items but contains factual errors.
Adequate The catalog includes well-written and accurate descriptions and illustrations for many items.
Exemplary The catalog is well designed, includes a complete sampling of regional crafts, and contains detailed, accurate descriptions and well-chosen images.

Answer to Photo Caption

Both nations deemed him a threat to international security.

Objectives

Upon completion of Section 4, students should be able to:

◆ explain how the discovery of oil changed the Arabian Peninsula;

◆ describe how Saudi Arabia has tried to balance modern-day changes and economic growth with respect for tradition;

◆ explain why Oman and Yemen are considered the least developed countries in the region.

 National Geography Standards

The following National Geography Standards are highlighted in this section: 1, 4, 5, 6, 11, 12, 14, 16, 18

 Bellringer

Ask students to make a list of the images that come to mind when they think of Saudi Arabia. Call on volunteers to share their images.

LESSON PLAN

1. Focus Point out that Saudi Arabia's rulers have adopted the motto "modernization without Westernization." Asks students to speculate about what this means. (The Saudis have tried to modernize their country while preserving Islamic religious values.)

2. Instruct Write the headings *Before Oil* and *After Oil* on the board. Ask students to describe what life was like on the Arabian Peninsula before and after the discovery of oil. Record their answers under the appropriate heading.

3. Close/Reteach Ask students to discuss the following questions: How have the oil-rich nations of the Arabian Peninsula improved the lives of their citizens? How are the oil-rich countries planning for the day when the oil runs out? Why has life changed less for people in Oman and Yemen than it has for people in other parts of the Arabian Peninsula?

4 Arabian Peninsula

Reading Focus

• In what ways did the discovery of oil change the Arabian Peninsula?

• How has Saudi Arabia tried to balance modern-day changes and economic growth with respect for tradition?

• Why are Oman and Yemen considered the least developed countries in the region?

Key Terms

desalination

infrastructure

falaj system

Main Idea The discovery of oil in the Arabian Peninsula has changed the lives of the people of this region.

Environmental Change This businessman has a clear view of how oil affects the Arabian Peninsula.

The Arabian Peninsula is a land of superlatives—of largests and leasts. Among the features that fall under the largest category is its desert, an enormous stretch of sand called the Rub' al-Khali, or the Empty Quarter. At 250,000 square miles (647,500 sq km), the desert is about the size of Texas. It is the world's largest sand desert. Among the leasts in the Arabian Peninsula is water. The peninsula, without one single body of fresh water, has the least amount of water of any large landmass. Instead it has the world's largest known petroleum reserves. Since oil is an important resource, the peninsula has seen the most change in the least amount of time of any place in the world.

Oil Changes a Region

In the early twentieth century, people in Saudi Arabia, Kuwait, Bahrain, Qatar, and the United Arab Emirates existed in much the same way as they had for centuries. Along the coasts, they fished and traded using *dhows*—Arab sailing ships. In the fertile oases of the desert, they lived in small towns and villages in houses made of sun-dried bricks. There they grew wheat, vegetables, and dates. They also tended small herds of camels, goats, and sheep. Groups of Bedouin herders roamed the deserts surrounding the fertile oasis settlements.

Oil Pays for Modernization The discovery of oil in the Arabian Peninsula in the 1930s greatly changed traditional ways of life. It brought enormous wealth to the region. Money from oil was used to pay for modernization. Hospitals, schools, roads, airports, and apartment buildings were built. Health and other services were provided free or heavily subsidized by the government.

These countries also spent billions of dollars to create more of their scarcest resource—water. Industrial plants were constructed to remove the salt from seawater so that it could be used for drinking and irrigation. This necessary and expensive process is called **desalination.**

Today most of the people have moved to cities such as Riyadh, Saudi Arabia's capital, and Abu

RESOURCE DIRECTORY

Teaching Resources

Unit 6, Chapter 23
• Section 4 Guided Reading and Review, p. 30

Guide to the Essentials (English/Spanish)
• Section Summary, Chapter 23, Section 4

Mental Mapping booklet
• Unit 6 Checklist, p. 79
• Outline Map 23, p. 87

Technology

Guided Reading Audiotapes (English/Spanish),
Chapter 23, Section 4

Section Reading Support Transparencies,
Chapter 23, Section 4

World Geography Map and Photo Transparencies
• Central and Southwest Asia: Maps and Photos

Book on CD, Chapter 23

Social Studies Skills Tutor CD-ROM

Companion Web site, www.phschool.com
• Chapter 23 Activities

Dhabi, the capital of the United Arab Emirates. There many live in modern, air-conditioned houses and apartments. Some work in gleaming chrome-and-glass buildings as engineers, computer programmers, and executives of international corporations.

OPEC In 1960 Iran, Iraq, Kuwait, and Saudi Arabia joined with Venezuela to form the Organization of Petroleum Exporting Countries (OPEC). These countries met regularly to decide how much oil to produce and at what price to sell it. Their goal was to decrease the influence of Western oil companies on their countries and to increase their profits. Between 1970 and 1980, high demand caused oil prices to soar. The impact of these soaring prices on the world economy

was great. Developing countries had to cancel social programs in order to pay for oil. Companies in wealthier countries passed along their increased costs for fuel by raising prices. Runaway inflation resulted in many countries. OPEC has expanded to include more nations from Africa, Latin America, Southwest Asia, and Southeast Asia. As world demand for oil has increased, so too has OPEC's power.

Planning for the Future The countries of the Arabian Peninsula will not always be able to depend on oil to support their economies. Some experts believe that Saudi Arabian and Kuwaiti oil will last another fifty to sixty years. Qatar's and Bahrain's oil may last for only another twenty to thirty years.

Arabian Peninsula: PHYSICAL-POLITICAL

KEY

Elevation

Feet	Meters
14,000	4,270
7,000	2,135
1,500	457
700	213
(sea level) 0	0 (sea level)

⊛ National capital
• Major city
▲ Mountain

Lambert Conformal Conic Projection

APPLYING THE GEOGRAPHIC THEMES

● **Movement** Many of the oil-producing countries of the Arabian Peninsula rely on the open passage of ships and oil tankers through the Persian Gulf.
• *Find the Strait of Hormuz on the map. What two bodies of water does it connect?*

Desalination

DIAGRAM SKILLS

● **Science and Technology** Many Middle Eastern countries turn to the sea for their water. Distillation is a common method of desalination. Salt water is heated and turned to steam in a low-pressure chamber. The steam condenses into fresh water on coils kept cool by incoming seawater.

• *Why has Saudi Arabia invested heavily in desalination?*

Aware that they will run out of oil one day, these countries have invested large sums of money to develop other industries. Bahrain has established itself as an international banking center. Saudi Arabia, Qatar, and the United Arab Emirates have built steel and petrochemical industries.

Such massive development efforts require workers. But because their own populations are so small and often lack necessary skills, the oil-rich countries have had to hire huge numbers of foreign workers. In some countries on the Arabian Peninsula, foreigners outnumber citizens. As one author wrote:

> 66 My hotel [in Jiddah, a city on the western coast of Saudi Arabia] was typical. The receptionist was Lebanese. . . . Yemeni and Pakistani construction workers were building an extension to the hotel under a Palestinian foreman. When I came to leave, a Jordanian made up the bill. But it was a Saudi Arabian who drove me to the airport because taxi driving, like the army and police, is reserved for nationals. 99

Saudi Arabia

Beginning in the late 1960s, the Saudi Arabian government spent billions of dollars of oil revenue to build the country's infrastructure. An **infrastructure** comprises a country's basic support facilities, including its roads, schools, airports, seaports, and communication systems.

Saudi Arabia opened schools throughout the country and provided children with free education. Universities began educating Saudi Arabians in engineering, science, and medicine so that one day they could run their own country.

Developing the Economy Two giant centers of commercial industry—Yanbu on the west coast and Jubail on the east coast—were constructed in Saudi Arabia. There, oil and gas are collected, processed, and shipped. Besides petrochemicals, other new industries are being introduced and developed.

Saudi Arabia spent billions of dollars on irrigation and desalination to increase agricultural production so that it would not have to rely on other countries for food. By the early 1980s, Saudi farmers were supplying much of the country's vegetables and poultry and most of its wheat.

Islam and Modernization In one generation, Saudi Arabia transformed itself from an ancient desert kingdom into a modern country. However, it did so cautiously. The government tried not to let modernization upset the Islamic and other traditions to which life in Saudi Arabia is rooted.

The family is still the most important social unit in Saudi Arabia. There are no public places of entertainment, such as movie theaters or nightclubs. Most people spend their free time at home with their families or visiting relatives.

Women, as wives and mothers, have an honored position in Saudi society. But they are limited members of society in other ways. Custom prohibits them from associating with men outside their immediate family. As a result, they must find professions where they are in contact only with other women, such as teaching in girls' schools. Some Saudi women would like the freedom to make more choices.

Saudi Arabia has tried to create a harmonious balance between change and tradition. Any radical changes in age-old traditions could upset more conservative members of society and cause social and political unrest. This balance between change and tradition can be seen in Saudi Arabia's role as guardian of Islam's most sacred cities, Mecca and Medina. Muhammad was born in Mecca, on the southwest coast of Arabia, around A.D. 570. Medina, which is about 200 miles (322 km) north of Mecca, is the city where Muhammad sought refuge after his departure, or *hegira,* from Mecca in A.D. 622.

Each year approximately two million Muslims from all over the world visit Saudi Arabia for the hajj, or pilgrimage to Mecca. Pilgrims to Mecca circle the cube-shaped holy shrine, known as the *Kaaba,* seven times, reciting prayers. Inside the Kaaba is a black stone that they believe was sent by God. During the hajj, hundreds of thousands of people are provided with sanitation and medical facilities. Saudi Arabia annually supports what Muslims believe to be the single most moving and meaningful religious ritual in Islam.

Deep tensions remain in Saudi society, however. While many Saudis embrace the economic benefits and trappings of Western society, others believe that the nation must return to its Islamic roots. Many of these Saudis share an intense hatred of the West—principally Israel and the United States—and their influence is growing. Saudi-born terrorist Osama bin Laden and his al-Qaida supporters justified their attacks on the United States on September 11, 2001, by arguing that thousands of "infidel" American troops were stationed on Islamic soil. Critics accuse the

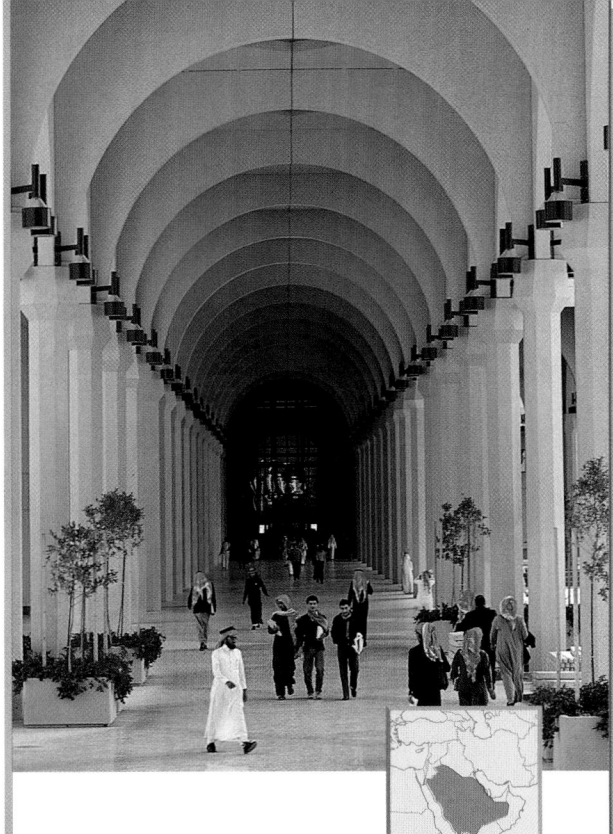

Change and Tradition

Cultures Saudi Arabia has sought a balance between its traditional culture and its attempt at modernization.

Place *How has Saudi Arabia preserved its culture? How has it modernized?*

Saudi government of doing little to counter terrorist activity.

Oman and Yemen

While life has changed greatly in Saudi Arabia, life for most people in the small southern Arabian nations of Yemen and Oman has changed little since ancient times. Although Yemen has some oil deposits, it only recently started to develop

GEOFacts

More than six million trees have been planted near oases in the Saudi Arabian province of Al-Hasa to stop the advance of the desert.

Answer to Photo Caption

Saudi Arabia has spent billions of dollars to develop new industries, infrastructure, and irrigation and desalination in its attempts to modernize the economy. Yet its citizens live in a traditional Islamic world. Women's activities are limited, and there are no nightclubs or movie theaters.

TEST PREPARATION

Have students read the subsection Islam and Modernization beginning on page 490 to answer the following question. When modernizing Saudi Arabia, the government proceeded cautiously so as not to upset the nation's —

  A sacred cities
  B freedoms
  C pilgrims
  (D) traditions

Answers to
Section 4 Assessment

1. (a) desalination, p. 488 **(b)** infrastructure, p. 490 **(c)** *falaj* system, p. 492

2. They used oil profits to build infrastructure and to bring in foreign workers to help build new industries, such as banking, steel, and petrochemical industries.

3. Abrupt changes to traditions, beliefs, and practices could lead to social and political unrest by provoking the strongly conservative elements of Saudi society.

4. Oman and Yemen are less modernized. Yemen has only recently started to develop its oil deposits.

5. He was implying that although Saudi Arabia would modernize, it would not give up traditional Islamic culture.

Activity Rubrics Share rubrics with students before they write their fact sheets and paragraphs.

Attempted The fact sheet and paragraph are incomplete or inaccurate.

Minimal The fact sheet is accurate, but the paragraph offers only a sketchy explanation of the effects of OPEC on the community.

Adequate The fact sheet is accurate. The paragraph adequately explains how OPEC affects the writer's community.

Exemplary The fact sheet is accurate, and the paragraph offers a comprehensive explanation of the effects of OPEC on the writer's community.

Achieving Literacy

Government and Citizenship Over thirty years ago, Oman had only three schools and illiteracy was common. Today Oman's school system supports around a half million students. The women shown here are participating in an adult literacy program.

Place *In what other ways is Oman trying to improve its standard of living?*

them. Oman began to use its oil revenues to improve life for its people in the early 1970s, but it has not undergone the large-scale modernization that countries like Saudi Arabia and Kuwait have.

Yemen is the poorest nation on the Arabian Peninsula. It was formed in 1990 when two smaller nations, North Yemen and South Yemen, agreed to merge. In 1993, Yemen's parliamentary elections were the first on the Arabian Peninsula in which women were allowed to vote.

Although Sanaa is Yemen's political capital, the port city of Aden is the economic center. Aden is located near the southern entrance to the Red Sea, and its port serves as a refueling center for huge oil tankers passing through the sea.

Most of the land in both Oman and Yemen is arid. Despite the harshness of the desert, many people make their living by farming and herding. Many farmers depend on an ancient system of underground and surface canals called the ***falaj system*** for water. These canals carry water from the mountains to villages many miles away.

Oman has used money from oil exports to improve its standard of living. The government has updated irrigation systems and built roads, hospitals, and schools. Oman is trying to reduce its dependence on oil and to develop its tourism and manufacturing sectors.

SECTION 4 ASSESSMENT

1. **Key Terms** Define **(a)** desalination, **(b)** infrastructure, **(c)** *falaj* system.

2. **Planning for the Future** How have the nations of the Arabian Peninsula used oil profits to develop new industry?

3. **Cultures** Why is Saudi Arabia cautious about the way in which it introduces changes into society?

4. **Economic Activities** How are Oman and Yemen different from the other countries on the Arabian Peninsula?

5. **Critical Thinking** **Recognizing Points of View** In 1966, King Faisal told the people of Saudi Arabia, "We are going ahead with extensive planning, guided by our Islamic laws and beliefs, for the progress of the nation." What did the king probably mean when he said this?

Activity

Take It to the NET

Writing a Paragraph OPEC is a powerful organization. Go online to learn more about OPEC. Create a fact sheet about the organization. In a short paragraph, discuss ways in which OPEC's power affects life in your community. Visit the World Geography section of **www.phschool.com** for help in completing this activity.

492   Chapter 23 ▪ The Countries of Southwest Asia

RESOURCE DIRECTORY

Teaching Resources

Unit 6, Chapter 23
- Section 4 Quiz, p. 31

Spanish Resources
- Section 4 Quiz, p. 59

Technology

Social Studies Skills Tutor CD-ROM, Analyzing and Interpreting Special Purpose Maps

---

Answer to Photo Caption

by updating irrigation systems, roads, and hospitals

Interpreting a Remote Sensing Image

Remote sensing uses data from long-distance satellites to gather information about the earth's surface. With expert interpretation, remote sensing images can help to explain the nature of surface features, environmental change, weather patterns, and historical information. Most remote sensing systems use cameras and scanners to record the amount of solar energy reflected from the earth's surface. Different objects can be identified because they reflect solar energy in unique ways.

Learn the Skill Study the satellite photograph below and use the following steps to learn how to interpret a remote sensing image.

1 *Identify the location.* Determine the location represented by the image. You can usually do this by reading the text that accompanies the image. *What place is represented by the remote sensing image?*

2 *Compare the image with another image.* Government agencies are often the providers of satellite photographs. They usually provide a map, such as the one at right, to help you understand the remote sensing image. *Approximately how many square miles are covered by the remote sensing image?*

3 *Look for significant features.* Experts interpreted the features shown by the remote sensing image of southern Oman, such as the region's main roads or waterways. Then, they labeled these features on the map. **(a)** *What do the various lines on the photograph indicate?* **(b)** *What physical characteristic is represented by the yellow region in the upper left-hand corner of the image?*

4 *Recognize patterns.* Remember that geographic features do not occur in random fashion. Look for patterns that occur because of the actions of physical processes or human activities. **(a)** *On which side of the wadi are most of the ancient caravan tracks and modern roads located?* **(b)** *Where do all the ancient caravan tracks converge?*

5 *Draw conclusions.* Now that you have identified some patterns, you can draw conclusions based on those patterns. For example, experts were able to use the

evidence to conclude that they had found the ruins of an ancient town. **(a)** *Why do all the transportation routes converge in one place?* **(b)** *Why do none of the transportation routes go across the northernmost portion of the region in the remote sensing image?*

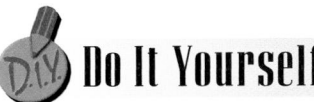

Do It Yourself

Practice the Skill Visit the Internet site of the National Weather Service. View the remote sensing images of the latest 24-hour surface forecast. Take notes on what you see. Use your notes to make generalizations about current weather conditions. Visit the World Geography section of **www.phschool.com** for help in completing this activity.

Apply the Skill See Chapter 23 Review and Assessment.

Southern Oman

0   10 mi
0   10 km
sand dunes
modern road
wadi
modern road
ruins
old caravan tracks
modern road

Chapter 23   **493**

Teaching the Skill
Ask students to read the introductory paragraph and study the photograph. Ask them to think of a more primitive form of remote sensing. Suggest that one might climb to the top of a hill or tree to survey the land and see what lay in the distance. As you work through the skill lesson with the class, compare the area shown in the photograph with the map of the Arabian Peninsula on page 489. Ask students to speculate on the advantages of radar imagery over our own senses.

ACTIVITY

Connecting With . . .

Science Point out to students that aerial photography is a form of remote sensing. Ask students to read more about photogrammetry, the science of making maps from aerial photographs and other data.

Answers to Learn the Skill
1. southern Oman
2. approximately 1,800 square miles (4,600 sq km)
3. **(a)** modern roads, old caravan tracks, a wadi **(b)** sand dunes
4. **(a)** on the east side **(b)** inside the triangle labeled "ruins"
5. **(a)** Possible answer: A city or a village, a souk, or an oasis might have once been there. **(b)** It is a desert; there are no settlements there.

Answer to Practice the Skill
Students' generalizations should reflect the data they have collected.

Objectives

Upon completion of this feature, students should be able to:

◆ identify worldwide uses for oil;

◆ describe the problems associated with the uneven supply and consumption of oil;

◆ explain how supply and demand affect oil prices.

 National Geography Standards

The following National Geography Standards are highlighted in this feature: 1, 4, 11, 14, 15, 16, 18

 Bellringer

Have students make a list of ways our society uses oil. Answers may include providing fuel for planes, trains, and automobiles and heat for homes. Discuss the kinds of problems that oil shortages can cause for our country.

LESSON PLAN

1. Focus Have students read the chart on this page. Ask: **How does the chart support the statement that Southwest Asia is the largest producer of oil?** (The total production of the four Southwest Asian OPEC nations exceeds the production in any other category.)

2. Instruct Explain supply and demand: When supply of a resource is lower than the demand for it, prices are high. When supply is higher than demand, prices are low. Then ask: **If Saudi Arabia stopped exporting oil, what would happen to global prices?** (They would rise.)

Answer to Photo Caption

The use of cars, planes, and machinery has increased.

Answers to Graph Skills

Saudi Arabia, Iran, Venezuela, Iraq, United Arab Emirates

Saudi Arabia, Iran, Iraq, United Arab Emirates

494 Chapter 23

People and Geography
Global Oil Trade

Dependence on Oil

Petroleum, or oil, is one of the world's most valuable resources. It is used as a fuel for producing electricity and heat. It also yields petrochemicals that are converted into plastics and other synthetic materials. However, it is the area of transportation in which oil reigns supreme. Petroleum products power most transportation systems, including automobiles, airplanes, and railroads. As a result, oil accounts for about 40 percent of global energy consumption. Simply put—the world depends on oil.

Saudi Arabian Oil Well
Why has the demand for oil dramatically increased over the past hundred years?

Production and Consumption

The world's supply of oil is limited and unevenly distributed. Today, more than 60 percent of known oil reserves are in Southwest Asia. Saudi Arabia, a member of OPEC, is the world's leading oil producer. It also has the largest proven oil reserves.

Oil consumption is also unevenly distributed. The leading industrialized nations of the world consume far more petroleum than other nations. In addition, most industrialized countries consume more petroleum than they produce. As a result, their economies depend on imported oil. The United States ranks first among oil importers with more than 7.5 million barrels per day, nearly half of its total petroleum needs. Japan ranks second with more than 4.5 million barrels per day, followed by Germany with about 2.1 million barrels. Other leading oil importers are South Korea, France, Italy, and the United Kingdom. Because these nations depend on oil imports, many of them are willing to use military force to protect the flow of oil. In the 1991 Persian Gulf War, for example, many nations joined together to expel the Iraqi forces that had seized control of oil-rich Kuwait.

WORLD OIL PRODUCTION

Rank	Country	Production Estimate*
1	Saudi Arabia	9.12
2	United States	9.08
3	Russia	6.71
4	Iran	3.81
5	Mexico	3.48
6	Norway	3.32
7	China	3.25
8	Venezuela	3.14
9	United Kingdom	2.75
10	Canada	2.74
11	Iraq	2.59
12	United Arab Emirates	2.51

Source: Energy Information Administration
*Million barrels per day in 2000.

Projected Production, 1997–2010 (Million barrels per day)

Source: International Energy Agency

■ Southwest Asian OPEC nations ■ Other OPEC nations ■ Non-OPEC nations

Oil Production
Which of the top 12 oil-producing countries are members of OPEC? Which of these OPEC countries are in Southwest Asia?

RESOURCE DIRECTORY

Teaching Resources
Simulations, Games, and Lab Activities
• Where to Build the Pipeline?, pp. 30–33

Technology
World Geography Map and Photo Transparencies
Central and Southwest Asia: Economic Activities and Resources

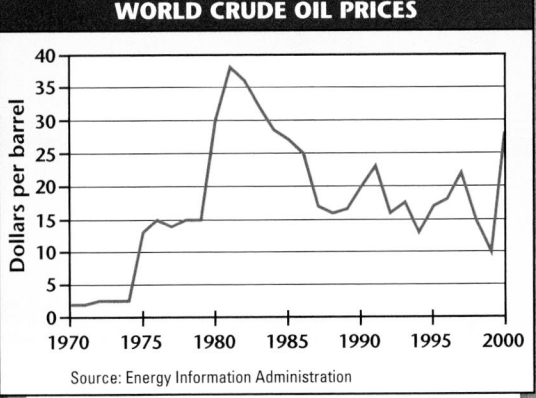

WORLD CRUDE OIL PRICES

Source: Energy Information Administration

Oil Prices
What happened to the price of oil at the end of the 1990s? What might have been a cause of this price change?

Supply, Demand, and Prices

Like any commodity, oil prices are affected by supply and demand. In 1973, Arab OPEC states refused to sell oil to nations that had recently supported Israel during an Arab-Israeli war. OPEC ended the embargo in 1974, but raised oil prices from $3 per barrel to more than $35 per barrel by 1981. In recent years, supply, demand, and international politics have continued to cause price fluctuations. When internal disputes have erupted within OPEC, some OPEC members have increased production in an attempt to increase their share of the profits. At these times, the global supply of oil has increased, causing oil prices to fall.

Planning for the Future

Most experts agree that known supplies of fossil fuels will last less than 100 years. Even so, it is unlikely that global oil supplies will suddenly run out during this century. New oil deposits are discovered every year, and technology for finding and extracting oil constantly improves. However, many predict that it will gradually become more and more difficult and expensive to find and extract new oil reserves. The challenge will probably intensify as India, China, and other developing countries increase their consumption of oil. Today, oil-importing countries are considering several options. These include finding new domestic oil supplies, conserving energy, and developing alternative energy sources.

ASSESSMENT: Making Decisions

1. Identify the Issue What is the oil issue that concerns the world?

2. Gather Information (a) How are oil production and consumption unevenly distributed? **(b)** How do changes in the supply of oil affect the price of oil?

3. Identify Options What options are oil-importing countries considering to meet their energy needs?

4. Make a Decision What do you think is the best way to supply the world with adequate energy supplies? Explain.

5. Plan for the Future How would you go about implementing the plan that you think is best?

Chapter 23   **495**

---

3. Close/Reteach Have students read Planning for the Future. Ask students to list one way to conserve oil supplies. Then have them discuss possible alternative energy sources that could someday serve as substitutes for oil.

ACTIVITY

Enrichment

Automobile Technology Remind the class that one way to reduce our reliance on oil is to create automobiles that use alternative fuels. Have students research the work that has been done to create cars that do not use gasoline. For instance, you might ask some students to research electric cars. Have them report their findings to the rest of the class. (Verbal/Linguistic)

Answers to Assessment

1. The world needs an available, reliable supply of oil since the largest consumers of oil do not produce enough to meet their needs.

2. (a) The United States is the world's largest oil consumer, but more than 60 percent of known oil reserves are in Southwest Asia. **(b)** Increased supply drives down the price; decreased supply drives up the price.

3. finding new domestic oil supplies, conserving energy, and developing alternative energy sources

4. Possible answer: developing alternative sources of energy, because as the world develops the need for energy will increase

5. Possible answer: support research and development for sources of energy that could be used in any area of the world

---

CUSTOMIZE FOR...

Less Proficient Readers

Using a Key Remind students that they must consult the key on the chart on page 494 to understand all the information. A *key* is a guide that makes clear different parts of a map or chart. In this case, the key is located below the table and graph. It helps readers see which nations produce the most oil. Have students use the key to find this information.

Answers to Chart Caption

It rose sharply. The cause may have been a decrease in supply or an increase in demand or a combination of both.

Objectives

Upon completion of Section 5, students should be able to:

◆ explain how Turkey became a modern nation after World War I;

◆ list the effects that an Islamic revolution had on the level of development of Iran;

◆ summarize the major issue that divides the people of Cyprus.

National Geography Standards

The following National Geography Standards are highlighted in this section: 1, 4, 5, 6, 10, 11, 13, 17

Bellringer

Ask students: **Are Turkey and Iran part of the Arab world?** (No. Although their populations are mostly Muslim, they are not Arab.)

LESSON PLAN

1. Focus Ask students to skim Section 5 and make a list of all the leaders of both Turkey and Iran. Ask each student to prepare two statements about each leader—including one about each leader's contribution to the nation's history. Then conduct a Who Am I? drill. Each student will read one statement, and the class will identify the leader. Continue until the clues start to be repeated.

2. Instruct Write the headings *Kemal Atatürk* and *Ayatollah Khomeini* on the board. Ask students to name ways in which these leaders changed their nations.

3. Close/Reteach Ask students to read the Reading Focus questions on this page. Based on what they have read, ask them to write answers to each question.

---

5 Turkey, Iran, and Cyprus

Reading Focus

- How did Turkey become a modern nation after World War I?
- What effects did an Islamic revolution have upon the level of development of Iran?
- What major issue divides the people of Cyprus?

Key Terms

secular

shah

ayatollah

Main Idea Turkey, Iran, and Cyprus are nations with diverse populations, new economies, and political unrest.

Cultures Ankara, Turkey's capital, is a planned city with boulevards, parks, and business districts.

T urkey and Iran are different from the other countries in Southwest Asia. Although the majority of people in Turkey and Iran are Muslims, they are not Arabs. They speak different languages, and they trace their ancestors back to different roots.

Turkey

The Persians, the Greeks, and the Romans—at various stages in history—all controlled what today is Turkey. However, it is the Turks, the last empire builders in Southwest Asia, from whom most of the people in Turkey today trace their ancestry.

The Turks originally came from Central Asia. Scholars and merchants who traveled from Southwest Asia to Central Asia introduced them to Islam. When the Turks began conquering Southwest Asia, they came as Muslim warriors. Although they were Muslims, their language and culture were Turkish, not Arab.

GEOFacts

About 72 percent of Turkish women over 15 can read and write. (U.S. = 97)

The "Father of the Turks" When World War I ended in 1918, the victors broke up the Otto-

man Empire. Turkey kept only Asia Minor—the peninsula south of the Black Sea—and the area around Istanbul. The Dardanelles—the strait linking the Sea of Marmara and the Aegean Sea—were kept under international control. Many Turkish nationalists were furious that a weak sultan had given up so much. Mustafa Kemal, a fiery young army officer, began a movement to establish Turkey as an independent republic. In 1923, Kemal and his revolutionaries overthrew the sultan and declared Turkey a republic. Kemal was elected president.

Immediately, Kemal set about making Turkey a modern country. He believed that Turkey would not survive without sweeping political and social reforms. One of his first changes was to break the bond between Islam and the government. Religious leaders were no longer involved in running the government. He replaced Islamic laws with laws based on European legal systems.

Many of Kemal's changes unraveled the fabric of social life. He outlawed the *fez*—a brimless, flat-topped hat worn by men—and he ridiculed the custom that required women to wear veils in public. After centuries of subservience, women were given the right to vote and hold office. Everyone was encouraged to attend school.

496 Chapter 23 ▪ The Countries of Southwest Asia

RESOURCE DIRECTORY

Teaching Resources

Unit 6, Chapter 23
- Section 5 Guided Reading and Review, p. 32
- Geography and World Literature, Memed, My Hawk, p. 43

Guide to the Essentials (English/Spanish)
- Section Summary, Chapter 23, Section 5

Mental Mapping booklet
- Unit 6 Checklist, p. 79

Technology

Guided Reading Audiotapes (English/Spanish), Chapter 23, Section 5

Section Reading Support Transparencies, Chapter 23, Section 5

World Geography Map and Photo Transparencies
- Central and Southwest Asia: Maps and Photos

Book on CD, Chapter 23

Social Studies Skills Tutor CD-ROM

Companion Web site, www.phschool.com
- Chapter 23 Activities

By the time Kemal died in 1938, Turkey was well on its way to becoming a modern country. Kemal had been such a force in establishing Turkey's identity after World War I that the Turks gave him the surname Atatürk, meaning "father of the Turks."

Turkey Today Turkey has faced challenges in its efforts to become a prosperous, modern nation. A large international debt and inflation have periodically troubled the country since the late 1960s. Political stresses have also been evident, as parties that believed Turkey's government should be **secular,** or that it should be run without religious influence, fought Islamic parties for control.

Another challenge facing Turkey is the Kurdish struggle for independence. Although Kurds make up roughly 20 percent of the population, they have been harshly repressed by the Turkish majority. Turkey has also faced resistance to its bid for entry into the European Union. Other EU nations have insisted Turkey admit to the massacre of 1.5 million Armenians during World War I—a claim the government denies—before it is admitted to the union.

Despite these challenges, Turkey has made progress. It is the most industrialized nation in Southwest Asia. Its farms continue to produce a broad range of crops and livestock. Turkish citizens also participate in their country's parliamentary government—one of the few freely elected governments in the region.

Islam Changes Iran

The Persians arrived in the area that is now Iran about 3,000 years ago. Today their descendants are the dominant cultural group in Iran. The Persians once ruled a vast empire that stretched west into what is now Libya and east to what is now the country of Pakistan. In 330 B.C., Alexander the Great conquered the empire. Later, the Persians won back much of their territory. By the time conquering Arab armies reached them in the mid-600s, the Persian culture was well established in Iran.

For about six hundred years, Persia was part of the Islamic empire. Even though most of Persia's people converted to Islam, they were not Arabs. They maintained their links to their Persian

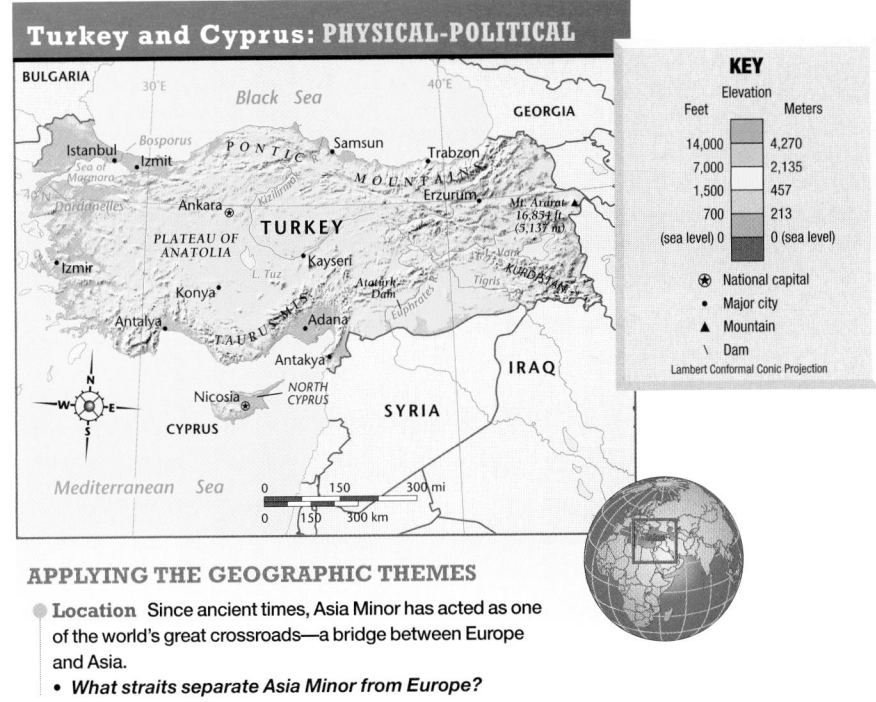

Turkey and Cyprus: PHYSICAL-POLITICAL

KEY

Elevation

Feet	Meters
14,000	4,270
7,000	2,135
1,500	457
700	213
(sea level) 0	0 (sea level)

⊛ National capital
• Major city
▲ Mountain
\ Dam

Lambert Conformal Conic Projection

APPLYING THE GEOGRAPHIC THEMES

● **Location** Since ancient times, Asia Minor has acted as one of the world's great crossroads—a bridge between Europe and Asia.
• *What straits separate Asia Minor from Europe?*

Articles From
NATIONAL GEOGRAPHIC

The following article may be used to extend the content in this section.

Allen, Thomas B., and Reza, photographer. "Turkey." *National Geographic,* Vol. 185, No. 5 (May 1994), pp. 2–35.

Turkey has been working to achieve stability and growth.

TEST PREPARATION

Have students read the subsection Turkey Today on this page to complete the following sentence.

When a government is run without religious influence, it is said to be —
  A Islamic
  B parliamentary
  C freely elected
  Ⓓ secular

Answer to Map Caption
Dardanelles and Bosporus

Ask students to read the subsection Modernization for Iran and write two questions based on their reading. Then, have students exchange questions with a partner and use the text to find the answers.

ACTIVITY

Vocabulary

Ayatollah Refer to the list of Key Terms on page 496. Write the term *ayatollah* on the board. Ask a volunteer to read its definition aloud from the Glossary. Ask students to speculate about what can make religious leaders powerful political figures. (Possible answers: They appeal to people's insecurity about the future; they ally themselves with the weak and oppressed; they base their authority on an otherworldly power.)

ACTIVITY

Enrichment

Taking Notes Have students research how the role of women in Turkey changed under Atatürk or how the role of Iranian women has changed, first under the shahs and then as a result of the Islamic revolution. Ask students to take notes and report their findings to the class. (Verbal/Linguistic)

Answer to Photo Caption

The village's level of development seems low because the farmers are not using machines to winnow the wheat.

498 Chapter 23

Winnowing Wheat

Economic Activities In a process called winnowing, Iranian farmers separate the unwanted chaff from their harvest of wheat. In the background is a traditional rural village.

Place *What can you tell about the level of development of this village?*

past and continued to speak Farsi, the language of their ancestors.

Modernization for Iran In 1921, an army officer, Reza Khan, seized power. In 1925, he declared himself Iran's **shah,** or ruler. When he came to power most of Iran's people were either nomadic herders or farmers, barely able to make a living from Iran's dry land. In the years of the shah's rule, Iran began to change. Like Atatürk in Turkey, the shah opened schools, built roads and railroads, encouraged industry, and gave women more rights.

When his son, Mohammad Reza Pahlavi, took over during World War II, he was even more determined than his father to make Iran into a modern, Westernized nation. In a very short time, great changes took place in Iran. Profits from its huge oil industry were channeled into industrial and agricultural development. Teachers and medical workers traveled into the villages to improve literacy and health care. Women began to vote, hold jobs outside the home, and dress in Western-style clothing.

However, resentment against the shah's rule developed. Although many Iranians benefited from the shah's reforms, many more still lived in great poverty. Some Iranians believed that Iran should be run as a democracy. Others, especially conservative

religious leaders known as **ayatollahs,** thought Iran should be governed in strict obedience to Islamic law. But the shah ran the country as a dictatorship. No one dared oppose the government for fear of being put in prison or exiled.

An Islamic Revolution In 1979, the people of Iran revolted. The shah and his supporters fled. The Ayatollah Khomeini set up a new government and declared Iran an Islamic republic.

Immediately, Khomeini's government set out to rid the country of all Western influences, which it saw as a threat to Islam. Westerners were forced to leave the country. Alcohol was outlawed. Women were discouraged from wearing Western-style clothing and once again donned their long, black cloaks called *chadors*.

Iran's new rulers belonged to the Shiite branch of Islam, as do most Iranians. They called on Shiites everywhere in Southwest Asia to overthrow their governments and establish Islamic republics. Their appeal was particularly powerful to Shiites who lived in countries run by Sunni Muslims where the Shiites were an oppressed minority. In 1980, angered by Khomeini's attempts to provoke Shiites in Iraq to take such action, Iraqi leaders launched a war against Iran. Hundreds of thousands of Iranians were killed in the fighting, which lasted eight years.

RESOURCE DIRECTORY

Teaching Resources

Unit 6, Chapter 23
- Section 5 Quiz, p. 33
- Reviewing Main Ideas, p. 34
- Test Forms A and B, pp. 37–42

Spanish Resources
- Section 5 Quiz, p. 60

Guide to the Essentials (English/Spanish)
- Chapter 23 Test

Mental Mapping booklet
- Chapter 23 Map Test, p. 89

Simulations, Games, and Lab Activities
- Place Location Review Games, pp. 58–63

Social Studies Skills Handbook
- Study and Research Skills, pp. 94–108

Technology

World Geography Map and Photo Transparencies
- Central and Southwest Asia: Maps and Photos

ExamView Test Bank CD-ROM
- Chapter 23 Test
- Unit 6 Test

Companion Web site, www.phschool.com
- Chapter 23 Self-Test

Iran Today Since the Ayatollah Khomeini died in 1989, Iran has begun to change. The revolution and the war with Iraq severely affected Iran's economy. Its radical position isolated it from the rest of the world.

Iran's economy has improved, but a political power struggle continues. On one side are reformers who want more reforms. On the other side are Islamic religious leaders who assert that increased freedom will endanger the security of the state. Resounding election victories by President Mohammad Khatami indicate strong popular support for reform.

Cyprus

Cyprus is an island country in the eastern part of the Mediterranean Sea. Greek colonists came to this island as early as 1200 B.C. Today about four fifths of the Cypriot people speak Greek as their first language and are Greek Orthodox Christians. However, Cyprus was also part of the Ottoman Empire from the 1570s until the British occupied it in 1878. One fifth of the island's people trace their roots back to Turkey and follow Islam. In the 1960s, civil war split the island in two. Some

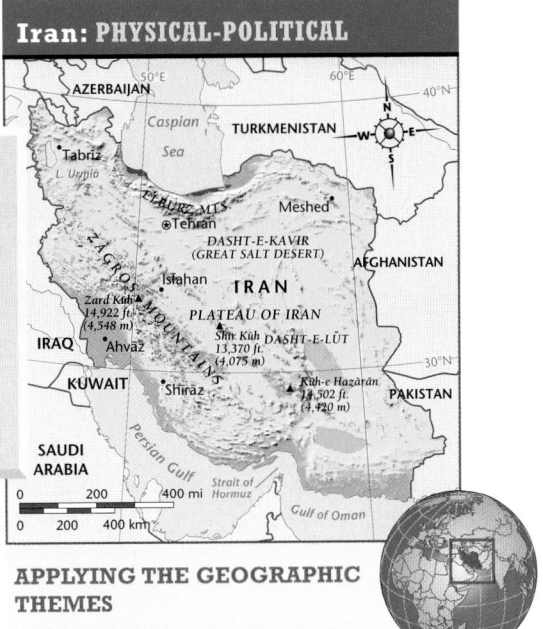

Iran: PHYSICAL-POLITICAL

KEY

Elevation

Feet	Meters
14,000	4,270
7,000	2,135
1,500	457
700	213
(sea level) 0	0 (sea level)

✪ National capital
• Major city
▲ Mountain

Lambert Conformal Conic Projection

APPLYING THE GEOGRAPHIC THEMES

● **Regions** Iran is a rugged country. Its mountains almost surround its central plateau.
• *What is the approximate elevation of the Plateau of Iran?*

Greek Cypriots wanted Cyprus to unite with Greece. In 1974, Turkey sent troops to Cyprus to prevent this. Turkey declared the northeastern part of Cyprus independent in 1983, though most countries do not formally recognize it.

SECTION 5 ASSESSMENT

1. **Key Terms** Define **(a)** secular, **(b)** shah, **(c)** ayatollah.

2. **Cultures (a)** How did Atatürk's policies affect Turkish culture? **(b)** How does ethnic and cultural diversity affect life in Turkey today?

3. **Cooperation and Conflict (a)** Why did Iranians revolt in 1979? **(b)** How did their country change as a result?

4. **Government and Citizenship** Why are there political tensions in Cyprus?

5. **Critical Thinking Making Comparisons** How are present-day conditions in Turkey and

Iran similar and different? Express your answer in the form of a table or graphic organizer.

Activity

Take It to the NET

Writing a News Bulletin Review the information in this section about the Cyprus problem. Then, conduct additional research on this topic on the Internet. Write a news bulletin about the latest steps taken toward peace in Cyprus. Visit the World Geography section of **www.phschool.com** for help in completing this activity.

CUSTOMIZE FOR...

Less Proficient Writers

Writing a Comparison Ask students to write two headings at the top of a piece of paper: *Iran Under Ayatollah Khomeini* and *Iran Today.* Have them read the subsections An Islamic Revolution and Iran Today and list facts about life in Iran under the correct heading. Then ask them to use the lists to write a paragraph comparing life under the ayatollah to life in Iran today.

Answer to Map Caption
1,500–7,000 feet (457–2,135 m)

Creating a Chapter Summary

As a reteaching opportunity, pair a more able student with a less able student to complete this chapter summary.

Chart entries may include:
600s: Islam begins to spread through Southwest Asia.
900s: Turks, led by the Seljuks, conquer most of the Middle East.
1400s–1700s: The Ottoman Empire rules the region but slowly loses control of diverse ethnic and religious groups.
1917: The Ottoman Empire is defeated in World War I, and the region is divided into many different countries.

Reviewing Key Terms

1–10. Students' puzzles should show a clear understanding of each term.

Understanding Key Ideas

11. The defeat of the Ottoman Empire during World War I allowed European victors to divide and set new boundaries for the empire's territory in what is today the Middle East.
12. Israelis have used technology to drain swamps and irrigate dry areas, making unusable land into farmland.
13. The government of Syria has modernized farming methods, created a market economy, and privatized banks.
14. Income earned from oil was used to modernize the nations of the region. Oil also gave the Arabian Peninsula control of an important part of the world's economy because it controls much of the world's oil supply and price.
15. Westernization brought modernization, more rights for women, and elements of Western culture. It also brought about a very strong reaction in the form of religious revolution.
16. (a) Jordan and Lebanon
(b) Palestinians in Jordan have pressured the government to support their claim to a homeland; Palestinians have used Lebanon as a base from which to attack Israel.

Critical Thinking and Writing

17. Israel, Jordan, Iraq
18. the terrorist attacks on the United States on September 11, 2001

Creating a Chapter Summary

On a sheet of paper, draw a chart like this one. Fill in events that have helped shape the Middle East. Add boxes as needed. One entry has been made to help you get started.

600s
Islam begins to spread through Southwest Asia

CREATING THE MODERN MIDDLE EAST

Take It to the NET
Chapter Self-Test For practice test questions for Chapter 23, go to the World Geography section of **www.phschool.com**.

Reviewing Key Terms

Use the following key terms to make a crossword puzzle. Exchange puzzles with a classmate. Complete the puzzles and then check each other's answers.

1. mandate
2. Zionist
3. drip irrigation
4. potash
5. anarchy
6. embargo
7. desalination
8. infrastructure
9. secular
10. ayatollah

Understanding Key Ideas

11. **Understanding the Past** How did the fall of the Ottoman Empire affect the emergence of the modern Middle East?
12. **Science and Technology** How has technology enabled Israel to develop more agriculture to support its growing population?
13. **Economic Activities** In what ways is the government of Syria attempting to modernize economic activities in the country?

14. **Natural Resources** How did the discovery of oil change life on the Arabian Peninsula?
15. **Government and Citizenship** How did Westernization affect Iran?
16. **Migration** (a) Which countries in this region have been most affected by the arrival of Palestinian refugees? (b) In what ways have some of those refugees attempted to influence their host countries?

Critical Thinking and Writing

17. **Interpreting Maps** Compare the map on page 468 with the one on page 471. Which present-day countries were part of the British mandate?
18. **Cooperation and Conflict** What event helped bring about the end of Saddam Hussein's leadership of Iraq?
19. **Distinguishing Fact From Opinion** Reread the comments from the Israeli couple on page 476. (a) Are the comments primarily facts or primarily opinions? Explain. (b) How do their comments highlight the challenge of developing Israel's desert areas?

---

19. (a) Most of the comments are opinions—Zvi's enthusiasm for life in a desert town and Rebecca's distaste for it. **(b)** They show that Israel is working hard to make desert communities attractive but also that many people find the challenges of such a life too great.

(Continued on next page.)

20. Defending a Position Do you think that the UN decision to impose an embargo against Iraq was a wise decision? Explain.

Applying Skills

Interpreting a Remote Sensing Image Refer to the Skills for Life lesson on page 493 to answer these questions:

21. What is the first step in interpreting a remote sensing image?

22. Why is it often necessary to have the help of experts when interpreting a remote sensing image?

23. Why might cloud coverage interfere with the interpretation of a remote sensing image?

Reading a Map Study the map below, and answer the following questions:

24. What regions of Iran probably have relatively low population density? Explain.

25. Why do you think nations have fought for control of the Strait of Hormuz in recent wars?

Iran: PHYSICAL-POLITICAL

Test Preparation

Read the question and choose the best answer.

26. Desalination plants are somewhat common in the Middle East because—

A there is a shortage of fresh water in the Middle East

B oil is plentiful in the Middle East

C most of the people in the region are Muslims

D Iraq has been involved in several wars

Activities

USING THE REGIONAL ATLAS

Review this chapter and the Regional Atlas for Central and Southwest Asia. Then, make some generalizations about the economic activities in this region. For example, how do climate and other physical characteristics affect economic activities?

ENTAL MAPPING

Study a map of Southwest Asia. On a separate piece of paper, draw a sketch map of Southwest Asia from memory. Label the following places on your map:

- Mediterranean Sea   • Israel
- Iran   • Saudi Arabia
- Turkey   • Persian Gulf
- Cyprus   • Beirut
- Red Sea   • Kuwait

Take It to the NET

Identifying Relationships On the Internet, find a news story about an event that took place in Southwest Asia within the past week. Explain how the news relates to what you have learned about the region from your study of this chapter. Visit the World Geography section of **www.phschool.com** for help in completing this activity.

20. Answers will vary but should demonstrate an understanding of the purpose and the consequences of the decision.

Applying Skills
21. identifying the location
22. Experts know how to identify and interpret significant features of a remote sensing image.
23. Most remote sensing systems record the amount of solar energy reflecting from the earth's surface. Cloud coverage could interfere with the solar energy reflection.
24. the Plateau of Iran and the Zagros Mountains; there are very few cities located in these regions
25. The Strait of Hormuz provides the oil-rich countries of the Persian Gulf with access to the Indian Ocean, and to the rest of the world.

Test Preparation
26. A

Activities

Using the Regional Atlas
Possible answer: In mountainous and desert regions there is little economic activity. Check students' generalizations for logic. Encourage students to provide facts to support their generalizations.

Mental Mapping
Review students' maps for relative and absolute location.

Take It to the Net
Students' work should reflect sound research. Check that they have accurately related the story to the chapter's content.

ENTAL MAPPING

Games for Review See pages 58–63 of the Simulations, Games, and Lab Activities booklet for games to review place names.

Chapter Map Test Students should use the completed outline maps and the Unit 6 Checklist in their Atlas Portfolios to prepare for the Chapter 23 Map Test.

Unit Map Test To prepare for the Unit 6 Map Test, students will need to study the location of all the place names on the Unit 6 Checklist.

Alternative Assessment

Final Evaluation

Class Discussion Hold the class discussion and then use the Class Discussion Evaluation Form on page 23 of the Alternative Assessment booklet in the Prentice Hall Assessment System to evaluate students' participation. Either teachers or students can complete the forms to indicate which level of work was achieved for each of the criteria. The evaluation should include specific examples and comments.

TEST PREPARATION

TEST PREPARATION

Use this sample exam to help your students prepare for standardized tests.

You might want to remind your students of the following:

Tips for Test Taking

1. Read the directions carefully.

2. Read each question carefully.

3. For multiple choice questions, try to answer the question before you look at the choices. Read all the choices. Then, eliminate those that are absolutely incorrect.

4. For short answer questions, be sure to answer the question completely if there is more than one part.

5. Answer the easy questions first. Then, go back to the ones that will take more time.

6. Pace yourself. Be sure to set aside enough time for the writing questions.

Write answers on a separate sheet of paper.

Multiple Choice

1 Over the years, one of the main causes of conflict in Israel has been that Arabs and Jews have different viewpoints on —

 A whether or not Israel should have a command economy

 B proposals for the creation of an independent Palestinian state

 C whether or not Israel should develop its vast petroleum reserves

 D how political power should be divided between shahs and ayatollahs

2 Which group of countries is most likely to enter into an agreement on how to share the water of the Euphrates River?

 A Israel, Jordan, and Lebanon

 B Oman, Yemen, and Saudi Arabia

 C Kazakhstan, Uzbekistan, and Turkmenistan

 D Turkey, Syria, and Iraq

3 Which agent of erosion plays the greatest role in shaping the landscape of the Arabian Peninsula?

 A Wind

 B Rain

 C Glacier

 D Geothermal energy

Use the pie graphs <u>and</u> your knowledge of social studies to answer the following question.

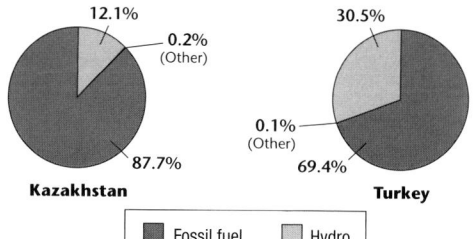

Electricity Production by Source

Source: *The World Factbook*

4 Which of the following conclusions about Turkey and Kazakhstan can be defended by citing the data in the pie graphs above?

 A Both countries depend mostly on petroleum or coal to produce their electricity.

 B Both countries are major exporters of fossil fuels.

 C Kazakhstan is a member of OPEC, but Turkey is not.

 D Neither Turkey nor Kazakhstan have the technology needed to develop nuclear energy.

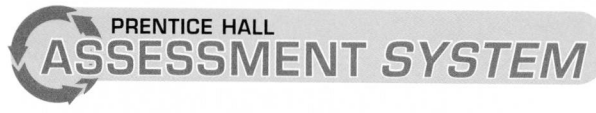

PRENTICE HALL

ASSESSMENT SYSTEM

Diagnose and Prescribe

 • Profile student skills with Diagnostic Tests A&B.

 • Address student needs with program materials identified in the test.

Review and Reteach

 • Provide cumulative content review with the Review Book.

Practice and Assess

 • Build test-taking skills with Test-Taking Strategies on Transparencies.

5 Which of the following was a significant cause of the Iraqi invasion of Kuwait in 1990?

A Saddam Hussein hoped to establish a Kurd homeland in Kuwait.

B The United Nations had imposed an embargo against Iraq.

C Saddam Hussein hoped to acquire the vast oil reserves in Kuwait.

D Kuwaiti forces attacked Iran, an ally of Iraq.

6 Which of the following developments has occurred as a result of cotton production and other agricultural activities in Central Asia?

A Tajikistan and Kyrgyzstan became independent of the Soviet Union.

B Unemployment and inflation have increased throughout much of the region.

C In Kazakhstan, there has been increased migration from rural to urban areas.

D Irrigation projects have caused the Aral Sea to decrease significantly in size.

7 Which of the following is the best example of religious and ethnic conflict?

A The war between Iraq and Kuwait

B The revolution that ended the shah's rule in Iran

C Fighting between Armenians and Azerbaijanis in the Caucasus

D Mustafa Kemal's successful revolution in Turkey

8 Commercial farming is a major economic activity in Israel because —

A Israelis have used technology so that they can grow crops on desert land

B many rivers flow through Israel

C erosion has enriched the soils in Israel

D Israel's climate benefits commercial farming much more than subsistence farming

9 After Shah Mohammad Reza Pahlavi of Iran was overthrown in 1979, Ayatollah Khomeini and the government of the new Islamic republic forced Westerners to leave Iran. This event is proof that —

A Khomeini did not have the support of most Iranians

B the new government opposed foreign influence and power in Iran

C the Islamic republic was opposed to Muslim fundamentalism

D Westerners had caused economic problems in Iran

Writing Practice

10 **(a)** How do the factors of supply and demand affect the price of gasoline and other petroleum products? **(b)** How does OPEC affect the prices that people pay for gasoline?

11 For centuries, nomadic herding was the chief economic activity in Central Asia. Today, in parts of the region, commercial farming and industry are also key economic activities. How did such a dramatic change occur?

12 How does the relationship between government and religion differ in the countries of Iran and Turkey?

Test Preparation Answers

Multiple Choice

1 B

2 D

3 A

4 A

5 C

6 D

7 C

8 A

9 B

Writing Practice

10 **(a)** A high demand and a limited supply of oil will cause prices to rise, and vice versa. **(b)** OPEC controls much of the world's oil supply. If OPEC withholds oil or increases prices, consumers will pay more for gasoline. Or if OPEC increases production, prices will drop.

11 Possible answer: Under Soviet control, herders were forced to give up their nomadic lifestyle and work on government farms and in government industries. Since the breakup of the Soviet Union, industrialization has continued, especially in Uzbekistan and Kazakhstan, and some people in the region have returned to herding.

12 Possible answer: In Iran, the government operates under religious principles, specifically those of Islam. In Turkey, the government is secular—that is, government and religion are independent of each other.

Introducing
UNIT
7
pp. 504–587

*A*frica

Activating Prior Knowledge
Have students share what comes to mind when they think of Africa. For example, do all people living in Africa speak the same language or share the same customs? Ask students to estimate how many countries make up Africa. (53) Have they heard or read anything in the news about the region?

Photo Study
The Nile River
The Blue Nile flows north from Ethiopia and joins the White Nile, which flows north from Lake Victoria, to form the longest river in the world. Although most commonly associated with Egypt, the Nile River basin covers about one tenth of the area of the entire African continent. From its most remote headstream, the Nile flows north to the Mediterranean Sea, where it empties through a delta 160 miles (250 km) wide. **Analyzing Causes and Effects** Ask students to locate the Nile and its tributaries on the physical map on page 509. How do the elevation data on this map explain why the Nile flows north? (The Nile and its tributaries flow from higher elevations in Ethiopia, Uganda, and Kenya to lower elevations in Sudan and Egypt.)

eTeach
Be sure to check out this month's online forum with a Master Teacher to join in an exchange of teaching ideas. **www.phschool.com**

UNIT
seven
*A*frica

Locating the Region
Africa lies south of Europe and the Mediterranean Sea and is connected to Asia in the northeast by a mere strip of land. To its west are the waters of the Atlantic Ocean, and to its east is the Indian Ocean. Deserts and rain forests, mountains and plateaus, city dwellers and nomads can all be found in Africa. As you read this unit, you will discover the role that Africa's location, landforms, and climates play in shaping the lives of the many people who live in the region.

Robinson Projection

RESOURCE DIRECTORY

Teaching Resources
Unit 7
- Geography and World Literature, Coffee for the Road, p. 58

Mental Mapping booklet
- Unit 7 Checklist, p. 91
- Unit 7 Map Test, p. 105

Simulations, Games, and Lab Activities
- Where on Earth? Games, pp. 76–77

Global Environmental Posters

Technology
TeacherExpress™ CD-ROM
World Geography: Building a Global Perspective Teaching Resources on CD-ROM offers lesson planning flexibility, test-generation capability, and resource manageability.

Prentice Hall Presentation Pro CD-ROM
This CD-ROM allows you to create custom lessons for instruction or review for every chapter.

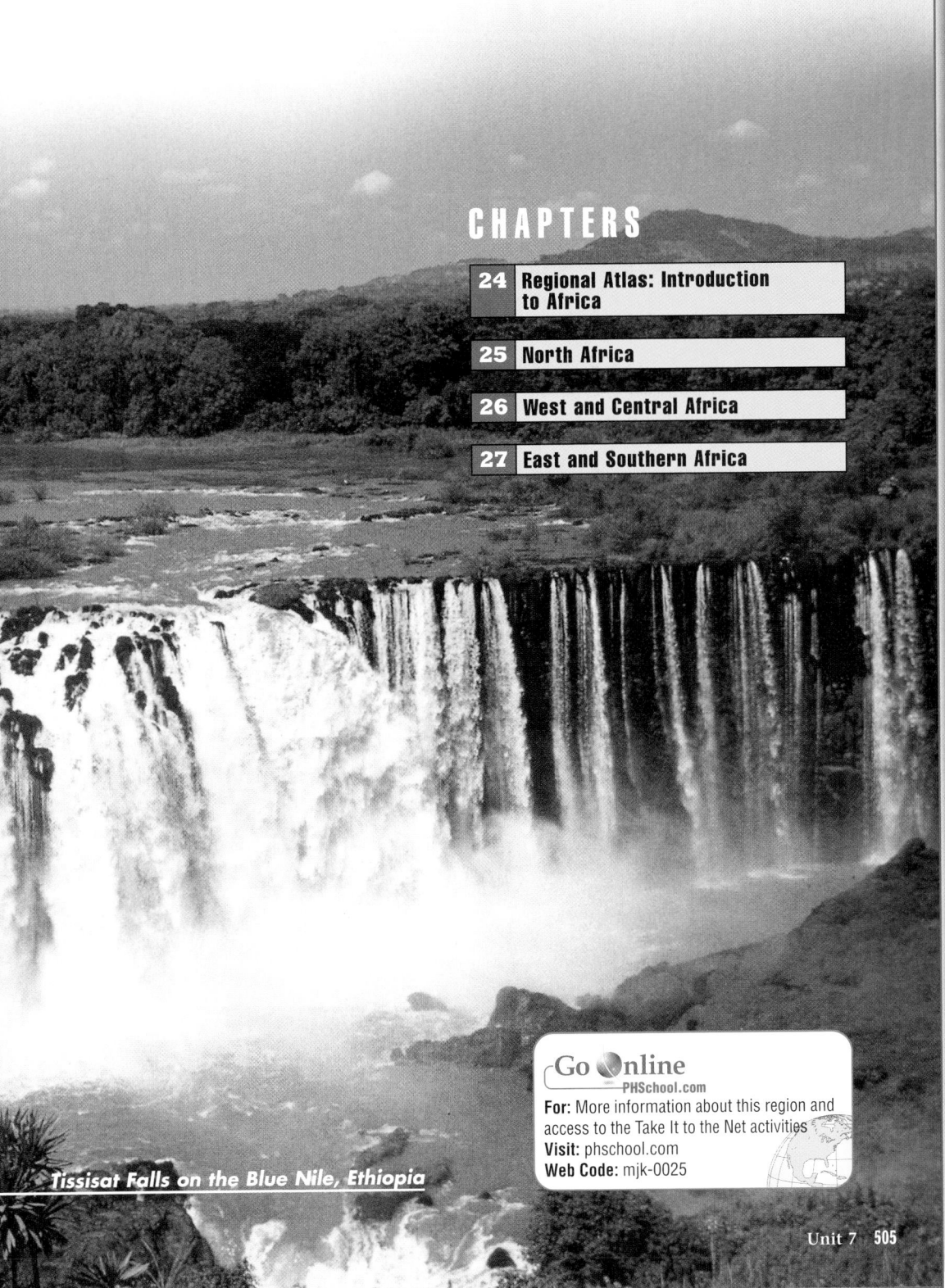

CHAPTERS

Go Online
PHSchool.com
For: More information about this region and access to the Take It to the Net activities
Visit: phschool.com
Web Code: mjk-0025

Tissisat Falls on the Blue Nile, Ethiopia

Promoting Geographic Understanding

Introduce the unit by using the themes below.

1. Location Help students identify Africa's location in relation to other regions by referring them to the Robinson projection map on the opposite page. Ask: **What bodies of water surround Africa?** (Atlantic Ocean, Indian Ocean, Mediterranean Sea, Red Sea) **What land regions border or lie close to Africa?** (Southwest Asia, southern Europe)

2. Location Have students trace the location of the Equator in Africa. Ask: **About how much of the African continent lies in the northern latitudes?** (approximately two thirds)

RESOURCE DIRECTORY

World Geography Map and Photo Transparencies
The World Geography Map and Photo Transparencies provide thematic maps and photos to help students understand key geographic concepts.

World Geography Videos
These chapter-level videos help students understand the key concepts and themes of geography through case studies.

ExamView Test Bank CD-ROM
The test bank CD-ROM allows you to create, edit, and print out chapter-level tests.

Social Studies Skills Tutor CD-ROM
This interactive CD-ROM provides students with the opportunity to learn and practice critical social studies skills.

Take It to the NET
Prentice Hall's Web site offers Internet activities and links that supplement *World Geography: Building a Global Perspective.* Visit us in the Social Studies area at **www.phschool.com**.

Chapter 24 Planning Guide

Resource Manager

	CORE INSTRUCTION	READING/SKILLS
Chapter-Level Resources	**Teaching Resources** ▪ **Unit 7**/Ch. 24 • Regional Atlas Study Guide, p. 2 ▪ **Mental Mapping booklet** • Unit 7 Checklist, p. 91 ▪ **Simulations, Games, and Lab Activities** • Place Location Review Games, pp. 58–63 ◉ **TeacherExpress™ CD-ROM,** Ch. 24 💻 **Companion Web site,** **www.phschool.com** • eTeach	**Teaching Resources** ▪ **Unit 7**/Ch. 24 • Regional Atlas Review, p. 3 ▪ **Guide to the Essentials (English/Spanish)** • Chapter 24 Summary ▪ **Spanish Resources** • Regional Atlas Review, p. 61 📼 **Guided Reading Audiotapes (English/Spanish),** Ch. 24 ▤ **Section Reading Support Transparencies,** Ch. 24 ◉ **Book on CD,** Ch. 24 ◉ **Social Studies Skills Tutor CD-ROM**
Historical Overview Describe significant events and developments in Africa's history.	**Teaching Resources** ▪ **Mental Mapping booklet** • Outline Map 24A, p. 92 ◉ **Prentice Hall Presentation Pro CD-ROM,** Ch. 24	**Teaching Resources** ▪ **Social Studies Skills Handbook** • Reading a Political Map, p. 19
Physical Characteristics Identify Africa's major physical characteristics.	**Teaching Resources** ▪ **Mental Mapping booklet** • Outline Map 24B, p. 93 ◉ **Prentice Hall Presentation Pro CD-ROM,** Ch. 24	**Teaching Resources** ▪ **Social Studies Skills Handbook** • Elevation on a Map, p. 20 • Four Types of Landforms, p. 21 • Relief on a Map, p. 22
Climates Compare Africa's climate regions.	◉ **Prentice Hall Presentation Pro CD-ROM,** Ch. 24	**Teaching Resources** ▪ **Social Studies Skills Handbook** • Reading a Climate Map, p. 26
Ecosystems Describe characteristics of major ecosystems in Africa.	**Teaching Resources** ▪ **Creative Teaching Activities** • Preserving Rain Forests, p. 26 ◉ **Prentice Hall Presentation Pro CD-ROM,** Ch. 24	**Teaching Resources** ▪ **Social Studies Skills Handbook** • Reading a Natural Vegetation Map, p. 25
People and Cultures Discuss elements of culture in Africa.	◉ **Prentice Hall Presentation Pro CD-ROM,** Ch. 24	**Teaching Resources** ▪ **Social Studies Skills Handbook** • Reading a Population Density Map, p. 31
Economics, Technology, and Environment Identify how the economy, technology, and the environment interact in Africa.	◉ **Prentice Hall Presentation Pro CD-ROM,** Ch. 24	**Teaching Resources** ▪ **Social Studies Skills Handbook** • Reading an Economic Activity Map, p. 27 • Reading a Natural Resources Map, p. 34
Database • Define *population density*. • Compare the population densities of select African countries and the United States.	**Teaching Resources** ▪ **Unit 7**/Ch. 24 • Regional Atlas Database Skills, p. 4 ◉ **Prentice Hall Presentation Pro CD-ROM,** Ch. 24	**Teaching Resources** ▪ **Unit 7**/Ch. 24 • Regional Atlas Database Skills, p. 4 ▪ **Social Studies Skills Handbook** • Reading a Table, p. 62

ENRICHMENT/HONORS/PREAP

Teaching Resources

Mental Mapping booklet
- Atlas Activity, p. 94

Social Studies Skills Handbook
- Study and Research Skills, pp. 94–108

Simulations, Games, and Lab Activities
- Where on Earth? Games, pp. 76–77

World Geography Map and Photo Transparencies
- Africa: Maps and Photos

World Geography Videos
- Regional Atlas: Africa, Tape 3

Companion Web site, www.phschool.com
- Chapter 24 Activities

World Geography Map and Photo Transparencies
- Africa: Political

World Geography Map and Photo Transparencies
- Africa: Physical

World Geography Map and Photo Transparencies
- World Climate Zones

World Geography Map and Photo Transparencies
- Africa: Natural Hazards

World Geography Map and Photo Transparencies
- Africa: Population Density

Teaching Resources

Social Studies Skills Handbook
- Recognizing Ideologies, p. 48

Simulations, Games, and Lab Activities
- Simulation: Global Hunger, p. 14

World Geography Map and Photo Transparencies
- Africa: Economic Activities

World Geography Map and Photo Transparencies
- Africa: Population Density

ASSESSMENT

PRENTICE HALL ASSESSMENT SYSTEM

Core Assessment
- ExamView Test Bank booklet, Ch. 24
- ExamView Test Bank CD-ROM, Ch. 24

Standardized Test Preparation

Diagnose and Prescribe
- Diagnostic Tests for High School Social Studies Skills

Review and Reteach
- Review Book for World Geography, pp. 15–16

Practice and Assess
- Test-taking Strategies With Transparencies for High School

  Test-taking Strategy Poster
- Alternative Assessment booklet
- Test Prep Book for World Geography

Teaching Resources

Unit 7/Ch. 24
- Test Forms A and B, pp. 5–10

Guide to the Essentials (English/Spanish)
- Chapter 24 Test

Mental Mapping booklet
- Chapter 24 Map Test, p. 95

Companion Web site, www.phschool.com
- Chapter 24 Self-Test

CUSTOMIZE FOR INDIVIDUAL NEEDS

Gifted and Talented
- Teacher's Edition, Customize for . . . , p. 515

Less Proficient Readers
- Guide to the Essentials (English), Ch. 24
- Guided Reading Audiotapes (English), Ch. 24
- Section Reading Support Transparencies, Ch. 24
- Book on CD, Ch. 24

Students Acquiring English/ESL
- Guide to the Essentials (English/Spanish), Ch. 24
- Guided Reading Audiotapes (English/Spanish), Ch. 24
- Section Reading Support Transparencies, Ch. 24
- Book on CD, Ch. 24

Less Proficient Writers
- Alternative Assessment, Writing Assignment Rubric, p. 6
- Teacher's Edition, Customize for . . . , p. 521

Introducing

CHAPTER........

24

pp. 506–519

Objectives

Upon completion of this Regional Atlas, students should be able to:

◆ describe significant events and developments in Africa's history;

◆ identify Africa's major physical characteristics;

◆ compare Africa's climate regions;

◆ describe characteristics of major ecosystems in Africa;

◆ discuss elements of culture in Africa;

◆ identify how the economy, technology, and the environment interact in Africa.

 National Geography Standards

The following National Geography Standards are highlighted in this Regional Atlas: 1, 2, 3, 4, 5, 7, 8, 9, 10, 11, 12, 13, 14, 15, 16, 17

 Bellringer

Divide students into groups and ask them to write as many words or phrases related to Africa's land, climate, and people as possible in 1–2 minutes. Work with the class to make a word web on the board that shows the students' perceptions of Africa.

Answers to Assessment

1. (a) Sahel, p. 506 **(b)** colonialism, p. 506

2. Possible answers: Cameroon, Central African Republic, Sudan, Ethiopia, Somalia, Equatorial Guinea, Congo, Gabon, Democratic Republic of the Congo, Uganda, Kenya, Rwanda, Burundi, Tanzania, Angola, Zambia, Malawi, Mozambique, Zimbabwe, Botswana, Namibia, Swaziland, Lesotho, and South Africa

3. Answers will vary, but students may suggest that if the borders drawn by African nations were along political and ethnic lines, conflict might be lessened.

Historical Overview

The first trace of modern humans emerged over 100,000 years ago in Africa. Some left to settle other parts of the world, while others remained there. One factor encouraging migration was climate change. About 7,000 years ago, what is now the Sahara had a wetter climate. People raised some of the world's first domesticated cattle on the fertile grasslands. As the climate became drier, these people moved to the moister lands north and south of the Sahara and into Egypt's Nile River valley.

Ancient Civilizations and Migrations

One of the world's first great civilizations arose in Egypt about 5,000 years ago. Egyptian civilization influenced both the Carthaginians and Romans who later controlled North Africa, and civilizations such as Kush and Aksum in modern Sudan and Ethiopia. Meanwhile, the Bantu peoples, originally from modern Cameroon, developed agriculture, spread to East Africa and learned to make iron tools. About 2,000 years ago, they spread south as far as modern South Africa. In the **Sahel** region, just south of the Sahara, there was a growing trade in salt and gold after A.D. 1000. It gave rise to the rich empires of Ghana and Mali. To the south, the Yoruba culture of Nigeria developed. In southern Africa, Great Zimbabwe emerged. Meanwhile, Muslim civilization spread across North Africa and down the coast of East Africa.

Trade and Enslavement

After 1500, Europeans began trading guns and other manufactured goods along the African coast for gold and ivory. Increasingly, however, they sought slaves for their colonies in the Americas. Coastal kingdoms such as Asante and Dahomey used European guns to round up Africans in the interior and sell these people as slaves to the Europeans. This trade sent millions of enslaved Africans to the Americas.

Colonialism In the 1800s, European countries abolished slavery and developed industry. They set up new colonies in Africa to secure sources of raw materials and markets for European products. This arrangement, known as **colonialism,** subjected African peoples to foreign rule. European countries divided the continent among themselves without regard to existing political and cultural divisions. However, colonialism also brought advantages such as highways and railroads, educational opportunities, and medical advances to the continent.

Independence and New Challenges

By the 1960s, most African countries had won independence. However, colonialism had left Africa in poverty. To promote economic advancement, many countries took on massive loans to finance projects. New nations generally maintained the borders imposed by Europeans. This contributed to ethnic turmoil and military conflict, both within and between nations. In many countries, military rulers seized power during the 1960s and 1970s. During the 1990s, however, free elections were held for the first time in South Africa, and democracy returned to such countries as Ghana and Tanzania. International campaigns to combat disease and malnutrition offered further hope to the people of Africa.

ASSESSMENT

1. **Key Terms** Define **(a)** Sahel, **(b)** colonialism.

2. **Map Skills** **Movement** In which present-day nations would you expect to find descendants of Bantu peoples?

3. **Critical Thinking** **Predicting Consequences** Suppose that African nations decided to draw new borders. What effect might this have on conflict? Explain.

RESOURCE DIRECTORY

Teaching Resources

Unit 7, Chapter 24
• Regional Atlas Study Guide, p. 2

Guide to the Essentials (English/Spanish)
• Chapter 24 Summary

Mental Mapping booklet
• Unit 7 Checklist, p. 91
• Outline Map 24A, p. 92

Social Studies Skills Handbook
• Reading a Political Map, p. 19

Technology

Guided Reading Audiotapes (English/Spanish),
Chapter 24

Section Reading Support Transparencies,
Chapter 24

World Geography Map and Photo Transparencies
• Africa: Maps and Photos

Book on CD, Chapter 24

World Geography Videos
• Regional Atlas: Africa, Tape 3

REGIONAL ATLAS

Africa: POLITICAL

Africa political map showing countries and capitals, with the following labels:

- MOROCCO — Rabat, Casablanca
- Algiers — ALGERIA
- TUNISIA — Tunis, Tripoli
- LIBYA
- EGYPT — Alexandria, Giza, Cairo
- WESTERN SAHARA (MOROCCO)
- MAURITANIA — Nouakchott
- MALI — Bamako
- NIGER — Niamey
- CHAD — N'Djamena
- SUDAN — Khartoum
- ERITREA — Asmara
- DJIBOUTI — Djibouti
- CAPE VERDE — Praia
- SENEGAL — Dakar
- GAMBIA — Banjul
- GUINEA-BISSAU — Bissau
- GUINEA — Conakry
- SIERRA LEONE — Freetown
- LIBERIA — Monrovia
- CÔTE D'IVOIRE — Yamoussoukro, Abidjan
- GHANA — Accra
- BURKINA FASO — Ouagadougou
- TOGO — Lomé
- BENIN — Porto-Novo
- NIGERIA — Kano, Abuja, Lagos
- CAMEROON — Yaoundé
- CENTRAL AFRICAN REPUBLIC — Bangui
- EQUATORIAL GUINEA — Malabo
- SÃO TOMÉ AND PRÍNCIPE — São Tomé
- GABON — Libreville
- CONGO — Brazzaville
- D.R. CONGO — Kinshasa, Kisangani, Lubumbashi
- CABINDA (ANGOLA)
- ANGOLA — Luanda
- ETHIOPIA — Addis Ababa
- SOMALIA — Mogadishu
- UGANDA — Kampala
- KENYA — Nairobi, Mombasa
- RWANDA — Kigali
- BURUNDI — Bujumbura
- TANZANIA — Dodoma, Dar es Salaam
- ZAMBIA — Lusaka
- MALAWI — Lilongwe
- COMOROS — Moroni
- ZIMBABWE — Harare
- MOZAMBIQUE — Maputo
- NAMIBIA — Windhoek
- BOTSWANA — Gaborone
- SOUTH AFRICA — Johannesburg, Pretoria, Cape Town, Durban
- SWAZILAND — Mbabane
- LESOTHO — Maseru
- MADAGASCAR — Antananarivo
- MAURITIUS — Port Louis
- RÉUNION (FR.)

Bodies of water and features: Strait of Gibraltar, Mediterranean Sea, Red Sea, Gulf of Aden, Gulf of Guinea, ATLANTIC OCEAN, INDIAN OCEAN, Mozambique Channel, Lake Nasser, L. Chad, L. Tana, L. Turkana, Lake Victoria, Tanganyika, L. Nyasa, Niger R., Benue R., Congo R., Nile, Blue Nile, White Nile, Zambezi, Limpopo, Orange R.

Lines: Tropic of Cancer, Equator, Tropic of Capricorn

KEY

- —— National boundary
- ⊛ National capital
- ⊙ Other city

Lambert Azimuthal Equal-Area Projection

Scale: 0 400 800 mi / 0 400 800 km

MENTAL MAPPING

Making a Political Map Study this political map and then draw your own sketch map of Africa. Label the countries and major cities of the region. Use various colors to outline and shade each country.

---

1. Focus Write these headlines on the board: *(1) Liberian Factions Sign Cease-fire; (2) African Farmers Fight Advancing Desert; (3) Nigeria Executes Political Dissidents.* Ask students what these headlines suggest about the challenges faced by the region today.

2. Instruct Ask students to complete the Mental Mapping activities and the study questions in each section of the Regional Atlas. Review the answers as a class.

3. Close/Reteach Ask students to imagine that they are visiting one of the places described in the Regional Atlas. Instruct them to write a letter to their friends at home that describes the landforms, climates, people, and cultures of the region.

MENTAL MAPPING

Unit Checklist Distribute the Unit 7 Checklist on page 91 of the Mental Mapping booklet in the Teaching Resources. This list includes all of the place names students should learn in the unit.

Making a Political Map Students can complete the mapping activity on this page either by sketching their own maps or by coloring and labeling the Chapter 24A Outline Map on page 92 of the Mental Mapping booklet. Ask students to label all of the countries and major cities listed under Part I of the Unit 7 Checklist.

Alternative Assessment

Introduce the Activity
Making Maps You may wish to distribute the Map Rubric found on page 14 of the Alternative Assessment booklet in the Prentice Hall Assessment System.

Africa's Ecosystems Ecosystems are formed by the relationships among plants, animals, humans, and the environments in which they live. Ecosystem distribution in Africa varies generally in continent-wide belts. North and south of the Equator, the ecosystems become progressively drier. Northern Africa mirrors southern Africa, although in East Africa ecosystems can vary with elevation. Understanding patterns of ecosystems can help students appreciate ways Africans depend on their environments.

AFRICA
Physical Characteristics

Africa's highest mountains rise along its northern and eastern edges. Most of the continent consists of **plateaus,** or elevated blocks of land with flat or gently rolling surfaces. Southern Africa forms a high plateau, while the Sahara in the north covers a low plateau dotted with scattered mountain ranges. The basins of rivers, such as the Congo and Zambezi, form low-lying areas on these plateaus. In eastern Africa, a number of lakes lie within the Great Rift Valley.

Movements within the crust cause cracks to appear on the surface.

Surface cracks

Block mountains

Lake   Volcano

Blocks of land slip down between faults created by cracks.

Rift Valleys
The Great Rift Valley stretches northward from Mozambique to Ethiopia. The valley is marked by volcanoes, lakes, and hot springs and has steep sides reaching about 6,562 feet (2,000 m). **PHYSICAL PROCESSES** *Would you expect a rift valley to widen or narrow over time?*

Major Rivers
A number of waterfalls and cataracts can be found along the Nile, the longest river in the world. Although many African rivers are navigable in inland areas, waterfalls and cataracts often make reaching the coast difficult. **PHYSICAL CHARACTERISTICS** *How might waterfalls and cataracts affect trade between inland and coastal areas?*

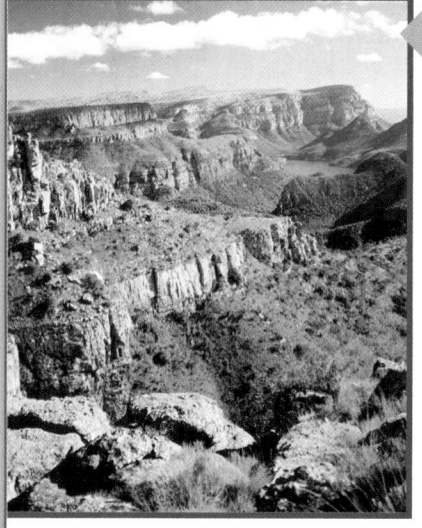

Drakensberg Mountains
Many areas near Africa's coasts are marked by **escarpments,** which are steep slopes or cliffs. Among these are the Drakensberg Mountains, which are the highest peaks in southern Africa. **PHYSICAL CHARACTERISTICS** *Based on the elevations on the map, identify areas where you would expect to find escarpments.*

ASSESSMENT

1. **Key Terms** Define **(a)** plateau, **(b)** escarpment.

2. **Map Skills** **Place** Many of the earth's oceans and seas began as long, narrow rift valleys that slowly widened and filled with water. Looking at the map, identify a sea that looks like a drowned rift valley.

3. **Critical Thinking** **Developing a Hypothesis** If the Great Rift Valley continued to widen in Africa, where would you expect a new sea to form?

REGIONAL ATLAS

Africa: PHYSICAL

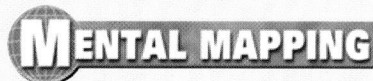

30°W · 20°W · 10°W · 0° · 10°E · 20°E · 30°E · 40°E · 50°E · 60°E

Strait of Gibraltar

Algiers

ATLAS MOUNTAINS

TUNISIA

Mediterranean Sea

Nile Delta

Suez Canal

ASIA

40°N

MOROCCO

30°N

Canary Islands

GREAT WESTERN ERG

GREAT EASTERN ERG

TASSILI N'AJJER

ALGERIA

LIBYA

QATTARA DEPRESSION

Cairo

EGYPT

30°N

N
W — E
S

WESTERN SAHARA (MOROCCO)

Tropic of Cancer

AHAGGAR MOUNTAINS

Lake Nasser

Aswan High Dam

Red Sea

20°N

S   A   H   A   R   A

PLATEAU DU MANGUENI

LIBYAN DESERT

NUBIAN DESERT

20°N

MAURITANIA

MALI

AIR

S   A   H   E   L

Cape Verde Islands

SENEGAL

GAMBIA

NIGER

CHAD

L. Chad

Khartoum

SUDAN

ERITREA

DJIBOUTI

Gulf of Aden

10°N

GUINEA-BISSAU

GUINEA

BURKINA FASO

JOS PLATEAU

MANDARA MTS

ETHIOPIA

ETHIOPIAN HIGHLANDS

HORN OF AFRICA

10°N

GUINEA HIGHLANDS

SIERRA LEONE

CÔTE D'IVOIRE

TOGO

BENIN

NIGERIA

Lagos

SUDD

Shebeli R.

LIBERIA

Lake Volta

GHANA

Bight of Benin

Niger Delta

Gulf of Guinea

CENTRAL AFRICAN REPUBLIC

CAMEROON

SOMALIA

Mogadishu

EQUATORIAL GUINEA

Congo R.

Boyoma Falls

L. Albert

UGANDA

KENYA

Equator

0°

SÃO TOMÉ AND PRÍNCIPE

GABON

CONGO

C O N G O
B A S I N

L. Edward

Lake Victoria

Nairobi

ATLANTIC OCEAN

L. Mai-Ndombe

Nyamuragira 10,017 ft. (3,053 m)

RWANDA

BURUNDI

SERENGETI PLAIN

Kilimanjaro 19,341 ft. (5,895 m)

INDIAN OCEAN

Seychelles Islands

Kasai R.

Kinshasa

CABINDA (ANGOLA)

DEMOCRATIC REPUBLIC OF THE CONGO

Tanganyika

Zanzibar

TANZANIA

Kalambo Falls

L. Mweru

Comoros Islands

10°S

ANGOLA

MALAWI

Lake Nyasa

ZAMBIA

L. Kariba

Zambezi R.

Harare

Victoria Falls

ZIMBABWE

MADAGASCAR

Mauritius

Réunion

NAMIB DESERT

NAMIBIA

Okavango Delta

Limpopo R.

BOTSWANA

MOZAMBIQUE

Mozambique Channel

KALAHARI DESERT

Johannesburg

Tropic of Capricorn

Vaal R.

Orange R.

SOUTH AFRICA

LESOTHO

DRAKENSBERG MTS.

SWAZILAND

Cape of Good Hope

Cape Town

Cape Agulhas

10°E · 20°E · 30°E · 40°E

KEY

Elevation

Feet	Meters
14,000	4,270
7,000	2,135
1,500	457
700	213
(sea level) 0	0 (sea level)

▲ Mountain
△ Volcano
• Major city
⌐ Waterfall
– Major dam
······ Canal

Lambert Azimuthal Equal-Area Projection

0 — 400 — 800 mi
0 — 400 — 800 km

MENTAL MAPPING

Making a Physical Map Study this physical map and then draw your own sketch map of Africa. Label the major physical features, including rivers and other bodies of water.

MENTAL MAPPING

Making a Physical Map Students can complete the mapping activity on this page either by adding labels to the political maps they have already completed or by coloring and labeling the Chapter 24B Outline Map on page 93 of the Mental Mapping booklet in the Teaching Resources. Ask students to label all major physical features and bodies of water listed under Part II of the Unit 7 Checklist.

ACTIVITY

Critical Thinking

Geography and History Use the following questions to help students analyze the links between a place's physical geography and its history: **What natural features of North America encouraged European exploration in the late 1400s and early 1500s?** (navigable waterways, coastal and inland plains) **What aspects of Africa's geography discouraged early exploration of the region south of the Sahara?** (The climate and terrain of the Sahara made travel to the region difficult. In addition, the many waterfalls and marshes of the region's major rivers prevented long-distance travel by boat.)

BACKGROUND

The Physical World

Lake Victoria Lake Victoria occupies a gentle depression on a section of the earth's crust between two arms of the Great Rift Valley. It is Africa's largest lake, and the third largest lake in area in the world.

Chapter 24 ▪ Regional Atlas: Africa **509**

AFRICA
Climates

Physical characteristics and location affect Africa's climate. The prevailing winds blow warm air toward the Equator before rising and cooling. During the summer, rain falls in broad zones on either side of the Equator. Farther to the north and south are regions with desert climates. Mediterranean climates, with wet winters and dry summers, occur at the extreme northern and southern edges of the continent.

Desert Climates
Although deserts are the hottest places on earth during the day, at night temperatures can plunge to below freezing. Deserts are extremely dry, and some receive no rainfall for years. **CLIMATES** *Based on the map, what is Africa's largest desert?*

Rain Forest in Sierra Leone
Tropical wet climates have high temperatures and heavy rainfall throughout the year. These conditions produce abundant plant and animal life in this tropical rain forest in Sierra Leone. **ECOSYSTEMS** *In what parts of Africa would you expect to find tropical rain forests like the one in the photograph?*

Zambian Grasslands
Grasslands, such as this one in Zambia, may appear in a variety of climate zones. The amount of rainfall affects what types of plants flourish in different areas. **PHYSICAL CHARACTERISTICS** *In which climate zone would you expect to find this grassland?*

ASSESSMENT

1. **Map Skills** **Regions** Which countries include marine west coast climate regions?

2. **Critical Thinking** **Synthesizing Information** How do prevailing winds and climate regions interact in Africa?

510   Chapter 24 ▪ Regional Atlas: Africa

REGIONAL ATLAS

Africa: CLIMATE REGIONS

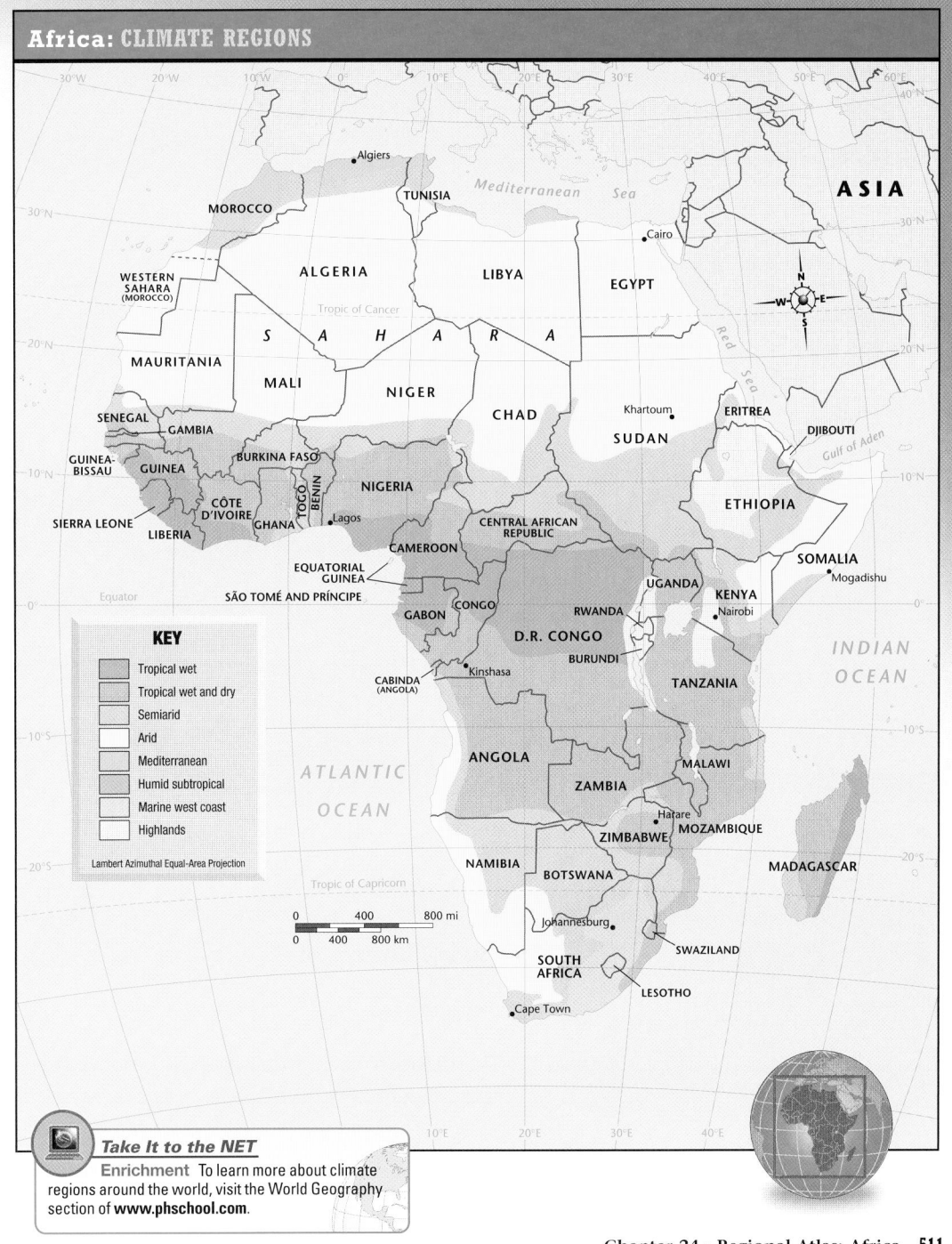

KEY

- Tropical wet
- Tropical wet and dry
- Semiarid
- Arid
- Mediterranean
- Humid subtropical
- Marine west coast
- Highlands

Lambert Azimuthal Equal-Area Projection

0   400   800 mi
0   400   800 km

Take It to the NET
Enrichment To learn more about climate regions around the world, visit the World Geography section of **www.phschool.com**.

Group Work

Activity: Presenting a weather report

Purpose: Assign each group one of the eight climate categories shown on the map on this page. Members of each group will work together to prepare a representative radio weather report for a city or country in their assigned climate region. The report should note the location, month, and day, as well as describe the current weather conditions.

Roles: Assign researchers, writers, and a news announcer.

Result: Announcers will read weather reports in class.

Articles From
NATIONAL GEOGRAPHIC

The following article may be used to extend the content in this section.

Webster, Donovan, and George Steinmetz, photographer. "Journey to the Heart of the Sahara." *National Geographic,* Vol. 195, No. 3 (Mar. 1999), pp. 2–33.

The harsh climate and collective poverty of the Sahara do not deter its inhabitants from maintaining a traditional nomadic way of life.

Map Study Extension

Use the questions below to develop additional geographic themes.

1. Movement The people of the Kalahari Desert were traditionally nomadic hunters and gatherers. Today they still move frequently to follow their herds of cattle. Instruct students to compare the area of the Kalahari Desert on the physical map on page 509 with the same area on the climate map on page 511 and the ecosystem map on the opposite page. Ask: **What role do climate and ecosystems play in the nomadic life of the people of the Kalahari Desert?** (The area in which the Kalahari is located is mostly semiarid; it supports tropical grasslands. However, because such climates have low annual precipitation, the grass is not lush and water is scarce. As a result, the people of the Kalahari must move frequently to find new grassland and sources of water.)

2. Place Many African countries encompass more than one ecosystem. Ask: **Which nations in Africa have the most ecosystems?** (Morocco, Algeria, Libya, Egypt, Sudan, and South Africa all have at least four different ecosystems within their borders.)

Answers to Assessment

1. (a) chaparral, p. 512 **(b)** savanna, p. 512

2. tropical grassland, desert scrub, temperate grassland, desert, and chaparral

3. Possible answer: A government can designate certain areas as natural reserves and pass laws that would make actions that could endanger the ecosystem (such as lumbering, hunting, and certain methods of farming) illegal in these areas.

Ecosystems

Africa supports a broad range of ecosystems. In the far north and far south, temperate grasslands and **chaparral**, or drought-resistant brush, support a variety of grazing animals and predators. Moving toward the Equator, desert ecosystems support a sparse population of drought-resistant plants and animals. Across much of the continent, the grassland and savanna ecosystems support much of Africa's unique wildlife. Along the Equator are tropical rain forests.

Arid Ecosystems

The **savanna** is a grassland with scattered trees. The ecosystem supports a rich variety of wildlife, which survive with limited water in the drier parts of Africa. Some animals, like these camels, also live in desert ecosystems. **ECOSYSTEMS** *What two desert ecosystems are shown on the map?*

Mali River

Rivers can create their own ecosystems, particularly in areas with limited or seasonal rainfall. Here, villagers wash laundry along the banks of the Mali River. **PATTERNS OF SETTLEMENT** *In an ecosystem with limited rainfall, why might human communities like this village tend to develop along rivers?*

Rain Forest Animals

In Africa, rain forest ecosystems are shrinking as people clear land for farming, grazing, and lumbering. Mountain gorillas, such as this one in the Democratic Republic of the Congo, are also in danger from hunters. **ENVIRONMENTAL CHANGE** *What human activities might threaten this ecosystem?*

ASSESSMENT

1. **Key Terms** Define **(a)** chaparral, **(b)** savanna.

2. **Map Skills** **Regions** Which ecological regions in northern Africa have counterparts in southern Africa?

3. **Critical Thinking** **Solving Problems** What actions might a government take to protect ecosystems?

Answers to Photo Captions

Arid Ecosystems desert and desert scrub

Mali River Water is needed for survival.

Rain Forest Animals farming, grazing, lumbering, and hunting

RESOURCE DIRECTORY

Teaching Resources
Creative Teaching Activities, Preserving Rain Forests, p. 26
Social Studies Skills Handbook
• Reading a Natural Vegetation Map, p. 25

Technology
World Geography Map and Photo Transparencies
• Africa: Maps and Photos

REGIONAL ATLAS

Africa: ECOSYSTEMS

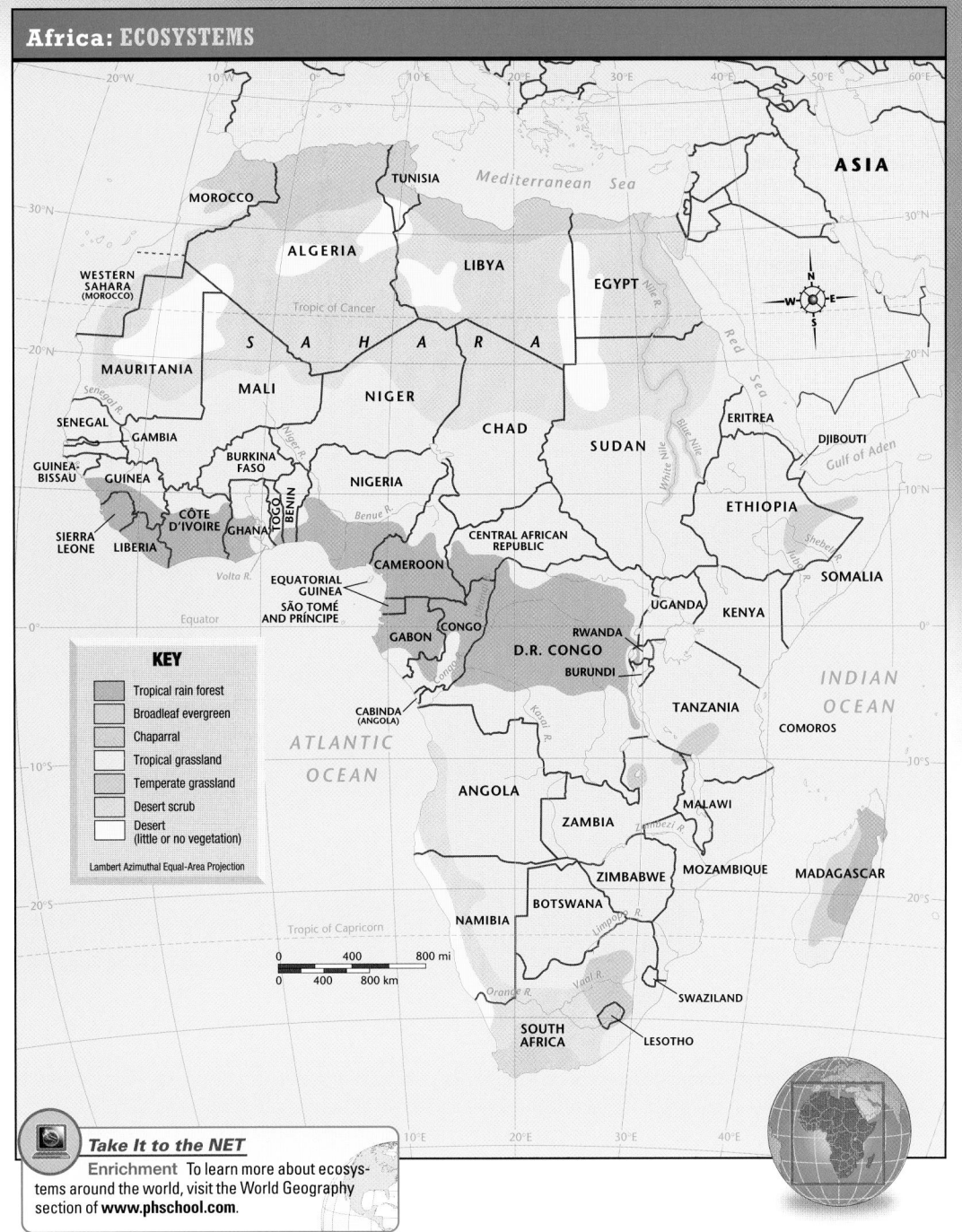

KEY
- Tropical rain forest
- Broadleaf evergreen
- Chaparral
- Tropical grassland
- Temperate grassland
- Desert scrub
- Desert (little or no vegetation)

Lambert Azimuthal Equal-Area Projection

0   400   800 mi
0   400   800 km

Take It to the NET
Enrichment To learn more about ecosystems around the world, visit the World Geography section of **www.phschool.com**.

AFRICA
People and Cultures

Africa is home to a wide range of peoples, languages, and cultures. The Arabs and Berbers of North Africa have close ties to the culture of Southwest Asia. South of the Sahara, peoples draw on a rich variety of cultural traditions and speak a total of more than 800 languages. Africa's population is particularly concentrated in regions such as the Nile Valley, Nigeria, the East African highlands, and certain coastal areas.

KEY

Portuguese	German
British	Spanish
French	Italian
Belgian	Independent

Politics and Culture

During the late 1800s, European powers divided Africa into colonies. Many elements of European cultures, such as language and political philosophies, are still evident today in African nations. **GOVERNMENT AND CITIZENSHIP** *Why might Africans have chosen to maintain some elements of European culture after gaining independence?*

Moroccan Storyteller

Africa's peoples maintain many traditions, including storytelling and **oral history,** or history passed down by word of mouth. This storyteller lives in Morocco. **CULTURES** *How do cultural traditions pass from one generation to the next?*

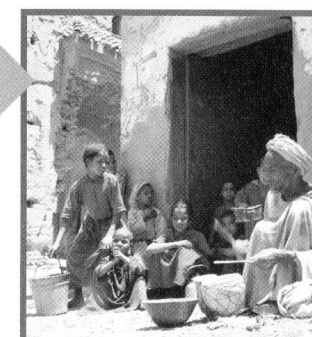

Housing Styles

In this photograph of Niamey, Niger, a high-rise apartment building towers over traditional grass homes. **SCIENCE AND TECHNOLOGY** *How do both of these types of housing reflect the ability of people to adapt to or change the environment?*

ASSESSMENT

1. **Key Term** Define oral history.

2. **Map Skills** **Human-Environment Interaction** Compare this map to the physical features map (page 509) and climate map (page 511). Which physical features and climates support the highest and lowest population densities?

3. **Critical Thinking** **Analyzing Information** Based on this map, which African countries would you expect to have the largest populations?

Africa: POPULATION DENSITY

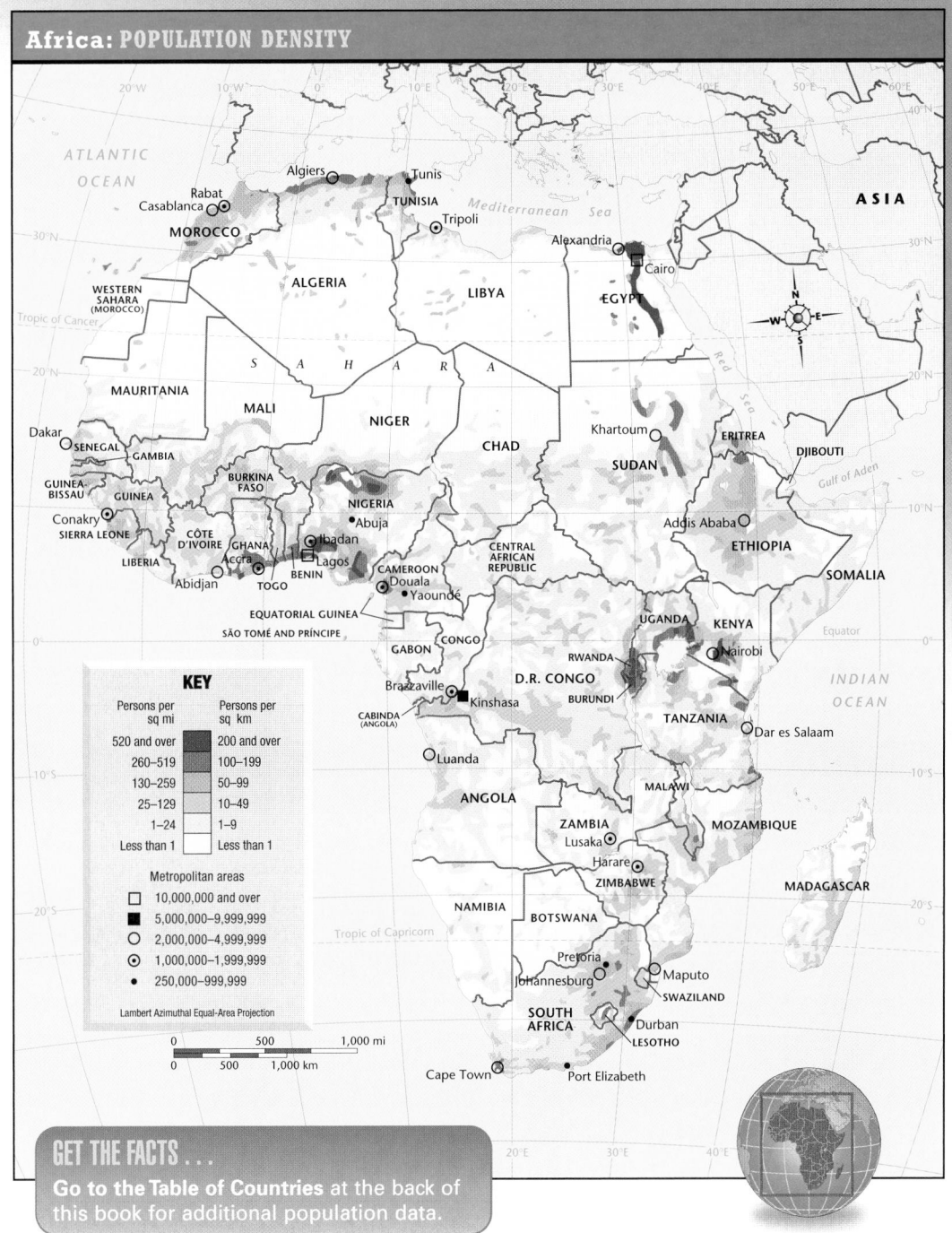

KEY

Persons per sq mi	Persons per sq km
520 and over	200 and over
260–519	100–199
130–259	50–99
25–129	10–49
1–24	1–9
Less than 1	Less than 1

Metropolitan areas
□ 10,000,000 and over
■ 5,000,000–9,999,999
○ 2,000,000–4,999,999
◉ 1,000,000–1,999,999
• 250,000–999,999

Lambert Azimuthal Equal-Area Projection

0   500   1,000 mi
0   500   1,000 km

GET THE FACTS . . .
Go to the Table of Countries at the back of this book for additional population data.

Chapter 24 ■ Regional Atlas: Africa   **515**

ACTIVITY

Area Comparison

Using the Table of Countries
Ask students to use the Table of Countries beginning on page 742 of their textbooks to compare the land areas and populations of the United States and Egypt. **Connections: Math** Ask: **Which country has a higher population density?** (While the population of the United States is roughly four times that of Egypt, its land area is about nine times greater. Therefore, Egypt has a higher population density.)

BACKGROUND

Daily Life

The Family The family is the central unit of African society. Most Africans live in villages. There, the typical family consists not only of parents and their children, but also of grandparents, aunts, uncles, and cousins. These extended families provide the most important relationships in a person's life. They offer security, financial help, and community. Relatives can be counted on to provide housing and food for indefinite periods as well as assistance with the harvest and care of the children.

Chapter 24 ■ Regional Atlas   **515**

AFRICA
Economics, Technology, and Environment

Africa's diverse environment supports a wide range of economic activities. The two most common activities are subsistence farming and **nomadic herding,** in which herders move their flocks to different pastures throughout the year. In some regions, commercial livestock raising and farming are more common; although, in some areas, the soil suffers from **leaching**—the dissolving and washing away of nutrients. Africa also has great mineral wealth, with some of the richest deposits of gold, diamonds, and petroleum in the world.

Tradition and Technology

Traditional economic activities and newer technologies coexist around the world. These Masai herders in Kenya are checking cattle blood for disease. **SCIENCE AND TECHNOLOGY** *How might technology improve economic conditions for groups such as the Masai?*

Urban Economies

Although most Africans still live in rural areas, many are moving to cities. In urban areas, economic activities center on manufacturing and service industries, such as this supermarket in Botswana. **ECONOMIC SYSTEMS** *What connections does this photograph show between the urban economy and the agricultural economy of the countryside?*

Land Degradation

Poverty in Africa often forces its people to overutilize resources. In Kenya, overgrazing by livestock has caused severe erosion, a type of **land degradation,** or reduction in the productive potential of the land. **ENVIRONMENTAL CHANGE** *How is poverty connected to environmental change caused by humans?*

ASSESSMENT

1. **Key Terms** Define **(a)** nomadic herding, **(b)** leaching, **(c)** land degradation.

2. **Map Skills** **Regions** In what regions is Africa's mineral wealth concentrated?

3. **Critical Thinking** **Predicting Consequences** What economic activities would you expect to gain in importance as more of Africa's population is concentrated in cities?

REGIONAL ATLAS

Africa: ECONOMIC ACTIVITIES AND RESOURCES

KEY

Nomadic herding	Iron
Hunting and gathering	Copper
Livestock raising	Bauxite
Commercial farming	Gold
Subsistence farming	Silver
Manufacturing and trade	Diamonds
Commercial fishing	Phosphates
Little or no activity	Uranium
Coal	Tin
Petroleum	Lead
Hydroelectric power	Tungsten

Lambert Azimuthal Equal-Area Projection

Take It to the NET
Enrichment To learn more about the economic activities and resources of this region, visit the World Geography section of **www.phschool.com**.

The Global Economy

Hydropower The interior plateau from which rivers plunge to the coast offers Africa great hydroelectric power. Hydroelectric power is a potentially cheap, renewable source of energy. It does not pollute the air, and it eliminates the need to import expensive oil. For example, Egypt's Aswan High Dam, finished in 1970, harnessed the power of the Nile River to produce 10 billion kilowatt-hours of electricity annually.

ACTIVITY

Reteach

Making a Chart To help students understand the economic challenges facing Africa, have them create cause-and-effect charts. Make a three-column chart on the board. Label the columns *Issues, Causes,* and *Effects*. In the first column, list the following statements: *(1) Farmers cannot grow enough food. (2) Many nations depend on the export of raw materials. (3) Some nations have large foreign debts. (4) In many parts of Africa water is scarce.* Have students copy and complete the chart by identifying causes and effects of each issue. (Visual/Spatial)

GLOBAL CONNECTIONS

Natural Resources

Africa's Mineral Wealth In some ways, Africa is the world's mineral storehouse. North and West Africa produce large amounts of petroleum and petroleum products. The mines of Central and South Africa supply nearly all of the gems and industrial diamonds used worldwide. A number of African countries also provide rare minerals such as radium, uranium, cobalt, and titanium. While most of the continent's abundant natural resources are developed by large multinational organizations, African nations are slowly gaining control of the production and export of their own mineral wealth.

Database:
Comparing Populations
pp. 518–519

Objectives
Upon completion of this lesson, students should be able to:
- define population density;
- compare the population densities of select African countries and the United States.

National Geography Standards
The following National Geography Standards are highlighted in this feature: 1, 4, 9, 12, 18

Bellringer
Read the definition of *population density* to the class. Remind students that many African nations are struggling with civil war, disease, and malnutrition. Ask: **How would any of these factors affect the population density of a nation?** (Population density would decrease.)

....

LESSON PLAN

1. Focus After students read the introductory paragraph, ask: **Which category on the population tables explains how many people are in each country?** (Total Population) **Which categories explain where people live in each country?** (Urban and Rural Population) **Which categories show trends in populations?** (Growth Rate, Doubling Time, Projections)

2. Instruct On the board, write the eight categories that the charts in the Regional Database use. Under each category, have students list the countries in order from highest to lowest.

3. Close/Reteach Discuss which of the statistics for the United States are similar to those of any of the African nations. Then compare statistics to see how these nations differ.

Some parts of Africa have rapidly growing populations, while other parts are gaining people much more slowly. Across much of Africa, birthrates are high, often because a large family can provide a safety net against poverty. In some parts of Africa, though, high death rates from diseases such as AIDS may cancel out high birthrates. Most Africans live in the countryside; but, in many countries, urban populations are rising faster than rural populations. Rural poverty drives many people to seek work in increasingly overcrowded cities.

Source: *Microsoft Encarta Interactive World Atlas*

Key Term: **population density**

GET THE FACTS . . .
Go to the Table of Countries at the back of this book to view additional data for the countries of Africa.

Take It to the NET
Data Update For the most recent update of this database, visit the World Geography section of **www.phschool.com**.

Egypt

Total Population	74,718,797
Population Density	194 people per sq mi
Population Growth Rate	1.88%
Population Projection, 2025	103,352,882
Population Projection, 2050	126,920,512
Urban Population	43%
Rural Population	57%

Egypt's population is heavily concentrated in the life-giving Nile River valley and delta, which contain more than 98% of the country's population in about 3% of the area. There, the **population density** (average number of people in a given unit of area) is more than 3,000 people per square mile. The rest of Egypt is mostly desert and lacks water to support a large population. Egypt's rapid population growth threatens the Nile River valley and delta with severe overcrowding and a risk of food shortages. Many rural Egyptians are moving to cities such as Cairo.

Nigeria

Total Population	133,881,700
Population Density	375 people per sq mi
Population Growth Rate	2.52%
Population Projection, 2025	206,397,510
Population Projection, 2050	307,420,055
Urban Population	45%
Rural Population	55%

Nigeria also faces the challenge of high population density and rapid population growth. However, population is less concentrated than in Egypt, and overcrowding is less of a danger to the economy and the environment. Although more than 50% of Nigerians still live in rural areas, the population of cities such as Lagos is rising quickly.

518 Chapter 24 ▪ Regional Atlas: Africa

RESOURCE DIRECTORY

Teaching Resources
Unit 7, Chapter 24
- Regional Atlas Review, p. 3
- Regional Atlas Database Skills, p. 4
- Test Forms A and B, pp. 5–10

Spanish Resources
- Regional Atlas Review, p. 61

Guide to the Essentials (English/Spanish)
- Chapter 24 Test

Mental Mapping booklet
- Chapter 24 Map Test, p. 95

Simulations, Games, and Lab Activities
- Place Location Review Games, pp. 58–63

Social Studies Skills Handbook
- Study and Research Skills, pp. 94–108

Prentice Hall Assessment System
Alternative Assessment booklet
- Map Evaluation Form, p. 15

Technology
ExamView Test Bank CD-ROM, Chapter 24 Test
Companion Web site, www.phschool.com
- Chapter 24 Self-Test

Mozambique

Total Population	17,479,266
Population Density	57 people per sq mi
Population Growth Rate	0.82%
Population Projection, 2025	17,496,393
Population Projection, 2050	19,010,691
Urban Population	33%
Rural Population	67%

Mozambique's population growth rate has slowed in recent years, and the country has a low population density. Almost two-thirds of its population is rural. For many years, civil wars limited population growth. More recently, the AIDS epidemic has begun to slow population growth. According to United Nations (UN) projections, deaths from AIDS will keep Mozambique's population from growing quickly.

South Africa

Total Population	42,768,678
Population Density	91 people per sq mi
Population Growth Rate	0.01%
Population Projection, 2025	34,045,336
Population Projection, 2050	30,955,486
Urban Population	58%
Rural Population	42%

South Africa is the most economically developed and most urbanized of these four countries. Partly as a result, the birthrate and population growth rate are lower. AIDS is an extremely serious problem here, and UN projections actually show South Africa's population decreasing by millions over the next several decades because of deaths from AIDS.

ASSESSMENT

1. **Key Term** Define population density.

2. **Population Growth** List at least three circumstances that tend to limit population growth in Africa.

3. **Urbanization** If current trends continue, would you expect Africa's population to be mostly rural or mostly urban in the future?

4. **Critical Thinking Analyzing Causes and Effects** How might continued urbanization affect the Nile River valley and delta?

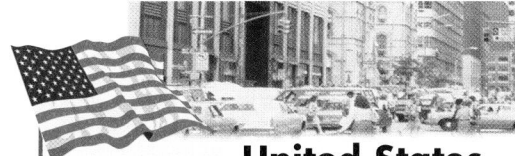

United States

Total Population	290,342,550
Population Density	78 people per sq mi
Population Growth Rate	0.92%
Population Projection, 2025	349,666,199
Population Projection, 2050	420,080,587
Urban Population	77%
Rural Population	23%

Chapter 24 ▪ Regional Atlas: Africa **519**

MENTAL MAPPING

Games for Review See pages 58–63 of the Simulations, Games, and Lab Activities booklet in the Teaching Resources for games to review place names in preparation for the Chapter 24 Map Test.

Chapter Map Test Students should use the completed outline maps and the Unit 7 Checklist in their Atlas Portfolios to prepare for the Chapter 24 Map Test. Point out to students that the test will cover all of the countries, cities, bodies of water, and landforms listed on the Unit 7 Checklist.

 Alternative Assessment

Final Evaluation

Making Maps Use the Map Evaluation Form on page 15 of the Alternative Assessment booklet in the Prentice Hall Assessment System to evaluate students' maps.

Answers to Assessment

1. population density, p. 518

2. Possible answers: food shortages, water shortages, civil wars, AIDS

3. mostly urban

4. Continued urbanization will create severe overcrowding and a risk of food shortages in the Nile River valley and delta.

Do-It-Yourself Skills

pp. 520–521

Objectives

Upon completion of this feature, students should be able to:
- explain the purpose of a diagram;
- follow a step-by-step process to create a diagram.

National Geography Standards

The following National Geography Standards are highlighted in this feature: 1, 2, 4, 7

Bellringer

Draw a diagram of a baseball diamond on the board. Ask students to identify for which sport a coach might use this diagram. Then have students identify what information the coach might include on it. (location of players and directions each should move) Have students explain the value to players of a diagram such as this.

LESSON PLAN

1. Focus Have students examine the diagram of irrigation on this page. Ask them to explain in their own words how qanat irrigation works. Ask: **How does a diagram like this help you understand a process?**

2. Instruct As students read the information in the tinted box on the opposite page, have them identify sentences that help them visualize how an oasis is formed. Then work with them to complete the diagram. When they finish, have them use the diagram to explain how an oasis forms.

3. Close/Reteach Ask students to locate another diagram in their textbook and explain in their own words the process it illustrates.

Do-It-Yourself Skills

Making Diagrams

What Is a Diagram?

A diagram is a visual representation of how something works. Diagrams help you to understand a process by outlining its parts. They also make it easier to understand corresponding data that are often difficult, complicated, or highly technical.

Qanat Irrigation

The wells are used as ventilation and repair shafts as well as to draw water.

Rainwater runs down and seeps into the ground.

The water flows along an underground channel, or qanat, that slopes gently downward.

A series of wells are used to dig the qanat and then to draw water from it.

A settlement often grows up near the mouth of a qanat.

How Can I Use This Skill?

Diagrams often can be found in instructional manuals, technical textbooks, and how-to guidebooks. They are used to explain processes that often are too complicated to understand without the aid of a visual. For example, when you take a driver's education course, your driver's manual will utilize diagrams to teach you the rules and regulations of driving.

Step by Step

Follow these steps to make a diagram. As you proceed, use the diagram of qanat irrigation above as a model.

 Select the data that you will need for your diagram. For this lesson, you are going to diagram the formation of an oasis.

RESOURCE DIRECTORY

Teaching Resources
Social Studies Skills Handbook
- Reading a Diagram, p. 56

Technology
Social Studies Skills Tutor CD-ROM, Sequencing

Find and collect data from a reliable source. An almanac and an atlas are examples of reliable sources. The data used in this lesson (right) came from a geographic atlas of the world.

Study the data and sketch a mental image. While you read, sketch a mental image of the data. Then, draw a diagram of the data. For this lesson, the diagram below is provided for you.

Provide a title and identify labels for your diagram. A label should be created for every step in the process. For example, a label should mark the location of rainfall, because this precipitation is a key step in the formation of an oasis.

Add leader lines to your diagram. A leader line is a dash that guides the eyes across a page. On your diagram, draw leader lines from the labels to the related parts of the image so that the information will be clear to a reader.

Sequence your diagram. Add numbers to your labels to show the order of events.

Analyze your diagram. Diagrams can help you to draw conclusions about why an event occurred. For example, by understanding how an oasis is formed, you can conclude why a community might arise in that area.

Oasis Formation

An oasis, due to the presence of a water source, is a fertile place in a desert. An oasis is formed by water from far away. Rain seeps underground and flows through an aquifer, or porous rock that holds water, to low places in the desert. The water cannot rise above or sink below the aquifer because it is blocked by impermeable rock. However, if there is a fault, or crack, in the earth's surface, then water can flow up the fault to form an oasis. An oasis provides nutrients for vegetation to grow. As a result, people and wildlife often live near oases.

TIP

Reading Diagrams

Diagrams can be complicated. Therefore, read the diagram more than once. Read first for a general outline of the process. Then, read again for details. Finally, redraw the diagram from memory to test whether or not you understand the process.

APPLY YOUR SKILL

Select another topic to diagram. You may choose something that you already know how to do, such as how to use the Internet, or you may find data from an encyclopedia or another reference work. Create a diagram for your topic. Then, summarize your diagram in a short paragraph.

Connecting With Science

Diagram of a Tool Have students create a diagram of equipment they have used or made in science classes, such as a microscope or an eclipse viewer. Have them use the diagram to explain how the equipment works.

Answers to Apply Your Skill

Check students' diagrams for clarity. Students' summaries will depend on the topic of their diagram.

CUSTOMIZE FOR...

Less Proficient Writers

Location Words As students read the information in the tinted box, help them identify words and phrases that describe location: *far away, underground, through an aquifer, low places in the desert.* Tell them that these words gave important clues to the person who designed the diagram on this page. Remind students that it is helpful to pay attention to words that indicate *where* as they draw their diagrams.

Resource Manager

Chapter-Level Resources	CORE INSTRUCTION	READING/SKILLS
	📗 Teaching Resources 📘 **Unit 7**/Ch. 25 • Reviewing Main Ideas, p. 15 📖 **Mental Mapping booklet** • Unit 7 Checklist, p. 91 📖 **Simulations, Games, and Lab Activities** • Place Location Review Games, pp. 58–63 💿 **TeacherExpress™ CD-ROM**, Ch. 25 💻 **Companion Web site,** **www.phschool.com** • eTeach	📗 Teaching Resources 📘 **Unit 7**/Ch. 25 • Map/Graph Skills, p. 17 📖 **Mental Mapping booklet** • Outline Map 25, p. 96 💿 **Book on CD**, Ch. 25 💿 **Social Studies Skills Tutor CD-ROM**
1 Egypt 1. Describe how physical characteristics influence patterns of settlement in Egypt. 2. Identify how Egypt's past has influenced its culture. 3. Explain how efforts to control the Nile River have affected agriculture in Egypt. 4. List the factors that influence economic activities in Egypt.	📗 Teaching Resources 📘 **Unit 7**/Ch. 25 • Guided Reading and Review, p. 11 📖 **Creative Teaching Activities** • Who Controls the Water?, p. 27 💿 **Prentice Hall Presentation Pro CD-ROM**, Ch. 25, Sec. 1	📗 Teaching Resources 📖 **Guide to the Essentials (English/Spanish)** • Section Summary, Ch. 25, Sec. 1 📖 **Social Studies Skills Handbook** • Asking Questions While You Read, p. 70 • Connecting Content to What You Already Know, p. 71 📼 **Guided Reading Audiotapes (English/Spanish)**, Ch. 25, Sec. 1 📑 **Section Reading Support Transparencies**, Ch. 25, Sec. 1
2 Libya and the Maghreb 1. Explain how physical characteristics and changing perceptions of geography have affected cultures in Libya and the Maghreb. 2. Describe how cooperation and conflict have led to cultural change in North Africa. 3. Identify the main settlement patterns in North Africa. 4. Describe how ideas of government and citizenship vary among North African nations.	📗 Teaching Resources 📘 **Unit 7**/Ch. 25 • Guided Reading and Review, p. 13 💿 **Prentice Hall Presentation Pro CD-ROM**, Ch. 25, Sec. 2	📗 Teaching Resources 📖 **Guide to the Essentials (English/Spanish)** • Section Summary, Ch. 25, Sec. 2 📖 **Social Studies Skills Handbook** • Reading a Time Zone Map, p. 24 📼 **Guided Reading Audiotapes (English/Spanish)**, Ch. 25, Sec. 2 📑 **Section Reading Support Transparencies**, Ch. 25, Sec. 2

ENRICHMENT/HONORS/PREAP

📗 **Teaching Resources**

📂 Unit 7/Ch. 25
- Critical Thinking, p. 16

📘 **Mental Mapping booklet**
- Atlas Activity, p. 97

📘 **Social Studies Skills Handbook**
- Study and Research Skills, pp. 94–108

📖 **World Geography Map and Photo Transparencies**
- Africa: Maps and Photos

📀 **World Geography Videos**
- Human-Environment Interaction: North Africa, Tape 3

💻 **Companion Web site, www.phschool.com**
- Chapter 25 Activities

📗 **Teaching Resources**

📘 **Social Studies Skills Handbook**
- Recognizing Bias, p. 47

💻 **Companion Web site, www.phschool.com**
- Chapter 25 Activities

💻 **Companion Web site, www.phschool.com**
- Chapter 25 Activities

ASSESSMENT

PRENTICE HALL
ASSESSMENT SYSTEM

Core Assessment

📘 ExamView Test Bank booklet, Ch. 25

💿 ExamView Test Bank CD-ROM, Ch. 25

Standardized Test Preparation

Review and Reteach

📘 Review Book for World Geography, pp. 15–16

Practice and Assess

📘 Test-taking Strategies With Transparencies for High School

Test-taking Strategy Poster

📘 Alternative Assessment booklet

📘 Test Prep Book for World Geography

📗 **Teaching Resources**

📂 Unit 7/Ch. 25
- Section Quizzes, pp. 12, 14
- Test Forms A and B, pp. 18–23

📘 **Guide to the Essentials (English/Spanish)**
- Chapter 25 Test

📘 **Spanish Resources**, Ch. 25
- Section Quizzes, pp. 62–63

📘 **Mental Mapping booklet**
- Chapter 25 Map Test, p. 98

💻 **Companion Web site, www.phschool.com**
- Chapter 25 Self-Test

CUSTOMIZE FOR INDIVIDUAL NEEDS

Honors/PreAP
- Teacher's Edition, Customize for . . . , p. 535

Less Proficient Readers
- Guide to the Essentials (English), Ch. 25, Section Summaries
- Guided Reading Audiotapes (English), Ch. 25
- Section Reading Support Transparencies, Ch. 25
- Book on CD, Ch. 25
- Teacher's Edition, Reading Strategy, pp. 527, 536
- Teacher's Edition, Activity: Vocabulary, pp. 524, 527, 534

Students Acquiring English/ESL
- Guide to the Essentials (English/Spanish), Ch. 25
- Guided Reading Audiotapes (English/Spanish), Ch. 25
- Section Reading Support Transparencies, Ch. 25
- Book on CD, Ch. 25
- Teacher's Edition, Customize for . . . , p. 527

Less Proficient Writers
- Alternative Assessment, Writing Assignment Rubric, p. 6

MENTAL MAPPING

Point out that North Africa includes five countries south of the Mediterranean Sea on the northern edge of the African continent. Have students name these five countries. (Egypt, Libya, Tunisia, Algeria, and Morocco) Ask: **Which are the three largest countries in the group?** (Egypt, Algeria, and Libya) **Which are the two smallest?** (Morocco and Tunisia)

Mapping the Region Have students study the map on this page. Then ask them to close their books and draw a sketch map of North Africa. Sketches should include labels for countries, capital cities, other major cities, and major bodies of water. Students needing extra assistance may label outline maps of North Africa. A Chapter 25 Outline Map can be found on page 96 of the Mental Mapping booklet in the Teaching Resources. Students should keep their maps in their Atlas Portfolios in order to prepare for the Chapter 25 Map Test.

eTeach

Be sure to check out this month's online forum with a Master Teacher to join in an exchange of teaching ideas. **www.phschool.com**

C H A P T E R

25

North Africa

SECTIONS

1 Egypt

2 Libya and the Maghreb

North Africa: POLITICAL

KEY

—— National boundary

⊛ National capital

• Other city

Lambert Azimuthal Equal-Area Projection

0   300   600 mi

0   300   600 km

Go Online
PHSchool.com

For: More information about North Africa and access to the Take It to the Net activities
Visit: phschool.com
Web Code: mjk-0026

RESOURCE DIRECTORY

Teaching Resources
Unit 7, Chapter 25
• Section 1 Guided Reading and Review, p. 11
Guide to the Essentials (English/Spanish)
• Section Summary, Chapter 25, Section 1
Mental Mapping booklet
• Atlas Activity, p. 97
• Unit 7 Checklist, p. 91

Technology
Guided Reading Audiotapes (English/Spanish),
Chapter 25, Section 1

Section Reading Support Transparencies,
Chapter 25, Section 1
World Geography Map and Photo Transparencies
• Africa: Maps and Photos
Book on CD, Chapter 25
World Geography Videos
• Human-Environment Interaction: North Africa, Tape 3
TeacherExpress™ CD-ROM, Chapter 25
Prentice Hall Presentation Pro CD-ROM, Chapter 25
Social Studies Skills Tutor CD-ROM
Companion Web site, www.phschool.com
• Chapter 25 Activities

1 Egypt

Reading Focus

- How do physical characteristics influence patterns of settlement in Egypt?
- How has Egypt's past influenced its culture?
- How have efforts to control the Nile River affected agriculture in Egypt?
- What factors influence economic activities in Egypt?

Key Terms

delta	basin irrigation
fellaheen	reservoir
sandstorm	perennial irrigation
bazaar	capital

Main Idea The Nile River, Muslim culture, and urbanization have helped form the distinctive character of modern Egypt.

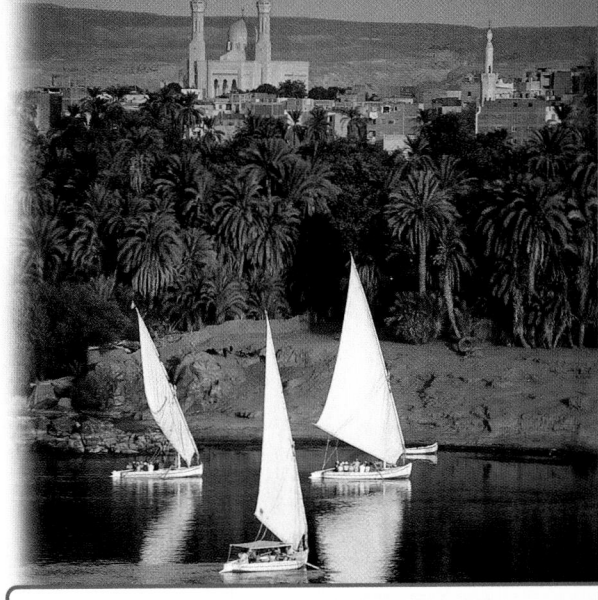
Cultures The Nile River valley is home to one of the world's oldest civilizations.

As the map on page 524 shows, the Arab nation of Egypt has a vital location: the northeast corner of Africa, where travelers and goods pass between two continents. It is large—about one-and-a-half times the size of Texas. It is also one of the most populous countries in the Arab world. These three factors—strategic location, size, and population—make Egypt a power to be respected in world affairs.

Physical Characteristics

Egypt is a land of wide, forbidding deserts divided by a single large river, the Nile. Without that river, all of Egypt would be desert. For this reason, Egypt is sometimes referred to as the Gift of the Nile.

The Nile River The Nile is the world's longest river. It begins in Central Africa and flows northward for 4,160 miles (6,695 km) before it empties into the Mediterranean Sea. On its way, it runs through Egypt from south to north.

As it nears the end of its course, the Nile forks into two major branches. Between these two branches is an area known as the Nile Delta. A **delta** is land formed by soil in the water that is

dropped as the river slows and enters the sea. The delta, which has been enriched by the Nile for centuries, is astoundingly fertile. The **fellaheen,** as Egyptian peasants are called, grow impressive crops without the aid of modern machinery. Like other Egyptian farmers, they rarely even use plows. With a population of 68 million people, Egypt relies on human labor rather than on machines to farm.

About 99 percent of Egypt's people live either in the Nile Valley or the delta region. Along the Nile's cultivated banks, population density averages about 2,700 people per square mile (1,100 per sq km). Egypt's two largest cities are Cairo, the capital, which straddles the Nile, and Alexandria, a major seaport and resort on the Mediterranean Sea.

The Desert Regions On either side of the Nile Valley are harsh wastelands. On the west is the Libyan Desert. On the east is a continuation of the Arabian Desert. The Sinai (SY ny) Peninsula, located in Asia to the east of the Suez Canal, is part of Egypt's eastern desert region.

Strong winds blow constantly across the Sahara. In the early summer a special wind, known

◄ **Great Pyramids at Giza, Egypt** *(photo left)*

Objectives

Upon completion of Section 1, students should be able to:

◆ describe how physical characteristics influence patterns of settlement in Egypt;

◆ identify how Egypt's past has influenced its culture;

◆ explain how efforts to control the Nile River have affected agriculture in Egypt;

◆ list the factors that influence economic activities in Egypt.

National Geography Standards

The following National Geography Standards are highlighted in this section: 1, 3, 4, 5, 6, 7, 8, 9, 10, 11, 12, 13, 14, 15, 16, 17

Bellringer

Tell students that Egyptian civilization is one of the oldest in the world. Have students guess its age. (between 5,000 and 7,000 years old)

LESSON PLAN

1. Focus Point out to students that 99 percent of Egypt's people live in the Nile Valley or the delta region. Population density along the Nile averages 2,700 people per square mile. Ask students to imagine what impact this population density must have on daily life, city infrastructures, and the environment.

2. Instruct Write these phrases on the board: *population growth, urbanization, agricultural production, lack of skilled workers, lack of capital.* Have students look for relationships between these factors and Egypt's economic development. Then have students write one sentence for each factor, explaining how it impacts modern Egypt.

3. Close/Reteach After students have read Section 1, instruct them to return to the list of Reading Focus questions on this page. Ask them to answer the questions based on what they have read.

TEACHING TIP
From A Master Teacher

Resources Across North Africa, two resources have played key roles in shaping geography: water and oil. Since ancient times, population distribution has mirrored the availability of water. In modern times, the presence of oil reserves has influenced the power, economic development, and prosperity of North African nations. Resources can change in importance over time. Oil has replaced cotton as Egypt's leading export just as salt and slaves are no longer valued trade items in the deserts of North Africa.

Pacing Suggestions

 For 90-minute Blocks

You will want to vary activities.

- Use the Creative Teaching Activity for Chapter 25 as the basis for a 90-minute lesson. After students have completed the activity, direct them to write a two or three paragraph essay based on the panel discussion. Students' essays should show an understanding of the five different points of view expressed by the panel members. Ask volunteers to read their essays to the class.

Vocabulary

Bazaar Point out the Key Terms list on page 523. Have students find the definition of *bazaar* in the Glossary or dictionary. Then ask: **What kinds of items do you think you might find in an Arab bazaar?** (rugs, hand-woven baskets or scarves, jewelry, various kinds of food)

Alternative Assessment

Introduce the Activity

Constructing a Time Line Ask students to use their text as well as outside sources to construct a time line showing North Africa's history. Distribute the Time Line Rubric found on page 12 of the Alternative Assessment booklet in the Prentice Hall Assessment System for students' reference during the project.

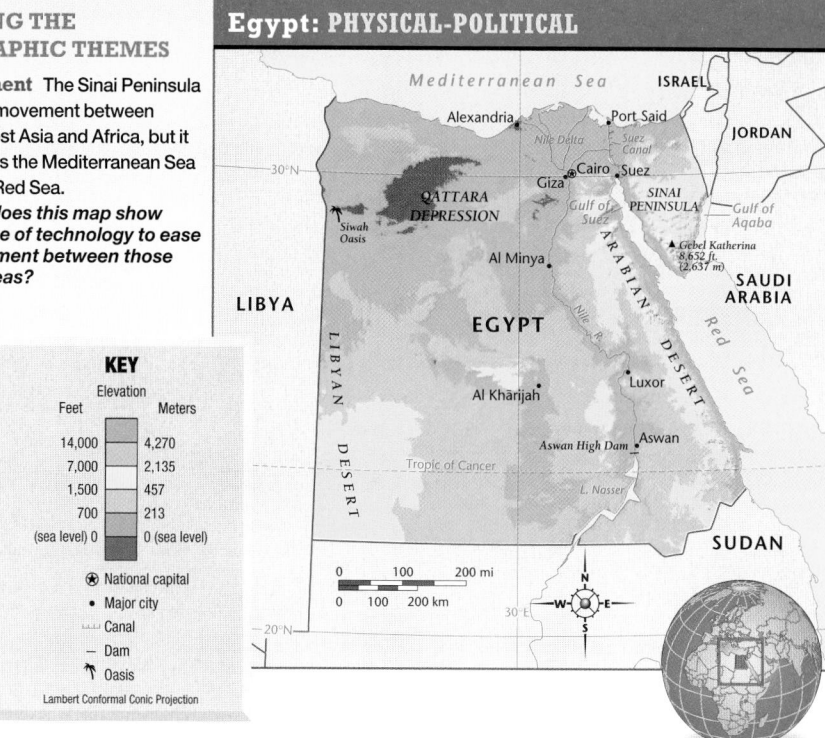

APPLYING THE GEOGRAPHIC THEMES

● **Movement** The Sinai Peninsula permits movement between Southwest Asia and Africa, but it separates the Mediterranean Sea and the Red Sea.

- *How does this map show the use of technology to ease movement between those two seas?*

Egypt: PHYSICAL-POLITICAL

KEY

Elevation

Feet		Meters
14,000		4,270
7,000		2,135
1,500		457
700		213
(sea level) 0		0 (sea level)

⍟ National capital
• Major city
⊔⊔ Canal
— Dam
↷ Oasis

Lambert Conformal Conic Projection

---

in Egypt as the *khamsin* (kam SEEN), creates **sandstorms** that blow hot air, dust, and grit into the Nile Valley. In bad years the *khamsin* blows so hard that the Egyptian sky turns orange with flying sand.

Oases, due to the presence of water, are the only arable land in the desert. But the desert does hold some resources. Phosphates, for example, which are used to make fertilizer, are extracted from the desert, as is some oil.

Patterns of Settlement

Over half of Egypt's population lives in rural areas. Yet, Egypt's urban areas have grown in recent decades, as more and more people have moved from rural villages to cities.

In some respects, village life in Egypt has remained unchanged for hundreds of years. The fellaheen live in small, low houses made of sun-dried mud bricks. These houses are often formed of rooms clustered around a central courtyard. If rural families can afford to, they keep domestic animals, such as chickens, goats, and donkeys, which provide food and transportation.

Life in the cities, however, has changed rapidly in recent times. After all, Cairo and Alexandria offer millions of people opportunities for jobs, schooling, culture, and entertainment. These opportunities constantly attract people from rural communities. Unfortunately, the cities cannot comfortably hold all the people who move to them. New arrivals from the countryside are often unable to find jobs or housing. Unwilling to return to their villages, they live in tents and other makeshift shelters. Cairo in particular has become a striking blend of new and old, rich and poor. Only blocks away from modern department stores that display the latest Paris fashions are the traditional Arab open-air markets, or **bazaars.**

Understanding the Past

Cities and their attractions have been a part of Egyptian life for well over 5,000 years. The civilization of the ancient Egyptians was unique and

---

RESOURCE DIRECTORY

Teaching Resources

Mental Mapping booklet
- Outline Map, p. 96

Social Studies Skills Handbook
- Recognizing Bias, p. 47
- Asking Questions While You Read, p. 70
- Connecting Content to What You Already Know, p. 71

Prentice Hall Assessment System

Alternative Assessment booklet
- Time Line Rubric, p. 12

Technology

World Geography Map and Photo Transparencies
- Africa: Maps and Photos

Answer to Map Caption

The Suez Canal was created to connect the two seas.

long-lasting. They were among the first people in the world to set up an organized government and religion and to invent a written language.

Ancient Egypt Among the accomplishments of the ancient Egyptians was the building of the world-famous pyramids, southwest of Cairo. The pyramids were built as tombs for the pharaohs, the rulers of ancient Egypt. Egyptians believed that a person's spirit might need to return to its body after death. Therefore, they preserved the bodies of the pharaohs in a process known as mummification. Egyptians also believed that a person's spirit might need nourishment and assistance in the afterlife. They placed many useful objects, including food, furniture, jewelry, and gold in the pharaohs' tombs.

Cultural Change The location of this rich kingdom at the crossroads of Asia, Africa, and Europe made it a tempting target for waves of invaders. Over the centuries, Egypt was ruled by Greek conquerors as well as by Roman conquerors. They brought the Greek language and Roman customs to the ancient land.

When the Arabs conquered Egypt in A.D. 642, Arabic became Egypt's official language and Islam its official religion. Today, more than 90 percent of Egyptians are Muslims. Most of the remaining minority are Copts, a very old Christian sect.

For more than one thousand years Egypt was ruled as part of various Muslim empires. The last of these was that of the Ottoman Turks.

European Interventions By the late 1700s, the Ottoman Turks' power was in decline, and European nations began to intervene in Egyptian affairs. The Suez Canal, which linked the Mediterranean and Red seas, opened in 1869 and made Egypt a vital link between Britain and its eastern colonies in Asia. In 1875, when Egypt's ruler faced heavy debts, Great Britain gladly purchased Egypt's share of ownership in the Suez Canal.

In 1879 Egyptian nationalists revolted, determined to regain control of the canal. Nationalists are people who want to form an independent nation to protect their common culture and interests. Britain responded by invading Egypt and defeating the new government in 1882. British troops remained in Egypt for decades.

Following World War I, Egyptian nationalists again pushed for independence. In 1922 Britain agreed to their demands. But, in effect,

Egyptian Agriculture

Science and Technology For many people in Egypt, daily life is a blend of ancient tradition (bottom) and modern technology. At right, a farmer uses a centuries-old method to thresh lentils, while in the distance power lines carry electricity.

Place *Would you expect to find this agricultural technique in a country that invests heavily in technology? Explain.*

Critical Thinking

Cause and Effect Use the following questions to help students see the link between Britain's occupation of Egypt and Egypt's economic development: **How did growing cotton for Great Britain affect Egypt and its agriculture?** (Egypt became dependent on a single cash crop, cotton, and cultivated this crop instead of growing food for its increasing population.) **How did British rule affect Egypt's modern development?** (British rule delayed Egypt's development because Britain did nothing to improve education or create new industries, both of which were important for Egypt's smooth entry into the modern world.)

BACKGROUND

The Global Economy

The Suez Canal The Suez Canal, separating Asia from Africa, extends for about 105 miles (168 kilometers). It provides the shortest maritime route between Europe and the Indian and western Pacific oceans. The canal reduces the 12,400-mile (19,950-km) journey between London and Bombay to 7,250 miles (11,670 km).

ACTIVITY

Connecting With . . .

History Have students read a biography of the Egyptian leader Gamal Abdel Nasser and give a brief report that addresses this question: What were Nasser's main beliefs, accomplishments, and failures?

GLOBAL CONNECTIONS

Economic Activities Cotton, Egypt's most valuable cash crop, is the world's most popular natural fiber. Although China and the United States are the two major cotton-producing countries, Egypt is the chief producer of long-staple cotton. This cotton is prized for its long fibers, which make it strong and durable. American farmers began using Egyptian plants about 100 years ago. Today, American-Egyptian cotton, a hybrid, is grown extensively in the United States.

the British continued to control Egypt, and Egyptian rulers had little power.

Independent Egypt In 1952 a group of nationalist army officers overthrew the government of Egypt. Colonel Gamal Abdel Nasser emerged as the new ruler. Nasser was determined to end Western domination of Egypt, modernize the country, and make it a major influence in world politics.

In 1956 Nasser seized control of the Suez Canal, creating an international crisis. Israel, Britain, and France jointly invaded Egypt in an attempt to retake the waterway. Both the United States and the Soviet Union supported a United Nations resolution demanding a cease-fire and the withdrawal of outside forces from Egyptian territory. This action forced the Western nations

to call off the attack. Nasser held the canal, and the British left Egypt in 1957. For the first time in more than two thousand years, Egypt was ruled solely by Egyptians.

Nasser formed close ties with the Soviet Union, the major Communist nation at that time. Helped by Soviet money and experts, the Egyptians implemented Nasser's many modernization projects. Under Nasser, industry was developed, and Egypt's dependence on cotton, its main export crop, was reduced.

When Nasser died in 1970, Anwar Sadat became president of Egypt. Sadat ended Egypt's alliance with the Soviet Union and forged new ties with the West.

Cooperation and Conflict After World War II, Egypt developed closer links with the Arab Middle East. The main cause of this trend was the establishment of the state of Israel in 1948. The Arabs were united in their opposition to the existence of Israel. Egypt took a major role in the 1948, 1967, and 1973 wars with Israel but suffered defeat in all three. In 1967 it lost control of the Sinai Peninsula to Israel.

When Egypt was defeated for the third time in 1973, Sadat decided to seek a permanent peace with Israel. In 1979 Egypt became the first Arab

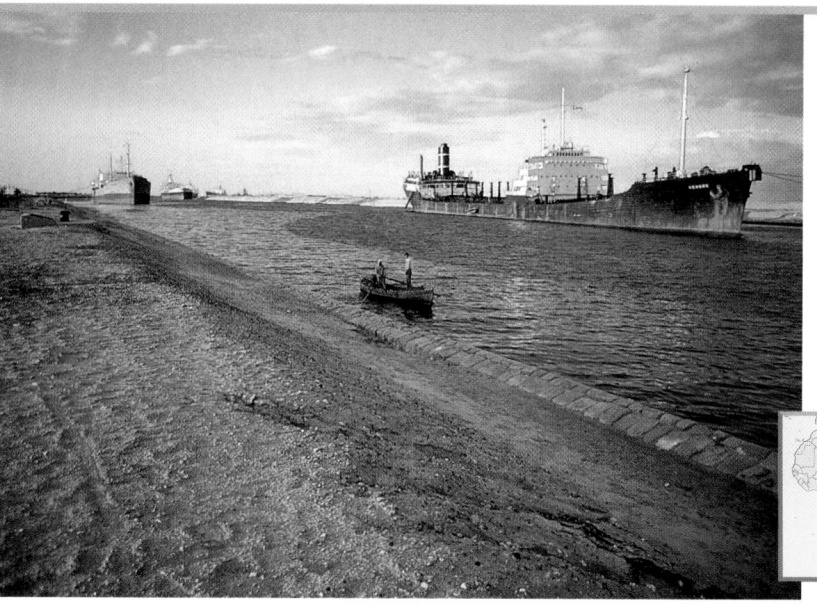

Suez Canal

Science and Technology Huge tankers and tiny rowboats share the Suez Canal. Completed in 1869, the canal links the Mediterranean and Red seas and is controlled by Egypt.

Location *Why do you think countries were willing to go to war over control of the Suez Canal in 1956?*

RESOURCE DIRECTORY

Teaching Resources
Creative Teaching Activities, Who Controls the Water?, p. 27

Answer to Photo Caption

The location of the Suez Canal made it important to world trade. Britain wanted to maintain its influence in Egypt by controlling the canal.

Aswan High Dam

Environmental Change
The building of the Aswan High Dam (at left of photo) created a giant reservoir, named Lake Nasser. Water from the reservoir is used to irrigate Egypt's farmland, which no longer receives yearly floods from the Nile.

Human-Environment Interaction *How does the Aswan High Dam illustrate the costs and benefits of changing the environment?*

nation to recognize Israel's right to exist. In return, Israel agreed to return the Sinai Peninsula to Egypt by 1982.

Sadat's peace treaty with Israel was harshly criticized by other Arab nations, who believed that he had betrayed the Arab cause. In 1981 Sadat was assassinated. His successor, Hosni Mubarak, continues to honor the Egypt-Israeli peace treaty.

Controlling the Nile

Until recently, the Nile River flooded every year, refreshing the fields with water and silt that formed a rich, fertile soil. Egypt's farmers have long built walls around their fields to trap this water and silt. This form of irrigation, **basin irrigation,** was good for growing crops, but it did not work year-round. And it could not control heavy flooding, which often brought disaster.

During the 1960s, President Nasser undertook an enormous new water project. He started building a dam that would store Nile floodwaters in a vast **reservoir**—a natural or artificial lake used to store water for human needs. The waters of Lake Nasser, as the reservoir was called, would be the basis of a **perennial irrigation** system— one that provides water for agriculture all through the year. The reservoir could also be tapped to provide extra water for Cairo and to generate electricity for modern industries.

The Aswan High Dam was completed in 1970. It promptly ended flooding of the Nile and

permitted Egyptian farmers to plant two or three crops every year. Lake Nasser's irrigation water has also allowed more and more desert to be reclaimed for farming.

North Africa and the United States
Education Data

Country	Education Expenditure (as percentage of GNP)	Literacy Rate (percentage)	Students in Secondary School (percentage of age group)
Algeria	5.2	61.6	63.2
Egypt	5.6	51.4	75.3
Libya	7.1	76.2	99.7
Morocco	5.3	43.7	39.3
Tunisia	6.7	66.7	65.6
United States	5.3	99.5	97.3

Source: *Encarta World Atlas*

CHART SKILLS

● **Cultures** *Which North African nation has the highest literacy rate?*
● **Planning for the Future** *Does this table suggest a connection between literacy and school attendance? Explain.*

Activity: Designing a television documentary

Purpose: Tell the class that its job is to develop a television documentary about Egypt. Assign each group one of the following topics: population density and growth, village life, city life, ancient Egyptian civilization, the conquest of Egypt, Egypt since independence, economic strengths and challenges, and Egypt's role in the Arab world. Have each group use Chapter 25 and library resources to research its topic and write a documentary script. The script should include the narrator's comments as well as the visual images and sound effects that accompany it. Have several students compile the topics to make a single script.

Roles: Director, scriptwriters, narrators, and script compilers.

Result: The narrator for each group should read his or her group's part of the finished script to the class in the order determined by the script compilers.

The dam has also caused some problems. Floodwaters no longer carry silt to fertilize the land on the banks of the Nile. Farmers now are forced to use chemical fertilizers to make up for the lack of natural fertilization. Another problem caused by the dam is that perennial irrigation makes salt build up in the soil. Some 35 percent of Egyptian farmlands now suffer from a high salt content. Solving this new problem would involve installing huge drainage systems and would cost a great amount of money.

Economic Activities

As you have read, a key trend in Egypt today is urbanization—the movement of rural people to the nation's cities. For about the last forty years, the urban population has been growing at the rate of 4 percent annually. Cairo, for example, grew from 2.1 million in 1947 to more than 6.8 million in the mid-1990s.

Population Growth A second key trend is rapid population growth throughout the nation. Egypt's overall population is growing at an annual rate of 1.7 percent, lower than in previous years, but still faster than other countries in the Arab world. Feeding, housing, educating, and providing other services for this fast-growing population strain the economy. But stemming population growth is not easy. Many Egyptians need the labor and income of every member of their large families. They resist government efforts to limit family size.

One of the major problems of Egypt's population growth is that it is outstripping the country's food supply. In 1960 Egypt produced nearly all its own food. Today, it imports more than one half of the food its people eat. The fertile land along the Nile is already intensively farmed. The Egyptian government has plans to increase the amount of arable land by irrigating farther into the desert, but this land will not be as naturally fertile as the soil in the Nile River valley. Large amounts of money will have to be spent on chemical fertilizers.

Global Trade Patterns In the past, Egypt's economy depended on a single export: cotton. When international cotton prices were high, Egypt's economy prospered; when they fell, Egypt faced potential economic disaster. Now oil and petroleum products have taken first place among Egyptian exports.

This change has not solved Egypt's economic problems. The country is still dependent upon the export of raw materials rather than manufactured goods. Most experts agree that to prosper, Egypt

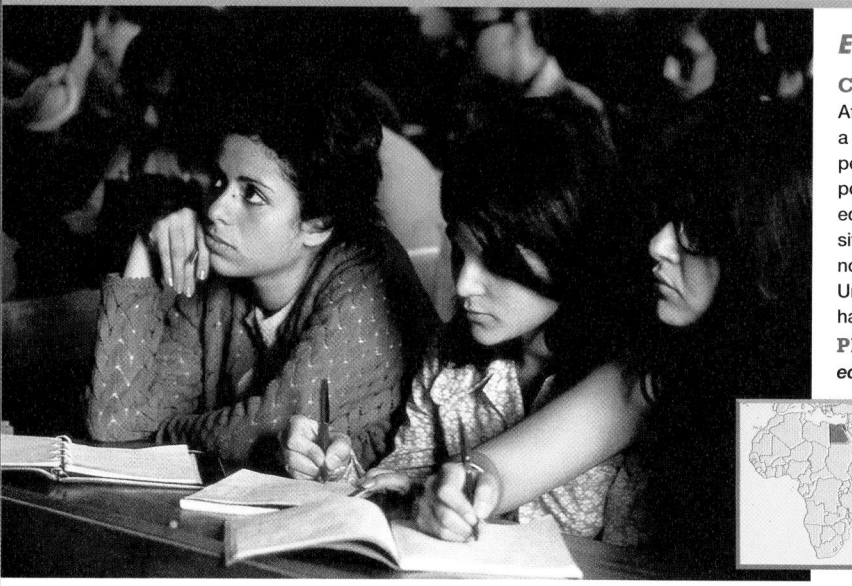

Egypt's Future

Cultures Like many African countries, Egypt has a large percentage of young people. To train this growing population, Egypt offers free education through the university level. Shown here taking notes are students at the University of Cairo, which has about 77,000 students.

Place *What will be the economic effect of educating present and future generations?*

Answer to Photo Caption

Possible answer: The cost of educating present and future generations may strain the economy. However, if Egypt can retain the people it educates, educating present and future generations will help Egypt's economy by strengthening its industry.

RESOURCE DIRECTORY

Teaching Resources
Unit 7, Chapter 25
• Section 1 Quiz, p. 12
Spanish Resources
• Section 1 Quiz, p. 62

Egypt's Major Imports

GRAPH SKILLS

- **Global Trade Patterns**
  Egypt's global trade is heavily dependent on machinery and equipment.
  - *What is the monetary value of Egyptian imports of base metals?*
  - *How might a major increase in the cost of imported machinery affect the Egyptian economy?*

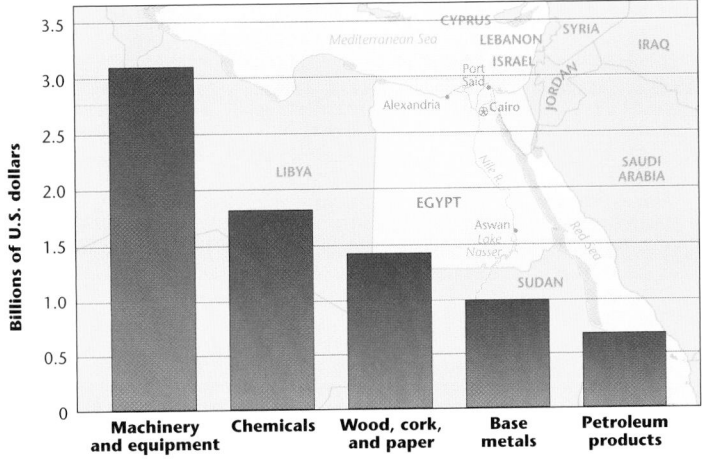

Source: Egypt State Information Service

needs an industrial base that will provide much-needed jobs and produce goods for sale abroad.

Obstacles to Development Efforts to promote industrialization began in the late 1950s and increased in the 1960s. But several factors have limited the growth of industries. One factor is the country's limited number of skilled workers. Although Egypt has the largest pool of educated people in the Arab world, it frequently loses these professionals to wealthier countries, where salaries are much higher.

A second major challenge facing Egypt is lack of **capital**—money that is invested in building and supporting new industries. Average annual per capita GDP in Egypt is about $1,250, compared with about $7,000 in Saudi Arabia or $33,900 in the United States. With relatively low incomes, few Egyptians have money left over, after paying for their basic needs of food and housing, to invest in new factories or industries. Lacking the oil reserves of some of its more fortunate neighbors, Egypt depends heavily on aid from Western and other Arab nations.

SECTION 1 ASSESSMENT

1. **Key Terms** Define **(a)** delta, **(b)** fellaheen, **(c)** sandstorm, **(d)** bazaar, **(e)** basin irrigation, **(f)** reservoir, **(g)** perennial irrigation, **(h)** capital.

2. **Patterns of Settlement** How do physical characteristics influence where people live in Egypt?

3. **Understanding the Past** How does Egypt's past influence modern culture?

4. **Environmental Change** What benefits and challenges have resulted from efforts to control the Nile?

5. **Economic Activities** How have recent changes in Egypt affected its economy?

6. **Critical Thinking Making Comparisons**
   Compare the flooding of the Nile in Egypt with the flooding of the Huang He in China. How are conditions in Egypt and China similar and different?

Activity

USING THE REGIONAL ATLAS

Review this section and the Regional Atlas for Africa. Suppose that you are an Egyptian government official. Develop a plan that would encourage economic development of Egypt's desert lands and reduce the population density along the Nile River.

Articles From NATIONAL GEOGRAPHIC

The following article may be used to extend the content in this section.

Theroux, Peter, and Reza, photographer. "The Imperiled Nile Delta." *National Geographic,* Vol. 191, No. 1 (Jan. 1997), pp. 2–35.
The Aswan Dam has created as many problems as it has solved. While it prevents flooding, the dam also blocks natural fertilizers from reaching the banks of the Nile.

TEST PREPARATION

Have students read Global Trade Patterns to answer the following question.
Which sentence best expresses the main idea of this subsection?

A Egypt has become extremely wealthy because of its petroleum resources.

B Egypt's dependence on the export of raw materials has kept its economy from prospering.

C Egypt's cotton industry provides jobs.

D Egypt's economy cannot thrive without an increased demand for cotton.

Teaching the Skill

Ask students to consider an important decision that they made at some point in the past year. Then have them look over the first four steps provided beneath Learn the Skill. Ask: **Did you use any of these steps in making your decision? If so, which ones? If not, how do you think using these steps might have helped you?** (Answers will vary.)

Answers to Learn the Skill

1. The Sphinx is crumbling away.
2. Pollution, wind, and humidity all wear away at the statue. Some repair attempts have caused further damage.
3. **(a)** Workers have replaced limestone blocks and injected chemicals into the stone. **(b)** Answers will vary. Archaeologists focus on draining seepage that damages the rock.
4. Answers will vary. Untrained workers have used methods that have proven ineffective in stemming the deterioration. The archaeologists' methods may be more successful.
5. **(a)** The Sphinx has continued to deteriorate. **(b)** Answers will vary, but students should be able to analyze the probable results of the options they have identified.

Answers to Practice the Skill

Students' proposals should be based on sound research into the issue and careful consideration of the possible options.

Making Decisions

Every day you have to make decisions, such as deciding what time to get up and what to eat for breakfast. Although most of your decisions are as routine as these, sometimes you face harder ones. A five-step process makes decision making easier, because it allows you to consider many aspects of the issue.

Learn the Skill Study the reading passage and the photograph below. Then, follow these steps to learn how to make informed decisions.

1. *Identify the issue.* Look carefully at the decision you are facing, and state the issue clearly. *What is the problem concerning the Sphinx in Egypt?*

2. *Gather information.* You cannot make an informed decision without an understanding of the issue and its origins. Research the problem and identify its causes. *What are the causes of the problem?*

3. *Identify options.* There is always more than one way to address an issue. Based on the information you have gathered, think of several possible courses of action. **(a)** *How have people tried to solve the problems facing the Sphinx?* **(b)** *What other options exist?*

4. *Make a decision.* Choose the option that seems to offer the best advantages and the least significant disadvantages. Remember that there may

be more than one good choice. *What are the advantages and disadvantages of each option you identified?*

5. *Plan for the future.* After you have put your decision into effect and have seen some results, take time to review it. If the problem has been solved, then stay with the decision. If the problem persists, has worsened, or has given rise to new problems, then start the process again and choose another option. **(a)** *What are the results of actions that have already been attempted?* **(b)** *What results might you expect for the other options you have identified?*

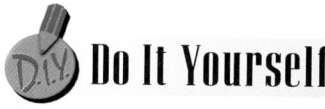

Practice the Skill Think of a geographic issue that exists in the United States or in your local community. Using the steps on this page, make a decision that addresses the issue. When you have finished the decision-making process, write a proposal for your recommended course of action.

Apply the Skill See Chapter 25 Review and Assessment.

Trouble for the Sphinx

The Sphinx, an ancient Egyptian monument that stands near the pyramids at Giza, is slowly crumbling away. Both environmental and human factors are to blame. Pollution, wind, and humidity all wear away at the statue. Even some repair attempts have caused further damage. During the 1980s, workers replaced limestone blocks and injected chemicals into the stone, but pieces continued to flake away. Untrained workers have used ineffective methods, and vandals have stolen pieces of the statue. Today, archaeologists focus on draining seepage that damages the rock.

RESOURCE DIRECTORY

Teaching Resources

Unit 7, Chapter 25
• Section 2 Guided Reading and Review, p. 13
• Map/Graph Skills, p. 17

Guide to the Essentials (English/Spanish)
• Section Summary, Chapter 25, Section 2

Mental Mapping booklet
• Unit 7 Checklist, p. 91

Technology

Guided Reading Audiotapes (English/Spanish), Chapter 25, Section 2

Section Reading Support Transparencies, Chapter 25, Section 2

World Geography Map and Photo Transparencies
• Africa: Maps and Photos

Book on CD, Chapter 25

Social Studies Skills Tutor CD-ROM, Decision Making

Companion Web site, www.phschool.com
• Chapter 25 Activities

2 Libya and the Maghreb

Reading Focus

- How have physical characteristics and changing perceptions of geography affected cultures in Libya and the Maghreb?
- How have cooperation and conflict led to cultural change in North Africa?
- What are the main settlement patterns in North Africa?
- How do ideas of government and citizenship vary among North African nations?

Key Terms

wadi

caravan

medina

souk

Main Idea Libya and the Maghreb nations share cultural patterns but have different resources, governments, and economies.

Economic Activities Moroccan women dry dates, a common fruit in North Africa and the Mediterranean.

Objectives

Upon completion of Section 2, students should be able to:

- ◆ explain how physical characteristics and changing perceptions of geography have affected cultures in Libya and the Maghreb;
- ◆ describe how cooperation and conflict have led to cultural change in North Africa;
- ◆ identify the main settlement patterns in North Africa;
- ◆ describe how ideas of government and citizenship vary among North African nations.

National Geography Standards

The following National Geography Standards are highlighted in this section: 1, 3, 4, 5, 6, 8, 9, 10, 11, 12, 13, 16, 17

Bellringer

Have students look at the physical map on page 532 and guess how far Morocco is from Europe. (approximately 8 miles, or 13 km)

LESSON PLAN

1. Focus Show students a picture of a North African coastal city, such as Casablanca, Tangier, Algiers, Tunis, or Tripoli. Then show them a picture of the Sahara. Have students identify the physical and cultural differences in the two photos.

2. Instruct Have students divide a sheet of paper into two columns. Instruct them to label the first column *Cause* and the second column *Effect.* Under *Cause,* have them list the following headings: North Africa's Mediterranean location; Arabs invade North Africa; camels are introduced; Europeans control North Africa; Oil is discovered in Algeria and Libya. Then have them list as many effects as possible for each cause.

3. Close/Reteach Have students work in pairs to develop five questions based on the material in this section. Divide the class into two teams. Have teams take turns asking and answering questions.

Chapter 25 ▪ Section 2 **531**

The North African countries west of Egypt are Libya and the Maghreb nations—Tunisia, Algeria, and Morocco. The word *Maghreb* comes from an Arabic term meaning "land farthest west." For a thousand years, these countries were the westernmost outposts of an Islamic empire that stretched across Asia, the Middle East, Africa, and into Europe. Today, they retain close ties to other Islamic countries, especially those of the Middle East.

The North African nations are similar in many respects. The majority of the people are Arabic-speaking Muslims who live along the Mediterranean coast. Away from this narrow coast, their lands are arid, forming the northern margins of the Sahara. The shared presence of the desert and their similar history give the cultures of these four countries many things in common.

There are, however, important differences among these nations. For example, Libya is a large country with rich oil reserves and very little arable land. Tunisia is small and much more agricultural, but it lacks oil.

Physical Characteristics of North Africa

In the coastal areas of North Africa the climate is Mediterranean, with hot, sunny summers and cool, rainy winters. Away from the seacoast, the extremely dry climate of the Sahara prevails. But, the landscape of the desert varies from area to area—sandy dunes flow into gravel and bare rock deserts. Dry riverbeds and sharp gullies, known as **wadis,** cut across the land, catching and temporarily holding water from sudden downpours. Low basins gradually rise to meet high, windswept plateaus and then mountains.

People who lived along the coast of North Africa found it easier to have contact with other countries than with interior regions of their own country. The people of the interior had limited contact with one another or with the outside world. No navigable rivers connected these places. The mountains and the desert were formidable barriers to travel and communication. For these reasons, the people of those interior regions have tended to maintain traditional ways.

Chapter 25 ▪ Section 2 **531**

Atlas Mountains Atlas is a mythical Greek character who was thought to support the heavens on his shoulders. According to one myth, Atlas was turned to stone by one of the Greek gods. The early Greeks believed that Atlas had stood on the mountains of North Africa, so they called them the Atlas Mountains.

History The salt route across the Sahara was one of the most important trade routes in Africa. Salt from the Mediterranean Sea was as precious as gold. People in the tropics needed salt to replenish what they lost through perspiration. Also, salt was used to preserve meat. Salt was so important that in ancient Rome soldiers were given a part of their wages as an allowance to buy salt (Latin *sal*) with. This is the origin of the word *salary*.

The Desert The desert of the Maghreb has not always been as dry as it is today. Because of the cycle of climatic changes, during the past 1 million years, there have been periods of abundant rainfall.

Alternative Assessment

Mid-Point Monitoring

Constructing a Time Line You may wish to monitor students' progress in constructing their time lines. Confer with students to see if they have completed their research and chosen the items that they will include on their time lines.

Answers to Map Caption

They are all coastal cities.

Away from the seacoast, the climate is extremely dry and inhospitable; mountains and the desert also form formidable barriers for travel and settlement in the interior regions.

Geography and Cultures

Located on the southern coast of the much-traveled Mediterranean Sea, coastal regions of North Africa have been influenced by centuries of contact with other peoples. Today, the region has a distinctive culture that is a blend of African, European, and Asian influences.

Early Movement Sometime after 5000 B.C. the Berbers—the original inhabitants of North Africa—became farmers and herders instead of nomads. They settled in villages along the Mediterranean coast and on the northern mountain slopes. Only a small portion of the population lived near oases. Over time, other groups came to power in the region, including the Carthaginians and the Romans.

During the period of Roman rule, camels imported from Central Asia were introduced to North Africa. Camels have been called "ships of the desert." They are well adapted to desert conditions. Even in very hot weather, camels can travel for several days without water. Their large, flat feet allow them to walk over sand dunes much as snowshoes allow people to walk over snow.

Camels changed perceptions of the geography of North Africa. For the first time, North Africans established regular trade with the people living south of the Sahara. They crossed the desert in **caravans,** large groups of merchants who have joined together to travel in safety. Southbound caravans carried salt, which was very valuable to people in tropical climates. Northbound caravans carried enslaved people as well as cargoes of ivory, gold, and feathers. They also transported wild animals such as hippopotamuses and elephants for contests in Roman amphitheaters.

Cooperation and Conflict

A dramatic change occurred in Libya and the Maghreb during the mid-600s A.D., when Arab armies invaded North Africa. The Arabs' impact upon the region was tremendous. They brought with them a new religion, Islam, and a new language, Arabic. The Arab conquest was the start

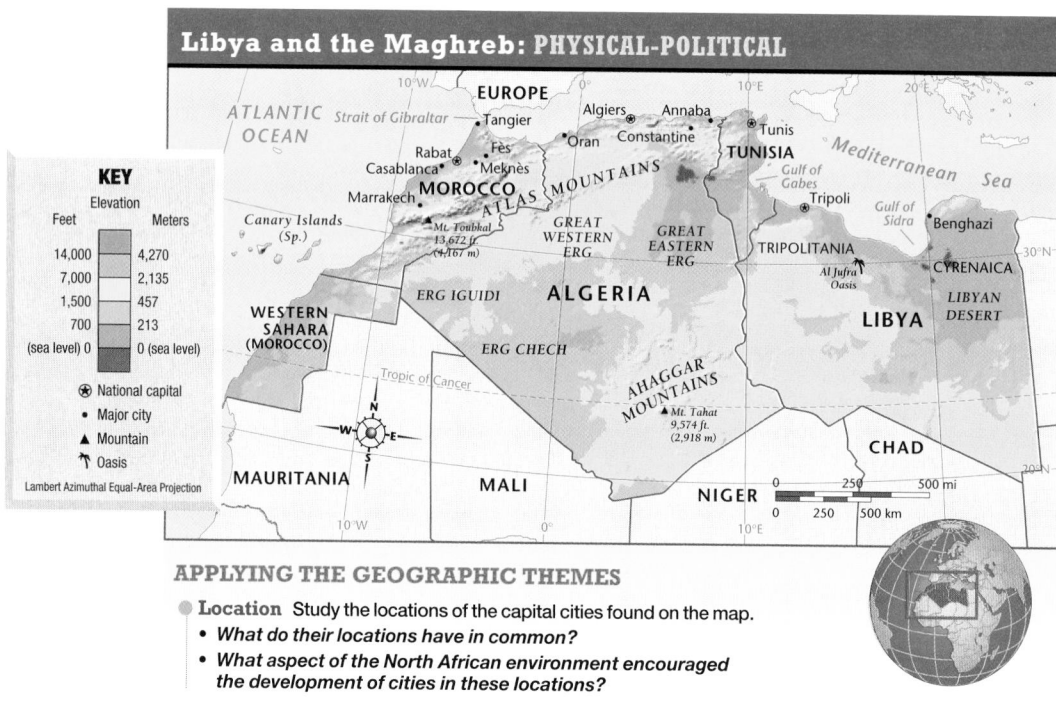

Libya and the Maghreb: PHYSICAL-POLITICAL

APPLYING THE GEOGRAPHIC THEMES

● **Location** Study the locations of the capital cities found on the map.
- *What do their locations have in common?*
- *What aspect of the North African environment encouraged the development of cities in these locations?*

RESOURCE DIRECTORY

Teaching Resources
Unit 7, Chapter 25
• Critical Thinking, p. 16
Social Studies Skills Handbook
• Reading a Time Zone Map, p. 24
Mental Mapping booklet
• Outline Map 25, p. 96

Technology
World Geography Map and Photo Transparencies
• Africa: Maps and Photos

of a long, golden age for North Africa. The region became a vital center of trade between Europe, Africa, and Asia and an important center of learning and scholarship.

Today, Arabs form the majority of the population in North Africa, with Berbers a substantial minority. Berbers in Algeria, for example, make up about 17 percent of the population.

European Influence In the nineteenth century some European powers sought to control North Africa. In 1830 France invaded Algeria. Algerian rebels battled French rule for more than seventy years but were eventually defeated.

During the late 1800s, France extended its empire to Tunisia. European conquest of the area was completed in 1912, when France gained control of Morocco and Italy conquered Libya.

Following Italy's defeat in World War II, in 1951 the United Nations declared Libya an independent nation. However, Algeria, Tunisia, and Morocco had to fight for their independence. In 1956 Morocco and Tunisia gained their freedom, followed by Algeria in 1962.

Patterns of Settlement

The most important cultural divisions in North Africa today are not between countries, but rather between rural and urban ways of life.

Rural Life Farmers living in Libya and the Maghreb still live in small rural villages, in mud or stone houses that may have only one room. For the sake of privacy, these houses usually do not have windows that face on the street. Instead, windows face the family's open courtyard. Water often comes not from a tap, but from a goatskin bag that hangs on a wall of the house. The family's supply of water must be carried from the village well each day.

People rise at dawn to begin their work. In the middle of the day, when temperatures are hottest, North Africans rest for several hours. Even in the cities, a three-hour midday break is the custom. When the sun's glare begins to lessen, people return to work until dusk. Some farmers own or rent small plots of land, raising wheat, barley, and livestock. The tools they use often are the same kind their ancestors used centuries ago. Wooden plows drawn by camels are not uncommon. Other

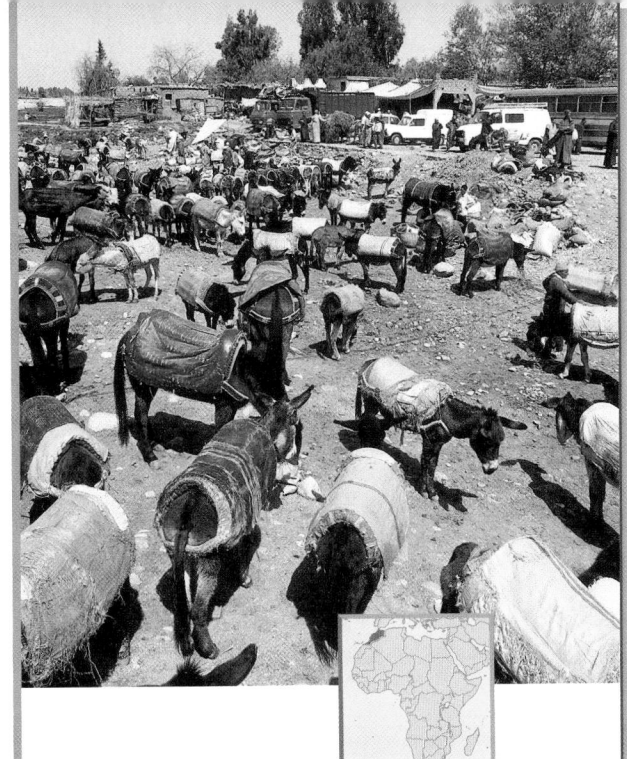

North African Market

Economic Activities At a market in Morocco, donkeys provide a method of transporting both people and goods.

Movement *What other method of transportation can be seen in this photograph?*

villagers hire themselves out to work for someone else on larger, more modern farms.

Desert Nomads Some North Africans have always followed a nomadic way of life. One of the most distinctive nomadic groups is the Tuareg (TWAR ehg), who live in small groups throughout the central and southern Sahara. The Tuareg speak their own language—the only Berber language that has a written form. They practice a unique form of Islam that preserves many elements of their previous religion.

The Tuareg's name for themselves means "free men." They have resisted giving up their nomadic ways and coming under the control of any government. Recently, severe droughts in the Sahara have forced many of the Tuareg to settle in villages and work on farms in order to

BACKGROUND

Daily Life

Shopping Souks have been part of North African life for hundreds of years. Like American shopping malls, nearly everyone goes there and you can buy almost everything you need. In North Africa this means that you are as likely to see men in business suits as you are to see veiled women in long robes. The goods displayed for sale range from state-of-the-art electronics to baskets filled with aromatic spices.

survive. It is possible that their ancient way of life—and that of other remaining North African nomads—will soon disappear.

Urban Life Like Egypt, the rest of North Africa is undergoing rapid urbanization. Recent estimates show that half or more of the populations of Algeria, Libya, and Tunisia live in urban areas.

The older Arab sections of North African cities, called **medinas**, usually are centered around a great mosque. **Souks**, or market areas, wind out from the mosque in a maze of narrow streets and alleyways lined with shops and workrooms. One visitor recently described the streets of a medina:

> ❝You walk past endless walls shiny from having been polished by generations of human beings wedged into narrow alleys. . . . Exquisite and often sumptuous houses are hiding behind these walls amid scented gardens filled with the murmur of fountains.❞

Like Cairo, the major cities of Libya and the Maghreb attract more rural people than they can absorb. Housing and jobs for unskilled laborers are scarce.

Since the 1950s, when European control of North Africa ended and oil wealth began, modern parts of cities have grown rapidly. Modern sections of North African cities look much like cities in Europe or the United States, with broad avenues, modern skyscrapers, internationally known stores, and corporate offices.

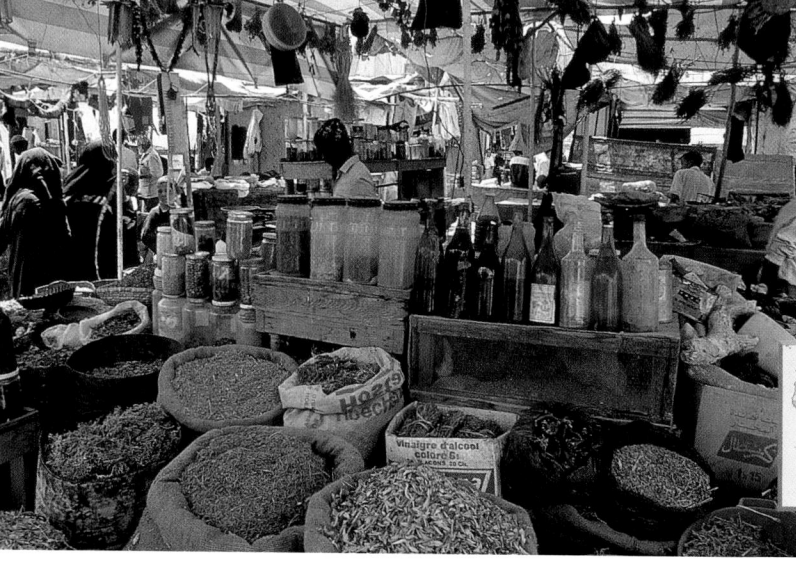

Living in the City

Cultures A street scene in Libya's capital city, Tripoli (above), contrasts with an open-air market in Morocco (left).

Place *What different styles of dress do you see in these photographs?*

Answer to Photo Caption

Both traditional and Western styles of dress can be seen in the photographs.

Libya's Black Gold

Natural Resources The fires visible in this photo of a Libyan oil field are caused by the burnoff of natural gas. Libya's economy depends heavily on money from exports of the country's large oil reserves.

Movement *What body of water provides a natural highway for transporting oil out of Libya?*

North Africa Today

Since independence, the four nations of North Africa have taken different paths politically and economically.

Libya After years of Italian control, in 1951 newly independent Libya was one of the poorest nations in Africa. Its revenues came almost entirely from foreign aid and rent from British and American military bases. That situation changed abruptly with the discovery of oil. By 1961 Libya's first oil wells were in production. Today oil makes up 99 percent of Libya's exports.

Money from oil paid for roads, schools, housing, hospitals, and airports. It brought electricity and new water wells to rural villages. It provided farmers with modern machinery. It also dramatically increased the income of many Libyans, especially those who found jobs in construction and the new oil industry.

It is hard to say which has changed Libya more, oil wealth or the government of Colonel Muammar Qaddafi. In 1969 Qaddafi led a military coup that overthrew the pro-Western king and abolished the monarchy. Qaddafi established a unique form of socialism that combined strict adherence to Islamic traditions with some modern economic and political reforms. One of

Qaddafi's goals was a more equal distribution of wealth in Libya. For example, he ordered that no Libyan could have more than one house or more than 1,000 dinar (about $3,400) in savings. The government seized the property of anyone who had more than it allowed.

Another of Qaddafi's goals was to root out Western influences, which he thought were unhealthy. His government closed bars and nightclubs. It banned blue jeans for men and any kind of pants or short skirts for women. To bring the country back to its Islamic traditions, Qaddafi established Islamic law as the law of the land.

In foreign policy, Qaddafi clashed both with Western nations and with Libya's neighbors. Libya used its oil revenues to buy billions of dollars worth of Soviet military equipment, which it then used in brief wars with Chad and Egypt during the 1970s and 1980s. Libya also supported terrorist groups around the world. In 1986 the United States launched an air strike against Libya in response to a terrorist bombing and, in 1992, imposed economic sanctions. The sanctions were lifted in 1999 when Libya turned over two suspects to the United Nations. Qaddafi abandoned terrorism and presented himself as a leader of Africa.

Many Libyans wonder why life has not improved since the sanctions were lifted. During

Summarizing Main Ideas

Read the subsection Algeria aloud with the class. At the end of each paragraph, pause and have students identify the main idea of that paragraph. Ask volunteers to share their main ideas with the class. Write their ideas on the board.

ACTIVITY

Connecting With . . .

Literature The Rock of Gibraltar on the Iberian Peninsula and Jebel Musa at Ceuta, Morocco, are the Pillars of Hercules. These two promontories mark the Strait of Gibraltar between Europe and Africa and remain the mythic gateway to the world of the Mediterranean. Have students research Greek mythology to find out why the Rock of Gibraltar and Jebel Musa are called the Pillars of Hercules.

Answer to Photo Caption

They are often seeking greater economic opportunities.

GLOBAL CONNECTIONS

Planning for the Future
Like Algeria, Latin America and Southeast Asia face the challenge of overcrowded coastal cities. Some nations encourage people to remain farmers. Others, like Brazil, build inland cities and promote resettlement.

opportunities of their own, Algerians had relied on French settlers to serve as professionals and government administrators. The new government began massive training and education programs to enable Algerians to fill the newly emptied positions.

Oil and natural gas, which were first discovered in the 1950s, make up about 96 percent of the value of all Algerian exports. Like Libya, Algeria's oil revenues have raised the country's general standard of living. Yet, Algeria still faces severe economic problems.

Although the oil industry produces most of Algeria's revenues, it employs few of the country's workers. With the population growing

the 1990s, rising oil prices should have brought increased wealth to Libya. Instead, people's incomes declined.

Algeria Nearly all the French colonists left Algeria after it became independent. Their flight had disastrous consequences. With no educational

rapidly, too few jobs are available. Many Algerians have emigrated to Europe to work, especially to France.

The Algerian government is trying to encourage rural Algerians to continue farming instead of flocking to the cities. If it is successful in its efforts, it will accomplish three goals. First, fewer Algerians will be unemployed, because agricultural workers are in great demand. Second, Algeria will be able to reduce its expensive dependence on food imports. Today, the country has to import more than one third of its food. And third, the severe problems of overcrowding in Algeria's coastal cities will be reduced. At present, two-room apartments house on average nine occupants.

The Algerian government has faced problems in the last few years. In 1988 economic discontent led to antigovernment riots. Algerians began to demand an end to the one-party rule that had controlled the government since independence. In time, new local and national elections were scheduled.

In 1992 an Islamist party nearly won the national elections. Many Algerians were alarmed that this party would impose on them a government similar to the Islamic government in Iran. They were afraid that they would never attain the democratic freedoms they hoped for in the

Onion Fields

Economic Activities
Near Algiers, farmers load a truck with onions. The Algerian government, hoping to reduce food imports and relieve overcrowding in the cities, has worked hard to strengthen the nation's farms.

Movement *Why do people choose to leave the farm for the city?*

RESOURCE DIRECTORY

Teaching Resources

Unit 7, Chapter 25
- Section 2 Quiz, p. 14
- Reviewing Main Ideas, p. 15
- Test Forms A and B, pp. 18–23

Spanish Resources
- Section 2 Quiz, p. 63

Guide to the Essentials (English/Spanish)
- Chapter 25 Test

Mental Mapping booklet
- Chapter 25 Map Test, p. 98

Simulations, Games, and Lab Activities
- Place Location Review Games, pp. 58–63

Social Studies Skills Handbook
- Study and Research Skills, pp. 94–108

Prentice Hall Assessment System

Alternative Assessment booklet
- Time Line Evaluation Form, p. 13

Technology

ExamView Test Bank CD-ROM, Chapter 25 Test
Companion Web site, www.phschool.com
- Chapter 25 Self-Test

future. To prevent radical Islamists from coming to power, the army took over the government and postponed the elections. Radical Islamists responded with a wave of assassinations and other terrorist attacks to undermine the army-run government.

Tunisia and Morocco Unlike Libya and Algeria, Tunisia and Morocco do not have large oil reserves. Some inhabitants view this as a blessing. As one Tunisian business leader stated, "We are lucky we didn't find much oil. Otherwise we wouldn't have worked so hard to develop our people." Tunisia spends more than 15 percent of its money on education, and education is free from the primary grades through the universities. One recent visitor to the Tunisian desert observed:

❝It is very touching to see groups of tiny children . . . trudging sturdily to classes across a wide, dusty landscape in which, as far as the eye can see, there is no obvious sign of home or school.❞

Aside from developing their human resources, Tunisia and Morocco also have begun to develop their manufacturing. Recently, both countries have increased their revenues by manufacturing clothing for export. Another important resource for Tunisia and Morocco is minerals. Phosphates are exported by both countries.

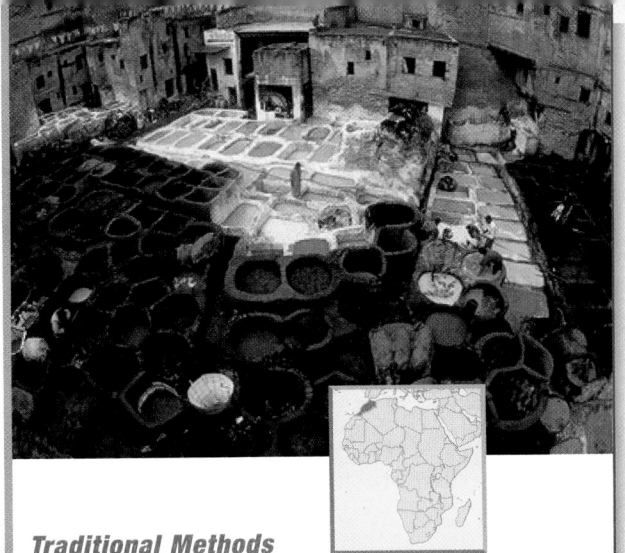

Traditional Methods

Economic Activities This scene from the Moroccan city of Fès shows giant tubs made of earth. The tubs contain vegetable dyes used to color sheepskins and cowhides. Clothing exports, especially to nearby Europe, are an increasingly important part of Morocco's economy.

Place *In what way does Morocco's economy differ from that of Libya or Algeria?*

They have also built up their chemical industries in order to process phosphates before exporting them. As in other parts of the region, rural areas are declining in population as new industrial projects lure workers from the countryside to the cities.

SECTION 2 ASSESSMENT

1. **Key Terms** Define **(a)** wadi, **(b)** caravan, **(c)** medina, **(d)** souk.

2. **Physical Characteristics** What are the key physical characteristics of North Africa?

3. **Cooperation and Conflict** How has conquest affected culture in Libya and the Maghreb?

4. **Patterns of Settlement** Identify cultural differences among **(a)** rural dwellers, **(b)** desert nomads, **(c)** urban dwellers.

5. **Government and Citizenship** How do the priorities of North African governments differ?

6. **Critical Thinking** **Synthesizing Information** Describe how geography and culture have affected economic activities in North Africa.

Activity

Take It to the NET

Making a Bar Graph Use Internet resources to learn more about quality of life in Libya and the Maghreb. Choose one quality-of-life indicator, such as literacy rate. Then, create a bar graph comparing that indicator in each of the four countries covered in this section. Visit the World Geography section of **www.phschool.com** for help in completing this activity.

TEST PREPARATION

Have students read the subsection Tunisia and Morocco on this page to complete the following sentence.

The economic activities of Morocco and Tunisia include all of the following *except* —

A manufacturing textiles
Ⓑ exporting oil
C mining phosphates
D exporting clothing

Answers to Section 2 Assessment

1. (a) wadi, p. 531 **(b)** caravan, p. 532 **(c)** medina, p. 534 **(d)** souk, p. 534

2. North Africa has a Mediterranean coastal climate and a dry desert climate in the interior region. The landscape is principally deserts and mountains.

3. Carthaginians, Romans, Arabs, and Europeans all conquered North Africa, bringing their customs and cultures to North Africa.

4. (a) Rural dwellers own or rent small plots of land to farm, or hire themselves out to work on larger farms. **(b)** The Tuareg follow an ancient nomadic way of life. They speak their own language and practice a unique form of Islam. **(c)** North African cities offer great variety. Many urban dwellers are poor and find housing and jobs scarce.

5. For the first 30 years of Qaddafi's rule, the Libyan government spent lavishly on military equipment and supported terrorism. Today, the Libyan government has abandoned terrorism and seeks to be a leader in Africa. The Algerian government has worked to improve the agriculture sector of the economy and to prevent radical Islamists from coming to power. Tunisia and Morocco have focused on education and are also working to develop manufacturing.

6. Answers will vary, but students should note the impact of oil reserves and other resources (or the lack thereof) on economic activities. They should also note that North Africa's location made it a center of trade.

Activity Rubrics Share rubrics with students before they begin their bar graphs.

Attempted The graph is not attempted or is messy and incomplete.

Minimal The graph contains the required elements but is messy.

Adequate The graph contains the required elements and is neat.

Exemplary The graph contains the required elements and is very well executed and visually attractive.

Answer to Photo Caption

Morocco lacks large oil reserves.

Creating a Chapter Summary

As a reteaching opportunity, pair a more able student with a less able student to complete this chapter summary.

Possible answers: **EGYPT Physical:** Nile River, Deserts **Economic:** Agriculture, Export of raw materials **Cultural:** Greeks and Romans, Arabs **Natural Resources:** Fertile delta, Oil reserves **LIBYA Physical:** Little arable land **Economic:** Oil exports **Cultural:** Arabs, Italians **TUNISIA Physical:** Mediterranean climate **Cultural:** French, Arabs **Natural Resources:** Minerals

Reviewing Key Terms

1–10. Students' crossword puzzles should reflect a clear understanding of each of the key terms.

Understanding Key Ideas

11. The Nile has made Egypt inhabitable and has provided fertile land for agriculture.
12. to provide water for agriculture year-round, to provide extra water for Cairo, and to generate electricity for modern industries
13. rapid population growth that is outstripping the food supply, lack of skilled labor, and lack of capital
14. Arabic was adopted as the primary language; Islam became the official religion; the region became a center for trade and scholarship.
15. farming, desert nomad, and urban
16. Tunisia spends more than 15 percent of its money to provide free education to its citizens.

Critical Thinking and Writing

17. Answers should reflect understanding of Egypt's proximity to Israel and the need to control the Sinai Peninsula and the Suez Canal.
18. The Nile flows south to north, depositing fertile silt in its delta. Cairo and Alexandria are located near the delta.
19. Answers will vary. Students should be able to support their positions with specific information on the positive or negative effects of Qaddafi's rule.

Creating a Chapter Summary

Copy this table on a sheet of paper. Add geographic information about the countries of North Africa. Add as many columns and rows as needed. Some information has been provided to help you get started.

CONCEPT	EGYPT	TUNISIA
PHYSICAL CHARACTERISTICS	• Nile River •	
		• Clothing; manufacturing
CULTURAL INFLUENCES		
NATURAL RESOURCES	• Oil	

Take It to the NET
Chapter Self-Test For practice test questions for Chapter 25, go to the World Geography section of **www.phschool.com**.

Reviewing Key Terms

Use the key terms listed below to create a crossword puzzle. Exchange puzzles with a classmate. Complete the puzzles, and then check each other's answers.

1. delta
2. fellaheen
3. bazaar
4. basin irrigation
5. reservoir
6. capital
7. wadi
8. caravan
9. medina
10. souk

Understanding Key Ideas

11. Understanding the Past How has the Nile River affected the history and economy of Egypt?

12. Environmental Change What three goals did Egypt hope to achieve through construction of the Lake Nasser reservoir?

13. Economic Activities What economic challenges face Egypt today?

14. Cooperation and Conflict How did the Arab conquest change North Africa?

15. Cultures What three distinct ways of life characterize Libya and the Maghreb?

16. Planning for the Future How is Tunisia developing human resources to meet future needs?

Critical Thinking and Writing

17. Asking Geographic Questions What role might location have played in Egypt's decision to make peace with Israel?

18. Drawing Conclusions How did the forks of the Nile River and the direction in which the Nile River flows influence the location of Egypt's two major urban areas?

19. Defending a Position Write an editorial discussing whether Qaddafi's rule has benefited or harmed the interests of the Libyan people.

20. Making Generalizations What economic problems are shared by the nations of North Africa?

20. Possible answers: They tend to rely on one main export; they do not produce enough of their own food; and they have experienced rapid urbanization.

Applying Skills

Making Decisions Refer to the skill lesson on page 530 and the subsection about Algeria on pages 536–537 to answer these questions:

21. What problem faces Algerian cities?

22. How has the Algerian government responded to this problem?

23. What other courses of action might the government take?

24. Which course of action would you recommend? Explain.

Analyzing a Photograph Study the photograph below, and answer the following questions:

25. In what kind of ecosystem does the oil field seem to be located?

26. How might climate conditions benefit or harm the operation of the oil field?

27. How might an accident at the oil field have a a negative effect on the environment?

Test Preparation

Read the question and choose the best answer.

28. In North Africa, population density is generally greatest —

  A along the Nile and the Mediterranean coast

  B in the middle of the Sahara

  C in southern Libya and Algeria

  D in the vast oasis that stretches several hundred miles across the Sahara

Activities

USING THE REGIONAL ATLAS

Review the Regional Atlas for Africa and Chapter 25. Create a table that lists economic activities and resources in North Africa and explains why they are important for the region. Develop a hypothesis to explain how a change in global trade patterns could have a negative impact on countries of the region.

 MENTAL MAPPING

Study a map of North Africa. On a separate piece of paper, draw a sketch map of the region from memory. Label the following places on your map:

- Egypt
- Libya
- Tunisia
- Algeria
- Nile River
- Sahara
- Cairo
- Tripoli
- Tunis
- Algiers

Take It to the NET

Creating a Time Line Search the Internet for information about Algerian history. Create a time line that shows major events in Algeria since the nation gained independence. Visit the World Geography section of **www.phschool.com** for help in completing this activity.

Applying Skills

21. overpopulation

22. The Algerian government is trying to encourage rural Algerians to continue farming instead of migrating to the cities.

23. Possible answer: Provide financial assistance to farmers to encourage agricultural production.

24. Answers will vary, but students should be able to support their recommendations.

25. desert

26. Possible answer: Severe weather—such as sandstorms or drought—could harm operations.

27. Air and land pollution are likely results.

Test Preparation

28. A

Activities

Using the Regional Atlas
Check that students' tables include all the available resources and that they have correctly explained the importance of each. Students' hypotheses should be well thought out and be based on logic.

Mental Mapping
Review students' maps for relative and absolute locations.

Take It to the Net
Students' time lines should reflect ample research and should be accurate and easy to read.

 MENTAL MAPPING

Games for Review See pages 58–63 of the Simulations, Games, and Lab Activities booklet for games to review place names in preparation for the Chapter 25 Map Test.

Chapter Map Test Students should use the completed outline maps and the Unit 7 Checklist in their Atlas Portfolios to prepare for the Chapter 25 Map Test. Point out to students that the test will cover only those place names relating to the region covered in this chapter.

Alternative Assessment

Final Evaluation

Constructing a Time Line Use the Time Line Evaluation Form on page 13 of the Alternative Assessment booklet in the Prentice Hall Assessment System to evaluate students' papers. Either teachers or students can complete the forms to indicate which level of work was achieved for each of the criteria. The person evaluating the paper should provide specific examples and comments.

Chapter 26 Planning Guide

Resource Manager

	CORE INSTRUCTION	READING/SKILLS
Chapter-Level Resources	**Teaching Resources** **Unit 7**/Ch. 26 • Reviewing Main Ideas, p. 32 **Mental Mapping booklet** • Unit 7, Checklist, p. 91 **Simulations, Games, and Lab Activities** • Place Location Review Games, pp. 58–63 **Creative Teaching Activities** • Ancient Folk Literature of Africa, p. 28 **TeacherExpress™ CD-ROM,** Ch. 26 **Companion Web site,** **www.phschool.com** • eTeach	**Teaching Resources** **Unit 7**/Ch. 26 • Map/Graph Skills, p. 34 **Book on CD,** Ch. 26 **Social Studies Skills Tutor CD-ROM**
1 The Sahel 1. Describe the role of trade and learning in the Sahel's history. 2. Identify environmental challenges facing the Sahel today. 3. List the three main goals of nations in the Sahel.	**Teaching Resources** **Unit 7**/Ch. 26 • Guided Reading and Review, p. 24 **Prentice Hall Presentation Pro CD-ROM,** Ch. 26, Sec. 1	**Teaching Resources** **Guide to the Essentials (English/Spanish)** • Section Summary, Ch. 26, Sec. 1 **Mental Mapping booklet** • Outline Map 26, p. 99 **Guided Reading Audiotapes (English/Spanish),** Ch. 26, Sec. 1 **Section Reading Support Transparencies,** Ch. 26, Sec. 1
2 The Coastal Countries 1. Show how location has encouraged the development of trade in the coastal countries of West Africa. 2. Explain how power struggles have affected West African nations since independence. 3. Describe the relationship between the traditional cultures and the economies of West Africa.	**Teaching Resources** **Unit 7**/Ch. 26 • Guided Reading and Review, p. 26 **Prentice Hall Presentation Pro CD-ROM,** Ch. 26, Sec. 2	**Teaching Resources** **Guide to the Essentials (English/Spanish)** • Section Summary, Ch. 26, Sec. 2 **Guided Reading Audiotapes (English/Spanish),** Ch. 26, Sec. 2 **Section Reading Support Transparencies,** Ch. 26, Sec. 2
3 Nigeria 1. Describe the regions of Nigeria. 2. Recognize the effect of military leadership on Nigeria's economy and politics.	**Teaching Resources** **Unit 7**/Ch. 26 • Guided Reading and Review, p. 28 **Prentice Hall Presentation Pro CD-ROM,** Ch. 26, Sec. 3	**Teaching Resources** **Guide to the Essentials (English/Spanish)** • Section Summary, Ch. 26, Sec. 3 **Guided Reading Audiotapes (English/Spanish),** Ch. 26, Sec. 3 **Section Reading Support Transparencies,** Ch. 26, Sec. 3
4 Central Africa 1. Describe how the physical characteristics of Central Africa affect movement in the region. 2. List the resources in Central Africa. 3. Explain how political turmoil has affected the Democratic Republic of the Congo.	**Teaching Resources** **Unit 7**/Ch. 26 • Guided Reading and Review, p. 30 **Prentice Hall Presentation Pro CD-ROM,** Ch. 26, Sec. 4	**Teaching Resources** **Guide to the Essentials (English/Spanish)** • Section Summary, Ch. 26, Sec. 4 **Guided Reading Audiotapes (English/Spanish),** Ch. 26, Sec. 4 **Section Reading Support Transparencies,** Ch. 26, Sec. 4

ENRICHMENT/HONORS/PreAP

Teaching Resources

Unit 7/Ch. 26
- Critical Thinking, p. 33

Mental Mapping booklet
- Atlas Activity, p. 100

Social Studies Skills Handbook
- Predicting Consequences, p. 50
- Study and Research Skills, pp. 94–108

People and Geography
- Environmental Degradation, pp. 36–41

World Geography Map and Photo Transparencies
- Africa: Maps and Photos

World Geography Videos
- Movement: West and Central Africa, Tape 3

Companion Web site, www.phschool.com
- Chapter 26 Activities

Companion Web site, www.phschool.com
- Chapter 26 Activities

Companion Web site, www.phschool.com
- Chapter 26 Activities

Companion Web site, www.phschool.com
- Chapter 26 Activities

Companion Web site, www.phschool.com
- Chapter 26 Activities

ASSESSMENT

PRENTICE HALL
ASSESSMENT SYSTEM

Core Assessment
- ExamView Test Bank booklet, Ch. 26
- ExamView Test Bank CD-ROM, Ch. 26

Standardized Test Preparation

Review and Reteach
- Review Book for World Geography, pp. 15–16

Practice and Assess
- Test-taking Strategies With Transparencies for High School

  Test-taking Strategy Poster

- Alternative Assessment booklet
- Test Prep Book for World Geography

Teaching Resources

Unit 7/Ch. 26
- Section Quizzes, pp. 25, 27, 29, 31
- Test Forms A and B, pp. 35–40

Guide to the Essentials (English/Spanish)
- Chapter 26 Test

Spanish Resources, Ch. 26
- Section Quizzes, pp. 64–67

Mental Mapping booklet
- Chapter 26 Map Test, p. 101

Companion Web site, www.phschool.com
- Chapter 26 Self-Test

CUSTOMIZE FOR INDIVIDUAL NEEDS

Gifted and Talented
- Teacher's Edition, Customize for . . . , p. 563

Honors/PreAP
- Teacher's Edition, Customize for . . . , p. 553

Less Proficient Readers
- Guide to the Essentials (English), Ch. 26, Section Summaries
- Guided Reading Audiotapes (English), Ch. 26
- Section Reading Support Transparencies, Ch. 26
- Book on CD, Ch. 26
- Teacher's Edition, Reading Strategy, pp. 543, 549, 553, 556
- Teacher's Edition, Activity: Vocabulary, pp. 544, 548, 558

Students Acquiring English/ESL
- Guide to the Essentials (English/Spanish), Ch. 26
- Guided Reading Audiotapes (English/Spanish), Ch. 26
- Section Reading Support Transparencies, Ch. 26
- Book on CD, Ch. 26
- Teacher's Edition, Customize for . . . , pp. 543, 557

Less Proficient Writers
- Alternative Assessment, Writing Assignment Rubric, p. 6
- Teacher's Edition, Customize for . . . , pp. 547, 551

MENTAL MAPPING

Ask students to look at the map on this page. Point out that West and Central Africa include the countries directly south of the Sahara (except Sudan), those bordering the Atlantic Ocean south to Angola, and the inland countries of Democratic Republic of the Congo and Central African Republic.

Mapping the Region Have students create a map like the one on this page. Ask them to sketch their own outline maps, or distribute the Chapter 26 Outline Map on page 99 of the Mental Mapping booklet in the Teaching Resources. Instruct students to lightly shade each country a different color and label the countries and bodies of water. Students should keep their maps in their Atlas Portfolios in order to prepare for the Chapter 26 Map Test.

eTeach

Be sure to check out this month's online forum with a Master Teacher to join in an exchange of teaching ideas. www.phschool.com

540   Chapter 26

C H A P T E R

26

West and Central Africa

SECTIONS

1   The Sahel

2   The Coastal Countries

3   Nigeria

4   Central Africa

West and Central Africa: POLITICAL

KEY
— National boundary
⊛ National capital
• Other city
Lambert Azimuthal Equal-Area Projection

Go Online
PHSchool.com
For: More information about West and Central Africa and access to the Take It to the Net activities
Visit: phschool.com
Web Code: mjk-0027

540   Chapter 26

RESOURCE DIRECTORY

Teaching Resources
Unit 7, Chapter 26
• Section 1 Guided Reading and Review, p. 24
Guide to the Essentials (English/Spanish)
• Section Summary, Chapter 26, Section 1
Mental Mapping booklet
• Atlas Activity, p. 100
• Unit 7 Checklist, p. 91

Technology
Guided Reading Audiotapes (English/Spanish),
   Chapter 26, Section 1

Section Reading Support Transparencies,
   Chapter 26, Section 1
World Geography Map and Photo Transparencies
• Africa: Maps and Photos
Book on CD, Chapter 26
World Geography Videos
• Movement: West and Central Africa, Tape 3
TeacherExpress™ CD-ROM, Chapter 26
Prentice Hall Presentation Pro CD-ROM, Chapter 26
Social Studies Skills Tutor CD-ROM
Companion Web site, www.phschool.com
• Chapter 26 Activities

1 The Sahel

Reading Focus

- **How were trade and learning important in the history of the Sahel?**
- **What environmental challenges face the Sahel today?**
- **What are the three main goals of nations in the Sahel?**

Key Terms

shifting agriculture
forage
deforestation
desertification
refugee
landlocked
inland delta

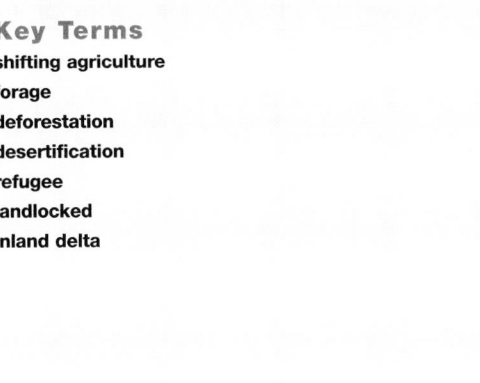

Main Idea Once the site of influential African cultures, the Sahel today is home to a number of countries that struggle to be self-sufficient.

Climates A dry climate means that nations of the Sahel are constantly in danger from drought and famine.

The Sahel, which extends across Africa, separates the Sahara to the north from the tropical grasslands to the south. Here is one journalist's description of the Sahel's many landscapes:

66 The forest thins out until it turns into the most characteristic of African landscapes, the savanna—undulating grasslands dotted with individual trees and occasional groves. . . . But this in turn shades off into sparser country, with scrubby trees and bushes and mottled patches of bare earth, and then into desert lands speckled only with thorn bushes and other tough growths and scarred by gullies and dry sand rivers; and at the final extreme, rocky, sandy, barren desert. 99

Many people in the West think of the Sahel as an arid region. They believe, as well, that its

history and culture are as barren as its dry climate. In fact, the Sahel was for centuries a busy crossroads and an important meeting point for different influential African cultures. Today, the area contains more than a dozen independent countries, each with its own complex and continuing vision of past, present, and future.

Understanding the Past

One of the many surprising facts about West Africa is that the Sahara was not always a desert. Rock paintings found there show that as recently as seven thousand years ago people hunted hippopotamuses in the region's rivers and chased buffalo on its wide, grassy plains. Over time, however, the climate grew drier. Some people of the Sahara migrated north toward the Mediterranean Sea; others migrated south toward the Sahel. Eventually, vast stretches of desert developed and separated them.

 Cattle grazing in Mali (photo left)

Chapter 26 • Section 1 **541**

Objectives

Upon completion of Section 1, students should be able to:

- ◆ describe the role of trade and learning in the Sahel's history;
- ◆ identify environmental challenges facing the Sahel today;
- ◆ list the three main goals of nations in the Sahel.

 National Geography Standards

The following National Geography Standards are highlighted in this section: 1, 2, 4, 5, 6, 7, 8, 9, 10, 11, 12, 13, 14, 15, 16, 17, 18

 Bellringer

Point out the nations of the Sahel on the World Political map in the Atlas. Ask: **Based on its location, why do you think that the Sahel was once a land of wealth?** (Its central location helped to make it a major trading center.)

LESSON PLAN

1. Focus Show students a photograph of a desert and one of a savanna. Have them guess what might cause a grassland to turn into desert.

2. Instruct Make a three-column chart on the board, labeling the columns *Past, Present,* and *Future.* Ask students to record the answers to the following questions on the chart: **Past:** *Why was the Sahel important to the development of Africa?* **Present:** *What are some of the problems that people living in the Sahel now face?* **Future:** *What are countries in the Sahel doing to improve their future?*

3. Close/Reteach Have students write a paragraph predicting what the Sahel will be like in 25 years.

TEACHING TIP
From A Master Teacher

Perceptions of West and Central Africa
Students may think of West and Central Africa as a uniform region. However, it is physically and culturally diverse, the home of numerous ethnic groups with various lifestyles living in environments ranging from near desert to tropical rain forest. Coherence in this area comes from a shared colonial experience, including being part of a worldwide slave system. Invite students to share their perceptions of the region and what factors have shaped them.

Pacing Suggestions

For 90-minute Blocks

You will want to vary activities.

- Use the Creative Teaching Activity for Chapter 26 as the basis for a 90-minute lesson. Extend the lesson by asking each student to write a folk tale in the style of the African stories they heard. Their tales should explain a mystery of nature that scientists have not solved, such as the origin of the universe. Ask volunteers to read their stories to the class.

Chapter 26 • Section 1 **541**

BACKGROUND

Word Origin

Sahel *Sahel* is the Arab word for "shore" or "border"—in the case of Africa's Sahel region, the shore that edges the Sahara desert.

BACKGROUND

Connecting With . . .

Literature Africa has a rich tradition of oral literature. The telling of myths and fables was one of the principal methods of moral, social, and spiritual instruction. The Brer Rabbit tales told by Uncle Remus and the *Just So Stories* popularized by Rudyard Kipling are all retellings of African tales.

Alternative Assessment

Introduce the Activity

Classroom Discussion Tell students that there will be a class discussion around the meaning of these lines from the play *A Dance of the Forests* by Nigerian playwright Wole Soyinka: ". . . You hold a doomed thing in your hand. It is no light matter to reverse the deed that was begun many lives ago." Distribute the Class Discussion Rubric found on page 22 of the Alternative Assessment booklet in the Prentice Hall Assessment System for students' reference.

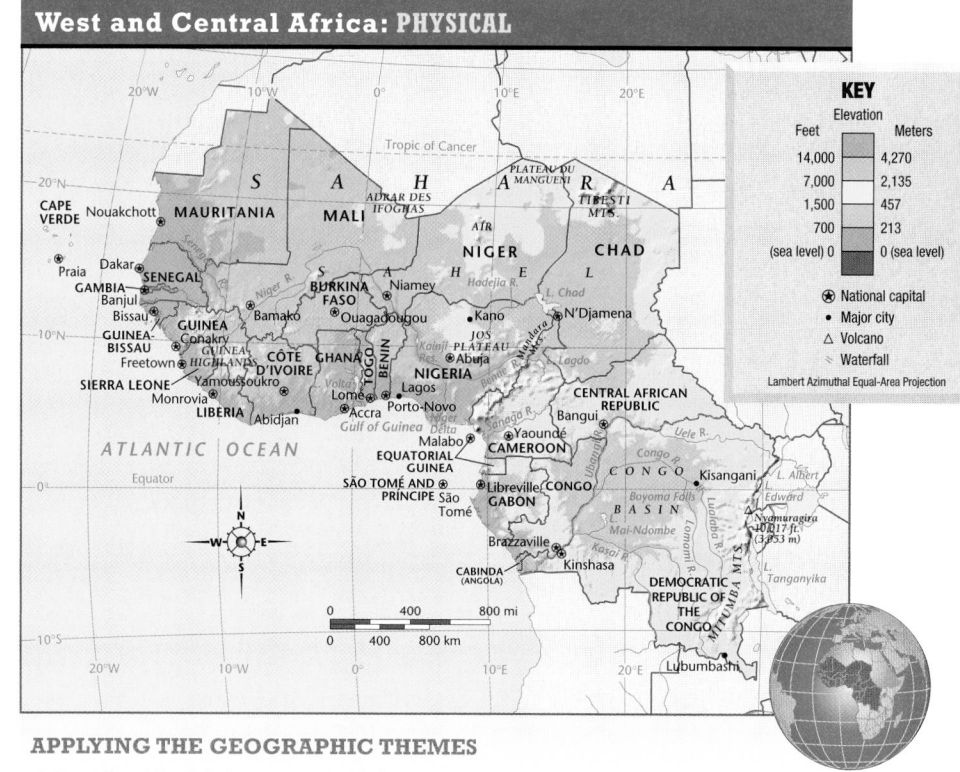

West and Central Africa: PHYSICAL

KEY

Elevation

Feet		Meters
14,000		4,270
7,000		2,135
1,500		457
700		213
(sea level) 0		0 (sea level)

⊛ National capital
• Major city
△ Volcano
⬚ Waterfall

Lambert Azimuthal Equal-Area Projection

APPLYING THE GEOGRAPHIC THEMES

● **Location** The Sahel separates the Sahara from grasslands to the south.
  • *Find the Equator on the map. Which important river basin is centered on the Equator?*

Trade Links and Empires The two groups never entirely lost touch with each other. Over the sea of sand came merchants from the north, bringing salt to trade. They sought ivory, enslaved people, and, most valued of all, the gold that patient miners panned from the two great rivers of the Sahel region—the Senegal and the Niger. Because of its central location, the Sahel's trade routes became a bridge between the Mediterranean coast and the rest of Africa.

The chiefs of the people of the Sahel found that they could grow wealthy by taxing the traders passing through their kingdoms. By A.D. 400 a great kingdom had emerged in the Sahel, then known as Ghana. By the year 800 its capital, Koumbi Saleh, had a substantial population. The Arab traveler and historian al-Bakri described the ruler of Ghana in these words:

66When he gives audience to his people . . . he sits in a pavilion around which stand his horses . . . in cloth of gold; behind him stand ten pages holding shields and gold-mounted swords; and on his right hand are the sons of the princes of his empire, splendidly clad and with gold plaited into their hair.99

A Center of Learning Ghana was defeated by conquerors who swept in from the desert in 1076. But new empires soon took its place in the Sahel.

Mali (MAH lee) was just one of them. At its height in the early 1300s, Mali was one of the largest empires in the world. Its most famous emperor, Mansa Musa, made a triumphal journey to

542   Chapter 26 ▪ West and Central Africa

RESOURCE DIRECTORY

Teaching Resources
Creative Teaching Activities, Ancient Folk Literature of Africa, p. 28
Mental Mapping booklet
• Outline Map 26, p. 99

Prentice Hall Assessment System
Alternative Assessment booklet
• Classroom Discussion Rubric, p. 22

Technology
World Geography Map and Photo Transparencies
• Africa: Maps and Photos

Answer to Map Caption

Congo River basin

Mecca. Under his rule the capital of the empire, Tombouctou (TOM book TOO), became an important trading city. It also developed into a cultural center, rich in the knowledge and arts of Islam.

After Mali's decline, the Songhai Empire dominated the region. Under one of the Songhai rulers, Mohammad Askia, Tombouctou reached the height of its intellectual influence. One report stated, "In Tombouctou there are numerous judges, doctors, and clerics, all receiving good salaries from the king. He pays great respect to men of learning." The Songhai remained a great power in the Sahel until about four hundred years ago.

The Sahel Today

Today, the Sahel is made up of independent countries. Mauritania (mawr i TAYN ee uh), Mali, named after the ancient empire, Niger (NY jer), Burkina Faso (boor KEE nuh FAH so), and Chad are the five northernmost countries of the Sahel.

To their south lie eleven countries that fit like jigsaw pieces around the shore of the Atlantic Ocean. These nations are discussed mainly in the following section on coastal countries, but most of them have at least some savanna in the interior. They are, therefore, linked with the Sahel. In fact, one of them is named Ghana, after the ancient kingdom that lay deep in the Sahel.

Farming Many people of the Sahel support themselves by farming. The dry climate and the poor soil determine how they farm the region.

Farmers cope with the dry climate by growing crops during the short rainy season. They meet the challenge of poor soil by using **shifting agriculture.** Under this system of land use, a site is cleared, prepared, and used to grow crops. After a year or two the soil has been stripped of its nutrients and is no longer useful. Then, the farmers move on to clear new areas of forest and do not return to the previously farmed land.

African Empires and Trade Across the Sahara, A.D. 900 to 1600

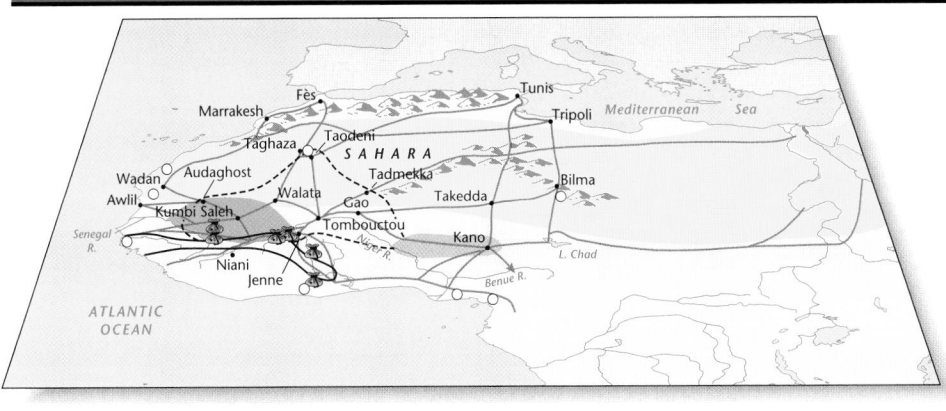

KEY

Empire boundaries:
- Ghana
- Mali
- Songhai
- Hausa states

Resources:
- Gold
- Salt

- Trade routes
- Desert

APPLYING THE GEOGRAPHIC THEMES

● **Movement** Mansa Musa, the Muslim king of the ancient kingdom of Mali, made Tombouctou a great commercial and cultural center.
- *According to the map, which regions of Africa were linked to Tombouctou by trade?*

As students read the subsection The Sahel Today, ask them to record the most important ideas in word webs that use *Farming* and *Herding* as their central ideas.

CUSTOMIZE FOR...

Students Acquiring English/ESL

Key Terms Point out the Key Terms list on page 541. Have students make up one fill-in-the-blank sentence about the Sahel region for each term. Then have students exchange sentences and fill in the missing terms.

Answer to Map Caption

West Africa, North Africa, and Northeast Africa

The Spread of the Desert A severe drought that struck the Sahel in 1968 caused the Sahara to spread south as much as 60 miles (97 km) in some places. Another drought that struck the region in the mid-1980s caused the desert to spread over farms and pastures, despite government reforestation programs.

Making a Diagram Explain that deserts are sometimes produced by the interaction of humans with the environment. To help students better understand the process of desertification, have them make a diagram illustrating the following cycle: (1) overgrazing leads to loss of vegetation; (2) depletion of vegetation reduces soil cover; (3) loss of soil cover destroys even more vegetation; (4) periods of drought destroy all remaining vegetation. (Visual/Spatial)

Landlocked Refer to the Key Terms list on page 541. Write the term *landlocked* on the board. Have students guess the meaning from this sentence: *The African country of Mali is landlocked.* Ask: **Why do you think landlocked countries often go to war against neighbors that have coastlines?** (to gain access to ocean trade)

Refugee The word *refugee* comes from two Latin words, *fugere,* "to flee," and *re,* meaning "back." A refugee is one who flees to escape danger or unfair treatment.

Answer to Photo Caption

Desertification forces people to migrate to urban locations to find work.

Change Over Time

Environmental Change

Patterns of Settlement The center of Nouakchott, the capital of Mauritania, has suffered the effects of desertification. As a result, houses and vegetation survive on the outskirts of the city's barren center.
Movement *How do environmental conditions, such as desertification, influence migration patterns?*

Two grains, millet and sorghum (SAWR guhm), are the vital crops that keep Sahel farmers alive. For cash they grow peanuts, which some sell to the distant cities of the coast for use there or for export.

Herding Instead of farming, many people in the Sahel herd camels, cattle, and sheep. The savannas of the Sahel might seem ideally suited to herding. They have low grasses and other edible plants, as well as trees such as the baobab (BAY o BAHB) and acacia (uh KAY shuh) with leaves that provide **forage,** or food for grazing animals. Unfortunately, such animals can destroy plants and trees when they graze too closely on the same range. This overgrazing has had a grim impact on the environment.

Overgrazing harms the Sahel by destroying the plants that hold the sandy soil in place. Moreover, the endless search for firewood to use for cooking and the tremendous demand for charcoal by a growing, urban population have further damaged the environment. Overharvested land is stripped of its trees through a process called **deforestation.** When there is a drought, vast areas of the Sahel may suffer a loss of all

vegetation, from grass to shrubs to trees, a phenomenon called **desertification.** In effect, the savanna turns to desert, and desertification is very difficult to reverse.

When a drought hits the Sahel region, desertification increases at a frightening pace. People throughout the Sahel flee to the cities, turning what would otherwise be modest, urban clusters into huge **refugee** camps. A refugee is a person who flees his or her home to escape danger or unfair treatment.

The more developed nations of the world can have difficulty aiding the Sahel, because all of the Sahel nations except for Mauritania are **landlocked.** A landlocked nation is cut off from the sea. Even the nations on the coast have poor transportation links. During one drought in Mauritania, the main road through the country could be kept open only by shoveling the sand off it every day.

Planning for the Future

The nations of the Sahel are directing their energies toward three goals: withstanding the harsh environment; developing natural resources; and

Teaching Resources
Unit 7, Chapter 26
• Critical Thinking, p. 33

making the most of their current human resources and cultures.

Holding On The Sahel countries need continuing foreign aid. Food, medicine, and technical help are always in demand. In Niger, for example, foreign aid has helped the country's people plant trees to form windbreaks for thousands of acres of land. In this way, the soil does not blow away during the dry season, and the crops have a better chance of growing when the rain does fall. The Sahel nations are trying to use their natural and human resources in a continuing effort to become self-sufficient.

Using Natural Resources One water resource has helped the people dwelling in the Sahel for thousands of years—the region's rivers. The Senegal and Niger rivers and their tributaries provide both transportation and water for irrigation.

The Niger's source is located in the mountains of the nation of Guinea only 150 miles (241 km) from the Atlantic Ocean, yet the river flows inland for 2,600 miles (4,183 km) before reaching the ocean. On its journey it brings water to countless villages within the Sahel. In Mali, the Niger expands into an **inland delta,** an area of lakes, creeks, and swamps away from the ocean. Here people grow rice, cotton, corn, and vegetables.

Sahel Countries and the United States
Transportation Data

Country	Total Railroad Track Length (miles)	Total Highway Length (miles)	Motor Vehicles (per 1,000 people)
Burkina Faso	386	7,754	6
Chad	0	20,708	4
Mali	452	9,362	4
Mauritania	436	4,749	12
Niger	0	6,262	6
United States	148,800	3,935,900	773

Sources: *Encarta World Atlas; The World Factbook*

CHART SKILLS

● **Economic Activities** *Which African nation has the greatest extent of highway?*

● **Migration** *In which of these African nations would you find it easiest to arrange for an automobile or bus ride between cities?*

The Sahel countries also possess valuable mineral resources that can be sold to buy food. Mauritania and Mali both have reserves of iron ore. Bauxite, the ore from which aluminum is made, is an important resource in Mali, as are Mauritania's

River Traffic

Patterns of Settlement The rivers of the Sahel provide water and transportation to the region's residents. This photograph shows boat traffic at Mopti, Mali. Since about two thirds of Mali is desert or semidesert, most of the country's residents cluster near rivers.

Human-Environment Interaction *Mopti is located at the meeting point of the Bani and Niger rivers. Why do settlements often develop at points where rivers meet?*

Activity: Holding a mock United Nations meeting

Purpose: Tell each group that it will become a mock United Nations delegation from one of the countries in the Sahel. Have groups divide themselves into two committees. One committee should determine the current economic problems in its country; the second committee should develop ideas for relief and aid.

Roles: Groups should include one ambassador, a secretary for each committee, and general delegates.

Result: The ambassador from each group reads his or her report to the class. Delegates propose and vote on aid to these countries.

ACTIVITY

Connecting With . . .

Art Have students research the art of one of the groups that live in the Sahel, such as the Songhai, Bambara, Mandingo, or Hausa, and make a presentation to the class. Encourage students to re-create a piece of art from the group that they have chosen and include it in their presentations.

TEST PREPARATION

Have students read the subsection Planning for the Future beginning on the opposite page to complete the following statement.
Important natural resources in the Sahel include —

A rivers and minerals
B rain and soil
C irrigation and windbreaks
D rice and vegetables

Answers to Chart Skills

Chad

Mauritania

Answer to Photo Caption

Such locations facilitate transportation of people and goods.

Answers to
Section 1 Assessment

1. (a) shifting agriculture, p. 543
(b) forage, p. 544 **(c)** deforestation, p. 544 **(d)** desertification, p. 544 **(e)** refugee, p. 544 **(f)** landlocked, p. 544 **(g)** inland delta, p. 545
2. The Sahel's trade routes across the Sahara formed a bridge between the Mediterranean coast and the rest of Africa.
3. (a) People of the Sahel have over-grazed their animals and deforested the region. Both of these practices remove the vegetation that holds the sandy soil in place. **(b)** Especially in times of drought, desertification pushes people into the cities. In some cases, desertification may result in abandoning land and property to the encroaching desert.
4. The people in the Sahel are trying to use their natural resources—the region's rivers and valuable mineral deposits—and their human resources in a continuing effort to become self-sufficient.
5. Possible answer: They are planting trees and developing water, mineral, and human resources.

Activity Rubrics Share rubrics with students before they prepare their oral reports.
Attempted The report contains factual errors, includes little or no description of the chosen topic, and is poorly delivered.
Minimal The report includes some factual errors, provides some details, and is understandable.
Adequate The report contains no factual errors, includes supporting details, and is well organized and presented.
Exemplary The report is exceptionally well organized and presented, includes many supporting details, and shows insight into the chosen topic.

Answer to Photo Caption

The Mali government has become more open and democratic.

Repair Shop

Economic Activities This Mali businesswoman is repairing hollow gourds, which are sold as containers. Government reforms aimed at encouraging private enterprise have spurred economic growth in Mali.

Place *How has the government of Mali changed in recent years?*

huge reserves of copper in that country. Niger has one of the world's largest and most valuable deposits of uranium.

Using Human Resources The descendants of the people of the Sahel's ancient empires still dwell in the region today. One of the larger groups is the Mossi of Burkina Faso. In Niger and in other countries of the Sahel, many of the Fulani (FOO lah nee) live as herders, and the Hausa (HOW suh) are famous as traders. In Mali, the Songhai people are known for their music and dance. The Mandingo (man DIN go) craft magnificent jewelry and the Bambara carve graceful objects of wood.

While many of the nations of Africa are struggling with repressive governments that simply do not work, one nation in the Sahel offers a model of how democracy and openness use human resources wisely. For 18 years, Mali was ruled by one political party. In 1992, Alpha Oumar Konare (AL fa OO mar ko NAR ay) was elected president in the first free and open elections. Under his leadership, the economy has been growing at a rate of approximately 5 percent per year. Private companies are taking over state-owned businesses and running them better. Newspaper publication encourages the free exchange of ideas. "The single-party system was a total failure in all countries which practiced it," President Konare has pointed out. "The logic of 'shut up and obey' gives immediate results, but offers no tomorrow."

SECTION 1 ASSESSMENT

1. Key Terms Define **(a)** shifting agriculture, **(b)** forage, **(c)** deforestation, **(d)** desertification, **(e)** refugee, **(f)** landlocked, **(g)** inland delta.

2. Understanding the Past Why was the Sahel a key region in the ancient world?

3. Environmental Change (a) Describe two ways in which people have contributed to the desertification of the Sahel. **(b)** How does desertification change patterns of settlement in the region?

4. Economic Activities How are people in the Sahel working to make their nations self-sufficient?

5. Critical Thinking Identifying Main Ideas Describe some of the ways in which the people of the Sahel are directing their energies toward protecting the future of the region.

Activity

Take It to the NET

Preparing an Oral Report Search the Internet for information about desertification in the Sahel. Choose one aspect of the topic that interests you—for example, to what extent the Sahara has spread in the past 50 years. After learning more about your topic, present an oral report to the rest of the class.

RESOURCE DIRECTORY

Teaching Resources
Unit 7, Chapter 26
• Section 1 Quiz, p. 25
• Section 2 Guided Reading and Review, p. 26
Spanish Resources
• Section 1 Quiz, p. 64
Guide to the Essentials (English/Spanish)
• Section Summary, Chapter 26, Section 2
Mental Mapping booklet
• Unit 7 Checklist, p. 91

Technology
Guided Reading Audiotapes (English/Spanish), Chapter 26, Section 2
Section Reading Support Transparencies, Chapter 26, Section 2
World Geography Map and Photo Transparencies
• Africa: Maps and Photos
Book on CD, Chapter 26
Social Studies Skills Tutor CD-ROM
Companion Web site, www.phschool.com
• Chapter 26 Activities

2 The Coastal Countries

Reading Focus

- In what ways has location encouraged the development of trade in the coastal countries of West Africa?
- How have power struggles affected West African nations since independence?
- What relationship exists between the traditional cultures of West African peoples and their countries' economies?

Key Terms

coup
ancestor worship
animism

Main Idea Most countries along the coast of West Africa have been in political and economic turmoil since achieving independence.

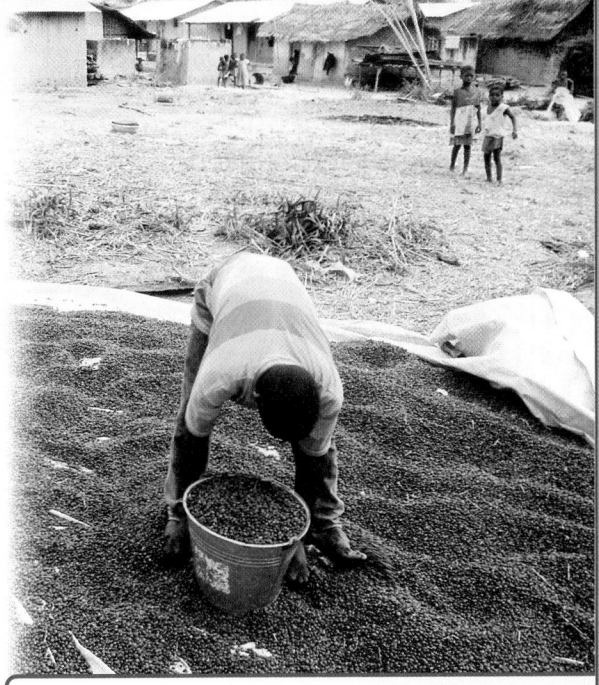

Economic Activities Agriculture is a vital part of the economies of many West African nations.

B esides the five Sahel nations, West Africa contains eleven other countries. One, Cape Verde, is a small island nation. The others line the coast of West Africa, beginning in the west with Senegal and continuing along the Atlantic coast to Nigeria.

Location Leads to Trade

Because of their location, the coastal countries of West Africa have two advantages over those of the Sahel. First, they have a wetter climate. Adequate rainfall allows successful farming and the growth of valuable trees. Second, they have access to the sea. The natural harbors along the West African coastline offer great economic potential to the developing nations in this region. Freetown, in Sierra Leone, has one of the largest harbors in the world, though it does not rank as a leading port.

Global Trade Patterns The coast of West Africa attracted European traders from the 1400s. They came for gold, ivory, palm oil, and enslaved people to use as laborers. This coastal trade made trade across the Sahara less important. Eager for economic prosperity, coastal kingdoms fought each other for control of the new foreign trade.

Today the nations on the West African coast export only a few products and raw materials. Senegal, Gambia (GAM bee uh), and Guinea-Bissau (GI nee bee SOW) export peanuts. Côte d'Ivoire (KOT dee VWAHR)—also called Ivory Coast—Ghana, Sierra Leone, and other nations largely depend upon the export of cocoa beans. Liberia exports iron ore.

Unequal Trade The economies of the West African countries suffer, in part, because their exports total less, in value, than their imports. Also, like many African countries, they are heavily in debt. Africa, as a whole, needs roughly 9 billion dollars every year just to pay the interest on its debts, and West Africa pays an enormous part of that.

Chapter 26 ▪ Section 2 **547**

Objectives

Upon completion of Section 2, students should be able to:

◆ show how location has encouraged the development of trade in the coastal countries of West Africa;

◆ explain how power struggles have affected West African nations since independence;

◆ describe the relationship between the traditional cultures and the economies of the countries of West Africa.

 National Geography Standards

The following National Geography Standards are highlighted in this section: 5, 6, 8, 9, 10, 11, 13, 16, 17, 18

 Bellringer

Ask: **What West African coastal country was founded by freed American slaves?** (Liberia)

LESSON PLAN

1. Focus Tell students to imagine that they have just heard the following report on the radio: "Last night the government was taken over by General Drill N. March. The President has fled; Congress and the Supreme Court have been dissolved." Have students discuss their reactions to this news.

2. Instruct Write this question on the board: *What is the most serious economic or political problem facing West African countries?* Have students work in groups to discuss the question and agree on an answer. Then have groups list evidence that supports their answers.

3. Close/Reteach Create a chart on the board, labeling the columns *Location (Pros and Cons), Government,* and *Economic Trends.* In the rows, list the names of the coastal countries. Have students fill in the information for each country. Encourage students to do research to find any information that is not included in Section 2.

Coastal West Africa and the United States
Health Care Data

Country	Infant Mortality Rate (per 1,000 births)	Life Expectancy (years)	Population per Hospital Bed
Benin	100	53.6	4,281
Cape Verde	48	70.5	631
Côte d'Ivoire	96	46.2	1,232
Gambia	77	53.9	1,637
Ghana	78	56.8	685
Guinea	129	46.0	1,816
Guinea-Bissau	112	49.1	677
Liberia	103	59.5	NA
Nigeria	71	53.5	599
Senegal	61	57.4	1,371
Sierra Leone	129	48.6	NA
Togo	80	58.8	662
United States	6	76.1	244

Source: *Encarta World Atlas*   NA = information not available.

CHART SKILLS

● **Science and Technology** *In which of these African nations does a newborn infant have the best chance of survival?*

● **Economic Activities** *In which of these nations might you expect to have the shortest hospital stay? Explain.*

Struggles for Power

European colonial powers ruled most of Africa until the 1960s. When the African countries gained their independence, their economies were often in very weak condition. Few new governments in Africa have been able to overcome or recover from these economic burdens.

Shifts in Power When governments are weak, the army often steps in and takes over. Sometimes, different factions, or groups within the army, fight for power.

In Benin, six **coups**—sudden political takeovers—took place from 1963 to 1972. Major Ahmed Mathieu Kérékou (AKH muhd mat YUH ker uh KOO) stayed in control from 1972 until 1990. In that year, with Benin's economy failing, Kérékou was faced with strikes and unrest. He then called for a new constitution that allowed others to share power. In 1991, a president was elected, and the military government resigned.

In some nations, setbacks occurred in the adoption of democracy. In Côte d'Ivoire, for example, the man who had ruled the nation for thirty years died and a new president was elected in 1995. Election laws and definitions of citizenship soon were changed, however, leading to growing conflict between different groups. The military overthrew the government in 1999. Although civilian leadership was reestablished by 2001, deep tensions remain between predominantly Christian people in the south and the mostly Muslim population of the north.

Liberia Founded in 1822 by freed American slaves, Liberia became independent in 1847 under an American-style constitution. The country began its slide into chaos in 1980 with a bloody military coup. A decade of oppression and corruption led to a civil war, which raged well into the 1990s. Peacekeepers from other West African nations proved unable to halt the violence, and attempts at a lasting cease-fire failed. During the war, some 200,000 Liberians were killed, hundreds of thousands fled the country, and more than a million others were left homeless. As armed gangs patrolled the streets, one resident commented:

> **❝**If I had the slightest opportunity to leave this country now, to go anywhere, even a slimy refugee camp, it would be better because I can expect a stray bullet or a direct bullet at any time. Nobody can guarantee my security.**❞**

As the violence worsened, humanitarian agencies withdrew. Their earlier shipments of aid, in the form of food and medical supplies intended for civilians, had been stolen by soldiers. However, by 1996, the war had ended with democratic elections. The new president soon proved to be as oppressive as his predecessors, and fighting broke out once again. By 2003, rebel forces controlled most of the country. Upon the arrival of peacekeeping forces from other West African nations, Liberia's president went into exile. Restoring normalcy to this devastated country will be a challenge for its new government.

Sierra Leone's Uncertain Future

Sierra Leone is another West African nation whose recent history has been bloody. After a series of coups and dictatorships over three decades, Sierra Leone held multiparty elections in 1996. Years of politically motivated violence seemed to be coming to an end. However, armed rebels overthrew the government in 1997. In response to the rebel actions, troops from eleven neighboring nations invaded and restored the elected leaders to power. The restoration was brief, though, and fighting resumed soon afterward.

In 2001, a cease-fire halted the violence and paved the way for national elections. However, Sierra Leone remained devastated by more than a decade of warfare. More than 50,000 people had been killed, and more than a third of the population was estimated to have been displaced. The banking system failed, and per capita GNP dropped to less than $500. The future of the nation's economy will depend upon the maintenance of peace and the continued receipt of financial aid from the international community.

People Power West Africans have learned that their governments alone often can do little to improve depressed economic conditions. One writer described a positive consequence of this realization:

> **❝** There are signs that some Africans already are taking matters into their own hands. As rural people have become disillusioned [disappointed] with outsiders and with their own governments, millions of them have begun grass-roots efforts . . . to organize local resources. **❞**

The key to this new economic approach is its grass-roots beginnings. Grass roots means that the effort begins with people. In West Africa, increasingly, it is women who make grass-roots efforts work.

Cultural Roles

Economic Opportunities Many of the women of West African countries, just as in the rest of the continent, are front-line troops in a hard-fought battle: they grow crops in the war

Democracy and Conflict

Government and Citizenship In 1996, Sierra Leoneans celebrated the nation's first free elections in three decades. In subsequent years, violence and political instability returned to the nation.

Regions *Why have many African countries in this region experienced military rule?*

against hunger. In many West African countries women are establishing agricultural cooperatives to improve the economic conditions of their villages. In the village of Malon in Sierra Leone, more than 200 women work together to grow

Chapter 26 ▪ Section 2 **549**

BACKGROUND

Word Origin

Sierra Leone The name *Sierra Leone*, which means "Mountains of the Lions," was first used by Portuguese sailors. Some say the sailors heard the sound of the thunder rolling through the mountains during storms and thought it sounded like the roar of lions.

READING STRATEGY

Summarizing Main Ideas

As students read the subsection Sierra Leone's Uncertain Future, have them write two or three sentences summarizing the major results of civil war in Sierra Leone.

ACTIVITY

Reteach

Writing Slogans Have students review the conflicts in Benin, Côte d'Ivoire, Liberia, and Sierra Leone. Then have them write a short political slogan that addresses one of the main ideas in one of the conflicts. Have volunteers read their slogans to the class. (Verbal/Linguistic)

TEST PREPARATION

Have students read the subsection Struggles for Power beginning on the opposite page to answer the following question.

The president of which African country went into exile in the early 2000s?

A Benin
Ⓑ Liberia
C Sierra Leone
D Côte d'Ivoire

Answer to Photo Caption

After they gained independence, these countries were vulnerable to military takeovers because their economies were weak and their governments were unstable.

Chapter 26 ▪ Section 2 **549**

Alternative Assessment

Mid-Point Monitoring

Classroom Discussion You may wish to remind students about the classroom discussion that will be held at the end of the chapter. Suggest to students that they make notes for the discussion as they think about the quotation.

Answers to Section 2 Assessment

1. (a) coup, p. 548 **(b)** ancestor worship, p. 550 **(c)** animism, p. 550
2. They have used their location to develop trade.
3. Since gaining independence, many of the countries of this region (Benin, Côte d'Ivoire, Liberia, Sierra Leone) have suffered one or more coups. Coups have threatened the establishment of a postindependence government and have slowed or overturned the democratic process.
4. a grass-roots effort to organize local resources
5. Answers will vary, but students should note that women are a key element in the economies of both the United States and African nations.

Activity Rubrics Share rubrics with students before they begin their line graphs.
Attempted The line graph contains factual errors, does not include the information requested, and is illegible.
Minimal The line graph contains some factual errors, includes most of the information requested, and is legible.
Adequate The line graph contains no factual errors, includes all of the information requested, and is easy to read.
Exemplary The line graph contains no factual errors, insightfully presents all of the information requested, and is well organized and attractive.

Answer to Photo Caption

Women have important roles raising crops and running markets. Children help grow and harvest crops.

550 Chapter 26

---

more crops. Women also run an important part of the economy—the markets where food is bought and sold. As Africa modernizes, women are constantly expanding their traditional roles and are becoming owners of small businesses. Children are also valuable workers in West African countries, helping to grow and harvest crops.

Religion Children are important for another reason, as can be seen in the case of the Asante (ah SAHN tay), a group of people who live in southern Ghana. The Asante, like many African peoples, believe that if their children continue to respect and honor them after death, they themselves will live on in the spirit world. An African chief once described his people as "a vast family, of which many are dead, few are living, and countless members are unborn." This belief in the spirits of the dead is called **ancestor worship.**

Ancestor worship is one aspect of the Asante religion; another is **animism.** According to this belief, ordinary things of nature—the sky, rivers, trees—all contain gods or spirits.

Population Growth In Africa, as in other places, social custom, religious beliefs, and economic conditions sometimes translate into large families and a fast-growing population. The birthrate in Ghana—29 per 1,000 population—is much higher than the average birthrate for the world. In fact, the population of Africa is growing faster than populations anywhere else on earth.

Asante King

Cultures The splendor of West African cultural tradition can be seen in this photograph of Asante king Koffi Yeebwa, shown at a festival with supporters.
Regions *What traditional roles remain important in West African life?*

SECTION 2 ASSESSMENT

1. Key Terms Define **(a)** coup, **(b)** ancestor worship, **(c)** animism.

2. Global Trade Patterns How have nations along West Africa's coast taken advantage of their location over the centuries?

3. Government and Citizenship How have coups played a part in the political history of this region?

4. Economic Systems What new economic practice is finding success in West Africa?

5. Critical Thinking Making Comparisons Compare women's roles in Africa with women's roles in the United States.

Activity

Making a Line Graph Choose one of the countries discussed in this section. Review the information about that country's history following its independence, and do more research on your own. Using your findings, create a line graph that expresses that country's movement toward democracy, beginning with its independence and extending to the most recent information you can find. Annotate your graph with notes that explain trends and any sudden "ups" and "downs" in the line.

RESOURCE DIRECTORY

Teaching Resources
Unit 7, Chapter 26
• Section 2 Quiz, p. 27
• Map/Graph Skills, p. 34
Spanish Resources
• Section 2 Quiz, p. 65
Social Studies Skills Handbook
• Predicting Consequences, p. 50

Predicting Consequences

Every day you make decisions about what course of action to take in a situation. Any action has consequences, or results. When choosing among possible courses of action, you can make a well-informed decision if you predict the consequences of each possible action.

Learn the Skill Study the text below. Then, follow these steps to learn how to predict consequences.

1 *Identify the issue or question.* Look carefully at the decision you are facing, and state the issue or question clearly. *What question does the Nigerian government face?*

2 *Identify the recommended action.* Consequences will vary from one situation to another and depend on the selection of a particular course of action. Clearly state the course of action that is being recommended. *How does the Nigerian government plan to respond to the question?*

3 *Predict possible benefits.* Determine the probable effects of the action. List the ways in which the action is likely to have positive results on the situation being addressed. *What benefits may result from the government's action?*

4 *Predict possible drawbacks.* Actions can also have drawbacks, or harmful effects. List the ways

in which the action is likely to have negative results on the situation being addressed. *How might the government's action affect taxpayers?*

5 *Draw conclusions.* Compare the possible benefits and possible drawbacks. If the benefits outweigh the drawbacks, you may conclude that the recommended action is a wise choice. If the drawbacks outweigh the benefits, however, you may need to address the central issue or question again, and develop an alternate course of action. **(a)** *Does the recommended course of action have more benefits or more drawbacks?* **(b)** *Does this course of action seem to be a wise choice? Explain.*

Do It Yourself

Practice the Skill Read a local newspaper to find out about an issue or question in your school or community. Using the steps in this lesson, predict the consequences of the course of action recommended to address the issue or question.

Apply the Skill See Chapter 26 Review and Assessment.

Free Meal Program Begins in Nigeria's Public Schools

The government has announced plans to provide free meals to students in public primary schools. Dr. Idowu Shobowale, the Commissioner for Education, announced the free lunch program at a press conference Sunday to mark the Year 2001 Children's Day celebration.

Only last year, the government announced its plan to introduce a one-meal-a-day program in the public schools. The goals are to improve the nutrition of the students and to make students ready for learning. The free lunch program will cost an estimated 1 billion naira a month.

The government has already spent more than 500 million naira to provide furniture to public schools. However, many students are still being asked to supply their own furniture.

Dr. Shobowale insisted that the government is still committed to ensuring that all schools in the state have adequate furniture. More than 70,000 pieces of furniture are currently being produced. By the time those pieces are delivered, he said, the problem of inadequate school furniture will be a thing of the past.

—adapted from *Vanguard,* May 22, 2001

Teaching the Skill

After students read the introductory paragraph on this page, ask: **How would you decide between studying for a big test and going out with your friends?** Record students' answers on the board, circling the responses that show that the students are predicting consequences. Have students work in groups to complete the five steps in the lesson. Review answers to the first four steps in Learn the Skill. Then call on a group spokesperson to explain each group's conclusion.

Answers to Learn the Skill

1. How can the government improve students' quality of life?
2. by providing free meals to students in public primary schools
3. Students will be healthy and prepared to learn.
4. The program is going to cost an estimated 1 billion naira a month, which will probably have to come from the taxpayers.
5. Answers will vary. Students should be able to recognize and analyze short-term benefits and drawbacks in comparison to long-term benefits and drawbacks.

Answer to Practice the Skill

Check that students have made reasonable predictions based on the possible benefits and drawbacks of the recommended course of action.

CUSTOMIZE FOR...

Less Proficient Writers

Predicting Consequences in Africa After the class has completed the Learn the Skill steps, focus students' attention on an issue discussed in this chapter, such as the Sahel's dependence on foreign aid or Sierra Leone's uncertain future. Have students work in small groups to follow the five steps with the chosen issue, making notes about each step as they discuss it within their groups. Then have students work independently, using their notes to write paragraphs summarizing their conclusions.

Objectives

Upon completion of Section 3, students should be able to:

◆ describe the regions of Nigeria;

◆ recognize the effect of military leadership on Nigeria's economy and politics.

National Geography Standards

The following National Geography Standards are highlighted in this section: 4, 5, 6, 8, 9, 10, 11, 12, 13, 16, 17, 18

Bellringer

Have students guess how many different ethnic groups live in Nigeria. (over 250)

LESSON PLAN

1. Focus Tell students to imagine that they are the leaders of a small country that produces oil. Have students list some things their country could do with the profits from selling that oil. Then have them suppose the price of oil suddenly drops. Discuss with the class what problems this drop in revenue might cause.

2. Instruct Write the following statements on the board: *(1) Rainfall varies in different parts of Nigeria; (2) When Nigeria became independent, its borders were drawn arbitrarily; (3) Large-scale oil drilling began in Nigeria in the 1950s; (4) The military takes over the Nigerian government.* Have students use the information in the text to create cause-and-effect chains that begin with each statement.

3. Close/Reteach Tell students to imagine that they own a manufacturing business and are considering opening a plant in Nigeria. Have them make a list of pros and cons to help them decide whether to locate there. Then have the students discuss their lists and reach a decision.

3 Nigeria

Reading Focus

- What characteristics define different regions in Nigeria?
- How has military leadership affected economic and political conditions in Nigeria?

Key Terms

World Bank

International Monetary Fund

structural adjustment program

Patterns of Settlement In Nigeria, different regions have been settled by specific cultural groups.

Main Idea If Nigeria can maintain political stability, its rich resources can offer the region great opportunity.

Not long ago, Nigeria was seen as the hope for Africa's future. A team of journalists summed up Nigeria's importance to Africa in this way:

> **❝**The best hope for Africa is that the continent's two giant economies—South Africa and Nigeria—can be harnessed. . . . Together, they could become a giant market to absorb the rest of Africa's products.**❞**

But ongoing problems have cast a shadow over that hope. The causes of Nigeria's problems are lack of unity and a weak central government, new to democracy.

Varying Regions

Nigeria's lack of unity stems from its varying regions. Of the coastal nations of West Africa, Nigeria, which is approximately twice the size of California, has the most varied climate and vegetation regions. A traveler going from south to north would find coastal swamps that give way to tropical rain forest, then a large area of savanna that gradually changes to desert scrub. Rainfall also varies widely over the country. Southern regions may receive up to 120 inches (305 cm) of rain a year, while the parched north gets only 20 inches (51 cm).

A variety of crops are grown throughout Nigeria. In the south, cocoa trees, oil palms, and rubber trees thrive. In the drier north, peanuts are cultivated. The middle belt of the country supports few crops because of its poor soil.

Patterns of Settlement Historically, the most powerful cultural groups have taken control of the most valuable land. For example, the Yoruba (yaw ROO buh) settled in the southwest, the Ibo (EE bo) lived in the southeast, and the Hausa traders and Fulani herders controlled the most fertile areas of the north. Small, weak groups were left to crowd into the least fertile lands in the middle belt of the country—an area about the size of New Mexico. Not surprisingly, more than 180 different languages are spoken in the middle belt, despite the fact that English is the official language of Nigeria.

RESOURCE DIRECTORY

Teaching Resources

Unit 7, Chapter 26
- Section 3 Guided Reading and Review, p. 28

Guide to the Essentials (English/Spanish)
- Section Summary, Chapter 26, Section 3

Mental Mapping booklet
- Unit 7 Checklist, p. 91

Technology

Guided Reading Audiotapes (English/Spanish), Chapter 26, Section 3

Section Reading Support Transparencies, Chapter 26, Section 3

World Geography Map and Photo Transparencies
- Africa: Maps and Photos

Book on CD, Chapter 26

Social Studies Skills Tutor CD-ROM

Companion Web site, www.phschool.com
- Chapter 26 Activities

Population Movement Nigeria is fractured between Muslim and Christian populations. By 2000, nine of Nigeria's thirty-six states adopted Islamic law called Shariah, a move that reflects Nigeria's new democratic ideals but threatens its overall unity. Because of vast differences in governing practices, Muslims are moving north to Shariah states and Christians are moving south. Religious conflict mars Nigeria's already messy democracy.

Military Leadership

Nigeria's governmental problems arose in the early 1980s. At that time, the sale of oil was providing most of the country's income, just as it does now. Unfortunately, countries that depend on selling only one crop, product, or resource often suffer economic disaster when prices fall on the world market. Such a disaster befell Nigeria when oil prices tumbled between 1981 and 1983.

As the economy broke down, the military staged a coup. Former government leaders who had stolen money were brought to trial. The new leaders promised to correct old economic problems. To do this, they turned for help to the **World Bank** and the **International Monetary Fund** (IMF), two agencies of the United Nations that give loans to countries for development projects. In 1986 Nigeria began to follow the **structural adjustment program** that the World Bank had suggested. A structural adjustment program is a set of guidelines that is supposed to make a country's economy work better. A country cannot borrow money from the World Bank and the IMF unless it agrees to follow the adjustment program guidelines.

During its structural adjustment, the Nigerian government sold state-run businesses to private companies, fired some government workers, and did not allow wages and prices to rise. But difficult times came with structural adjustment, and students and workers often protested, keeping up pressure on the military and calling for democratic elections.

The military began to give up power in 1993, and some democratic elections occurred in the following years. A candidate named Moshood Abiola won several elections and was close to becoming president when the military suddenly

GLOBAL CONNECTIONS

Economic Activities A number of foreign oil companies participate in joint ventures designed to make the most of Nigeria's petroleum reserves. Many local communities complain that the profits from oil production benefit these companies rather than local residents. In 1998, sabotage to an oil pipeline near the village of Warri resulted in the deaths of more than 700 people. Many had been trying to collect gasoline from the damaged pipeline.

Fulani Cattle Herders

Economic Activities Fulani herdsmen seek out grazing land for their cattle in the Sahel. Despite its abundance of natural resources, Nigeria must import large amounts of food to feed its people.

Human-Environment Interaction *What effect does overgrazing have on the natural landscape in the Sahel?*

553

Nigerian Oil

Economic Activities Nigerian oil workers prepare a drilling shaft. Oil exports earn Nigeria billions of dollars each year, but oil drilling has caused widespread environmental damage. Foreign governments condemned the Nigerian government's crackdown on environmental and human rights protesters.

Human-Environment Interaction *How did Nigeria's dependence on oil exports probably affect its environmental policies?*

declared the elections void. A new military ruler ruthlessly suppressed all opposition. He jailed Abiola and executed several human-rights activists, including well-known environmentalist Ken Saro-Wiwa. The international community expressed outrage over the continuing violence. The structural adjustment program was suspended, and interest payments on Nigeria's enormous debt were delayed.

Following a change in military leadership in 1998, democratic reform slowly resumed. A new constitution was adopted, and Nigerians later elected Olusegun Obasanjo as president. A former military leader himself, Obasanjo gradually sought to restore the economy and fight government corruption.

As it moves into the twenty-first century, Nigeria faces the challenge of reducing its dependence on petroleum while improving agricultural productivity. The nation also must deal with ethnic and religious tensions among its many different cultural groups.

SECTION 3 ASSESSMENT

1. Key Terms Define **(a)** World Bank, **(b)** International Monetary Fund, **(c)** structural adjustment program.

2. Physical Characteristics How has regional variety affected patterns of settlement and population movement in Nigeria?

3. Government and Citizenship (a) What promises did military leaders make after staging a coup? **(b)** How did international organizations try to influence the Nigerian government?

4. Critical Thinking Predicting Consequences How do you think that the movement of Christians and Muslims might affect Nigerian politics?

Activity

USING THE REGIONAL ATLAS

Review the Regional Atlas for Africa and this section. Using the maps as a guide, think about how Nigeria's economy might change if the land were used differently or if the nation pursued new or additional economic activities. What challenges would your ideas introduce?

4 Central Africa

Reading Focus

- In what ways do the physical characteristics of Central Africa affect movement in the region?
- What kinds of renewable and nonrenewable resources exist in Central Africa?
- How has political turmoil affected the Democratic Republic of the Congo?

Key Terms

watershed

mercenary

barter

Main Idea Although Central Africa is rich in resources and culture, some areas face economic and political hardship.

Natural Resources The Congo River provides transportation for the people of Central Africa.

East of Nigeria, the coast of Africa turns sharply to the south. Along this southward stretch lie the seacoasts of Cameroon, Equatorial Guinea, Gabon, Congo, and the Democratic Republic of the Congo. Offshore is the island nation of the Republic of São Tomé (SOW tuh MAY) and Príncipe (preen SEEP), as well as five islands that make up the bulk of Equatorial Guinea. East of the coastal nations is the Central African Republic. Together these seven countries make up Central Africa. They range in size from the Republic of São Tomé and Príncipe, a little larger than New York City, to the Democratic Republic of the Congo, which is as large as the part of the United States east of the Mississippi River.

A Region Built by Movement

Movement of people has affected this region possibly more than any other in Africa. The region's physical characteristics have, in turn, affected the ways in which that movement has taken place.

The Big River The largest river of the region is the Congo, also called the Zaire River. Like the Niger River, its source is only a short distance from the ocean, yet it flows inland for a great many miles. The Congo winds 2,900 miles (4,666 km) through a huge basin before finding its outlet in the Atlantic Ocean. The river and its many tributaries total more than 9,000 miles (14,481 km) of waterway. The entire Congo River system is a great living highway that provides food, water, and transportation for much of the region.

Most of the Congo River is located in the Democratic Republic of the Congo. Boats can travel from Boyoma Falls in the northeast of the country to its capital, Kinshasa (kin SHAHS uh), located in the west. Below Kinshasa the course of the river is blocked by cataracts. Because boats cannot pass this stretch of the river, goods are carried overland by the railroad that links Kinshasa with the lower reaches of the Congo.

Through Forest and Savanna The basin that feeds the Congo River system is over 1 million square miles (2.6 million sq km) in area.

Chapter 26 ▪ Section 4 **555**

Articles From NATIONAL GEOGRAPHIC

The following article may be used to extend the content in this section.

Caputo, Robert, text and photographs. "Lifeline for a Nation—Zaire River." *National Geographic*, Vol. 180, No. 5 (Nov. 1991), pp. 5–35.

In a nation with few roads, river barges serve as public transportation and mobile markets, bringing goods to people throughout the former Zaire.

Section 4 *pp. 555–559*

Objectives

Upon completion of Section 4, students should be able to:

◆ describe how the physical characteristics of Central Africa affect movement in the region;

◆ list the resources in Central Africa;

◆ explain how political turmoil has affected the Democratic Republic of the Congo.

🌐 National Geography Standards

The following National Geography Standards are highlighted in this section: 5, 7, 8, 9, 11, 12, 13, 14, 15, 16, 17, 18

🔔 Bellringer

Have students make a list of what they would need to bring if they were planning a journey by foot through the African rain forest.

LESSON PLAN

1. Focus Write this phrase on the board: *the Dark Continent, darkest Africa*. Tell students that these terms were used by nineteenth-century Europeans to describe Africa. Ask: **If you heard this phrase, what would you think Africa looks like?** Then brainstorm a list of facts that students can use to dispel many common stereotypes of Africa.

2. Instruct Make a three-column chart on the board, labeling the columns *Resources, Importance*, and *Problems*. In the first column, list the following: *rivers, rain forest, oil, minerals*. Have students complete the chart.

3. Close/Reteach Have students work in pairs to brainstorm a list of possible news stories that could come out of the region in the next decade. Ask volunteers to submit their lists for class discussion.

Critical Thinking

Movement Use the following exercises and questions to help students understand how Central Africa's physical geography has affected movement in the region. Instruct students to turn to the ecosystem map on page 513 and identify the areas of rain forest and savanna in Central Africa. Ask: **Where is travel easier—on the savanna or through the rain forest? Why?** (on the savanna, because the rain forest is too dense) Ask students to find the Zaire River and its tributaries on the physical map on page 509. Ask: **Why is the Zaire River compared to a highway?** (Like a highway, it provides a passage for transport.) **Where are cities and towns located in the rain forest? Why?** (Settlements are located along rivers because the rain forest is too thick for inland travel.)

The Physical World

The Doldrums A wet and hot climate and lush tropical rain forest vegetation dominate the region of Central Africa. This area falls in the Intertropical Convergence Zone (ITCZ), or doldrums, where a permanent low-pressure system prevails with strong convectional updrafts resulting in daily heavy rainfall.

Visualizing

Have students use the subsection Through Forest and Savanna beginning on page 555 to create a simple sketch of the basin that feeds the Congo River system.

Answers to Chart Skills

Democratic Republic of the Congo
The Central African Republic does not import or export petroleum.

In the center of the basin is a dense rain forest. It is easy to see why in the distant past people shied away from entering this dark and forbidding maze of trees.

If the forest presented a frightening barrier to movement, travel on the savannas was relatively easy. These grasslands stretch around the rain forests to the north, east, and south. From ancient times people of the savanna were able to conquer others, trade, or communicate without obstacles.

Today, the forest is still a barrier to travel. Moreover, its valuable wood, such as mahogany, ebony, walnut, and iroko, can be easily harvested and exported only along rivers or where a railroad has been carved through the forest. And, in spite of the rich vegetation it supports, the forest soil is actually of little use for farming. Soil in the savanna lands, too, is often poor. People have migrated from both of these areas either to plantations located on more fertile soil or to great cities like Kinshasa or Brazzaville, the capital of Congo.

Kinshasa and Urbanization Migration has turned Kinshasa into a major world city. Its population of more than 6 million is larger than that of Vienna, Austria.

The city grew explosively in the second half of the twentieth century. Some of the people who moved to Kinshasa during those decades found wealth by working in the city's businesses or in the national government. They built expensive homes on Kinshasa's tree-lined avenues. Others continued the subsistence way of life they had known in the countryside, scraping together a living in Kinshasa's vast slums.

Rich and poor alike, however, take part in a culture that has grown from ancient African roots and has blended with the modern world. For example, Kinshasa has gained an international reputation for its popular music. A lively blend of African, rock, and pop rhythms, this music style known as Afro Pop is popular throughout the world.

Interdependence Across the Congo River from Kinshasa lies Brazzaville. Although their two countries frequently disagree politically, these two cities share the river that forms the border between them.

Brazzaville, like Kinshasa, has a rail connection with the coast, and not surprisingly the route

---

Central Africa and the United States
Energy Data

Country	Electricity Consumption Total (per capita kilowatt-hours)	Petroleum Imports (thousand barrels per year)	Petroleum Exports (thousand barrels per year)
Cameroon	174	0	27,361
Central African Republic	29	0	0
Congo	208	0	64,189
D.R. Congo	129	351	8,314
Equatorial Guinea	42	0	1,812
Gabon	731	0	127,953
São Tomé and Príncipe	96	0	0
United States	12,235	2,742,208	40,129

Source: *Encarta World Atlas*

CHART SKILLS

● **Economic Activities** *Which of these African nations both imports and exports petroleum?*

● **Science and Technology** *How does this chart suggest reliance on hydroelectric power in the Central African Republic?*

is dotted with industrial towns. The railroad also serves the inland nations of Chad and the Central African Republic, which ship mineral resources down the Ubangi (yoo BANG ee) and Congo rivers to Brazzaville and from there to the Atlantic Ocean.

Many countries of West and Central Africa belong to an African financial community known as the CFA. The CFA countries use a currency, or form of money, called the CFA franc, which has solid value on international markets because it can be exchanged for the French franc. Use of this common currency promotes trade, travel, and general interdependence among countries in the region.

Diverse Natural Resources

The rivers and forests of Central Africa not only affect movement, they are resources in themselves. In theory, they are renewable—that is, if properly used, they can be maintained and never run out. Other resources are nonrenewable—once they are used up, they are gone forever. Sometimes, however, even renewable resources in Africa are destroyed as they are exploited.

Renewable Resources The continent of Africa consists of a group of basins set in a vast plateau. When the rivers that drain the basins cut through the edge of the plateau to the coastal plain, they drop sharply. At this escarpment, the rivers have great potential for creating hydroelectric power. The Democratic Republic of the Congo, for instance, is believed to be capable of producing 100,000 megawatts of hydroelectricity; at present it produces only about 2,500. Similarly, the Central African Republic lies on a **watershed,** or dividing ridge between two basins. About 80 percent of its electricity is produced by hydropower.

But, as you read in the case of the Nile River, a river does more than serve as a power source. It provides fish to eat. Its floods deposit fresh, fertile soil on farmland and sweep the riverbanks clear of disease-carrying insects. Once a river is dammed for hydropower, fishing and farming downstream are never the same. Diseases in the region increase as well. In short, the river is not allowed to renew itself.

Rain forests in Africa, too, are often treated like a nonrenewable resource. But deforestation has been less of a problem in Central Africa than in the coastal nations of West Africa, where loggers can get to forest areas more easily. In Côte d'Ivoire, for example, 85 percent of the rain forest has been destroyed since the 1940s. At this rate, the forests may be completely cut down early in the twenty-first century.

The rain forests are valuable for many reasons. In addition to supplying lumber, they provide habitats for thousands of animal species and shelter for thousands of plants. They also absorb carbon dioxide. Increasing amounts of carbon dioxide left unabsorbed in the atmosphere may lead to what scientists call global warming—a gradual rise in global temperatures.

The nations of Central Africa are still in a position to control logging within their borders. But planting new forests costs more than most African countries can afford. Instead, countries are looking at ways in which to practice conservation

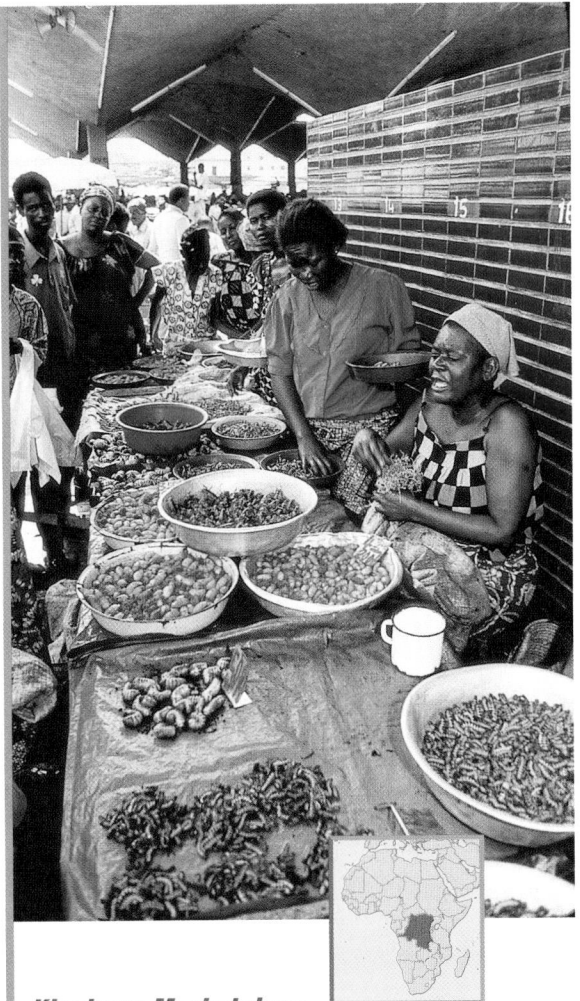

Kinshasa Marketplace

Economic Systems Kinshasa benefits from its location on the Congo River. Here women in the central market sell food fresh off the boat.

Movement *Why do goods travel from Kinshasa to the mouth of the Congo by rail rather than boat?*

and still take economic advantage of their rain forests.

Nonrenewable Resources Central African nations have many other resources besides rivers and forests. The larger Central African nations have huge deposits of minerals. The Democratic Republic of the Congo has vast copper reserves in the southeastern region of the country.

Chapter 26 ▪ Section 4   **557**

Economics Have students research the environmental challenges of one Central African country and develop a conservation plan that addresses the needs of that country.

ACTIVITY

Reteach

Paraphrasing Information Have students work in small groups. Have each member of the group read aloud a paragraph from one of the main subsections in Section 4. When a student is finished reading a section, have another member of the group paraphrase what she or he has heard. (Verbal/Linguistic)

ACTIVITY

Vocabulary

Mercenary Refer to the Key Terms list on page 555. Write the term *mercenary* on the board. Have a volunteer look up the term in the Glossary and paraphrase its definition. Ask students how mercenaries differ from other kinds of soldiers.

GL BAL CONNECTIONS

Cooperation and Conflict
International involvement in civil unrest is depriving the Democratic Republic of the Congo of its mineral wealth. As of early 2001, diamonds were being looted by warring Congolese factions backed by Uganda, Rwanda, Angola, Zimbabwe, and Namibia. Although the conflict has a political basis, the looting is so widespread that a representative for the organization Global Witness has concluded, "The war is all about diamonds."

It has more cobalt than any other country in the world, and one third of the world's industrial diamonds lie within its borders. Because of its resources, the Democratic Republic of the Congo once promised to be the same kind of economic giant in Central Africa that Nigeria was supposed to be in West Africa. But like Nigeria, the Democratic Republic of the Congo ran into economic and political troubles.

Democratic Republic of the Congo

The history of the Democratic Republic of the Congo is marked by periods of civil war and coups. Within a week of gaining independence from Belgium in 1960, it faced a revolt by its armed forces. Also, the southern province of Shaba seceded and declared itself the republic of Katanga.

A Country Divided The country was torn apart for four years as Belgian troops, United Nations forces, rebel armies, and **mercenaries**—hired soldiers—battled for power. Eventually a general who took the name Mobutu Sese Seko established himself as dictator and changed the country's name to Zaire.

Under Mobutu, Zaire regained control of Katanga and improved its mining and industries. By the 1980s, however, the nation fell deeply into debt. Mobutu was forced to begin a structural adjustment program, but it did little good. By the early 1990s, Zaire owed foreign banks nearly 9 billion dollars. Mobutu's personal wealth was also estimated to be billions of dollars. The citizens of Zaire had little difficulty guessing where their wealth had gone.

Continuing Conflict The wind of democratic change that swept over the world in the late 1980s seemed for a time to blow through Zaire as well. In April 1990, its dictator of twenty-five years announced that he was permitting the formation of other political parties and allowing a premier to rule in his place.

Copper Mining

Natural Resources The discovery of immense copper resources brought heavy industrial development to the Katanga (formerly Shaba) region of the Democratic Republic of the Congo.

Place *What were the cause and effect of violence in Katanga during the 1960s?*

558

Answer to Photo Caption

Katanga tried to secede from the newly independent nation. After four years of civil war, Katanga was reunited with the rest of the country.

RESOURCE DIRECTORY

Teaching Resources
Unit 7, Chapter 26
• Section 4 Quiz, p. 31
• Reviewing Main Ideas, p. 32
• Test Forms A and B, pp. 35–40
Spanish Resources
• Section 4 Quiz, p. 67
Guide to the Essentials (English/Spanish)
• Chapter 26 Test
Mental Mapping booklet
• Chapter 26 Map Test, p. 101
Simulations, Games, and Lab Activities
• Place Location Review Games, pp. 58–63

Social Studies Skills Handbook
• Study and Research Skills, pp. 94–108

Prentice Hall Assessment System
Alternative Assessment booklet
• Classroom Discussion Evaluation Form, p. 23

Technology
ExamView Test Bank CD-ROM, Chapter 26 Test
Companion Web site, www.phschool.com
• Chapter 26 Self-Test

Effects of Civil War

Cooperation and Conflict Over the years, civil wars have plagued Congo, Democratic Republic of Congo, and other Central African nations. Here a group of women in Brazzaville continue with their daily routine as they walk past an abandoned military tank—evidence of an outbreak of recent fighting.

Place *How does war affect daily life for the inhabitants of a place?*

But even after a new premier was installed in office, supposedly to run the country, Mobutu refused to give up power. From a compound in his native village in northern Zaire, he controlled the armed forces and police. In the resulting turmoil, people resorted to **barter,** the exchange of goods without the use of money, to get basic necessities.

In 1997, forces led by Laurent Kabila overthrew Mobutu's government. Kabila changed the nation's name to the Democratic Republic of the Congo. When Kabila was sworn in as president, civil war erupted. Neighboring nations intervened, fighting each other as well as Congolese factions for the nation's natural resources.

After Kabila was assassinated in 2001, his son, Joseph, became president. The new leader persuaded some foreign troops to leave, and in 2003, leaders of opposition parties and rebel groups joined him in a power-sharing arrangement. However, fighting continued to rage in some parts of the nation.

SECTION 4 ASSESSMENT

1. **Key Terms** Define **(a)** watershed, **(b)** mercenary, **(c)** barter.

2. **Physical Characteristics** How has the forest of Central Africa influenced human movement in this region?

3. **Natural Resources** **(a)** How does overuse of renewable resources affect nations in West and Central Africa? **(b)** How are nations responding to such overuse?

4. **Economic Systems** What problems face the Democratic Republic of the Congo?

5. **Critical Thinking** **Identifying Main Ideas** What advantages does interdependence bring to Central African countries?

Activity

Making a Map Draw a sketch map of the Congo River. Indicate the origins of the river, and plot major cities along its route. Include the locations of waterfalls that prevent travel along some stretches of the river.

TEST PREPARATION

Have students read the subsection Democratic Republic of the Congo beginning on the opposite page to complete the following statement.
From the 1960s through the 1980s, the Democratic Republic of the Congo was ruled by —
(A) a military dictator
B an army of mercenaries
C a democratically elected premier
D UN forces

Creating a Chapter Summary

As a reteaching opportunity, pair a more able student with a less able student to complete this chapter summary.

Possible answers: **Niger:** *Cause:* Valuable mineral resources that can be sold to buy food *Effect:* Sales of uranium deposits **Sierra Leone:** *Cause:* Political anarchy *Effect:* Steep drop in per capita GNP **Nigeria:** *Cause:* Dependence on a single resource *Effect:* Economic disaster when world oil prices fall **Democratic Republic of the Congo:** *Cause:* Dictatorship *Effect:* Economic turmoil and high debt

Reviewing Key Terms

1–8. Students' terms should be listed under the appropriate concepts, and their sentences should be clear and accurate.

Understanding Key Ideas

9. Peoples of the Sahel struggle to grow crops and graze livestock; in times of drought, the expanded desert area can uproot communities.
10. Under democratic leadership, private companies are taking over state-owned businesses and running them better, and newspaper publication encourages the free exchange of ideas.
11. Their economies suffer because their exports total less, in value, than their imports.
12. It has made it difficult for Nigeria to be united.
13. It provides food, water, and transportation.
14. (a) The country gained its independence from Belgium in 1960; a period of internal strife ended when General Mobutu Sese Seko took power. It was Mobutu who renamed the country Zaire. **(b)** Mobutu's government was overthrown in 1997 by Laurent Kabila, who renamed the country the Democratic Republic of the Congo.

Critical Thinking and Writing

15. It is a factual description of the region's physical characteristics. One could verify in other sources that the

---

Creating a Chapter Summary

On a sheet of paper, draw a cause-and-effect chart like this one. Identify causes and effects about economic conditions. Some information has been filled in to help you get started.

CAUSE		EFFECT
•	NIGER	• Sales of uranium deposits
• Political anarchy	SIERRA LEONE	•
•	NIGERIA	•
•	DEMOCRATIC REPUBLIC OF THE CONGO	•

Take It to the NET
Chapter Self-Test For practice test questions for Chapter 26, go to the World Geography section of **www.phschool.com**.

Reviewing Key Terms

(a) Classify each of the key terms listed below under one of the following concepts: Physical Characteristics; Economic Systems; Cultures; Cooperation and Conflict. **(b)** Choose one word in each category and write a sentence explaining how that word relates to the concept.

1. deforestation
2. inland delta
3. coup
4. ancestor worship
5. animism
6. structural adjustment program
7. watershed
8. barter

Understanding Key Ideas

9. Environmental Change How does desertification affect life in the Sahel?
10. Government and Citizenship How does Mali demonstrate wise use of human resources as a result of democracy?
11. Economic Activities How does unequal trade affect West African countries?

12. Cultures What effects has cultural diversity had on Nigeria?
13. Physical Characteristics What role does the Congo River play in Central Africa?
14. Understanding the Past **(a)** How did the country once known as the Belgian Congo come to be known as Zaire? **(b)** How did Zaire come to be known as the Democratic Republic of the Congo?

Critical Thinking and Writing

15. Distinguishing Fact From Opinion Reread the description of the Sahel on page 541. Does that description consist primarily of facts or primarily of opinions? Explain.
16. Recognizing Patterns Why have the nations of the Sahel had difficulty establishing global trade?
17. Analyzing Causes and Effects **(a)** Why have West Africans become involved in grass-roots economic efforts? **(b)** How might such efforts increase unity within a country?

savanna is the most characteristic African landscape, what a savanna region looks like, and how the landscape of the Sahel changes as one moves through it.
16. With the exception of Mauritania, these countries are landlocked, making global transportation difficult.

17. (a) They have seen that their governments often have been unable to achieve economic reform or revival. **(b)** Possible answer: People may be unified by the common purpose of improving local economic activities.

Applying Skills

Predicting Consequences Refer to the Skills for Life lesson on page 551 to answer these questions:

18. Why is predicting consequences an important skill?

19. What factors did the Nigerian government consider in developing the meal program?

20. What other consequences might result from this program?

Analyzing Data Study the table below, and answer the following questions:

21. How long might you expect to live, on average, if you were born in Ghana?

22. How does life expectancy in Cape Verde compare to life expectancy in Sierra Leone?

23. (a) Would you expect to find a relationship between life expectancy and the availability of hospital beds? (b) Does the data in this table support your conclusion? Explain.

Coastal West Africa and the United States
Health Care Data

Country	Infant Mortality Rate (per 1,000 births)	Life Expectancy (years)	Population per Hospital Bed
Benin	100	53.6	4,281
Cape Verde	48	70.5	631
Côte d'Ivoire	96	46.2	1,232
Gambia	77	53.9	1,637
Ghana	78	56.8	685
Guinea	129	46.0	1,816
Guinea-Bissau	112	49.1	677
Liberia	103	59.5	NA
Nigeria	71	53.5	599
Senegal	61	57.4	1,371
Sierra Leone	129	48.6	NA
Togo	80	58.8	662
United States	6	76.1	244

Test Preparation

Read the question and choose the best answer.

24. Overgrazing and overharvesting are major causes of —

A foraging

B coups

C watersheds

D desertification

Activities

USING THE REGIONAL ATLAS

Review the Regional Atlas for Africa and this chapter. If you were president of an organization that sent advisors into an area whose people were struggling economically, what three locations in this region would you target? Explain your choices, and describe the kinds of work that would be done by your advisors.

 MENTAL MAPPING

Study a map of Africa. Then, on a separate piece of paper, draw a sketch map of West and Central Africa from memory. Label the following places on your map:

- Democratic Republic of the Congo
- Nigeria
- Mali
- Ghana
- Sierra Leone
- Liberia
- Chad
- Kinshasa
- Congo River
- Niger River
- Atlantic Ocean

 Take It to the NET

Preparing an Oral Report On page 556, you learned about the influential musical style known as Afro Pop. Search the Internet for more information about Afro Pop and other influential elements of this region's culture. Write an oral report of your findings, including audio and video clips if possible. Visit the World Geography section of **www.phschool.com** for help in completing this activity.

Applying Skills

18. It allows people to make well-informed decisions.

19. Students need better nutrition; better nutrition will better prepare students for learning.

20. The program will probably cost taxpayers.

Analyzing Data

21. 57 years

22. Life expectancy in Cape Verde is more than 20 years longer than in Sierra Leone.

23. (a) Possible answer: A likely relationship would be that the greater the availability of hospital beds, the higher the life expectancy. (b) Possible answer: No. There does not seem to be a correlation between the two statistics.

Test Preparation
24. D

Activities

Using the Regional Atlas
Check students' choices of locations and type of work for relevance.

Mental Mapping
To check their work, have students compare their maps to those in the Regional Atlas.

Take It to the Net
Students should explain their findings clearly, giving a sense of the influential quality of the subject. You may want to have several students pool their resources and give a multimedia presentation to the class.

MENTAL MAPPING

Games for Review See pages 58–63 of the Simulations, Games, and Lab Activities booklet for games to review place names in preparation for the Chapter 26 Map Test.

Chapter Map Test Students should use the completed outline maps and the Unit 7 Checklist to prepare for the Chapter 26 Map Test. The test will cover only those place names on the checklist that relate to the region covered in this chapter.

Alternative Assessment

Final Evaluation

Classroom Discussion Use the Classroom Discussion Evaluation Form on page 23 of the Alternative Assessment booklet in the Prentice Hall Assessment System to evaluate students' participation. Either teachers or students can complete the forms to indicate which level of participation was achieved for each of the criteria. The evaluation should include specific examples and comments.

Objectives

Upon completion of this feature, students should be able to:

◆ explain the importance of biodiversity;

◆ identify why elephant and rhinoceros populations are threatened;

◆ describe conservation efforts.

 National Geography Standards

The following National Geography Standards are highlighted in this feature: 4, 8, 14, 16

 Bellringer

Write the following statistics for African elephant population (est.) on the board: *1979: 1,300,000; 1989: 600,000; 1998: 487,000.* Ask students to make a generalization about the status of the African elephant population. (The population is declining, but the rate of decline has slowed.) Ask students to speculate why the rate of decline dropped.

LESSON PLAN

1. Focus Write the word *biodiversity* on the board, and have students identify its benefits. Ask: **What human activities affect biodiversity?** (overhunting, pollution, economic development)

2. Instruct Have students read the text. Ask: **What circumstances have contributed to a decline of elephant and rhinoceros populations in Africa?** (expansion of land settlements, hunting) **What steps have people taken to reverse this decline?** (international treaty; preservation of natural habitats; ecotourism; captive breeding)

Answer to Graph Caption

They declined from approximately 65,000 to below 20,000 in 10 years.

Answer to Photo Caption

This trade promotes animal hunting and killing, which leads to a decline in population.

People and Geography
Environmental Conservation and Africa

Black Rhino Population

Endangered Species
Why did people become alarmed about rhinoceros populations in the 1980s?

Biodiversity Threatened

Biodiversity, or the variety of all life on earth, provides essential benefits. We rely on plants and animals for food, medicine, clothing, and other products. Many species provide ecological benefits by limiting soil erosion, influencing the atmosphere, changing solar energy into food energy, and performing other functions. If these benefits were no longer provided, the earth could become less suitable for all life.

Around the world, thousands of species of plants and animals are threatened. If a species is greatly reduced in number or becomes extinct, there may be negative effects on others species and even on entire ecosystems. Human activities such as overhunting, pollution, and economic development are part of the problem. In Africa, for example, human activities have contributed to great reductions in the populations of elephants and black rhinoceroses.

African Elephants and Rhinos

As people in Africa use more land for settlements and agriculture, the natural habitats of elephants and rhinos are lost. Hunting is another threat to these animals. For centuries, people have used ivory from elephants' tusks to make piano keys, jewelry, and other decorative items. At the same time, the international market for rhino horn has encouraged hunters to kill rhinos. In China, the Koreas, and other parts of East Asia, the horn is used to make traditional medicines. In the Southwest Asian country of Yemen, people pay high prices for daggers with handles made of rhino horn. For years, laws have limited the hunting of elephants and rhinos. However, illegal hunting continues because of the huge profits that can be made.

African Elephants

1979: 1.3 million
1989: 600,000

Global Trade
How does the international trade in traditional medicines and ivory goods affect animal populations?

RESOURCE DIRECTORY

Technology

World Geography Map and Photo Transparencies
• Africa: Physical

Conservation Efforts

In Africa and around the world, people are working together to reduce the threats to elephants, rhinos, and other species. The Convention on Trade in Endangered Species (CITES) is an international treaty ratified by more than 150 member nations. By this treaty, nations have agreed to control or prohibit trade in over 40,000 species of animals and plants. As part of this agreement, there is a ban on international trade in ivory and rhino horn. However, levels of law enforcement vary from country to country and illegal trade continues.

Another conservation effort is the preservation of natural habitats. In Africa, there is a growing number of national parks and reserves. Populations of black rhinos were stabilized in the early 1990s, largely because of thriving populations in protected habitats in South Africa. African governments have also promoted ecotourism. Tourists visiting national parks and reserves bring in millions of dollars to the economies of African nations.

Captive breeding is yet another effort at conserving species. In 2000, for example, there were around 200 black rhinos in at least 70 different zoos. Most of these rhinos were born in captivity. Zoos around the world cooperate in efforts to breed more rhinos.

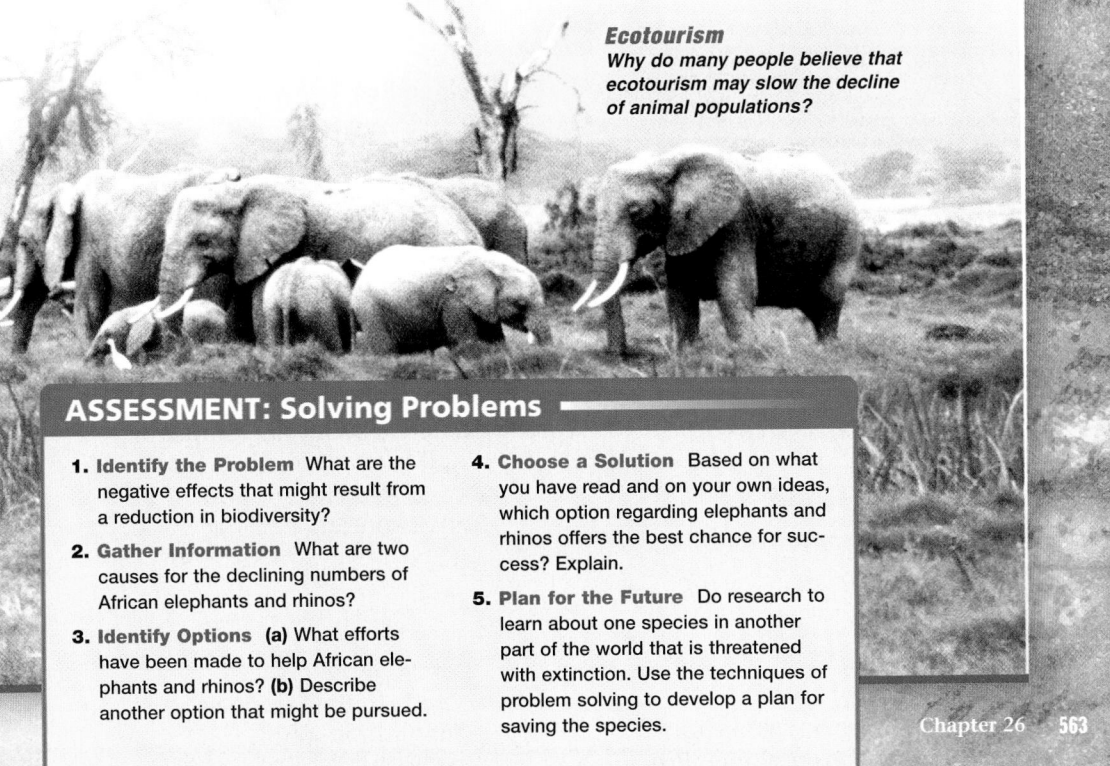

KENYA WILDLIFE SERVICE
ABERDARE NATIONAL PARK
WARNING – DANGER
VISITORS ENTER THIS NATIONAL PARK ENTIRELY AT THEIR OWN RISK PLEASE EXERCISE CARE AND KEEP A SAFE DISTANCE FROM ANY DANGEROUS ANIMALS—THEY HAVE THE RIGHT OF WAY

A Possible Solution
How are the governments of Kenya and other African countries trying to solve the problem of endangered species?

Ecotourism
Why do many people believe that ecotourism may slow the decline of animal populations?

ASSESSMENT: Solving Problems

1. **Identify the Problem** What are the negative effects that might result from a reduction in biodiversity?

2. **Gather Information** What are two causes for the declining numbers of African elephants and rhinos?

3. **Identify Options** **(a)** What efforts have been made to help African elephants and rhinos? **(b)** Describe another option that might be pursued.

4. **Choose a Solution** Based on what you have read and on your own ideas, which option regarding elephants and rhinos offers the best chance for success? Explain.

5. **Plan for the Future** Do research to learn about one species in another part of the world that is threatened with extinction. Use the techniques of problem solving to develop a plan for saving the species.

Chapter 26   **563**

CUSTOMIZE FOR...

Gifted and Talented

Return of Animals to the Wild Have students use the library or the Internet to research the controversy over the reintroduction of an endangered species to the wild. Some examples of animals that students could choose would be California condors reintroduced in the western United States, wolves reintroduced in the Yellowstone Park area, black-footed ferrets reintroduced in Arizona, and grizzly bears reintroduced in Idaho and Montana. After students gather their information, have them write a short oral report and present their findings to the class.

3. Close/Reteach Have students review the reasons that they originally offered for why the rate of decline of the elephant population had slowed. Ask: **Based on what you now know, how might you change this list of reasons?**

ACTIVITY

Group Work

Activity: Planning an ecotourism trip

Purpose: Have students research and plan an ecotourism trip they would like to take. To show where they would travel, what they would do, and which types of animals they would see, have them create a scrapbook with pictures and captions that would illustrate their travel itinerary.

Roles: Researchers, photo editors, writers, and editors

Result: Display the scrapbooks in the classroom. Have groups present their scrapbooks to the class.

Answers to Assessment

1. fewer sources of food, medicine, clothing, and other products; loss of ecological benefits such as limiting soil erosion

2. loss of natural habitats and hunting

3. (a) More than 150 nations have agreed to a treaty to control or prohibit trade in more than 40,000 species of plants and animals; natural habitats are being preserved; animals are being bred in captivity. **(b)** Possible answer: public campaign to discourage purchase or use of goods made from endangered species.

4. Possible answer: A combination of all the options would probably work best since no single solution provides the whole answer; however, the strongest single option is probably to enforce existing laws. Unless people feel immediate consequences, they will not be motivated to stop illegal hunting.

5. The answer will depend on each student's choice.

Answers to Photo Captions

by developing wildlife preserves
The money brought into nations by ecotourism will decrease the need for income from hunting.

Chapter 26   **563**

Chapter 27 Planning Guide

Resource Manager

	CORE INSTRUCTION	READING/SKILLS
Chapter-Level Resources	**Teaching Resources** **Unit 7**/Ch. 27 • Reviewing Main Ideas, p. 49 **Mental Mapping booklet** • Unit 7 Checklist, p. 91 **Simulations, Games, and Lab Activities** • Place Location Review Games, pp. 58–63 **TeacherExpress™ CD-ROM**, Ch. 27 **Companion Web site, www.phschool.com** • eTeach	**Teaching Resources** **Unit 7**/Ch. 27 • Map/Graph Skills, p. 51 **Mental Mapping booklet** • Outline Map 27, p. 102 **Book on CD**, Ch. 27 **Social Studies Skills Tutor CD-ROM**
1 Kenya 1. Identify some major physical characteristics of Kenya. 2. Describe how British rule affected the settlement of Kenya. 3. Identify the economic activities that improved Kenya's economy. 4. Explain why Kenyans are concerned about the government's stability.	**Teaching Resources** **Unit 7**/Ch. 27 • Guided Reading and Review, p. 41 **Creative Teaching Activities** • Preserving the Wildlife of Africa, p. 29 **Prentice Hall Presentation Pro CD-ROM**, Ch. 27, Sec. 1	**Teaching Resources** **Guide to the Essentials (English/Spanish)** • Section Summary, Ch. 27, Sec. 1 **Guided Reading Audiotapes (English/Spanish)**, Ch. 27, Sec. 1 **Section Reading Support Transparencies**, Ch. 27, Sec. 1
2 Other Countries of East Africa 1. Show how several countries on the Horn of Africa are strategically located. 2. Identify the issues that divide the people of the Sudan. 3. Describe the effects of drought and political conflict on the region's landlocked countries. 4. Explain why Tanzania changed its system of government.	**Teaching Resources** **Unit 7**/Ch. 27 • Guided Reading and Review, p. 43 **Prentice Hall Presentation Pro CD-ROM**, Ch. 27, Sec. 2	**Teaching Resources** **Guide to the Essentials (English/Spanish)** • Section Summary, Ch. 27, Sec. 2 **Guided Reading Audiotapes (English/Spanish)**, Ch. 27, Sec. 2 **Section Reading Support Transparencies**, Ch. 27, Sec. 2
3 South Africa 1. Identify the conditions that divided life in South Africa. 2. Describe the international backlash against the white South African government. 3. Explain how South Africa transformed from a repressive police state to a model for peaceful political change.	**Teaching Resources** **Unit 7**/Ch. 27 • Guided Reading and Review, p. 45 **Prentice Hall Presentation Pro CD-ROM**, Ch. 27, Sec. 3	**Teaching Resources** **Guide to the Essentials (English/Spanish)** • Section Summary, Ch. 27, Sec. 3 **Guided Reading Audiotapes (English/Spanish)**, Ch. 27, Sec. 3 **Section Reading Support Transparencies**, Ch. 27, Sec. 3
4 Other Countries of Southern Africa 1. Describe how Malawi and Botswana have been affected by South Africa. 2. Summarize how colonialism affected Angola and Mozambique. 3. Explain the effect of farming policy on Zambia and Zimbabwe.	**Teaching Resources** **Unit 7**/Ch. 27 • Guided Reading and Review, p. 47 **Prentice Hall Presentation Pro CD-ROM**, Ch. 27, Sec. 4	**Teaching Resources** **Guide to the Essentials (English/Spanish)** • Section Summary, Ch. 27, Sec. 4 **Guided Reading Audiotapes (English/Spanish)**, Ch. 27, Sec. 4 **Section Reading Support Transparencies**, Ch. 27, Sec. 4

ENRICHMENT/HONORS/PREAP

📕 **Teaching Resources**

📘 **Unit 7**/Ch. 27
- Critical Thinking, p. 50

📘 **Mental Mapping booklet**
- Atlas Activity, p. 103

📘 **Social Studies Skills Handbook**
- Study and Research Skills, pp. 94–108

📖 **World Geography Map and Photo Transparencies**
- Africa: Maps and Photos
- How the Earth Works, Unit 7

📺 **World Geography Videos**
- Physical Characteristics: East and Southern Africa, Tape 3

💻 **Companion Web site,**
www.phschool.com
- Chapter 27 Activities

💻 **Companion Web site,**
www.phschool.com
- Chapter 27 Activities

💻 **Companion Web site,**
www.phschool.com
- Chapter 27 Activities

📕 **Teaching Resources**

📘 **Unit 7**/Ch. 27
- Geography and World Literature, p. 58

💻 **Companion Web site,**
www.phschool.com
- Chapter 27 Activities

💻 **Companion Web site,**
www.phschool.com
- Chapter 27 Activities

ASSESSMENT

PRENTICE HALL ASSESSMENT SYSTEM

Core Assessment

📘 ExamView Test Bank booklet, Ch. 27

💿 ExamView Test Bank CD-ROM, Ch. 27

💿 ExamView Test Bank CD-ROM, Unit 7

Standardized Test Preparation

Review and Reteach

📘 Review Book for World Geography, pp. 15–16

Practice and Assess

📘 Test-taking Strategies With Transparencies for High School

Test-taking Strategy Poster

📘 Alternative Assessment booklet

📘 Test Prep Book for World Geography

📕 **Teaching Resources**

📘 **Unit 7**/Ch. 27
- Section Quizzes, pp. 42, 44, 46, 48
- Test Forms A and B, pp. 52–57

📘 **Guide to the Essentials (English/Spanish)**
- Chapter 27 Test

📘 **Spanish Resources**, Ch. 27
- Section Quizzes, pp. 68–71

📘 **Mental Mapping booklet**
- Chapter 27 Map Test, p. 104
- Unit 7 Map Test, p. 105

💻 **Companion Web site, www.phschool.com**
- Chapter 27 Self-Test

CUSTOMIZE FOR INDIVIDUAL NEEDS

Gifted and Talented
- Teacher's Edition, Customize for . . . , p. 579

Honors/PreAP
- Teacher's Edition, Customize for . . . , p. 571

Less Proficient Readers
- Guide to the Essentials (English), Ch. 27, Section Summaries
- Guided Reading Audiotapes (English), Ch. 27
- Section Reading Support Transparencies, Ch. 27
- Book on CD, Ch. 27
- Teacher's Edition, Reading Strategy, pp. 566, 572, 574, 581
- Teacher's Edition, Activity: Vocabulary, pp. 567, 570, 575, 579, 583
- Teacher's Edition, Customize for . . . , p. 573

Students Acquiring English/ESL
- Guide to the Essentials (English/Spanish), Ch. 27
- Guided Reading Audiotapes (English/Spanish), Ch. 27
- Section Reading Support Transparencies, Ch. 27
- Book on CD, Ch. 27
- Teacher's Edition, Customize for . . . , pp. 567, 581

Less Proficient Writers
- Alternative Assessment, Writing Assignment Rubric, p. 6
- Teacher's Edition, Customize for . . . , p. 577

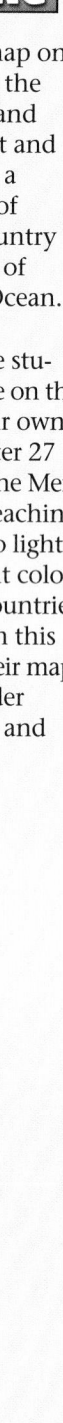

(M)ENTAL MAPPING

Ask students to look at the map on this page, and point out that the countries that make up East and Southern Africa lie to the east and south of the Sahara, forming a crescent around the bottom of Central Africa. The island country of Madagascar is located east of Mozambique in the Indian Ocean.

Mapping the Region Have students create a map like the one on this page. Ask them to sketch their own maps, or distribute the Chapter 27 Outline Map on page 102 of the Mental Mapping booklet in the Teaching Resources. Instruct students to lightly shade each country a different color. Then ask them to label the countries and bodies of water shown on this map. Students should keep their maps in their Atlas Portfolios in order to prepare for the Chapter 27 and Unit 7 map tests.

eTeach

Be sure to check out this month's online forum with a Master Teacher to join in an exchange of teaching ideas. **www.phschool.com**

C H A P T E R

27

East and Southern Africa

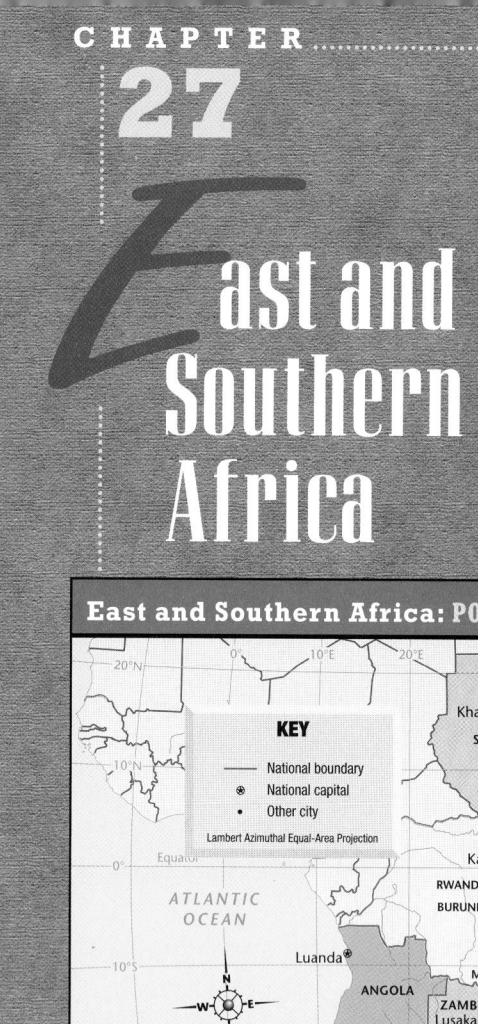

SECTIONS

1	**Kenya**
2	**Other Countries of East Africa**
3	**South Africa**
4	**Other Countries of Southern Africa**

East and Southern Africa: POLITICAL

KEY
— National boundary
⊛ National capital
• Other city

Lambert Azimuthal Equal-Area Projection

Go Online
PHSchool.com

For: More information about East and Southern Africa and access to the Take It to the Net activities
Visit: phschool.com
Web Code: mjk-0028

RESOURCE DIRECTORY

Teaching Resources

Unit 7, Chapter 27
• Section 1 Guided Reading and Review, p. 41

Guide to the Essentials (English/Spanish)
• Section Summary, Chapter 27, Section 1

Mental Mapping booklet
• Atlas Activity, p. 103
• Unit 7 Checklist, p. 91

Technology

Guided Reading Audiotapes (English/Spanish),
Chapter 27, Section 1

Section Reading Support Transparencies,
Chapter 27, Section 1

World Geography Map and Photo Transparencies
• Africa: Maps and Photos

Book on CD, Chapter 27

World Geography Videos
• Physical Characteristics: East and Southern Africa, Tape 3

TeacherExpress™ CD-ROM, Chapter 27

Prentice Hall Presentation Pro CD-ROM, Chapter 27

Social Studies Skills Tutor CD-ROM

Companion Web site, www.phschool.com
• Chapter 27 Activities

1 Kenya

Reading Focus

- What are some major physical characteristics of Kenya?
- In the past, how did British rule affect patterns of settlement in Kenya?
- What economic activities helped Kenyans to build a solid economy for their country?
- Why are the citizens of Kenya concerned about the political stability of their government?

Key Terms

harambee

pyrethrum

malnutrition

Main Idea A spirit of cooperation has helped Kenya to develop its economy, especially in cash crop agriculture.

Natural Resources The fertile landscape of Kenya's highland region is ideal for herding.

Kenya has many features that have become symbols of Africa—rolling savanna lands, highland coffee plantations, the nomadic Masai (mah SY) people, and spectacular national parks where elephants, lions, and other protected wildlife roam freely.

Kenya is, of course, more than just these symbols. It is a vibrant country with a population of more than 30 million and a varied and beautiful landscape.

Physical Characteristics

Kenya is located on the east coast of Africa and extends deep into the interior of the continent. As the map on page 566 shows, the Equator runs right through the center of the country, so parts of Kenya are bathed in steamy heat. In addition, the Great Rift Valley slices through Kenya's highlands, where elevation makes the climate cooler.

Most of Kenya's people live in the fertile highlands of the country's southwest region. Rainfall is uncertain in northern Kenya, making the area prone to drought. The plateau that leads toward the center of the country, gradually rising toward

the west, is the driest part of Kenya. In contrast, the highlands receive adequate rainfall, and forests and grasslands cover much of the area. In the westernmost corner of the region is magnificent Lake Victoria, the largest lake in Africa.

Understanding the Past

The most fertile land in Kenya, found in the central highlands along the Great Rift Valley, has been a main area of activity for centuries. When Kenya came under British rule in the early 1890s, two groups occupied the highlands: a group of herders called the Masai, and another group, the Kikuyu (ki KOO yoo). Under the British, however, these groups lost their most fertile farmland and all political power.

The Railroad Arrives In an effort to encourage economic development and to gain access to the rich farmland in the central highlands, the British decided to build a railroad from the coast to Lake Victoria. It was an extremely difficult task that cost thousands of lives and millions of dollars. One writer described the hazards involved as follows.

 Cape Town, South Africa *(photo left)*

Chapter 27 • Section 1 **565**

Section 1 *pp. 565–568*

Objectives

Upon completion of Section 1, students should be able to:

◆ identify some major physical characteristics of Kenya;

◆ describe how British rule affected the settlement of Kenya;

◆ identify the economic activities that improved Kenya's economy;

◆ explain why Kenyans are concerned about the government's stability.

 National Geography Standards

The following National Geography Standards are highlighted in this section: 1, 4, 5, 6, 7, 8, 9, 10, 11, 12, 13, 16, 17

 Bellringer

Read students this passage by Jomo Kenyatta, Kenya's first president: "If you woke up one morning and found that somebody had come to your house, and had declared that the house belonged to him, you would naturally . . . like to know by what arrangement." Ask students what they think Kenyatta meant by this.

LESSON PLAN

1. Focus Tell students to look at the map and the photographs in this section. Then have them write captions for three photographs they might have taken on a trip to Kenya.

2. Instruct Tell students they have been asked to write a chapter on Kenya for a guide book. Ask them to list the topics they will include.

3. Close/Reteach To play a quiz game, write the following "answers" on the board: (1) *Lake Victoria* (2) *Kikuyu* (3) *Kenya's first president*. Then have students supply questions to go with the answers. Ask volunteers to write more answers.

TEACHING TIP
From A Master Teacher

East and Southern Africa When teaching about East and Southern Africa, it is difficult not to focus on the region's problems. Students should be told that the causes of some of these problems came from outside the region. The legacy of slavery and colonialism and the consequent development of export-oriented economies still affect the region's economies. The struggles for democracy and ethnic tensions that plague the region are a remnant of the imposition of national boundaries on diverse groups of people.

Pacing Suggestions

For 60-minute Blocks

You will want to vary activities.

- Hand out copies of Outline Map 27 from the Mental Mapping booklet. Have students label the countries, capital cities, and major rivers and lakes. Ask them to list bodies of water that serve as national boundaries and cities that are located on waterways. Then ask them to write a brief essay about the role they think waterways play in the region.

Chapter 27 • Section 1 **565**

READING STRATEGY

Summarizing Main Ideas

For each subheading in Section 1, have students write a sentence that explains the main idea introduced by the heading. Tell students to keep these sentences to help them review what they have learned about Kenya.

BACKGROUND

The Global Economy

Ecotourism Kenya has created huge wildlife preserves where elephants, rhinos, lions, and other large game animals can roam freely. These preserves attract hundreds of thousands of tourists from the United States, Europe, and other places each year, making ecotourism, or tourism based on the environment, an important part of Kenya's economy.

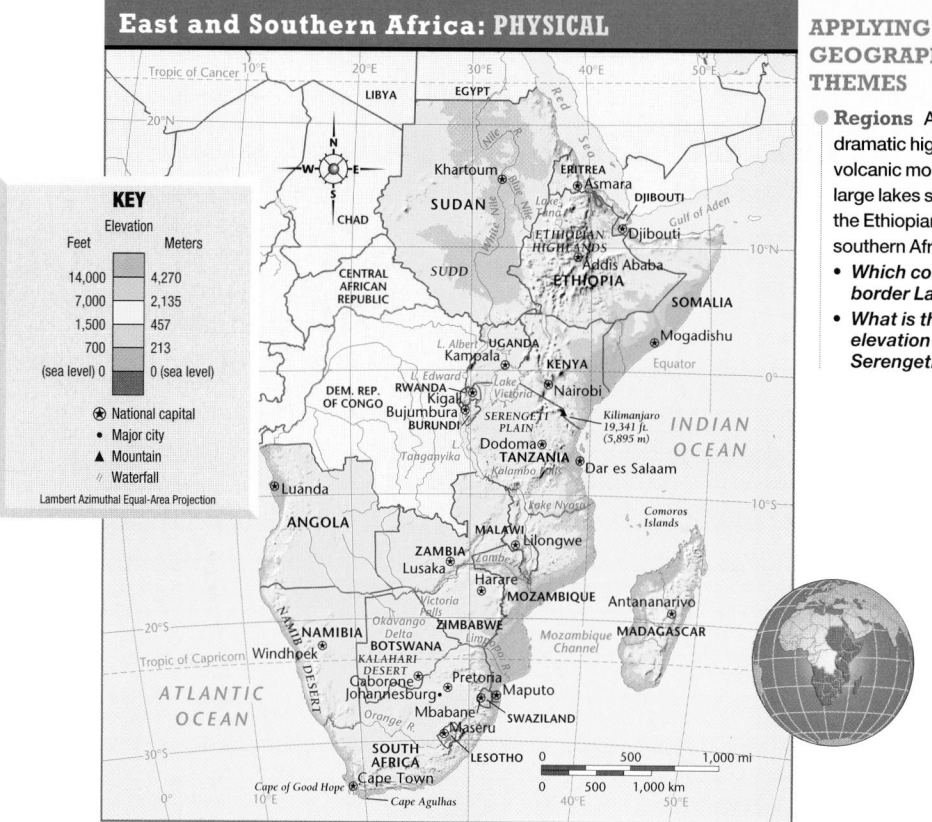

East and Southern Africa: PHYSICAL

KEY

Elevation

Feet	Meters
14,000	4,270
7,000	2,135
1,500	457
700	213
(sea level) 0	0 (sea level)

⊛ National capital
• Major city
▲ Mountain
⌇ Waterfall

Lambert Azimuthal Equal-Area Projection

APPLYING THE GEOGRAPHIC THEMES

● **Regions** A line of dramatic highlands, volcanic mountains, and large lakes stretches from the Ethiopian Plateau to southern Africa.

• *Which countries border Lake Victoria?*
• *What is the average elevation of the Serengeti Plain?*

66Waterless deserts, man-eating lions who preyed on and terrorized the [workers] . . . fever and sickness, the scaling of mountains, the spanning of valleys, the bridging of rivers that turned into swollen torrents in the rain—all these, and many more obstacles, had to be overcome.99

Despite the many challenges of the physical environment, the railroad was finally completed in 1903.

The new transportation link across Kenya brought changes. The British government encouraged its citizens and other Europeans to settle in Kenya and develop the highlands. White settlers, some from South Africa, were eager to move into the cool climate of the highlands. A new town was built on the railroad line. It was called Nairobi (ny RO bee) and it grew very rapidly.

Kenyans Challenge the British

The white settlers took over much of the land that the Kikuyu had traditionally considered their own. Many were forced to work on farms run by settlers.

In the 1950s, the Kikuyu went to war against the British settlers in Kenya in a fierce confrontation called the Mau Mau Rebellion. The rebellion was crushed, but one of the leaders of the Kikuyu, Jomo Kenyatta, became president one year after Kenya emerged from British rule in 1963. Under Kenyatta, the Kikuyu regained some of their farms in the central highlands.

Economic Activities

Kenyatta encouraged all parts of the economy—the government, privately held companies, and individuals—to work together to strengthen

RESOURCE DIRECTORY

Teaching Resources

Creative Teaching Activities, Preserving the Wildlife of Africa, p. 29

Mental Mapping booklet
• Chapter 27 Outline Map, p. 102

Technology

World Geography Map and Photo Transparencies
• Africa: Maps and Photos

Answers to Map Caption

Uganda, Kenya, and Tanzania
1,500–7,000 feet (457–2,135 m)

Nairobi Skyline

Government and Citizenship The city of Nairobi is Kenya's capital and main center of industry. Roads and railways connect Nairobi to the port of Mombasa on the Indian Ocean.

Movement *How did location along a railroad line benefit Nairobi?*

Kenya's economy. He called this working together *harambee,* from a Swahili word that means "pulling together."

Working Together *Harambee* grew as a grass-roots movement of people pulling together to help themselves and each other. Many foreign investors were pleased with Kenyatta's attitude and willingly pulled together with the Kenyans.

The result of this cooperation was solid economic growth. Because Kenya has little mineral wealth, the growth was based mostly on expanding agriculture. Kenyatta encouraged farmers to raise cash crops—coffee and tea—which grow well on the fertile central highland farms of the Kikuyu. Many government officials were Kikuyu, and they soon grew wealthy from their own farming.

Not Enough Food Rather than growing food, the government has concentrated on growing cash crops—especially certain flowers used to produce **pyrethrum** (py REE thrum), a pesticide, as well as luxuries like coffee and tea. As more land is used for cash crops, there is less land available for subsistence agriculture. For example, 30 percent of the country's wheat has to be imported, even while fresh flowers, fruits, and vegetables are rushed out of the country by air

freight for sale in Europe. As a result, many Kenyans suffer from **malnutrition,** a disease caused by not having a healthy diet.

Government and Citizenship

Since independence, Kenya has been one of the most admired and stable countries in Africa. In the 1980s, however, Kenya began to face hard times. The population grew at an astounding rate, at times more than 4 percent a year. Kenya was unable to supply its rapidly growing population with enough food or jobs. Social and political unrest developed, and ethnic groups that had lived in peace with one another since independence began to clash.

GLOBAL CONNECTIONS

Economic Activities Kenya's wildlife reserves draw millions of tourists from around the world each year. But with one of the fastest-growing populations in Africa, Kenya suffers a severe shortage of land. The Masai need open rangeland in two of Kenya's biggest reserves to continue their traditional way of life. To offer them an alternative, the government is giving them a share of the profits from tourism.

Chapter 27 ▪ Section 1 **567**

Nairobi Founded in the 1890s as a railroad depot, Nairobi has grown into a cosmopolitan capital with many international links. Tourists from Asia, Europe, and the Americas land in the city before going on safari. Representatives from around the world address global issues at the United Nations Environmental Program, based in Nairobi.

Answers to
Section 1 Assessment
1. (a) *harambee*, p. 567
(b) pyrethrum, p. 567
(c) malnutrition, p. 567
2. Physical characteristics include fertile highlands in the southwest, covered with forests and grasslands; a dry central plateau; and Lake Victoria, the largest lake in Africa.
3. The railroad led to the creation of the capital, Nairobi, and encouraged settlement of the central highlands.
4. There is less land available for subsistence agriculture, and many Kenyans suffer from malnutrition.
5. (a) Rapid population growth, government corruption, and ethnic violence have caused problems.
(b) Possible answer: Kenya's future stability relies on cooperation.
6. The elevation of the highlands gives them a cool climate.

Activity Rubrics Share rubrics with students before they plan their safaris.
Minimal The plan is incomplete or messy.
Attempted The plan includes basic information about key places and costs but contains some errors in content.
Adequate The plan shows sufficient research and includes information about key sites.
Exemplary The plan reflects extensive research, is well organized, and includes a complete overview of key sites and costs.

Answer to Photo Caption
It has led to malnutrition.

568 Chapter 27

Kenyan Cash Crop

Economic Activities The fertile soil in the Great Rift Valley is good for farming. Lush coffee plantations cover the hilly terrain. Yet, because the government wants farmers to focus on cash crops for export, many Kenyans lack adequate food.

Place *How does concentration on cash crop production affect the health of Kenyans?*

Political Reforms Many Kenyans blamed the country's president, Daniel arap Moi, for their troubles. They accused him of corruption and mismanagement of the economy. Like citizens in other countries south of the Sahara, they demonstrated for democratic reforms in the government.

At first, President Moi refused to allow multiparty elections. He punished independent judges, threw critics in jail, and closed down newspapers that protested his policies. Moi finally agreed to permit multiparty elections after Western nations withheld loans the government needed badly. In both 1992 and 1997, he won the presidency by narrow margins in elections marred by violence. However, after another election in 2002, Mwai Kibaki won the office, and Moi stepped aside peacefully.

Search for Peace The struggle for unity and peace continues, despite setbacks. Ethnic violence has forced thousands of farmers in the Great Rift Valley off their land, which has further hurt food production. Though the violence has quieted, many worry that a government stained by corruption will again bring bloodshed at election time.

Still, Kenyans are hopeful of regaining their unity and prosperity, and they draw inspiration from the symbols of their nation. Kenya's flag has stripes of three colors: black, for the people of Kenya; red, representing their struggle for independence; and green, symbolizing the country's agriculture. The seal of the Republic of Kenya shows two lions leaning on a shield. Beneath them is the word *harambee*, reminding Kenyans of the importance of pulling together for their nation's future.

SECTION 1 ASSESSMENT

1. **Key Terms** Define **(a)** *harambee*, **(b)** pyrethrum, **(c)** malnutrition.

2. **Physical Characteristics** Describe the physical characteristics of Kenya.

3. **Understanding the Past** What changes did the British railroad bring to Kenya?

4. **Economic Activities** How has the growth of cash crop agriculture affected Kenyans?

5. **Government and Citizenship** **(a)** Why has Kenya been unstable since the 1980s? **(b)** How is the future stability of Kenya linked to *harambee*?

6. **Critical Thinking** **Analyzing Causes and Effects** Why are the highlands of Kenya cool even though they are on the Equator?

Activity

Planning a Safari Ecotourism is an important economic activity in Kenya. Gather some additional information about Kenya's wildlife reserves from the library or on the Internet. Then, plan a safari for tourists. Include information about key places to visit and the approximate cost. Keep in mind that ecotourism is responsible travel to natural areas, meaning that all efforts should be made by visitors to conserve the environment and maintain the well-being of the local community.

2 Other Countries of East Africa

Reading Focus

- **In what ways are several countries on the Horn of Africa strategically located?**
- **What physical characteristics and regional issues divide the people of the Sudan?**
- **How has drought and political conflict slowed the growth of many of the landlocked countries of this region?**
- **Why did Tanzania change its government?**

Key Terms

strategic value   villagization

ethnocracy

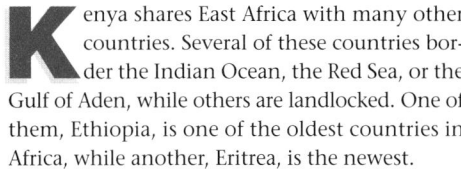

Main Idea   Regional conflicts and drought leading to famine have disrupted many East African nations.

Cooperation and Conflict   UN workers help Ethiopians rebuild a road destroyed by war.

Section 2   *pp. 569–572*

Objectives

Upon completion of Section 2, students should be able to:

 show how several countries on the Horn of Africa are strategically located;

 identify the physical characteristics and regional issues that divide the people of the Sudan;

◆ describe the effects of drought and political conflict on the region's landlocked countries;

◆ explain why Tanzania changed its system of government.

National Geography Standards

The following National Geography Standards are highlighted in this section: 2, 3, 4, 5, 6, 9, 10, 11, 13, 17

Bellringer

Tell students that Eritrea gained its independence from Ethiopia in 1991. Ask: **How would this change have affected Ethiopian trade?** (Ethiopia lost its access to the sea.)

LESSON PLAN

1. Focus Point out that the recent history of East Africa has included civil wars and severe droughts. Have students make a list of the effects of war and drought on people.

2. Instruct Write the following country names on the board: *Sudan, Ethiopia, Eritrea, Djibouti, Somalia, Uganda, Rwanda, Burundi, Tanzania.* Have students take turns writing on the board a fact about one of the countries. Remind students that they can learn facts from charts and maps, as well as from text. Then have students decide if each fact is a "plus" or a "minus" for the country's future.

3. Close/Reteach Have students write a one- or two-sentence prognosis for each of the countries in the region. Then have students discuss what they have written.

Kenya shares East Africa with many other countries. Several of these countries border the Indian Ocean, the Red Sea, or the Gulf of Aden, while others are landlocked. One of them, Ethiopia, is one of the oldest countries in Africa, while another, Eritrea, is the newest.

The Horn of Africa

The region's coastal location gives some of its countries special opportunities for trade as well as **strategic value**—the value of the location to nations planning large-scale military actions. The countries of Ethiopia, Eritrea, Djibouti (ji BOO tee), and Somalia are located on a landmass known as the Horn of Africa. These countries have particularly strategic locations. They lie near both the oil supplies of the Middle East and the shipping lanes of the Red Sea and the Gulf of Aden. These countries are also strategically located at the midpoint between Europe and Southeast Asia.

Djibouti Djibouti is a vital link between neighboring Ethiopia's capital city of Addis Ababa and the sea. Djibouti earns most of its income from its strategic ports. France pays large fees to

Djibouti for the right to maintain a military base in the country. When civil war broke out in 1991, France tried to bring the two sides to the negotiating table. Even though the ruling party agreed to a new constitution, unrest continued to strangle the country for many years. A presidential election was held in 1999, followed by a peace agreement in 2000. Djibouti has started to repair its agriculture, its educational and health care facilities, and its infrastructure.

Ethiopia Ethiopia has one of the longest histories of all the nations in Africa. Ruins and ancient Egyptian writings record the history of the Kushite civilization in Ethiopia about 3,500 years ago. The region's high, fertile plateaus, which enjoy temperate climates, rise like massive walls above the deserts of the Sudan to the west and Somalia to the east. In recent years, regional conflict and drought have brought this ancient nation almost to the edge of collapse.

Droughts in 1984 and 1986 caused famine and starvation in Ethiopia. In addition, war with Somalia, as well as civil war in the coastal province of Eritrea, caused grave crises. Other nations sent aid to Ethiopia, but the civil war prevented food

GLOBAL CONNECTIONS

Science and Technology In 2000, experts estimated that more than 25 million people in Africa were infected with the virus believed to cause AIDS. Although AIDS has spread around the world, Africa is the continent most strongly affected. According to the United Nations, African nations need $3 billion annually to improve AIDS education, prevention, and care. Such efforts have been successful in Uganda, where infection rates dropped during the 1990s.

from reaching those who needed it.

In 1991 the Ethiopian government was overthrown; and at about the same time, the Ethiopian army was beaten by Eritrean guerrillas. Ethiopia was forced to allow Eritrea its independence, and as a result Ethiopia's relative location changed. Once situated strategically on the Red Sea, Ethiopia is now landlocked. It is still badly torn by ethnic division. Within the first few years of its new government, at least 100 political parties appeared, most of them based on ethnic grouping.

Eritrea After winning its independence, Eritrea began to rebuild an economy damaged by three decades of fighting. Economic reconstruction replaced independence as the major national goal. Said one Eritrean:

> 66 There is almost a demonic [fierce] determination to get things done. It's one of those things I think comes out of suffering. The thirty years of war—one of the dividends . . . was this tremendous sense of discipline. 99

Progress was made at first. The capital city of Asmara was rebuilt and its streets filled with bustling taxis and buses. A new steel mill melted down old military equipment for peaceful uses. Steam engines from the 1930s were refurbished for use on the rail line to the main port. Much of this was accomplished with little borrowing from other nations.

Unfortunately, a border war with Ethiopia from 1998 to 2000 and a successive downturn in the world economy slowed progress significantly. Subsistence farming and herding remained the mainstays of the Eritrean economy. The situation would be more precarious were it not for money

East Africa and the United States
Economic Data

Country	GDP per Capita (U.S. dollars)	GDP Growth Rate (percentage)	Inflation Rate (percentage)
Burundi	600	1.4	14.0
Djibouti	1,400	0.0	2.0
Eritrea	740	7.0	15.0
Ethiopia	700	7.3	6.8
Kenya	1,000	1.0	3.3
Rwanda	1,000	5.0	5.0
Somalia	550	3.0	100.0+
Sudan	1,360	5.5	10.0
Tanzania	610	5.0	5.0
Uganda	1,200	5.1	3.5
United States	36,300	0.3	2.8

Source: *The World Factbook*

CHART SKILLS

- **Economic Activities** *Which country has the lowest gross domestic product?*
- **Cooperation and Conflict** *Which country has the highest inflation rate? How do you think conditions in this country have affected the inflation rate?*

sent home by many Eritreans working in other nations, including the United States.

Somalia Since Somalia gained its independence in 1960, fighting between clans, border wars with Ethiopia, and drought have prevented it from becoming a strong, unified nation. In the late 1980s, full-scale civil war erupted. By 1991, Somalia was in a state of anarchy.

The situation worsened when a severe drought struck the region in the early 1990s. An estimated 1.5 million Somalis were threatened with starvation. International relief agencies donated food, but chronic civil strife hampered its distribution.

Somalia has no effective national government. From 2000 to 2003, a group of leaders in southern Somalia claimed to govern the nation, but this group had only marginal control in the capital of Mogadishu and no control elsewhere.

570 Chapter 27 ▪ East and Southern Africa

The Sudan

The Sudan—the largest nation in area in all of Africa—is much like the Sahel nations discussed in Chapter 26. To the north the country is largely a desert of bare rock or ergs—shifting sand dunes; in the south are clay plains and an extensive swamp area called the Sudd, which means "the Barrier."

The people of the Sudan are divided. Muslim Arabs live in the north. In the south, the people belong to several different African ethnic groups, and they practice animism or Christianity. North and south have been at war almost continuously since independence in 1956, resulting in widespread suffering. During the 1990s, UN estimates of Sudanese in danger of starvation ranged into the millions, despite international aid missions.

Landlocked Countries

Along with Ethiopia, the three countries of Uganda, Rwanda, and Burundi are landlocked, or entirely surrounded by land. All three nations are heavily populated, agricultural countries. Coffee is the most important export crop, but Rwanda and Burundi lack the means to get their goods to foreign buyers.

Uganda   Located to the west of Kenya, Uganda is for the most part a plateau with fertile soils. It prospered first by growing cotton and then by raising coffee. But when the nation gained independence from Britain in 1962, civil war broke out and disrupted the country's prosperity. People in the north, who had won most of the military power, struggled against southern groups, which had most of the economic might. Under a ruthless dictator, Idi Amin (EE dee ah MEEN), as many as 300,000 Ugandans died or "disappeared" in the violent struggles that took place in the country during the 1970s. By the mid-1990s, Uganda was rebuilding itself and moving closer to a more democratic government. In 2001, an election was held for president.

Rwanda and Burundi   An **ethnocracy** is a government in which one ethnic group rules over others. Rwanda (roo AHN duh) and Burundi (boo ROON dee), two of the smallest African nations, are both ethnocracies.

In Rwanda, 80 percent of the population belongs to the Hutu (HOO too) group. Most of the remainder are Tutsi (TOOT see), sometimes called Watusi (wah TOO see). The Hutu remained firmly in power for 35 years after they successfully overthrew the Tutsi-controlled government in 1959, killing some 100,000 of the minority. In 1994, hundreds of thousands of Tutsi were murdered and about 2 million Rwandans were driven from their homes in a brief and horrifying civil war. Hutu and Tutsi currently share power in Rwanda.

Ugandan Bus Station

Patterns of Settlement
This photograph shows a crowded bus station in Kampala, the capital of Uganda, at rush hour. Most Ugandans, however, are farmers rather than city dwellers. Uganda's economy depends heavily upon agriculture, especially coffee exports.

Movement *Why does a country that exports farm products need good transportation as well as fertile soil?*

571

Before students read the subsection Tanzania, have them examine the photo and caption on this page. Ask them to jot down predictions regarding Tanzania's economic potential. After students have read the text, have them revise and expand their predictions as needed.

Answers to
Section 2 Assessment

1. (a) strategic value, p. 569
(b) ethnocracy, p. 571
(c) villagization, p. 572
2. They lie near the oil supplies of the Middle East and the shipping lanes of the Red Sea and the Gulf of Aden and are at the midpoint between Europe and Southeast Asia.
3. The strife results from religious differences between the people of the north and the south. Muslim Arabs live in the north; the African peoples of the south practice Christianity or animism.
4. Drought has caused famine and starvation in some of the countries of East Africa.
5. (a) Tanzania's government abandoned socialism. **(b)** The economy has improved.
6. Ethiopia had been strategically located, with a long shore on the Red Sea through which oil shipments passed. When it lost Eritrea, Ethiopia no longer had a shore on the Red Sea. It became a landlocked country. Eritrea gained the Red Sea advantage and began to build up its economy.

Activity Rubrics Share rubrics with students before they create their maps.
Minimal The map and explanations are incomplete.
Attempted The map is complete, but the explanation of the challenges and benefits is sketchy.
Adequate The map is neatly executed, and the explanation has sufficient detail.
Exemplary The map is very well executed, and the explanation includes extensive detail.

Answer to Photo Caption

Tanzania's location along the coast provides ports for shipping, and the ports employ many workers.

Copper for Export

Natural Resources This worker is loading copper ingots onto a ship in Tanzania. Tanzania's lands are a rich source of copper, iron ore, and other minerals.
Location *How does Tanzania's location benefit this worker?*

In Burundi, the Tutsi are in power, although they account for only 14 percent of the population. They control the army and use it to maintain power. In mid-1993, when Burundi held its first free elections, the people chose a Hutu president. Within months, the army overthrew him. Tens of thousands of Tutsis and Hutus have been massacred since Burundi gained independence in 1962. Efforts to reach peace in 2001 failed again after violence erupted.

Tanzania

To the east of Rwanda and Burundi lies Tanzania (tan zuh NEE uh). Like many African nations, it is a land of great potential wealth. Its soils are fertile in many areas. Its lands include the hot, humid coastal lands, the cool highlands, the varied terrain around Lake Victoria, and the dry central plains. Beneath its surface lie iron ore, coal, diamonds, and other minerals.

However, because of poor development, it remains the second poorest country in the world, after neighboring Mozambique. During an experiment in socialism between 1961 and 1985, Tanzania's rural people were subjected to **villagization**—forced to move into towns and to work on collective farms. The nation's economy ground to a halt. Not until socialism was abandoned did the economy turn around. The key to recovery was paying farmers a fair price for their crops. When they saw that they could profit by growing corn and cotton, they once again farmed land that had been idle for years.

SECTION 2 ASSESSMENT

1. Key Terms Define **(a)** strategic value, **(b)** ethnocracy, **(c)** villagization.

2. Global Trade Patterns Why is location a great asset to the nations on the Horn of Africa?

3. Cooperation and Conflict What are the causes of conflict in the Sudan?

4. Natural Hazards How has drought contributed to the poor standard of living in some of the landlocked countries of East Africa?

5. Government and Citizenship **(a)** What shift has taken place in the government of Tanzania? **(b)** What effect has that shift had on the economy?

6. Critical Thinking Analyzing Change Compare the changes that took place in Ethiopia and Eritrea after Eritrea won its independence from Ethiopia.

Activity

USING THE REGIONAL ATLAS
Review the Regional Atlas for Africa and this section. Draw a sketch map of the region. Then, draw three waterways that would connect the landlocked countries to the sea. Explain the challenges of construction at each site and the benefits that each waterway would produce.

3 South Africa

Reading Focus

- What racial and economic conditions divided life in South Africa for most of the twentieth century?
- What systems of control released an international backlash against the white South African government?
- In the 1990s, how did the government of South Africa transform the nation from a repressive police state to a model for peaceful political change?

Key Terms

apartheid
segregation
sanction

Main Idea After many years of colonial rule and racial segregation, South Africa is now a free society.

Science and Technology At a modern plant in South Africa, workers inspect part of a pipeline.

The Republic of South Africa is one of the powerhouse economies of the African continent. In fact, it is the wealthiest, most highly developed nation in Africa. Yet, it has not had an untroubled past. Black South Africans became equal citizens in their country only at the beginning of the 1990s, after years of protest and violence.

A Country Divided by Race

Much can be told about the Republic of South Africa with a few numbers. Some 75 percent of South Africa's population is black; about 2 percent is Asian; about 9 percent is of mixed race; and 14 percent is white. Yet, the white minority ruled South Africa for over a century.

Minority Rule Whites controlled not only the South African government, but about two thirds of the land in South Africa and most of its highly paid jobs as well. The whites owned the gold mines, the diamond mines, and the mines

where some seventy other minerals were dug from beneath the soil.

White South Africans owned the best farmland as well. The Republic of South Africa is mostly a high plateau. Around the edges of the plateau is an escarpment that drops to a narrow coastal plain. The plateau itself is generally dry, but in places where there is good rain, corn, wheat, and a wide variety of fruits grow abundantly. Whites also owned the thriving industries of South Africa, where the metals of the mines were manufactured into machines and other goods. In other words, the white population possessed nearly all of the country's wealth. How did this nation's minority come to possess so much wealth and power?

Migration Into African Lands The inequality of ownership in South Africa came about, first of all, through migration. Europeans came to South Africa beginning in the 1600s—first the Dutch, then some Germans and a few French. Over time, these groups together came to be known as Afrikaners (AF ri KAHN erz), or Boers.

Objectives

Upon completion of Section 3, students should be able to:

- identify the racial and economic conditions that divided life in South Africa for most of the twentieth century;
- describe the systems of control that released an international backlash against the white South African government;
- explain how South Africa transformed from a repressive police state to a model for peaceful political change.

National Geography Standards

The following National Geography Standards are highlighted in this section: 3, 5, 6, 9, 10, 11, 12, 13, 16, 17, 18

Bellringer

Divide the class in half. Tell both halves to imagine that the other half has been given all the class resources—books, paper, pens, desks, chairs, etc. Then ask students how they feel about this situation.

LESSON PLAN

1. Focus Write the following sentence on the board: *Apartheid feels like _____, sounds like _____, looks like _____, and smells like _____.* Based on their reading of the section, have students supply sensory images to complete the sentence.

2. Instruct Divide students into three groups. Assign each group one of the following questions and have them present their answer orally to the class: (1) What is apartheid? (2) Describe apartheid's historical background. (3) How have recent developments in South Africa changed apartheid?

(continued on next page)

CUSTOMIZE FOR...

Less Proficient Readers

Identifying Clue Words Focus students' attention on the terms "In fact" and "Yet" introducing two sentences in the opening paragraph of the lesson. Explain that "In fact" is used to affirm and reinforce information in the previous statement. "Yet" is used to introduce information that contrasts with that in the previous statement. Have students identify three other examples of contrasting information introduced by clue words. For each example, ask them to write a sentence restating the contrasting concepts in their own words.

They spoke their own distinctive language, called Afrikaans (AF ri KAHNZ). The Afrikaners pushed the native Africans inland, gradually claiming the Africans' land both by treaty and by force. Then, British settlers arrived in South Africa in great numbers. The Afrikaners continually moved inland to escape from the British, and the British moved after them repeatedly, reasserting British control.

An armed conflict called the Boer War broke out in 1899 and raged for three years. In the end, the Afrikaners accepted British rule. The final effect of this movement was a combined colony of Afrikaners and English-speaking settlers. The majority African population was driven into separate lands called reserves or put to work on plantations or in factories owned primarily by whites and Asians.

Migration Into White Lands By the time South Africa left the British Commonwealth to become an independent nation in 1961, a new pattern of movement had appeared. Africans were moving out of the confining reserves into the cities. The reserves promised nothing but subsistence farming on arid land, while jobs were available in the cities.

From about 1950 until 1980 the economy of South Africa grew faster than that of any country on the continent, and faster than that of most nations in the world. There were four reasons for this growth.

First, South Africa had an inexpensive energy source from its abundant coal reserves. Second, the country also had capital, or money, to invest. Third, South Africa's excellent connections with Britain and the rest of Europe provided the technology, knowledge, and skills that South Africans needed to build productive factories and mills.

The fourth and most important element in South Africa's great expansion was the black South Africans themselves. They formed a vast pool of labor, and worked for low wages because they had little choice.

Artificial Regions

The white government was frightened by the migration of black South Africans toward the cities. Whites were afraid that the blacks who were crowding into the townships, or settlements near the cities, might claim a right to live there permanently.

Soweto Township

Understanding the Past Soweto, shown here, is a large, black township near the city of Johannesburg. Many black South Africans were once forced to live in townships. Many blacks remain there today, living in tin shacks like those in the foreground, because they are too poor to move.
Place *What role did the townships play in opposing apartheid?*

Southern Africa and the United States

Trade Data

Country	Total Exports (billions of dollars)	Total Imports (billions of dollars)	Trade Balance (billions of dollars)
Angola	7.00	2.70	4.30
Botswana	2.50	2.10	0.40
Lesotho	0.25	0.72	−0.47
Madagascar	0.68	0.92	−0.24
Malawi	0.42	0.46	−0.04
Mozambique	0.75	1.25	−0.50
Namibia	1.58	1.71	−0.13
South Africa	32.30	28.10	4.20
Swaziland	0.70	0.85	−0.15
Zambia	0.88	12.05	−11.17
Zimbabwe	2.10	1.50	0.60
United States	723.00	1,148.00	−425.00

Source: *The World Factbook*

CHART SKILLS

- **Economic Activities** *Which countries export more than they import?*
- **Global Trade Patterns** *How would this table probably appear different if there were still economic sanctions against South Africa?*

Attempts at Control In order to control black South Africans, the South African government created arbitrary regions called homelands. Under the homelands plan, the blacks—about 75 percent of the total population—were forced to live on only 14 percent of the country's land. Every African in the nation was assigned to a homeland and was supposed to stay in it unless a pass had been issued allowing him or her to live somewhere else.

Along with the homelands plan, whites created a system of laws known as **apartheid** (uh PAR tate), which means "apartness." Under apartheid, nonwhite South Africans were **segregated**, or forced to live apart, from whites. By law, blacks were required to use separate public facilities of all types, including schools and colleges. The facilities for black South Africans were never as good as those that were available to whites. For example, in 1990 the average-size class in the black South African school system was 41, whereas the average size of white classes was only 15 students.

International Backlash Apartheid and the homelands plan was an unjust system, and much of the world refused to let it continue without protest. In 1986, South Africa's major trading partners, Europe and the United States, placed economic **sanctions** against South Africa. Sanctions are actions that punish a country for behavior of which the international community does not approve.

The United States sanctions prohibited Americans from investing in South Africa and banned the import of certain South African products. Imports from South Africa fell 40 percent in the first nine months. One expert estimated that sanctions were costing South Africa 2 billion dollars a year. Meanwhile, Africans in the townships kept up the pressure with protests that not even police violence could stop. Finally, South African whites began to admit that changes had to take place.

Government and Citizenship

In 1989, a new president, F. W. de Klerk, came to power in South Africa. He proved to be a reformer, and in spite of angry opposition from some whites, he started making changes.

Moving Toward Majority Rule One of de Klerk's most important actions was the release of prominent black South African activist Nelson Mandela from prison. Mandela had been held for 27 years for his antiapartheid activities.

As a leader of the African National Congress (ANC), Mandela entered into negotiations with the white government on behalf of blacks in South Africa. In 1990 and 1991, apartheid and

GLOBAL CONNECTIONS

Economic Activities After the peaceful transition to majority rule, it seemed that South Africa would not be able to attract investment money. In 1993, for example, fleeing whites took 15 billion rand (the South African currency) from the country. But, one year later, the flow had reversed, and 5.2 billion rand in investment money was flowing into South Africa.

ACTIVITY

Vocabulary

Apartheid Refer to the Key Terms list on page 573. Write the term *apartheid* on the board. Ask a volunteer to look up the term in the Glossary and read its definition aloud. Tell students that the Dutch word *apartheid* comes from the French phrase *à part*, which means "apart," and the Dutch *-heid*, or "-hood." Have students give examples of how their lives might be different if they lived under apartheid.

BACKGROUND

Daily Life

Education Under apartheid, blacks and whites were taught in separate schools. Many schools tried to break this pattern of segregation on their own when apartheid ended. In 1996, the government of South Africa made it official—no school could discriminate on the basis of race.

ACTIVITY

Group Work

Activity: Creating an editorial page

Purpose: Have each group work together to create a mock editorial page on the transition to majority rule. Pages should include background information, editorials, political cartoons, and letters to the editor.

Roles: Groups should include a researcher, writers, a cartoonist, and an editor.

Result: Have groups share their pages with the class.

Articles From NATIONAL GEOGRAPHIC

The following article may be used to extend the content in this section.

Cobb, Charles E., Jr., and James Nachtwey, photographer. "The Twilight of Apartheid." *National Geographic*, Vol. 183, No. 2 (Feb. 1993), pp. 66–93.

After overcoming apartheid, South Africa faced the challenge of negotiating peace.

TEST PREPARATION

Have students read the subsection **Artificial Regions** beginning on the opposite page to answer the following question.

What was the purpose of international sanctions against South Africa in the mid-1980s?

- **A** To end the system of apartheid
- **B** To create new black homelands
- **C** To increase foreign investment
- **D** To incite protests in the townships

Answers to Chart Skills

Angola, Botswana, South Africa, and Zimbabwe

South Africa's export and import totals would probably be lower because the sanctions restricted its trade.

576 Chapter 27

Connecting With . . .

Government Write the following statement on the board: *The South African government is working hard to shape a new country for its citizens.* Have students locate newspaper and magazine clippings that address this statement and display the clippings on a bulletin board.

Answers to Section 3 Assessment

1. (a) apartheid, p. 575
(b) segregation, p. 575
(c) sanction, p. 575
2. A white minority gained power in South Africa through a long period of migration into black territory, during which whites gradually took lands from blacks.
3. Foreign governments imposed economic sanctions; black South Africans pressured the government through protests.
4. Nelson Mandela was released from prison, apartheid was repealed, and black South Africans were allowed to vote for the first time.
5. Students may suggest that economic sanctions are controversial because innocent people often suffer the effects as much as do government and industry leaders.

Activity Rubrics Share rubrics with students before they create their summaries.
Minimal The summary is incomplete or reveals a lack of understanding of the topic.
Attempted The summary shows some understanding of the lasting effects of apartheid but is poorly written and organized.
Adequate The summary shows good understanding of the lasting effects of apartheid and is well written and organized.
Exemplary The summary shows thorough understanding of the lasting effects of apartheid and is very well written and organized.

Answer to Photo Caption

Mandela had been imprisoned for many years for his antiapartheid activities.

South African Peacemakers

Government and Citizenship As president, F. W. de Klerk (right) dismantled apartheid. His reforms led to South Africa's first all-race elections in 1994, which resulted in the selection of Nelson Mandela (left) as the first president of the new South Africa. De Klerk and Mandela received the Nobel Peace Prize for their work.

Place *Why had Mandela been imprisoned for many years?*

all the laws that supported it were repealed, or removed. A gradual transition of power to African majority rule ensued. In 1994 South Africa held its first truly free elections, in which blacks as well as whites were allowed to vote. Despite some violence, and despite fears that extremist whites and blacks would prevent the transition to majority rule, South Africans of all backgrounds went to the polls. This historic election paved the way for Nelson Mandela to become South Africa's first black president.

Looking Ahead In 1996, a new constitution was certified by the Constitutional Court. It guaranteed equality and the right to housing, health care, water, food, and education to all South Africans. Virtually overnight, South Africa went from a repressive police state to a model for peaceful political change. Today, South Africa works to heal the wounds of the apartheid era. In 2000, President Thabo Mbeki promised to fight poverty by strengthening the economy and opening doors for those who have been disadvantaged.

SECTION 3 ASSESSMENT

1. **Key Terms** Define **(a)** apartheid, **(b)** segregation, **(c)** sanction.

2. **Understanding the Past** How did a white minority come to gain power in predominantly black populated South Africa?

3. **Global Trade Patterns** Give two reasons for the change in the white South African government's policy toward black South Africans.

4. **Government and Citizenship** What changes took place in South Africa after the presidential election of F. W. de Klerk?

5. **Critical Thinking** **Recognizing Points of View** Why do you think that economic sanctions are sometimes considered controversial?

Activity

Take It to the NET
Creating a Summary Use the Internet to locate some articles about present-day issues in South Africa. Then, create a summary about the lasting effects of apartheid. Visit the World Geography section of **www.phschool.com** for help in completing this activity.

RESOURCE DIRECTORY

Teaching Resources
Unit 7, Chapter 27
• Section 3 Quiz, p. 46
• Map/Graph Skills, p. 51
Spanish Resources
• Section 3 Quiz, p. 70

Technology
Social Studies Skills Tutor CD-ROM, Synthesizing Information

Synthesizing Information

If you want to know whether or not a movie is worth seeing, you can read a review, watch a television commercial, view a film clip on the Internet, and talk to people who have seen the movie. You can combine the different pieces of information to develop a more complete impression of the movie. This process of combining pieces of information is called synthesizing.

Learn the Skill Refer to the subsection on racial divisions beginning on page 573, the subsection on government beginning on page 575, and the questionnaire below. Then, follow the steps to learn how to synthesize information.

1 *Focus on a topic.* It is usually not very fruitful to synthesize bits of information that have little or nothing in common. The different pieces of information should be on some common topic. Read the different sources of information and look for an overall theme or position. *Which question on the questionnaire most closely relates to government?*

2 *Analyze each source of information.* The purpose of synthesizing is to gather information on a topic from more than one source. As you study, take notes on the main idea and supporting details found in each source. Try to put what you've read into your own words. *(a) What ethnic group is in the majority in South Africa? (b) What kind of system of government does South Africa have today?*

3 *Look for similarities.* Information is more complete and reliable if more than one source

provides the same or similar information. Identify the ideas about which all the sources are in agreement. *For each ethnic group, do most people feel they are playing an active role in the new democratic government?*

4 *Look for differences.* Identify any inconsistent information about the topic. Consider why there may be variations across the data. Perhaps the information provided is biased or can be interpreted differently from another perspective. *(a) Which one group is most dissatisfied with the new political situation? (b) Does this group form a majority or a minority group in South Africa?*

5 *Draw conclusions.* Our knowledge of a topic becomes more complete when we draw conclusions based on information from a variety of sources. *Why is the group you identified above dissatisfied?*

 Do It Yourself

Practice the Skill Select a current economics topic in South Africa, such as international trade or stock market trends. Find three different pieces of information on the topic. Write questions to analyze and synthesize the information. Trade papers with a partner and answer each other's questions.

Apply the Skill See Chapter 27 Review and Assessment.

Questionnaire on the Quality of Life in South Africa

Background Periodically, the democratic government of South Africa distributes questionnaires to its citizens. Responses are categorized by race (in South Africa, the term "coloured" refers to people of mixed race).

1. How do you feel about life now compared to twelve months ago?

	All Races	Black	Coloured	Asian	White
Life has improved	19.4%	17.9%	24.7%	29.5%	21.8%
Life is the same	47.8%	47.2%	49.5%	45.8%	50.6%
Life has gotten worse	32.4%	34.6%	25.6%	24.3%	26.7%
Undecided	0.4%	0.3%	0.2%	0.4%	0.9%

2. Do you think you have a say in decisions that affect the country?

	All Races	Black	Coloured	Asian	White
Yes	41.4%	42.4%	42.7%	44.6%	34.9%
No	57.9%	57.0%	56.7%	54.7%	63.9%
Undecided	0.7%	0.6%	0.6%	0.7%	1.2%

Chapter 27 **577**

Teaching the Skill
Ask a volunteer to read the first paragraph of the lesson aloud. Then ask students: **When would you use the skill of synthesizing information?** (to make decisions, form opinions, draw conclusions) **What sources of information would you consult?** After students have offered several suggestions, have them read the five bold headings in the lesson. Comment that this lesson will focus on synthesizing geographic information. Then proceed through the steps in the lesson.

Answers to Learn the Skill
1. the second question
2. (a) Black (b) democratic
3. No
4. (a) White (b) minority
5. South Africa has changed to majority rule, and the white population, which had previously been in control, is in the minority.

Answer to Practice the Skill
Check that students have gathered sufficient information, written pertinent questions to synthesize the information, and drawn valid conclusions.

CUSTOMIZE FOR...

Less Proficient Writers
Concluding Statement When students reach step 5 in Learn the Skill, ask them to brainstorm a list of reasons the group they named is dissatisfied. Encourage them to include information from Section 3 as well as information from this page. List the reasons on the board, and have students copy the list. Then instruct students to organize their lists by order of importance. Have students use their prioritized lists to write a paragraph that explains why the group they identified is dissatisfied.

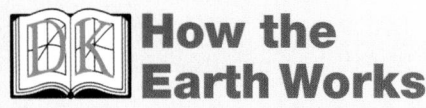

How the Earth Works

pp. 578–579

Objectives

Upon completion of this feature, students should be able to:

♦ describe the location and climate of the world's major grasslands;

♦ identify the types of animals that live on grasslands and explain how they survive in their environments.

National Geography Standards

The following National Geography Standards are highlighted in this feature: 1, 4, 8

Bellringer

Write the word *grasslands* on the board. Have students recall movies, television shows, or books that are set in the North American prairies. Tell students that the prairie is a particular type of grassland. Have them draw on prior knowledge to describe what prairies are like. Discuss the climate and the plants and animals that live on this type of grassland.

LESSON PLAN

1. Focus Write on the board the words *savannas, prairies, pampas,* and *steppes*. Have students use the Glossary or a dictionary to define these words. Ask: **How are these words related?**

2. Instruct At the center of the board, write *Food Chain*. Have students use details from the feature to create a chain that shows the relationship among carnivores, herbivores, and plants on the African savannas.

3. Close/Reteach Remind students that plants and animals often have special adaptations or habits that help them survive in their environment. Discuss how the baobab tree, giraffes, and herding animals are well suited to life on the savanna.

How the Earth Works

Grasslands

Grasslands comprise about a quarter of the earth's natural vegetation. They grow where it is too dry for forests but too wet for deserts. Tropical grasslands, or **savannas,** grow in warm lands near the Equator. Temperate grasslands are found in cooler parts of the world and are known by several names. They are called **prairies** in North America, **pampas** in South America, and **steppes** in Europe and Asia. All grasslands support a rich variety of insects, birds, and mammals.

Distribution of world's major grasslands

Central Asian steppes

North American prairies

South American pampas

African savanna

Maned wolf

HUNTERS
On grasslands, the many varieties of **herbivores,** or plant-eaters, provide food for the **carnivores,** or meat-eaters. Carnivores of the grasslands include lions, hyenas, wolves, and coyotes. Many of these species hunt together in packs. The prairies of North America were once home to wolves, but coyotes are now the main hunters.

South American maned wolves have long legs that help them move through tall grasses.

SAVANNA
The word *savanna* means "treeless plain," although the African savanna usually has scattered trees. The weather is hot all year-round, but there are long dry seasons separated by wet seasons. The African savanna is home to vast herds of grazing animals as well as to large predators, such as lions.

Wildebeests migrate hundreds of miles in search of fresh grass.

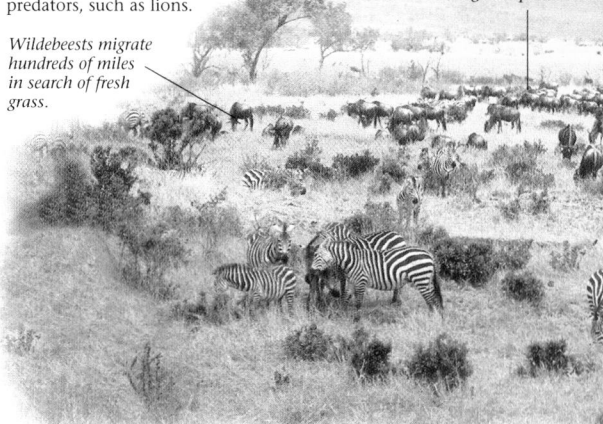

Herding animals cooperate for defense against predators.

GRAZERS AND BROWSERS
On the African savanna, many species of herbivores can live in the same area because they feed on different plants or on different parts of the grasses. Elephants and giraffes, for example, browse on bushes and trees, whereas zebras and wildebeests graze on grass.

BURROWING ANIMALS
Many small grassland mammals live underground where they can escape predators or fires and survive the heat or cold. Some use their burrows to store food or to hibernate in winter. The nine-banded armadillo, whose range stretches from South America to the southern United States, digs into the earth to find insects for food.

Long necks allow giraffes to browse on high branches.

Dik-diks feed on young leaves of small bushes.

Zebras graze on the course, tough tops of grasses.

Wildebeests eat the leafy middles of grass plants.

Thomson's gazelles eat young grass shoots and seeds.

Nine-banded armadillo

578

RESOURCE DIRECTORY

Teaching Resources

World Geography Map and Photo Transparencies
• How the Earth Works, Unit 7

Technology

Companion Web site, www.phschool.com
• Chapter 27 Activities

TREES AND SHRUBS
In savanna grasslands, scattered trees and shrubs shade the ground, keeping the soil moist. Their fallen leaves enrich the soil and help grass grow. Many trees and bushes, such as acacias, have thorns to deter grazing animals and deep roots to reach water underground. Baobab trees have tough bark for protection against fire.

Baobab tree

Baobab trees have thick trunks to store water for the dry season.

Trees and bushes provide shade from the hot sun.

SCAVENGERS
No food is wasted on the savanna. The remains of animals that have died or have been killed are quickly devoured by **scavengers** such as vultures, jackals, marabou storks, and carrion beetles. Vultures often crowd around the same carcass, squabbling noisily as they fight for scraps.

White-backed vulture

ASSESSMENT

1. **Key Terms** Define **(a)** savanna, **(b)** prairie, **(c)** pampa, **(d)** steppe, **(e)** herbivore, **(f)** carnivore, **(g)** scavenger.

2. **Ecosystems** What is the difference between a tropical grassland and a temperate grassland?

3. **Physical Characteristics (a)** How are some species of vegetation well suited for survival on grasslands? **(b)** How are some species of animals well suited for survival on grasslands?

4. **Critical Thinking Analyzing Processes** Increases or decreases in animal populations on the savanna can have lasting effects on the entire ecosystem. **(a)** What might happen to the population of herbivores if the plant population declines? Explain. **(b)** How might a decline in the herbivore population have a negative effect on another part of the grasslands ecosystem?

579

CUSTOMIZE FOR...

Gifted and Talented

Tourist Information Guide In some parts of the United States, grasslands have been turned into state parks or national parks. Have students use the Internet or library to find information on the grassland park that is located closest to your community. Then have them create a guidebook that contains facts about the park.

Objectives

Upon completion of Section 4, students should be able to:

◆ describe how Malawi and Botswana have been affected by the wealth and policies of South Africa;

◆ summarize how colonialism affected Angola and Mozambique;

◆ explain the effect of farming policy on conditions in Zambia and Zimbabwe.

National Geography Standards

The following National Geography Standards are highlighted in this section: 2, 4, 5, 6, 9, 10, 11, 12, 13, 15, 16, 17

Bellringer

Ask students: **Which countries of southern Africa are completely surrounded by another country?** (Swaziland and Lesotho)

LESSON PLAN

1. Focus Refer students to the physical map on page 566 and point out the proximity of the countries of southern Africa to South Africa. Have students brainstorm a list of ways in which South Africa might influence these countries politically, socially, and economically.

2. Instruct Draw a large circle on the board and label it South Africa. Around this, draw smaller circles representing the countries of southern Africa and label them. Have students identify each southern African country that has been influenced by South Africa and draw a line connecting it with the larger circle. Then have students list the way(s) the country has been influenced by South Africa. Erase the countries that have not been influenced by South Africa.

3. Close/Reteach Write the names of the countries of southern Africa on the board. Have students contribute concepts and summary statements to write under each country's name.

4 Other Countries of Southern Africa

Reading Focus

- In what ways are the countries of Malawi and Botswana affected by the wealth and policies of the Republic of South Africa?
- How has colonialism affected Angola and Mozambique in the past?
- How do attitudes toward farming explain the current conditions in the countries of Zambia and Zimbabwe?

Key Terms

enclave
white flight
land redistribution

> **Main Idea**
> The other countries of southern Africa rely on natural resources to improve their economies.

Cultures A man weaves grass into the thatched roof of his hut in Botswana.

The Republic of South Africa is so powerful that it overshadows other nations in the region. Lesotho (luh SO to), for example, is an **enclave** of South Africa. That means it is completely surrounded by the larger country—and dependent on it. Swaziland, although richer in resources than Lesotho, is in much the same position. Namibia, on the west coast, was almost a colony of South Africa until recently. It even had its own version of apartheid, including African homelands. The rest of the southern African nations have dealt with their powerful neighbor in different ways.

Malawi and Botswana

Landlocked Malawi (muh LAH wee) and Botswana have worked to keep relations friendly with the Republic of South Africa because they have economic ties to the country. Malawi, a crowded nation on the western shore of Lake Nyasa in the Great Rift Valley, has many migrant workers who are under labor contracts in South Africa. Botswana is less dependent on South Africa than Malawi only because Botswana is wealthier.

A comparison of Malawi and Botswana reveals the impact of physical geography on their economies. Malawi has fertile land and an excellent water supply, so that over time it has attracted a large population. Its resources must therefore be stretched to meet the needs of more people. Botswana, on the other hand, is an arid country that is sparsely populated. Its yearly profits from the sale of diamonds, copper, coal, and the millions of beef cattle it raises every year benefit a large part of its relatively small population.

Angola and Mozambique

Angola on the west coast and Mozambique on the east coast are separated from one another by the other countries of southern Africa. However, they share similar characteristics. Both coastal states were once Portuguese colonies. Both countries

580 Chapter 27 ▪ East and Southern Africa

RESOURCE DIRECTORY

Teaching Resources

Unit 7, Chapter 27
- Section 4 Guided Reading and Review, p. 47

Guide to the Essentials (English/Spanish)
- Section Summary, Chapter 27, Section 4

Mental Mapping booklet
- Unit 7 Checklist, p. 91

Technology

Guided Reading Audiotapes (English/Spanish), Chapter 27, Section 4

Section Reading Support Transparencies, Chapter 27, Section 4

World Geography Map and Photo Transparencies
- Africa: Maps and Photos

Book on CD, Chapter 27

Social Studies Skills Tutor CD-ROM

Companion Web site, www.phschool.com
- Chapter 27 Activities

won their independence in 1975 after fighting long wars with Portugal. At the end of the wars, many Portuguese settlers fled, taking their wealth with them. This **white flight,** or departure of trained white administrators and technicians, made the task of the new government doubly difficult.

Conflict Reacting to the problems that colonialism and capitalism had created in their countries, both governments committed themselves to a Communist economic system. This angered their capitalist neighbor, South Africa. In Angola a rebel group known as UNITA waged war against the new government. In Mozambique a group known as Renamo played a similar role. South Africa backed both rebel groups with weapons, money, and, in the case of Angola, troops.

The human cost of these wars was horrifying. Hundreds of thousands of people in Angola and Mozambique died in the fighting. Refugees fled the battle zones and packed themselves into urban areas, where they lived in terrible conditions. Under the stress of civil war, the economies of both nations fell apart. Disease and malnutrition were also widespread. In Angola, one child in four died before the age of five. Once able to feed its own people, Angola had to import most of its food.

Peace and Potential By the beginning of the 1990s, a glimmer of hope for peace began to emerge. South Africa and other nations ended their military involvement in Angola, which held its first free election in 1992. Although fighting erupted again between the new government and UNITA, the rebel group soon lost all international support because it would not agree to peace terms. In Mozambique, the civil war ended, and the government and the rebels worked out a peace agreement.

The outlook for these countries is, therefore, more promising than it has been for decades. Although Mozambique has been ranked as one of the world's poorest nations, its economy grew at a high rate between 1996 and 1998. It has a wealth of natural resources and a huge labor force. In 2000, however, Mozambique suffered devastating floods. The government reported that more than one million people lost their homes as a result of the natural disaster. As for Angola, observers are hoping that it may soon again produce enough food for its population.

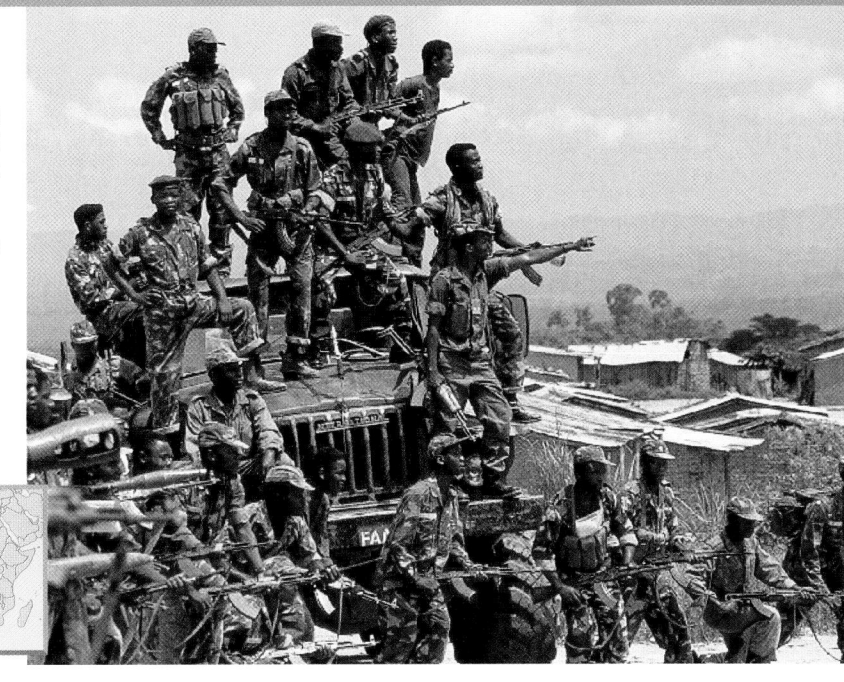

Government Troops in Angola

Cooperation and Conflict In Angola, a long-running civil war between the government and UNITA rebels took many lives and devastated the economy. Here, a government patrol searches for rebel troops. In 1992 Angola held its first free elections, raising hopes for a peaceful future.

Place *How did events outside Angola help end the war there?*

Articles From NATIONAL GEOGRAPHIC

The following special issue may be used to extend the content in this section.

"Botswana." *National Geographic,* Vol. 178, No. 6 (Dec. 1990), pp. 5–97.

This issue includes several articles exploring the natural and cultural aspects of Botswana.

The Physical World

Victoria Falls Victoria Falls, on the Zambezi River between Zambia and Zimbabwe, is one of the outstanding physical features of Africa. Measuring roughly 350 feet (107 m) high and more than a mile (1.6 km) wide, the falls were named in honor of Queen Victoria in 1855. Local people call them Musi-O-Tunya, which means "the smoke that thunders." The name is appropriate: The roar of the water can be heard miles away.

Critical Thinking

Comparing and Contrasting Use the following questions to help students compare and contrast the countries of southern Africa: **Why is Botswana less dependent on South Africa than Malawi is?** (Botswana is wealthier than Malawi.) **What do Angola and Mozambique have in common?** (Both are coastal countries that were once Portuguese colonies. Also, civil war has brought suffering to both countries.) **Why has Zimbabwe been more successful than Zambia in achieving economic independence?** (Zambia has depended solely on copper, while Zimbabwe has pursued a successful policy of land redistribution.)

Enrichment

Designing Magazine Covers Have students design a magazine cover to highlight a nation or group of nations in southern Africa. Ask students to include a table of contents on the cover. Suggest that they use current newsmagazines as models. (Visual/Spatial)

Answer to Diagram Skills

The force of the incoming water turns the turbine wheel, which turns the shaft. The shaft turns the armature inside the generator, thus producing electricity.

GEOFacts

A drought in Zimbabwe in 1992–1995 forced crocodiles out of streams near the Zambezi River. They took over spring-fed pools in the area, creating danger for people and livestock. At the same time, hungry elephants foraging for food came close to villages, causing serious damage.

Zambia and Zimbabwe

Two countries in the region, Zambia and Zimbabwe (zim BAHB way), have tried with some success to keep themselves out of South Africa's long-reaching shadow. In spite of this shared goal, they have fared very differently.

Missed Opportunity

Zambia has over 880 million tons of copper reserves in an area adjoining the Democratic Republic of the Congo known as the Copperbelt. When Zambia achieved independence in 1964, the new president, Kenneth Kaunda, counted on copper to provide the country with a solid source of revenue.

Following independence, Zambia prospered. The government, certain that revenues from copper would always provide the nation with money to buy food, allowed Zambia's agricultural economy to decline.

In the long run, however, Zambia's reliance on copper proved to be a mistake. During the 1980s and 1990s, the price of copper on the world market plunged. Zambia could not get enough money to feed its people. The country became poor just as fast as it had become rich.

In 1991, President Kaunda, who had held office for 27 years, was defeated by Frederick Chiluba. Chiluba initiated reforms to kick-start the economy. He relaxed agricultural policies and allowed businesses to privatize. Unfortunately, he also began to erode the rule of law for which he had campaigned, leaving many Zambians discouraged as they looked to the future.

Making Farming Work The experience of Zimbabwe was different, in part because the country's citizens learned to work together. In 1965, the white minority government of Rhodesia—as Zimbabwe was then known—declared independence from Britain. But Britain and the United Nations demanded that Rhodesia's white leaders first respect the rights of the black majority. After

Hydroelectric Power

1. **Water tunnel** brings water into the power plant.
2. **Turbine wheel** turns as water is driven against blades.
3. **Water outlet** carries water out after passing through turbine.
4. **Turbine shaft** connects the turbine wheel to the generator.
5. The shaft turns the armature inside the **generator** to produce electricity.
6. **Transformer** boosts the voltage of electricity from the generator and transmits through high-voltage **power lines**.

DIAGRAM SKILLS

● **Science and Technology** Water power is an important resource for many African nations. Hydroelectric plants are powered by rivers such as the Zambezi and by the rushing waters of Victoria Falls, shown at right.
• *How does water provide power for electricity?*

RESOURCE DIRECTORY

Teaching Resources
Unit 7, Chapter 27
• Reviewing Main Ideas, p. 49
• Critical Thinking, p. 50
• Section 4 Quiz, p. 48
• Test Forms A and B, pp. 52–57
Spanish Resources
• Section 4 Quiz, p. 71
Guide to the Essentials (English/Spanish)
• Chapter 27 Test
Mental Mapping booklet
• Chapter 27 Map Test, p. 104

Simulations, Games, and Lab Activities
• Place Location Review Games, pp. 58–63
Social Studies Skills Handbook
• Study and Research Skills, pp. 94–108

Technology
ExamView Test Bank CD-ROM
• Chapter 27 Test
• Unit 7 Test
Companion Web site, www.phschool.com
• Chapter 27 Self-Test

years of conflict and negotiations, free elections were finally held in 1980. Later that same year, Rhodesia became the fully independent nation of Zimbabwe.

Zimbabwe's new leader, Robert Mugabe, was very cautious about making changes. At the time of independence, white farmers owned most of the nation's land. For this reason, Mugabe pursued a policy of **land redistribution.** Under such a policy, land is taken from those who have plenty and given to those who have little or none. According to Zimbabwe's constitution, white farmers had to be paid for their land, and they had to be willing to sell it.

Land redistribution took place slowly in Zimbabwe. This schedule gave the government more time to develop the necessary infrastructure for the new farmers. An infrastructure is a country's basic support systems, such as transportation, education, water, electricity, and other necessities.

However, Mugabe's care and caution were not to last. In 2000, President Mugabe announced that Zimbabwe planned to seize thousands of white-owned farms and give them to black Zimbabweans. He refused to compensate the white farmers, as the law required. As squatters began to camp on white-owned land, violence erupted. When people criticized Mugabe's moves, he began to knock down two important pillars of democracy: freedom of speech and freedom of the press. The government arrested anyone who criticized it, including judges and journalists. The peace that blacks and whites had shared was shattered.

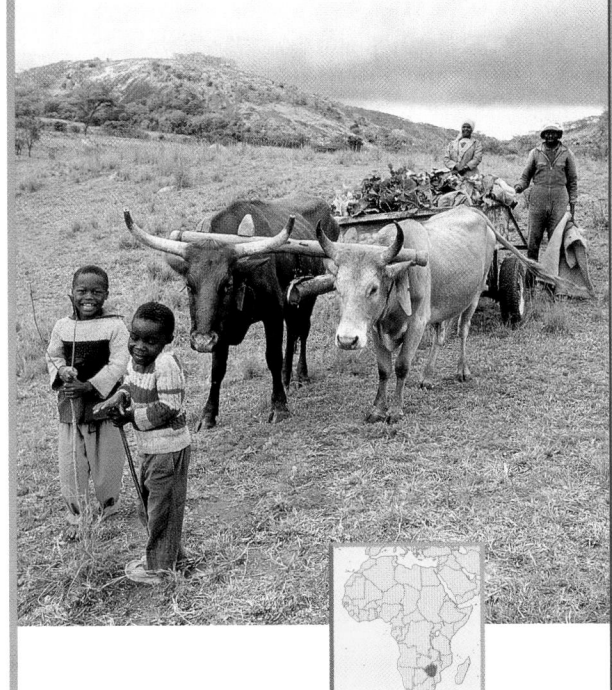

Farming Family

Economic Activities Corn, tobacco, and cotton are among Zimbabwe's important crops. But less than 10 percent of the land is good for farming, and drought can make even these areas unproductive.

Human-Environment Interaction *How might technology be used to reduce the impact of drought?*

SECTION 4 ASSESSMENT

1. **Key Terms** Define **(a)** enclave, **(b)** white flight, **(c)** land redistribution.

2. **Global Trade Patterns** How does proximity to the Republic of South Africa affect the countries of Malawi and Botswana?

3. **Understanding the Past (a)** List three ways in which the southern African countries of Angola and Mozambique share a similar past. **(b)** What events occurred in the 1990s to improve the outlook for these countries?

4. **Economic Activities (a)** Why did agriculture fail to develop in Zambia? **(b)** Why did agriculture develop successfully in Zimbabwe?

5. **Critical Thinking** **Predicting Consequences** How might the political and economic changes in the Republic of South Africa affect the other countries of southern Africa?

Activity

Presenting an Oral Report Many of the countries in this region gained independence from Great Britain. Research how British culture continues to shape life in the region. Share your findings in a short oral report.

Vocabulary

Land redistribution Refer to the Key Terms list on page 580. Write the term *land redistribution* on the board. Ask a student to look up the term in the Glossary and read its definition aloud. Have students restate the definition in their own words. Ask: **How might land redistribution change the lives of rural people?** (Poor farmers would receive more land.)

Answers to Section 4 Assessment

1. (a) enclave, p. 580 **(b)** white flight, p. 581 **(c)** land redistribution, p. 583

2. Both countries have economic ties to South Africa. Botswana is less dependent on South Africa because it is wealthier than Malawi.

3. (a) Possible answers: Both were Portuguese colonies; both won independence in 1975; both adopted communism; both have suffered from civil war. **(b)** Angola held its first free election in 1992. In Mozambique, the civil war ended, and the economy grew at a high rate.

4. (a) Zambia neglected agriculture to develop its copper reserves. **(b)** Zimbabwe redistributed land and developed its infrastructure to support farmers.

5. Answers will vary, but students should see that political and economic improvements in South Africa will improve relations and trade with other African nations.

Activity Rubrics Share rubrics with students before they present their oral reports.

Minimal The report is incomplete and shows little understanding of how British culture shapes life in the region.

Attempted The report shows some understanding of how British culture shapes life in the region but is disorganized and poorly presented.

Adequate The report is well researched and thorough.

Exemplary The report is very well researched and organized and has interesting and relevant information.

TEST PREPARATION

Have students read the section Making Farming Work beginning on the opposite page to complete the following sentence. In 2000, President Mugabe announced a new land policy that involved —

  A   expanding freedom of the press
  B   seizing white-owned farms
  C   purchasing land from squatters
  D   releasing critics of the government from prison

Answer to Photo Caption

Possible answer: Irrigation could be used to reduce the impact of drought.

Creating a Chapter Summary
As a reteaching opportunity, pair a more able student with a less able student to complete this chapter summary.

Possible entries: **Regional Ties With Great Britain** 1. The British railroad in Kenya establishes the city of Nairobi. 2. British settlers asserted control in South Africa. 3. Britain demanded that white leaders of Rhodesia respect the rights of the country's black majority. **Regional Ties With Other European Countries** 1. France maintains a military base in Djibouti. 2. Dutch, German, and French settlers claimed land in South Africa. 3. Angola and Mozambique were both Portuguese colonies. **Regional Agricultural Challenges** 1. In Zimbabwe, a land redistribution plan has recently collapsed. 2. Kenya's emphasis on cash crops has led to malnutrition. 3. Droughts in Ethiopia have caused famine and starvation. **Regional Political Conflicts** 1. Ethnic violence has pushed many Kenyan farmers off their land. 2. The people of north and south Sudan have been at war almost continuously since 1956. 3. Land redistribution attempts in Zimbabwe have led to violence.

Reviewing Key Terms
1–10. Students' sentences should show a clear understanding of the meaning of each of the key terms.

Understanding Key Ideas
11. The Kikuyu and the Masai first occupied the area; they were followed by the British; later other Europeans arrived.
12. Kenyans, working together to strengthen the economy, attracted foreign investment.
13. Djibouti has strategic ports.
14. Rwanda is controlled by the Hutu majority and Burundi by the Tutsi minority.
15. The plan required Africans to remain in assigned regions. Although black South Africans accounted for about 75 percent of the population, they were squeezed onto only 14 percent of the land.
16. There were abundant coal deposits, ample capital investment,

584 Chapter 27

Creating a Chapter Summary

On a sheet of paper, draw a chart like this one. Beneath each heading, fill in key details from the text. Some information has been filled in to help you get started.

REGIONAL TIES WITH GREAT BRITAIN
1. The British railroad in Kenya establishes the city of Nairobi.
2.

REGIONAL TIES WITH OTHER EUROPEAN COUNTRIES
1.
2.

REGIONAL AGRICULTURAL CHALLENGES
1. In Zimbabwe, a land redistribution plan has recently collapsed.
2.

REGIONAL POLITICAL CONFLICTS
1.
2.

Take It to the NET
Chapter Self-Test For practice test questions for Chapter 27, go to the World Geography section of **www.phschool.com**.

Reviewing Key Terms

Use the key terms listed below to write sentences. Leave blanks where the key terms belong. Trade papers with those of a partner and fill in each other's blanks.

1. *harambee*
2. malnutrition
3. strategic value
4. ethnocracy
5. apartheid
6. segregation
7. sanction
8. enclave
9. white flight
10. land redistribution

Understanding Key Ideas

11. Migration Describe the movement of various groups to Kenya's fertile highlands over the centuries.
12. Cultures How did *harambee* benefit Kenya?
13. Cooperation and Conflict Why does France keep a military base in Djibouti?
14. Government and Citizenship Why are Rwanda and Burundi considered to be ethnocracies?

15. Patterns of Settlement How did the homelands plan affect where people in South Africa lived?
16. Understanding the Past List four reasons for the boom in South Africa's economy between 1950 and 1980.
17. Climates How has the arid environment of Botswana actually helped that country?
18. Cooperation and Conflict Why did South Africa support rebels fighting against the governments of Angola and Mozambique?

Critical Thinking and Writing

19. Analyzing Change In Kenya, how did the Kikuyu people overcome British rule and become an important political force in their nation?
20. Analyzing Causes and Effects Push factors are conditions that drive people to migrate from the location in which they have been living. **(a)** In South Africa's past, what push factors caused the native

---

technological skill, and a large labor pool.
17. The arid environment kept the population small, so Botswana's profits can be divided among fewer people.
18. South Africa was a capitalist nation, and the governments of Angola and Mozambique were communist.

Critical Thinking and Writing
19. In the 1950s, the Kikuyu led the Mau Mau Rebellion against the British. After independence, Jomo Kenyatta,

a Kikuyu, became Kenya's first president.
20. (a) The Afrikaners pushed the Africans inland by claiming their land. The Afrikaners were pushed inland by the British settlers. **(b)** Both countries had won independence only after wars with Portugal. The long period of war, followed by the end of Portuguese rule, drove the settlers out.

(Continued on next page.)

Africans to move inland? **(b)** When Angola and Mozambique became independent, what push factors drove out Portuguese settlers?

21. Developing a Hypothesis Why do you think that the villagization program that Tanzania implemented a generation ago failed?

22. Identifying Main Ideas (a) Give two examples of ethnic strife between native African peoples who live in the same area. **(b)** Why do you think such strife exists?

Applying Skills

Synthesizing Information Refer to the Skills for Life lesson on page 577 and the subsection on South Africa's government beginning on page 575. Then, answer these questions:

23. How did South Africa's government change in the 1990s?

24. Based on the evidence, do you think that the people of South Africa feel that the new form of democratic government has improved their lives? Explain.

Recognizing Points of View Study the passage below, and answer the following questions:

25. What are some major changes that have taken place in South Africa in recent history?

26. What are some examples of how countries in East Africa have improved their economies in recent years?

27. If you were a diplomat trying to help Africa become self-sufficient in food and settle its ethnic and religious differences, what positive plan of action would you propose?

> 66 Africa never runs out of surprises. The lesson here is that things can always change for the better, and it is never too late to save a situation. 99

Test Preparation

Read the question and choose the best answer.

28. The British never controlled which of the following pairs of countries?

 A Mozambique and Eritrea

 B Somalia and Uganda

 C Zambia and Zimbabwe

 D Kenya and South Africa

Activities

USING THE REGIONAL ATLAS

Study the photographs in the Regional Atlas for Africa and Chapter 27. Then, make a two-column chart that shows human-environment interaction in the region. In one column, list ways in which people change the environment. In the other column, list ways in which the natural environment affects people.

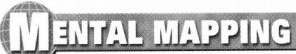 **MENTAL MAPPING**

Study a map of Africa. Then, on a separate piece of paper, draw a sketch map of East and Southern Africa from memory. Label the following places on your map:

- Lake Victoria
- Cape Town
- Somalia
- Sudan
- Nairobi
- Indian Ocean
- Zimbabwe
- Rwanda
- Atlantic Ocean
- Angola

Take It to the NET

Investing in the Region Invest 10 million dollars in the country of your choice in East or Southern Africa. Research the economic, health, and infrastructure needs of your chosen country on the Internet. Explain where and why you invested the money. Visit the World Geography section of **www.phschool.com** for help in completing this activity.

 MENTAL MAPPING

Games for Review See pages 58–63 of the Simulations, Games, and Lab Activities booklet for games to review place names.

Chapter Map Test Students should use the completed outline maps and the Unit 7 Checklist in their Atlas Portfolios to prepare for the Chapter 27 Map Test.

Unit Map Test To prepare for the Unit 7 Map Test, they will need to study the location of all the place names on the Unit 7 Checklist.

Alternative Assessment

Final Evaluation

Giving an Oral Presentation Use the Oral Presentation Evaluation Form on page 21 of the Alternative Assessment booklet in the Prentice Hall Assessment System to evaluate students' presentations. Either teachers or students can complete the forms to indicate which level of work was achieved for each of the criteria. The evaluation should include specific examples and comments.

Critical Thinking and Writing (cont.)

21. Students may suggest that the people of Tanzania resented being forced to live in certain places and work on collective farms. They were not being paid what they felt was a fair price for their crops and so had little incentive to be productive.

22. (a) Examples include warfare between Eritreans and Ethiopians, clan warfare in Somalia, and strife between the Hutu and the Tutsi in Rwanda and Burundi. **(b)** Answers will vary but may suggest that competition for political and economic power and access to land and other resources can lead to strife.

Applying Skills

23. In the 1990s, all the laws that supported apartheid were repealed, and majority rule ensued.

24. No, according to the statistics, the majority felt that their quality of life had remained about the same or declined, and that they did not have a say in decisions affecting the country.

25. South Africa has shifted from a repressive police state run by a small minority to a democratic nation with majority rule.

26. Possible answers: Eritrea modernized its capital, reopened the rail line to its port, and built new industries and housing; Tanzania improved its economy by abandoning socialism and allowing farmers to earn profits from their crops.

27. Answers will vary but should demonstrate an ability to analyze which methods have been successful in accomplishing these aims in Africa.

Test Preparation
28. A

Activities

Using the Regional Atlas
Check students' charts for accuracy regarding human-environment interaction.

Mental Mapping
Review students' maps for relative and absolute location.

Take It to the Net
Students' work should reflect sound research. Check that they have accurately identified the needs of the country and proposed reasonable investments to address those needs.

Use this sample exam to help your students prepare for standardized tests.

You might want to remind your students of the following:

Tips for Test Taking

1. Read the directions carefully.

2. Read each question carefully.

3. For multiple choice questions, try to answer the question before you look at the choices. Read all the choices. Then, eliminate those that are absolutely incorrect.

4. For short answer questions, be sure to answer the question completely if there is more than one part.

5. Answer the easy questions first. Then, go back to the ones that will take more time.

6. Pace yourself. Be sure to set aside enough time for the writing questions.

Write answers on a separate sheet of paper.

Multiple Choice

1 Which two economic activities are the most common ways of producing goods and services in countries across Africa?

   A   Subsistence farming and commercial farming

   B   Livestock raising and commercial farming

   C   Nomadic herding and hunting and gathering

   D   Subsistence farming and nomadic herding

2 In West and Central Africa, CFA member nations use a common currency, much like members of —

   A   the United Nations

   B   NAFTA

   C   the European Union

   D   NATO

3 Which statement best contrasts the aftermath of independence movements in Algeria and South Africa?

   A   An Islamist political movement gained control of the government in Algeria but lost power in South Africa.

   B   The Algerian government created regions called homelands for specific groups, whereas the South African government encouraged diversity.

   C   South Africa promoted agriculture, whereas Algeria promoted industrial development.

   D   Most of the European colonists left Algeria but remained in South Africa.

4 Why are many species of herbivores able to live in the same area of grasslands?

   A   They feed on different plants or on different parts of the grasses.

   B   Herbivores eat very little.

   C   Some herbivores supplement their diets with meat.

   D   Grasses grow back quickly after fires because their root systems survive.

Use the map _and_ your knowledge of social studies to answer the following question.

European Powers in Africa, 1914

British
French
German
Other European powers
Independent

0   1,000 mi
0   1,000 km

5 In which parts of Africa would you expect to find the largest number of French speakers?

   A   East Africa

   B   Southern Africa

   C   North Africa

   D   Central Africa

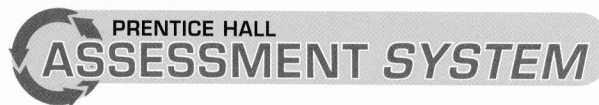

PRENTICE HALL
ASSESSMENT SYSTEM

Diagnose and Prescribe
- Profile student skills with Diagnostic Tests A&B.
- Address student needs with program materials identified in the test.

Review and Reteach
- Provide cumulative content review with the Review Book.

Practice and Assess
- Build test-taking skills with Test-Taking Strategies on Transparencies.

6 Which of the following responses to poaching represents an international influence on public policies regarding the management of natural resources?

A The ban on the ivory trade by the Convention on Trade in Endangered Species

B Increased use of antipoaching units by the Kenya Wildlife Service

C Use of tourist income on environmental protection programs

D Establishment of national parks and national game preserves

7 How does location affect nations of the Sahel?

A The Sahara has always been impossible to cross, preventing contact among nations.

B Many rivers make agriculture profitable, as surplus crops are exported to other countries.

C Foreign aid often has difficulty reaching Sahel nations because of limited transportation networks in the region.

D Many Sahel nations have busy ports on the Atlantic Ocean, making them centers of international trade.

8 How did the introduction of camels to North Africa change the region's geography?

A Domesticating the camels turned the nomadic Berbers into herders and farmers.

B Desert-hardy camels enabled North Africans to establish regular trade with peoples south of the Sahara.

C Increased access to transportation encouraged the growth of large cities away from the coast.

D Soldiers on camelback successfully fought the arrival of European colonists.

9 The end of apartheid in South Africa marked a change in cultural beliefs that led to an expansion of —

A citizenship practices such as voting

B economic sanctions by other countries

C segregation of different groups into race-based homelands

D the Boer War

10 Which characteristic would best support the identification of Cameroon, Gabon, and Congo as a formal region?

A They contain tributaries that supply water to the Congo River.

B Tropical rain forest covers much of all three nations.

C All three nations have an arid climate.

D All of these nations border the Indian Ocean.

Writing Practice

11 How is population growth in Egypt contributing to environmental change?

12 What economic challenges face landlocked countries in Africa?

13 Suppose that you were to hear of a project to build a dam along the Congo River. Would you promote or oppose the project? Use specific details to support your answer.

Unit 7 ▪ Test Preparation **587**

Multiple Choice

1 D

2 C

3 D

4 A

5 C

6 A

7 C

8 B

9 A

10 B

Writing Practice

11 In response to population growth in Egypt, the Egyptian government plans to increase the amount of arable land by irrigating farther into the desert. To make the desert arable, chemical fertilizers need to be used. The runoff of fertilizers can do damage to the waters of the Nile.

12 Students should recognize that without an outlet to an ocean, a country faces challenges bringing in products from the outside and getting exports out to foreign markets.

13 Students might cite problems that have resulted from dam projects in other places—for example, the flooding of villages, the loss of farmland, and the rise in disease. Students also should point out some of the benefits of the Congo River that would be compromised, if not destroyed, by a dam—namely, the river's value as a system of transportation and provider of food and water to the region. Students also might mention that the rain forest of the region might suffer as a result of the proposed project.

Unit 7 ▪ Test Preparation **587**

Introducing
U N I T
8
pp. 588–631

South Asia

Activating Prior Knowledge
Have students share what comes to mind when they think of South Asia. Ask: **What countries does the South Asian region include?** (Afghanistan, Pakistan, India, Bangladesh, Bhutan, Nepal, Sri Lanka) **What are some of the mountain ranges in the region?** (Hindu Kush, Karakoram, Paropamisus, Himalayas) Finally, ask students if they have heard or read anything recently in the news about the region.

Photo Study
Sagarmatha National Park, Nepal
The Himalayas dominate the landscape of the northern regions of South Asia. Tourists flock to this beautiful region. As the tourist industry has grown in the area, deforestation has become a problem along main hiking trails. **Analyzing Causes and Effects** Ask: **What are some of the causes and effects of deforestation in this region?** (Possible causes: Villagers and tourists use wood fuel for heat and cooking, selling lumber commercially. Possible effects: flooding, erosion, depletion of natural resources, loss of beauty that attracts tourists)

eTeach
Be sure to check out this month's online forum with a Master Teacher to join in an exchange of teaching ideas. **www.phschool.com**

UNIT eight
South Asia

Locating the Region
South Asia looks like a giant triangle extending out into the Indian Ocean. Millions of years ago, the part of the earth's crust containing the subcontinent of South Asia collided with the rest of Asia. The force of this huge collision drove the earth skyward, creating the world's highest mountains, the Himalayas. These mountains formed a barrier that allowed the people of South Asia to develop their own unique cultures. Yet, peoples and ideas did move into and out of the region, helping to transform South Asia and its neighbors.

Robinson Projection

RESOURCE DIRECTORY
Teaching Resources
Unit 8
• Geography and World Literature, Nectar in a Sieve, p. 26
Mental Mapping booklet
• Unit 8 Checklist, p. 106
• Unit 8 Map Test, p. 114
Simulations, Games, and Lab Activities
• Where on Earth? Games, pp. 78–79
Global Environmental Posters

Technology
TeacherExpress™ CD-ROM
World Geography: Building a Global Perspective Teaching Resources on CD-ROM offers lesson planning flexibility, test-generation capability, and resource manageability.
Prentice Hall Presentation Pro CD-ROM
This CD-ROM allows you to create custom lessons for instruction or review for every chapter.

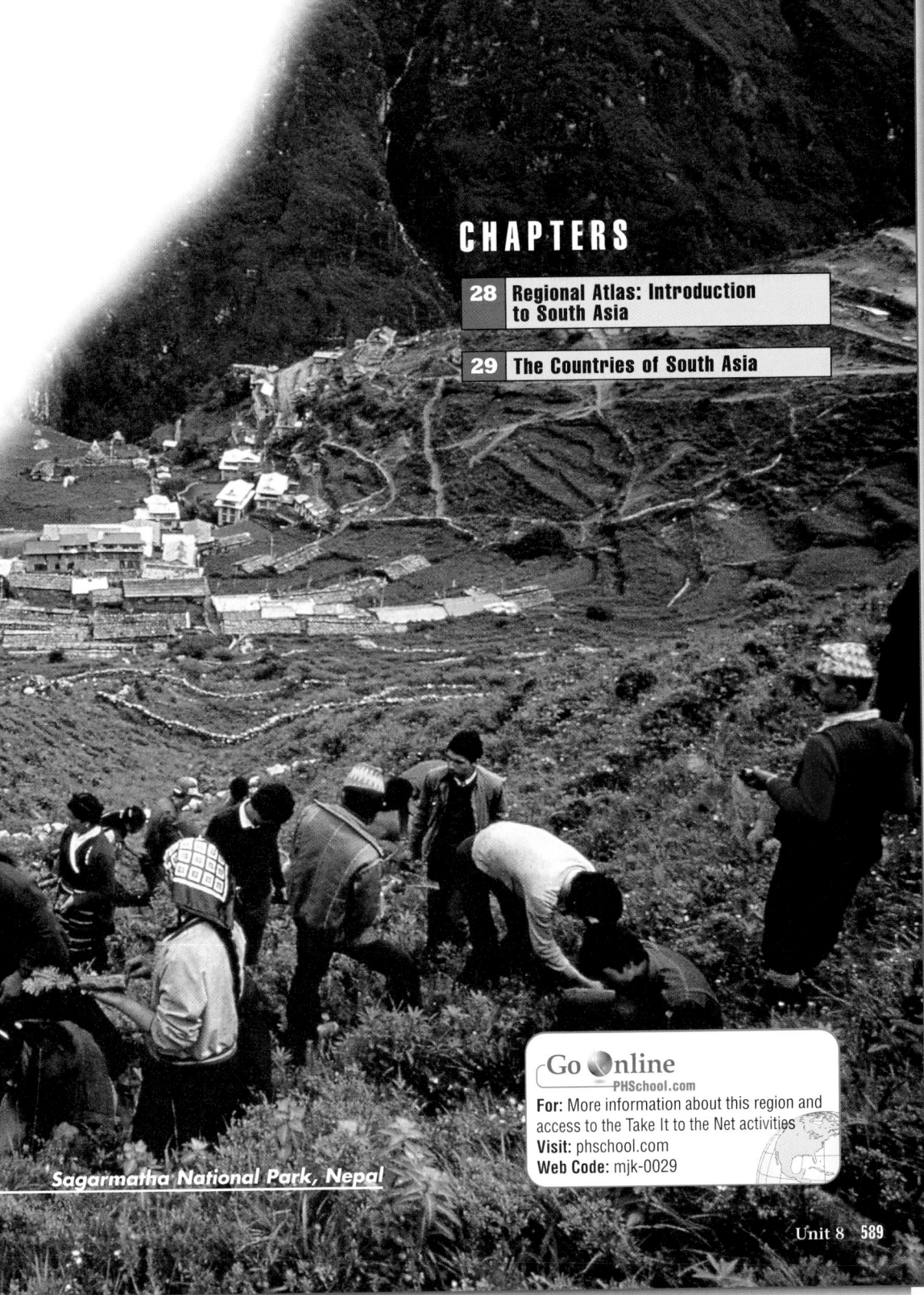

CHAPTERS

Go Online
PHSchool.com

For: More information about this region and access to the Take It to the Net activities
Visit: phschool.com
Web Code: mjk-0029

Sagarmatha National Park, Nepal

Unit 8 **589**

Promoting Geographic Understanding

Introduce the unit using the themes below.

1. Location Help students identify South Asia's location in relation to other regions by referring them to the Robinson projection map on page 588. Ask: **What bodies of water surround South Asia?** (Indian Ocean, Bay of Bengal, Arabian Sea)

2. Place Tell students to look at the political map of Asia in the Atlas of their textbooks. Ask: **What countries border South Asia?** (Iran, Turkmenistan, Uzbekistan, Tajikistan, China, and Myanmar)

RESOURCE DIRECTORY

World Geography Map and Photo Transparencies
The World Geography Map and Photo Transparencies provide thematic maps and photos to help students understand key geographic concepts.

World Geography Videos
These chapter-level videos help students understand the key concepts and themes of geography through case studies.

ExamView Test Bank CD-ROM
The test bank CD-ROM allows you to create, edit, and print out chapter-level tests.

Social Studies Skills Tutor CD-ROM
This interactive CD-ROM provides students with the opportunity to learn and practice critical social studies skills.

Take It to the NET
Prentice Hall's Web site offers Internet activities and links that supplement *World Geography: Building a Global Perspective.* Visit us in the Social Studies area at **www.phschool.com**.

Resource Manager

	CORE INSTRUCTION	READING/SKILLS
Chapter-Level Resources	**Teaching Resources** 📗 **Unit 8**/Ch. 28 • Regional Atlas Study Guide, p. 2 📘 **Mental Mapping booklet** • Unit 8 Checklist, p. 106 📘 **Simulations, Games, and Lab Activities** • Where on Earth? Games, pp. 78–79 • Place Location Review Games, pp. 58–63 💿 **TeacherExpress™ CD-ROM**, Ch. 28 💻 **Companion Web site,** **www.phschool.com** • eTeach	**Teaching Resources** 📗 **Unit 8**/Ch. 28 • Regional Atlas Review, p. 3 📘 **Guide to the Essentials (English/Spanish)** • Chapter 28 Summary 📘 **Spanish Resources** • Regional Atlas Review, p. 72 📼 **Guided Reading Audiotapes (English/Spanish)**, Ch. 28 📄 **Section Reading Support Transparencies**, Ch. 28 💿 **Book on CD**, Ch. 28 💿 **Social Studies Skills Tutor CD-ROM**
Historical Overview Describe significant events and developments in the history of South Asia.	**Teaching Resources** 📘 **Mental Mapping booklet** • Outline Map 28A, p. 107 💿 **Prentice Hall Presentation Pro CD-ROM**, Ch. 28	**Teaching Resources** 📘 **Social Studies Skills Handbook** • Reading a Political Map, p. 19
Physical Characteristics Identify major physical characteristics of South Asia.	**Teaching Resources** 📘 **Mental Mapping booklet** • Outline Map 28B, p. 108 💿 **Prentice Hall Presentation Pro CD-ROM**, Ch. 28	**Teaching Resources** 📘 **Social Studies Skills Handbook** • Elevation on a Map, p. 20 • Four Types of Landforms, p. 21 • Relief on a Map, p. 22
Climates Compare climate regions in South Asia.	**Teaching Resources** 📘 **Creative Teaching Activities** • The Effects of Monsoons, p. 30 💿 **Prentice Hall Presentation Pro CD-ROM**, Ch. 28	**Teaching Resources** 📘 **Social Studies Skills Handbook** • Reading a Climate Map, p. 26 • Reading a Climate Graph, p. 65 • Comparing Climate Graphs, p. 66
Ecosystems Describe characteristics of major ecosystems in South Asia.	💿 **Prentice Hall Presentation Pro CD-ROM**, Ch. 28	**Teaching Resources** 📘 **Social Studies Skills Handbook** • Reading a Natural Vegetation Map, p. 25
People and Cultures Discuss elements of culture in South Asia.	💿 **Prentice Hall Presentation Pro CD-ROM**, Ch. 28	**Teaching Resources** 📘 **Social Studies Skills Handbook** • Reading a Population Density Map, p. 31
Economics, Technology, and Environment Identify how the economy, technology, and the environment interact in South Asia.	💿 **Prentice Hall Presentation Pro CD-ROM**, Ch. 28	**Teaching Resources** 📘 **Social Studies Skills Handbook** • Reading an Economic Activity Map, p. 27 • Reading a Natural Resources Map, p. 34
Database • Discuss how a nation's economy influences the development of its communications systems. • Compare the communications statistics of India, Pakistan, Sri Lanka, Bangladesh, and the United States.	**Teaching Resources** 📗 **Unit 8**/Ch. 28 • Regional Atlas Database Skills, p. 4 💿 **Prentice Hall Presentation Pro CD-ROM**, Ch. 28	**Teaching Resources** 📗 **Unit 8**/Ch. 28 • Regional Atlas Database Skills, p. 4 📘 **Social Studies Skills Handbook** • Reading a Table, p. 62

ENRICHMENT/HONORS/PREAP

📗 **Teaching Resources**

📖 **Mental Mapping booklet**
- Atlas Activity, p. 109

📖 **Social Studies Skills Handbook**
- Study and Research Skills, pp. 94–108

📱 **World Geography Map and Photo Transparencies**
- South Asia: Maps and Photos

📺 **World Geography Videos**
- Regional Atlas: South Asia, Tape 4

💻 **Companion Web site, www.phschool.com**
- Chapter 28 Activities

📱 **World Geography Map and Photo Transparencies**
- South Asia: Political

📱 **World Geography Map and Photo Transparencies**
- South Asia: Physical

📱 **World Geography Map and Photo Transparencies**
- World Climate Zones

📱 **World Geography Map and Photo Transparencies**
- South Asia: Natural Hazards

📱 **World Geography Map and Photo Transparencies**
- South Asia: Population Density

📱 **World Geography Map and Photo Transparencies**
- South Asia: Economic Activities

📱 **World Geography Map and Photo Transparencies**
- Per Capita GDP: Access to the Internet

ASSESSMENT

PRENTICE HALL ASSESSMENT SYSTEM

Core Assessment

📖 **ExamView Test Bank booklet,** Ch. 28

💿 **ExamView Test Bank CD-ROM,** Ch. 28

Standardized Test Preparation

Diagnose and Prescribe

📖 **Diagnostic Tests for High School Social Studies Skills**

Review and Reteach

📖 **Review Book for World Geography,** pp. 17–18

Practice and Assess

📖 **Test-taking Strategies With Transparencies for High School**

📖 **Test-taking Strategy Poster**

📖 **Alternative Assessment booklet**

📖 **Test Prep Book for World Geography**

📗 **Teaching Resources**

📒 **Unit 8**/Ch. 28
- Test Forms A and B, pp. 5–10

📖 **Guide to the Essentials (English/Spanish)**
- Chapter 28 Test

📖 **Mental Mapping booklet**
- Chapter 28 Map Test, p. 110

💻 **Companion Web site, www.phschool.com**
- Chapter 28 Self-Test

CUSTOMIZE FOR INDIVIDUAL NEEDS

Gifted and Talented
- Teacher's Edition, Customize for . . . , p. 605

Honors/PreAP
- Teacher's Edition, Customize for . . . , p. 603

Less Proficient Readers
- Guide to the Essentials (English), Ch. 28
- Guided Reading Audiotapes (English), Ch. 28
- Section Reading Support Transparencies, Ch. 28
- Book on CD, Ch. 28

Students Acquiring English/ESL
- Guide to the Essentials (English/Spanish), Ch. 28
- Guided Reading Audiotapes (English/Spanish), Ch. 28
- Section Reading Support Transparencies, Ch. 28
- Book on CD, Ch. 28

Less Proficient Writers
- Alternative Assessment, Writing Assignment Rubric, p. 6

Introducing

CHAPTER

28

pp. 590–603

Objectives

Upon completion of the Regional Atlas, students should be able to:

◆ describe significant events and developments in the history of South Asia;

◆ identify major physical characteristics of South Asia;

◆ compare climate regions in South Asia;

◆ describe characteristics of major ecosystems in South Asia;

◆ discuss elements of culture in South Asia;

◆ identify how the economy, technology, and the environment interact in South Asia.

 National Geography Standards

The following National Geography Standards are highlighted in this Regional Atlas: 1, 4, 5, 7, 8, 9, 10, 12, 13, 14, 17

 Bellringer

Instruct each student to write three questions that they would like to ask a student from South Asia about his or her region.

Answers to Assessment

1. (a) sultanate, p. 590 **(b)** nonaligned nation, p. 590

2. Pakistan, India, and Bangladesh

3. The religion of foreign invaders led to new religions and ways of governing. Also, when colonialism ended, Britain divided its possessions (present-day Pakistan and India) into two states on the basis of religion.

CHAPTER 28 — Introduction to SOUTH ASIA

Historical Overview

South Asia is home to one of the world's oldest civilizations. The Indus Valley civilization, centered in present-day Pakistan, flourished from about 2500 to 1500 B.C. Toward the end of that period, the first of several waves of invaders arrived from Central Asia and Afghanistan.

Religions and Ancient Empires The religious beliefs of the invaders and the earlier inhabitants merged to form Hinduism, one of the world's major religions. Later, around 500 B.C., another of the world's major religions, Buddhism, was founded in India. Over the next few centuries, a series of invaders from Central Asia and Afghanistan founded and conquered empires in South Asia.

Muslim Dominance In the early A.D. 700s, Arab conquerors brought Islam to the Sind region in modern Pakistan. Over the next several centuries, Islam spread across the region through conquest and trade. In 1206, Muslim invaders from Afghanistan established the Sultanate of Delhi. This **sultanate,** or state ruled by a sultan, expanded across South Asia during the 1300s. It held off Mongol invaders but fragmented into smaller states during the 1400s. During the 1520s, Babur, a Muslim from Central Asia, invaded northern India and defeated the last sultan. His successors ruled the Mughal Empire, which covered most of South Asia by the 1600s. Like earlier Muslim states, the Mughal Empire included members of the Hindu majority in its power structure.

British Imperialism In 1618, the English East India Company gained the right to set up trading posts along the coast. Over time, the company edged out rivals from other European countries. Starting in the mid-1700s, the company began to build a colonial empire across South Asia. The peoples of Afghanistan remained independent.

Resistance and Independence Resistance to British rule led to the foundation of the Indian National Congress in 1885. The Muslim League, founded in 1906, represented the Muslim minority. In 1920, Congress leader Mohandas Gandhi launched a campaign of boycotts and peaceful demonstrations. However, tensions grew between Hindus and Muslims.

Unable to maintain control in South Asia or to overcome religious conflict, Britain divided its possessions into two new states on the basis of religion. India and Pakistan became independent in 1947. The two countries frequently fought over disputed territory. India was one of the **nonaligned nations,** which adopted neutrality during the Cold War. Pakistan at first consisted of two large areas on the eastern and western flanks of India, but easterners sought more political power. Civil war broke out, and aided by India, East Pakistan gained independence as Bangladesh in 1971. In recent decades, Soviet occupation and civil war have wrecked Afghanistan. Its government was toppled in 2001 as the United States and other nations fought terrorism following the September 11 attacks.

ASSESSMENT

1. **Key Terms** Define **(a)** sultanate, **(b)** nonaligned nation.

2. **Map Skills** **Place** Through which modern countries do the Indus and Ganges rivers flow?

3. **Critical Thinking** **Analyzing Change** How has religion led to changes throughout South Asian history?

590 Chapter 28 ▪ Regional Atlas: South Asia

RESOURCE DIRECTORY

Teaching Resources

Unit 8, Chapter 28
• Regional Atlas Study Guide, p. 2

Guide to the Essentials (English/Spanish)
• Chapter 28 Summary

Mental Mapping booklet
• Unit 8 Checklist, p. 106
• Outline Map 28A, p. 107

Social Studies Skills Handbook
• Reading a Political Map, p. 19

Technology

Guided Reading Audiotapes (English/Spanish), Chapter 28

Section Reading Support Transparencies, Chapter 28

World Geography Map and Photo Transparencies
• South Asia: Maps and Photos

Book on CD, Chapter 28

World Geography Videos
• Regional Atlas: South Asia, Tape 4

590 Chapter 28

REGIONAL ATLAS

South Asia: POLITICAL

KEY

— National boundary
⊛ National capital
• Other city

Lambert Azimuthal Equal-Area Projection

Countries and cities shown on map:

AFGHANISTAN — Kabul, Peshawar, Islamabad

PAKISTAN — Lahore, Amritsar, Karachi

INDIA — Delhi, New Delhi, Kanpur, Varanasi, Ahmadabad, Kolkata (Calcutta), Mumbai (Bombay), Hyderabad, Bangalore, Chennai (Madras)

NEPAL — Kathmandu

BHUTAN — Thimphu

BANGLADESH — Dhaka

SRI LANKA — Colombo

MALDIVES — Male

Water/physical features: Arabian Sea, Bay of Bengal, Indian Ocean, Gulf of Kutch, Gulf of Khambhat, Tropic of Cancer, Indus R., Yamuna R., Ghaghara R., Ganges R., Brahmaputra R., Meghna R., Narmada R., Godavari R., Krishna R., Mouths of the Ganges, Andaman Islands (India), Nicobar Islands (India), Palk Strait

Scale: 0 250 500 mi / 0 250 500 km

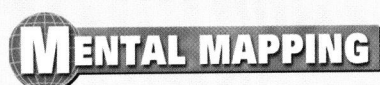

MENTAL MAPPING

Making a Political Map Study this political map and then draw your own sketch map of South Asia. Label the countries and major cities of the region. Use various colors to outline and shade each country.

LESSON PLAN

1. Focus Ask each student to pack an imaginary suitcase for a journey through South Asia. Ask students to consult the maps in the Regional Atlas in order to list what they would pack.

2. Instruct Have students complete the Mental Mapping activities and answer the Photo Caption questions in the Regional Atlas. Review the answers as a class.

3. Close/Reteach Divide the class into pairs. Ask each pair to create a "Map of Errors" of South Asia, labeling an outline map to include 10 errors. Then have pairs exchange maps and try to find all the errors.

Map Study Extension
Use the question below to develop an additional geographic theme.

Location The mountainous country of Nepal lies along the northern border of South Asia. Ask: **What is the capital of Nepal?** (Kathmandu)

MENTAL MAPPING

Unit Checklist Distribute the Unit 8 Checklist on page 106 of the Mental Mapping booklet in the Teaching Resources. This list includes all of the place names students should learn in this unit.

Making a Political Map Students can complete the mapping activity on this page by sketching their own maps or by coloring and labeling the Chapter 28A Outline Map on page 107 of the Mental Mapping booklet. Ask students to label all of the countries and major cities listed under Part I of the Unit 8 Checklist.

Alternative Assessment

Introduce the Activity

Making a Map You may wish to distribute the Map Rubric found on page 14 of the Alternative Assessment booklet in the Prentice Hall Assessment System.

TEACHING TIP
From a Master Teacher

Human-Environment Interaction Students should comprehend the impact one of the world's densest populations has on this region's environment. Millions of people depend on South Asia's ecosystems for their livelihoods as subsistence farmers. Consequently, they alter the balance of nature. One result has been severe deforestation. The environment affects people, as well. Flooding in the lowlands of Bangladesh, made worse by deforestation in the highlands of India, is particularly destructive.

Map Study Extension

Use the questions below to develop additional geographic themes.

1. Movement Instruct students to compare the physical map with the locations of major cities on the political map. Ask: **What do many of the cities have in common?** (Most are located on rivers or coasts.)

2. Place The Himalayas form the highest mountain system in the world. They are relatively young mountains and have not eroded much. In fact, they continue to shift, move, and rise. The Himalayas also contain some of the world's largest glaciers, so that India contains the world's largest body of ice outside subpolar regions. Ask: **Which is higher: Mt. Everest in the Himalayas or Aconcagua in the Andes of South America?** (Mt. Everest: It is 29,028 feet above sea level; Aconcagua is 22,831 feet.)

3. Movement Three great rivers flow through the northern region of the Indian subcontinent: the Indus, the Ganges, and the Brahmaputra. These rivers begin their journey to the sea as thin streams moving slowly down the Himalayan slopes. They continue to grow in size as they flow southward over lower and flatter land. Ask: **What is the plain the Ganges River flows through?** (Indo-Gangetic Plain)

Answers to Assessment

1. (a) subcontinent, p. 592 **(b)** alluvial plain, p. 592

2. the Khyber Pass

3. It would lose a significant water supply, which would likely damage its agricultural production.

Because of its size, South Asia is often referred to as a **subcontinent,** or large landmass forming a distinct part of a continent. The geographic landscape of the region varies greatly. Deserts stretch throughout Pakistan, while lush rain forests spread across the slopes of India's west coast. Glacier-covered mountains tower above the villages of Nepal.

Himalayas

The Himalayas include more than 30 of the world's highest mountains. The mountain system is made up of several parallel ranges and is often referred to as "the rooftop of the world." **PHYSICAL CHARACTERISTICS** *Through what countries do the Himalayas run?*

Indus River

The Indus River is one of three great rivers in South Asia and was home to the region's oldest civilizations. The river begins in the Himalayas and runs to the Arabian Sea, forming **alluvial plains** as it deposits rich silt in flat areas. **NATURAL RESOURCES** *How would you expect the Indus River to affect farming?*

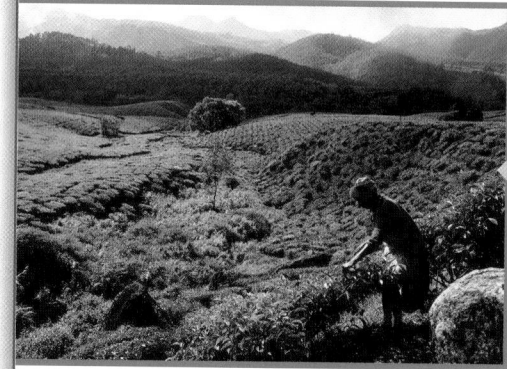

Western Ghats

The Western Ghats, one of two mountain ranges that run along the coasts of southern India, marks the western edge of the Deccan Plateau. **CLIMATES** *Would you expect rainfall levels to be higher on the western or eastern slopes of the Western Ghats? Explain.*

ASSESSMENT

1. **Key Terms** Define **(a)** subcontinent, **(b)** alluvial plain.

2. **Map Skills** **Movement** What physical feature would allow people to travel through the mountains between Afghanistan and Pakistan?

3. **Critical Thinking** **Developing a Hypothesis** How might Bangladesh be affected by the construction of dams in the Indo-Gangetic Plain?

Answers to Photo Captions

Himalayas Nepal, Bhutan, India
Indus River The Indus River is extremely beneficial to farming.

Western Ghats the western slopes; Rain is usually heavier on the coast than in the interior.

REGIONAL ATLAS

South Asia: PHYSICAL

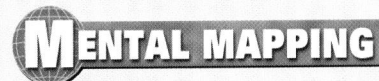

KEY

Elevation

Feet	Meters
14,000	4,270
7,000	2,135
1,500	457
700	213
(sea level) 0	0 (sea level)

• Major city
▲ Mountain
)(Mountain pass

Lambert Azimuthal Equal-Area Projection

HINDU KUSH
Kabul
Peshawar
AFGHANISTAN
Islamabad
KASHMIR
SULAIMAN RANGE
Mangla Reservoir
CHAGAI HILLS
BOLAN PASS
PUNJAB
Lahore • Amritsar
Sutlej R.
PAKISTAN
Indus R.
BALUCHISTAN PLATEAU
GREAT INDIAN DESERT (THAR DESERT)
Delhi
New Delhi
Yamuna R.
MAKRAN
• Karachi
Kanpur
Chambal R.
INDO-GANGETIC PLAIN
• Varanasi
Gandhi Reservoir
NEPAL
Kathmandu
HIMALAYAS
Mt. Everest 29,035 ft. (8,850 m)
BHUTAN
Thimphu
Brahmaputra R.
KHASI HILLS
BANGLADESH
Dhaka
Meghna R.
Govind Ballabh Pant Reservoir
Kolkata (Calcutta)
Tropic of Cancer
Gulf of Kutch
Ahmadabad
VINDHYA MOUNTAINS
Narmada R.
Arabian Sea
Gulf of Khambhat
Tapti R.
INDIA
Godavari R.
Mouths of the Ganges
L. Chilka
Mumbai (Bombay)
DECCAN PLATEAU
Hyderabad
Krishna R.
Nagarjuna Reservoir
EASTERN GHATS
Bay of Bengal
WESTERN GHATS
Hirakud Reservoir
Chennai (Madras)
Bangalore
Coromandel Coast
Andaman Islands
Malabar Coast
INDIAN OCEAN
Nicobar Islands
SRI LANKA
Palk Strait
MALDIVES
Colombo
• Male

0   250   500 mi
0   250   500 km

MENTAL MAPPING

Making a Physical Map Study this physical map and then draw your own sketch map of South Asia. Label the major physical features, including rivers and other bodies of water.

MENTAL MAPPING

Mapping Physical Features Students can complete the mapping activity on this page either by adding labels to the political maps they have completed or by coloring and labeling the Chapter 28B Outline Map on page 108 of the Mental Mapping booklet in the Teaching Resources. Ask students to label all of the bodies of water and landforms listed under Part II of the Unit 8 Checklist.

ACTIVITY

Connecting With . . .

Literature Instruct students to read about the mountaineers who have climbed in the Himalayas, including Sir Edmund Hillary. Suggestions include: *Everest: Expedition to the Ultimate*, by Reinhold Messner, and *Annapurna: A Woman's Place*, by Arlene Blum, about the 1978 American Women's Himalayan Expedition.

BACKGROUND

History

The Indus Civilization The Indus Civilization, which was at its height around 4,500 years ago, rivaled the better-known civilizations of Egypt and Mesopotamia in its accomplishments. Large cities had populations of 35,000 or more. While most of the people would have been occupied with raising crops and livestock, arts, crafts, and architecture also flourished. The Indus Civilization developed its own alphabet, a system of weights and measures, a huge trade network, and a political system. The Indus religion created many of the ideas and symbols that are common in India today.

Map Study Extension

Use the questions below to develop additional geographic themes.

1. Region Ask: **Name a city located in a semiarid region.** (Delhi)

2. Place Ask: **What are the four most prevalent climate types in the region?** (arid, semiarid, humid subtropical, and tropical wet and dry)

3. Region Ask: **Where in South Asia is the climate tropical wet?** (southern half of Sri Lanka, southwest India, Bangladesh)

Answers to Assessment

1. monsoon, p. 594

2. the northwest

3. Bangladesh would likely be more affected by flooding because it experiences summer monsoon winds from the ocean, which cause great amounts of rainfall.

SOUTH ASIA
Climates

Altitude and distance from the Indian Ocean affect climates in South Asia. In portions of the region, seasonal rainfall varies dramatically. The **monsoons** are winds that blow dry air from the northeast during the winter and carry moisture from the southwest in the summer.

Monsoons

The monsoons bring much-needed rain, but can also cause flooding. Here, oxen are herded through a downpour. **CLIMATES** *What countries in South Asia have tropical wet and tropical wet and dry climates?*

Thar Desert

Jaisalmer, India, is a caravan center in the Thar Desert. Also called the Great Indian Desert, the arid region spans the border between India and Pakistan. **ECONOMIC ACTIVITIES** *Based on this photograph, would you expect farming to play an important role in the local economy?*

Annual Precipitation

Precipitation levels vary greatly throughout South Asia. Areas out of the path of the monsoon winds receive little rain. **PHYSICAL CHARACTERISTICS** *Which of these five cities seems least likely to be affected by monsoons?*

IN.

100	
80	
60	
40	
20	
0	Dhaka Colombo Kabul Islamabad Kolka (Calcu

Source: www.worldclimate.com
Bars show average annual rainfall in inches.

ASSESSMENT

1. **Key Term** Define monsoon.

2. **Map Skills Place** What part of India has an arid climate?

3. **Critical Thinking Drawing Conclusions** Would you expect Bhutan or Bangladesh to be more affected by flooding? Explain.

594 Chapter 28 ▪ Regional Atlas: South Asia

RESOURCE DIRECTORY

Teaching Resources
Creative Teaching Activities, The Effects of Monsoons, p. 30
Social Studies Skills Handbook
• Reading a Climate Map, p. 26
• Reading a Climate Graph, p. 65
• Comparing Climate Graphs, p. 66

Technology
World Geography Map and Photo Transparencies
• South Asia: Maps and Photos

Answers to Photo Captions

Monsoons India, Bangladesh, and Sri Lanka

Thar Desert no

Annual Precipitation Kabul

REGIONAL ATLAS

South Asia: CLIMATE REGIONS

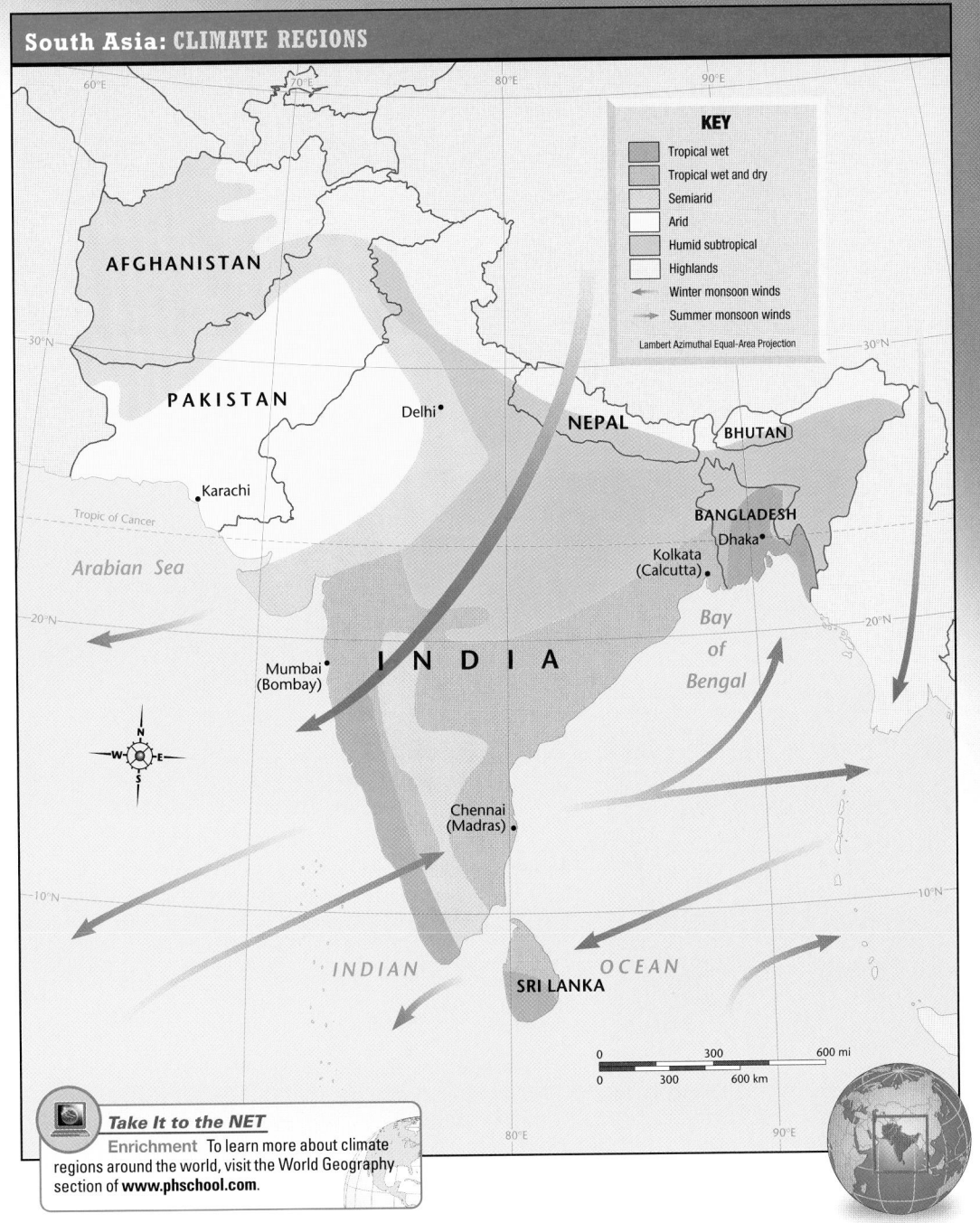

KEY

- Tropical wet
- Tropical wet and dry
- Semiarid
- Arid
- Humid subtropical
- Highlands
- ← Winter monsoon winds
- → Summer monsoon winds

Lambert Azimuthal Equal-Area Projection

AFGHANISTAN

PAKISTAN

Delhi

NEPAL   BHUTAN

Karachi

Tropic of Cancer

BANGLADESH

Dhaka

Kolkata
(Calcutta)

Arabian Sea

Bay
of
Bengal

Mumbai
(Bombay)

I N D I A

Chennai
(Madras)

INDIAN   OCEAN

SRI LANKA

0   300   600 mi
0   300   600 km

Take It to the NET

Enrichment To learn more about climate regions around the world, visit the World Geography section of **www.phschool.com**.

ACTIVITY

Critical Thinking

Climate Use the following questions to help students see the links between prevailing winds and climate. **How do prevailing winds from the northeast during winter affect the climate of South Asia?** (Winds coming from inland, snow-covered mountains are cooler and drier.) **How do prevailing winds from the southwest during the summer affect the region's climate?** (Winds from the ocean are warmer and more humid, causing greater rainfall.)

BACKGROUND

Word Origin

Monsoon The word *monsoon* is derived from the Arabic word *mausim*, meaning "time" or "season." Very heavy rains—the "burst of the monsoon"—start the rainy season. A weak monsoon can cause crop failure, which may result in widespread famine.

TEST PREPARATION

Have students review the captions on the opposite page to answer the following question.

Since most of South Asia is hot and dry for half the year, monsoons provide water for farmers' dry fields. What might happen if the monsoons were late?

   A Flooding
   B Earthquakes
   C Drought
   D Sinkholes

Map Study Extension

Use the questions below to develop additional geographic themes.

1. Location Ask: **Where would you go to find forest in South Asia?** (northern Afghanistan; northeastern Pakistan; northern and eastern India; southern and western Indian coasts; southern and eastern Nepal; southern Bhutan; Bangladesh; Sri Lanka)

2. Region When summer monsoon winds meet mountain ranges, they release their moisture as they are pushed upward. Because the Western Ghats block the rain, the land to the east is hot and dry. Compare the physical map with the ecosystem map. Ask: **What is the predominant ecosystem of the land east of the Western Ghats?** (grassland) **What kinds of vegetation grow there?** (grasses, short bushes, and shrubs)

3. Place Ask: **What type of ecosystem dominates Afghanistan?** (temperate grassland)

Answers to Assessment

1. (a) Bangladesh and Sri Lanka
(b) mid-latitude deciduous forest

2. Possible answer: Increased conservation efforts would probably help national economies in South Asia by encouraging tourism.

Answers to Photo Captions

Ibex Herd desert scrub
Asian Elephants tropical grassland
Wetlands Poaching and destruction of habitat negatively affect the natural environment in South Asia.

Ecosystems

South Asia's size and its variety of elevations and landforms give the region a wide range of ecosystems. Plant life varies with precipitation levels and elevation. Wildlife is plentiful, although poaching and loss of habitat are serious threats to many animals, such as rhinoceroses, elephants, and tigers. A strong conservation movement in the region works to protect plants and animals.

Ibex Herd

Kirthar National Park in Pakistan is home to Sind ibexes, such as the ones in this herd. Although the region has strong, dry winds and soil with few nutrients, a variety of plants and animals can be found. **CLIMATES** *In which climate region would you expect to find a desert ecosystem like Kirthar National Park?*

Asian Elephants

Elephants are one of the species living within Bandhavgarh National Park in central India. Here, a young elephant uses its trunk to get water from a stream while an adult elephant stands guard. **ECOSYSTEMS** *In what ecosystem would you expect to find these elephants?*

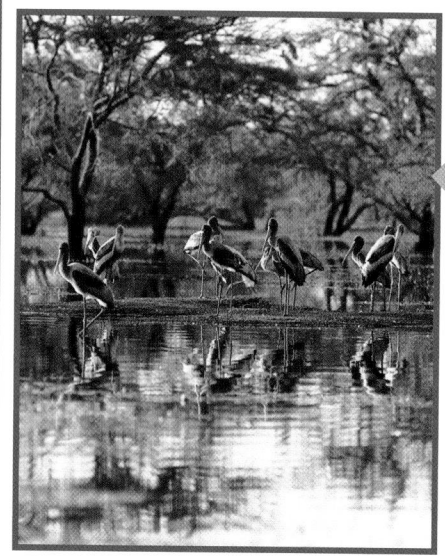

Wetlands

Bird sanctuaries provide refuge for animals such as these painted storks. India alone has over 1,200 species of birds. **ENVIRONMENTAL CHANGE** *In what ways do people's actions affect the environment in South Asia?*

ASSESSMENT

1. **Map Skills** **Regions** **(a)** Which South Asian countries have only one ecosystem? **(b)** In South Asia, which ecosystem is found only in Afghanistan?

2. **Critical Thinking** **Predicting Consequences** What effects might increased conservation efforts have on national economies in South Asia?

REGIONAL ATLAS

South Asia: ECOSYSTEMS

AFGHANISTAN

PAKISTAN

Delhi

Karachi

Tropic of Cancer

Gulf of Kutch

Arabian Sea

Gulf of
Khambhat

INDIA

Mumbai
(Bombay)

NEPAL

BHUTAN

BANGLADESH

Kolkata
(Calcutta)

Mouths of
the Ganges

Indus R.
Sutlej R.
Chambal R.
Yamuna R.
Ganges R.
Ghaghara R.
Son R.
Brahmaputra R.
Meghna R.
Narmada R.
Tapti R.
Mahanadi R.
Godavari R.
Krishna R.

Bay
of
Bengal

MALDIVES

Palk Strait

SRI LANKA

INDIAN

OCEAN

| 0 | 300 | 600 mi |
| 0 | 300 | 600 km |

KEY
- Tropical rain forest
- Mid-latitude deciduous forest
- Mixed forest (deciduous and coniferous)
- Tropical grassland
- Temperate grassland
- Desert scrub
- Highlands (vegetation varies with elevation)

Lambert Azimuthal Equal-Area Projection

Take It to the NET
Enrichment To learn more about ecosystems around the world, visit the World Geography section of **www.phschool.com**.

Enrichment

India's Wildlife Parks Tell students that India has a long history of practicing conservation. In the third century B.C., Emperor Ashoka ordered people to stop killing certain animals and destroying forests. Today, India maintains over 400 parks, sanctuaries, and reserve areas to protect its plant and animal life. Instruct students to use library and Internet travel guides to research some of India's reserves. Have students create bumper stickers characterizing the flora or fauna in an area of their choice. Display finished stickers in the classroom. (Verbal/Linguistic, Visual/Spatial)

SOUTH ASIA
People and Cultures

South Asia has one of the most densely settled populations on earth. India's population alone is more than 1 billion. More and more people are moving to cities in search of jobs. By the early 2000s, Kolkata, formerly Calcutta, and Mumbai were among the ten most populated cities in the world. About half of the people in India speak Hindi, but many languages are spoken throughout the region. Although many religions are practiced in the region, the dominant religions are Hinduism in India and Nepal; Islam in Afghanistan, Bangladesh, and Pakistan; and Buddhism in Bhutan.

Tradition and Convergence

Cattle are commonplace sights in cities and rural areas throughout South Asia. In Hinduism, cows are sacred and are not used for food. **CULTURES** (a) *In which South Asian nations would you be most likely to encounter a scene like the one shown here? Explain.* (b) *What evidence of cultural convergence appears in this photograph?*

Overpopulation

India has a population growth rate of 1.6 percent, which will lead the nation's population to double in 36 years. This mural encourages families to limit the number of children they have to two. **POPULATION GROWTH** *Why might officials want to limit population growth?*

Urban Landscape

Colombo, the capital of Sri Lanka, shows a mixture of old and new building styles. Arab traders settled in the area beginning in the 700s. **URBANIZATION** *How does this photo suggest that population density is increasing in South Asian cities?*

ASSESSMENT

1. **Map Skills** **Regions** Which South Asian nation appears to be the least densely populated?

2. **Critical Thinking** **Synthesizing Information** What languages would you expect to hear in Chennai?

REGIONAL ATLAS

South Asia: POPULATION DENSITY

KEY

Persons per sq mi	Persons per sq km
Over 520	Over 200
260–519	100–199
130–259	50–99
25–129	10–49
1–24	1–9
Less than 1	Less than 1

Metropolitan areas

☐ Over 10,000,000
■ 5,000,000–10,000,000
○ 2,000,000–5,000,000
◉ 1,000,000–2,000,000
● 250,000–1,000,000
○ Under 250,000

Lambert Azimuthal Equal-Area Projection

South Asia: MAJOR LANGUAGES

KEY

Indo-European family
Dravidian family
Sino-Tibetan
Austroasiatic family
Burushaski
Altaic family

Lambert Azimuthal Equal-Area Projection

GET THE FACTS ...

Go to the Table of Countries at the back of this book for additional population data.

ACTIVITY

Group Work

Activity: Creating a skit

Purpose: Have each group research, write, and perform a skit based on an Indian myth or legend.

Roles: Each group should have researchers, scriptwriters, performers, and a director.

Result: Groups should take turns performing their skits.

BACKGROUND

Daily Life

Language Language, rather than ethnic origin, is the primary distinction among India's people. Officially, the Indian constitution recognizes 15 regional languages, in addition to Hindi, which is the national language. English is used for national and international communication.

ACTIVITY

Area Comparison

Using the Table of Countries Ask students to use the Table of Countries beginning on page 742 of their textbooks to compare the land areas and populations of the United States and India. **Connections: Math** Ask: **Which country —the United States or India— has the greater population density?** (While India's land area is about one third that of the United States, its population is more than 3.5 times greater. Therefore, India has a much higher population density.)

Articles From
NATIONAL GEOGRAPHIC

The following article may be used to extend the content in this Regional Atlas.

McCarry, John, and Steve McCurry, photographer. "Bombay: India's Capital of Hope." *National Geographic*, Vol. 187, No. 3 (Mar. 1995), pp. 42–67.

Overpopulation and religious conflict challenge the prosperity of Bombay's free market economy.

Economics, Technology, and Environment

Agriculture dominates South Asia's economy. About two thirds of workers depend directly on the land for their livelihood. At the same time, many people are leaving farms and rural areas to seek employment in cities.

Bollywood
Movies are extremely popular in India, which produces more movies than any other country in the world. The Indian film industry is often referred to as Bollywood, a combination of the words *Bombay* and *Hollywood*. **ECONOMIC ACTIVITIES** *What factor would help make filmmaking a profitable industry in India?*

Economic Opportunities
New technology and businesses offer economic opportunities to some Indian women. Here, a woman employed in the computer industry installs a motherboard. **GLOBAL TRADE PATTERNS** *How might industrial development affect India's economy?*

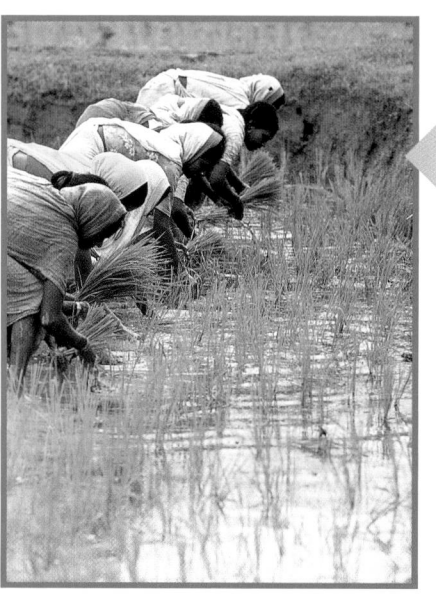

Agriculture
Most people in South Asia earn a living from farming, like these women planting rice. In spite of this, growing enough food to feed its people continues to be a challenge for the region. **ECONOMIC ACTIVITIES** *What kind of farming takes place throughout most of the region?*

ASSESSMENT

1. **Map Skills** **Regions** Compare the map on the opposite page with the physical map on page 593. What physical feature contributes to the lack of economic activity along the northern border of South Asia?

2. **Critical Thinking** **Drawing Conclusions** Does hydroelectricity or fossil fuels appear to be more important as a power source in South Asia? Explain.

REGIONAL ATLAS

South Asia: ECONOMIC ACTIVITIES AND RESOURCES

KEY

Nomadic herding		Coal
Commercial farming		Petroleum
Subsistence farming		Hydroelectric power
Manufacturing and trade		Iron
Commercial fishing		Gold
Little or no activity		Phosphates

Lambert Azimuthal Equal-Area Projection

Arabian Sea

Tropic of Cancer

Bay of Bengal

INDIAN OCEAN

0   250   500 mi
0   250   500 km

Take It to the NET
Enrichment To learn more about the economic activities and resources of this region, visit the World Geography section of **www.phschool.com**.

Chapter 28 ▪ Regional Atlas: South Asia **601**

Database:
Comparing Communications
pp. 602–603

Objectives
Upon completion of this lesson, students should be able to:
◆ discuss how a nation's economy influences the development of its communications systems;
◆ compare the communications statistics of India, Pakistan, Sri Lanka, Bangladesh, and the United States.

National Geography Standards
The following National Geography Standards are highlighted in this feature: 9, 11, 16, 18

Bellringer
Ask students to suggest some effects that would result from a six-month loss of all radio, television, telephone, and print communications in their city or state.

LESSON PLAN

1. Focus After students have read the Regional Database, have them list the three main obstacles standing in the way of building effective communications among the people of South Asian nations. (poverty, power shortages, social disorder)

2. Instruct Arrange students in small groups. Assign each group one of the following categories: radio receivers, television receivers, daily newspaper circulation, personal computers, and telephone mainlines per 1,000 people. Ask each group to use the database tables and the population figures from the Table of Countries (beginning on page 742 of their texts) to calculate theoretically how many people have to share each form of communication in each country. Have group spokespeople report the findings. As a class, compare each South Asian country's figures with those of the United States.

3. Close/Reteach Ask students to write a paragraph explaining which forms of communication they think South Asian countries should concentrate on developing first.

SOUTH ASIA
Database: Comparing Communications

By comparing the data below, you will learn that countries in South Asia have different economic situations, which influence their ability to afford communications. For example, Pakistan and Bangladesh have struggled to provide adequate communications systems for their citizens. In contrast, Sri Lanka is comparatively wealthy and can afford more of this technology. You will note even greater differences when you compare the South Asian data with the United States data on page 603.

Sources: *Encyclopedia Britannica Almanac; World Factbook*

GET THE FACTS . . .
Go to the Table of Countries at the back of this book to view additional data for the countries of South Asia.

Take It to the NET
Data Update For the most recent update of this database, visit the World Geography section of **www.phschool.com**.

India

Total Radio Stations	312
Number of Radios per 1,000 People	120
Total Television Stations	562
Number of Televisions per 1,000 People	75
Personal Computers in Use per 1,000 People	3.3
Internet Users per 1,000 People	2.8
Number of Telephones per 1,000 People	27
Cellular Telephones per 1,000 People	1.9

India's future economic growth is tied up in telecommunications. Traditionally, this industry has not been one of the country's strengths. Although India has about 4,500 daily newspapers and a strong tradition of freedom of the press, many people cannot afford a subscription and thus have very limited access to news and information. The government hopes to reduce poverty by expanding communication.

Pakistan

Total Radio Stations	49
Number of Radios per 1,000 People	102
Total Television Stations	22
Number of Televisions per 1,000 People	119
Personal Computers in Use per 1,000 People	4.3
Internet Users per 1,000 People	0.6
Number of Telephones per 1,000 People	22
Cellular Telephones per 1,000 People	2.1

A poor, heavily populated country, Pakistan is finding it hard to provide communications luxuries to many of its people. Most Pakistanis living in rural areas cannot afford televisions or radios. Also, a general power shortage has been a constant problem, such that even people with telecommunications are hard-pressed to use them. Projects have therefore been started to increase electricity production, which could also benefit new businesses and industries.

Sri Lanka

Total Radio Stations	72
Number of Radios per 1,000 People	211
Total Television Stations	21
Number of Televisions per 1,000 People	102
Personal Computers in Use per 1,000 People	5.6
Internet Users per 1,000 People	3.5
Number of Telephones per 1,000 People	36
Cellular Telephones per 1,000 People	12

Although it is financially better off than its neighbors and better able to afford communications instruments, social problems prevent Sri Lanka from fully realizing its potential. Recurring civil war weakens its economy, and overexpansion places too much pressure on existing power plants and telecommunications facilities. Therefore, despite having one of the best communications industries in South Asia, Sri Lanka is also seeking improvement.

Bangladesh

Total Radio Stations	26
Number of Radios per 1,000 People	64
Total Television Stations	15
Number of Televisions per 1,000 People	7.4
Personal Computers in Use per 1,000 People	1.0
Internet Users per 1,000 People	0.4
Number of Telephones per 1,000 People	3.4
Cellular Telephones per 1,000 People	1.2

One of the world's poorest and least developed nations, Bangladesh has an almost entirely rural population that cannot afford telecommunications technology. Power shortages, as in Pakistan, are common. Service industries that rely on communications are expanding, but their growth is slowed by the lack of such products. Overall, poverty is such a huge factor that basic human needs have priority over communications.

ASSESSMENT

Use the data for South Asia and the United States (at right) to answer the following questions.

1. **Science and Technology** Which South Asian nation has the most personal computers in use per 1,000 people?
2. **Economic Activities** Are people in India or in Bangladesh more likely to use the Internet?
3. **Global Trade Patterns** In which South Asian nation would you have the easiest time borrowing a cell phone?
4. **Critical Thinking** **Recognizing Patterns** What type of communications technology is most available to people in South Asian nations and the United States?

United States

Total Radio Stations	10,340
Number of Radios per 1,000 People	2,116
Total Television Stations	1,500+
Number of Televisions per 1,000 People	843
Personal Computers in Use per 1,000 People	510
Internet Users per 1,000 People	290
Number of Telephones per 1,000 People	664
Cellular Telephones per 1,000 People	307

Chapter 28 ▪ Regional Atlas: South Asia **603**

MENTAL MAPPING

Games for Review See pages 58–63 of the Simulations, Games, and Lab Activities booklet in the Teaching Resources for suggested games to review place names in preparation for the Chapter 28 Map Test.

Chapter Map Test Students should use the completed Chapter 28 outline maps and the Unit 8 Checklist to prepare for the Chapter 28 Map Test. Point out that the test will cover all of the countries, cities, bodies of water, and landforms listed on the Unit 8 Checklist.

 Alternative Assessment

Final Evaluation

Making a Map Use the Map Evaluation Form on page 15 of the Alternative Assessment booklet in the Prentice Hall Assessment System to evaluate students' maps. Either teachers or students can complete the forms to indicate which level of work was achieved for each of the criteria.

Answers to Assessment

1. Sri Lanka
2. India
3. Sri Lanka
4. Radio receivers

CUSTOMIZE FOR...

Honors/PreAP

Covering South Asian News in Print Have students work together to research recent news from South Asia. Instruct the class to use the collected data to create a newspaper to be distributed and read in South Asia. The newspaper should include social, political, and economic news stories; editorial(s); letters to the editor; feature stories; and graphics. Display the newspaper in the classroom.

Do-It-Yourself Skills

pp. 604–605

pp. 604–605

Objectives

Upon completion of this feature, students should be able to:

◆ explain the purpose of the Geographic Information System (GIS);

◆ describe how GIS technology is used;

◆ analyze information produced by a GIS.

 ### National Geography Standards

The following National Geography Standards are highlighted in this feature: 1, 3, 4, 17, 18

 ### Bellringer

Tell students that it is their job to determine where to build a new park in their community. Ask: **What kind of information would you need to gather in order to help you make the decision?** (land availability, location of population, public transportation, traffic patterns, dangers such as overhead power lines) Draw a map on the board showing these kinds of elements. Have students analyze how such a map would be of value to them as urban planners.

LESSON PLAN

1. Focus Write *Geographic Information System* on the board. Ask students if they know how this technology can be used in the study of geography. Explain that it is a type of computer technology that can be used to combine thematic maps (or other geographic information) for a region.

2. Instruct Have students list professions that interest them. Work together as a class to determine which professions might use information presented with GIS technology. Identify the kinds of information that could be plotted on maps that would be useful for each profession. (Possible answer: A map showing population distribution and the location of hospitals might help a doctor determine the best place to put a new office.)

 # Do-It-Yourself Skills

Using GIS

What Is a GIS?

A GIS, or Geographic Information System, is a computerized system for inputting, manipulating, displaying, and analyzing geographic data. It is like having a set of map transparencies for some place or region, as shown below. Each transparency could represent one feature, such as population density, per capita income, soil types, etc. You can map points, lines, and areas. You can add and remove layers of information or can change scale by zooming in and out.

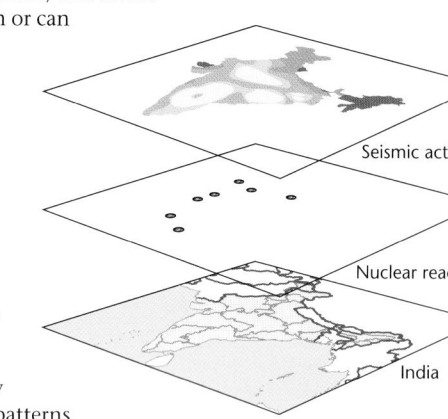

Seismic activ

Nuclear react

India

How Can I Use This Skill?

By using a GIS, people can combine layers of information about a place to discover patterns and relationships among data. GIS technology is used in a variety of fields including business, health care, government, and environmental science. In business, GIS can be used in decision making, for example, by comparing regional data such as sales, inventory, total potential customers, etc. Health care officials, meanwhile, might study the effects of waste facilities on local health patterns.

Step by Step

Follow these steps to learn how to use GIS. In this lesson, we will show how GIS can be used to analyze geographic data for India.

1 Start by deciding what information you want to analyze. It is usually best to form a question. Be as specific as possible. For this lesson, our question is: Are India's nuclear reactors jeopardized by earthquake activity?

2 Now you need a basic outline map of India. Various GIS software programs come with base maps. Outline maps can also be digitized or scanned into a computer.

> **TIP**
>
> **Learn More About It**
>
> The United States Geological Service (USGS) is an excellent source for learning more about GIS. Link to the World Geography section of **www.phschool.com** and connect to the USGS Homepage.

---

3 Select your data. GIS software includes databases. Also, you can input data yourself or download data from government and commercial providers via the Internet. Data may be available for free or for a fee. For this lesson, we are using two sets of data: the locations of nuclear reactors in India and the areas of seismic activity in India.

4 Process the data. If you are mapping the locations of things, you may need to assign geographic coordinates, such as latitude and longitude. If you are mapping quantities, such as per capita income per state, you will need to devise a classification scheme and decide how to represent the scheme through thematic symbolism. You may also need to measure areas and combine different layers of information.

5 Add a layer of data to the base map. Here, we have added a layer showing the locations of major nuclear plants in India. Note that a key explains the symbolism. GIS programs enable you to decide on symbolism as you design your own thematic maps.

6 Now you can add another layer of data. Here we have added a thematic layer showing areas or zones of seismic activity in India.

7 The final step is to analyze the information that you have displayed on maps. To develop a theory, compare the two layers of data and look for patterns. Ask yourself questions such as these:

- Are there any reactors in zones 4 and 5?
- Do you think the threat of earthquakes was taken into account by the people who decided where to build India's nuclear reactors? Explain.
- Which reactors are in the greatest danger of earthquake damage?
- Based on your analysis, what steps would you recommend to reduce the likelihood of nuclear reactor accidents in India?

KEY
⊕ Nuclear reactor

KEY
⊕ Nuclear reactor
☐ Zone 1 (least earthquake-prone)
☐ Zone 2
☐ Zone 3
☐ Zone 4
■ Zone 5 (most earthquake-prone)

APPLY YOUR SKILL

If you are a beginner, you can find GIS sites that provide demonstrations of how GIS works. You can also download free or trial versions of GIS software. If you are already experienced with GIS, then design and execute a project by following the steps above, from formulating a question to analyzing the results.

3. Close/Reteach After students finish analyzing the maps on this page, tell them to pretend that they have an additional map that shows population density in India. Ask: **How would this map help the power company determine the shape of its power distribution grid?** (Possible answer: It would help determine which power plant should supply which population and how many transmission lines would be needed.)

ACTIVITY

Reteach

Writing Cause-and-Effect Research Questions Remind students that some research questions are designed to determine whether a cause-and-effect relationship exists between two phenomena. For instance, the question "Are India's nuclear reactors jeopardized by earthquake activity?" asks whether earthquakes in India might have a negative *effect* on the reactors. Have students study the format of this cause-and-effect question. Then have them write similar research questions for other regions and topics that interest them. They might look for regions of the world affected by hurricanes, floods, or other natural disasters that would affect the location of an industry or government. (Visual/ Spatial, Verbal/Linguistic)

ACTIVITY

Critical Thinking

Examining Purpose Tell students that city planners and regional planners use GIS maps to make decisions that affect many people. Ask: **If planners used GIS technology to study our school district, what kinds of questions would they ask? What kinds of information would the different layers represent? What decisions might be made with the results?**

Answers to Apply Your Skill

Check students' projects for accuracy and understanding of how to analyze data using GIS.

Chapter 29 Planning Guide

Resource Manager

	CORE INSTRUCTION	READING/SKILLS
Chapter-Level Resources	**Teaching Resources** 📖 **Unit 8**/Ch. 29 • Reviewing Main Ideas, p. 17 📘 **Mental Mapping booklet** • Unit 8 Checklist, p. 106 📘 **Simulations, Games, and Lab Activities** • Exploring Local Geography, Local Immigration Patterns, p. 11 • Simulation, The Immigrant Experience, p. 12 • Place Location Review Games, pp. 58–63 📘 **Creative Teaching Activities** • Determining Population Growth, p. 31 💿 **TeacherExpress™ CD-ROM**, Ch. 29 🖥 **Companion Web site,** **www.phschool.com** • eTeach	**Teaching Resources** 📖 **Unit 8**/Ch. 29 • Map/Graph Skills, p. 19 📘 **Social Studies Skills Handbook** • Reading a Cartogram, p. 67 💿 **Book on CD**, Ch. 29 💿 **Social Studies Skills Tutor CD-ROM**
1 Road to Independence 1. Describe the role Mohandas Gandhi played in India's struggle for independence. 2. Explain how religious conflict contributed to independence for Pakistan and Bangladesh.	**Teaching Resources** 📖 **Unit 8**/Ch. 29 • Guided Reading and Review, p. 11 💿 **Prentice Hall Presentation Pro CD-ROM**, Ch. 29, Sec. 1	**Teaching Resources** 📘 **Guide to the Essentials (English/Spanish)** • Section Summary, Ch. 29, Sec. 1 📘 **Mental Mapping booklet** • Outline Map 29, p. 114 📼 **Guided Reading Audiotapes (English/Spanish)**, Ch. 29, Sec. 1 📄 **Section Reading Support Transparencies**, Ch. 29, Sec. 1
2 India's People and Economy 1. Analyze the role of religion in the lives of most Indians. 2. Identify both the traditional and the modern aspects of village life in India. 3. Discuss how urbanization has changed the character of India. 4. Explain how India's government is attempting to raise the country's standard of living.	**Teaching Resources** 📖 **Unit 8**/Ch. 29 • Guided Reading and Review, p. 13 💿 **Prentice Hall Presentation Pro CD-ROM**, Ch. 29, Sec. 2	**Teaching Resources** 📘 **Guide to the Essentials (English/Spanish)** • Section Summary, Ch. 29, Sec. 2 📘 **Mental Mapping booklet** • Outline Map 29, p. 114 📘 **Social Studies Skills Handbook** • Reading a Climate Graph, p. 65 📼 **Guided Reading Audiotapes (English/Spanish)**, Ch. 29, Sec. 2 📄 **Section Reading Support Transparencies**, Ch. 29, Sec. 2
3 Other Countries of South Asia 1. Explain how limited rainfall affects Pakistanis. 2. Describe how political and cultural issues have affected Afganistan. 3. Describe the difficulties facing the people and government of Bangladesh. 4. Differentiate the cultures and landscapes of Nepal, Bhutan, and Sri Lanka.	**Teaching Resources** 📖 **Unit 8**/Ch. 29 • Guided Reading and Review, p. 15 💿 **Prentice Hall Presentation Pro CD-ROM**, Ch. 29, Sec. 3	**Teaching Resources** 📘 **Guide to the Essentials (English/Spanish)** • Section Summary, Ch. 29, Sec. 3 📘 **Mental Mapping booklet** • Outline Map 29, p. 114 📼 **Guided Reading Audiotapes (English/Spanish)**, Ch. 29, Sec. 3 📄 **Section Reading Support Transparencies**, Ch. 29, Sec. 3

ENRICHMENT/HONORS/PREAP

Teaching Resources
Unit 8/Ch. 29
- Critical Thinking, p. 18

Mental Mapping booklet
- Atlas Activity, p. 112

Social Studies Skills Handbook
- Study and Research Skills, pp. 94–108

People and Geography
- Population, pp. 42–46

World Geography Map and Photo Transparencies
- South Asia: Maps and Photos
- World Population Cartogram
- How the Earth Works, Unit 8

World Geography Videos
- Science and Technology: The Countries of South Asia, Tape 4

Companion Web site, www.phschool.com
- Chapter 29 Activities

Teaching Resources
Social Studies Skills Handbook
- Predicting Consequences, p. 50

Companion Web site, www.phschool.com
- Chapter 29 Activities

Teaching Resources
Unit 8/Ch. 29
- Geography and World Literature, p. 26

Social Studies Skills Handbook
- Identifying Central Issues, p. 42

Companion Web site, www.phschool.com
- Chapter 29 Activities

Companion Web site, www.phschool.com
- Chapter 29 Activities

ASSESSMENT

PRENTICE HALL ASSESSMENT SYSTEM

Core Assessment
- ExamView Test Bank booklet, Ch. 29
- ExamView Test Bank CD-ROM, Ch. 29
- ExamView Test Bank CD-ROM, Unit 8

Standardized Test Preparation
Review and Reteach
- Review Book for World Geography, pp. 17–18

Practice and Assess
- Test-taking Strategies With Transparencies for High School
- Test-taking Strategy Poster
- Alternative Assessment booklet
- Test Prep Book for World Geography

Teaching Resources
Unit 8/Ch. 29
- Section Quizzes, pp. 12, 14, 16
- Test Forms A and B, pp. 20–25

Guide to the Essentials (English/Spanish)
- Chapter 29 Test

Spanish Resources, Ch. 29
- Section Quizzes, pp. 73–75

Mental Mapping booklet
- Chapter 29 Map Test, p. 113
- Unit 8 Map Test, p. 114

Companion Web site, www.phschool.com
- Chapter 29 Self-Test

CUSTOMIZE FOR INDIVIDUAL NEEDS

Gifted and Talented
- Teacher's Edition, Customize for . . . , pp. 613, 621, 627

Honors/PreAP
- Teacher's Edition, Customize for . . . , p. 615

Less Proficient Readers
- Guide to the Essentials (English), Ch. 29, Section Summaries
- Guided Reading Audiotapes (English), Ch. 29
- Section Reading Support Transparencies, Ch. 29
- Book on CD, Ch. 29
- Teacher's Edition, Reading Strategy, pp. 608, 618, 623
- Teacher's Edition, Activity: Vocabulary, pp. 608, 618, 622
- Teacher's Edition, Customize for . . . , p. 609

Students Acquiring English/ESL
- Guide to the Essentials (English/Spanish), Ch. 29
- Guided Reading Audiotapes (English/Spanish), Ch. 29
- Section Reading Support Transparencies, Ch. 29
- Book on CD, Ch. 29

Less Proficient Writers
- Alternative Assessment, Writing Assignment Rubric, p. 6

Introducing
CHAPTER
29
pp. 606–629

MENTAL MAPPING

Referring to the map on this page, point out that the nations labeled on this map comprise the Indian subcontinent. Ask students to name the southernmost point in the region. (Sri Lanka) Have students name the bodies of water that surround the subcontinent. (Indian Ocean, Bay of Bengal, Arabian Sea)

Mapping the Region Have students study the map on this page. Then instruct them to close their books and create a sketch map of South Asia, or distribute the Chapter 29 Outline Map on page 111 of the Mental Mapping booklet in the Teaching Resources. Ask students to lightly shade each country a different color and add labels for countries and bodies of water on their maps. Students should keep their maps in their Atlas Portfolios in order to prepare for the Chapter 29 Map Test.

eTeach

Be sure to check out this month's online forum with a Master Teacher to join in an exchange of teaching ideas. **www.phschool.com**

The Countries of South Asia

SECTIONS

1. **Road to Independence**
2. **India's People and Economy**
3. **Other Countries of South Asia**

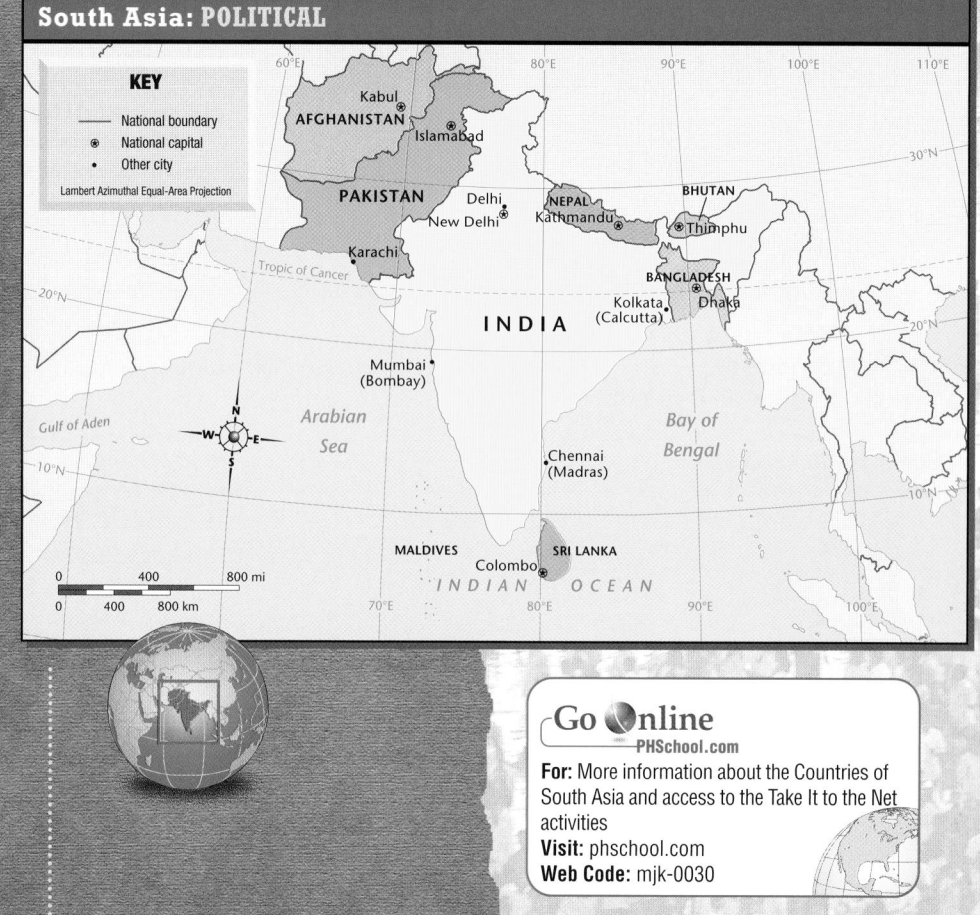

South Asia: POLITICAL

KEY
— National boundary
⊛ National capital
• Other city
Lambert Azimuthal Equal-Area Projection

AFGHANISTAN — Kabul
Islamabad
PAKISTAN
Karachi
Delhi
New Delhi
NEPAL — Kathmandu
BHUTAN — Thimphu
BANGLADESH — Dhaka
Kolkata (Calcutta)
INDIA
Mumbai (Bombay)
Gulf of Aden
Arabian Sea
Chennai (Madras)
Bay of Bengal
MALDIVES
Colombo — SRI LANKA
INDIAN OCEAN

0   400   800 mi
0   400   800 km

Go Online
PHSchool.com

For: More information about the Countries of South Asia and access to the Take It to the Net activities
Visit: phschool.com
Web Code: mjk-0030

RESOURCE DIRECTORY

Teaching Resources
Unit 8, Chapter 29
• Section 1 Guided Reading and Review, p. 11
Guide to the Essentials (English/Spanish)
• Section Summary, Chapter 29, Section 1
Mental Mapping booklet
• Atlas Activity, p. 112
• Unit 8 Checklist, p. 106

Technology
Guided Reading Audiotapes (English/Spanish),
  Chapter 29, Section 1
Section Reading Support Transparencies,
  Chapter 29, Section 1

World Geography Map and Photo Transparencies
• South Asia: Maps and Photos
Book on CD, Chapter 29
World Geography Videos
• Science and Technology: The Countries of South Asia, Tape 4
TeacherExpress™ CD-ROM, Chapter 29
Prentice Hall Presentation Pro CD-ROM, Chapter 29
Social Studies Skills Tutor CD-ROM
Companion Web site, www.phschool.com
• Chapter 29 Activities

1 Road to Independence

Reading Focus

- **What role did Mohandas Gandhi play in India's move from a British colony to an independent nation?**
- **How did religious conflict contribute to independence for Pakistan and Bangladesh?**

Key Terms

nationalism

nonviolent resistance

boycott

partition

Main Idea India's independence movement was largely nonviolent, but open conflict preceded independence for Pakistan and Bangladesh.

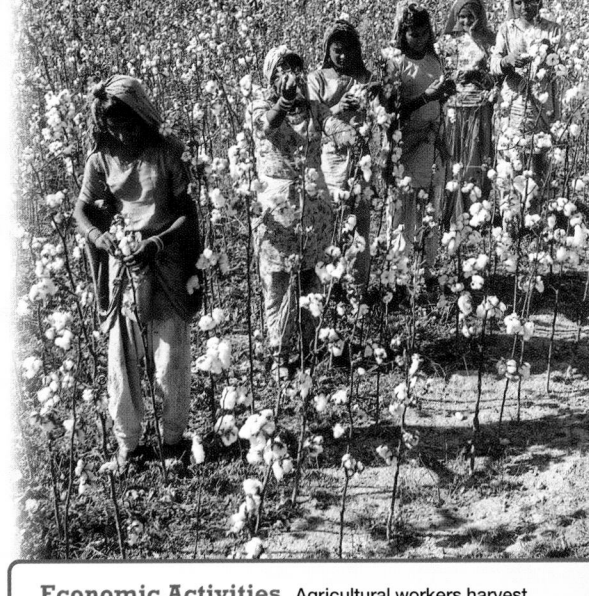

Economic Activities Agricultural workers harvest cotton in India.

On August 14, 1947, thousands of Indians crowded outside the Assembly building in New Delhi to hear these words:

> ❝At the stroke of the midnight hour, while the world sleeps, India will awake to life and freedom. A moment comes, which comes but rarely in history, when we step out from the old to the new, when an age ends, and when the soul of a nation, long suppressed, finds utterance.❞

The speaker was Jawaharlal Nehru (juh WAH huhr lahl NAY roo), the first prime minister of India, just hours before India's independence.

Indian Independence

Since the mid-1700s, Britain had controlled India. The colonial rulers made many changes, such as ending slavery, improving schools, and building a large railroad network, that benefited India. Other changes, however, did not.

India once had a flourishing textile industry. The Indians were among the first people to grow cotton. Indian artisans spun the cotton into thread and wove new fabrics such as calico, cashmere, chintz, and muslin. The British, however, wanted to use India as a market for their own cheaper, machine-made textiles. The British colonial system imported raw cotton from India, made it into cloth, and shipped the finished product back to India for sale. As a result, millions of Indian textile workers lost their jobs.

In addition, the British did not treat their subjects as equals. For example, both the government and the army were organized with British officials in all of the positions of power. Indians were expected to take positions at the lower levels. This situation angered many Indians.

Mohandas Gandhi During the late 1800s, Indians developed a strong sense of **nationalism,** or pride in one's nation. In addition, Western ideas of individual rights and self-government began to spread among the country's English-speaking middle class—its lawyers, doctors, and teachers. Many middle-class Indians traveled to England to study. One was a young law student named Mohandas Gandhi (moh HAHN dahs GAHN dee). It was Gandhi—later called Mahatma, meaning "the Great Soul"—who led India to independence.

◀ Worshippers near Mumbai (Bombay) during a festival *(photo left)*

Chapter 29 ▪ Section 1   **607**

Objectives

Upon completion of Section 1, students should be able to:

◆ describe the role Mohandas Gandhi played in India's struggle for independence;

◆ explain how religious conflict contributed to independence for Pakistan and Bangladesh.

 National Geography Standards

The following National Geography Standards are highlighted in this section: 1, 2, 5, 6, 9, 10, 11, 13, 16, 17

Bellringer

Ask: **What problems might arise if a country where two religions are practiced were to divide into two nations, one for each religious group?** (Possible answers: massive migrations, struggles for resources)

LESSON PLAN

1. Focus Write this quotation on the board: *"Control over the mind alone is necessary, and when that is attained, man is free, like the king of the forest, and his very glance withers the enemy."* Explain that it expresses the philosophy of Mohandas Gandhi, who led India to independence from Britain. Discuss what Gandhi meant by this quote.

2. Instruct Have students make a time line of the history of the Indian subcontinent using these dates: 1935, 1946, 1947, 1965, 1971.

3. Close/Reteach Draw a chart on the board, labeling the columns *Event, Cause, Date, Geographic Impact.* In the first column list the following: *Indian Independence, Partition, Pakistan Civil War.* Have students complete the chart.

TEACHING TIP
From A Master Teacher

Effects of Globalization A study of South Asia should focus on how globalization creates cultural tensions and threatens traditional cultures in the region. One reaction is the growth of religious identities and calls for a return to fundamentalism. In India, Hindu nationalism plays a significant role in politics and causes friction with other religious groups. In Pakistan, some Muslims support extreme anti-Western policies. In Sri Lanka, Hindu nationalists (the Tamil) wage a civil war against their Buddhist neighbors, the Sinhalese.

Pacing Suggestions

 For 90-minute Blocks

You will want to vary activities.

- Tell students that they will design a travel brochure titled "Beautiful India." Each student should do research on major sites and attractions in India and include pictures and descriptions of a variety of these in the brochure. Have students exchange completed brochures with each other. Then call on volunteers to explain which attractions they would choose to visit first.

Vocabulary

Boycott Refer to the Key Terms list on page 607. Write the term *boycott* on the board. Ask a volunteer to look up the term in the Glossary and read its definition aloud. Have students give examples of boycotts they have heard or read about. (Examples include those used by the U.S. civil rights movement and migrant farm workers in the 1960s.) Ask: **Is a boycott an example of nonviolent protest?** (Yes, because it does not involve violence.)

Making Inferences

As students read this section, ask them to create a sequence chart titled *Steps Toward Indian Independence*. Have students use completed charts to infer how the actions of Indians and others affected the British.

GL🌐BAL CONNECTIONS

Cooperation and Conflict
The term *boycott* comes from the name of a person—Capt. Charles Boycott, a British land agent of the 1800s, whose Irish tenants refused to work the land in protest of his methods of rent collection. The principle was practiced earlier, as well, when colonial Americans refused to buy highly taxed British imported goods.

Gandhi's belief in using **nonviolent resistance** against injustice was his most powerful weapon against the British. Nonviolent resistance means opposing an enemy or oppressor by any means other than violence. Gandhi also believed that peace and love were more powerful forces than violence. Everywhere he went, he won the hearts of the Indian people.

One way that Gandhi peacefully resisted British rule was to **boycott**—refuse to purchase or use—British cloth. Gandhi stopped wearing Western clothes, and instead wore clothes made from yarn he had spun himself. He devoted two hours each day to spinning his own yarn and urged other Indians to follow his example. The spinning wheel became a symbol of national pride. As a result of Gandhi's leadership and the boycott by the Indian people, the sale of British cloth in India fell sharply.

Gandhi's program of nonviolent resistance developed into a mass movement involving millions of Indians. In spite of Gandhi's pleas to avoid violence, however, some protests against British rule led to riots. Hundreds of people were killed or hurt.

Gandhi and his followers attracted support from other countries. In 1935, the British gave in to mounting Indian and international pressures and agreed to establish provinces that were governed entirely by Indians.

Religious Conflict

In the early 1940s, the conflict between India's Hindus and Muslims deepened. For hundreds of years, the relationship between the two groups had often been hostile, but in recent years economic differences divided the two groups even further. The Muslims were generally the poorer peasants or landless workers, whereas the Hindus were often landowners.

For a time, Hindus and Muslims worked together for independence. But, as they drew nearer to their goal, both groups began to fear being ruled by the other. In 1946, Britain offered independence to India on condition that Indian leaders could agree on a form of government. However, Hindus and Muslims were unable to reach an agreement. Riots broke out in which thousands of people died.

Gandhi yearned for a united India, but the violence persisted. Finally, in 1947, British and

Unrest in India

Cooperation and Conflict The conflict between Hindus and Muslims that led to the partition of India in 1947 continues today. In 1992, militant Hindus destroyed a historic Muslim mosque in northern India and sparked violence across the nation.

Place *Why didn't the partition of India bring a lasting peace?*

Teaching Resources
Unit 8, Chapter 29
• Critical Thinking, Understanding Gandhi's Creed, p. 18
Social Studies Skills Handbook
• Predicting Consequences, p. 50

Answer to Photo Caption

The partition did not solve the problem of economic inequality. Each country remained home to minorities who resented their lack of power.

Indian leaders agreed that the only solution to the conflict was to **partition**—divide into parts—the subcontinent into separate Hindu and Muslim countries. Part of the subcontinent became the mostly Hindu Republic of India. The northwestern and northeastern parts of the subcontinent, where most Muslims lived, formed the nation of Pakistan.

Violent Partition Independence came to India and Pakistan on August 15, 1947. The event brought joyous scenes of celebration. But independence also brought confusion and suffering. In one of the greatest migrations in history, some 12 million people moved. To avoid the rule of a majority religion to which they did not belong, Hindus moved to India, where Hindus were in the majority, and Muslims moved to Pakistan, where Muslims were in the majority.

The journey was long and torturous. Ashwini Kumar, a young police officer who witnessed the migration, stated:

> 66They passed in eerie silence. They did not look at each other. . . . The creak of wooden wheels, the weary shuffling of thousands of feet, were the only sounds rising from the columns.99

Most of the refugees left their possessions along the road or traded them for lifesaving water. Many people died from hunger, thirst, or exhaustion. Fighting between Hindus and Muslims killed an estimated one million people.

Since independence, India and Pakistan have fought three wars. The third war, in 1971, led to the creation of the new nation of Bangladesh. Tensions rose when both nations tested nuclear weapons in 1998, and disputes persist over control of the border territory of Kashmir.

Bangladesh When Pakistan became independent, it consisted of two regions—West Pakistan and East Pakistan—separated by 1,100 miles (1,770 km) of Indian territory. The boundaries of East and West Pakistan were not based on any physical landforms but rather on the predominance of Islam in these two regions. In fact, Islam was the only thread that connected these two very different regions. The people of West

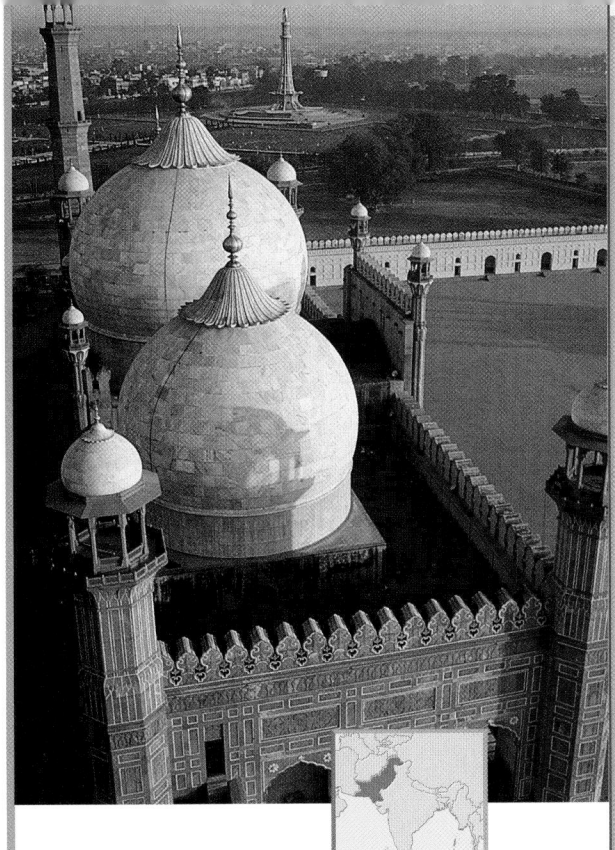

A Place of Worship

Cultures The traditional Muslim place of worship is called a mosque. From the towers, or minarets, a crier calls the faithful to prayer five times a day.

Place *How did religion play a role in the creation of Pakistan?*

Pakistan belonged to several ethnic groups, but most residents of East Pakistan were Bengalis (ben GAHL eez). Many people in West Pakistan spoke Urdu (OOR doo), which became the official language of the new country. This situation upset the East Pakistanis, who were proud of their Bengali language and their literary tradition.

Economics and politics further complicated the already difficult situation. West Pakistan contained some factories, while East Pakistan was largely agricultural. But, despite being economically less developed, East Pakistan paid more taxes than West Pakistan. At the same time, more than half the national budget was spent in West

610 Chapter 29

Entrepreneurs

Economic Activities
Their country's struggle for independence a distant memory, these Bangladeshi women today make baskets for the business they created with the help of collateral-free loans from the Grameen Bank.

Place *Why do you think the Grameen Bank does not require collateral, or property given to a lender as a pledge to repay a loan?*

Pakistan, where the government was located. Moreover, most positions of power in the government and the army were held almost exclusively by West Pakistanis.

Unrest continued to grow as many people in East Pakistan began to feel that their region was being treated merely as a colony of West Pakistan. Then, in 1970, more than 300,000 East Pakistanis died in a devastating flood caused by a cyclone and tidal wave. Many people in East Pakistan accused the government of deliberately delaying shipments of food and relief supplies to the victims.

The disaster touched off fighting between the two regions. India joined the conflict on the side of the East Pakistanis. In the face of such opposition, the West Pakistani forces surrendered and on December 16, 1971, East Pakistan became the independent country of Bangladesh, meaning "Bengali Nation." Bangladesh is shown on the map on page 591.

SECTION 1 ASSESSMENT

1. **Key Terms** Define **(a)** nationalism, **(b)** nonviolent resistance, **(c)** boycott, **(d)** partition.

2. **Cooperation and Conflict** How did Mohandas Gandhi use nonviolent resistance to oppose British rule?

3. **Understanding the Past** How did the nations of Pakistan and Bangladesh gain their independence?

4. **Critical Thinking** **Predicting Consequences** Do you think that other nations would have been as likely to support Indian independence if leaders like Gandhi had not promoted a program of nonviolent resistance? Explain.

Activity
Identifying Relationships In the United States, Dr. Martin Luther King, Jr., studied the writings of Mohandas Gandhi and encouraged nonviolent resistance in the civil rights movement. Gather more information about both leaders, their philosophies, and their campaigns. In a class discussion, share and explain at least one similarity.

Analyzing a Cartogram

A cartogram is a special-purpose map used to present statistics geographically. Countries on a cartogram are not drawn in proportion to their land area. Instead, some other feature—such as population growth or GDP—determines the size of each nation. On the cartogram below, the size of a country's population determines its size on the cartogram.

Learn the Skill Use the following steps to learn how to understand and analyze cartograms.

1 *Identify the kind of information represented on the cartogram.* Look for the title and the key, which will help you interpret the cartogram. **(a)** *What kind of information does this cartogram show?* **(b)** *According to the key, how is population represented on the cartogram?*

2 *Compare the cartogram with a conventional land-area map.* By comparing the two, you can determine the degree of distortion involved. For example, compare the cartogram below with the land-area map on pages 16–17. *When compared with their appearance on the land-area map, which countries look very different on the cartogram?*

3 *Practice reading the information shown on the cartogram.* You might begin by determining which countries show very large populations and very small populations. **(a)** *Which two countries*

have the largest populations? **(b)** *Name one country that appears about the same size on both the cartogram and the land-area map.*

4 *Analyze the information.* Look for relationships among the data depicted on the cartogram. *How would you explain the relatively large sizes of Japan, Taiwan, the Philippines, and Indonesia on the cartogram, in contrast to the tiny size of Australia?*

 Do It Yourself

Practice the Skill Search the Internet for the latest U.S. census data, and study the population density map in the Regional Atlas on page 599. Then, create a cartogram for one region of the United States. Show the population of the states in that region through the relative size of each state. Be sure to include a key to help readers interpret the cartogram. Given what else you know about that region of the country, how would you explain the differences or similarities in the sizes of the states?

Apply the Skill See Chapter 29 Review and Assessment.

World Population Cartogram

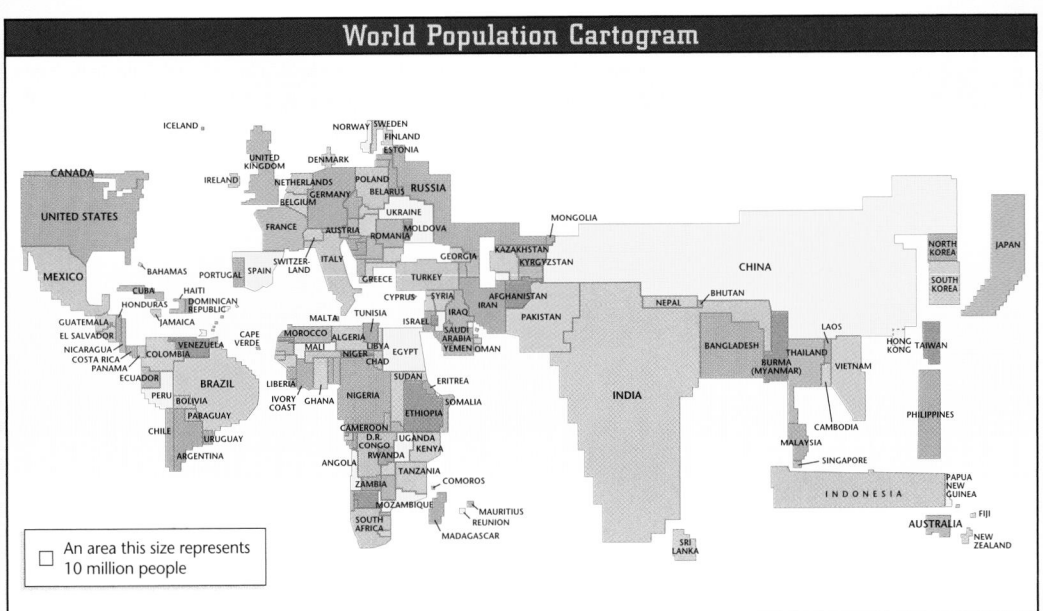

☐ An area this size represents 10 million people

 Career Prep

Careers in Geography

Cartographer Cartographers are people trained in making maps. Cartography was once a specialty done by hand. Today, however, cartography is done mainly with computers. Cartographers are hired by government agencies and by mapping companies.

People and Geography

Objectives

Upon completion of this feature, students should be able to:

◆ summarize how migration has affected cultural change in South Asia;

◆ explain the factors that have led to cultural convergence and cultural divergence in South Asia.

 ### National Geography Standards

The following National Geography Standards are highlighted in this feature: 1, 4, 9, 10, 12, 13, 17, 18

 ### Bellringer

Have a volunteer find and read aloud the definitions of *cultural convergence* and *cultural divergence* in the Glossary. Ask each student to give at least one example of how cultural convergence has affected culture in the United States. Students can use examples from categories such as food, music, art, or literature.

LESSON PLAN

1. Focus Write the word *migration* on the board. Have students explain what it is and discuss why migration often causes cultural change.

2. Instruct Draw two columns on the board. Label them *Cultural Convergence* and *Cultural Divergence*. Have students use the text to fill in the columns with examples of how each wave of migration has caused either convergence or divergence.

Answer to Map Caption

The Aryan culture came into contact with the culture of the people of the Indus River valley.

Answer to
Graph and Photo Caption

These migrations had a lasting religious impact, introducing Islam to the region. Their influence can also be seen in the Urdu language as well as in art and architecture.

612 Chapter 29

People and Geography
Migration and Cultural Change in South Asia

Ancient Invaders

Migration is a key component of cultural change. As people move, their cultures move with them. Several thousand years ago, the Aryans, a nomadic people, migrated to South Asia. As a result, cultural convergence occurred. The Aryan culture came into contact with the culture of the people living in the Indus River valley. Cultural changes took place that are still evident today. For example, Hinduism, the major religion in India today, has its roots in Aryan culture. The language of Sanskrit also has Aryan origins, as does India's caste system.

Cultural Convergence
In ancient times, what cultures came into contact as a result of migration into South Asia?

Muslim Migration Into India

Between the 1000s and 1500s, Afghans, Turks, Persians, and Mongols entered South Asia and introduced Islam to the region. Conflict between Hindus and Muslims became common, but Muslim rulers of the Mughal dynasty maintained peace for a time. A new language, Urdu, combined Persian, Arabic, and Hindi. Muslim and Hindu styles of art and architecture blended to create a unique Indian style. One of the greatest examples of this style is the Taj Mahal, shown below.

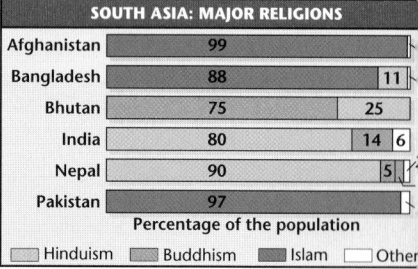

SOUTH ASIA: MAJOR RELIGIONS

	Percentage of the population
Afghanistan	99
Bangladesh	88 / 11
Bhutan	75 / 25
India	80 / 14 / 6
Nepal	90 / 5
Pakistan	97

Hinduism   Buddhism   Islam   Other

Muslim Influence
What are some lasting effects of migration by Afghans, Turks, Persians, and Mongols into South Asia?

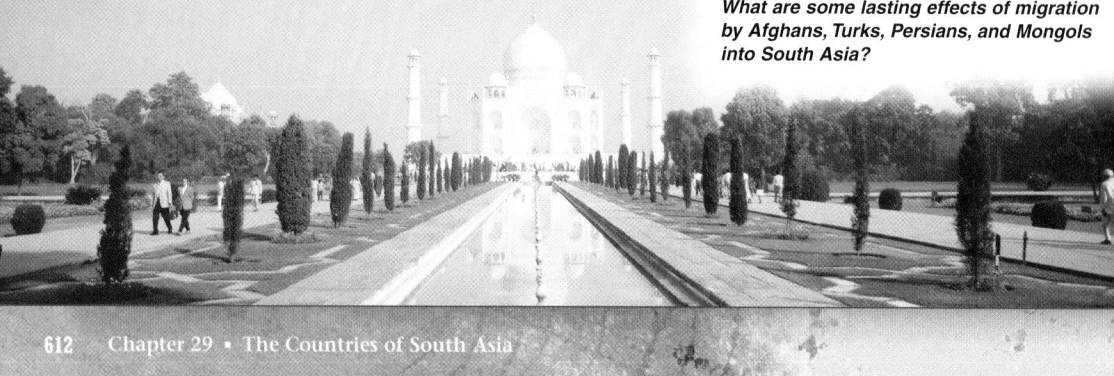

RESOURCE DIRECTORY

Teaching Resources

People and Geography
• Population, pp. 42–46

Simulations, Games, and Lab Activities
• Exploring Local Geography, Local Immigration Patterns, p. 11
• Simulation, The Immigrant Experience, p. 12

Technology

World Geography Map and Photo Transparencies
• South Asia: Political

British Imperialism

In the early 1600s, British merchants established the East India Company to trade for India's spices. By the mid-1800s, Britain ruled most of India. British imperialism introduced the English language, which quickly became the standard for business and government in India. The British also built an extensive railroad system. When India gained its independence in 1947, it adopted a parliamentary system of democratic government similar to Britain's.

British Influence
How did British rule affect government and transportation in South Asia?

BRITISH INFLUENCE
Railroads
English language
Government

Migration and Cultural Divergence

As you have learned, the end of British rule was followed by violence and mass migration. Millions of Muslims moved from India to Pakistan, and millions of Hindus moved from Pakistan to India. Today, national and religious rivalries contribute to cultural divergence, which limits cross-cultural influences and cooperation. Relations between Pakistan and India remain fragile and tense. One of the main sources of tension is border disputes. Fears were heightened in 1998, after Pakistan and India both tested nuclear weapons.

ASSESSMENT: Analyzing Causes and Effects

1. **Identify the Issue** How are migration and cultural change in South Asia related?

2. **Identify Possible Causes** (a) How can migration lead to cultural convergence? (b) How can migration lead to cultural divergence?

3. **Identify Possible Effects** What were the effects of migration between Pakistan and India in the late 1940s?

4. **Make Generalizations** In general, how can migration affect language in a region?

5. **Make Recommendations** Do you think it is likely that South Asia's culture will change in the future? Explain your answer.

Chapter 29 613

CUSTOMIZE FOR...

Gifted and Talented

Immigration and Its Effects Have students choose an English-speaking country and find out how much of the population is Indian. Also have them find out how Indian immigrants have contributed to the culture of their adopted countries. Students can present what they learn in an oral report, using visual aids such as maps of immigration routes and population graphs.

3. Close/Reteach Have students write on the board the languages that make up Urdu. Ask: **Is Urdu an example of cultural convergence or cultural divergence?** (cultural convergence) **What cultures contributed to the development of Urdu?** (Persian, Arabic, and Hindi)

BACKGROUND

History

Gandhi's Influence One of the most influential figures in the history of India was Mohandas Gandhi, who was also known as Mahatma Gandhi. (*Mahatma* means "great soul.") Gandhi encouraged nonviolent protest against British control of India. As a member of Congress, he encouraged Indians to disobey repressive laws passed by British officials. He also inspired Indian nationalists to boycott British goods, schools, courts, and elections. His campaign of resistance was known as *satyagraha* ("devotion to truth"). It attracted a mass following and helped India achieve independence from Britain.

Answers to Assessment

1. Migration introduced new cultures into South Asia, which brought about cultural convergence.

2. (a) Migration brings different cultures into contact with one another, which can lead to cultural convergence. **(b)** Migration introduces national and religious differences among people of a region, which can often lead to rivalries that contribute to cultural divergence.

3. The migration contributed to cultural divergence, a result of the fragile and tense relationship between India and Pakistan.

4. Immigrants can introduce new words into the native language, or a new hybrid language, such as Urdu, may develop.

5. Answers will vary, but students should be able to support their answers with observations.

Answer to Photo Caption

India adopted a parliamentary system of democratic government similar to Britain's, and the British built an extensive railroad system in India.

Chapter 29 **613**

Objectives

Upon completion of Section 2, students should be able to:

◆ analyze the role of religion in the lives of most Indians;

◆ identify both the traditional and the modern aspects of village life in India;

◆ discuss how urbanization has changed the character of India;

◆ explain how India's government is attempting to raise the country's standard of living.

National Geography Standards

The following National Geography Standards are highlighted in this section: 1, 2, 3, 4, 5, 6, 9, 10, 11, 12, 13, 14, 16, 17, 18

Bellringer

Have students think of pairs of contrasts between rural life and urban life. (Possible answers: slow pace versus fast pace, not crowded versus crowded)

LESSON PLAN

1. Focus Tell students that experts predict that by the year 2025, India's population will be close to 1.4 billion. India already has more people than all of the countries of Africa combined. Ask: **What challenges might this population growth create for the region?** (overcrowding, shortages of food and other resources)

2. Instruct Have students make a three-column chart. In the first column, have them list: *Agriculture, Industry, Education,* and *Health Care.* The second and third columns will describe the signs of progress in each area and obstacles to further progress. Discuss ways in which progress in one area might affect other areas.

3. Close/Reteach Have students tell whether each of the following terms is associated with traditional India or changing India and why: *purdah, joint family system, middle class, cottage industries, consumer goods, cholera, primary schools.*

---

2 India's People and Economy

Reading Focus

- How does religion shape the lives of most people in India?
- In what ways has village life in India remained essentially the same for generations, and in what ways has it changed in recent years?
- How has urbanization changed the character of India?
- In what ways is India's government attempting to raise the country's standard of living?

Key Terms

reincarnation	purdah
caste system	joint family system
charpoy	cottage industry
sari	

Main Idea Ancient cultural traditions continue to affect daily life for many people throughout modern India.

Population Growth The city of Mumbai is India's financial center and busiest port.

"The city air makes a man free," runs a medieval European saying. And, adds one modern journalist, "It is in the cities that twentieth-century India is casting off . . . the past." But most Indians still live in small, rural villages and carry on cultural traditions and religious customs.

Religious Life

The majority of people in India practice Hinduism, an ancient, polytheistic religion that teaches the unity of all life. Hindus believe that every living thing has a spirit, or soul, which comes from the Creator, Brahma. Because every creature possesses a soul, Hindus treat animals with great respect. Cows are especially sacred to Hindus and may wander freely through the city streets.

Hindus also consider the Ganges River to be holy. The Ganges is believed to purify the souls of people who bathe in it or drink its water. As a result, the banks of the Ganges often are lined with Hindus who have come there for healing.

According to Hinduism, the final goal of every living thing is unity with Brahma—a state of bliss without change or pain. In order to achieve this goal, the soul passes through cycles of **reincarnation.** Reincarnation is the belief that the souls of human beings and animals go through a series of births, deaths, and rebirths. Hindus believe that the soul does not die, but passes from body to body until it becomes pure enough to be united with Brahma.

The Caste System For hundreds of years, Hindu society has been organized according to the **caste system.** This system is a social hierarchy in which people are born into a particular group that has been given a distinct rank in society. Each caste has its own duties and obligations. Among these duties are obedience to caste rules

---

as well as to moral laws. People can improve their position in the next life by carrying out their duties in this life.

At the top of the caste system are Brahmans—the priests, teachers, and judges. Beneath the Brahmans are the Kshatriyas (kuh SHAHT ree yuhz), or warriors. Below these two groups are the Vaisyas (VY ee syuhs), farmers and merchants. The fourth group are the Sudras, craftworkers and laborers.

A group called "untouchables," or outcasts, holds the lowest rank in the caste system. Traditionally, untouchables do the work that is considered "unclean," such as street sweeping and tanning hides.

Today, the caste system continues to shape people's lives despite the fact that it has become less rigid. Although some people take up professions that follow the traditions of their caste, many do not. However, social relationships are often, though not always, confined to people within the same caste. Untouchables continue to have fewer educational and employment opportunities than citizens who belong to higher castes. Efforts are being made by the Indian government to offer greater opportunities to untouchables.

Other Religions Although the majority of Indians are Hindu, other religions practiced in India include Islam, Christianity, Sikhism (SEEK iz uhm), and Jainism (JY nihz uhm). Sikhism began as a movement to combine Hinduism and Islam. Sikhs are not divided into castes. Today, many are farmers in their native province of Punjab in northwest India. Jainism, which developed in reaction to Hinduism, teaches that violence of any kind is wrong. Jains are taught to avoid harming any living creature.

Village Life

About seven out of ten Indians live in villages and farm for a living. Most Indian villages consist of a group of houses surrounded by fields. Dirt paths may lead to the village school, the pool used for washing clothes, and private vegetable gardens. A larger path may lead to the next village. Sometimes a bus goes by on its way to a larger town. Many people own bicycles; almost no one has a car. Each section, or social division, of the village shares a well.

The Caste System

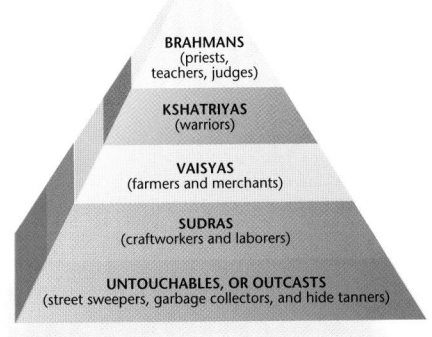

BRAHMANS
(priests, teachers, judges)

KSHATRIYAS
(warriors)

VAISYAS
(farmers and merchants)

SUDRAS
(craftworkers and laborers)

UNTOUCHABLES, OR OUTCASTS
(street sweepers, garbage collectors, and hide tanners)

GRAPH SKILLS

● **Cultures** Untouchables have traditionally been denied common privileges and have lived bleak lives outside the social system.

• *Why do you think "untouchables" traditionally have held the lowest rank in Indian society?*

Rural Housing Houses belonging to the more prosperous families in a village are often built of brick and have tiled roofs and cement floors. Houses owned by poor villagers may be made of mud and thatched with dried grass. The floor is usually made of packed earth. Mud houses have no windows, which would only let in wind and rain.

Usually the only furniture is a **charpoy** (CHAR poy)—a wooden bed frame with knotted string in place of a mattress. Most families move the charpoy outside to the courtyard when the weather turns especially hot. The cooking is often carried out in the courtyard as well.

Food For both religious and economic reasons, Indians follow a mostly vegetarian diet. Hindus generally do not eat beef because the cow has religious importance, and Muslims are forbidden to eat pork. Some Indians do, however, eat goat meat and chicken. Those who live near rivers or the sea also eat fish.

Most Indians eat some form of rice every day. With it, they may eat a lentil soup called *dal* (DAHL). In northern India, the people make *rotis*

B A C K G R O U N D

Word Origin

Caste The word *caste* comes from a Portuguese word meaning "race." Its early roots go back to a Latin word meaning "pure."

 Alternative Assessment

Introduce the Activity

Writing a Position Paper Ask students to conduct research and write a two-page position paper agreeing or disagreeing with the following statement: The democratic government of India adequately protects the rights of Muslim, Christian, and Sikh minorities in India today. Distribute the Position Paper Rubric found on page 8 of the Alternative Assessment booklet in the Prentice Hall Assessment System for students' reference during the project.

CUSTOMIZE FOR...

Honors/PreAP

Exploring Indian Cuisine Ask students to conduct research on the foods and recipes of India. Have them use their research to create a menu of Indian dishes for a restaurant in the United States. A description of the dish should appear under the name of each selection on the menu.

Answer to Graph Skills

because they do work that is considered "unclean"

Word Origin

Purdah The word *purdah* comes from the Persian word *pardah,* which means "veil."

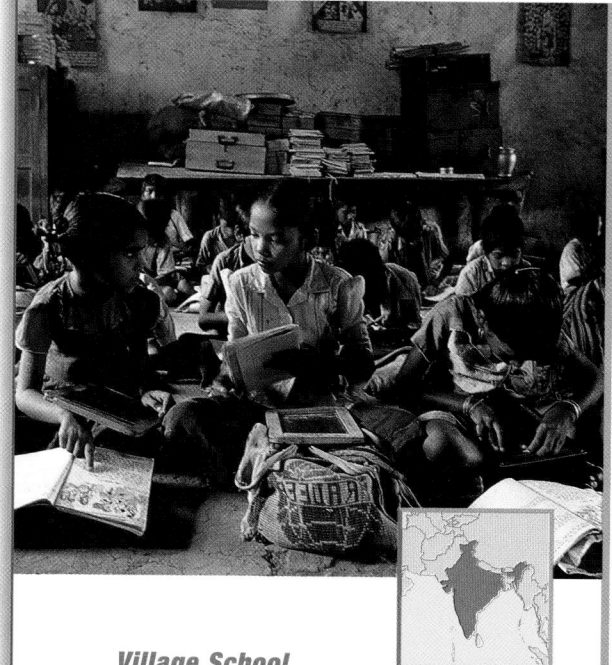

Village School

Cultures Education is compulsory in India until age 14, but only 50 percent of India's population is literate. Literacy rates are highest in urban areas and among males.

Human-Environment Interaction *Why might access to education be easier in urban areas?*

(RO teez), or flat cakes of wheat or sorghum that are baked on an iron griddle. In southern India, the people eat *idlis* (ID lees), or steamed pancakes of rice.

Clothing Because most of India is so hot and humid, clothing is light and loose. Many Indian women wear a **sari** (SAH ree)—brightly colored cloth that is draped over the body like a long dress. Some Indian women cover their faces with a veil when they are in public. This custom, called **purdah** (PUR duh), began among Muslims but is followed by Hindus as well.

Family Life Families in India are generally large. When a man marries, he usually brings his new wife to live in his parents' house. Often the household includes uncles and other relatives. This is known as the **joint family system.**

Everyone in the family has a role to play. Even the youngest children can take care of the chickens, goats, or sheep. Older children carry water and help their parents in the fields. People who are too old to help in the fields do light jobs around the house, such as shelling peas or washing rice.

Life is very demanding for village women. Here is how one writer describes a typical day:

> 66 The women . . . work an 18-hour day, which begins at four in the morning with millet grinding—two women to a stone for more than two hours. After breakfast, the dung must be cleared and carried to the fields. . . . Then there is water to fetch and firewood to chop, the children to dress, and always a pile of clothes to wash and mend, not to mention the toil in the fields . . . planting, weeding, clearing stones, harvesting, gathering fodder and fuel. After a long day's work, there is still the rice to husk, the children to wash, and the supper to cook and serve. 99

Signs of Change Some modern technologies have made their way into many Indian villages. Most villages now have electricity, and television reaches 75 percent of all Indians. Because illiteracy is still widespread, television, radio, and movies are more powerful media than newspapers for spreading new ideas to villagers. Indians are avid moviegoers, and the Indian film industry produces hundreds of films annually.

India's leaders hope that as villagers come to learn more about modern life and better farming techniques, they will be able to produce more food. The constant threat of a shortage of food in the face of an increasing population is a major concern of the Indian government.

Urbanization

India's urban areas are growing rapidly because of widespread immigration from rural villages. India's urban areas range in size from towns with 20,000 inhabitants to enormously crowded cities that swell with populations of more than 10 million.

RESOURCE DIRECTORY

Teaching Resources
Unit 8, Chapter 29
• Geography and World Literature, Nectar in a Sieve, p. 26

Answer to Photo Caption

Possible answer: Urban areas have more modern technology than rural areas, so inhabitants can dedicate more time and resources to education. In rural areas, children often have to help their families make a living.

Life in Towns Many of India's people live in small or medium-sized towns. India's towns are far more populated and lively than its rural villages. A writer who taught in India described a typical town:

66 Cows wander through the streets, washermen bang clothing against rocks in nearby streams, homes built of mud and tar paper and corrugated tin and planks and cardboard lean against one another, ready to be toppled by the first big storm. But the pace of the Indian town nearly terrifies the villager. The streets are often a wild free-for-all, with buses bearing down on pedestrians, dogs and goats scurrying out of the way of three-wheeled taxis and cars, bicycles weaving past the carters who wearily push their loads of flour sacks uphill. 99

Life in Cities India's cities are even busier, because they are far more crowded. While New York City has almost 25,000 people per square mile (9,687 per sq km), the Indian city of Mumbai (Bombay) has an astonishing 714,000 inhabitants per square mile (275,676 per sq km)! The writer V. S. Naipaul described Mumbai's bulging population in this way:

66 In Bombay there isn't room for [the newcomers]. There is hardly room for the people already there. The older apartment blocks are full; the new skyscrapers are full; the small, low huts of the squatters' settlements on the airport road are packed tightly together. 99

Despite the extreme crowding and poverty that exist, most families consider themselves better off in a city than in a village. Most people believe the cities offer far more opportunities for work and education than do rural areas. India's rural population therefore has been drawn to many of India's large cities. Mumbai, on India's west coast, is the country's busiest port and its financial center. Chennai, once called

India's Holy City

Cultures Varanasi contains hundreds of temples to accommodate the many Hindu as well as Buddhist pilgrims who travel to the holy city each year. The worshippers shown here are using ghats, the brick steps built into the riverbank, to wash away their sins in the sacred waters of the Ganges.

Movement *Why do you think peoples of different religions make pilgrimages to holy sites?*

ACTIVITY

Reteach

The Growth of Cities Write the following statement on the board: *India's major cities have grown because of their relative location.* Have students point out Mumbai (Bombay), Kolkata (Calcutta), Chennai (Madras), New Delhi, and Varanasi on a map of South Asia and explain how the statement applies to each city. (Mumbai, Kolkata, and Chennai are trade centers because of their coastal locations. New Delhi became the capital because of its central location. Varanasi's location on the Ganges River, sacred to Hindus, helped it grow.) (Visual/Spatial)

BACKGROUND

Daily Life

Urbanization Migration from farms to cities is a common phenomenon in India and elsewhere in the developing world. About one fourth of all Indians now live in urban areas. Most of the cities are very crowded. However, cities offer more educational, cultural, and employment opportunities than rural areas do, which results in a constant influx of people.

TEST PREPARATION

Have students use the photograph and caption on this page to complete the following statement.

Varanasi is a destination for Hindu pilgrims because —

A it has a pleasant climate

B there are many jobs available

C it is located on the Ganges River

D it has the most interesting temples

Answer to Photo Caption

Possible answers: because of religious obligation, or to feel connected to something holy or sacred

618 Chapter 29

Vocabulary

Cottage Industry Refer to the Key Terms list on page 614. Write the term *cottage industry* on the board. Have students use the meanings of both words to suggest possible definitions. Then have a volunteer look up the term in the Glossary and restate the definition. Ask: **What would be the opposite of a cottage industry?** (factory work)

READING STRATEGY

Predicting

Before students read the subsection Advances in Farming on this page, ask them to predict one or two farming improvements that India may have attempted. Have them compare actual improvements with their predictions as they read.

GLOBAL CONNECTIONS

Science and Technology

India's Talent in Demand Many of India's highly skilled Information Technology (IT) specialists have been recruited to work at companies around the world. Australian businesses are attempting to attract Indian IT professionals both through programs designed to improve Australia-India industry relations and by encouraging joint ventures between companies in both countries. In the United States, Indian computer entrepreneurs have founded nearly half of the companies in California's famous Silicon Valley.

Change Over Time

Monsoons

Climates Much of South Asia is hot and dry for half the year (left). Farmers wait anxiously for the summer monsoons (right), but hope that the rains will not cause flooding that spoils crops and farmlands.

Human-Environment Interaction *What might happen if the monsoons were late?*

Madras, and Kolkata, once called Calcutta, are major east coast centers of commerce and the shipping industry. The city of New Delhi, India's capital and center of government, is located in the country's interior on the banks of the Yamuna River.

Varanasi (vah RAH na see), one of India's oldest cities, is built on the banks of the Ganges. Hindus regard it as the holiest city in the world. Anyone lucky enough to die within the city limits of Varanasi, Hindus believe, is released from the reincarnation cycle of birth, death, and rebirth. Devout Hindus hope to visit the city at least once within their lifetime to wash in the sacred Ganges River. Many pilgrims collect Ganges water, which they take home for use in family worship.

GL🌐BAL CONNECTIONS

Science and Technology While public health efforts have reduced a number of diseases, others continue to spread. In 2000, international officials estimated that some 3.7 million Indians were infected with HIV, the virus that causes AIDS. Some predicted that the infection rate might soon exceed that of many African countries.

Economic Improvements

India's government has tried to raise the standard of living for its people, whether they live in remote villages or teeming cities. It has been partially successful, but enormous challenges remain.

Advances in Farming One of India's main goals has been to feed its growing population. More land has been farmed. Better farming methods, increased irrigation, and higher quality seeds have produced more and better crops.

Despite these advances, only a few families own enough land to support themselves. Almost half of the farmers do not own any land at all.

To add to their income, many farmers have set up **cottage industries.** People in these industries make goods in their own homes, using their own tools and machines. They may spin yarn and weave cloth or make things like jewelry or pottery. These goods can then be sold in the cities and towns.

Expanded Industry Although about 65 percent of Indians are farmers, the country is one of the world's leading industrial nations. India has made great advances in computers and

RESOURCE DIRECTORY

Teaching Resources
Unit 8, Chapter 29
• Section 2 Quiz, p. 14
Spanish Resources
• Section 2 Quiz, p. 74
Social Studies Skills Handbook
• Identifying Central Issues, p. 42
• Reading a Climate Graph, p. 65

Answer to Photo Caption

Drought conditions might cause the crops to fail, resulting in hunger and possibly famine.

in space research, and in recent years has placed several satellites in orbit. Another recent growth industry is consumer goods, such as televisions and videocassette recorders.

Many of the new customers for these consumer goods are members of India's growing urban middle class. Traditionally, Indian society has been sharply divided between a wealthy minority and a poor majority. Over the past decades, however, teachers, doctors, and government workers have become part of an expanding middle class. Others have moved into the middle class after building their own successful businesses.

Education In 1950, only about 16 percent of Indians could read and write. By the mid-1990s, the figure was nearly 50 percent and was still rising. As a result of intensive government efforts, almost every village now has a primary school. Yet many children still fail to complete their schooling. Often their families need them to work in the fields or to care for younger brothers and sisters.

Health Care The Indian government has also worked to improve people's health. In 1950, the average Indian's life expectancy was only 32 years. By the mid-1990s, it had risen to 60 years; and the government aims to increase that figure to 64 years by the early twenty-first century. Yet, many Indians cannot afford even basic medical care. In cities like Mumbai, many people live on the street. Millions of others live in slums, without healthy water or sanitation.

Availability of Electricity in India

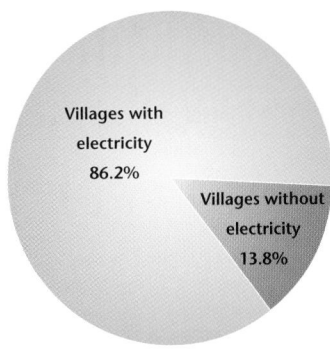

Villages with electricity 86.2%

Villages without electricity 13.8%

Source: Press Information Bureau, Government of India

GRAPH SKILLS

● **Science and Technology** Rural electrification has put village people in touch with more of the world.
• *How might the introduction of television, telephones, and movies change village life?*

Unhealthy water is also a problem in many rural areas. In the past, most Indians drank from open wells, which were breeding grounds for bacteria. Since the 1970s, the government has drilled hundreds of thousands of deep, machine-made wells with covers that reduce the risk of contamination. As a result, diseases such as malaria and cholera have become much less common.

SECTION 2 ASSESSMENT

1. **Key Terms** Define (a) reincarnation, (b) caste system, (c) charpoy, (d) sari, (e) purdah, (f) joint family system, (g) cottage industry.

2. **Cultures** How do most Hindus regard their journey through life? Explain.

3. **Science and Technology** What are elements of village life in India?

4. **Urbanization** Why do most Indians prefer to live in a city rather than in a village?

5. **Planning for the Future** In what ways could education in India be related to the country's economic improvement?

6. **Critical Thinking** **Recognizing Points of View** Think about the influence of the caste system in India. Why do you think many people support it? Why do you think many people want it to be changed or abolished?

Activity

Take It to the NET

Making a Poster As you studied Section 2, what aspect of India's culture interested you the most? Use Internet resources to find out more about that cultural interest. Then, create an attractive, fact-filled poster to interest your classmates in that aspect of India's culture.

Articles From
NATIONAL GEOGRAPHIC

The following article may be used to extend the content in this section.

Ward, Geoffrey C., and Steve McCurry, photographer. "India: Fifty Years of Independence." *National Geographic,* Vol. 191, No. 5 (May 1997), pp. 2–57.

After 50 years of freedom from British rule, India is making advances slowly but steadily while continuing to struggle with relentless population growth.

Objectives

Upon completion of Section 3, students should be able to:

◆ explain how limited rainfall affects Pakistanis;

◆ describe how political and cultural issues affected Afghanistan;

◆ describe the difficulties facing the people and government of Bangladesh;

◆ differentiate the cultures and landscapes of Nepal, Bhutan, and Sri Lanka.

National Geography Standards

The following National Geography Standards are highlighted in this section: 1, 4, 5, 6, 7, 8, 9, 10, 11, 12, 13, 14, 15, 17

Bellringer

Ask students what problems a region might face if it received too much or too little water. (Possible answers: floods and destruction, drought and starvation)

LESSON PLAN

1. Focus Divide students into groups and assign each group one of the following environments: desert, flood plain, high mountain range, and tropical island. Give group members three minutes to discuss how they think their assigned environment might affect clothing, housing, history, and way of life.

2. Instruct Divide students into two teams. Have each team write and answer 10 questions that begin with the phrase, "In which country . . . ?" (Example: In which country are most people Buddhists?) Have teams ask each other questions in turn. The group with the most correct answers wins.

3. Close/Reteach Have students describe the physical features of each country described in this section and identify at least one effect of these features.

3 Other Countries of South Asia

Reading Focus

• How does the availability of water influence the lives of people in Pakistan?

• How have political and cultural issues affected Afghanistan?

• What ongoing difficulties challenge the people and government of Bangladesh?

• How are the cultures and landscapes of Nepal, Bhutan, and Sri Lanka distinct?

Key Terms

hydroelectric power
irrigate
embankment dam
buffer state
malnutrition
deforestation

Main Idea Although their physical characteristics differ, India's neighbors share many of India's political and social challenges.

Natural Resources In Pakistan, limited rainfall forces many farmers to irrigate dry lands.

India's neighbors share many of India's challenges—poverty, overpopulation, and internal conflict between religious and ethnic groups. But, from the crowded cities of Bangladesh to the remote mountaintop villages of Afghanistan, each country is physically and culturally distinct.

Pakistan

The physical map on page 593 shows that Pakistan is made up of three physical regions. Along its northern and western borders, one of the world's highest mountain ranges, the Hindu Kush, reaches majestically toward the sky. Several passes cut through the mountains, making transportation possible. The Khyber (KY ber) Pass allows movement between Peshawar (puh SHAH wuhr) in northwest Pakistan and Kabul (KAH buhl), the capital of Afghanistan.

Just as in India, the towering mountains keep the cold air from central Asia from penetrating the subcontinent during the winter. As a result,

except at high elevations, temperatures in Pakistan are generally warm or hot. Temperatures in the city of Islamabad average 50°F (10°C) in January and 90°F (32°C) in July.

Much of western Pakistan is covered by the rugged Baluchistan (bah LOO chi STAN) Plateau. To the east lie barren stretches of the Thar Desert and brown, dusty plains. Sandwiched between these two forbidding regions is the fertile valley created by the Indus River as it flows south out of the mountains to the Arabian Sea.

Irrigation and Electricity The Indus River is the lifeline of a largely dry country. The river basin contains most of Pakistan's agricultural areas, as well as its major **hydroelectric power** stations. Hydroelectric power is electricity produced by the movement of water.

Since much of Pakistan receives less than 10 inches (25 cm) of rain annually, farmers must **irrigate** the land, or supply it with water. The Tarbela Dam was built to control the extreme

---

seasonal changes of the Indus River. It holds more water than any other **embankment dam** in the world. An embankment dam is a wall of soil and rock built to hold back water.

The Tarbela Dam is one of the world's biggest producers of hydroelectric power. It has also turned millions of acres of arid desert into lush cropland. The dam has created problems, however. The river picks up silt as it flows through northern Pakistan, and this silt is piling up behind the dam. Engineers estimate that within 20 years the dam will be unable to supply irrigation water.

Cultural Patterns As in India, most of the people of Pakistan live in farming villages. Almost all Pakistanis are Muslims, and prayers are an important part of daily life.

Tradition also plays an important role in their lives. For example, women generally have far fewer freedoms and economic opportunities than do men. Many women avoid contact with men outside the home and cover their faces with a veil in the presence of strangers.

National Challenges Islam holds Pakistan together, but other forces threaten to split it apart. About 60 percent of Pakistanis speak Punjabi or a Punjabi variant, but Urdu, which is spoken by only about 8 percent of the people, is the official language. Disputes among different ethnic groups often turn violent.

Tensions rose when Pakistan allowed American and other foreign troops to use its territory as a base for removing the Taliban government from neighboring Afghanistan in 2001. Periodic demonstrations and terrorist attacks challenged the control of the military government.

Afghanistan

In many ways, Afghanistan's history has been influenced by its location and terrain. The map on page 593 shows that the towering Hindu Kush forms the central backbone of the country. These mountains are nearly as high and certainly as rugged as the Himalayas. The word *kush* means "death," a name that probably stems from the danger posed to people crossing the mountains. The Hindu Kush also marks the boundaries of three regions. The first consists of the mountains themselves. At their feet lie several fertile valleys, where most Afghans live. North of the Hindu Kush is a region of semiarid plains. The land to the south is mostly desert.

Civil War

Cooperation and Conflict Decades of invasion and civil war inflicted great damage on many parts of Afghanistan. Here, a tank in the capital city of Kabul sits near buildings destroyed by fighting.

Location *How has location influenced Afghanistan's involvement in wars?*

Vocabulary

Buffer State Refer to the Key Terms list on page 620. Write the term *buffer state* on the board. Define *buffer* as any device used as a protective barrier or to cushion an object against shock. Ask students what shocks countries experience. (invasion, war) Have students guess the definition of the term *buffer state* and then look it up to check the accuracy of their guesses.

Daily Life

Women Under the Taliban Under the Taliban, Muslim women in Afghanistan were forced to follow strict regulations. Women were required to wear the *burqa,* a traditional garment covering them from head to toe with only a small opening to see through. Additionally, women were prohibited from working and going to school, and could not even leave their homes unless escorted by a male relative. Anyone who did not follow these rules might be beaten. After the Taliban lost power, some women chose to abandon the *burqa,* while others decided to continue wearing it. One farmer said, "Our women have used the *burqa* long before Taliban time, and they will continue to use it. This is part of our religion and culture. What we did not like about the Taliban was that they beat women who did not wear them."

Answer to Photo Caption

Possible answer: Refugees might never feel safe enough to return to their homeland.

Displaced by War

Migration This Afghan child is carrying freshly baked bread to her family in a refugee camp in Pakistan.

Movement *How might continuing social unrest in Afghanistan affect the 5 million refugees?*

For centuries, merchants and soldiers crossed Afghanistan on their way to or from China, Southwest Asia, and India. Although the Hindu Kush formed a barrier, openings such as the Khyber Pass allowed some movement.

Ethnic Diversity As a result of invasions and migrations, Afghanistan includes many ethnic groups. The country has two official languages, but many others are also spoken. Over the centuries, local groups isolated themselves as protection against invaders. As a result, some groups are unable to communicate with one another. In addition to these ethnic and linguistic differences, groups have conflicting opinions about Islamic beliefs and practices.

Buffer State During the 1800s, Britain and Russia competed for influence in southern Asia. When they failed to conquer Afghanistan, the two countries agreed to leave it alone. Afghanistan thus became a **buffer state**—a country separating opposing powers.

In December 1979, Soviet troops marched into Afghanistan to help put down a revolt at the request of the Afghan government. Millions of people fled the country, many settling in refugee camps in Pakistan. Pakistan and the United States helped arm and train Afghan resistance fighters who attacked Soviet forces.

Terrorism and War After the Soviet withdrawal in 1989, civil war broke out. By the mid-1990s, a radical Muslim group called the Taliban controlled most of the nation. The Taliban imposed harsh rule and harbored Muslim extremists from other countries.

One of the extremists was Osama bin Laden, an exiled Saudi millionaire who led an international terrorist organization called al-Qaida. In 1998, bin Laden issued a statement to Muslims, proclaiming that "the killing of Americans and their civilian and military allies is a religious duty." Al-Qaida members were linked to a number of attacks against Americans, including bombings of U.S. embassies in east Africa and a navy ship at port in Yemen.

On September 11, 2001, al-Qaida hijackers crashed airplanes into the World Trade Center towers in New York City and into the Pentagon near Washington, D.C. Thousands of innocent civilians from many nations were killed in the attacks. Al-Qaida personnel were also suspected of trying to develop chemical, biological, and nuclear weapons.

Despite international pressure, leaders of the Taliban continued to shelter bin Laden. In response, an international coalition led by the United States launched military attacks on Taliban and al-Qaida strongholds in Afghanistan.

The Taliban were quickly driven from power. The coalition helped establish a new democratic government that involved representatives of many ethnic groups. However, al-Qaida and Taliban sympathizers persist in parts of the nation.

RESOURCE DIRECTORY

Teaching Resources
Creative Teaching Activities, Determining Population Growth, p. 31

Bangladesh

As the map on page 593 shows, most of Bangladesh is an enormous delta formed by three powerful rivers—the Ganges, the Brahmaputra, and the Meghna (MAYG nuh). As a result, the soil is very fertile. However, because the country is so close to sea level, floods occur regularly.

Challenging Climate The climate of Bangladesh is primarily tropical wet. Temperatures rarely drop below 80°F (27°C). Because of the monsoon winds, large amounts of rain fall within a four- to five-month period.

The climate and geography of Bangladesh create a delicate balance between prosperity and disaster. In good times, the warm temperatures, abundant water supply, and fertile soil enable farmers to plant and harvest three crops a year. In bad times, the raging rivers overflow and fierce, tropical storms sweep in from the Bay of Bengal, submerging the land in salt water.

Record monsoon rains lashed at Bangladesh in 1989 and 1990, causing severe flooding. Millions of people were rendered homeless; power lines were knocked down; and roads, bridges, and railway lines were washed away. Transporting food and medicine from one part of the country to another proved almost impossible.

These successive disasters forced the government of Bangladesh to seek a lasting solution to the chronic flood problem. The first phase of a Flood Action Plan was launched in the early 1990s, funded with the help of the international aid community. The goal is to identify ways to lessen the effects of flooding and to improve future disaster management and relief.

Overpopulation Like India, Bangladesh struggles with overpopulation. It is the ninth most populous country in the world. With about 131 million people, it has almost as many people as Mexico and Canada combined, squeezed into an area the size of Wisconsin.

Overpopulation and natural hazards have combined to create another problem: hunger. **Malnutrition**—a lack of food or an unbalanced diet—is an almost constant problem. The Green Revolution has helped to increase agricultural production. Still, the population is growing at a faster rate than the food supply.

Flooding in Bangladesh

Economic Activities This Bangladeshi ricksha driver goes about business as usual, despite the monsoon waters.

Human-Environment Interaction *Why is flooding a particular problem in Bangladesh?*

To add to its problems, Bangladesh has few roads or bridges. Most travel is by boat along its many waterways. Without massive aid, Bangladesh cannot improve its communications and transportation system. Bangladesh thus faces

Articles From
NATIONAL GEOGRAPHIC

The following article may be used to extend the content in this section.

Cobb, Jr., Charles E., and James P. Blair, photographer. "Bangladesh." *National Geographic*, Vol. 183, No. 6 (June 1993), pp. 118–134.

The monsoons bring both sustenance and destruction to the people of Bangladesh.

The Physical World

Challenge of the Mountain
Mount Everest is the highest mountain in the world. It would take 191 Statues of Liberty stacked top to bottom to equal its height of 29,030 feet (8,848 m). Among the many climbers who have challenged it, more than 150 have died. In May 1953, Sir Edmund Hillary of New Zealand and Sherpa Tenzing Norgay were the first to successfully reach the peak. At 15 years old, Nepal's Temba Tsheri became the youngest successful climber in 2001. In 1999, at 61 years old, Lev Sarkisov of Armenia became the oldest person to reach the "top of the world."

Critical Thinking

Comparing and Contrasting
Use the following questions to help students compare and contrast Nepal and Bhutan. **What are some similarities between Nepal and Bhutan?** (Both contain a great range of elevation: hot and tropical lowlands, where tropical crops are grown, and highlands, where other types of crops are grown on terraces.) **What are some differences?** (Nepal is mostly Hindu; Bhutan is largely Buddhist. Bhutan has been isolationist, while Nepal has encouraged contact with the outside world.) Point out that while religious differences eventually led to partition in India, Buddhism and Hinduism coexist peaceably in Nepal and Bhutan.

Enrichment

Trekking in Nepal Nepal has encouraged tourism and is a favorite destination for adventurous travelers. Have students use travel brochures and guidebooks to write an itinerary for a five-day tour of Nepal. (Visual/Spatial)

Answer to Photo Caption

By limiting contact with tourists and foreigners, the government limits new ideas and influences and thereby preserves the existing way of life.

Cultural Divergence

Government and Citizenship In Thimpu, Bhutan, traditional architecture reflects the government's efforts to maintain a distinct culture.

Place *How might the Bhutanese government's limits on tourism support this goal?*

some of the greatest challenges of any country in the world.

Nepal and Bhutan

The countries of Nepal (nuh PAHL) and Bhutan (boo TAHN) span a great range in altitude, from a low elevation of about 230 feet (70 m) to that of the highest mountains in the world, the Himalayas. The tallest of the towering Himalayan peaks, Mount Everest in Nepal, towers 29,030 feet (8,848 m) high.

The southern lowlands of Nepal and Bhutan are hot and humid. Monsoon rains pour down every summer. Tropical crops flourish here, including citrus fruits, sugar cane, and rice. In the cooler, high areas, people grow wheat, millet, and potatoes. Most crops are grown in terraced fields built into the hillsides.

Nepal is about 90 percent Hindu, while Bhutan is about 75 percent Buddhist. Hinduism is more common in the lowlands, while Buddhism is the religion of the high areas. Yet, each religion has influenced the other. For example, people often celebrate festivals honored by both religions.

Both high mountains and politics kept Nepal and Bhutan somewhat separated from the rest of the world until the middle of the twentieth century. Today, Bhutan continues to discourage contact with tourists and other foreigners in an effort to preserve its traditional culture. Nepal, on the other hand, welcomes those who come to hike in its mountains and enjoy its magnificent scenery. The Sherpas, who live high in the mountains of Nepal, are skilled mountaineers. Many of them make a living by guiding climbers through the challenging mountain terrain.

Sri Lanka

Sri Lanka, meaning Magnificent Island, is located in the Indian Ocean 33 miles (53 km) southeast of the tip of India. Sri Lanka is often referred to as "a tear dropped off the subcontinent of India."

Environmental Change As the climate map on page 595 shows, Sri Lanka's climate is tropical, but is made cooler by ocean breezes. The heaviest rains fall in the southwestern part of the island, which contains plantations where crops like coconuts and rubber are grown for export. Another major crop is tea, which comes mainly from the higher slopes of the island's mountains. Sri Lanka produces about one eighth of the world's tea.

RESOURCE DIRECTORY

Teaching Resources
Unit 8, Chapter 29
• Section 3 Quiz, p. 16
• Reviewing Main Ideas, p. 17
• Test Forms A and B, pp. 20–25
Spanish Resources
• Section 3 Quiz, p. 75
Guide to the Essentials (English/Spanish)
• Chapter 29 Test
Mental Mapping booklet
• Chapter 29 Map Test, p. 113
Simulations, Games, and Lab Activities
• Place Location Review Games, pp. 58–63

Social Studies Skills Handbook
• Study and Research Skills, pp. 94–108

Prentice Hall Assessment System
Alternative Assessment booklet
• Position Paper Evaluation Form, p. 9

Technology
ExamView Test Bank CD-ROM
• Chapter 29 Test
• Unit 8 Test
Companion Web site, www.phschool.com
• Chapter 29 Self-Test

Sri Lanka was once covered with a thick rain forest. Today, almost two thirds of that forest is gone, cut down for farming and development. Scientists think that this **deforestation** may have helped change the island's weather and caused droughts. Restoring the rain forest is a major government challenge.

Social Unrest Another challenge is to keep the peace. About three fourths of Sri Lankans are Sinhalese (sin hah LEEZ), descendants of Aryans who migrated from northern India about 500 B.C. Later, the Tamils (TAHM uhlz), a people of Dravidian origin, came to Sri Lanka from southern India. The Sinhalese and the Tamils often fought each other. Religion and language differences further split the two groups. The Sinhalese practice Buddhism, while the Tamils practice Hinduism. The two groups speak different languages and have different alphabets.

Since Sri Lanka gained its independence from Britain in 1948, the Sinhalese have controlled the government. But that government has faced serious obstacles. In 1971, a radical Sinhalese group tried to overthrow the government. In addition, Tamils have long argued that Sinhalese discrimination has denied them equal rights to education, jobs, and land ownership. Attempts to repress the Tamil language led to calls for the creation of an independent Tamil nation on part of the island.

Tamil rebels began a guerrilla war against the Sinhalese in 1983. The conflict led to bloody fighting between government forces and guerrillas, with many civilians caught in the crossfire. The fighting disrupted development in the industry and service sectors of the economy. In late 2001, Norway helped negotiate a cease-fire, but two years of fitful peace talks after that had not made much progress.

South Asia and the United States
Population Data

Country	Total Population	Population Density (persons per square mile)	Population Growth Rate (percent)
Afghanistan	28,717,213	114	3.38
Bangladesh	138,448,210	2,430	2.06
Bhutan	2,139,549	118	2.13
India	1,049,700,100	859	1.47
Nepal	26,469,569	466	2.26
Pakistan	150,694,740	490	2.01
Sri Lanka	19,742,439	779	0.83
United States	290,342,550	78	0.92

Source: *Encarta World Atlas*

CHART SKILLS

● **Patterns of Settlement** *Which one of these countries has the greatest level of population density?*

● **Planning for the Future** *Which one of these countries seems most likely to face problems with its existing infrastructure?*

SECTION 3 ASSESSMENT

1. **Key Terms** Define **(a)** hydroelectric power, **(b)** irrigate, **(c)** embankment dam, **(d)** buffer state, **(e)** malnutrition, **(f)** deforestation.

2. **Environmental Change** How has the Tarbela Dam affected Pakistan?

3. **Cooperation and Conflict** How has Afghanistan been involved in international conflict?

4. **Planning for the Future** If Bangladesh is to deal with malnutrition, what key factors will its leaders and people have to consider?

5. **Physical Characteristics** Compare and contrast the physical geography of Nepal, Bhutan, and Sri Lanka.

6. **Critical Thinking** **Analyzing Information** Many years ago, Afghanistan was a buffer state. What advantages and disadvantages might a country experience as a result of that status?

Activity

USING THE REGIONAL ATLAS

Review the Regional Atlas for South Asia and this section. Suppose that you were leaving New Delhi, India, on a journey. If you were to travel to the northeast, what physical characteristics would you expect to encounter in this region's lands? Compare that area with the areas east of New Delhi.

TEST PREPARATION

Have students read the subsection Sri Lanka beginning on the opposite page to complete the following statement. The major goal of the Tamil guerrillas in Sri Lanka is to —

  A control coconut and rubber plantations
  B establish a separate state
  C put the Sinhalese in power
  D restore the rain forest

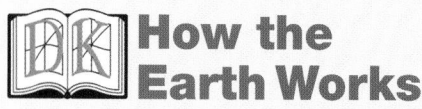
Objectives

Upon completion of this feature, students should be able to:

◆ explain what causes wind and what factors affect wind speed;

◆ describe the development of the different types of storms;

◆ summarize the impact of storms.

National Geography Standards

The following National Geography Standards are highlighted in this feature: 1, 4, 7, 15, 17

Bellringer

Have students read the feature caption heads that name different types of storms. Ask: **Do any of these kinds of storms occur in your region?** If so, have students estimate how frequently the storms occur. Discuss how location and regional climate account for the frequency of storms.

LESSON PLAN

1. Focus Write the Key Terms on the board. Ask students to define them. Then have students explain what causes wind and what factors affect wind speed.

2. Instruct Have students compare and contrast the development of the different types of storms described in the feature (monsoons, thunderstorms, tornadoes, blizzards, and tropical cyclones). Then have students draw diagrams on the board that show how these storms form.

3. Close/Reteach Ask students to discuss which kind of storm seems most threatening. Then have them explain their answers.

How the Earth Works

Winds and Storms

The world's atmosphere is forever on the move. **Wind,** or air in motion, occurs because solar radiation heats up some parts of the sea and land more than others. Air above these hot spots becomes warmer and lighter than the surrounding air and therefore rises. Elsewhere, cool air sinks because it is heavier. Winds blow because air squeezed out by sinking, cold air is sucked in under rising, warm air. Wind may move slowly as in a gentle breeze. In extreme weather, wind moves rapidly, creating terrifyingly destructive storms.

Southwest Monsoon
During the early summer, the hot, dry lands of Asia draw in cooler, moist air from the Indian Ocean.

Northeast Monsoon
The cold, dry winter air from Central Asia brings chilly, dusty conditions to South Asia.

MONSOONS
Seasonal winds called monsoons affect large areas of the tropics and subtropics. They occur in South Asia, southern North America, eastern Australia, and other regions of the world. In South Asia, southwest monsoons generally bring desperately needed rain from May until October.

THUNDERSTORMS
Thunderclouds are formed by powerful updrafts of air that occur along cold fronts or over ground heated very strongly by the sun. Ice crystals and water droplets high in the cloud are torn apart and smashed together with such ferocity that they become charged with electricity. Thunderstorms can unleash thunder, lightning, wind, rain, and hail.

LIGHTNING AND THUNDER
Electricity is discharged from a thundercloud in the form of lightning. A bolt of lightning can heat the air around it to a temperature four times as hot as the sun. The heated air expands violently and sends out a rumbling shock wave that we hear as thunder.

RESOURCE DIRECTORY

Technology

World Geography Map and Photo Transparencies
• How the Earth Works, Unit 8

Companion Web site, www.phschool.com
• Chapter 29 Activities

TORNADOES

Tornadoes may strike wherever thunderstorms occur. A **tornado** begins when a column of strongly rising warm air is set spinning by high winds at a cloud's top. A funnel is formed and may touch the ground. With winds that can rise above 200 mph, tornadoes can lift people, cars, and buildings high into the air and then smash them back to the ground.

BLIZZARDS
In a **blizzard,** heavy snowfall and strong winds often make it impossible to see. Winds pile up huge drifts of snow. Travel and communication can grind to a halt.

IMPACT OF TROPICAL STORMS

Tropical storms are often devastating. The strongest winds, with gusts sometimes more than 200 mph, occur at the storm's center, or eye. When a tropical storm strikes land, raging winds can uproot trees and destroy buildings. Vast areas may be swamped by torrential rain, and coastal regions may be overwhelmed by a **storm surge,** a wall of water some 25 feet (8 m) high sucked up by the storm's eye.

These women wade through the streets of Dhaka, Bangladesh, flooded by a tropical cyclone. In 1991, a cyclone killed more than 130,000 Bangladeshis.

A Pacific typhoon struck this ship off the coast of Taiwan in November 2000. Many of the crew members fell victim to the raging sea.

HOW TROPICAL STORMS DEVELOP

Tropical storms begin when water evaporates over an ocean in a hot tropical region to produce huge clouds and thunderstorms. When the storms cluster together and whirl around a low-pressure center, they form a **tropical cyclone.** Tropical cyclones with winds of at least 74 mph are called hurricanes in some regions and **typhoons** in other regions. The sequence below shows satellite images of an Atlantic hurricane.

Stage 1: Thunderstorms develop over the ocean.

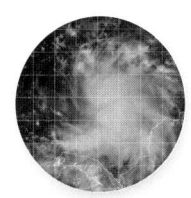

Stage 2: Storms group to form a swirl of cloud.

Stage 3: Winds grow and a distinct center forms in the cloud swirl.

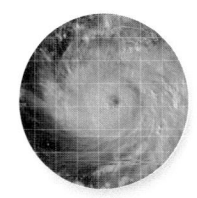

Stage 4: Eye forms. The hurricane is now at its most dangerous.

Stage 5: Eye passes over land. The hurricane starts to weaken.

Chapter 29　**627**

ASSESSMENT

1. **Key Terms** Define **(a)** wind, **(b)** tornado, **(c)** blizzard, **(d)** tropical cyclone, **(e)** typhoon, **(f)** storm surge.

2. **Physical Processes** How do thunderstorms come into being?

3. **Economic Activities** **(a)** How can storms have a negative impact on economic activities? **(b)** How can monsoons benefit economic activities?

4. **Natural Hazards** How can a tropical cyclone result in the loss of thousands of lives?

5. **Critical Thinking** **Developing a Hypothesis** Since 1991, the Bangladeshi government has constructed hundreds of concrete storm shelters in coastal regions of the country. **(a)** Why do you think the government decided on this policy? **(b)** How do you think the policy has benefited the country?

Creating a Chapter Summary

As a reteaching opportunity, pair a more able student with a less able student to complete this chapter summary.

Students may add the following entries: **India** *Cultures:* Predominantly Hindu, Caste system, Joint family system, Village life but increasing urbanization *Challenges:* Improving the standard of living, including education and health care **Pakistan** *Physical:* Mountain ranges, Plateau, Desert *Cultures:* Predominantly Muslim, Farming village lifestyle *Challenges:* Fighting among Muslim groups, Improving the standard of living **Bangladesh** *Physical:* Tropical wet climate, Delta with fertile soil, Low elevation *Cultures:* Predominantly Bengali *Challenges:* Chronic flooding, Malnutrition **Afghanistan** *Physical:* Hindu Kush, Desert, Fertile valleys *Cultures:* Variety of ethnic groups, united by Islamic faith *Challenges:* Recovering from Soviet occupation in the 1980s **Sri Lanka** *Physical:* Tropical climate, Rain forests largely deforested *Cultures:* Sinhalese majority, Tamil minority *Challenges:* Strife between Sinhalese and Tamils

Reviewing Key Terms

1–10. Students' quizzes should demonstrate a clear understanding of the key terms.

Understanding Key Ideas

11. He played a great role in India's move to independence and did so in a nonviolent manner.

12. People migrated to avoid being ruled by a majority religion to which they did not belong.

13. Cities are more crowded and busier than rural areas, but they offer more opportunities for work and education than rural areas do.

14. Cottage industries allow farmers to supplement their income. Goods that are made by farmers are sold in cities and towns.

15. Pakistan receives little rainfall; the dam was built to supply water for irrigation.

16. After years of civil war and international conflict, Afghanistan

---

Creating a Chapter Summary

Copy this chart on a piece of paper. Complete the chart with information about the countries of South Asia. Some entries have been completed to serve as an example.

COUNTRY	PHYSICAL CHARACTERISTICS	CULTURES	CHALLENGES
INDIA	• Hot, humid climate in most of country		
PAKISTAN			
BANGLADESH			• Overpopulation •
AFGHANISTAN			
SRI LANKA			

Take It to the NET
Chapter Self-Test For practice test questions for Chapter 29, go to the World Geography section of **www.phschool.com**.

Reviewing Key Terms

Review the key terms listed below. Then, use the words and their definitions to create a matching quiz. Exchange your quiz with another student's quiz. Check each other's answers when you are finished.

1. nationalism
2. boycott
3. partition
4. reincarnation
5. caste system
6. purdah
7. joint family system
8. buffer state
9. malnutrition
10. deforestation

Understanding Key Ideas

11. Understanding the Past Mohandas Gandhi was also called Mahatma, meaning "the Great Soul." How does that title reflect his contribution to India?

12. Migration What was the main reason for the great migration of people after India achieved independence?

13. Cultures Describe some differences between rural and urban life in India today.

14. Economic Systems What role do cottage industries play in India's economy?

15. Science and Technology In what way was the building of the Tarbela Dam a response to Pakistan's climate?

16. Cooperation and Conflict What challenges does Afghanistan face?

Critical Thinking and Writing

17. Analyzing Change Why do you think that Gandhi's use of nonviolent resistance was successful?

18. Recognizing Bias Reread Jawaharlal Nehru's announcement of India's independence on page 607. Which parts of his statement do you think are meant to inspire feelings of national pride among the listeners?

19. Analyzing Causes and Effects Describe the causes and effects of the growth of India's middle class.

20. Making Comparisons (a) How do Nepal and Bhutan differ in their attitudes about outsiders? **(b)** How might each country's attitude affect its economy?

---

needs to rebuild its economy and government.

Critical Thinking and Writing

17. It demonstrated to Britain that the Indian independence movement was disciplined and committed. Nonviolence also attracted world sympathy for the Indian cause.

18. Students may point to the expression "awake to life and freedom," the emphasis on the rarity of the moment and the end of an age, and the description of India as a once-suppressed soul that now has found utterance.

19. Possible causes: India has become a major economic power; people have greater opportunities to start their own businesses or enter teaching, medicine, and other professions. Possible effects: The middle class is spending money on consumer goods, thereby strengthening that industry.

(Continued on next page.)

21. **Recognizing Patterns** (a) Which two religions have the most followers in South Asia? (b) How does religion affect regional conflict?

22. **Drawing Conclusions** Why is hunger still a major problem in South Asia?

Applying Skills

Analyzing Cartograms Refer to the cartogram on page 611 to answer these questions:

23. According to the cartogram, which country has the largest population in (a) South Asia, (b) Africa, and (c) Latin America?

24. Why is Russia's appearance on the cartogram so different from its appearance on a land-area map?

Reading a Diagram Study the diagram below, and answer the following questions:

25. What reasons might exist for ranking farmers and merchants above craftworkers and laborers in the traditional caste system?

26. How would a caste system conflict with the idea of personal initiative?

The Caste System

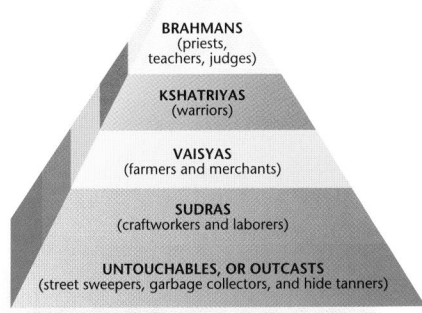

BRAHMANS
(priests, teachers, judges)

KSHATRIYAS
(warriors)

VAISYAS
(farmers and merchants)

SUDRAS
(craftworkers and laborers)

UNTOUCHABLES, OR OUTCASTS
(street sweepers, garbage collectors, and hide tanners)

Test Preparation

Read the question and choose the best answer.

27. The country of Bangladesh was formed as a direct result of —

A protests against human-rights violations in Pakistan

B control of Afghanistan by the Taliban

C Indian independence from Britain

D conflict between East Pakistan and West Pakistan

Activities

USING THE REGIONAL ATLAS

Review the Regional Atlas for South Asia and Chapter 29. Using information about climates, ecosystems, and economic activities, write a paragraph explaining why the monsoons are important to large portions of South Asia and how the seasonal wind patterns affect different aspects of daily life in the region.

MENTAL MAPPING

Study a map of South Asia. Then, on a separate piece of paper, draw a sketch map of it from memory. Label the following places on your map:

- India
- Pakistan
- Bangladesh
- Afghanistan
- Sri Lanka
- Nepal
- Mumbai (Bombay)
- Kolkata (Calcutta)
- Kabul
- Islamabad
- Indian Ocean
- Arabian Sea
- Bay of Bengal

Take It to the NET

Completing a Time Line Search the Internet for information about the history of Afghanistan. Create a time line that shows major political developments and social changes within the country, as well as information about international events related to Afghanistan. You may wish to illustrate your time line with photographs.

Critical Thinking and Writing (cont.)

20. (a) Nepal welcomes visitors; Bhutan discourages visitors and remains isolationist in an attempt to preserve traditional culture. (b) Nepal's economy might benefit from tourism, whereas Bhutan's economy might experience slower growth.

21. (a) Hinduism and Islam (b) Possible answer: Religious differences can intensify regional conflict.

22. In many areas, poor farming techniques mean that farmers cannot produce large quantities of food. In addition, droughts and floods disrupt the supply of food.

Applying Skills

23. (a) India (b) Nigeria (c) Brazil

24. Russia is vast in terms of land area, but its cold climate does not encourage settlement.

25. Possible answer: Farmers and merchants may earn more money and be more autonomous than craftworkers and laborers.

26. People are born into their positions in the caste system, and ambition or personal initiative cannot change their rank in society.

Test Preparation
27. D

Activities

Using the Regional Atlas
Check students' paragraphs for accuracy, comprehensiveness, and an understanding of the weather patterns of South Asia and their impact on daily life.

Mental Mapping
To check their work, have students compare their maps to those in the Regional Atlas.

Take It to the Net
Students' work should reflect sound research. Check time lines for accuracy and scale.

MENTAL MAPPING

Games for Review See pages 58–63 of the Simulations, Games, and Lab Activities booklet for games to help students review place names.

Chapter Map Test Students should use their completed outline maps and the Unit 8 Checklist to prepare for the Chapter 29 Map Test.

Unit Map Test Students will need to study the location of all the place names on the Unit 8 Checklist.

Alternative Assessment

Final Evaluation

Writing a Position Paper Use the Position Paper Evaluation Form on page 9 of the Alternative Assessment booklet in the Prentice Hall Assessment System to evaluate students' papers. Either teachers or students can complete the forms to indicate which level of work was achieved for each of the criteria. The evaluation should include specific examples and comments.

TEST PREPARATION

Use this sample exam to help your students prepare for standardized tests.

You might want to remind your students of the following:

Tips for Test Taking

1. Read the directions carefully.

2. Read each question carefully.

3. For multiple choice questions, try to answer the question before you look at the choices. Read all the choices. Then, eliminate those that are absolutely incorrect.

4. For short answer questions, be sure to answer the question completely if there is more than one part.

5. Answer the easy questions first. Then, go back to the ones that will take more time.

6. Pace yourself. Be sure to set aside enough time for the writing questions.

Write answers on a separate sheet of paper.

Multiple Choice

1 Most Indians speak languages belonging to the —

   A Austro-Asiatic family

   B Indo-European family

   C Sino-Tibetan family

   D Dravidian family

2 In the economies of both India and California, —

   A wine grapes are grown in all vineyards

   B monsoon rains have a significant impact on agriculture

   C tea, rice, and jute are leading agricultural products

   D motion picture production is a major industry

Use the graph <u>and</u> your knowledge of social studies to answer the following question.

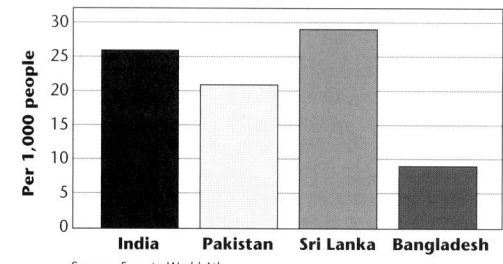

Daily Newspaper Circulation

Source: *Encarta World Atlas*

3 Based on newspaper circulation, in which of these countries would you expect to find the highest literacy rate?

   A India

   B Pakistan

   C Sri Lanka

   D Bangladesh

4 Which two South Asian countries are most likely to have a dispute over how much Indus River water each country can draw for its own use?

   A India and Pakistan

   B Bangladesh and Sri Lanka

   C Sri Lanka and Pakistan

   D India and Bangladesh

5 Which of the following most clearly illustrates Britain's enduring colonial influence upon India?

   A Constitutional government

   B Existence of many different languages

   C Increasing population density in cities

   D Recent growth of cottage industries

Use the quotation <u>and</u> your knowledge of social studies to answer the following question.

> I do not believe in armed risings. They are a remedy worse than the disease sought to be cured. . . . We have a better method. Unlike that of violence it certainly involves the exercise of restraint and patience; but it requires also resoluteness of will. This method is to refuse to be party to the wrong.

6 Which Indian most likely made this statement, and about which issue?

   A Ashwini Kunar, about ending the conflict between India and Pakistan

   B V. S. Naipaul, about the rise of crime in India's overpopulated cities

   C Mohandas Gandhi, about opposing British control of India

   D Jawaharlal Nehru, about the people's response to the death of Mohandas Gandhi

---

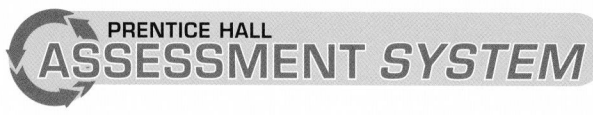

PRENTICE HALL

ASSESSMENT *SYSTEM*

Diagnose and Prescribe

- Profile student skills with Diagnostic Tests A&B.

- Address student needs with program materials identified in the test.

Review and Reteach

- Provide cumulative content review with the Review Book.

Practice and Assess

- Build test-taking skills with Test-Taking Strategies on Transparencies.

7 In which of the following ways are Pakistan and Bangladesh similar?

 A Hindi is the major language of both countries.

 B Both countries have democratic governments modeled after the government of the United States.

 C In both countries, Islam is the predominant religion.

 D Both countries receive vast quantities of monsoon rains.

Use the statements <u>and</u> your knowledge of social studies to answer the following question.

- The Taj Mahal is a monument in which both Hindu and Muslim artistic and architectural styles are evident.
- The Urdu language is a blend of Arabic, Persian, and Hindi.
- The Sanskrit language of India has its origins in the culture of the Aryans.
- In 1947, India adopted a parliamentary system of democratic government.

---

8 What geographic concept do all of these facts best illustrate?

 A Environmental change

 B Cultures

 C Planning for the future

 D Global trade patterns

9 A street sweeper in Mumbai who states, "My son will grow up to be a street sweeper, as I am, not a merchant or teacher" is expressing the Hindu idea of —

 A caste

 B polytheism

 C cultural divergence

 D ahimsa

10 Unlike the civil unrest in Pakistan, the civil unrest in Sri Lanka —

 A is driven by water rights issues

 B has been nonviolent

 C occurs between Hindus and Muslims

 D occurs between Hindus and Buddhists

Writing Practice

11 **(a)** How and why did the Soviet Union play a direct role in the affairs of a South Asian country? **(b)** What was the outcome of that intervention?

12 What factors contribute to tensions between Pakistan and India?

13 How do monsoons affect life in South Asia?

14 How is the government of Bangladesh working to reduce the destruction caused by typhoons?

Test Preparation Answers

Multiple Choice

 1 B

 2 D

 3 C

 4 A

 5 A

 6 C

 7 C

 8 B

 9 A

10 D

Writing Practice

11 **(a)** In 1979, Soviet troops invaded Afghanistan to help put down a revolt against an Afghan government that the Soviets supported. **(b)** With the help of the United States and Pakistan, the rebels were able to drive out the Soviet forces by 1989. Civil war continued in Afghanistan. Several million Afghans fled the country.

12 When British rule ended in 1947, the subcontinent was divided into two countries—India, with a Hindu majority, and Pakistan, with a Muslim majority. As Muslims migrated from India to Pakistan and Hindus migrated from Pakistan to India, fighting erupted and over a million people died. Since then, border disputes have added to the tension between India and Pakistan.

13 In winter, monsoons from the northeast bring very dry air into South Asia. In summer, monsoons from the south pick up moisture from the Indian Ocean and drop heavy rains over South Asia. The seasonal monsoons affect agriculture and other human activities.

14 Possible answers: As a result of intensive government efforts, almost every Indian village now has a primary school. To reduce the spread of disease from unhealthy water, the government has drilled deep wells with covers to reduce the risk of contamination.

East Asia and the Pacific World

Activating Prior Knowledge

Ask students to brainstorm a list of countries located in East Asia and the Pacific. Have students share what comes to mind when they think of these places. Ask: **Which countries are most familiar to you? Why?** (Answers will vary.)

Photo Study

The Great Wall of China

Qin ruler Shi Huangdi ruled China from 221 B.C. until 210 B.C. During his rule, he extended Chinese power to the south and west. Using forced labor, he organized the building of the Great Wall. Before that time, local lords had built walls to defend their lands against nomadic invaders. Shi Huangdi joined and extended these walls across northern China. The Great Wall eventually stretched 4,500 miles (7,300 km) and was rebuilt many times. **Analyzing Change** Ask: **What is one technological advance that has made walls less of a barrier in modern times?** (Possible answers: airplanes, rockets, missiles)

eTeach

Be sure to check out this month's online forum with a Master Teacher to join in an exchange of teaching ideas. **www.phschool.com**

Locating the Region

Located partly in the Asian continent, the region known as Southeast Asia includes a host of island nations. The continent "down under," Australia, is itself an island. Its frozen neighbor to the south, Antarctica, anchors the world.

Robinson Projection

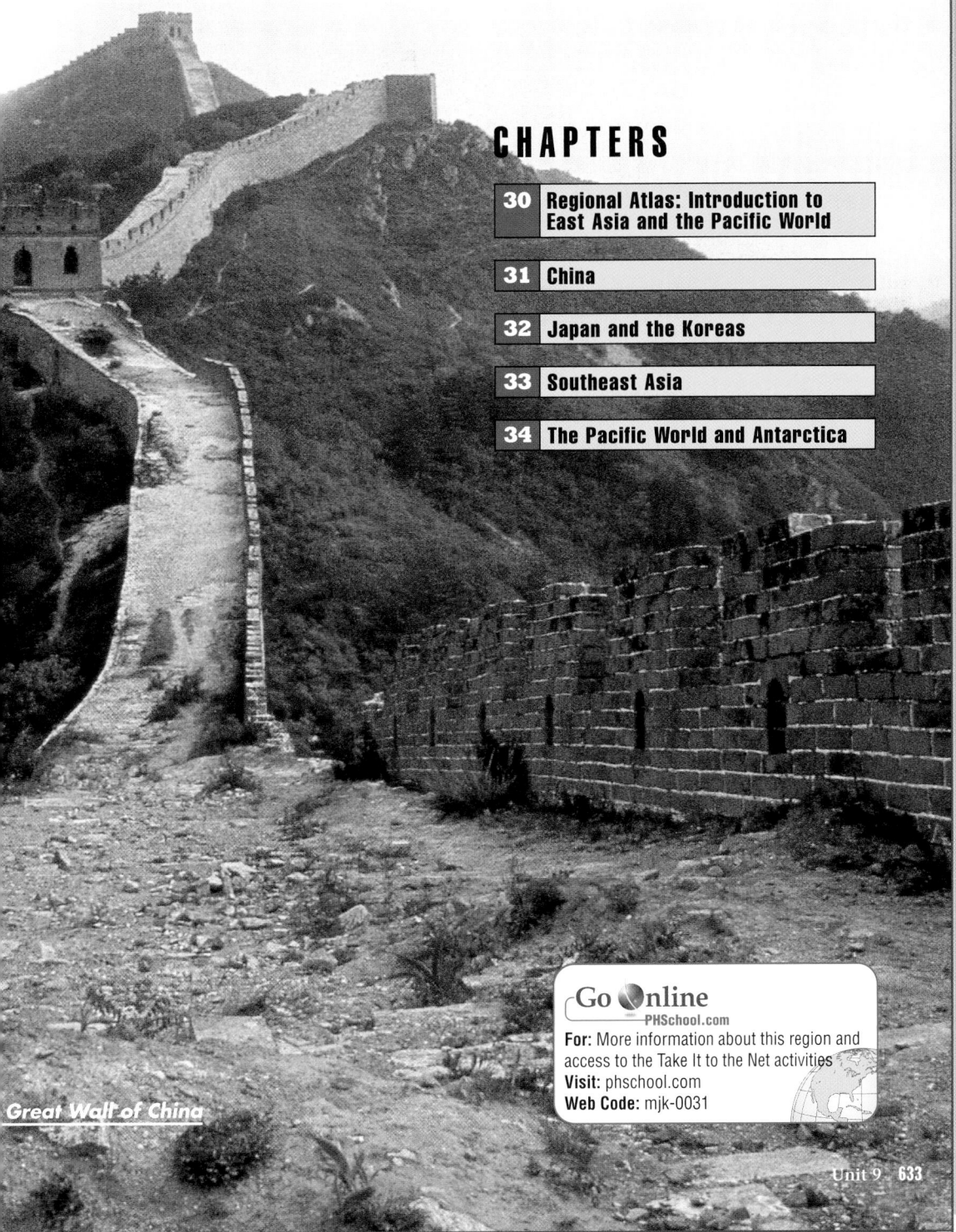

CHAPTERS

Great Wall of China

Go Online
PHSchool.com
For: More information about this region and access to the Take It to the Net activities
Visit: phschool.com
Web Code: mjk-0031

Unit 9 **633**

Promoting Geographic Understanding

Introduce the unit using the themes below.

1. Location Help students identify the Pacific World's location in relation to East Asia by referring them to the Robinson projection map on page 632. Ask: **What is the relative location of the Pacific Islands to East Asia?** (south and east)

2. Region The Pacific Rim is an economic region made up of countries that border the Pacific Ocean. Ask: **Which is the largest Pacific Rim country below the Equator?** (Australia)

3. Place Ask: **Which is the largest nation in the region?** (China)

RESOURCE DIRECTORY

World Geography Map and Photo Transparencies
The World Geography Map and Photo Transparencies provide thematic maps and photos to help students understand key geographic concepts.

World Geography Videos
These chapter-level videos help students understand the key concepts and themes of geography through case studies.

ExamView Test Bank CD-ROM
The test bank CD-ROM allows you to create, edit, and print out chapter-level tests.

Social Studies Skills Tutor CD-ROM
This interactive CD-ROM provides students with the opportunity to learn and practice critical social studies skills.

Take It to the NET
Prentice Hall's Web site offers Internet activities and links that supplement *World Geography: Building a Global Perspective.* Visit us in the Social Studies area at **www.phschool.com**.

Resource Manager

Chapter-Level Resources	CORE INSTRUCTION	READING/SKILLS
Chapter-Level Resources	**Teaching Resources** 📘 **Unit 9**/Ch. 30 • Regional Atlas Study Guide, p. 2 📖 **Mental Mapping booklet** • Unit 9 Checklist, p. 115 📖 **Simulations, Games, and Lab Activities** • Where on Earth? Games, pp. 80–81 • Place Location Review Games, pp. 58–63 💿 **TeacherExpress™ CD-ROM**, Ch. 30 🖥 **Companion Web site,** **www.phschool.com** • eTeach	**Teaching Resources** 📘 **Unit 9**/Ch. 30 • Regional Atlas Review, p. 3 📖 **Guide to the Essentials (English/Spanish)** • Chapter 30 Summary 📖 **Spanish Resources** • Regional Atlas Review, p. 76 📼 **Guided Reading Audiotapes (English/Spanish)**, Ch. 30 📄 **Section Reading Support Transparencies**, Ch. 30 💿 **Book on CD**, Ch. 30 💿 **Social Studies Skills Tutor CD-ROM**
Historical Overview Describe significant events and developments in the history of East Asia and the Pacific World.	**Teaching Resources** 📖 **Mental Mapping booklet** • Outline Map 30A, p. 116 📖 **Creative Teaching Activities** • Historical and Cultural Landmarks, p. 32 💿 **Prentice Hall Presentation Pro CD-ROM**, Ch. 30	**Teaching Resources** 📖 **Social Studies Skills Handbook** • Reading a Political Map, p. 19
Physical Characteristics Identify major physical characteristics of East Asia and the Pacific World.	**Teaching Resources** 📖 **Mental Mapping booklet** • Outline Maps 30B and 30C, pp. 117–118 💿 **Prentice Hall Presentation Pro CD-ROM**, Ch. 30	**Teaching Resources** 📖 **Social Studies Skills Handbook** • Elevation on a Map, p. 20 • Four Types of Landforms, p. 21 • Relief on a Map, p. 22
Climates Compare climate regions in East Asia and the Pacific World.	💿 **Prentice Hall Presentation Pro CD-ROM**, Ch. 30	**Teaching Resources** 📖 **Social Studies Skills Handbook** • Reading a Climate Map, p. 26
Ecosystems Describe characteristics of major ecosystems in East Asia and the Pacific World.	💿 **Prentice Hall Presentation Pro CD-ROM**, Ch. 30	**Teaching Resources** 📖 **Social Studies Skills Handbook** • Reading a Natural Vegetation Map, p. 25 • Analyzing a Photograph, p. 58
People and Cultures Discuss elements of culture in East Asia and the Pacific World.	💿 **Prentice Hall Presentation Pro CD-ROM**, Ch. 30	**Teaching Resources** 📖 **Social Studies Skills Handbook** • Reading a Population Density Map, p. 31
Economics, Technology, and Environment Identify how the economy, technology, and the environment interact in East Asia and the Pacific World.	💿 **Prentice Hall Presentation Pro CD-ROM**, Ch. 30	**Teaching Resources** 📖 **Social Studies Skills Handbook** • Reading an Economic Activity Map, p. 27 • Reading a Natural Resources Map, p. 34 • Using the Map Key, p. 3 • Reading a Cartogram, p. 67
Database • Discuss how a nation's economy, population, and geographic size influence the development of its transportation system. • Compare the transportation systems in China, Japan, Australia, Thailand, and the United States.	**Teaching Resources** 📘 **Unit 9**/Ch. 30 • Regional Atlas Database Skills, p. 4 💿 **Prentice Hall Presentation Pro CD-ROM**, Ch. 30	**Teaching Resources** 📘 **Unit 9**/Ch. 30 • Regional Atlas Database Skills, p. 4 📖 **Social Studies Skills Handbook** • Reading a Table, p. 62

ENRICHMENT/HONORS/PREAP

Teaching Resources

📖 **Mental Mapping booklet**
- Atlas Activity, p. 119

📖 **Social Studies Skills Handbook**
- Study and Research Skills, pp. 94–108

🖥 **World Geography Map and Photo Transparencies**
- East Asia and the Pacific World: Maps and Photos

📺 **World Geography Videos**
- Regional Atlas: East Asia and the Pacific World, Tape 4

💻 **Companion Web site, www.phschool.com**
- Chapter 30 Activities

🖥 **World Geography Map and Photo Transparencies**
- East Asia and the Pacific World: Political

🖥 **World Geography Map and Photo Transparencies**
- East Asia and the Pacific World: Physical

🖥 **World Geography Map and Photo Transparencies**
- World Climate Zones

🖥 **World Geography Map and Photo Transparencies**
- East Asia and the Pacific World: Natural Hazards

🖥 **World Geography Map and Photo Transparencies**
- East Asia and the Pacific World: Population Density

🖥 **World Geography Map and Photo Transparencies**
- East Asia and the Pacific World: Economic Activities

🖥 **World Geography Map and Photo Transparencies**
- East Asia and the Pacific World: Transportation

ASSESSMENT

PRENTICE HALL ASSESSMENT SYSTEM

Core Assessment

📖 **ExamView Test Bank booklet**, Ch. 30

💿 **ExamView Test Bank CD-ROM**, Ch. 30

Standardized Test Preparation

Diagnose and Prescribe

📖 **Diagnostic Tests for High School Social Studies Skills**

Review and Reteach

📖 **Review Book for World Geography**, pp. 19–20

Practice and Assess

📖 **Test-taking Strategies With Transparencies for High School**

Test-taking Strategy Poster

📖 **Alternative Assessment booklet**

📖 **Test Prep Book for World Geography**

Teaching Resources

📖 **Unit 9**/Ch. 30
- Test Forms A and B, pp. 5–10

📖 **Guide to the Essentials (English/Spanish)**
- Chapter 30 Test

📖 **Mental Mapping booklet**
- Chapter 30 Map Test, p. 120

💻 **Companion Web site, www.phschool.com**
- Chapter 30 Self-Test

CUSTOMIZE FOR INDIVIDUAL NEEDS

Gifted and Talented
- Teacher's Edition, Customize for . . . , p. 637

Honors/PreAP
- Teacher's Edition, Customize for . . . , p. 649

Less Proficient Readers
- Guide to the Essentials (English), Ch. 30
- Guided Reading Audiotapes (English), Ch. 30
- Section Reading Support Transparencies, Ch. 30
- Book on CD, Ch. 30

Students Acquiring English/ESL
- Guide to the Essentials (English/Spanish), Ch. 30
- Guided Reading Audiotapes (English/Spanish), Ch. 30
- Section Reading Support Transparencies, Ch. 30
- Book on CD, Ch. 30

Less Proficient Writers
- Alternative Assessment, Writing Assignment Rubric, p. 6

Introducing

CHAPTER

30

pp. 634–649

Objectives

Upon completion of the Regional Atlas, students should be able to:

◆ describe significant events and developments in the history of East Asia and the Pacific World;

◆ identify major physical characteristics of East Asia and the Pacific World;

◆ compare climate regions in East Asia and the Pacific World;

◆ describe characteristics of major ecosystems in East Asia and the Pacific World;

◆ discuss elements of culture in East Asia and the Pacific World;

◆ identify how the economy, technology, and the environment interact in East Asia and the Pacific World.

National Geography Standards

The following National Geography Standards are highlighted in this Regional Atlas: 1, 4, 5, 8, 9, 10, 11, 12, 13, 14, 16, 17

Bellringer

Write these names on the board: *China, Australia, Antarctica*. Have students envision the landscape of each place. Ask volunteers to share their images.

Answers to Assessment

1. concession, p. 634

2. The countries of Southeast Asia were the first to be conquered by the Europeans: Portugal and the Netherlands colonized Indonesia, Spain colonized the Philippines, and Britain colonized Australia and New Zealand.

3. The Europeans forced cultural change in East Asia and the Pacific through trade and military action. For example, China was forced to grant concessions to European merchants and governments.

Introduction to EAST ASIA AND THE PACIFIC WORLD

Historical Overview

East and Southeast Asia were the sites of some of humanity's earliest technological advances. The oldest known pottery was made in Japan by 10,000 B.C., and rice may have been domesticated in northern Thailand or Vietnam by 4000 B.C. By 2000 B.C., people had migrated from Taiwan to the Philippines, and their descendants crossed vast stretches of ocean to colonize the Pacific Islands.

Chinese Civilization Probably the most influential development in this region occurred in China, which by about 1500 B.C. had developed a complex society and a unique writing system that remains in use today. By 60 B.C. China's Han empire had expanded to include nearly all of present-day China except for Manchuria and Tibet, as well as parts of present-day Vietnam and the Koreas. Several other empires followed the Han in China.

China was the birthplace of Confucianism and Daoism. It passed these belief systems, along with Buddhism and other aspects of its culture, to neighboring countries. Technologies such as printing, gunpowder, and the compass all originated in China.

European and Japanese Imperialism European traders began to arrive in East and Southeast Asia in the 1500s and 1600s. They were not widely welcomed in China, Korea, or Japan, each of which restricted the movement of Western traders. However, the Portuguese established trading colonies in Indonesia, and Spain colonized the Philippines during the 1500s. Beginning in the 1600s, the Netherlands conquered most of Indonesia, including most Portuguese

possessions. During the 1700s and 1800s, British settlers colonized Australia and New Zealand.

Military action by Britain and other European industrial powers forced China to grant increasing **concessions,** or exemptions from local law, to European merchants and governments, while the United States forced Japan to allow greater foreign trade. After 1868, a new Japanese government developed and, in the 1920s and 1930s, launched its own program of industrialization and colonial conquest. By 1940, Japan had conquered Korea, Taiwan, parts of mainland China, and many Pacific islands. In World War II, the Western allies defeated Japan and liberated its colonial possessions.

Communism and Economic Systems A civil conflict between the Chinese Communists and the ruling Nationalists began in the 1930s and continued after World War II. In 1949, the Nationalists fled to Taiwan, and the Communists established the People's Republic of China on the mainland. Communist governments also took power in North Vietnam and North Korea.

By 1960, most of the former European colonies in the region gained independence. The non-Communist countries, particularly Japan, enjoyed rapid economic growth and prosperity between 1950 and 1990 under market economies. A recession slowed growth in Japan and other Asian nations after 1990, but Communist China adopted some capitalist reforms and experienced an economic boom.

ASSESSMENT

1. **Key Term** Define concession.

2. **Map Skills Location** Describe the locations of countries conquered earliest by Europeans.

3. **Critical Thinking Drawing Conclusions** How did European imperialism impact cultural change in East Asia and the Pacific world?

634 Chapter 30 ▪ Regional Atlas: East Asia and the Pacific World

---

RESOURCE DIRECTORY

Teaching Resources

Unit 9, Chapter 30
• Regional Atlas Study Guide, p. 2

Guide to the Essentials (English/Spanish)
• Chapter 30 Summary

Mental Mapping booklet
• Unit 9 Checklist, p. 115
• Outline Map 30A, p. 116

Social Studies Skills Handbook
• Reading a Political Map, p. 19

Technology

Guided Reading Audiotapes (English/Spanish), Chapter 30

Section Reading Support Transparencies, Chapter 30

World Geography Map and Photo Transparencies
• East Asia and the Pacific World: Maps and Photos

Book on CD, Chapter 30

World Geography Videos
• Regional Atlas: East Asia and the Pacific World, Tape 4

REGIONAL ATLAS

East Asia and the Pacific World: POLITICAL

KAZAKHSTAN

RUSSIA

Sea of Okhotsk

KYRGYZSTAN

TAJIKISTAN

Ulan Bator

MONGOLIA

PAKISTAN

Hokkaido

Sea of Japan

Huang He

Beijing

N. KOREA

P'yŏngyang

Seoul

JAPAN

Honshu

Tokyo

(Yellow R.)

S. KOREA

NEPAL

BHUTAN

Lhasa

CHINA

Xi'an

Yellow Sea

Osaka

Shikoku

Shanghai

Kyushu

INDIA

Yangzi R.

East China Sea

BANGLADESH

Okinawa

Taipei

Ryukyu Islands

Tropic of Cancer

MYANMAR (BURMA)

Macao

TAIWAN

Bay of Bengal

Yangon

LAOS

Hanoi

Vientiane

Hainan

Hong Kong

South China Sea

PACIFIC OCEAN

THAILAND

Gulf of Tonkin

Luzon

Bangkok

VIETNAM

CAMBODIA

Manila

PHILIPPINES

Philippine Sea

Phnom Penh

Ho Chi Minh City

Strait of Malacca

Sulu Sea

Mindanao

0   500   1,000 mi

0   500   1,000 km

BRUNEI

Bandar Seri Begawan

Celebes Sea

Kuala Lumpur

MALAYSIA

SINGAPORE

Singapore

Equator

Sumatra

Borneo

Celebes

INDIAN OCEAN

I N D O N E S I A

Moluccas

PAPUA NEW GUINEA

SOLOMON ISLANDS

Jakarta

Java

Java Sea

Banda Sea

Flores

New Guinea

Honiara

Bali

EAST TIMOR

Arafura Sea

Port Moresby

Timor Sea

Gulf of Carpentaria

Coral Sea

VANUATU

Port-Vila

Tropic of Capricorn

NEW CALEDONIA (FR.)

Noumea

AUSTRALIA

Brisbane

Lake Eyre

Perth

Great Australian Bight

Darling R.

Sydney

Lachlan R.

Murray R.

Canberra

Tasman Sea

Auckland

NEW ZEALAND

Melbourne

Bass Strait

Wellington

110°E   120°E   130°E   140°E   170°E   180°

KEY

— National boundary

⊛ National capital

• Other city

Lambert Azimuthal Equal-Area Projection

MENTAL MAPPING

Making a Political Map Study this political map and then draw your own sketch map of East Asia and the Pacific world. Label the countries and major cities of the region. Use various colors to outline and shade each country.

Chapter 30 ▪ Regional Atlas: East Asia and the Pacific World   **635**

LESSON PLAN

1. Focus Ask small groups to review the maps and photos in the Regional Atlas and discuss the places they would like to visit.

2. Instruct Have students complete the Mental Mapping activities and answer the Photo Caption questions in each section of the Regional Atlas. Go over the answers as a class.

3. Close/Reteach Assign groups an area in the region. Give each group index cards and have students write 10 questions and answers about their area. Instruct groups to swap cards and answer the questions.

Map Study Extension

Use the question below to develop an additional geographic theme.

Movement Singapore's location at the junction of important trade routes has helped it become one of the world's busiest ports. Ask: **Between which two oceans is Singapore situated?** (Indian and Pacific)

Unit Checklist Distribute the Unit 9 Checklist on page 115 of the Mental Mapping booklet in the Teaching Resources.

Making a Political Map Students can complete the mapping activity on this page by sketching their own maps or by coloring and labeling the Chapter 30A Outline Map on page 116 of the Mental Mapping booklet. Ask students to label all of the countries and major cities listed under Part I of the Unit 9 Checklist.

Alternative Assessment

Introduce the Activity

Creating a Map You may wish to distribute the Map Rubric found on page 14 of the Alternative Assessment booklet in the Prentice Hall Assessment System.

TEACHING TIP
From A Master Teacher

Environment and Society The interplay between societies and the environments in which they live provides a useful theme with which to study East Asia and the Pacific. Throughout the region, people live close to the edge of survival, depending upon an environment under stress from the growing population. At the same time, the volatile nature of the region's environments affects the population. Earthquakes, volcanic eruptions, tsunamis, typhoons, and other natural hazards shape the lives of millions of people.

Map Study Extension

Use the questions below to develop additional geographic themes.

1. Place Australia is the flattest continent. Along its eastern edge, however, stretches a line of hills and mountains. Much of Australia west of this range is arid plain or dry plateau. East of the range the climate is moist. Ask: **What is the name of the mountain range that prevents moisture from reaching most of the Australian interior?** (Great Dividing Range)

2. Movement Rivers are an important means of transportation in China. Ask: **What three rivers extend far into the Chinese interior?** (Mekong, Huang He, Yangzi)

Answers to Assessment

1. Indonesia, Papua New Guinea, Australia, New Zealand

2. northeast

Physical Characteristics

The collision of the Eurasian and Indian tectonic plates has raised the Himalayas, the Plateau of Tibet, the Kunlun Shan, the Altun Shan, and the Tian Shan. Southeast Asia has a complex geography of mountain chains, river valleys, peninsulas, and islands. Farther to the southeast, Australia and New Zealand form blocks of continental crust that rise above the Pacific Ocean, which is dotted with volcanic islands.

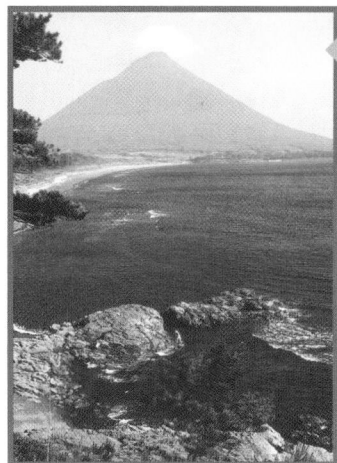

Volcanic Islands

Volcanic islands such as Kyushu, Japan, surround East and Southeast Asia. Volcanic islands such as Kyushu form part of the Ring of Fire—a fringe of volcanic and earthquake-related activity that surrounds the Pacific Ocean. **PHYSICAL CHARACTERISTICS** *Based on this description and the map, which islands besides Kyushu would you expect to have volcanoes?*

Mekong River

Powerful rivers such as the Mekong, shown here in Laos, have carved valleys through the highlands of East and Southeast Asia. River valleys often contain fertile land for farming. **PHYSICAL CHARACTERISTICS** *What other river valleys can you identify on the map?*

Desert Landforms

With few permanent bodies of water, the continent of Australia is largely arid. Wind erosion shapes desert landforms such as the Pinnacles, shown here. **PHYSICAL CHARACTERISTICS** *Based on the map, where else might you expect to find desert landforms?*

ASSESSMENT

1. **Map Skills Location** Which countries in this region lie south of the Equator?

2. **Critical Thinking Analyzing Processes** In which direction do you think the Indian plate is moving in order to create mountains in the interior of East Asia?

Answers to Photo Captions

Volcanic Islands Hokkaido, Honshu, Shikoku, Taiwan, the Philippines, and the islands of Indonesia

Mekong River Irrawaddy, Red, Yangzi, Huang He, Songhua, Liao, Tarim, Amur, Yalu, Darling, Lachlan, and Murray river valleys

Desert Landforms China and Mongolia

REGIONAL ATLAS

East Asia and the Pacific World: PHYSICAL

KAZAKHSTAN

KYRGYZSTAN

TAJIKISTAN TIEN SHAN

PAKISTAN

TAKLA MAKAN DESERT

ALTUN SHAN

KUNLUN SHAN

PLATEAU OF TIBET

NEPAL Lhasa

INDIA

Mt. Everest
29,035 ft
(8,850 m) BHUTAN

BANGLADESH

MYANMAR
(BURMA)

Bay
of
Bengal Yangon

THAILAND

Bangkok

Phnom
Penh

Strait of Malacca

Malay
Peninsula

Kuala Lumpur

MALAYSIA

SINGAPORE
Singapore

Sumatra

INDIAN
OCEAN

Jakarta

Java

Bali

ALTAI MTS.

KHANGAI MTS.

Ulan Bator

MONGOLIA

GOBI DESERT

Beijing

CHINA Xi'an NORTH
CHINA
PLAIN

SICHUAN
BASIN

Yangzi

YUNNAN PLATEAU

Hanoi

LAOS

Vientiane Hainan

Gulf
of Tonkin

VIETNAM

CAMBODIA

Ho Chi Minh City

BRUNEI

Bandar Seri Begawan

I N D O N E S I A

Java Sea

RUSSIA

GREATER KHINGAN RANGE

Songhua

Liao R.

Yalu R.

Huang He (Yellow River)

P'yongyang

N. KOREA

Seoul S. KOREA

Shandong
Peninsula

Yellow
Sea

Shanghai

Macao

Hong Kong

South
China
Sea

Luzon

Manila PHILIPPINES

Sulu
Sea

Celebes
Sea

Celebes

Flores

Timor

Amur R.

Sea
of
Okhotsk

Hokkaido

Sea
of
Japan

Honshu

JAPAN Tokyo

Osaka

Shikoku

Kyushu

East
China
Sea

Okinawa

Taipei

TAIWAN

Ryukyu Islands

Mindanao

Philippine
Sea

Banda
Sea

Moluccas

PAPUA
NEW GUINEA

Arafura
Sea

Timor
Sea

Cape
York
Peninsula

Gulf of
Carpentaria

PACIFIC
OCEAN

SOLOMON
ISLANDS

Honiara

Port
Moresby

Coral
Sea

Tropic of Cancer

Equator

KEY

Elevation	
Feet	Meters
14,000	4,270
7,000	2,135
1,500	457
700	213
(sea level) 0	0 (sea level)

• Major city
▲ Mountain

Lambert Azimuthal Equal-Area Projection

0 — 500 — 1,000 mi
0 — 500 — 1,000 km

VANUATU
Port-Vila

NEW
CALEDONIA
(FR.) Noumea

AUSTRALIA

GREAT SANDY
DESERT

GIBSON
DESERT

MACDONNELL
RANGES

SIMPSON
DESERT

Lake
Eyre

Perth

Great
Australian Bight

Tropic of Capricorn

GREAT DIVIDING RANGE

Great Barrier Reef

Brisbane

Darling R.

Lachlan R.

Murray R.

Sydney

Canberra

Melbourne

Tasman
Sea

Bass Strait

Mt. Cook
12,316 ft
(3,754 m)

Auckland

NEW
ZEALAND

Taupo

Wellington

SOUTHERN ALPS

MENTAL MAPPING

Making a Physical Map Study this physical map and then draw your own sketch map of East Asia and the Pacific world. Label the major physical features, including rivers and other bodies of water.

MENTAL MAPPING

Mapping Physical Features Students can complete the mapping activity on this page either by adding labels to the political maps they have completed or by coloring and labeling the Chapter 30B and 30C Outline Maps on pages 117 and 118 of the Mental Mapping booklet in the Teaching Resources. Ask students to label all of the bodies of water and landforms listed under Part II of the Unit 9 Checklist.

BACKGROUND

The Physical World

Volcanoes The 1991 eruption of Mt. Pinatubo in the Philippines was one of the most powerful volcanic eruptions in the twentieth century. Ashes and hot lava covered entire towns and destroyed crops. Falling ash and debris killed more than 700 people and left at least 100,000 homeless.

BACKGROUND

The Physical World

Natural Phenomena A large red sandstone formation in the center of Australia's vast desert, known as Uluru, or Ayers Rock, is the world's largest monolith. Stretching almost 1.5 miles (2.4 km) and rising to 1,100 feet (335 m), this rock appears to change color at sunrise and sunset, when it becomes fiery orange-red. Uluru is sacred to Australia's indigenous people, the Aborigines.

Articles From
NATIONAL GEOGRAPHIC

The following article may be used to extend the content in this Regional Atlas.

O'Neill, Thomas, and Michael S. Yamashita, photographer. "The Mekong—A Haunted River's Season of Peace." *National Geographic,* Vol. 183, No. 1 (Feb. 1993), pp. 2–35.

Travel the twelfth longest river in the world, the Mekong, as it flows 2,600 miles from the snowy interior of China to the South China Sea.

CUSTOMIZE FOR...

Gifted and Talented

Building Mountains Note that the great mountains of East Asia's Himalayan range were formed by tectonic activity. Ask student pairs to research this physical process. Instruct pairs to use materials of their own choosing to build models that illustrate the formation of the Himalayas. Models should clearly show the various layers of the earth's crust and the action of colliding plates.

Map Study Extension

Use the questions below to develop additional geographic themes.

1. Region Rice, which requires large amounts of water to grow, is East Asia's staple food crop. Ask: **Where would you expect rice to be grown in East Asia? Why?** (Rice is grown throughout most of Southeast Asia, Japan, the Koreas, and eastern and southern China because these areas have tropical wet, tropical wet and dry, and humid subtropical climates, which receive plenty of rain.)

2. Place Unlike Australia, which is an island of many climates, New Zealand primarily has one type. Ask: **What climate dominates New Zealand?** (marine west coast)

3. Location Tell students to compare the climate map on page 639 with the climate map of the United States and Canada on page 131. Ask: **What generalizations can be made about 40°N latitude in Japan, Eastern China, and the eastern half of the United States?** (All three areas are mainly humid subtropical and humid continental.)

Answers to Assessment

1. mainly between 1,500 and 7,000 feet (457–2,135 meters)

2. Winds that blow over water take on the water's temperature. These winds moderate land temperatures as they blow onshore. Such areas often have milder, more stable climates than other areas that are at the same latitude but are far from a large body of water.

Climates

Across much of this region, rain falls seasonally. Summer monsoons bring rain to much of East Asia and to the tropical wet and dry climate regions of Southeast Asia and northern Australia. The Mediterranean and marine west coast climates of southern Australia and New Zealand tend to have heavier winter rainfall.

City/Country	Average January Temperature (°F)	Average July Temperature (°F)
Bangkok, Thailand	79	83
Beijing, China	24	79
Jakarta, Indonesia	79	81
Sydney, Australia	72	53
Tokyo, Japan	41	77
Ulan Bator, Mongolia	−12	62

Sources: www.weather.com; www.worldclimate.com

Seasonal Temperatures

Cities in the tropics have little seasonal temperature change. Temperate coastal locations show modest temperature swings. Places farther inland and farther from the Equator have greater seasonal variation. **CLIMATES** *Why might distance from the ocean affect the temperature variation of a location?*

Tropical Climates

South of the Equator, monsoons in Southeast Asia generally peak around January. To the north, July is usually the peak monsoon season. Heavy downpours occur during typhoons—tropical storms known as hurricanes in the Americas. **CLIMATES** *During which months would you expect the heaviest average rainfall in Manila?*

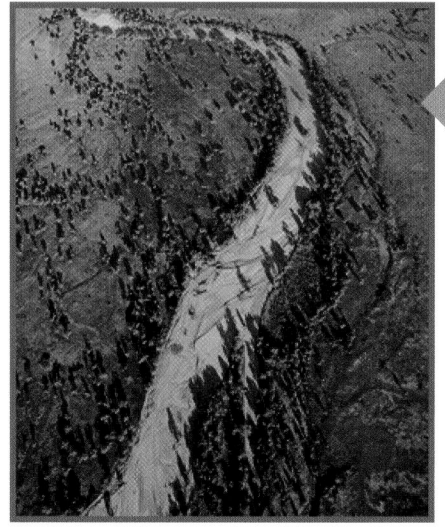

Dry Climates

Arid and semiarid climates cover most of Australia, where many rivers and lakes become full after heavy rains and then dry up in the burning sun. **CLIMATES** *Based on the map, what parts of Asia have arid or semiarid climates?*

ASSESSMENT

1. **Map Skills Place** Compare this map with the physical map on page 637. At what elevations are the region's deserts found?

2. **Critical Thinking Developing a Hypothesis** Why might coastal locations show less seasonal variation in temperature than other locations?

Answers to Photo Captions

Seasonal Temperatures Land and water absorb and store heat at very different rates. Land temperatures can have great extremes, while water temperatures vary much less and tend to moderate coastal temperatures.

Tropical Climates the summer months

Dry Climates northern and central East Asia

RESOURCE DIRECTORY

Teaching Resources
Social Studies Skills Handbook
• Reading a Climate Map, p. 26

Technology
World Geography Map and Photo Transparencies
• East Asia and the Pacific World: Maps and Photos

REGIONAL ATLAS

East Asia and the Pacific World: CLIMATE REGIONS

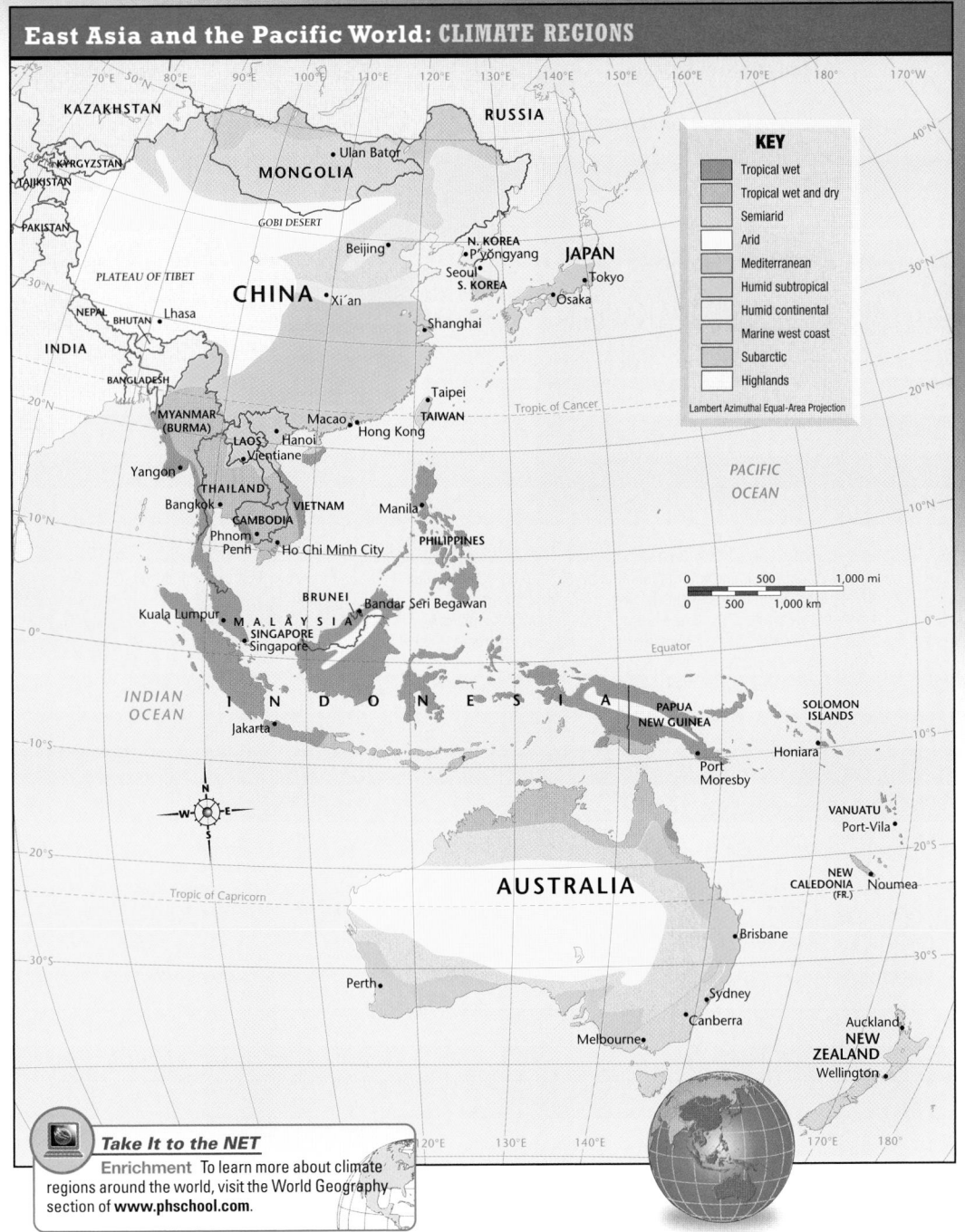

KEY

- Tropical wet
- Tropical wet and dry
- Semiarid
- Arid
- Mediterranean
- Humid subtropical
- Humid continental
- Marine west coast
- Subarctic
- Highlands

Lambert Azimuthal Equal-Area Projection

0   500   1,000 mi
0   500   1,000 km

Take It to the NET
Enrichment To learn more about climate regions around the world, visit the World Geography section of **www.phschool.com**.

Chapter 30 ▪ Regional Atlas: East Asia and the Pacific World **639**

BACKGROUND

The Physical World

Typhoons A typhoon is potentially one of nature's most devastating storms. The low pressure, high winds, tidal surge, heavy rains, and floods associated with a typhoon can exact a great toll on human life. Originating in the warm Pacific waters, these storms track westward across the Philippines toward China's coast before turning northeast to cross South Korea or Japan. One of the strongest typhoons to hit the Pacific Islands in recent years, Typhoon Utor, struck the northern half of the Philippine Islands in July 2001, with peak winds of 100 miles per hour (150 km/h). The storm resulted in mudslides, landslides, and downed power lines. Over 120 people were killed, and about 12,000 homes were damaged or destroyed.

ACTIVITY

Group Work

Activity: Creating an advertisement

Purpose: Arrange students in pairs and assign each pair a city chosen from the various climate zones on the map. Tell students they own a clothing and accessories store in that city. Instruct student pairs to create an illustrated newspaper advertisement showing how certain items sold in their store equip customers for the local weather.

Roles: Writers and illustrators

Result: Display advertisements in the classroom.

Ecosystems

This region is home to a rich variety of plants and animals in many different environments. Forests include the coniferous forests of the far north and mountains, mid-latitude forests of deciduous trees, and the rain forests of the tropics. Grasslands cover drier interior regions, while scrub and sparse vegetation grow in the deserts. Each of these plant communities supports a community of animal wildlife.

Tropical Rain Forests
High average temperatures and high rainfall produce tropical rain forests, such as this forest in Malaysia. These forests line the coasts of northern Australia and East and Southeast Asia. **ECOSYSTEMS** *What conditions might keep tropical rain forests from growing in the interior of Australia or Mongolia?*

Grasslands
Grasslands cover large parts of interior China and Mongolia. They are home to grazing animals, including these wild horses. Australian grasslands support kangaroos and other species. **ECOSYSTEMS** *What domestic animals do you think that temperate grasslands might support?*

Deciduous Forests
Parts of East Asia, Australia, and New Zealand have forests of deciduous trees. Japanese deciduous forests such as this one on Miyajima Island are home to bears, wild monkeys, and other animals. **ECOSYSTEMS** *Which Asian countries have deciduous forests?*

ASSESSMENT

1. **Map Skills Regions** What type of ecosystem covers most of the islands of Southeast Asia?

2. **Critical Thinking Interpreting Maps** Compare this map with the climates map on page 639. What is the most common ecosystem in the highland and semiarid regions of China?

REGIONAL ATLAS

East Asia and the Pacific World: ECOSYSTEMS

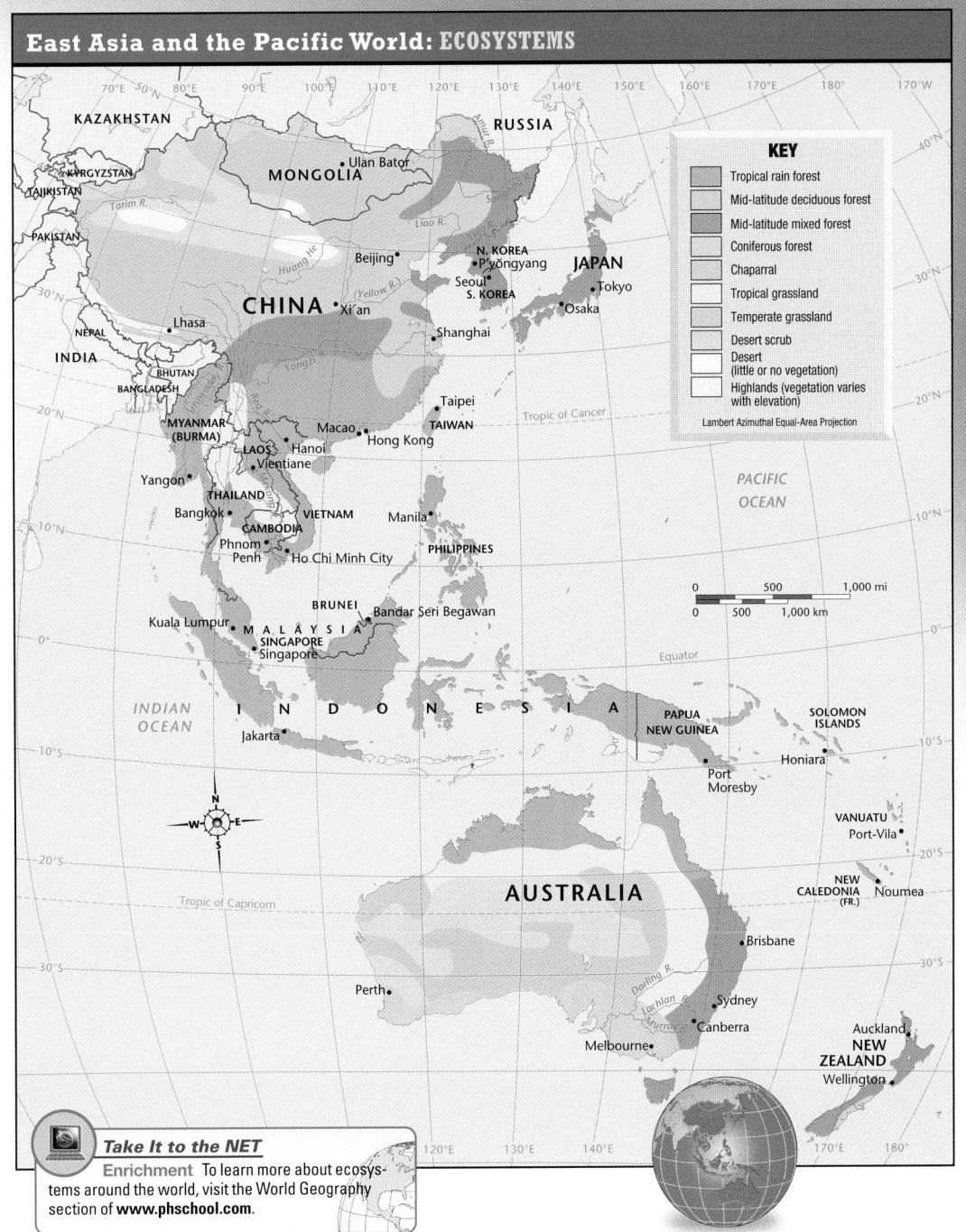

KEY

- Tropical rain forest
- Mid-latitude deciduous forest
- Mid-latitude mixed forest
- Coniferous forest
- Chaparral
- Tropical grassland
- Temperate grassland
- Desert scrub
- Desert (little or no vegetation)
- Highlands (vegetation varies with elevation)

Lambert Azimuthal Equal-Area Projection

Take It to the NET

Enrichment To learn more about ecosystems around the world, visit the World Geography section of **www.phschool.com**.

Chapter 30 ▪ Regional Atlas: East Asia and the Pacific World **641**

Take It to the NET

Enrichment To learn more about ecosystems around the world, visit the World Geography section of **www.phschool.com**.

ACTIVITY

Enrichment

Creating Animal Data Sheets Assign each student one of these four areas to conduct research on native animals: China and Mongolia, Japan and the Koreas, Southeast Asia, or Australia and New Zealand. Have students collect photos and data on individual species' physical characteristics, habitats, behavior patterns, and possible endangered status. Instruct students to prepare a data sheet for each species. Bind the sheets into a notebook of regional fauna. (Verbal/Linguistic)

BACKGROUND

Environmental Issues

Threats to the Grasslands Overgrazing, by livestock or by wild animals, can wreak havoc on grassland ecosystems. Overgrazing in northern China has increased desertification so severely that sandstorm forecasts have become part of Chinese television broadcasts. In Australia, rabbits introduced by Europeans in the mid-1800s have diminished vegetation on grazing lands. They have also caused the extinction of some native animals that were unable to compete with the rabbits for food or burrows.

Map Study Extension

Use the questions below to develop additional geographic themes.

1. Regions Throughout East Asia and the Pacific World, the population is unevenly distributed. Ask: **What countries are the least densely populated?** (Mongolia, Papua New Guinea, Australia, New Zealand, and the majority of Indonesia)

2. Human-Environment Interaction Tell students to compare the population density map with the physical and climate maps. Point out that in East Asia the areas of dense population match lowland areas that have mild and wet climates. Ask: **Why does much of western China have a low population density?** (The western part of China is mountainous and arid.)

Answers to Assessment

1. most densely populated: Java, Bali, Sumatra; least densely populated: Borneo, Flores, Timor, Celebes, the Moluccas, New Guinea

2. Buddhism and Islam

People and Cultures

East and Southeast Asia are some of the most heavily populated parts of the world, with about 2 billion inhabitants. China alone has a population of over 1 billion, concentrated on the north-central plains, on the southern coast of eastern China, and in the Yangtze River valley. To the south, Australia is the world's most sparsely inhabited continent, with its population concentrated in a very small portion of the nation. The many peoples of these regions have remarkably diverse cultures.

KEY
Buddhism
Buddhism and Shinto
Buddhism and Daoism
Islam
Christianity
Traditional religions

Lambert Azimuthal Equal-Area Projection

Religious Diversity

The variety of religions in East Asia reflects the region's great cultural diversity. As this map shows, religious boundaries do not conform to national borders. **CULTURES** *What are the major religions of the Philippines?*

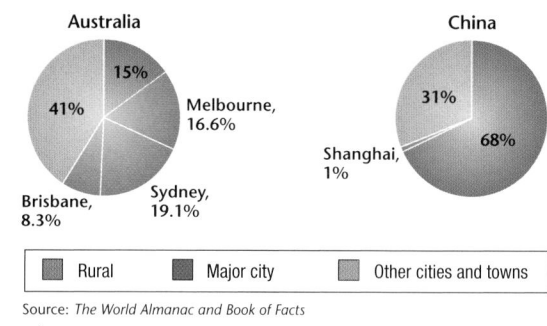

Australia
15%
41%
Melbourne, 16.6%
Brisbane, 8.3%
Sydney, 19.1%

China
31%
68%
Shanghai, 1%

■ Rural   ■ Major city   ■ Other cities and towns

Source: *The World Almanac and Book of Facts*

Urban and Rural Populations

Although China's large population is densely settled, almost three quarters of its population is rural. In contrast, even though Australia is sparsely populated, 85 percent of its people live in cities. **PATTERNS OF SETTLEMENT** *Based on these charts and the map, where is the population of Australia concentrated?*

Cultural Convergence

In cities around the world, daily life is often a blend of local culture and international influence. **GLOBAL TRADE PATTERNS** *How can trade affect a region's culture?*

ASSESSMENT

1. **Map Skills Place** What are the most densely and least densely populated parts of Indonesia?

2. **Critical Thinking Interpreting Maps** Compare the maps of religions and population density in East Asia. Which religions would you expect to have the most believers in this region?

Answers to Photo Captions

Religious Diversity Christianity and Islam

Urban and Rural Populations in the urban areas along the coast

Cultural Convergence Trade introduces different cultures to a region, which may influence the existing culture of that region.

RESOURCE DIRECTORY

Teaching Resources
Creative Teaching Activities, Historical and Cultural Landmarks, pp. 30–32
Social Studies Skills Handbook
• Reading a Population Density Map, p. 31

Technology
World Geography Map and Photo Transparencies
• East Asia and the Pacific World: Maps and Photos

REGIONAL ATLAS

East Asia and the Pacific World: POPULATION DENSITY

KEY

Persons per sq mi	Persons per sq km
520 and over	200 and over
260–519	100–199
130–259	50–99
25–129	10–49
1–24	1–9
Less than 1	Less than 1

Metropolitan areas
- ☐ 10,000,000 and over
- ■ 5,000,000–9,999,999
- ◯ 2,000,000–4,999,999
- ◉ 1,000,000–1,999,999
- • 250,000–999,999
- ◦ Less than 250,000

Lambert Azimuthal Equal-Area Projection

GET THE FACTS . . .
Go to the **Table of Countries** at the back of this book for additional population data.

Group Work

Activity: Creating murals
Purpose: Show two pictures: a suburban neighborhood and an inner-city neighborhood. Discuss the adaptations made in each setting to the different amounts of available space (size of houses and lots, number of cars). Divide students into small groups and explain that half of the groups will do research on how the Chinese have adapted to population density and the other half will do research on Japanese adaptations to population density. Then have groups create murals to show what they have learned. (Topics covered could include housing, education, work, customs, transportation, and law.)
Roles: Researchers and artists
Result: Exhibit murals in the classroom.

BACKGROUND

Daily Life

Religion It is thought that missionaries and traders introduced Buddhism to China from India around A.D. 100. During the 300s, Buddhism became firmly established in China. The religion taught strict moral standards and was accepted by the Chinese because of its emphasis on personal behavior. The Chinese integrated Buddhism into their traditional belief systems— Taoism and Confucianism. In this way, strains of Buddhism that are particular to China developed.

ACTIVITY

Area Comparison

Using the Table of Countries Ask students to use the Table of Countries beginning on page 742 of their textbooks to compare the land areas and populations of the United States and China. **Connections: Math** Ask: **Which country will have the greater population density in the year 2025?** (While the land area of China and the United States is roughly the same, China's population in 2025 is projected to be more than four times greater than that of the United States. Therefore, China will have a much higher population density.)

TEST PREPARATION

Have students use the map on this page to answer the following question.
Which country in this region would most likely be interested in resettling people in its western lands because of extreme crowding in the east?
- **A** Australia
- **B** Japan
- **C** Laos
- **Ⓓ** China

Map Study Extension

Use the questions below to develop additional geographic themes.

1. Human-Environment Interaction Rain forests cover large areas of China and Southeast Asia but they are rapidly being cleared. Have students compare the ecosystems map on page 641 to the economic activities map on the opposite page. Ask: **How is most of the land in China's and Southeast Asia's rain forest regions being used?** (Most of the land is being used for farming—commercial farming in China and subsistence farming in Southeast Asia.)

2. Place Several nations in East Asia and the Pacific World rely on sales of oil to help fund development. Ask: **What nations in East Asia and the Pacific World produce petroleum?** (Malaysia, Brunei, Indonesia, China, Myanmar, and Australia)

Answers to Assessment

1. (a) intensive farming, p. 644
(b) terrace, p. 644

2. North Korea, Papua New Guinea, and Australia

3. Environmental damage in such a region could reduce or poison food and water supplies, leading to starvation or sickness.

Answers to Photo Captions

Dam Construction China

Intensive Agriculture In densely populated areas there is little land, so farmers use intensive farming to make the most out of every piece of available land.

Industry Japan, China, and Australia

Economics, Technology, and Environment

Sharp contrasts mark the economies and environments of East Asia and the Pacific world. Highly industrialized urban areas in Japan and Australia exist alongside large populations of subsistence farmers in China and Southeast Asia. The interior of East Asia includes large areas devoted to nomadic herding and desert areas with little economic activity. In many countries, rapid economic development has caused pollution and other environmental harm.

Dam Construction

Economic development in China has included projects such as the Three Gorges Dam on the Yangtze River, which will produce hydroelectricity. Many people oppose the project because it may cause pollution and harm downstream economic activities. **SCIENCE AND TECHNOLOGY** *Based on the map, which country has the most hydroelectric facilities?*

Intensive Agriculture

East and Southeast Asians practice **intensive farming,** which is farming that requires much labor, to produce food. To use all available land, farmers in hilly areas have reshaped the land into **terraces,** or level, narrow ledges. **ECONOMIC ACTIVITIES** *Why might farmers in densely populated regions use labor-intensive methods?*

Industry

East Asia is one of the world's industrial powerhouses. East Asian products, such as these gas ranges manufactured in Korea, are exported around the world. **ECONOMIC ACTIVITIES** *Based on the map, which countries have substantial areas devoted to manufacturing and trade?*

ASSESSMENT

1. **Key Terms** Define **(a)** intensive farming, **(b)** terrace.

2. **Map Skills Location** Which countries have gold deposits?

3. **Critical Thinking Predicting Consequences** What dangers might environmental damage pose in a region where large populations rely on limited land areas for food and water?

RESOURCE DIRECTORY

Teaching Resources
Mental Mapping booklet
• Atlas Activity, p. 119
Social Studies Skills Handbook
• Reading an Economic Activity Map, p. 27
• Reading a Natural Resources Map, p. 34
• Using the Map Key, p. 3
• Reading a Cartogram, p. 67

Technology
World Geography Map and Photo Transparencies
• East Asia and the Pacific World: Maps and Photos

REGIONAL ATLAS

East Asia and the Pacific World: **ECONOMIC ACTIVITIES AND RESOURCES**

KEY

Nomadic herding	Hydroelectric power
Hunting and gathering	Copper
Livestock raising	Bauxite
Commercial farming	Iron
Subsistence farming	Silver
Manufacturing and trade	Phosphates
Commercial fishing	Lead
Little or no activity	Tin
Coal	Nickel
Petroleum	Tungsten
	Gold
	Uranium

Lambert Azimuthal Equal-Area Projection

PACIFIC OCEAN

Tropic of Cancer

INDIAN OCEAN

Equator

Tropic of Capricorn

0   500   1,000 mi
0   500   1,000 km

Take It to the NET
Enrichment To learn more about the economic activities and resources of this region, visit the World Geography section of **www.phschool.com**.

Chapter 30 ▪ Regional Atlas: East Asia and the Pacific World **645**

The Global Economy

World Trade On the northern coast of Borneo is Brunei, one of the smallest and most unusual countries in East Asia. Independent since 1984, Brunei is an Islamic, oil-exporting country ruled by a sultan who is reputedly one of the wealthiest people in the world. Its high per capita GDP is supported by export earnings from oil shipped primarily to Japan, South Korea, Singapore, and the European community. Although the coastal area is wealthy and urban, the interior is a subsistence agricultural region, so that Brunei must import 70 percent of its food.

GLOBAL CONNECTIONS

Science and Technology

The Question of Dams The construction of dams is controversial in many parts of the world. Protests against new dam building have recently erupted in Turkey and India. China's Three Gorges Dam has also been controversial. While providing beneficial water for the lands nearby, dams can have several negative effects. In addition to flooding human settlements, dams can harm river ecosystems and erode soil and vegetation. The United States, which has more than 100,000 dams, is considering a program of dam removal to restore some of its rivers.

Database:
Comparing Transportation
pp. 646–647

Objectives
Upon completion of this lesson, students should be able to:

◆ discuss how a nation's economy, population, and geographic size influence the development of its transportation system;

◆ compare the transportation systems in China, Japan, Australia, Thailand, and the United States.

National Geography Standards
The following National Geography Standards are highlighted in this feature: 4, 9, 11, 18

Bellringer
Ask students to complete this sentence: "Of all the countries in East Asia and the Pacific, China's transportation needs are the greatest because—" (Possible answer: It has the largest population.)

LESSON PLAN

1. Focus After the class has read the introductory paragraph on this page, ask volunteers to list on the board three factors that determine the status of a nation's transportation system. (population, geographic size, wealth)

2. Instruct Arrange students into teams. Each team will write five comparison statements based on data from the five tables. For example, Australia has 54 more motor vehicles per thousand people than Japan. Have teams take turns reading their five statements to the competing team, which responds by identifying which of the three factors—population, geographic size, or relative wealth of a country—relates to the statistic.

3. Close/Reteach Have each team create five political cartoons, each depicting the status of transportation in the countries featured in this Regional Database.

EAST ASIA AND THE PACIFIC WORLD
Database: Comparing Transportation

By comparing the data below, you will learn how transportation systems differ among countries. You will see how the population, geographic size, and relative wealth of each country affect its transportation system. Keep these differences in mind when you compare the East Asian and Pacific world countries with the United States.

Sources: *Encarta World Atlas; The World Factbook*

Key Term: **bullet train**

GET THE FACTS . . .
Go to the Table of Countries at the back of this book to view additional data for the countries of East Asia and the Pacific world.

Take It to the NET
Data Update For the most recent update of this database, visit the World Geography section of **www.phschool.com**.

China

Railroad Track Length		41,932 miles
Highways	Total length:	869,400 miles
	Paved length:	168,477 miles
	Unpaved length:	700,923 miles
Airports	Total:	489
	With paved runways:	324
	With unpaved runways:	165
Motor Vehicles per 1,000 People		8.2

China's road and railroad networks are larger than those of the other countries considered here, with the exception of the United States. China covers an area about as large as the United States, and China's population is more than four times larger than that of the United States. As a result, China's railroads and roads are often overcrowded. Because there are about eight motor vehicles per 1,000 people, many Chinese rely on bicycles. China's relative poverty explains the lack of both motor vehicles and airports.

Japan

Railroad Track Length		14,689 miles
Highways	Total length:	715,521 miles
	Paved length:	535,925 miles
	Unpaved length:	179,596 miles
Airports	Total:	173
	With paved runways:	142
	With unpaved runways:	31
Motor Vehicles per 1,000 People		560

Even though Japan's land area is only about 4 percent that of China, its road network is almost as large. Japan's railroad system includes the reliable **bullet train,** which travels at speeds greater than 160 miles per hour. Japan has 560 motor vehicles per 1,000 people, far more than China. The wealth of Japan's population explains these differences.

RESOURCE DIRECTORY

Teaching Resources
Unit 9, Chapter 30
• Regional Atlas Review, p. 3
• Regional Atlas Database Skills, p. 4
• Test Forms A and B, pp. 5–10

Spanish Resources
• Regional Atlas Review, p. 76

Guide to the Essentials (English/Spanish)
• Chapter 30 Test

Mental Mapping booklet
• Chapter 30 Map Test, p. 120

Simulations, Games, and Lab Activities
• Place Location Review Games, pp. 58–63

Social Studies Skills Handbook
• Study and Research Skills, pp. 94–108

Prentice Hall Assessment System
Alternative Assessment booklet
• Map Evaluation Form, p. 15

Technology
ExamView Test Bank CD-ROM, Chapter 30 Test
Companion Web site, www.phschool.com
• Chapter 30 Self-Test

REGIONAL ATLAS

Australia

Railroad Track Length		21,002 miles
Highways	Total length:	566,973 miles
	Paved length:	219,419 miles
	Unpaved length:	347,554 miles
Airports	Total:	421
	With paved runways:	282
	With unpaved runways:	139
Motor Vehicles per 1,000 People		601

Australia's road network is nearly as large as China's, and its railroad network is about half as large, despite a smaller area and a much smaller population. Many of Australia's airports are unpaved airstrips that serve isolated communities in the country's interior. Heavy air travel and motor vehicle use reflect both the long distances between cities in Australia and the country's wealth.

Thailand

Railroad Track Length		2,528 miles
Highways	Total length:	40,117 miles
	Paved length:	39,114 miles
	Unpaved length:	1,003 miles
Airports	Total:	110
	With paved runways:	59
	With unpaved runways:	51
Motor Vehicles per 1,000 People		104

With 104 vehicles per 1,000 people, Thailand's small road network is very crowded. Huge traffic jams tie up its big cities, especially Bangkok. Thailand is a major tourist destination in the region, and its 110 airports primarily serve that industry. Its reliance on air and motor vehicle travel shows that Thailand's population is wealthier than China's but less wealthy than that of Australia or Japan.

ASSESSMENT

1. **Key Term** Define bullet train.

2. **Patterns of Settlement** How have Australia's settlement patterns affected its transportation system?

3. **Economic Systems** How can differences in transportation systems reflect differences in wealth?

4. **Critical Thinking Predicting Consequences** If China becomes more prosperous, what changes might be expected in its transportation system?

United States

Railroad Track Length		131,920 miles
Highways	Total length:	3,955,789 miles
	Paved length:	3,560,210 miles
	Unpaved length:	395,579 miles
Airports	Total:	14,695
	With paved runways:	5,127
	With unpaved runways:	9,568
Motor Vehicles per 1,000 People		759

Chapter 30 ▪ Regional Atlas: East Asia and the Pacific World **647**

Games for Review See pages 58–63 of the Simulations, Games, and Lab Activities booklet in the Teaching Resources for games to review place names in preparation for the Chapter 30 Map Test.

Chapter Map Test Students should use the completed Chapter 30 outline maps and the Unit 9 Checklist to prepare for the Chapter 30 Map Test. Point out to students that the test will cover all of the countries, cities, bodies of water, and landforms listed on the Unit 9 Checklist.

 Alternative Assessment

Final Evaluation

Creating a Map Use the Map Evaluation Form on page 15 of the Alternative Assessment booklet in the Prentice Hall Assessment System to evaluate students' maps. Either teachers or students can complete the forms to indicate which level of work was achieved for each of the criteria.

Answers to Assessment

1. bullet train, p. 646

2. Because Australia's cities and the nation's wealth are separated by long distances and because many small communities are isolated in the country's interior, Australia has developed an extensive road and air travel network.

3. Little air travel and motor vehicle use may indicate that a nation's people cannot afford such transportation, whereas heavy air travel and motor vehicle use often mark wealthier nations.

4. With a more prosperous economy, China will likely increase its number of airports and expand its highways and its motor vehicle use.

Do-It-Yourself Skills

pp. 648–649

Objectives

Upon completion of this feature, students should be able to:

◆ explain the advantage of following a step-by-step process to solve problems;

◆ describe the five steps in the problem-solving process;

◆ use the process to solve a problem.

National Geography Standards

The following National Geography Standards are highlighted in this feature: 4, 13, 17, 18

Bellringer

Have students think about stories they have read in which a character solves a problem. Ask: **How does the character solve the problem?** Work together as a class to evaluate the effectiveness of the solution.

LESSON PLAN

1. Focus Ask students to read Step 1. Ask: **Can you think of a similar situation in which no one took action? What happened?** Then have them explain what might have happened in China and Japan.

2. Instruct As students brainstorm advantages and disadvantages of solutions, ask: **Does the solution actually solve the problem? Is it harmful or expensive? Is there a better or less expensive way to solve the problem?** Have students copy the table into their notebooks and include their responses to these questions.

3. Close/Reteach After students evaluate the effects of solutions chosen by China and Japan, ask them to explain what solution they would recommend to countries facing a similar problem. Have them explain their answers.

Do-It-Yourself Skills

Solving Problems

How Do We Solve Problems?

Some people just ignore problems and hope they will go away. This approach, however, usually fails. A better method is a step-by-step system. First, identify the problem. Next, gather information. Then, list options and consider their advantages and disadvantages. After doing this, choose and implement a solution. The final step is to evaluate the effects of the chosen solution.

How Can I Use This Skill?

Today, your problem might be how to prepare for two difficult school exams on the same day. Perhaps you need to help a friend who is unhappy. In the future, you may face problems as the head of a family or encounter problems at the workplace. As a citizen, you will have the power to help solve problems by voting and by participating in political and social organizations.

Step by Step

Study the problem, such as the one faced by China and Japan in the 1800s, as described below. Then, follow the steps to participate in the process of problem solving.

> ### A Problem for Japan and China
>
> In the 1800s, industrialized nations developed machinery and weapons that were superior to what the Japanese and Chinese had. Some industrialized nations used their new power to demand special trading privileges in Asia.

1 Identify the problem clearly and concisely. Determine the central issues of the problem, and state them as specifically as possible. For example, list what you think would have happened to China and Japan if they had taken no action in response to their problem.

2 Gather information about the problem. Identify as many of its causes as you can. Do research to increase your understanding of the situation. In this case, identify the kinds of machinery and weapons that the industrial powers had that China and Japan did not have.

RESOURCE DIRECTORY

Teaching Resources
Social Studies Skills Handbook
• Identifying Alternatives, p. 51

Technology
Social Studies Skills Tutor CD-ROM, Problem Solving

3 List and consider options. Identify advantages and disadvantages for each option. It is often a good idea to work with others to brainstorm as many alternatives as possible. You may also find it helpful to record your ideas in a concept chart or graphic organizer. Copy the graphic organizer at right. Add other possible options. For each option, fill in advantages and disadvantages.

4 Choose a solution by weighing the advantages and disadvantages of the various options. Identify the solution that seems to offer the most significant advantages and the least significant disadvantages. List specific steps for carrying out the chosen solution. Do research to learn what China and Japan did to implement their chosen solutions.

5 After a while, evaluate the effectiveness of the chosen solution. Consider whether conditions have improved or worsened as a result of the solution. If the situation did not significantly improve, you should start the problem-solving process again and try a different solution. Evaluate the effects of the solutions chosen by China and Japan. Determine if one or both nations should have reconsidered their options and chosen new solutions. Explain.

Options for Japan and China

OPTIONS	ADVANTAGES	DISADVANTAGES
1. Give in to demands of the industrialized powers	• Avoid conflict	• Native merchants lose profits to foreigners
2. Give in to demands, but also build new machines and weapons and pursue imperialism	•	•
3. Refuse the demands and reject much of the new technology	•	•

The Solutions and Their Effects

• After choosing option 3, China was defeated in several wars, first by Great Britain and then by Japan. Foreign nations gained special privileges in China. Today, China has a Communist government and is still struggling to become a leading industrial power.

• After choosing option 2, Japan quickly became an industrial, military, and imperialist power. After suffering defeat in World War II, Japan demilitarized. Today, it remains one of the world's leading industrial powers.

TIP

Be Willing to Reconsider

People sometimes make the mistake of not evaluating solutions after implementing them. Sticking with a poor solution too long often leads to additional problems.

APPLY YOUR SKILL

Review the chapters in this unit. Find a problem that faces one or more of the countries in the region. Using the steps in this lesson, identify the problem and analyze possible solutions to the problem. Identify which alternative seems best to you, and predict results.

Chapter 30 649

Resource Manager

Chapter-Level Resources	CORE INSTRUCTION	READING/SKILLS
	Teaching Resources **Unit 9**/Ch. 31 • Reviewing Main Ideas, p. 19 **Mental Mapping booklet** • Unit 9 Checklist, p. 115 **Simulations, Games, and Lab Activities** • Place Location Review Games, pp. 58-63 **Creative Teaching Activities** • Asian Music, p. 33 **TeacherExpress™ CD-ROM**, Ch. 31 **Companion Web site, www.phschool.com** • eTeach	**Teaching Resources** **Unit 9**/Ch. 31 • Map/Graph Skills, p. 21 **Book on CD**, Ch. 31 **Social Studies Skills Tutor CD-ROM**
1 The Emergence of Modern China 1. Describe the results of China's early contacts with the West. 2. Identify internal conflicts that led to a Communist takeover. 3. Describe the purposes and results of the Great Leap Forward. 4. Explain how a series of modernizations attempted to change China.	**Teaching Resources** **Unit 9**/Ch. 31 • Guided Reading and Review, p. 11 **Prentice Hall Presentation Pro CD-ROM**, Ch. 31, Sec. 1	**Teaching Resources** **Guide to the Essentials (English/Spanish)** • Section Summary, Ch. 31, Sec. 1 **Guided Reading Audiotapes (English/Spanish)**, Ch. 31, Sec. 1 **Section Reading Support Transparencies**, Ch. 31, Sec. 1
2 Regions of China 1. Describe how China's Northeast region has served as the center of population, industry, and government. 2. Explain why the Southeast region of China is ideal for agriculture and transportation. 3. Explain how the Silk Road promoted development of China's barren Northwest region. 4. Identify how Communist rule has affected Southwestern China.	**Teaching Resources** **Unit 9**/Ch. 31 • Guided Reading and Review, p. 13 **Prentice Hall Presentation Pro CD-ROM**, Ch. 31, Sec. 2	**Teaching Resources** **Guide to the Essentials (English/Spanish)** • Section Summary, Ch. 31, Sec. 2 **Mental Mapping booklet** • Outline Map 31, p. 121 **Guided Reading Audiotapes (English/Spanish)**, Ch. 31, Sec. 2 **Section Reading Support Transparencies**, Ch. 31, Sec. 2
3 China's People and Culture 1. Describe how China's Communist government has changed its attitudes about population growth. 2. Identify the factors that create a common Chinese culture and encourage unity throughout China.	**Teaching Resources** **Unit 9**/Ch. 31 • Guided Reading and Review, p. 15 **Prentice Hall Presentation Pro CD-ROM**, Ch. 31, Sec. 3	**Teaching Resources** **Guide to the Essentials (English/Spanish)** • Section Summary, Ch. 31, Sec. 3 **Guided Reading Audiotapes (English/Spanish)**, Ch. 31, Sec. 3 **Section Reading Support Transparencies**, Ch. 31, Sec. 3
4 China's Neighbors 1. Describe how Taiwan has become an industrial power in Asia. 2. Explain how Hong Kong's relationship with China makes Hong Kong's future uncertain. 3. Discuss how the standard of living in Mongolia has improved in recent years.	**Teaching Resources** **Unit 9**/Ch. 31 • Guided Reading and Review, p. 17 **Prentice Hall Presentation Pro CD-ROM**, Ch. 31, Sec. 4	**Teaching Resources** **Guide to the Essentials (English/Spanish)** • Section Summary, Ch. 31, Sec. 4 **Guided Reading Audiotapes (English/Spanish)**, Ch. 31, Sec. 4 **Section Reading Support Transparencies**, Ch. 31, Sec. 4

ENRICHMENT/HONORS/PREAP

📦 **Teaching Resources**

📘 **Unit 9**/Ch. 31
  • Critical Thinking, p. 20

📘 **Mental Mapping booklet**
  • Atlas Activity, p. 122

📘 **Social Studies Skills Handbook**
  • Study and Research Skills, pp. 94–108

📘 **People and Geography**
  • Human Rights, pp. 47–52

📙 **World Geography Map and Photo Transparencies**
  • East Asia and the Pacific World: Maps and Photos

📺 **World Geography Videos**
  • Population Growth: China, Tape 4

💻 **Companion Web site, www.phschool.com**
  • Chapter 31 Activities

💻 **Companion Web site, www.phschool.com**
  • Chapter 31 Activities

📦 Teaching Resources

📘 **Simulations, Games, and Lab Activities**
  • Simulation, Should the Sian River Dam Be Funded?, pp. 34–48

💻 **Companion Web site, www.phschool.com**
  • Chapter 31 Activities

💻 **Companion Web site, www.phschool.com**
  • Chapter 31 Activities

💻 **Companion Web site, www.phschool.com**
  • Chapter 31 Activities

ASSESSMENT

PRENTICE HALL
ASSESSMENT *SYSTEM*

Core Assessment

📘 ExamView Test Bank booklet, Ch. 31
💿 ExamView Test Bank CD-ROM, Ch. 31

Standardized Test Preparation

Review and Reteach

📘 **Review Book for World Geography,** pp. 19–20

Practice and Assess

📘 **Test-taking Strategies With Transparencies for High School**

  Test-taking Strategy Poster

📘 **Alternative Assessment booklet**

📘 **Test Prep Book for World Geography**

📦 Teaching Resources

📘 **Unit 9**/Ch. 31
  • Section Quizzes, pp. 12, 14, 16, 18
  • Test Forms A and B, pp. 22–27

📘 **Guide to the Essentials (English/Spanish)**
  • Chapter 31 Test

📘 **Spanish Resources,** Ch. 31
  • Section Quizzes, pp. 77–80

📘 **Mental Mapping booklet**
  • Chapter 31 Map Test, p. 123

💻 **Companion Web site, www.phschool.com**
  • Chapter 31 Self-Test

CUSTOMIZE FOR INDIVIDUAL NEEDS

Gifted and Talented
  • Teacher's Edition, Customize for . . . , p. 653

Honors/PreAP
  • Teacher's Edition, Customize for . . . , p. 677

Less Proficient Readers
  • Guide to the Essentials (English), Ch. 31, Section Summaries
  • Guided Reading Audiotapes (English), Ch. 31
  • Section Reading Support Transparencies, Ch. 31
  • Book on CD, Ch. 31
  • Teacher's Edition, Reading Strategy, pp. 656, 662, 667, 673
  • Teacher's Edition, Activity: Vocabulary, pp. 657, 663, 668, 673
  • Teacher's Edition, Customize for . . . , pp. 665, 671

Students Acquiring English/ESL
  • Guide to the Essentials (English/Spanish), Ch. 31
  • Guided Reading Audiotapes (English/Spanish), Ch. 31
  • Section Reading Support Transparencies, Ch. 31
  • Book on CD, Ch. 31
  • Teacher's Edition, Customize for . . . , p. 659

Less Proficient Writers
  • Alternative Assessment, Writing Assignment Rubric, p. 6
  • Teacher's Edition, Customize for . . . , p. 673

Introducing
C H A P T E R
31
pp. 650–679

MENTAL MAPPING

Referring to the map on this page, point out that China, Mongolia, and Taiwan are located in East Asia. China, the largest country in East Asia, and Mongolia lie on the mainland. The island of Taiwan is situated off China's southeast coast.

Mapping the Region Have students study the map on this page. Then instruct them to close their books and create their own sketch maps of the region. You may also distribute the Chapter 31 Outline Map on page 121 of the Mental Mapping booklet in the Teaching Resources. Ask students to lightly shade each country a different color and to label the countries and bodies of water. Students should keep their maps in their Atlas Portfolios in order to prepare for the Chapter 31 Map Test.

eTeach

Be sure to check out this month's online forum with a Master Teacher to join in an exchange of teaching ideas. www.phschool.com

---

CHAPTER
31
China

SECTIONS

1	The Emergence of Modern China
2	Regions of China
3	China's People and Culture
4	China's Neighbors

China, Taiwan, and Mongolia: POLITICAL

KEY
— National boundary
⊛ National capital
• Major city
Two-Point Equidistant Projection

Go Online
PHSchool.com
For: More information about China and access to the Take It to the Net activities
Visit: phschool.com
Web Code: mjk-0032

RESOURCE DIRECTORY

Teaching Resources
Unit 9, Chapter 31
• Section 1 Guided Reading and Review, p. 11
Guide to the Essentials (English/Spanish)
• Section Summary, Chapter 31, Section 1
Mental Mapping booklet
• Atlas Activity, p. 122
• Unit 9 Checklist, p. 115

Technology
Guided Reading Audiotapes (English/Spanish),
Chapter 31, Section 1

Section Reading Support Transparencies,
Chapter 31, Section 1
World Geography Map and Photo Transparencies
• East Asia and the Pacific World: Maps and Photos
Book on CD, Chapter 31
World Geography Videos
• Population Growth: China, Tape 4
TeacherExpress™ CD-ROM, Chapter 31
Prentice Hall Presentation Pro CD-ROM, Chapter 31
Social Studies Skills Tutor CD-ROM
Companion Web site, www.phschool.com
• Chapter 31 Activities

1 The Emergence of Modern China

Reading Focus

- What were the results of China's early contacts with Western powers?
- What conflicts within China left the country open to a Communist takeover?
- What were the purposes and results of the program known as the Great Leap Forward?
- How did a series of modernizations attempt to change China?

Key Terms

sphere of influence
abdicate
warlord
light industry
martial law

Main Idea China is a vast and ancient country that has seen far-reaching changes over the past two centuries.

Economic Activities Families work the land together in rural China.

Since its birth along the Huang He in northern China around 3000 B.C., Chinese civilization has been deeply rooted in an agricultural way of life. Guided by the principles of Confucianism, the emperors of China ruled as if they were the fathers of their people. Their main responsibilities were to make sure their people's needs were met and to rule by setting an example of fairness.

Feeding China's large population has required large amounts of rice and other crops. One of the main duties of the Chinese emperors was to make sure that surplus food was stored for use in times of drought or flooding. The government also oversaw a system of trade among the different parts of the country. As a result, food shortages in one region could be met with surpluses from another region. This storage and distribution system worked well. Because China always had a large supply of agricultural workers, new technology did not come to be valued as it was in the West. In fact, according to the ideals of government in China, moral traits such as

cooperation were more important than new technical knowledge.

Lack of military technology proved a serious disadvantage in the mid-1800s. The industrialized countries of Europe and the United States used their military strength to force their way into China. The changes forced on China by these Western powers upset the country's internal trade network. These changes, combined with a series of natural and other disasters, resulted in widespread famine. A series of rebellions then broke out across the country. As a result, China entered a period of turmoil that would last for decades.

The March to Communism

By 1900 the United States and a number of European powers had carved China into **spheres of influence.** These are areas in which these countries had some political and economic control, but did not directly govern. Angered by the

◄ Terraced farmland in China *(photo left)*

Section 1 *pp. 651–658*

Objectives

Upon completion of Section 1, students should be able to:

◆ describe the results of China's early contacts with the West;

◆ identify internal conflicts that led to a Communist takeover;

◆ describe the purposes and results of the Great Leap Forward;

◆ explain how a series of modernizations attempted to change China.

 ### National Geography Standards

The following National Geography Standards are highlighted in this section: 1, 4, 5, 6, 9, 10, 11, 12, 13, 14, 16, 17, 18

Bellringer

Ask: **What aspects of Chinese culture have been incorporated into American life?** (Possible answers: food, art, philosophical beliefs, martial arts)

LESSON PLAN

1. Focus Explain that Confucius, perhaps the most influential Chinese philosopher, said that society functions best if people respect and obey those in authority. Ask students how this teaching could affect a society's ability to achieve political reform.

2. Instruct On the board, write *Great Leap Forward, Cultural Revolution,* and *Four Modernizations.* Have students write questions beginning with the words *who, what, when,* and *why* for each program. Have them find the answers in the text.

3. Close/Reteach Have students defend or disprove this statement: "Since the Communist Revolution, the Chinese government has had the best interests of China's people in mind."

TEACHING TIP
From A Master Teacher

Population China has been a site of dense human settlement for thousands of years. Its long-established patterns of population distribution persist today but are changing with new economic opportunities; environmental stress such as deforestation, erosion, and pollution; and changing population dynamics. Explain to students that China's cities are growing and expanding into agricultural lands, making food production for its peoples a continuing problem.

Pacing Suggestions

 For 90-minute Blocks

You will want to vary activities.

- Tell students that they will create a Chinese art exhibit. Have student pairs select an art form: visual art, music, dance, theater, or crafts. Ask each pair to do research and create a poster illustrating and explaining an example of that Chinese art form. Display posters and have students tour the exhibit.

Word Origin

China The name *China* was given to the country by foreigners. It may have come from *Qin,* pronounced "chihn," the name of an early Chinese dynasty.

Enrichment

Making a Time Line Have students make a time line to show the significant events in the history of modern China from the early 1900s to the present. (Visual/Spatial)

Connecting With . . .

History In 1900, Chinese peasants revolted against foreign intervention and the influx of Western ideas and customs in an uprising known as the Boxer Rebellion. The Boxer uprising got its name from the secret society that led this peasant protest. The members of the society practiced a form of martial arts that aimed to prepare the mind and body for combat. Loosely translated, the society's name was "Righteous and Harmonious Fists," which led Westerners to refer to its followers as "Boxers."

Answer to Photo Caption
6,000 miles (9,700 km)

treatment they were receiving from the Western powers, many Chinese people called for changes. They disagreed, however, on what course to take. Some favored giving up their traditional ways and accepting the Western culture of their enemies. Others wanted to totally reject Western influences. A third group wished to take on parts of Western culture, like technology, as a means to defend and protect their own culture. During this struggle, a new political party emerged—the Nationalist People's party. Many Nationalists, although they disliked the foreign powers in China, were greatly influenced by Western ideas.

After a series of revolts in 1911, the Nationalists seized power, forcing the emperor to **abdicate,** or give up his throne. The Nationalists then declared China a republic, choosing Sun Yat-sen (soon yaht sen) as the country's first president. Sun, who had been educated in the United States, wanted China to adopt a government based on Western democratic principles.

A Struggle for Power The Nationalists found that seizing control was far easier than keeping it. As fighting broke out between the Nationalists and the former army, local **warlords,** regional leaders with their own armies, seized power in their own areas. The Nationalists realized that to gain control of the whole country, they would have to defeat the warlords.

In the mid-1920s, Sun Yat-sen died and Chiang Kai-shek (chyahng ky shek) took over the leadership of the party. Chiang, a trained soldier, quickly molded the Nationalist troops into a disciplined fighting force. In a two-year campaign, Chiang defeated one warlord after another, taking control of much of the country. By 1928 he had established himself as president of the Nationalist Republic of China.

The Long March In the 1920s, a split developed in the Nationalist party. Some members of the party had adopted an ideology based on Karl Marx's communism. Marxism seemed to suggest an answer to the age-old problem of achieving prosperity for all Chinese. It also offered a means of defeating the imperialist powers in China through a revolution led by the working class.

To achieve these goals, Communists within the Nationalist party wanted to give more power

The Long March

Cooperation and Conflict In 1934 the Communists, under the leadership of Mao Zedong (shown on horseback), left their stronghold in Jiangxi to evade a blockade by Nationalist forces. Their Long March, as it came to be known, was planned to engage Nationalist forces at their weakest points.

Movement *How many miles did the Long March cover?*

652 Chapter 31 ▪ China

Route of the Long March

DIAGRAM SKILLS

● **Physical Characteristics** One of the biggest challenges of the Long March was the difficult terrain.
  • *What geographic obstacles did Mao and his troops face on their trek?*

to the workers and to give land to the landless peasants. But Chiang Kai-shek disagreed. In 1927 he ordered those who favored Communist ideas to be killed.

Some Communists survived Chiang's executions, fleeing to the mountainous region of south central China. There they built a stronghold in the province of Jiangxi (jyahng shee). Over the next six years, their numbers grew. Fearful that they would soon challenge his hold on the government, in 1933 Chiang sent a huge army to hunt them down and destroy them. After months of fighting, the Nationalists' superior numbers and resources began to prevail. In late 1934, the Communists left their positions in Jiangxi and started a year-long, northward journey known as the Long March.

The illustration on this page shows the long, winding route of the Long March. The Communists had to cross 18 mountain ranges and more than 20 rivers on their 6,000-mile (9,700-km) journey. Hunger, disease, and almost constant attacks by Nationalist troops made the march even more hazardous. Of the 100,000 Communists who had left Jiangxi, only about 8,000 reached their goal—safety in the northern province of Shaanxi (shah ahn shee). There, in the mountain town of Yan'an (yahn ahn), they set up their new headquarters under the leadership of Mao Zedong (mow zhuh doong).

Communists Take Over

During the early 1930s, the Japanese took advantage of the fighting in China. They invaded the northern Chinese province of Manchuria. Then, in 1937, the Japanese attempted to take over other areas of China. This hostile invasion forced the Nationalists and Communists to unite against their common enemy.

After the war ended in 1945, however, the two factions once again fought for control of China. But, while fighting against Japan, the Communists had carried out major social reforms in the areas they controlled. These reforms

BACKGROUND

Literature

The Communist Manifesto In 1848, Karl Marx and Friedrich Engels published *The Communist Manifesto.* This pamphlet became the platform for communism, a form of socialism that views history as a struggle between classes—the bourgeoisie (the owners of the means of production) and the proletariat (the workers). In the *Manifesto,* Marx and Engels argued that the working class would eventually win this struggle and create a classless, Communist society.

Answer to Diagram Skills
many mountain ranges and rivers

Communist Work Project

Government and Citizenship In 1985, workers who lived along the 30-mile stretch of road between Chengdu and Guanxian widened the road on the orders of the Communist party's Central Committee. The task was completed in a single week.

Place *How do road construction projects in the United States differ from this project?*

included lowering the peasants' rents. Many of these peasants now joined the Communist struggle against the Nationalists. By 1949 the Nationalists had been defeated.

Chiang Kai-shek fled the mainland, seeking safety on the island of Taiwan. There he vowed he would one day reconquer China. In Beijing, Mao Zedong made a different statement. On October 1, 1949, he announced the establishment of a new Communist state: the People's Republic of China.

A Communist Nation

Much of China lay in ruins after years of war. Even so, Mao indicated that he had great plans for the nation. He wanted to increase agricultural productivity. He believed that improvements in farm production could be achieved only according to the Communist principle of replacing private ownership with common ownership. In 1953, therefore, he called for the establishment of collective farms. On a collective, people work together as a group and then share whatever they

harvest. By 1956, 110 million families—about 88 percent of all Chinese peasants—were working on collective farms.

The Great Leap Forward Despite these economic changes, China still failed to meet Mao's goals. In 1958 he introduced yet another plan: the Great Leap Forward into communism. Under this plan, some 750,000 collectives were combined into about 23,500 People's Communes. These self-sufficient communal settlements, some of which had as many as 25,000 people, contained both farms and industries. Life in a People's Commune resembled life in the military. Communist party officials made all the decisions about what goods were made and who received them. The people's task was simply to work in the fields or factories.

Mao hoped that this new economic organization would, in a matter of years, increase China's production greatly. But the Great Leap Forward resulted, according to one Chinese official, in "a serious leap backward." Rather than increasing, production fell. The difficult life in the communes offered people no incentive to work hard. They received the same rewards regardless of the amount they produced. In addition, bad weather conditions hindered farm production. The harvests from 1958 to 1960 were among China's worst. The Chinese government abandoned its Great Leap Forward after only two years.

The Cultural Revolution Many political leaders criticized Mao Zedong for the failure of the Great Leap Forward. Even Mao's closest advisers charged him with making mistakes. Deng Xiaoping (dung shau ping), for example, felt that Mao had tried to do too much too quickly. "A donkey is certainly slow, but at least it rarely has an accident," Deng remarked.

Stung by this criticism, Mao responded that if the revolution was failing, then even more drastic measures were needed. In 1966, he called for a Great Cultural Revolution to smash the old order completely and establish a new, socialist society. Mao unleashed an army of radical young men and women, called Red Guards, to enforce his policies. Their job and command was to destroy the Four Olds: old ideology, old thought, old habits, and old customs.

No part of society was safe from the Red Guards. Communists who favored slower change, teachers, artists, writers—in fact, all those who disagreed with Mao—were publicly humiliated, beaten, and even killed. Those enemies who survived the wrath of the Red Guards lost their jobs and were imprisoned or sent to the country to work as peasants.

Farm production fell, factory work ground to a halt, and schools closed as the Red Guards moved through the country. Mao approved of their actions by saying, "To rebel is justified." The destruction was so great that Mao called for an end to the Cultural Revolution in 1969. He also ordered the army to disband the Red Guards.

The Cultural Revolution was an enormous failure for China. At its end the economy was almost completely ruined. Hundreds of thousands of innocent people were in jail or had been driven into remote, rural areas. An entire generation of

Mao's Little Red Books

Cultures During the Chinese Cultural Revolution, Mao's sayings were collected and distributed in what became known as Mao's little red book. In the frenzy of the Cultural Revolution, Mao was feverishly revered and his words were considered the final authority.

Place *What were the Four Olds that Mao wished to destroy?*

BACKGROUND

Connecting With . . .

History The Great Leap Forward and the Cultural Revolution—programs that forced the Chinese people to comply with communism—may be seen as reactions to the Hundred Flowers campaign, an earlier Mao program that failed. In a 1956 speech, Mao invited Chinese intellectuals to openly share their ideas about the government. It took a while for the Chinese intellectuals to speak up. When they did, they criticized Mao's government harshly. Mao took the response as a personal insult. In 1957, he revised the speech that had granted the freedoms to include stifling rules about which ideas were correct and which were not. Many people who had criticized the Chinese Communist Party were punished. The party later claimed that the campaign had been an elaborate trap designed to expose those who were not supporters of the party.

BACKGROUND

Daily Life

Government Control In 1949, the Chinese government began to control how people made a living and where they resided. From 1954 to 1960, peasants were recruited as laborers by the state and relocated to urban and mining areas. By 1961, growing urban areas could no longer absorb the laborers, so the government began to restrict migration into cities. From 1966 to 1969, huge numbers of students and intellectuals were forced out of the cities and into the countryside to work as manual laborers. The vast majority of these people streamed back into the cities in the late 1970s.

TEST PREPARATION

Have students read the subsection The Cultural Revolution beginning on this page to answer the following question.
Mao most likely targeted the Four Olds because —

A he feared that other governments would consider China old-fashioned

B he was trying to industrialize China

C many of the Four Olds contradicted his ideas

D farm production fell and factory work halted

Answer to Photo Caption

old ideology, old thought, old habits, and old customs

Chapter 31 ▪ Section 1 **655**

Before reading the subsection The Four Modernizations, ask students to scan the subheadings and note any key words. Have students brainstorm what they think might be discussed in the text under each heading. After reading the subsection, instruct students to check if their predictions were correct.

Alternative Assessment

Introduce the Activity

Writing a Position Paper Ask students to conduct current events research and to write a two-page position paper agreeing or disagreeing with the following statement: In the near future, China will undertake democratic reforms to give the Chinese people more freedom. Distribute the Position Paper Rubric found on page 8 of the Alternative Assessment booklet in the Prentice Hall Assessment System for students' reference during the project.

young people had lost their chance for an education. This loss of talent alone made China's economic recovery very difficult.

The Four Modernizations

Mao Zedong died in 1976. A power struggle followed that pitted the Gang of Four—a group of politicians led by Mao's widow, who wanted to continue the Cultural Revolution—against a group led by Deng Xiaoping. Most people sided with Deng because they were tired of death and disorder. Deng took a more practical approach to solving China's problems than Mao.

To begin the changes, Deng started a program called the Four Modernizations. The goals of the program were to improve agriculture, industry, science and technology, and defense as quickly as possible. To accomplish this, Deng said, any ideas would be considered, even if they approached the ideas of a free-enterprise economy. Said Deng, "It doesn't matter if a cat is black or white, as long as it catches mice."

Changes in Agriculture
First, Deng took steps to repair the damage done to farm production during the Great Leap Forward. In place

of the communes, he established the contract responsibility system. Under this arrangement, the government rented land to individual farm families. Each family then decided for themselves what to produce. The families contracted with the government simply to provide a certain amount of crops at a set price. Once the contract was fulfilled, they were free to sell any extra crops at markets for whatever prices they could get.

This chance to make more money by growing more crops led farmers to increase their

China's New Economy

Global Trade Patterns Home-grown industries, such as the ceramics-making business shown here (top photo), now exist side by side with international businesses. Deng Xiaoping's economic reforms included a new openness to the West. The Chinese have allowed U.S. soft drink makers to open bottling plants in China (left), in return for a share of the profits.

Place *What were China's experiences with foreign trade prior to modernization under Deng?*

656 Chapter 31 ▪ China

Answer to Photo Caption

Under communism, the economy faltered and, therefore, China had limited trade.

production by about 8 percent more each year than they had in the previous year. In the first eight years, farmers' incomes tripled.

Industrial Development When the Communists came to power, they used most of China's resources to increase heavy industry. Heavy industries produce goods such as iron, steel, and machines that are used in other industries. At first, heavy-industry production grew rapidly. By the time Deng came to power, however, Chinese technology was outdated and inefficient.

Deng's program for industry had two goals. First, he wanted people to spend more money on consumer goods. Therefore, he changed the focus from heavy industry to **light industry.** This refers to the production of small consumer goods such as clothing, appliances, and bicycles. He also wanted factories to step up production. Deng gave more decision-making power to factory managers. He started a system of rewards for managers and workers who found ways to make factories produce more.

In addition, Deng set up four Special Economic Zones along China's east coast. By locating the zones near Hong Kong and Taiwan, Deng hoped to attract foreign capital, companies, and technology from these offshore economic giants. As described in the next section, the zones have proven enormously successful. Indeed, China now has not just four but more than 2,000 of these zones.

About 1.5 million industrial firms were in operation in 1978. Fifteen years later, that number had grown to almost 8 million. This shift from agriculture to industry has changed the face of rural China in ways both good and bad.

Unexpected Results Unfortunately, China's rapid economic growth has taken place very unevenly. Spurred by the establishment of Special Economic Zones, the coastal cities grew rich, but the interior regions lagged far behind. Drawn by the booming economy, millions of people left their villages to make their fortunes in the cities. Unable to find adequate work, between 50 and 100 million workers now drift from job to job. Rapid urban growth has resulted in an increase in crime that the weak and sometimes corrupt police force has trouble handling. To combat these problems, the government has planned more Special Economic Zones in the interior and in the north. Concentrating on high-tech industries, these efforts will help strengthen the economy in areas that previously had lagged behind.

China's economy is stronger today than it has ever been. Since the start of Deng's reforms in 1978, China's gross domestic product has more than quadrupled. The growth rate has been as high as 8 percent per year. Chinese leaders believe their nation's economy will be the third largest in the world by 2020 and the second largest by 2050.

Residents of China have noticed this growth through the many improvements in their daily lives. In the early 1980s, for example, few households had any modern appliances. Only a decade later, 80 percent of urban households owned washing machines.

Country	Number of Radios (per 1,000 people)	Number of Televisions (per 1,000 people)	Daily Newspaper Circulation (per 1,000 people)
China	335	292	23
Mongolia	142	58	27
Taiwan	402	418	20
United States	2,116	843	215

China, Mongolia, Taiwan and the United States — Communications Data

Sources: *Encyclopedia Britannica Almanac*

CHART SKILLS

● **Cultures** Which country has the least amount of televisions? What does that suggest about the level of development of that country?

● **Science and Technology** Which countries rely more on radio receivers than on newspapers for access to information?

GLOBAL CONNECTIONS

Global Trade Patterns
After the International Olympic Committee chose Beijing to host the 2008 Games, China began spending billions of dollars to improve the capital city's infrastructure. Officials expect foreign investment and tourism to boost China's GDP by about 3 percent annually between 2002 and 2008.

An International Symbol

Cultures As global communications improve, the
world's nations borrow ideas from each other. These student protestors adopted the symbol of the Statue of Liberty, sending an unmistakable signal to their government.
Place *What was the "Fifth Modernization" that students demanded in 1989?*

More Political Upheaval

As they became accustomed to economic reform,
many Chinese citizens began to demand a "Fifth
Modernization"—political freedom. They were
eager to enjoy democratic rights, such as the
freedom to express their political beliefs openly
and without fear. They also called for a voice in
running the government.

Early in 1989, thousands of Chinese, mostly
students, began a series of demonstrations in Beijing to demand democratic reforms. As many as
100,000 people crowded into Tiananmen Square
in the center of the city. In May, the government
decided to end the protests. The country's leaders
imposed **martial law** and ordered demonstrators to leave the square. Martial law is law that is
administered during periods of strict military control. Some demonstrators disobeyed the government's orders. On the night of June 3, the army
moved in to disperse those who remained.

The troops opened fire without warning,
killing as many as 2,000 people and wounding
hundreds more. In the days that followed, other
dissident leaders were arrested, and some were executed. When other nations expressed outrage at
these actions, Chinese authorities accused them of
interfering in China's internal affairs.

In the decade that followed, China continued
to periodically repress some of its citizens. Political activists were given long prison terms, and
spiritual groups were outlawed, as Chinese leaders
expressed their belief that economic growth can
only continue if people keep "in line" politically.

SECTION 1 ASSESSMENT

1. **Key Terms** Define **(a)** sphere of influence,
   (b) abdicate, **(c)** warlord, **(d)** light industry,
   (e) martial law.

2. **Understanding the Past** **(a)** Why did Western
   powers divide China into spheres of influence?
   (b) How did their actions lead to the establishment of China as a republic?

3. **Cooperation and Conflict** How did the Communists gain control of China?

4. **Economic Systems** What was the purpose of
   the Great Leap Forward?

5. **Government and Citizenship** **(a)** What were
   the goals of the Four Modernizations? **(b)** How
   did a "Fifth Modernization" differ from the previous four?

6. **Critical Thinking Drawing Conclusions**
   Why do you think that the Chinese authorities
   responded so violently to the prodemocracy
   demonstrations in Tiananmen Square?

Activity

Making a Time Line Gather more information about
China's history. Then, chronicle your findings on a
time line. Be sure to represent China's ancient history,
its contacts with the West, and the rise and effects of
communism.

2 Regions of China

Reading Focus

- In the past, how has China's Northeast region served as the center of population, industry, and government?
- Why is the Southeast region of China ideal for agriculture and transportation?
- In what way did the Silk Road promote development of China's barren Northwest region?
- What effect has Communist rule had on China's Southwest region?

Key Terms

double cropping
theocrat
autonomous region

Main Idea China's geographic vastness and cultural diversity are reflected in the character of its four major regions.

Understanding the Past Beijing's Imperial Palace lies within an enclosure known as the Forbidden City.

A journey through China's four major regions provides a vivid picture of the country's geographic diversity. Locate the regions of China on the map on page 660. Compare this map with the physical map on page 637. As you can see, China's regions are largely defined by geography. Each region has developed its own character. A densely populated area, the Northeast has served as the country's administrative and industrial center. However, the Southeast, once China's major agricultural region, has become the center of its booming economy. China's frontier lies to the west and is characterized by two sparsely populated regions—the desert Northwest and the mountainous Southwest.

The Northeast

The Northeast region includes eastern China from the Amur River in the north to the North China Plain in the south. The region is bounded on the west by the Greater Khingan (shinj ahn) Range. China's major lowland areas are in the Northeast.

For centuries the Northeast formed China's core. It contains Beijing, the country's capital, and the greatest concentration of China's population. The Northeast was the site of one of the world's earliest culture hearths, centered on the Huang He. Each dynasty that ruled in China added more territory to its empire, extending Chinese influence far beyond the country's original boundaries. But no matter how far these empires extended, the capital remained in the Northeast.

Beijing Beijing continues to function as the seat of power for today's Communist government. Like other cities in the Northeast, Beijing is a major industrial center. But because the Southeast region has prospered so enormously with the establishment of the Special Economic Zones, Beijing may be losing its status as China's nerve center. Investment dollars are flowing south, and when people request permission from the government to change residence, they are often hoping to move south. A professor at Beijing Normal University explains the attraction in the following way.

Chapter 31 ■ Section 2 **659**

CUSTOMIZE FOR...

Students Acquiring English/ESL
Designing Souvenir Plates Tell students that the Chinese have a long tradition of making beautifully painted ceramic plates. In fact, this is where the term *china* comes from. Give each student four white paper plates. Tell them to draw or paint a design for a souvenir plate for each of China's four regions. Each plate should show what is significant about the region. Have students show their plates to the class and explain why they chose to symbolize the region in the way that they did.

Section 2 *pp. 659–664*

Objectives

Upon completion of Section 2, students should be able to:

◆ describe how China's Northeast region has served as the center of population, industry, and government;

◆ explain why the Southeast region of China is ideal for agriculture and transportation;

◆ explain how the Silk Road promoted development of China's barren Northwest region;

◆ identify how Communist rule has affected Southwestern China.

National Geography Standards

The following National Geography Standards are highlighted in this section: 1, 2, 3, 4, 5, 6, 7, 8, 10, 11, 12, 13, 14, 15, 16, 17

Bellringer

Tell students that China has four distinct geographic regions. Then, have students create a list of characteristics that make the region in which they live unique.

LESSON PLAN

1. Focus Explain that Cantonese, Peking, Szechuan, and Hunan are four types of Chinese cooking that originated in different areas. Have students list examples of regional cooking in the United States, such as Tex-Mex barbecue and New England clam chowder. Ask: **Why do regional cooking styles differ?** (use of local ingredients, climate, tradition)

2. Instruct Make a four-column chart on the board, labeling the columns *Landforms, Climate, Economic Activities,* and *Unique Aspects.* Have students complete the chart for each of China's four regions.

3. Close/Reteach Have each student write one statement that describes a region of China beginning with the expression *This region. . .* As a class quiz, ask students to match each statement with a region.

Chapter 31 ■ Section 2 **659**

Word Origin

Loess The term *loess* stems from the German word *lösch,* which means "loose." In China, people who lived in densely populated agricultural areas used to dig out the steep slopes formed by loess to construct cellar-like dwellings.

Connecting With . . .

Art The dragon, a common symbol in China, was said to live in clouds and rivers and so was often connected with water in China. Like water itself, which sometimes came as floods and at other times as badly needed rain, a dragon could signify both good and bad.

Group Work

Activity: Developing new businesses

Purpose: Tell each group that its job is to attract foreign businesses to China. Assign each group one of the four Chinese regions. Have groups find out what resources their area has to offer, such as mineral wealth or access to transportation. Then have them decide what kind of businesses might be successful in their region. Each group must create and deliver a sales presentation to the class explaining what the region has to offer foreign businesses. Presentations should include visuals such as maps, pictures, tables, and graphs.

Roles: Researchers, writers, illustrators, and a salesperson

Result: Salespeople should deliver their presentations to the class.

Answer to Map Caption

Possible answer: Northwest; It is mostly desert.

660 Chapter 31

China: REGIONS

APPLYING THE GEOGRAPHIC THEMES

● **Regions** China's regions are divided between sparsely settled, dry, and mountainous lands in the west, and densely settled, well-watered lands in the east.
  • *In which region of China would you expect relatively few people to be engaged in farming? Why?*

❝Beijing was considered the best city in China [in which] to study, but that's changing. Now students want to stay in the south or be on the coast because they have more opportunities and can make more money.❞

Loess: Fertile Soil In addition to having industrial centers like Beijing, the Northeast is also the site of a vast agricultural area. Here the soil has been made fertile by loess—a fine, yellow-brown loam deposited by seasonal dust storms. Strong winds blow the loess from Mongolia and the Gobi Desert, depositing it along the upper reaches of the Huang He. In fact, the Huang He is sometimes called the Yellow River because of the color the loess gives the water. The loess is carried to the Huang He's lower reaches. During

660   Chapter 31 ▪ China

---

floods, it is deposited as silt across the lowland area of the North China Plain.

Loess, which is highly fertile, can become productive agricultural soil with the use of irrigation. As a result, the North China Plain is among the most intensely farmed areas in China.

China's Sorrow In addition to carrying rich, fertile soil to the lowland areas, the Huang He also serves as a transportation route. It flows 3,395 miles (5,464 km) on a tortuous path to the sea. Originating in the Tibetan Plateau, it makes its way north through the Gobi Desert to the North China Plain. At about 40°N latitude it makes a sudden bend east and southward. It picks up the Wei River at around 35°N latitude and turns east, coursing its way to the sea.

However, the river that helps transportation has also brought death and destruction to the region in the past. Some people call it "China's Sorrow."

In the years when the spring thaw and rains were very heavy, the river's swollen waters spilled over its banks, flooding the surrounding areas. Countless numbers of people lost their lives in these destructive floods. Those who survived saw their homes and crops washed away or buried under thick layers of silt. In 1887 flooding along the Huang He resulted in one of history's greatest flood disasters, in which close to 1 million people died.

Incredibly, China now has a new problem with the Huang He. Because its water is used by millions of people in the region, it can dry up completely for months at a time. As population increases, the region will need more water than the river delivers. To solve this crisis, the Chinese government is considering projects that will divert water from the Yangzi River in the south to the Huang He in the north. The cost and the impact on people and the environment would be vast. However, as one Canadian expert put it:

❝They will go ahead with these schemes, because to them it will be the simpler solution to increase the supply of water rather than manage the supply through conservation. That is the typical Communist party solution.❞

RESOURCE DIRECTORY

Teaching Resources
Mental Mapping booklet
• Outline Map 31, p. 121
Simulations, Games, and Lab Activities
• Simulation, Should the Sian River Dam Be Funded?, pp. 34–48

Technology
World Geography Map and Photo Transparencies
• East Asia and the Pacific World: Maps and Photos

The Southeast

Southeast China stretches from the North China Plain to the country's southern border, and from the eastern coast to the western highland areas. As the map on page 637 shows, the Southeast region is more mountainous than the Northeast. In addition, the Southeast has a warmer, wetter climate than the Northeast.

This climate, together with the fertile soil of the region's river valleys, makes the region excellent for farming. Farmers use a number of intensive farming methods to get the greatest yield from the land. In some areas, farmers practice **double cropping**—growing more than one crop a year on the same land. Elsewhere, farmers carve steplike terraces into the slopes of hills to increase the area of arable land. Rice, rather than wheat, dominates agriculture in the Southeast.

Movement on the Yangzi The valley of the Yangzi, or Ch'ang, River is the location of some of China's most productive farmland. With an average population density greater than 5,000 people per square mile (1,900 per sq km), the Yangzi valley ranks among the country's busiest and most crowded areas.

The Yangzi serves as China's east-west highway. Oceangoing ships can navigate some 600 miles (950 km) inland to the city of Wuhan. Small steamers travel even farther upstream, carrying goods to and from many towns deep in China's interior. Shanghai, China's major port, is located at the mouth of the Yangzi. Farther inland, the massive Three Gorges Dam is being constructed. Experts estimate that it will help control the Yangzi's flooding and generate much of China's energy. However, many fear that shoddy construction could lead to disaster for the 400 million people who live downstream. Furthermore, many towns will be submerged when the lake forms behind the dam. Residents are being resettled forcibly.

Special Economic Zones One goal of the Four Modernizations was to spur economic growth by attracting foreign investment and technology to China. As discussed in Section 1, in the late 1970s, the Chinese government created four Special Economic Zones in the Southeast. Three of the original zones, Zhuhai, Shenzhen,

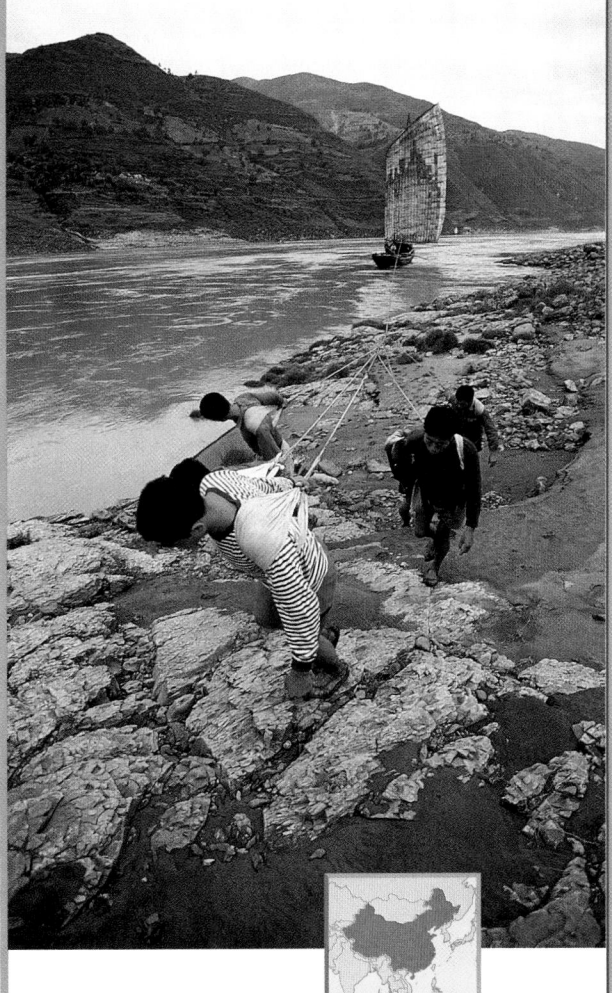

Inland on the Yangzi River

Economic Activities The Yangzi River connects China's vast interior with the coast. However, recent economic advances in the coastal regions have not reached far inland. Here the power of human physical effort is still as common as the power of modern engines is in modern cities.

Regions *How does China's population size keep human power economically viable in some regions?*

and Shantou, are located in Guangdong province, north of Hong Kong. The fourth, Xiamen, is in Fujian province just across the Taiwan Strait from Taiwan. Thousands of new economic zones have

---

Articles From ·······

NATIONAL GEOGRAPHIC

The following article may be used to extend the content in this section.

Zich, Arthur, and Bob Sacha, photographer. "China's Three Gorges." *National Geographic*, Vol. 192, No. 3 (Sept. 1997), pp. 2–33.

One of China's biggest architectural undertakings, the building of the Three Gorges Dam seems to have as many drawbacks as it does advantages.

The Physical World

Shanghai's Coastline The Yangzi River meets the sea at Shanghai, where the river current slows. Every year it deposits approximately 500 million tons of sand along the coastline, extending Shanghai's territory hundreds of feet into the sea. Chingming Island, located east of Shanghai proper, has doubled in area since 1958.

Daily Life

Food With the advent of better milling machinery in the first millennium A.D., ancient China's staple crop, millet, was replaced by wheat. Soon after, irrigated farming in the Yangzi River valley made rice an important grain. In the late 1600s, the Spanish brought crops such as maize and potatoes. Today the term *fan* refers to any staple grain used in regional cuisine. In the north, *fan* is wheat; in the west, it is rice or maize. In the east, *fan* is rice or sweet potatoes; in the south, *fan* is always rice.

Critical Thinking

Physical Geography and Economic Activity Refer students to the physical map on page 637 and use the following questions to help students see the links between physical geography and economic activity. Ask: **Where do you think most of China's agricultural activity takes place? Why?** (in the eastern region; The land is flat and has large rivers.) **Why do you think the Yangzi River is an important trade route?** (It has many tributaries and canals, and the major port city of Shanghai is at its mouth.)

Answer to Photo Caption

China's vast population provides a source of inexpensive labor.

READING STRATEGY

Visualizing

Ask students to skim the subsection The Northwest beginning on this page and look for any descriptive words that might help in visualizing the physical features of this region. Ask volunteers to share their thoughts about what living in this region would be like. Then, have students read the section to determine if their assumptions were correct.

since been added. The government hoped to lure to these zones the foreign investment and technological expertise available from Chinese industrialists and financiers of Hong Kong and Taiwan. To entice these business people, the government set low tax rates. It also reduced the number of official forms and licenses required to operate a business in the economic zones. The strategy worked. By 1991, foreign investors had poured $22 billion into the Special Economic Zones. Foreign investors from Hong Kong, Taiwan, and other countries from around the Pacific Rim have been racing to tap into the fastest-growing market in the world.

Evidence of the economic boom abounds. Scores of new apartment and office buildings have been constructed. Cars and electronic equipment, once considered luxuries, are now readily available. To take advantage of this wealth, hundreds of thousands of people have migrated to the cities of the Southeast from other parts of China. According to recent estimates, Shanghai's population is expected to soar to 23.5 million by 2015.

The Northwest

The landscape of China's Northwest region is stark, rugged, and barren when compared with the landscape of the country's eastern sections. The Gobi Desert forms China's northern boundary. Apart from leathery grasses that anchor the thin, sandy soil, very little grows in this rough, rock-strewn land. Few people find the region hospitable, and population is low. Mountains in this region surround and separate two large basins. The Takla Makan Desert occupies much of the western Tarim Basin. Steppe grasses cover most of the other basin.

The Silk Road, one of the great trade routes of ancient times, crossed the bare landscape of Northwest China. Along the road, way stations developed around oases fed by mountain streams. Over time, some of these way stations grew into large towns. For example, Kashgar, on the western

Shoemakers in Urumqi

Economic Activities In the city of Urumqi, in China's Northwest region, shoemakers make and repair shoes on simple sewing machines at roadside stands.

Location *How has Urumqi's location near the Tien Shan range benefited the economy of the city and the surrounding region?*

Answer to Photo Caption

Oases fed by streams from the Tien Shan range encouraged the development of towns, such as Urumqi. Since the time of the Silk Road, travelers have stopped at these towns to trade.

662 Chapter 31

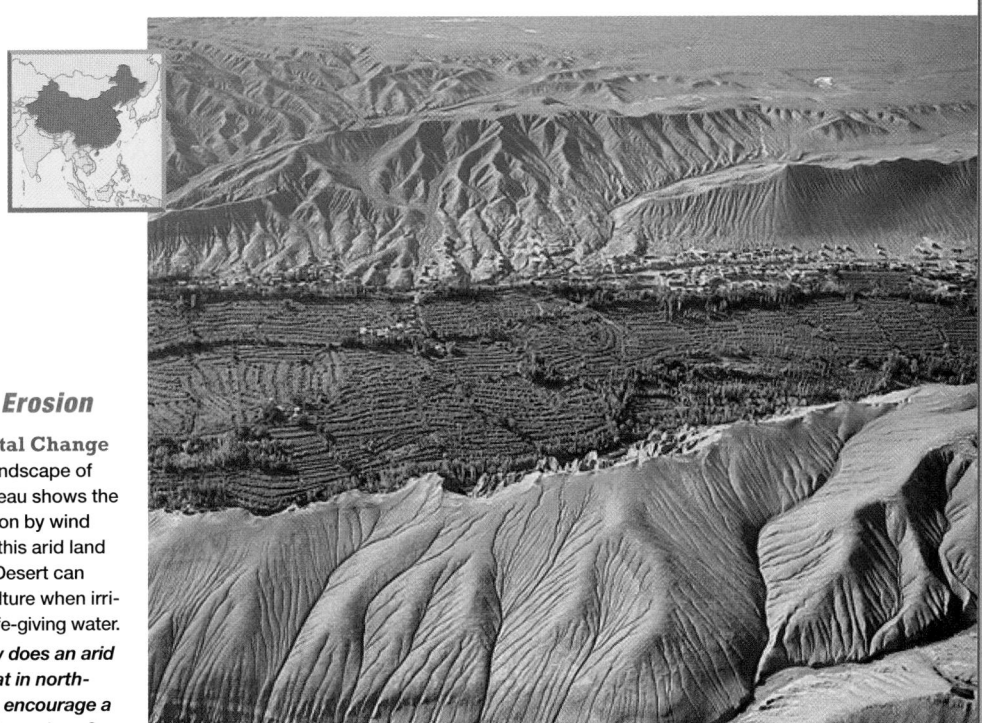

Effects of Erosion

Environmental Change
The tortured landscape of this inland plateau shows the effects of erosion by wind and water. Yet this arid land near the Gobi Desert can support agriculture when irrigation brings life-giving water.
Regions *How does an arid climate like that in northwestern China encourage a nomadic herding culture?*

ACTIVITY

Vocabulary

Theocrat Refer to the Key Terms list on page 659. Write the term *theocrat* on the board. Have a volunteer look up the term in the Glossary and read its definition aloud. Ask: **What countries, past or present, have been theocracies?** (most European monarchies before the nineteenth century; currently Iran)

ACTIVITY

Enrichment

Making a Regional Map Have students make a map of China's regions, illustrating the unique features of each region. Then have students display their maps. (Visual/Spatial)

edge of the Takla Makan, has a population of about 300,000. About 1.5 million people live in Urumqi (oo room chi), in the foothills of the lofty Tien Shan range (tyen shahn).

In these and other oasis towns, many people make a living through farming. For example, in Turpan (toor pahn), about 95 miles (150 km) southeast of Urumqi, a system of underground irrigation canals fed by streams flowing from the Tien Shan has helped to make grape growing an important occupation. Nomadic herding, however, is the major economic activity throughout the region. When spring arrives, herders drive their animals to higher elevations in search of fresh pastures. Then, with the onset of cold weather, they return their herds to their lowland meadows.

Tibet: The Southwest

If you look at the maps on pages 637 and 660, you will notice that one landform—the cold, dry Plateau of Tibet—dominates China's Southwest region. Its elevations exceed 14,000 feet (4,300 m)

and surrounding mountains soar above 20,000 feet (6,100 m). Being the highest region in the world, the plateau is largely isolated from the rest of the world.

Occupying the plateau is Tibet—a distinct, traditional society based on the Buddhist religion. For most of their history the farmers and herders of Tibet lived quiet, simple lives ruled by Buddhist custom and the decrees of their theocratic leader, the Dalai Lama. A **theocrat** is someone who claims to rule by religious or divine authority.

In 1950 a Chinese invasion ended Tibet's isolation. By 1959, the Chinese reduced Tibet's Buddhist monasteries

GLOBAL CONNECTIONS

Cultures One of the main religions of Asia, Buddhism, has become increasingly popular in other nations, particularly the United States. According to a survey conducted at the beginning of the 1990s, American Buddhists number an estimated 800,000. Tibetan Buddhism in particular has seen a sharp rise in interest.

Chapter 31 ▪ Section 2 **663**

TEST PREPARATION

Have students read the subsection Tibet: The Southwest beginning on this page to complete the following sentence.
The takeover of Tibet by the Chinese government led to —
(A) the exile of its leader
B economic reforms
C increased religious freedom
D agricultural reforms

Answer to Photo Caption

Since the climate is arid, the pastureland quality changes throughout the year; the herders must take their animals to where the pastureland is best.

Tibet

Cultures Tibet has been called the Rooftop of the World because of its altitude. Its average elevation is 16,000 feet (4,900 m) above sea level. It is surrounded on the north, south, and west by the highest mountains in the world. These pilgrims have come to this remote temple to honor Buddha on the anniversary of his birth.

Human-Environment Interaction *How has Tibet's physical geography protected the country's unique culture in the past?*

to rubble. Farmers were required to join agricultural communes unsuitable for their nomadic lifestyle. Furthermore, the Dalai Lama was driven into exile in India.

After an uprising in Tibet in 1959, the Chinese government instituted a policy designed to destroy Tibet's ancient culture. In 1965 China installed a Communist government and designated Tibet an **autonomous region.** An autonomous region is a political unit with limited self-government. The Chinese also gave Tibet a new name—Xizang (shee zahng), meaning "hidden land of the west." Even so, the Tibetans held on to their traditions and culture. After a series of reforms that relaxed limits on religion, the Chinese government clamped down on Tibet once again. This new Chinese interference in their affairs has only increased the Tibetans' desire to regain their independence.

SECTION 2 ASSESSMENT

1. **Key Terms** Define **(a)** double cropping, **(b)** theocrat, **(c)** autonomous region.

2. **Understanding the Past** Why was the Northeast region considered the center of China?

3. **Physical Characteristics** **(a)** What factors encourage agriculture in the Southeast region? **(b)** Why is the Yangzi River important to this region?

4. **Global Trade Patterns** How did the Silk Road encourage development of China's barren Northwest region?

5. **Government and Citizenship** How has Tibet, in the Southwest region, been affected by Communist rule?

6. **Critical Thinking** **Making Comparisons** What are the major differences between eastern and western China?

Activity

USING THE **REGIONAL ATLAS**

Review the Regional Atlas for East Asia and the Pacific World and this section. For each of China's four major regions, identify the greatest environmental challenge. Then, explain your thoughts in an oral report.

3 China's People and Culture

Reading Focus

- Through the years, how has China's Communist government changed its attitudes about population growth?
- What factors create a common culture throughout China, encouraging unity across the nation?

Key Terms

ideogram
atheism
acupuncture

Main Idea China draws strength from its rich culture and traditions as it struggles with overpopulation.

Urbanization More than 7 million commuters take to their bicycles each day in Shanghai.

magine standing on a street corner watching a parade in which the entire population of China marched by. If the people marched in rows of four, how long do you think it would take for the parade to pass? Would it take a few minutes, or would the time run into hours, or days? Actually, if the whole population of China took part in the parade, you would have to stand on that street corner for more than ten years to see everyone pass by! With nearly 1.3 billion people, China ranks as the world's most populous nation. Despite their numbers, the vast majority of China's people share a common language and culture.

A Huge Population

Mao Zedong, China's first Communist leader, believed that power lay in numbers. A huge number of people, he suggested, could never be overrun by outsiders. He urged the Chinese people to have more children. By the mid-1960s the population of China was growing annually by about 2.07 percent, a rate above that of most other countries. The growth rate in the United States, for example, stood at 1.46 percent.

For decades, Mao failed to recognize the problems his policy was causing. Demographers warned him that rapid population growth would mean serious shortages of food and shelter. By the 1960s, their predictions had come true. Overcrowding and hunger were a part of everyday life for many Chinese. The worst overcrowding was along China's eastern coast. Even today, population densities in this area rank among the highest in the world.

Population Control Policies Finally realizing his country's predicament, Mao agreed to a new population policy. He called for families to have no more than two children. This policy slowed China's rate of growth a little. Nevertheless, overpopulation remained a social and economic problem.

Chapter 31 • Section 3 **665**

CUSTOMIZE FOR...

Less Proficient Readers

Developing an Outline On the board write the title *China's People and Culture.* Then help students develop an outline of Section 3. Direct students to find heads, subheads, and supporting details. Have students copy the completed outline to use as a study guide.

Section 3 *pp. 665–669*

Objectives

Upon completion of Section 3, students should be able to:

◆ describe how China's Communist government has changed its attitudes about population growth;

◆ identify the factors that create a common Chinese culture and encourage unity throughout China.

National Geography Standards

The following National Geography Standards are highlighted in this section: 2, 3, 4, 5, 6, 9, 10, 12, 17

Bellringer

Ask students to list the pros and cons of being an only child. Tell students that they will read about restrictions the Chinese government put on families desiring children.

LESSON PLAN

1. Focus Draw the international symbol for "no smoking" on the board and have students identify its meaning. Explain that this symbol is an ideogram because we understand its meaning from a picture. Chinese writing is also made of pictures, or ideograms. Have students write messages with simple pictures, exchange messages, and attempt to decode them.

2. Instruct List the following on the board: *Mao encourages large families; Deng imposes one-child policy; Chinese use ideograms to write; Communists discourage religious practices.* Next to each action, have students list at least one effect it has had on China.

3. Close/Reteach Have students discuss the Chinese government's cultural policies since the Communists gained control. Ask: **Do you think these policies have been justified? Explain.**

Chapter 31 • Section 3 **665**

Population of China: 1950–2050

Sources: Population Reference Bureau;
China Population Information and Research Center
*Projected population.

GRAPH SKILLS

● **Population Growth** Despite China's efforts to limit population growth, experts project that China's population will continue to rise.

• *How would you describe China's growth rate between 1950 and 2000? How might strict enforcement of the one-child policy alter population projections?*

When Deng Xiaoping came to power in the late 1970s, he argued that one sure way to improve the standard of living of the Chinese people was to reduce population growth still further. To achieve this goal, he set up a one-couple, one-child policy. Couples who followed this policy received special rewards, such as better housing and better jobs, or pay increases at work. In contrast, couples who had more than one child faced fines, wage cuts, loss of their jobs, and the prospect of social disapproval.

Results To ensure the success of the new policy, the government started a large publicity campaign. It flooded the country with posters and billboards that listed the virtues of one-child families.

Propaganda did not convince people in rural areas. The contract responsibility system, the government's agricultural reform policy described in Section 1, was clearly at odds with government requests to limit population growth. The responsibility system shifted agricultural production away from communes and back to a system of family labor. As a result, rural couples began to have more children who would help in the fields. Children also represented security for parents, who eventually would become too old or sick to work. In rural areas, therefore, people simply accepted the punishments. City dwellers, however, generally complied with the policy. By 2000, the annual population growth rate had slowed to 0.9 percent—a significant change.

The Chinese government's one-child policy received worldwide criticism. As a result, the Chinese government has begun recently to relax the policy. China now favors noncoercive approaches, such as family planning and counseling. Ethnic minorities now are required to limit the size of their families as well. Slowing population growth remains a major challenge for China. Despite the government's policies, China's population is expected to reach 1.4 billion by the middle of this century.

Chinese Culture

Occupying a vast area and possessing a huge population, China is a land of great ethnic diversity. At the same time, the majority of the Chinese people share a common cultural background.

Ethnic Differences About 56 ethnic minority groups live in China, mostly in the frontier areas of western and northwestern China. Each of these groups has its own language, and the Chinese government officially recognizes no fewer than 52 separate languages. Different culture groups also have their own traditions, encompassing everything from the foods they eat to the clothes they wear. They practice many different religious faiths.

However, even the largest of these ethnic groups, the Mongols, Uighurs, Tibetans, and Kazakhs, are relatively small in number. Together, all the ethnic minorities represent only 8 percent of China's population. The remaining 92 percent, more than 1 billion people, belong to the Han ethnic group. Taking its name from the Han Dynasty—established about 2,200 years ago—the Han have been the dominant ethnic group in China for centuries.

The Chinese Language The Han people speak Chinese. Written Chinese is unusual in that it is nonphonetic. Most other forms of writing use alphabets that give an indication of the sounds of words. The written form of Chinese, however, generally gives no clues to its pronunciation.

Written Chinese involves the use of **ideograms**—pictures or characters representing a thing or an idea. To perform a simple task like reading a newspaper, a person needs to master as many as 2,000 to 3,000 characters. To achieve a solid grasp of the entire written Chinese language, however, requires knowledge of at least 20,000 different characters.

Though these characters are pronounced in different ways in different parts of China, people throughout the nation can always communicate in writing. Why? Because they use the same characters. To help bridge the gap between spoken dialects, in 1956 the Chinese government declared Mandarin, the northern dialect, to be the official language. When students learn to read and write Chinese characters, they are taught Mandarin, whether or not they speak a different dialect locally.

Religions and Beliefs Ancient philosophies still have a great impact in China.

GEOFacts

For more than 500 years before the European printing press was invented in the mid-1400s, Chinese printers were using wood blocks, with ideograms carved in relief, to print texts.

The Art of Writing

Cultures Calligraphy is an important art form in East Asia, but even basic literacy requires dedication and concentration.

Place *How many characters, or ideograms, must one learn to master Chinese?*

Word Origin

Nonphonetic Written Chinese is nonphonetic—the way it looks does not relate to speech sounds. The word *phonetic* comes from the Greek *phonetikos,* meaning "vocal."

Connecting With . . .

Art Calligraphy, an ornate form of writing, has a special place in Chinese culture. In calligraphy, a brush and ink are used to "paint" Chinese characters on paper or silk. The calligrapher must learn only eight basic strokes, but to become accomplished at the art of calligraphy takes years of practice. One great calligrapher, Wang Hsi-chih, is said to have spent 15 years practicing a single character.

Building Vocabulary

Ask students to scan the subsection Religions and Beliefs beginning on this page and list any bolded terms or uncommon words they find. Ask students to determine the meaning of the unknown terms by reading the surrounding text. After reading the section, instruct students to look up their words in the Glossary or a dictionary to determine if their definitions were correct. Ask volunteers to share their definitions with the class.

TEST PREPARATION

Have students read the subsection The Chinese Language on this page to complete the following sentence.
The written Chinese language is difficult to master because it is composed primarily of —
   A   an extensive alphabet
   B   over 30,000 letters
   C   nonphonetic ideograms
   D   vowels

Answer to Photo Caption

A person needs to master at least 2,000 to 3,000 characters to read a newspaper and at least 20,000 different characters to grasp the entire written language.

ACTIVITY

Connecting With...

History Have students research the philosophy of Confucius and how it influences Chinese society. Ask students to list the virtues of a good person in Confucian society. Then write the following saying by Confucius on the board: *"When you see a good person, try to emulate his or her example, and when you see a bad person, search yourself for his or her faults."* Have students put together a skit to illustrate this saying.

ACTIVITY

Vocabulary

Atheism Refer to the Key Terms list on page 665. Ask a volunteer to look up *atheism* in the Glossary and read its definition aloud. Ask another volunteer to paraphrase the definition. Ask: **Why would a government impose atheism?** (Possible answer: It does not want any competing ideologies to influence people.)

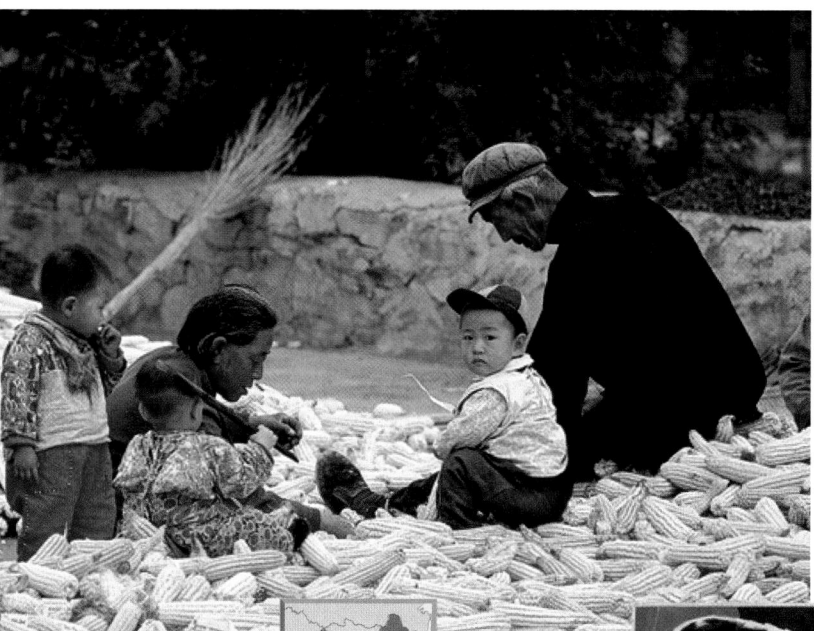

The Chinese Family

Cultures Confucian tradition encourages settled roles in families to promote a stable and harmonious society. Rural families rely on large families to do the farm work.

Place *How might Chinese philosophy and the needs of the rural poor make it difficult to persuade people to limit the size of their families?*

The Chinese practice a variety of belief systems, but the traditional faiths of Buddhism, Daoism, and Confucianism are the most popular.

Daoism is based on the teachings of Laozi (low DZEE), who lived from 604 to 531 B.C. According to Daoism, the path to true happiness lies in living in a harmonious relationship with the natural world. This path is called the right way, or Dao (dow).

Confucianism is the most widely practiced faith. It is a philosophy based on a collection of the teachings of Confucius, called the *Analects*. Confucius, who lived from about 551 to 479 B.C., believed that society functioned best if every person respected the laws and behaved according to his or her position. For example, Confucius taught that parents should set good examples for their children and that children should obey their parents. Similarly, he stressed the importance of honoring one's ancestors. Today, many Chinese homes have altars where candles burn in memory of loved ones. Also, certain holidays are devoted to ancestors.

Although these philosophies, and religions such as Buddhism, still have a powerful effect on Chinese life, China is officially an atheist state. **Atheism** denies the existence of God. According to communism, religion is nothing more than a set of myths designed to keep workers under the domination of the ruling classes.

On coming to power in China, the Communists discouraged all religious practice. They seized churches, temples, and other places of worship, turning some of them into meeting halls, schools, and museums. During the Cultural Revolution a few years later, the Red Guards destroyed many of these buildings in order to tear down the Four Olds.

Still, neither laws nor the violent Red Guards could wipe out 2,000 years of tradition. Many Chinese people continued to practice their religions. In the 1980s, the government eased restrictions

RESOURCE DIRECTORY

Teaching Resources
Unit 9, Chapter 31
• Section 3 Quiz, p. 16
Spanish Resources
• Section 3 Quiz, p. 79

Answer to Photo Caption

Rural families depend on their children to help with the workload. Children are also expected to take care of their aging parents. This, in addition to the strong philosophical belief of respect for the family, makes it difficult to limit family size.

Tai Chi

Cultures Many Chinese seek the health benefits of the ancient martial art Tai Chi (ty chee).

Place *What other ancient practices are used to promote health in modern China?*

on religious practices. One group that is not tolerated is Falun Gong. Falun Gong is a self-described spiritual movement that combines meditation, exercises, and principles from Buddhism and Daoism. It claims 70 million members in China alone. The Chinese government outlawed Falun Gong in 1999. As many as 10,000 Falun Gong members were arrested and sent to labor camps for "reeducation." Falun Gong supporters responded by protesting against the Chinese government in many other nations.

Traditional Medicine Although Western medicine is practiced in China, many people prefer traditional Chinese medicine. This discipline, dating back 2,000 years, is based on the idea that good health results from harmony between people and the environment. Traditional Chinese medicine relies on special diets, herbal remedies, breathing exercises, massage, and acupuncture. **Acupuncture** is the practice of inserting needles at specific points on the body to cure diseases or to ease pain.

SECTION 3 ASSESSMENT

1. **Key Terms** Define **(a)** ideogram, **(b)** atheism, **(c)** acupuncture.

2. **Population Growth** **(a)** Why did China's population grow dramatically during the rule of Mao Zedong? **(b)** How did Deng Xiaoping later try to control that growth?

3. **Cultures** In spite of China's vast area, why is its culture similar throughout the country?

4. **Critical Thinking** **Analyzing Information** How does the Chinese government's contract responsibility system for farmers conflict with its efforts to reduce population growth?

Activity

Take It to the NET

Writing a News Report *Time* magazine called China "cyberworld's hottest battlefield." Research the chief issues regarding online technology in China on the Internet. Then, summarize your findings in a news report. Visit the World Geography section of **www.phschool.com** for help in completing this activity.

Articles From ················
NATIONAL GEOGRAPHIC

The following article may be used to extend the content in this section.

Allen, Thomas B., and Reza, photographer. "Xinjiang." *National Geographic,* Vol. 189, No. 3 (Mar. 1996), pp. 2–43.

Once a remote area of many cultures, this western region of China has now opened its markets to the world.

People and Geography

pp. 670–671

Objectives

Upon completion of this feature, students should be able to:

◆ identify rights outlined in the Universal Declaration of Human Rights;

◆ describe human rights violations in China;

◆ explain the effects of these human rights violations.

National Geography Standards

The following National Geography Standards are highlighted in this feature: 1, 4, 9, 10, 12, 13

Bellringer

Ask students to list on the board activities that they consider rights. Remind them that "human rights" are rights that people are entitled to simply because they are born. As a group, determine which of the items listed are human rights, rather than privileges (such as driving a car). Explain what makes human rights different from privileges.

LESSON PLAN

1. Focus On the board, draw a circle and label it *Cultural Beliefs/ Governmental Practices*. Ask students to fill the circle with beliefs and practices that help create discrimination against women in China. Create similar circles for Xinjiang Muslims and Tibetan Buddhists.

2. Instruct Discuss how human rights violations in China have affected the economy and the lives of women, Buddhists, and Muslims. Have students make projections about how today's violations may affect future generations in China.

Answer to Photo Caption

It is widely accepted that the more education a person has, the better chance he or she has for employment.

People and Geography
Human Rights and China

A Global Issue

The Universal Declaration of Human Rights, adopted by the United Nations in 1948, states the issue: "Disregard and contempt for human rights have resulted in barbarous acts which have outraged the conscience of mankind." The declaration goes on to outline rights to which all are entitled. Life, liberty, and personal security are chief among these. Other rights include the freedoms of speech, religion, and assembly. The declaration also states that everyone has a right to an education, just working conditions, and equal pay for equal work. Additionally, government authority should be based on the people's will as expressed in free elections.

Unfortunately, disregard for human rights continues today. In southeastern Europe and central Africa for example, ethnic conflict has led to torture, mass murder, and forced migration. In South Asia, Southwest Asia, and other regions, human rights abuses stem from religious conflict. In China, abuse of human rights occurs in a variety of ways.

Women in China

Historically, women in China have had limited educational opportunities. One reason is that a son, who is expected to care for his parents in old age, is perceived by some to have more economic value than a daughter. Chinese families that cannot afford to have all their children attend school often keep the girls at home. As a result, Chinese women suffer economic disadvantages. Job opportunities are often limited for those with inadequate education.

However, the Chinese government recognizes the need for an educated population. They have made attempts at educating rural women. They have offered training in agricultural studies and literacy. Nevertheless, some women from rural areas have migrated to the city, seeking higher wages and jobs that require less physical labor.

> Female*
> 13%
> Male*
> 4%
> *Aged 15–24
> **Illiteracy Rates**

Economic Inequality
How can lack of education limit a person's ability to obtain a secure financial future?

RESOURCE DIRECTORY

Teaching Resources
People and Geography
• Human Rights, pp. 47–52

Technology
World Geography Map and Photo Transparencies
• East Asia and the Pacific World: Political

Muslims in Xinjiang Province

Religious and ethnic minorities face discrimination in China. In Xinjiang (shin she ong) Province in Northwest China, the Uighurs (WEE gars), who practice Islam, are an ethnic minority. The Chinese government has placed strict restrictions on when and where they can practice their religion. The government has also encouraged members of the majority ethnic group, the Han Chinese, to migrate into the area. Statistically, the Han Chinese obtain higher-paying jobs and own more businesses than the Uighurs. Believing their rights are being violated, some Uighurs hope to win independence from China. However, the government is particularly intolerant of unrest in Xinjiang Province because it values the province as a key military location and as an important source of petroleum and other natural resources.

A Minority in China
What evidence is there that the Uighurs do not enjoy the same rights as the majority Han Chinese?

A History of Conflict
How can the rapid economic development of an area mask human rights issues?

Buddhists in Tibet

China's relationship to Tibet is a study in geopolitics, or the way one nation exerts control over another nation. In geopolitics, the political attitudes and actions of the past influence current world conditions. In Tibet's past, the area was ruled by a Buddhist leader, the Dalai Lama. Then, the Chinese government invaded and took control of Tibet in 1950. The Chinese government restricted the practice of Buddhism and encouraged Chinese people to move into the area. Just like the Uighurs in Xinjiang, Tibetans found themselves a minority group in their native land.

As the Chinese population in Tibet increased, the government improved the infrastructure of the area and encouraged economic development. Tourism has increased in Tibet, which has helped the economy to grow. The denial of Tibetan independence and religious freedom, however, remain important local and global issues.

Turning Points in Tibet: 1911–1990s

1911
Tibet gains independence from China.

1950
Chinese forces invade Tibet.

1959
Tibetan uprising crushed by Chinese.

1989
Dalai Lama awarded Nobel Peace Prize.

1990s
Tibetan monasteries rebuilt.

ASSESSMENT: Analyzing Causes and Effects

1. **Identify the Issue** Why do you think the United Nations felt it was necessary to issue the Universal Declaration of Human Rights?

2. **Identify Possible Causes** What are some of the causes of human rights violations?

3. **Identify Possible Effects** (a) What kinds of economic opportunities are available to women in rural China? (b) How does ethnic tension affect the economy of Xinjiang Province?

(c) How does Chinese rule violate the political rights of Tibetans?

4. **Make Generalizations** (a) Are all people treated equally in China? (b) Provide evidence to support your generalization.

5. **Make Recommendations** What are some ways in which nations and international organizations can promote human rights?

CUSTOMIZE FOR...

Less Proficient Readers

Find the Main Idea As students read the section Women in China, remind them that the main idea of a paragraph is sometimes mentioned twice: once near the beginning of the paragraph, and again at the end. Have them look for the main idea of the first paragraph. Also have them identify supporting details by looking for key words or expressions that introduce them, such as *one reason*.

---

3. Close/Reteach Have students write a paragraph that begins with the following sentence stem: "Economic opportunity is a human rights issue because. . ." Have them read their paragraphs aloud when they finish writing.

ACTIVITY

Enrichment

Human Rights Have students investigate how the United States government has responded to China's human rights record since 1989. Students should arrange their findings on a time line that begins in 1989 and continues to the present. Ask students to identify areas of controversy related to the U.S. response to China's human rights violations. (Verbal/Linguistic, Visual/Spatial)

Answers to Assessment

1. because there were many areas of the world in which people's basic rights were being denied

2. Answers include ethnic conflict, religious conflict, economic discrimination, and geopolitics.

3. (a) training in agricultural studies and literacy (b) Uighurs experience economic discrimination. (c) Tibetans have come under Chinese control.

4. (a–b) No; students' answers should reflect information from the text.

5. Possible answers: support the International Declaration of Human Rights; speak out against injustice; apply economic sanctions

---

Answer to Photo Caption

because statistically the Han Chinese have higher-paying jobs and own more businesses

Answer to Time Line Caption

If people have material goods, their lack of freedom is less apparent.

Objectives

Upon completion of Section 4, students should be able to:

◆ describe how Taiwan has become an industrial power in Asia;

◆ explain how Hong Kong's relationship with China makes Hong Kong's future uncertain;

◆ discuss how the standard of living in Mongolia has improved in recent years.

National Geography Standards

The following National Geography Standards are highlighted in this section: 2, 3, 4, 5, 6, 8, 9, 10, 11, 12, 13, 16, 17, 18

Bellringer

Ask students how they would feel if they found out that the United States would soon become part of another country. Tell students they will be reading about a region that experienced a similar situation.

LESSON PLAN

1. Focus Tell students that in 1997 Hong Kong, a small, prosperous island off the coast of China, ended its temporary status as a British colony and once again became part of China. Have students speculate on what problems this transition could create for the residents of Hong Kong.

2. Instruct Make a four-column chart on the board with the following labels: *Physical Geography, Economic Activities, Political System,* and *Relations with China.* Have students use their textbooks to complete the chart for Taiwan, Hong Kong, and Mongolia.

3. Close/Reteach List the following on the board: *Taiwan, Hong Kong,* and *Mongolia.* Have students vote on which country is "the most likely to succeed." After the vote is in, have students explain why they voted the way they did.

4 China's Neighbors

Reading Focus

• How did Taiwan become an industrial power in Asia?

• In what way does Hong Kong's relationship with China make Hong Kong's future uncertain?

• How has the standard of living in Mongolia improved in recent years?

Key Terms

buffer

provisional government

exodus

Main Idea Taiwan, Hong Kong, and Mongolia have distinct characteristics and unique roles in Asian concerns.

Cultures Modern buildings surround the Chiang Kai-shek Memorial Hall located in Taipei, Taiwan.

The island state of Taiwan lies off China's southeastern coast. Hong Kong is part peninsula and part island, lying off China's southern coast. Mongolia fringes China's northern border, forming a **buffer,** or protective zone, between China and Russia. During the second half of the twentieth century, China cast a large shadow over its three smaller neighbors.

Taiwan: A World Apart

The small volcanic island of Taiwan lies 100 miles (160 km) off China's southeast coast. Mountains, its major landform, rise in tiers to an elevation of about 13,000 feet (3,960 m). This distinctive landscape gives the island its name. In Chinese, *Taiwan* means "terraced bay."

The Emergence of Taiwan The Nationalists, led by Chiang Kai-shek, fled China and Communist rule and arrived in Taiwan in 1949. This new group of immigrants, primarily business

people and military and government leaders, joined native Taiwanese living on the island. On their arrival, Chiang Kai-shek set up a temporary **provisional government.** Although repressive, Chiang's government allowed free enterprise to flourish. Meanwhile, on the mainland, Marxist collectivism was ruling political and economic life.

During the next few decades, a dispute raged between the Chinese and Taiwanese governments. The Nationalist government in Taipei (ty PAY), Taiwan's capital, claimed it represented all of China. The Communist government on the mainland claimed that it was the official government of China.

Much of the Western world backed the Nationalists in the hope that Chiang Kai-shek could oust the Communists. By the 1960s, however, many Western powers recognized that the Communists in China were there to stay. They began to seek better relations with the Beijing government. Then, in 1971, the United Nations accepted

672 Chapter 31 ▪ China

RESOURCE DIRECTORY

Teaching Resources

Unit 9, Chapter 31
• Section 4 Guided Reading and Review, p. 17
Guide to the Essentials (English/Spanish)
• Section Summary, Chapter 31, Section 4
Mental Mapping booklet
• Unit 9 Checklist, p. 115

Technology

Guided Reading Audiotapes (English/Spanish), Chapter 31, Section 4

Section Reading Support Transparencies, Chapter 31, Section 4
World Geography Map and Photo Transparencies
• East Asia and the Pacific World: Maps and Photos
Book on CD, Chapter 31
Social Studies Skills Tutor CD-ROM
Companion Web site, www.phschool.com
• Chapter 31 Activities

mainland China as a member. It voted to expel Taiwan, which had represented China at the United Nations since 1949. Immediately, most countries also recognized Beijing as the legal seat of government for China.

Since the 1970s, Taiwan has existed in an international limbo. Much of the world has refused to recognize it as a country. Yet, many countries that do not recognize Taiwan still provide it with money and technical assistance. They also trade with Taiwan, helping make it one of the leading economic powers in Asia.

Taiwan's Economy When the Nationalist government arrived in 1949, it instituted a sweeping land-reform program that placed the land in the hands of tenant farmers. The government also encouraged farmers to use more fertilizers, plant more productive seeds, and practice intensive farming methods such as double cropping. As a result, Taiwan's farm production almost doubled.

The Nationalists also set in motion an industrial modernization program. With the help of foreign investment—especially from the United States—Taiwan quickly developed textile, food-processing, plastics, and chemical industries. This industrial growth was truly remarkable, given that nearly all the raw materials for these industries had to be imported.

In recent years Taiwan has pursued new industrial goals, concentrating on high-technology industries, such as electronics. Selling their products to huge markets in the United States and Europe, Taiwanese companies have greatly contributed to their country's rapid economic growth. This growth has allowed most Taiwanese to enjoy a high standard of living while holding on to their cultural heritage. In 1996, Taiwan's president noted:

66Taiwan has been able in recent decades to preserve traditional culture on the one hand and to come into wide contact with Western democracy and science and modern business culture on the other.**99**

Taiwan's Future Until 1987, Taiwan had no official contact with China. In November of

Road Hazard

Environmental Change Many people, even whole families, travel by motor scooter in Taiwan's crowded cities. Air quality, however, is a constant worry.
Human-Environment Interaction *How might Taiwan's rapid economic growth have contributed to air pollution?*

that year, the Taiwanese were finally permitted to visit relatives on the mainland. Soon bans on trade and investment were lifted. Taiwanese investors began pouring huge sums into China's Special Economic Zones.

Reteach

Writing a Telegram Tell students to imagine that they are traveling in Taiwan, Hong Kong, and Mongolia. Have them send a telegram from each place to friends back home. Each telegram should be no more than 25 words and should summarize what the traveler has found there. (Visual/Spatial)

Taiwan's Export Economy

Economic Activities Taiwan's economy is based on foreign trade. It imports raw materials, like oil and basic metals, and exports manufactured goods, like the microchips shown here.

Place *How has Taiwan's economic development changed its standard of living?*

China, however, still viewed Taiwan as a province, not an independent country. In 1996 it conducted war games in the Taiwan Strait, hoping to persuade Taiwan to vote against the pro-independence candidate, Lee Teng-hui. The tactic failed utterly, and Lee was elected. But Lee spoke softly on the topic of independence. He pointed out that Taiwan had "proved eloquently that the Chinese are capable of practicing democracy." He hoped Taiwan could serve as a leader and model to China as it modernized and someday became a democracy as well.

Relations between China and Taiwan remain tense. In 2000, Taiwan's president stated that Taiwan would claim its independence only if attacked. China responded that it would attack if Taiwan refused to talk of reunification.

Hong Kong Returns to China

Hong Kong faces an even more uncertain future. Located on China's southern coast, Hong Kong consists of the Kowloon Peninsula, several large islands, and many smaller islands. It covers only about 400 square miles (1,000 sq km), yet it is home to more than 6 million people. With average population densities in excess of 15,000 people per square mile (5,800 per sq km), Hong Kong ranks as one of the most crowded places in the world.

The Growth of Hong Kong Hong Kong did not always bustle with human activity. Before the 1800s, it was largely uninhabited. During the 1800s, Britain used the site both as a naval base and as a way station for ships sailing to its far-flung Pacific empire. In 1898, the British forced China to agree to lease Hong Kong and other land in the area to them for ninety-nine years. During these years, Hong Kong enjoyed the benefits of free enterprise.

During the twentieth century, Hong Kong's deep, natural harbor and its central location on East Asian sea routes helped the port to become a leader in world trade. Hong Kong also became an important manufacturing center, specializing in textiles, clothing, and electrical appliances. In developing these industries, Hong Kong took advantage of a large pool of human resources.

674 Chapter 31 ▪ China

Answer to Photo Caption

Due to economic growth, Taiwan's standard of living is high.

Following World War II, millions of people, fleeing war and political unrest elsewhere in Asia, sought a safe haven in Hong Kong. During the first fifteen years of Communist rule in China, Hong Kong took in more than 1 million Chinese refugees. It was this **exodus,** or mass departure, that provided a vast supply of inexpensive labor for the factories of Hong Kong.

Hong Kong exports about 90 percent of the goods its factories produce. Recent estimates set the value of Hong Kong's trade—both imports and exports—at about $170 billion, about that of China, its giant neighbor to the north.

The End of the Lease Throughout its short history, Hong Kong developed with little interference from China. But the two places have developed an interdependence. Hong Kong has long obtained most of its vital resources—fresh water, for example—from the mainland. Also, China has used Hong Kong as an exchange point for its trade with the West. Furthermore, since the establishment of the Special Economic Zones, Hong Kong has been a leading investor in the Chinese economy.

Hong Kong became part of China again on July 1, 1997. An agreement between Britain and China had provided that for the 50 years following that date, Hong Kong was to function as a Special Administrative Region. It would be free to carry on as before, both economically and politically.

Events prior to the handover put the agreement in doubt, however. In 1992 the governor of Hong Kong introduced a plan for democratic reform. The plan called for an increase in the number of eligible voters, from 110,000 to 2.7 million. The Chinese were outraged. One Chinese official responded, "[The governor] cannot install Western-style democracy in Hong Kong

GLOBAL CONNECTIONS

Government Formerly controlled by the Portuguese, Macao was one of the oldest European settlements in East Asia. Macao consists of a peninsula and two small islands. It is only about 10 square miles (26 sq km) in area, but has about 446,000 inhabitants. Macao returned to Chinese rule in 1999.

Hong Kong's Future

Government and Citizenship As Great Britain sailed out of Hong Kong's future, many wondered what would become of the former British colony as it reverted to Chinese rule. Many feared that the Chinese Communist government would bring an end to the free enterprise system to which Hong Kong owes its success.

Location *How did Hong Kong's location help it become a leader in world trade?*

BACKGROUND

The Global Economy

A Shopper's Paradise To help promote tourism by encouraging jet-set shopping, Hong Kong's government has a duty-free policy on all goods except liquor, tobacco, cosmetics, hydrocarbon oils, and methyl alcohol. Many items, including electronics, often make their first appearance on the world market in Hong Kong.

ACTIVITY

Group Work

Activity: Conducting market research

Purpose: Have all students look in their homes and in stores for products made in Hong Kong, particularly clothing, electronics, small appliances, and plastic goods. Each group should compile a list of these goods, including the names of manufacturers.

Roles: Researchers, a scribe, and a spokesperson

Result: Have each spokesperson present group findings to the class. Point out that many U.S. companies manufacture goods in East Asia. Discuss why this is done and how it affects U.S. workers.

Answer to Photo Caption

Hong Kong's deep, natural harbor and its central location on East Asian sea routes helped it become a leader in world trade.

Chapter 31 ▪ Section 4   **675**

TEST PREPARATION

Have students read the subsection Hong Kong Returns to China to complete the following sentence.

As a Special Administrative Region, Hong Kong is allowed many freedoms. However, it is not allowed to —

A hold democratic elections
B trade freely with other nations
C have a free press
Ⓓ govern itself independently of China

designed to infect China." Soon after the July 1, 1997, handover, Hong Kong's new political leader, Tung Chee-hwa, replaced the democratically elected members of the assembly with pro-China lawmakers.

Hong Kong's worst fears did not come to pass. The local government permits modest protests and a free press. When limited elections were held in May 1998, many democrats won seats in the new assembly. However, as one professional explained, "If you elect someone who is against China, then Hong Kong is in trouble. But if you elect someone who follows everything China says, then Hong Kong is also in trouble."

China knows that Hong Kong must remain healthy economically. A policy of "one country, two systems" allows Hong Kong's economy to continue to flourish.

Mongolia

Mongolia is a vast, dry land more than twice the size of Texas. The Gobi Desert occupies the southern areas, while steppe vegetation covers much of the rest of the land.

In the thirteenth century, Mongolia was one of the world's great powers. The Mongols, under Genghiz Khan and his descendants, ruled an empire that extended from China in the east to Hungary and Poland in the west. In later centuries, however, Mongolia came under Chinese rule.

Mongolia remained a province of China until 1921 when, with the backing of the Soviets, the Mongols declared their independence. Ten years later, following Russia's example, Mongolia adopted communism. After Russia democratized its government in the early 1990s, Mongolia too held its first democratic elections. The winners were former Communists who had renounced communism and promised to create a free market economy. Since the 1990s, people have been allowed to purchase state-owned businesses, and a stock exchange has opened its doors to investors.

Traditionally, the Mongols have made a living through nomadic herding. Even today, herding still ranks as the major economic activity on Mongolia's steppes, which are pasture for about 33 million livestock. However, Mongolia has developed some industries. Among the most important rank coal and copper mining; food processing; and manufacturing leather goods, chemicals, and cement. With industrialization, Mongolia has become more urban. About 63 percent of the population now live in urban areas, many in Ulan Bator (oo lahn BAH tawr), the capital.

Many Mongolians still live as nomads in mobile tents, but they are becoming increasingly connected to the rest of the world. Mongolians visit Internet cafes and surf the Web via mobile phones. The Mongolian government hopes to make the Internet accessible to all citizens by 2010. Mongolia realizes that it is cheaper to use wireless technology than it is to install traditional telephone lines.

SECTION 4 ASSESSMENT

1. Key Terms Define **(a)** buffer, **(b)** provisional government, **(c)** exodus.

2. Economic Systems How did Taiwan become an economic power in Asia?

3. Government and Citizenship Why does Hong Kong's relationship with China make its future uncertain?

4. Economic Activities How has the standard of living in Mongolia improved in recent years?

5. Critical Thinking Recognizing Points of View How do you think the Communist Chinese reacted to Taiwan president Lee Teng-hui's promise that Taiwan would lead China into democracy?

Activity

Designing a Poster Review this section on Taiwan, Hong Kong, and Mongolia, taking notes on reasons why people would want to travel to each place. Then, design a poster for one of the three places. The poster should showcase a person, a place, or an event that represents the country.

676 Chapter 31 ▪ China

Analyzing Primary Sources

A primary source is information produced during or soon after an event, usually by a participant or observer. Examples of primary sources are letters, journals, news photos, paintings, and eyewitness accounts. A writer's personal involvement in an event may make the account biased or inaccurate. For that reason, primary sources must be analyzed critically to determine their reliability.

Learn the Skill Use the following steps to learn how to understand and analyze primary sources.

1 *Identify the nature of the document.* Below are two primary sources describing events that occurred when Chinese authorities used their army to end a mass protest in Beijing's Tiananmen Square in June 1989. Passage A is the statement of a student who was there. Passage B is a quote from a Chinese officer who helped direct the army. His statement, released in March 1990, was among the few given by Chinese leaders after the killings. *What makes each of these documents a primary source?*

2 *Identify the purpose of the document.* It is important to try to determine the purpose or goal of the author of a primary source. *What is the main point of view of the author of each of the passages below?*

3 *Decide how reliable the source is.* It is also important to judge if the author's point of view is biased. You may need other information about the author or the event in order to determine

how reliable the source is. **(a)** *How convincing is the speaker in each passage?* **(b)** *Do you think that the two speakers may have any interests that might lead them to conceal or distort the truth?* **(c)** *What other information do you think would help you determine the reliability of each source?*

4 *Draw conclusions.* You can understand the meaning of historical events with greater accuracy by identifying and analyzing primary source documents. **(a)** *Based on what you have read, what happened in Tiananmen Square?* **(b)** *Which speaker is more directly responsible for the events in Tiananmen Square? Why?*

 ## Do It Yourself

Practice the Skill Find another primary source document about the student protest in Tiananmen Square in 1989. (Remember that a primary source can be a photograph, a sound recording, a newspaper article, or any other eyewitness account.) Analyze the document and draw conclusions. Compare your document to the passages below. Has your opinion about the incident changed? Explain.

Apply the Skill See Chapter 31 Review and Assessment.

Passage A	Passage B
We expected tear gas and rubber bullets. But they used machine guns and drove over people with tanks. . . . It was like a dream. From where I was, the sound of crying was louder than gunfire, but I kept seeing people falling. One line of students would stand and then get shot down, and then another line of students would stand and the same thing would happen. There was gunfire from all directions. The soldiers were shooting everyone. —Student protester	The People's Liberation Army intervention in Tiananmen was a matter of necessity. . . . At the beginning, we stressed to our forces, "When beaten don't fight back; when scolded don't reply." First the PLA fired into the air as a warning. But a small minority shot at the PLA and snatched weapons. Under these circumstances, the PLA had to fire back in self-defense. —Chinese army officer

---

Teaching the Skill
After students have read the introductory paragraph and passages A and B, ask them to explain how each passage made them feel. Note the sometimes personalized nature of primary sources. Discuss situations in which primary sources might be helpful and situations in which primary sources might not be reliable. Finally, work through the steps of Learning the Skill with the students.

Answers to Learn the Skill
1. People who witnessed the event made the statements.
2. The speaker of Passage A believes the army responded with excessive force and cruelty. The speaker of Passage B states that the army had to respond the way it did for self-defense purposes.
3. (a) Students should recognize that Passage A paints a vivid scene, while Passage B relies more on general description. As a result, Passage A seems more convincing. **(b)** Since the speakers were participants, their observations may have been influenced by their roles. **(c)** Possible answer: an account from a reference book, such as an encyclopedia
4. (a) Answers will vary. **(b)** Answers will vary but should include an explanation of the student's choice.

Answers to Practice the Skill
Encourage students to explain their opinions of the demonstration after analyzing the new primary source.

CUSTOMIZE FOR...

Honors/PreAP
Creating a Poster Have students use books, magazines, and the Internet to find out more about the specific political reforms that students were demanding during the protest in Tiananmen Square in 1989. Ask them to design a poster that captures the message that the students were trying to send to the Chinese government.

Creating a Chapter Summary
As a reteaching opportunity, pair a more able student with a less able student to complete this chapter summary.

Possible entries: **Regions:** Northwest, Northeast, Southwest, Southeast **Government:** Nationalist until 1949, Communist to present **Culture:** Huge population, Ethnic differences, Traditional medicines **Economy:** Four Modernizations, Light industry, New openness to the West

Reviewing Key Terms
1–10. Students' puzzles should demonstrate a clear understanding of the key terms.

Understanding Key Ideas
11. Mao's Cultural Revolution resulted in the exile or death of hundreds of thousands of innocent people and a ruined economy. Many youths lost their chance for an education, making economic recovery very difficult.
12. They introduced elements of free enterprise into the economic system.
13. **(a)** to control the flooding of the Yangzi and to generate power **(b)** Many Chinese will be forced to resettle elsewhere. Others fear the shoddy construction of the dam.
14. Tibetans wish to practice their traditions and culture freely. Since China took control, it destroyed many symbols of Tibet's Buddhist tradition, replaced its theocracy with Communist rule, forced nomads onto farms, and recently placed further restrictions on Tibetans' freedoms.
15. Their economic and political practices differ from China's. Proximity and past experiences with China make them fearful that China will exert its influence over them.

Critical Thinking and Writing
16. Possible answer: The Long March strengthened the resolve of those who survived it. Also, once the Communists were settled in Shaanxi, they were free to recruit new members and strengthen their power.

Creating a Chapter Summary

On a sheet of paper, draw a graphic organizer like this one. Fill in each oval with information from the chapter. You may wish to add more ovals. Some information has been filled in to help you get started.

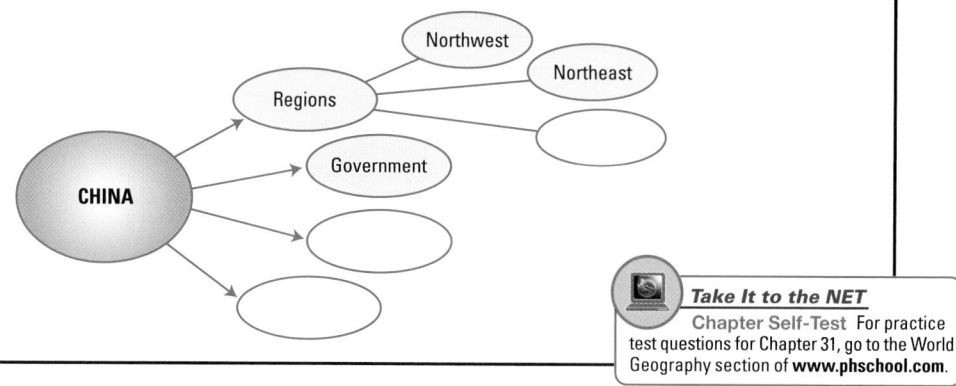

Take It to the NET
Chapter Self-Test For practice test questions for Chapter 31, go to the World Geography section of **www.phschool.com**.

Reviewing Key Terms

Use the chapter key terms below to create a crossword puzzle. Exchange puzzles with a classmate and complete the puzzles.

1. sphere of influence   6. autonomous region
2. abdicate   7. ideogram
3. warlord   8. acupuncture
4. double cropping   9. provisional government
5. theocrat   10. exodus

Understanding Key Ideas

11. Understanding the Past What effect did the Cultural Revolution have on Chinese society?

12. Economic Systems How did the Four Modernizations change China's economic focus?

13. Environmental Change (a) What are the purposes of the Three Gorges Dam? **(b)** Why has its construction stirred such controversy?

14. Cooperation and Conflict Why do the people of Tibet wish to regain independence from China?

15. Government and Citizenship Why are Taiwan, Hong Kong, and Mongolia wary of China?

Critical Thinking and Writing

16. Developing a Hypothesis How might the Long March have helped the growth of communism in China instead of destroying it?

17. Analyzing Causes and Effects What problems resulted from China's establishment of Special Economic Zones?

18. Identifying Alternatives What alternative courses could the Chinese government have taken in dealing with the prodemocracy movement in 1989?

19. Analyzing Causes and Effects Why have the south and the coast of China started to become more popular places to live than Beijing, the capital?

---

17. a shortage of jobs for the millions who migrated to the coastal cities and increased urban crime
18. Possible answer: The government could have made a greater effort to negotiate with the demonstrators or could have used a less harsh method to disperse them.

19. With the establishment of the Special Economic Zones, the south and the coast have grown economically at a far faster rate than has Beijing. Foreign investment and growth have attracted more people in search of better jobs.

Applying Skills

Analyzing Primary Sources Refer to the Skills for Life lesson on page 677 to answer these questions:

20. Why can a photograph be considered a primary source?

21. Do you think that the authors of Passage A and Passage B may have any interests that might lead them to conceal or distort the truth? Explain.

Reading a Map Study the map below, and answer the following questions:

22. (a) In which region is it most likely that water scarcity is an issue? (b) Why would water scarcity be an issue there?

23. Why do you think the Southeast region is so densely populated?

24. (a) In which region do the major rivers of China have their sources? (b) How might a drought in this region affect irrigation projects in other regions? Explain.

China: REGIONS

[Map of China with regions labeled: NORTHWEST, NORTHEAST, NORTH CHINA PLAIN, SOUTHWEST (XIZANG), PLATEAU OF TIBET, SOUTHEAST. Features include TAKLA MAKAN DESERT, GOBI DESERT, Tropic of Cancer, INDIAN OCEAN, South China Sea. Scale bars show 0–1,000 mi and 0–1,000 km.]

Test Preparation

Read the question and choose the best answer.

25. Economic reforms during the 1970s and 1980s encouraged many Chinese citizens to push for —

A an end to the one-child policy

B an end to martial law

C political reforms

D changes in environmental policy

Activities

USING THE REGIONAL ATLAS

Review the Regional Atlas for East Asia and the Pacific World and Chapter 31. Write a list of questions that compares China to its neighbors, Taiwan, Hong Kong, and Mongolia. Then, exchange lists with a partner and answer the questions.

MENTAL MAPPING

Study a map of China and its neighbors. Then, on a separate piece of paper, draw a sketch map of the area from memory. Label the following places on your map:

- Shanghai
- Yangzi River
- Hong Kong
- South China Sea
- Mongolia
- Plateau of Tibet
- Ulan Bator
- Beijing
- Taiwan
- Huang He (Yellow River)

Take It to the NET

Creating a Diagram Some Mongolians live a nomadic lifestyle. Other Mongolians live a more cosmopolitan lifestyle. Search the Internet to find examples of each. Then, create a diagram that compares how nomadic living and urban living are alike and different. Visit the World Geography section of **www.phschool.com** for help in completing this activity.

Applying Skills

20. A photograph is a primary source because someone who is either a participant in or observer of the event produces it.

21. Possible answer: The author of Passage B might be trying to conceal the truth because if the Chinese government were discovered to be suppressing human rights, this revelation could jeopardize its political and economic ties with foreign countries.

22. (a) the Northwest region (b) Most of the region is desert with no coastline, no lakes, and limited access to rivers.

23. The region offers many economic opportunities: The climate and fertile soil are ideal for agriculture; its location along the coasts allows for industrial growth and overseas trade; and its waterways allow transportation of goods into the interior.

24. (a) Southwest (b) A lack of precipitation in the Southwest would decrease the rivers' flow, so there would be less water for irrigation projects in other regions.

Test Preparation
25. C

Activities

Using the Regional Atlas
Encourage students to ask about a variety of topics—such as physical characteristics, history, economic activities, and political challenges. After checking students' answers for accuracy, work with students to create an in-class game that tests their knowledge.

Mental Mapping
To check their work, have students compare their maps to those in the Regional Atlas.

Take It to the Net
Students' work should reflect sound research. Diagrams should have several entries and be easy to read.

MENTAL MAPPING

Games for Review See pages 58–63 of the Simulations, Games, and Lab Activities booklet for games to review place names.

Chapter Map Test Students should use the completed outline maps and the Unit 9 Checklist in their Atlas Portfolios to prepare for the Chapter 31 Map Test. Point out to students that the test will cover only those place names on the Unit Checklist relating to China, Mongolia, and Taiwan.

Alternative Assessment

Final Evaluation

Writing a Position Paper Use the Position Paper Evaluation Form on page 9 of the Alternative Assessment booklet in the Prentice Hall Assessment System to evaluate students' papers. Either teachers or students can complete the forms to indicate which level of work was achieved for each of the criteria. The evaluation should include specific examples and comments.

Resource Manager

	CORE INSTRUCTION	READING/SKILLS
Chapter-Level Resources	**Teaching Resources** ■ **Unit 9**/Ch. 32 • Reviewing Main Ideas, p. 34 ■ **Mental Mapping booklet** • Unit 9 Checklist, p. 115 ■ **Simulations, Games, and Lab Activities** • Place Location Review Games, pp. 58–63 ■ **Creative Teaching Activities** • The Balance of Trade, p. 34 ● **TeacherExpress™ CD-ROM**, Ch. 32 ■ **Companion Web site,** **www.phschool.com** • eTeach	**Teaching Resources** ■ **Unit 9**/Ch. 32 • Map/Graph Skills, p. 36 ● **Book on CD**, Ch. 32 ● **Social Studies Skills Tutor CD-ROM**
1 Japan: The Land of the Rising Sun 1. List the chief physical characteristics of Japan. 2. Explain why Japan has a variety of climates. 3. Describe what factors encourage unity among the Japanese people.	**Teaching Resources** ■ **Unit 9**/Ch. 32 • Guided Reading and Review, p. 28 ● **Prentice Hall Presentation Pro CD-ROM**, Ch. 32, Sec. 1	**Teaching Resources** ■ **Guide to the Essentials (English/Spanish)** • Section Summary, Ch. 32, Sec. 1 ■ **Mental Mapping booklet** • Outline Map 32, p. 124 ▦ **Guided Reading Audiotapes (English/Spanish)**, Ch. 32, Sec. 1 ⚏ **Section Reading Support Transparencies**, Ch. 32, Sec. 1
2 Japan's Economic Development 1. Discuss why Japan isolated itself from the West and what happened when new relations were established in the 1800s. 2. Explain why Japan attempted to gain control of neighboring countries. 3. Summarize Japan's role in World War II and how it affected Japan's status at the war's end. 4. Describe how Japan was able to prosper economically after World War II.	**Teaching Resources** ■ **Unit 9**/Ch. 32 • Guided Reading and Review, p. 30 ● **Prentice Hall Presentation Pro CD-ROM**, Ch. 32, Sec. 2	**Teaching Resources** ■ **Guide to the Essentials (English/Spanish)** • Section Summary, Ch. 32, Sec. 2 ▦ **Guided Reading Audiotapes (English/Spanish)**, Ch. 32, Sec. 2 ⚏ **Section Reading Support Transparencies**, Ch. 32, Sec. 2
3 The Koreas: A Divided Peninsula 1. Identify the cultural elements the Koreans adapted from the Chinese. 2. Explain how the Korean Peninsula became two separate countries. 3. Describe how the physical characteristics of North Korea and South Korea differ. 4. Explain why reunification is a challenge to both North Korea and South Korea.	**Teaching Resources** ■ **Unit 9**/Ch. 32 • Guided Reading and Review, p. 32 ● **Prentice Hall Presentation Pro CD-ROM**, Ch. 32, Sec. 3	**Teaching Resources** ■ **Guide to the Essentials (English/Spanish)** • Section Summary, Ch. 32, Sec. 3 ▦ **Guided Reading Audiotapes (English/Spanish)**, Ch. 32, Sec. 3 ⚏ **Section Reading Support Transparencies**, Ch. 32, Sec. 3

ENRICHMENT/HONORS/PreAP

Teaching Resources

Unit 9/Ch. 32
- Critical Thinking, p. 35

Mental Mapping booklet
- Atlas Activity, p. 125

Social Studies Skills Handbook
- Study and Research Skills, pp. 94–108

World Geography Map and Photo Transparencies
- East Asia and the Pacific World: Maps and Photos

World Geography Videos
- Location: Japan and the Koreas, Tape 4

Companion Web site, www.phschool.com
- Chapter 32 Activities

Teaching Resources

Social Studies Skills Handbook
- Identifying Alternatives, p. 51

Companion Web site, www.phschool.com
- Chapter 32 Activities

Companion Web site, www.phschool.com
- Chapter 32 Activities

Companion Web site, www.phschool.com
- Chapter 32 Activities

ASSESSMENT

PRENTICE HALL
ASSESSMENT SYSTEM

Core Assessment
- ExamView Test Bank booklet, Ch. 32
- ExamView Test Bank CD-ROM, Ch. 32

Standardized Test Preparation

Review and Reteach
- Review Book for World Geography, pp. 19–20

Practice and Assess
- Test-taking Strategies With Transparencies for High School

  Test-taking Strategy Poster

- Alternative Assessment booklet
- Test Prep Book for World Geography

Teaching Resources

Unit 9/Ch. 32
- Section Quizzes, pp. 29, 31, 33
- Test Forms A and B, pp. 37–42

Guide to the Essentials (English/Spanish)
- Chapter 32 Test

Spanish Resources, Ch. 32
- Section Quizzes, pp. 81–83

Mental Mapping booklet
- Chapter 32 Map Test, p. 126

Companion Web site, www.phschool.com
- Chapter 32 Self-Test

CUSTOMIZE FOR INDIVIDUAL NEEDS

Gifted and Talented
- Teacher's Edition, Customize for . . . , p. 685

Honors/PreAP
- Teacher's Edition, Customize for . . . , pp. 691, 695

Less Proficient Readers
- Guide to the Essentials (English), Ch. 32, Section Summaries
- Guided Reading Audiotapes (English), Ch. 32
- Section Reading Support Transparencies, Ch. 32
- Book on CD, Ch. 32
- Teacher's Edition, Reading Strategy, pp. 685, 688, 694
- Teacher's Edition, Activity: Vocabulary, pp. 683, 694
- Teacher's Edition, Customize for . . . , p. 697

Students Acquiring English/ESL
- Guide to the Essentials (English/Spanish), Ch. 32
- Guided Reading Audiotapes (English/Spanish), Ch. 32
- Section Reading Support Transparencies, Ch. 32
- Book on CD, Ch. 32

Less Proficient Writers
- Alternative Assessment, Writing Assignment Rubric, p. 6

SECTIONS

1 Japan: The Land of the Rising Sun

2 Japan's Economic Development

3 The Koreas: A Divided Peninsula

Japan and the Koreas

MENTAL MAPPING

Ask students to look at the map on this page, and point out that North and South Korea lie on the Korean Peninsula, which extends south from northeastern China. Japan lies off the east coast of Asia. Have students name the bodies of water that lie between Japan and the Koreas. (Sea of Japan and Korea Strait)

Mapping the Region Ask students to sketch their own outline maps like the one on this page, or distribute the Chapter 32 Outline Map on page 124 of the Mental Mapping booklet in the Teaching Resources. Instruct students to lightly shade each country a different color. Then ask them to label the countries, cities, and bodies of water shown on this map. Students should keep their maps in their Atlas Portfolios in order to prepare for the Chapter 32 Map Test.

Japan and the Koreas: POLITICAL

0 200 400 mi	
0 200 400 km	

Sinŭiju
P'yŏngyang
Namp'o
NORTH KOREA
Wŏnsan
Inch'ŏn
Seoul
SOUTH KOREA
Taejŏn
Taegu
Kwangju
Pusan
Yellow Sea
Cheju
Hiroshima
Korea Strait
Nagasaki
Kyushu
Shikoku
Kobe
Osaka
Kyoto
Nagoya
Yokohama
Tokyo
Honshu
Sendai
JAPAN
Sea of Japan (East Sea)
Sapporo
Hokkaido
Kuril Islands (administered by Russia, claimed by Japan)
Etorofu
Kunashiri
Shikotan
Habomai
PACIFIC OCEAN
East China Sea
Ryukyu Islands (JAPAN)
Okinawa
Philippine Sea

KEY

— National boundary
⊛ National capital
• Other city

Lambert Conformal Conic Projection

Go Online
PHSchool.com

For: More information about Japan and the Koreas and access to the Take It to the Net activities
Visit: phschool.com
Web Code: mjk-0033

eTeach

Be sure to check out this month's online forum with a Master Teacher to join in an exchange of teaching ideas. www.phschool.com

RESOURCE DIRECTORY

Teaching Resources
Unit 9, Chapter 32
• Section 1, Guided Reading and Review, p. 28
Guide to the Essentials (English/Spanish)
• Section Summary, Chapter 32, Section 1
Mental Mapping booklet
• Atlas Activity, p. 125
• Unit 9 Checklist, p. 115

Technology
Guided Reading Audiotapes (English/Spanish),
Chapter 32, Section 1

Section Reading Support Transparencies,
Chapter 32, Section 1
World Geography Map and Photo Transparencies
• East Asia and the Pacific World: Maps and Photos
Book on CD, Chapter 32
World Geography Videos
• Location: Japan and the Koreas, Tape 4
TeacherExpress™ CD-ROM, Chapter 32
Prentice Hall Presentation Pro CD-ROM, Chapter 32
Social Studies Skills Tutor CD-ROM
Companion Web site, www.phschool.com
• Chapter 32 Activities

1 Japan: The Land of the Rising Sun

Reading Focus
- What are Japan's chief physical characteristics?
- What geographic factors contribute to the variety of climates found in Japan?
- What factors encourage national unity and identity among the majority of the Japanese people?

Key Terms
seismograph

typhoon

homogeneous

Main Idea Japan is a culturally unified, densely populated country in a geologically unstable region.

Urbanization A Japanese farmer cultivates a narrow strip of land in an urban neighborhood.

Objectives
Upon completion of Section 1, students should be able to:
- list the chief physical characteristics of Japan;
- explain why Japan has a variety of climates;
- describe what factors encourage unity among the Japanese people.

National Geography Standards
The following National Geography Standards are highlighted in this section: 4, 9, 10, 17

Bellringer
Tell students that the Japanese people live on islands and most of them share a common heritage. Ask: **How do you think this would affect their view of the world?**

LESSON PLAN

1. Focus Have students imagine living in a densely populated country like Japan, with limited space for housing and farming. Ask students what challenges they might face.

2. Instruct Write the following phrases on the board: *Ring of Fire, high population density, homogeneous population, large middle class.* Ask students to tell how each affects life in Japan.

3. Close/Reteach Give each student three index cards. Have students use the material in the section to write a question about Japan on the front of each card and the answer on the back. Collect the cards, remove duplicate questions, and shuffle the rest. Divide the class into two teams and have them take turns drawing a card and answering a question. Assign one point for each correct answer.

In ancient times, the Japanese knew of no people who lived to their east. They thought the sea was endless and that Japan was the land on which the rising sun first shed its light. According to legend, Amaterasu, the goddess of the sun, was the protector of Japan. The flag of modern Japan, a red circle on a white background, symbolizes Japan's special relationship with the rising sun.

Physical Characteristics

Japan consists of an archipelago (AR kuh PELL uh GO), or chain of islands, that lies about 100 miles (160 km) off the coast of East Asia. The stormy Korea Strait and the Sea of Japan separate Japan from the mainland. The archipelago includes thousands of small islands, many of which are little more than large rocks. It also includes four large islands where almost all of Japan's people live. The largest, Honshu, is home to about 80 percent of Japan's population. South of Honshu are the islands of Shikoku and Kyushu. The farthest north of Japan's main islands is Hokkaido.

In the past, the seas surrounding Japan served to both isolate and protect it from invaders. The seas also provided links within Japan. Honshu, Kyushu, and Shikoku surround a body of water known as the Inland Sea. Sheltered from dangerous Pacific storms, the Inland Sea served as a major highway between islands.

The islands of Japan are actually the peaks of a great underwater mountain range. Millions of years ago these mountains began pushing up from the ocean floor when two tectonic plates collided in a subduction zone.

Because of its mountainous terrain, only about 13 percent of Japan's land is arable. Small and often inefficient farms are squeezed into small valleys between mountain ridges. To create more farmland, the Japanese carved terraces into hillsides and drained marshes, swamps, and deltas. Japan's best farmland has been created by the alluvial deposits of its rivers, including the Ishikari River, which cuts across the western half of the island of Hokkaido. These narrow plains, which make up only about one eighth of Japan's land area, hold most of its population.

◄ **Mt. Fuji, Japan** *(photo left)*

Chapter 32 ▪ Section 1 **681**

TEACHING TIP
From A Master Teacher

Urbanization One way to approach the study of Japan and the Koreas is to look at their cities. In South Korea, 40 percent of the total population is highly concentrated in one city, Seoul. In contrast, Japan has a better developed network of cities throughout the archipelago, with a concentration along the southern coast from Tokyo-Yokohama, Nagoya, Osaka-Kyoto-Kobe, and Hiroshima to Fukuoka. Both nations are seeking ways to better distribute their population because of congestion and environmental impacts.

Pacing Suggestions

For 90-minute Blocks
You will want to vary activities.
- Use the Creative Teaching Activity for Chapter 32 as the basis for a 90-minute lesson. Extend the activity by asking student pairs to scan recent newspapers and magazines for articles about South Korean or Japanese trade. Have each pair present to the class a news flash that summarizes one of its findings and suggests how the news might relate to balance of trade.

The Physical World

Earthquakes Mount Usu, located 50 miles (80 km) south of Sapporo on the island of Hokkaido, Japan, has erupted ten times since 1626. In March and April of 2000, Usu spewed ash, smoke, and steam for many days. The pressure of the steam underground caused roads to crack, and rain mixed with ash triggered large-scale mudslides. Thousands of people were evacuated from towns in the path of destruction.

Word Origin

Japan The Japanese call their country *Nippon* or *Nihon,* meaning "source of the sun." Created by Japanese scholars in A.D. 670, this name was translated into Chinese and eventually into Malay as *Japang.* Portuguese traders in Asia may have brought the Malay term to Europe in the 1500s. It first appears in English records in 1577, spelled *Giapan.*

The Ring of Fire Although Japan's islands are millions of years old, they are relatively new additions to the earth's surface. Japan is part of the Ring of Fire—a region of spectacular tectonic activity along the rim of the Pacific Ocean. Earthquakes and volcanoes are common in the region. In fact, Japan experiences more earthquakes than any other country in the world. Sensitive **seismographs**—machines that register movements in the earth's crust—record about 7,500 earthquakes in Japan each year. About 1,500 of these are strong enough to be felt by people.

The Japanese have learned to adapt to most of these mild earthquakes. About once every two years, however, Japan experiences an earthquake that causes serious damage and loss of life. If the epicenter of the earthquake is on land, the earth shifts and buckles, causing landslides in mountainous areas. Buildings, farmland, and whole villages may be destroyed. When an earthquake occurs offshore, the vibration can cause an enormous ocean wave, called a tsunami, which can devastate coastal lands.

As part of the Ring of Fire, Japan also has about 170 volcanoes, 75 of which are active. From time to time they erupt, sending showers of hot ash or molten lava down onto the surrounding countryside. The diagram on the next page shows how the region's tectonic forces result in Japan's volcanic activity.

Despite the dangers, volcanic activity has benefited Japan. In many places, volcanoes generate heat that warms underground water, creating hot springs. Resorts have been built up around these natural hot tubs.

Climates

If Japan were set along the east coast of the United States, it would stretch all the way from Maine to Florida. Japan's climates, like those of

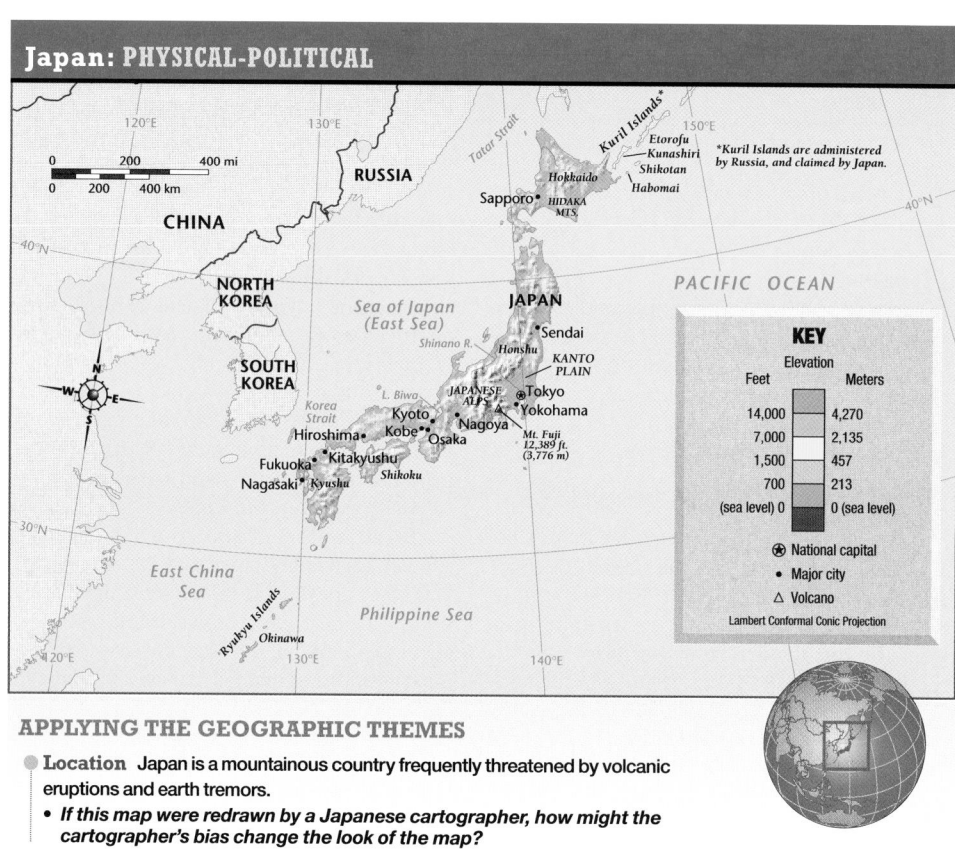

Japan: PHYSICAL-POLITICAL

KEY

Elevation

Feet	Meters
14,000	4,270
7,000	2,135
1,500	457
700	213
(sea level) 0	0 (sea level)

⊛ National capital
• Major city
△ Volcano

Lambert Conformal Conic Projection

Kuril Islands are administered by Russia, and claimed by Japan.

APPLYING THE GEOGRAPHIC THEMES

● **Location** Japan is a mountainous country frequently threatened by volcanic eruptions and earth tremors.
  • *If this map were redrawn by a Japanese cartographer, how might the cartographer's bias change the look of the map?*

682   Chapter 32 ▪ Japan and the Koreas

RESOURCE DIRECTORY

Teaching Resources
Mental Mapping booklet
• Outline Map 32, p. 124

Technology
World Geography Map and Photo Transparencies
• East Asia and the Pacific World: Maps and Photos

Answer to Map Caption

Possible answer: Kurile Islands might be shaded as part of Japan, with label indicating Russian claims rather than Japanese.

Volcano

Asia
Japan
PACIFIC OCEAN
Volcano
Earthquake
PLATE
PLATE
Plate melts and rises through cracks
Slow-moving currents push plates together
MANTLE (molten rock)

DIAGRAM SKILLS

● **Natural Hazards** The diagram above illustrates the shaky ground on which Japan stands.

• *Explain in your own words how the region's tectonic plate activity results in Japan's earthquakes and volcanic activity.*

the eastern United States coast, vary according to latitude. The northern island of Hokkaido has a climate like that of New England, with long winters and cool summers. Northern Honshu's climate is similar to that of the mid-Atlantic states. In southern Honshu, the climate is similar to that of North Carolina, with hot summers and mild but sometimes snowy winters. Kyushu and Shikoku, on the other hand, have climates more like that of Florida.

Monsoons Japan's seasons are affected by monsoons, or prevailing winds. In the summer, the monsoon blows onto the land from the east, bringing heavy rains and hot temperatures. From late summer to early fall is the season for **typhoons.** A typhoon is a tropical hurricane that forms over the Pacific Ocean, often causing floods and landslides. In winter the monsoon shifts, blowing in cold, dry air from the Asian mainland.

Ocean Currents Ocean currents also affect Japan's climate. The Japan Current, which flows northward from tropical waters along the southern and eastern coasts, warms the air. As a result, much of Japan has a long growing season that averages between 200 and 260 days. The cold Oyashio Current, on the other hand, flows southeastward along the east coast of Hokkaido and northeastern Honshu, cooling the air above it. Consequently, the Oyashio region supports high fish harvests. (Review the ocean currents map on page 67.)

GLOBAL CONNECTIONS

Natural Hazards A tsunami can affect countries that are at a great distance from its site of origin. In 1960, for example, a strong earthquake off the coast of Chile created a tsunami that swept westward, causing destruction in Hawaii and ultimately killing 200 people in Japan.

Chapter 32 ▪ Section 1   **683**

Chapter 32 ▪ Section 1   **683**

Environmental Issues

Wetlands Some of the world's most endangered wetlands are in East Asian countries, including Japan. The Wetlands International Asia Pacific, which was established with international funding, helps to protect these wetlands through education programs and by recommending sites for protection.

Connecting With . . .

Art Origami, the art of paper folding, has been practiced for centuries in Japan. The oldest known book on origami was devoted to the making of one shape—that of the crane. Show the class an image of a crane in a Japanese work of art, and explain that the Japanese regard this graceful bird as a symbol of long life and good fortune. Ask students to research origami instructions and have them make a crane.

Connecting With . . .

Literature Explain to students that a haiku is a short Japanese poem that creates a single, intense image. Find an example of a haiku and write it on the board. Have students count the syllables in each line. (5, 7, 5) Then ask each student to write a haiku. Invite volunteers to share their poems with the class.

Answer to Photo Caption

With so many people competing for so little land, the price of land is pushed very high.

Capsule Hotels

Population Growth Space is tight in Japan, and highly valued. Shown here is a capsule hotel where patrons rent tiny rooms. In 2000, Japan had a population density of 870 people per square mile. At the same time, the United States had 74 people per square mile.

Human-Environment Interaction *What effect does Japan's high population density have on land prices?*

People and Culture

Japan is one of the world's most densely populated countries. Since 1880, its population has grown from about 35 million to more than 127 million. Although Japan's entire area is about the size of California, it has nearly four times that state's population. Adding to the crowding is the fact that three quarters of the population live on the narrow coastal plain between Tokyo and Hiroshima. (See the population density map on page 643.)

Crowded Cities Population density has had far-reaching effects in Japan. For example, the shortage of space has driven up the prices of land and housing. Many families live in apartments in large high-rise buildings rather than in single-family homes. A family of four may share two or three small rooms.

This trend has had profound effects on the Japanese family. Traditionally, aging parents lived with their eldest son and his family. Now, older people often live by themselves or in special housing for the elderly. However, great respect for the elderly is still part of the Japanese way of life.

Japan's large population and limited land area also pose great problems with respect to pollution and waste disposal. Japan has developed aggressive recycling and waste-treatment programs. One study found that about 10 percent of Japan's solid waste was recycled or composted, while more than 70 percent was burned (often to produce electricity), and less than 20 percent was buried in landfills. In contrast, only about 7 percent of the solid waste in the U.S. was recycled or composted and only 8 percent was incinerated, while almost 85 percent was buried. Japan's industries have also developed energy-efficient technologies that generate less pollution.

Uniformity Most of Japan's people have a common heritage. Shared ancestry makes Japan's population **homogeneous,** or uniform. In fact, more than 99 percent of Japan's people have ancestors who lived in Japan thousands of years ago. Koreans are the only significant ethnic minority in Japan, and they make up only 0.6 percent of the population. Both ethnic and cultural similarities have enabled the Japanese to build a strong sense of national unity and identity.

Japan's isolated island setting helped to shape its society and its view of the world. From earliest times, the Japanese had a sense of their own separate, special identity. For years the Japanese actively tried to keep foreigners off their island.

A strong national identity has strengthened Japan but has also contributed to prejudice against the Ainu and the *burakumin.* The Ainu were the early native inhabitants of northern Japan who were excluded from Japanese society. The *burakumin,* although ethnically Japanese, are social outcasts and generally live in segregated communities. They are descendants of butchers and leather tanners who lived during feudal times. The Buddhist view against the taking of life led to negative feelings against the *burakumin.* The Koreans, the Ainu, and the *burakumin* all suffer from discrimination today.

Similar Religions Most of Japan's people also share similar religious beliefs and traditions. Japan's earliest people followed a religion known as Shinto. Shintoists worshipped the forces of nature and the spirits of their dead ancestors. Each household had an altar at which family members prayed and offered sacrifices. Today, while most of the holidays the Japanese celebrate are Shinto, the religion is no longer the focus of daily life. Nonetheless, it has had a great influence on Japanese culture, especially the Japanese people's great love of nature. To adapt this love of nature to crowded living conditions, the Japanese create miniature gardens that imitate nature. As one garden architect observed:

> 66 When I am arranging one stone after another, I am always entangling the stone with my dream and pursuing an ideal world of beauty. 99

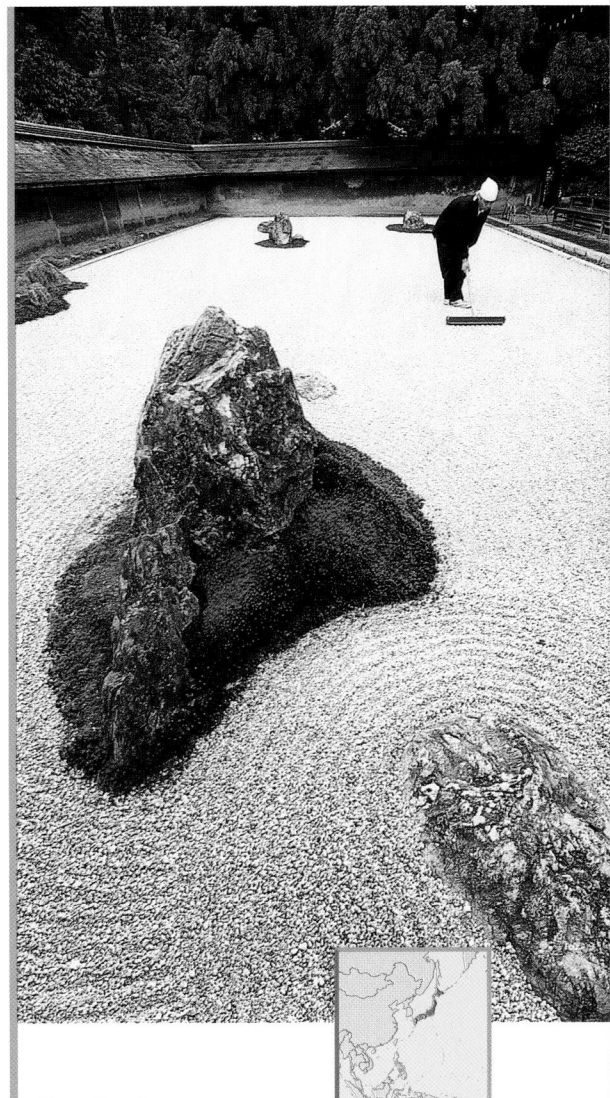

Zen Garden

Cultures In "dry landscaping," the few elements of the Zen Buddhist rock garden represent nature. Individual rocks represent entire mountains, while the patterns raked into the bed of small stones represent water. **Place** *How does such a garden reflect Japanese religion?*

The majority of Japanese also practice Buddhist traditions. Buddhism teaches that people should seek spiritual enlightenment or knowledge by living selflessly and modestly. The Japanese

Chapter 32 ▪ Section 1 **685**

**Answers to
Section 1 Assessment**

1. (a) seismograph, p. 682
(b) typhoon, p. 683 **(c)** homogeneous,
p. 685
2. Answers may include islands, seas,
mountains, and volcanoes.
3. The islands' climates vary according to latitude. Monsoons bring
warm, wet weather in the summer
and cold, dry weather in the winter.
Ocean currents also affect the climate.
The Japan Current warms the air; the
Oyashio Current cools the air.
4. ethnic heritage and language, religious beliefs, and membership in the
middle class
5. Answers will vary. Possible answer:
It would affect housing and patterns
of family life.

Activity Rubrics Share rubrics
with students before they prepare
their explanations.
Attempted The explanation is
incomplete or shows insufficient
research.
Minimal The explanation shows
sufficient research but is poorly
written.
Adequate The explanation is well
written and informative.
Exemplary The explanation shows
excellent understanding of the patterns of settlement in Japan and is
thoughtful and well written.

Japan, the Koreas, and the United States
Education Data

Country	Education Expenditure (as percentage of GNP)	Literacy Rate (percentage)	Secondary School Students (per teacher)
Japan	3.8	99.0	14
North Korea	NA	99.0	NA
South Korea	3.7	98.0	24
United States	5.3	99.5	15

Source: *Encarta World Atlas*   NA = information not available.

CHART SKILLS

● **Economic Activities** *What percentage of its gross national product does Japan spend on education?*
● **Cultures** *Does this table suggest a connection between literacy and the teacher-to-secondary-school-student ratio? Explain.*

integrated or added Buddhist teachings into their Shinto beliefs.

Shinto beliefs about the forces of nature and Buddhist teachings about the impermanence of life have both played a role in shaping the distinctive style of Japanese art. In accordance with Buddhist beliefs, artists suggest an idea, a thought, or a feeling with a minimum of detail. A few bold lines, for example, could suggest to the viewer the artist's impression of a mountain.

Japanese culture has also been greatly influenced by Confucianism, a philosophy that began in China. Confucianism stresses respect for the wisdom of older people and obedience to people in positions of authority, such as leaders, employers, parents, and teachers. Japanese society reflects the influence of Confucianism in its belief in the importance of the common good and in the high value it places on loyalty and respect for authority.

A Large Middle Class In most countries, modernization has gone hand in hand with the growth of the middle class. Nowhere is this more true than in Japan. Japan once had a small upper class of aristocrats and a large lower class of illiterate peasants. Today, the vast majority of people belong to a highly educated middle class. This social and economic uniformity contributes to the homogeneity of the Japanese population.

Japanese popular culture is influenced by both Japanese traditions and ideas from the West. Like their Western counterparts, middle-class Japanese spend their leisure time watching television, going to the movies, or attending both modern and traditional sports events. Styles and ideas travel both in and out of Japan. The Japanese have adopted many Western sports, such as baseball, golf, tennis, and volleyball. On the other hand, sushi bars, architectural styles, and landscape gardening are all popular cultural "exports" to the West.

SECTION 1 ASSESSMENT

1. **Key Terms** Define **(a)** seismograph, **(b)** typhoon, **(c)** homogeneous.

2. **Physical Characteristics** Name and describe three of Japan's most important physical characteristics.

3. **Climates** What factors cause Japan to have a variety of climates?

4. **Cultures** What shared characteristics give the majority of Japan's people a strong sense of national unity?

5. **Critical Thinking** **Predicting Consequences** How would a high population density, such as is found in Japan, influence the culture of a country?

Activity
USING THE REGIONAL ATLAS
Review the Regional Atlas for East Asia and the Pacific World; then, review this section. Using the maps as your basis, prepare a brief explanation of patterns of settlement in Japan. Why is the population concentrated in some areas but not in others? What, if anything, might be done to distribute the population more evenly?

Answers to Chart Skills

3.8

The table does not indicate a link. (Although South Korea has the most pupils per teacher, it also has a very high literacy rate.) In order to make a valid generalization, more data from countries around the world would be required.

RESOURCE DIRECTORY

Teaching Resources
Unit 9, Chapter 32
• Section 1 Quiz, p. 29
• Section 2 Guided Reading and Review, p. 30
Spanish Resources
• Section 1 Quiz, p. 81
Guide to the Essentials (English/Spanish)
• Section Summary, Chapter 32, Section 2
Mental Mapping booklet
• Unit 9 Checklist, p. 115

Technology
Guided Reading Audiotapes (English/Spanish), Chapter 32, Section 2
Section Reading Support Transparencies, Chapter 32, Section 2
World Geography Map and Photo Transparencies
• East Asia and the Pacific World: Maps and Photos
Book on CD, Chapter 32
Social Studies Skills Tutor CD-ROM
Companion Web site, www.phschool.com
• Chapter 32 Activities

2 Japan's Economic Development

Reading Focus

- Why did Japan isolate itself from the West, and what happened when new relations were established in the 1800s?
- Why did Japan attempt to gain control of neighboring countries?
- What was Japan's role in World War II, and how did it affect Japan's status at the war's end?
- How was Japan able to prosper economically after World War II?

Key Terms

militarism   tariff

downsize   quota

Main Idea Japan became an industrial power by adapting Western ideas to the needs of its own society.

Economic Activities Busy downtown Tokyo is a center for commerce and industry.

A hundred and fifty years ago, Japan was an agricultural nation that had shut itself off from contact with other cultures. No one then could have foreseen that Japan would become one of the world's great industrial powers.

First Contacts

At the time of its first contact with the West, Japan had a highly developed civilization and was a prosperous nation. Trade between Japan and neighboring Korea, China, and Southeast Asia flourished. Its beautiful textiles were in great demand. From the court of the emperor in the charming city of Heian, now Kyoto, came impressive works of art and literature.

In 1543 the first Portuguese trading ships arrived in Japan. Traders were followed by Roman Catholic missionaries, who hoped to bring Christianity to Japan. At first, the Japanese welcomed the Europeans, but soon they began to worry that European nations might try to conquer them. As a result, in 1639 the government closed Japan's

doors to the West, ordering most Europeans to leave the country.

A Forced Reopening

Japan's isolation lasted for more than 200 years. Then, in 1853, the United States government sent Commodore Matthew C. Perry to Japan to negotiate a trade agreement. Perry's request was backed up by a fleet of steam-powered warships. Outmatched, the Japanese agreed to Perry's terms. In the next 15 years, Japan was forced to sign treaties with other Western nations as well. These unequal treaties gave all the economic advantages to foreigners.

An Era of Reforms

In 1868 a new government took control in Japan. Its leaders were determined to modernize and industrialize the country so that it would no longer be at the mercy of foreign powers. The new emperor took the name Meiji (MAY jee), which means "enlightened rule."

Section 2 *pp. 687–692*

Objectives

Upon completion of Section 2, students should be able to:

- discuss why Japan isolated itself from the West and what happened when new relations were established in the 1800s;
- explain why Japan attempted to gain control of neighboring countries;
- summarize Japan's role in World War II and how it affected Japan's status at the war's end;
- describe how Japan was able to prosper economically after World War II.

National Geography Standards

The following National Geography Standards are highlighted in this section: 6, 11, 13, 14, 17

Bellringer

Ask students to make a list of Japanese-made goods that they have used in their daily lives.

LESSON PLAN

1. Focus Tell students to look at the economic activity map on page 645 and list Japan's major resources. Ask: **What two major resources needed for industry are lacking in Japan?** (petroleum and iron ore) Have students suggest how Japan could become a major industrial nation with so few raw materials.

2. Instruct Write these years on the board: *1543, 1639, 1853, 1868, 1900, 1939, 1945, 1960s, Today.* Have students write one sentence summarizing significant ideas about Japanese history and economics for each of these dates.

3. Close/Reteach Ask students to list the factors, including cultural traits, that have contributed to Japan's economic success.

Activity: Writing an update letter

Purpose: Have each group write a letter to Commodore Perry informing him of events in Japan since 1853. Letters should provide a historical update as well as a description of and explanations for Japan's economic situation today.

Roles: Groups should include researchers, a scribe, and a group leader.

Results: Have volunteers read their letters to the class.

Direct students' attention to the illustration caption on this page. Point out the slogan from the Meiji era, "Rich country, strong arms!" Ask students to create two concept webs: one with "Rich Country" in the center, the other with "Strong Arms" in the center. As students read pages 688 and 689, have them draw examples from their reading to complete the webs.

Answer to Photo Caption

Possible response: In order to become richer and fuel its industries, Japan sought to dominate other countries. Japan could do this because of its powerful military.

The Meiji Era in Japan

Understanding the Past One slogan from the Meiji era was "Rich country, strong arms!" During the Meiji era, Japan industrialized rapidly. Industrialism and militarism were central to Japan's efforts to become competitive with the West in the late 1800s.

Place *How might this spirit have led to Japanese imperialism?*

During the period of the Meiji reforms, from 1868 to 1912, Japan underwent revolutionary changes. Meiji reformers sent hundreds of Japanese to the United States and Europe to study Western institutions. Politically, the country became more democratic. A parliament, called the Diet, was created, and legal reforms made all Japanese men equal before the law. The government also established a new school system, so that all Japanese children could be offered a basic education. To promote rapid industrialization, the government paid for the development of railroads, mines, telegraph systems, and new industries. By 1900 Japan was strong enough to force an end to the unfair treaties and to deal with the West on equal terms.

Although Japan adopted many of the West's political and economic institutions, it did not wish to become a Western society. The Japanese practiced selective borrowing. They brought in only those ideas and innovations that seemed useful, adapting them to Japanese society. One of the Meiji leaders expressed his attitude in the following poem:

> ❝May our country,
> Taking what is good,
> And rejecting what is bad,
> Be not inferior
> To any other.❞

Japanese Imperialism

Lack of natural resources was a serious obstacle to Japan's goal of becoming an industrial power. The two major resources needed for industry, iron ore to make steel and petroleum for energy, are almost nonexistent in Japan. These and other items needed by Japan's developing industries had to be imported. Following the Western example of imperialism, Japanese officials began efforts to gain control of weaker countries that were rich in natural resources.

At the turn of the century Japan fought and won wars with China and Russia, thereby gaining new territory and trading rights. The Russian defeat stunned Western nations. It was the first time in modern history that an Asian nation had defeated a major European power. The treaty ending the war gave Japan a foothold on the mainland in Manchuria. In 1910, Korea was forced to become part of Japan. During World War I, Japan joined the Allies. After the war, it was rewarded with control of Germany's former colonies in the Pacific Ocean.

The worldwide economic depression that began in 1929 took a terrible toll on Japanese industry. Many businesses were ruined, and unemployment soared. The government's inability to solve the crisis led to domestic troubles. Military leaders argued that the path to recovery was

Change Over Time

Recovery From War

Science and Technology Japan's emphasis on technological innovation allowed the nation to recover quickly from the destruction of World War II. Although the city of Hiroshima was devastated by an atomic blast (PAST), the city was soon rebuilt (PRESENT). One section, however, was set aside and not restored to illustrate the effects of an atomic bomb.

Place *How did Japan's government change after World War II?*

PRESENT

PAST

through more aggressive expansion in Asia. An overseas empire would provide Japan with markets, raw materials, and new land for its expanding population. As conditions grew worse, militarists were able to gain control of the government. In 1931 Japan invaded Manchuria, and in 1937, China. During the 1930s, Japan gradually became a military dictatorship. The new leaders promoted **militarism,** or the glorification of the military and a readiness for war. Military leaders encouraged people to believe that Japan's mission in the world was to free Asian nations from Western imperialism.

World War II

With the outbreak of World War II in Europe in 1939, Japan's leaders sided with Nazi Germany. When France and the Netherlands fell under Nazi occupation, Japan seized French and Dutch colonies in Southeast Asia.

On December 7, 1941, Japan attacked the United States naval fleet at Pearl Harbor, Hawaii, and the two countries went to war. Both suffered

heavy casualties. The United States and its allies gradually destroyed Japan's ability to wage war. In August 1945, the United States dropped atomic bombs on the Japanese cities of Hiroshima and Nagasaki. Faced with the destruction caused by this new superweapon and the threat of more attacks, Japan quickly surrendered.

American Military Occupation

From 1945 to 1952, Japan was occupied by the United States army. It was the first time in Japanese history that the country had been ruled by a foreign power.

The United States introduced democratic reforms into Japan. The military leaders of Japan were removed from power. The Japanese emperor, who had been worshipped as a god, was stripped of his political powers. Finally, Japan's armed forces were disbanded, and Japan was forbidden ever to rebuild its military. The United States occupation forces introduced a democratic constitution giving women legal equality with men.

Critical Thinking

Economics and History Use the following questions to help students see the links between economics and history. Ask: **Why did the Meiji rulers want to modernize Japan?** (so that it would no longer be at the mercy of foreign powers) **What was the major obstacle to Japan's industrial development?** (lack of natural resources) **How did the Japanese plan to get the natural resources they needed?** (by taking control of countries that were rich in natural resources) **What did Japan hope to gain by entering World War II?** (an overseas empire that would provide Japan with raw materials)

BACKGROUND

History

Power of Petroleum A key factor in Japan's decision to attack the United States was a need for petroleum. Until 1941, American companies had sold oil to the Japanese. However, when Japan continued a takeover of Indochina that the United States had protested, the U.S. government declared an embargo on further oil shipments to Japan. The Japanese attempted to secure an oil supply from the Dutch in Indonesia, but negotiations failed. Alarmed, the Japanese high command decided to make war with the United States unless an immediate agreement could be reached. No agreement came, and on December 7, 1941, Japan attacked the U.S. naval fleet at Pearl Harbor, Hawaii.

Articles From NATIONAL GEOGRAPHIC

The following article may be used to extend the content in this section.

Gup, Ted, and Jodi Cobb, photographer. "Hiroshima." *National Geographic,* Vol. 18, No. 2 (Aug. 1995), pp. 78–101.

Economically recovered from the atomic bomb's devastation, the people of Hiroshima vow to work diligently for global peace and to never forget.

TEST PREPARATION

Have students read the subsection American Military Occupation to complete the following statement.

U.S. occupation of Japan after World War II resulted in all of the following *except* —

  A elevation of women's legal status
  B disbanding of the military
  (C) restoring power to the emperor
  D introduction of democracy

Answer to Photo Caption

Japan's military leaders were removed from power, the emperor was stripped of his political powers, and the United States introduced a democratic constitution.

Industry Over the past several decades, Japan has been finding ways to minimize the effects of industry and automobile traffic on its environment. Air quality regulations have reduced the amount of pollutants being released into the air. In 2001, Japan's legislature passed even stricter laws to regulate diesel-powered vehicles and reduce their harmful effects. However, air pollution from the East Asian mainland still contributes to Japan's acid rain.

Alternative Assessment

Introduce the Activity

Cooperative Learning Project Ask students to set up an exhibit for a trade show featuring advertisements for new products from Japan and the Koreas. Divide the class into three groups and assign each group one of the countries. Distribute the Cooperative Learning Project Rubrics found on pages 16 and 18 of the Alternative Assessment booklet in the Prentice Hall Assessment System for students' reference during the project.

Large farms and businesses were broken up and sold to poor citizens.

The Economic Boom

In the years following World War II, the Japanese economy grew faster than any other economy in the world. Instead of seizing raw materials from conquered nations as they had done in the past, Japan now obtained them through trade. Japan became known as the world's workshop because it imported raw materials and made them into finished goods for export.

At first, Japanese industries produced poorly made toys and novelties. Then, the government encouraged a switch to expensive, high-quality goods such as cameras, electronic equipment, and motorcycles. By studying the methods used in Europe and the United States, the Japanese rapidly increased the efficiency of their factories. The quality of their goods gradually came to equal or surpass goods made elsewhere. By the 1960s, Japan had become one of the most powerful industrial nations in the world.

Sources of Japan's Success

All over the world, people have admired Japan's economic success. Despite recent setbacks, Japan remains an economic superpower. How did this country, which began with so many seeming disadvantages, succeed so rapidly?

An Educated Work Force Japan's greatest natural resource has turned out to be its people. Education has always been very important in Japan. Today, its people are among the most highly educated in the world. Almost all of its citizens attend high school, and a third go on to college.

Japanese schools have very high standards. The school day is long, and vacations are short. Students have a great deal of homework, and complete assignments during summer vacations.

To enter high school, students must take a special examination. To get into college, they must score well on another exam. Competition for places in the best schools is fierce, so many students take extra classes after school to help them perform better on these exams.

A Literate Nation

Cultures "Cram schools" like this calligraphy class give Japan's highly competitive students extra preparation for their exams. Japan's efforts in education are repaid by a literacy rate of 99 percent and have helped Japan keep a very low level of unemployment.

Place *Why is education so important in an advanced economy like Japan's?*

RESOURCE DIRECTORY

Teaching Resources
Unit 9, Chapter 32
• Critical Thinking, p. 35

Prentice Hall Assessment System
Alternative Assessment booklet
• Cooperative Learning Project Rubrics, pp. 16 and 18

Answer to Photo Caption

Advanced economies rely on people who can master complex information.

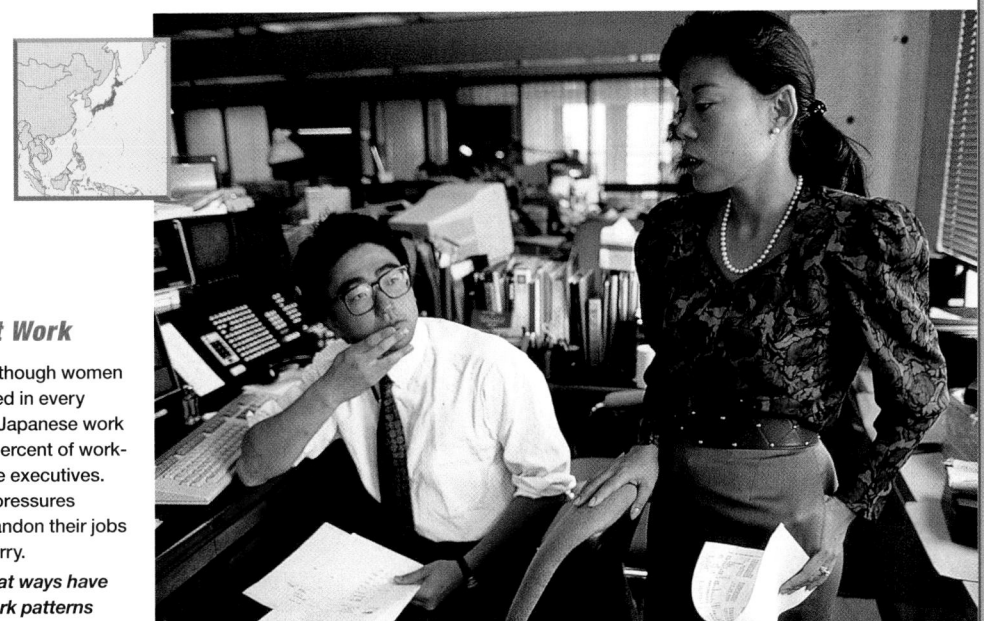

Women at Work

Cultures Although women are represented in every sphere of the Japanese work force, only 1 percent of working women are executives. Tradition still pressures women to abandon their jobs when they marry.

Place *In what ways have traditional work patterns begun to change in Japan?*

The Pacific Rim After Europeans colonized the Americas, the greatest volume of world trade traveled back and forth across the Atlantic Ocean. In the early 1990s, however, the value of goods traded among countries around the rim of the Pacific Ocean began to exceed that of goods traded across the Atlantic. Today Japan and the United States dominate Pacific Rim trade, although South Korea, Taiwan, Singapore, and Hong Kong are strong competitors. An association of 18 Pacific Rim countries has vowed to create a free-trade zone like that of the European Union or NAFTA by the year 2020.

The Workplace Another reason for Japan's success during the boom years was the attitude and cooperative skills of its workers. Japanese employees worked hard and for long hours. They took pride in the success of their company and wanted to contribute to that success. In return for this dedication, Japanese companies provided many benefits for their employees.

During the growth years, large Japanese companies were frequently compared to families. Workers were often hired as soon as they graduated from high school or college. Once hired, Japanese workers were rarely fired or laid off, and very few workers ever quit their jobs.

Companies encouraged loyalty and team spirit in a variety of ways. Workers often assembled every morning to sing and exercise together. Many companies offered their employees low-cost apartments, making coworkers into neighbors. Coworkers often vacationed together on trips sponsored by the company. Companies also provided benefits like medical clinics, child care, and low-interest loans.

Today, some of these traditional patterns are changing as the Japanese compete in the fierce international battle for profits. Like workers in

the United States, Japanese workers now are finding themselves **downsized,** or fired, as their companies trim workers to save costs. Sometimes workers who refuse to retire early are given demeaning jobs to force them to leave.

Global Trade Patterns In recent years, Japan's growth was aided by shifts in patterns of global trade. Other Asian nations began to develop economically. As a result, instead of being far from the countries with which it trades, Japan is now at the center of active trade networks.

Government Planning In Japan, the government takes an active role in business. The Ministry of International Trade and Industry (MITI) is made up of leaders from business and government. MITI works to coordinate the efforts of Japan's many companies. For example, it sponsors research to find out what kinds of products are wanted and needed in foreign markets and shares its findings with potential producers. MITI

In crowded Tokyo, people find space for recreation by building golf putting greens on top of office buildings.

Answer to Photo Caption

Workers, who in the past were employed for life, are being fired or forced into retirement in order to save companies money.

High-Tech Robotics

Science and Technology
The word *robot* comes from the Czech word *robota*, which means "drudgery." Robots, such as the ones pictured here in a Japanese car factory, are machines that are programmed to do routine, repetitive work in place of humans.

Place *How might increased reliance on robots affect the Japanese work force?*

plans far into the future, deciding what kinds of economic activity will bring the greatest benefit not to individual companies, but to Japan as a whole.

During the growth decades, the government aided businesses by controlling trade. For example, it passed laws requiring **tariffs.** Tariffs are taxes on imports that make foreign goods more costly than their domestic equivalents. The government also sets **quotas,** or fixed total quantities, which limit the number of foreign-made goods sold in Japan.

However, in the late 1990s, Japan suffered a significant recession. Japan strengthened its banking system and analyzed its business practices. Japan's door now is open a little wider, realizing the benefits of healthy trade relationships with other countries.

SECTION 2 ASSESSMENT

1. Key Terms Define **(a)** militarism, **(b)** downsize, **(c)** tariff, **(d)** quota.

2. Global Trade Patterns **(a)** Why did Japan cut off trade with the West in 1639? **(b)** Why was trade reopened in 1853?

3. Understanding the Past For what reasons did Japan seek to build an empire in Asia?

4. Cooperation and Conflict **(a)** Summarize Japan's participation in World War II. **(b)** Describe Japan's status at the war's end.

5. Economic Systems What factors contributed to Japan's rapid economic growth after 1945?

6. Critical Thinking Synthesizing Information What marketing problems would be encountered by an American film company selling its products in Japan?

Activity

Making a Chart Prepare a three-column posterboard chart about the history of Japan. In the first column, summarize Japan's early experiences with the West. In the second column, make some notes about the Japanese imperialistic era. In the third column, provide information about Japan from 1945 to the present. You may wish to do additional research and illustrate the chart.

3 The Koreas: A Divided Peninsula

Reading Focus

- **What cultural elements did the Koreans adapt from the Chinese?**
- **How did the Korean Peninsula become two separate countries?**
- **How do the physical characteristics of North Korea and South Korea differ?**
- **Why is reunification a challenge to both North Korea and South Korea?**

Key Terms

demilitarized zone

proliferation

Main Idea Despite their shared history and ancient culture, the Korean people have been divided since 1945 by communism.

Cooperation and Conflict Even in times of peace, military forces continue to patrol a divided Korea.

The Korean Peninsula extends off the east coast of Asia between China and Japan. In area, the peninsula is about the same size as Minnesota. Though small, the peninsula is divided into two nations. North Korea, or the Democratic People's Republic of Korea, is a Communist country. South Korea, or the Republic of Korea, has a non-Communist government. Despite their political differences, the people of the Korean Peninsula share a common history and an ancient culture.

A Common Culture

Historians believe that the first people who lived in Korea came from the northwestern regions of Asia. Through the more than 2,000 years of Korea's recorded history, invading armies from Mongolia, China, and Japan have swept through the peninsula on numerous occasions.

Koreans adapted Chinese cultural ways to their own existing culture. They borrowed extensively from the Chinese writing system and adapted many Chinese words. The Korean language, however, is actually a branch of the Altaic group, which includes Finnish, Turkish, and Hungarian.

As did the Japanese, many Koreans accepted and integrated more than one religion and philosophy into their way of life. Daoism and Confucianism, for example, came from China. Later, many Koreans also adopted Buddhism, but they modified its teachings to fit their own existing culture. Today, Buddhism is the most common religion among Koreans; though in the north, the Communist government discourages people from holding any religious beliefs.

The Korean War

In 1945, at the end of World War II, the Korean Peninsula became caught up in the Cold War struggle between Communists and non-Communists. The Soviet Union administered northern Korea, and the United States administered southern Korea. Both powers were expected to remove their

TEST PREPARATION

Have students read the subsection A Common Culture to answer this question.
Which of the following best explains why Korean culture includes elements of various Asian traditions?

- **A** Two separate nations occupy the Korean Peninsula.
- **B** The Korean language belongs to the Ural-Altaic group.
- Ⓒ Armies from other parts of Asia have invaded the peninsula many times.
- **D** The Communists discouraged religion.

Objectives

Upon completion of Section 3, students should be able to:

- ◆ identify the cultural elements the Koreans adapted from the Chinese;
- ◆ explain how the Korean Peninsula became two separate countries;
- ◆ describe how the physical characteristics of North Korea and South Korea differ;
- ◆ explain why reunification is a challenge to both North Korea and South Korea.

 National Geography Standards

The following National Geography Standards are highlighted in this section: 5, 9, 13, 15, 16, 18

 Bellringer

Write the following proverb on the board: *When the whales fight, it is the shrimp that get hurt.* Call on student volunteers to explain what they think this proverb means.

LESSON PLAN

1. Focus Have students locate the Koreas on the map on page 694. Tell students that throughout its history, Korea has been the focus of rivalry between neighboring China, Russia, and Japan. Ask students to use the map to draw a conclusion about the meaning of the proverb from the Bellringer in relation to the history of the Koreas.

2. Instruct Write these headings on the board: *Physical Geography, Culture, Government, Economy.* Have students list them on a piece of paper. Under each heading they should list the similarities and/or differences between North Korea and South Korea.

3. Close/Reteach Separate the class into small groups and ask each group to write ten sentences, some true and others false, based on Section 3. Then have each group read its sentences aloud. Classmates should identify false statements and provide corrected ones.

Vocabulary

Demilitarized Zone Refer to the Key Terms list on page 693. Have a volunteer look up *demilitarized zone* in the Glossary and read the definition aloud. Explain that in the Koreas, the demilitarized zone was a strip of land 2.5 miles (4 km) wide along the final battle line. Ask: **What would be the advantages of establishing a demilitarized zone in a region that had been at war?** (It would separate troops and help to avoid small incidents that could reignite fighting.)

Summarizing Main Ideas

Write the following headings on the board: *A Common Culture, The Korean War, Different Environments, A Changing Economy, Planning for the Future.* Work with students to develop an outline of Section 3. Identify each heading with a Roman numeral. As they read, have students find supporting details and arrange them under the appropriate heading.

Alternative Assessment

Mid-Point Monitoring

Cooperative Learning Project You may wish to monitor students' progress on preparing their exhibits. Confer with students to see if they will soon complete their research.

Answer to Map Caption

P'yŏngyang; Seoul

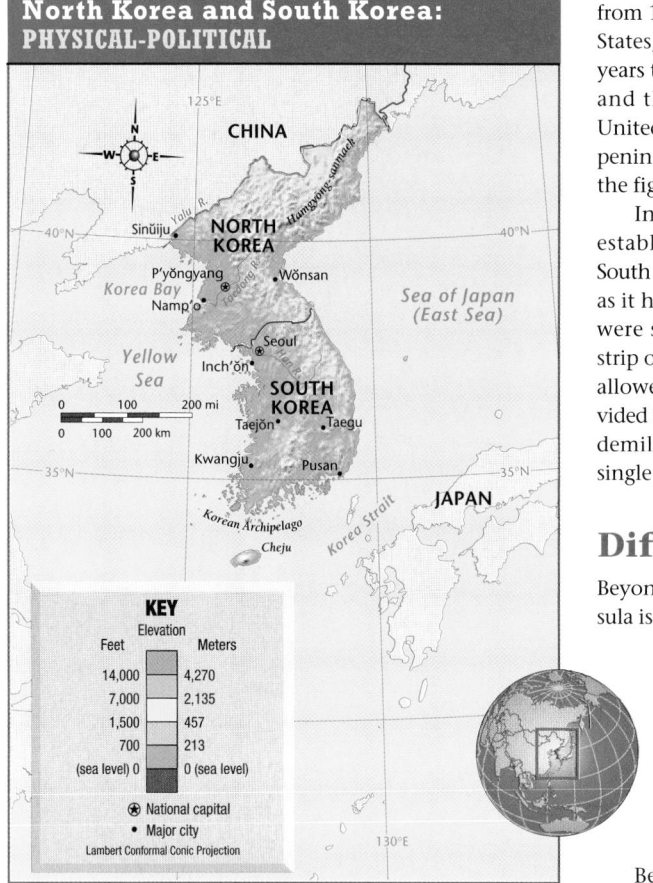

North Korea and South Korea: PHYSICAL-POLITICAL

KEY

Elevation	
Feet	Meters
14,000	4,270
7,000	2,135
1,500	457
700	213
(sea level) 0	0 (sea level)

⊛ National capital
• Major city

Lambert Conformal Conic Projection

APPLYING THE GEOGRAPHIC THEMES

● **Place** As it extends toward the East China Sea, the Korean Peninsula separates the Yellow Sea from the Sea of Japan.
  • *What is the capital of North Korea? Of South Korea?*

troops as soon as Korea was able to govern itself. Instead, the Soviet Union established a Communist government in North Korea. In South Korea an election was held and American troops pulled out in 1949. Fearing life in a Communist state, more than 2 million Koreans fled to the south.

In 1950, the North Koreans launched a surprise attack on South Korea. Their objective was to unite the country under the rule of a single, Communist government. United Nations forces from 15 different countries, including the United States, came to the aid of South Korea. For three years the army of North Korea, helped by China, and the army of South Korea, helped by the United Nations, fought back and forth across the peninsula. An estimated 4 million people died in the fighting.

In 1953, a cease-fire agreement was signed establishing the division between North and South Korea near 38°N latitude—roughly the same as it had been before the fighting. The countries were separated by a **demilitarized zone**—a strip of land on which troops or weapons are not allowed. The Korean Peninsula remains thus divided today. More hostile forces are massed at this demilitarized zone, or DMZ, than at any other single place on the planet.

Different Environments

Beyond its political divisions, the Korean Peninsula is a land of opposites. The two countries that occupy its regions have different climates, landforms, and resources.

North Korea North Korea has about 23 million people and is less densely populated than South Korea. P'yŏngyang, the capital, is the only city with a population of more than 1 million.

Because it is located near the Asian mainland, North Korea is influenced by nearby continental climate regions. The climate is similar to that of southern Siberia, with short, cool summers and bitterly cold winters. The land itself is mountainous and rugged. Its fast-flowing mountain rivers have been harnessed to create hydroelectric power for its industries. North Korea also has some of the richest natural resources in East Asia, including coal, copper, iron ore, lead, tungsten, and zinc.

South Korea In contrast, South Korea, which is home to about 47 million people, is one of the most densely populated countries in the world. Almost a quarter of the population is concentrated in the capital city of Seoul.

South Korea is influenced by the moderating effects of the surrounding seas, and parts of South Korea are actually subtropical in climate.

Teaching Resources
Creative Teaching Activities, The Balance of Trade, p. 34

It is less mountainous than North Korea and has wide, rolling plains. Because of its terrain and warmer climate, South Korea is better suited for agriculture than is its neighbor to the north.

A Changing Economy

At the time of the cease-fire in 1953, South Korea was economically at a disadvantage. The best industries and hydroelectric plants were in Communist North Korea, and South Korea was overflowing with battle-weary refugees.

Communist states, such as China and the Soviet Union, became North Korea's new trading partners. South Korea, on the other hand, allied itself with the United States and Japan. With aid from its new economic partners, South Korea became industrialized. The government actively encouraged the development of both heavy and light industries. To solve its energy problems, South Korea built nuclear power plants. As a result, the country witnessed an impressive rate of economic growth in the ensuing years. South Korea also experienced the development of a new middle class, as well as an increase in its role in international trade and politics.

Today, South Korea is a major exporter of textiles, clothing, automobiles, and electronic goods. It is considered one of the new industrial powers of the region surrounding the Pacific Ocean.

Industrialization Rapid industrialization has pulled at the social fabric of Korean culture. In an effort to compete economically with Japan and Western countries, family-owned businesses in South Korea have often treated workers unfairly. As a result of this conflict, massive labor strikes and political struggles have at times disrupted the country's economic growth.

Under Communist leadership, North Korea has continued to evolve from an agricultural to an industrial society. Despite the fact that it has greater natural resources than does South Korea,

GLOBAL CONNECTIONS

Cultures North Korea has used technology to enforce cultural divergence. In 1990, radios could receive only one station, which was approved by the government. By 1999, there were nearly 30 AM and FM stations, but censorship continued. Recent agreements with South Korea have eased some travel restrictions, but contact is still limited.

A Consumer Society Takes Shape

Economic Systems The stores of Seoul, South Korea, are full of consumer goods. In recent years the nation has become a leading economy in the region, far outstripping North Korea's economy.

Regions *Has South Korea outperformed North Korea economically because its natural resources are richer? Explain your answer.*

Chapter 32 ▪ Section 3   **695**

Reteach

Making a Mobile Ask students to make mobiles that illustrate important facts and ideas about Korea from Section 3. They may use sketches, words, phrases, "artifacts," or pictures cut from magazines. (Bodily/Kinesthetic)

Answers to Section 3 Assessment

1. (a) demilitarized zone, p. 694 **(b)** proliferation, p. 696

2. Koreans borrowed the Chinese writing system and adapted many Chinese words. They also modified Chinese religions and philosophies to fit their culture.

3. war between the Communist north (with its ally China) and the non-Communist south (with various United Nations allies)

4. North Korea: rugged, mountainous, with fast-moving rivers and rich mineral resources; short, cool summers and bitterly cold winters. South Korea: less mountainous, with wide, rolling plains; more moderate climate, subtropical in areas.

5. Both countries seem unwilling to compromise their political/economic views and forms of government.

6. Possible answer: Common history and culture that is thousands of years old ultimately could help to unite the two countries.

Activity Rubrics Share rubrics with students before they write their summaries.

Minimal The summary does not include two items or does not adequately explain them.

Attempted The summary meets basic requirements but is poorly written.

Adequate The summary is well written and demonstrates good understanding of the topic.

Exemplary The summary is very well written and insightful and demonstrates a thorough understanding of current attitudes toward reunification.

Answer to Photo Caption

The main obstacle is that North Korea is Communist and South Korea is capitalist, and neither country wishes to give up its form of government.

Korea's Political Scene

Government and Citizenship This North Korean poster is promoting reunification of North and South Korea.

Regions *What are the political obstacles to reunification?*

North Korea lags far behind its neighbor in its standard of living. With the fall of the Soviet Union in 1991, North Korea lost its main economic supporter. Immediately, supplies dwindled. Fuel and spare parts still are scarce, so factories have closed. Hospitals sometimes have no heat or running water. When a severe food shortage hit in 1997, international aid came to North Korea's rescue. People are less hungry now, but the situation remains dire.

Planning for the Future

After 1953, North Korea and South Korea sometimes discussed reunification but could not agree on conditions. North Korea wanted an exclusively Communist Korean Peninsula. As a successful capitalist state, South Korea did not want to jeopardize its free system of government.

In 1993, North Korea withdrew from the Nuclear Non-Proliferation Treaty. This treaty was designed to stop the **proliferation,** or increase in number, of atomic weapons around the world. North Korea agreed to shut down its nuclear facilities the following year in return for economic assistance from the United States.

Leaders from North Korea and South Korea began talks again in 2000, but in 2002, North Korea announced that it was resuming development of its nuclear program. The United States and other nations worked together to try to persuade North Korea to stop this effort.

SECTION 3 ASSESSMENT

1. Key Terms Define **(a)** demilitarized zone, **(b)** proliferation.

2. Cultures In what sense did the Koreans adapt Chinese cultural elements to their own culture?

3. Understanding the Past What caused the division of the Korean Peninsula?

4. Physical Characteristics In terms of physical characteristics, how are North Korea and South Korea different from each other?

5. Government and Citizenship Why have North Korea and South Korea found it difficult to discuss reunification?

6. Critical Thinking Solving Problems What cultural and economic factors do you think might encourage the reunification of Korea?

Activity

Take It to the NET

Summarizing Information How have attitudes about reunification changed (if at all) since this book was published? To find out, go online. Find and summarize two recent items related to the topic—either two items that reinforce a particular point of view or two items that seem to take opposing views. Share your findings with classmates who also have researched this topic.

RESOURCE DIRECTORY

Teaching Resources

Unit 9, Chapter 32
• Map/Graph Skills, p. 36
• Section 3 Quiz, p. 33
• Reviewing Main Ideas, p. 34
• Test Forms A and B, pp. 37–42

Spanish Resources
• Section 3 Quiz, p. 83

Guide to the Essentials (English/Spanish)
• Chapter 32 Test

Mental Mapping booklet
• Chapter 32 Map Test, p. 126

Simulations, Games, and Lab Activities
• Place Location Review Games, pp. 58–63

Social Studies Skills Handbook
• Study and Research Skills, pp. 94–108

Technology
ExamView Test Bank CD-ROM, Chapter 32 Test
Companion Web site, www.phschool.com
• Chapter 32 Self-Test

Using a Spreadsheet

A spreadsheet is a tool that allows you to organize information so that data can be analyzed. Often, spreadsheets are computerized, allowing you to make calculations as well as input data.

Learn the Skill Use the sample below and the following steps to learn how to use a spreadsheet.

1 *Identify the topic and organization.* A spreadsheet contains information about a specific topic. The data within the spreadsheet provide information about that topic and are organized into categories. Often, you can determine the topic by reading the title bar of the document. **(a)** *What is the topic of the spreadsheet below?* **(b)** *What are the major categories?*

2 *Understand the structure.* A spreadsheet is organized into columns and rows. The point at which each column and row intersect is called a cell. You may find that columns are labeled with numbers and rows with letters, which gives each cell an easily identifiable label. For example, the point at which column 5 meets row B is cell B5. **(a)** *In the sample below, what does column 1 indicate?* **(b)** *What does row A indicate?*

3 *Navigate and edit.* In a computer-based spreadsheet, a cell can be selected by clicking on the cell itself, or by entering the cell number into a window. Data can be entered into the cell and can be edited later. **(a)** *What information appears in cell B2?* **(b)** *If you wanted to update statistics about nuclear energy use in China, which cell would you edit?*

4 *Analyze the statistics.* Look for relationships between the data. In statistics, the mode is the value of the variable occurring most often in a set of data. In statistics, the mean is the average value for a set of data. **(a)** *For the set of data in row E, what value represents the mode?* **(b)** *For the set of data in row C, what is the average value of electricity produced from hydropower?*

5 *Draw conclusions.* Use the data to form some conclusions. Be careful to recognize what can be learned and what cannot be learned. Avoid drawing conclusions that cannot be supported by the data. For example, the data in the table indicate that North Korea and the Philippines rely entirely on fossil fuels and hydroelectric power. **(a)** *Can you use the data below to determine how many hydroelectric plants exist in each country?* **(b)** *Based on the data presented, which two countries are most likely to be concerned about the disposal of radioactive waste?*

Do It Yourself

Practice the Skill Select a topic about East Asia and the Pacific World, and collect data. Using the steps above, organize the data into a spreadsheet. Be sure to give your spreadsheet a title. After you have completed your spreadsheet, analyze the data and draw conclusions.

Apply the Skill See Chapter 32 Review and Assessment.

Electricity–Production by Source (percentage)					
	1	**2**	**3**	**4**	**5**	**6**
		Japan	South Korea	North Korea	China	Philippines
A						
B	Fossil fuels	56.7	59.6	34.4	80.3	70.1
C	Hydro	9.0	1.9	65.6	18.5	10.7
D	Nuclear	31.9	38.5	0	1.2	0
E	Other	2.4	0	0	0	19.1

Page 1 / Page 2 / Page 3

Creating a Chapter Summary

As a reteaching opportunity, pair a more able student with a less able student to complete this chapter summary.

Completed charts might include the following entries: **Japanese Imperialism** 1. Japan sought natural resources for industrialization. 2. led to Japan's attempts at conquest in World War II **Japan's Economic Success** 1. studied production methods used in Europe and the United States 2. Japanese workers tend to be well educated and hard-working. **Korean War** 1. Korea was divided at the end of World War II. 2. North Korea's attack on South Korea in 1950 resulted in a conflict that ended in 1953. **Two Koreas Today** 1. South Korea has become a major industrial power in the region. 2. North Korea struggles to supply its people's needs.

Reviewing Key Terms

1–9. Students' sentences should show a clear understanding of each term.

Understanding Key Ideas

10. (a) Shinto, Buddhism **(b)** Shinto: forces of nature, spirits of ancestors; Buddhism: spiritual enlightenment through modest, selfless living
11. Many Japanese traveled to Europe and the United States to study Western institutions. Japan became more democratic. A new school system provided basic education to all children. Government funded new industry and improved transportation and communication systems.
12. During Japan's economic boom, many Japanese had great job opportunities and benefits. Recently, many companies have tried to increase profits by firing workers, giving them early retirement, or assigning them to demeaning jobs to force them to quit.
13. (a) At the end of World War II, Korea was divided, with the Soviet Union governing the north and the United States governing the south. The Soviet Union established a Communist government in the north. **(b)** to bring all of the Korean Peninsula under Communist control

---

Creating a Chapter Summary

On a sheet of paper, draw a chart like this one. Beneath each heading, fill in two key details from the text. Some information has been filled in to help you get started.

JAPANESE IMPERIALISM
1.
2.

JAPAN'S ECONOMIC SUCCESS AFTER WORLD WAR II
1. Studied successful production methods used in Europe and the United States
2.

THE KOREAN WAR
1.
2.

THE TWO KOREAS TODAY
1.
2.

Take It to the NET
Chapter Self-Test For practice test questions for Chapter 32, go to the World Geography section of **www.phschool.com**.

Reviewing Key Terms

Write sentences, using the key terms listed below and leaving blanks where the key terms should go. Exchange your sentences with those of another student, and fill in the blanks in each other's sentences.

1. seismograph
2. typhoon
3. homogeneous
4. militarism
5. downsize
6. tariff
7. quota
8. demilitarized zone
9. proliferation

Understanding Key Ideas

10. Cultures (a) What are the main religious traditions in Japan? **(b)** Summarize the main focus of each religious tradition.
11. Understanding the Past How did the Meiji era (1868–1912) change attitudes and actions in Japan?
12. Economic Activities How have working conditions changed for many Japanese in the recent past?

13. Cooperation and Conflict (a) How did communism take hold in North Korea? **(b)** Why did North Korea attack South Korea in 1950?
14. Economic Systems Why were the 1990s a time of great economic hardship for the people of North Korea?

Critical Thinking and Writing

15. Making Decisions Suppose that you could visit Japan at any time of the year. How would a knowledge of typhoons help you decide when to visit?
16. Analyzing Information The term *cultural divergence* refers to the practice of isolating a culture or trying to protect it from outside influences. **(a)** How was cultural divergence an important part of Japan's history? **(b)** How does cultural divergence continue to be a part of Japanese life today?
17. Identifying Relationships What did Japanese officials hope to gain from an alliance with Nazi Germany in World War II?

---

14. When the Soviet Union fell, North Korea lost its main source of economic support. Widespread shortages of food, fuel, machinery, and other supplies followed.

Critical Thinking and Writing
15. Possible answer: You would avoid visiting in late summer and early fall, when typhoons often cause floods and landslides.

16. (a) For many years, the Japanese tried to keep Westerners out of Japan. **(b)** Most Japanese come from the same ethnic group and have a similar culture; minorities such as Koreans, Ainu, and *burakumin* are often discriminated against.
17. Japan hoped to take control of the Pacific possessions of European countries that fell to the Nazis.

(Continued on next page.)

18. Predicting Consequences How do you think Japan's history would have been different if Japan had had an abundant supply of natural resources?

19. Making Comparisons How does the practice of religion differ between North Korea and South Korea?

Applying Skills

Using a Spreadsheet Refer to the Skills for Life lesson on page 697 to answer these questions:

20. If you wanted to update statistics for hydropower use in the Philippines, which cell would you edit?

21. Based on the data presented, which country relies most heavily on fossil fuels to produce electricity?

Reading a Map Study the map below, and answer the following questions:

22. What body of water separates South Korea from Japan?

23. What physical feature marks the border between North Korea and China?

North Korea and South Korea

Test Preparation

Read the question and choose the best answer.

24. Why does Japan have effective recycling programs and strict energy efficiency laws?

  A Japan's government is bowing to pressure from other countries.

  B Japan has a strong grass-roots environmental movement.

  C These measures are necessary because of Japan's high population density.

  D These reforms are a result of the American occupation of Japan.

Activities

USING THE **REGIONAL ATLAS**

Review the Regional Atlas for East Asia and the Pacific World and Chapter 32. Working on your own or with a partner, make a list of ten geographical statements about Japan, North Korea, and South Korea. Some statements should be true and some false, but be sure to keep a correct answer key handy. Exchange lists with classmates for an informal quiz about this region.

MENTAL MAPPING

Study a map of East Asia and the Pacific World. Then, on a separate piece of paper, draw a sketch map of Japan and the Koreas from memory. Label the following places on your map:

- North Korea
- Kanto Plain
- South Korea
- East China Sea
- Pacific Ocean
- Honshu
- Seoul
- P'yŏngyang
- Sea of Japan
- Tokyo
- Hiroshima

Take It to the NET

Making a Poster How has culture in the United States been influenced by contact with Japan and the Koreas—and vice versa? Make a poster that shows some of these cultural influences. Visit the World Geography section of **www.phschool.com** for help in completing this activity.

---

18. Possible answer: Japan might not have felt the need to gain control of its neighbors and their resources, so its history may not have been marked by such militarism.
19. North Korea: Communist government discourages religious practice. South Korea: freedom of worship and many religions are practiced, with Buddhism dominant.

Applying Skills
20. C6
21. China
22. Korea Strait
23. Yalu River

Test Preparation
24. C

Activities

Using the Regional Atlas
Lists will vary but may touch upon political characteristics, physical characteristics, climates, and economic activities.

Mental Mapping
To check their work, have students compare their maps to those in the Regional Atlas.

Take It to the Net
Students' work should reflect sound research. Posters may include a variety of cultural areas, such as music, fashion, entertainment, and religion.

MENTAL MAPPING

Games for Review See pages 58–63 of the Simulations, Games, and Lab Activities booklet in the Teaching Resources for games to review for the Chapter 32 Map Test.

Chapter Map Test Students should use the completed outline maps and the Unit 9 Checklist in their Atlas Portfolios to prepare for the Chapter 32 Map Test.

Alternative Assessment

Final Evaluation

Cooperative Learning Project Use the Cooperative Learning Project Evaluation Forms on pages 17 and 19 of the Alternative Assessment booklet in the Prentice Hall Assessment System to evaluate students' papers. Teachers or students can complete the forms to indicate the level of work achieved for each of the criteria. Evaluations should include specific comments.

Resource Manager

Chapter-Level Resources	CORE INSTRUCTION	READING/SKILLS
	Teaching Resources **Unit 9**/Ch. 33 • Reviewing Main Ideas, p. 47 **Mental Mapping booklet** • Unit 9 Checklist, p. 115 **Simulations, Games, and Lab Activities** • Place Location Review Games, pp. 58–63 **TeacherExpress™ CD-ROM**, Ch. 33 **Companion Web site,** **www.phschool.com** • eTeach	**Teaching Resources** **Unit 9**/Ch. 33 • Map/Graph Skills, p. 49 **Book on CD**, Ch. 33 **Social Studies Skills Tutor CD-ROM**
1 Historical Influences on Southeast Asia 1. Explain how the migration of people into Southeast Asia has affected the region's culture. 2. Describe how Europeans changed the economy, environment, and political boundaries of Southeast Asia.	**Teaching Resources** **Unit 9**/Ch. 33 • Guided Reading and Review, p. 43 **Creative Teaching Activities** • Learning About Batik, p. 35 **Prentice Hall Presentation Pro CD-ROM**, Ch. 33, Sec. 1	**Teaching Resources** **Guide to the Essentials (English/Spanish)** • Section Summary, Ch. 33, Sec. 1 **Guided Reading Audiotapes (English/Spanish)**, Ch. 33, Sec. 1 **Section Reading Support Transparencies**, Ch. 33, Sec. 1
2 The Countries of Southeast Asia 1. Explain why Myanmar struggles with its national identity but Thailand does not. 2. Describe how years of conflict affected Vietnam, Laos, and Cambodia. 3. Explain what keeps the diverse nations of Indonesia and the Philippines united. 4. List the natural resources that support the economies of Singapore, Malaysia and Brunei, and Papua New Guinea.	**Teaching Resources** **Unit 9**/Ch. 33 • Guided Reading and Review, p. 45 **Prentice Hall Presentation Pro CD-ROM**, Ch. 33, Sec. 2	**Teaching Resources** **Guide to the Essentials (English/Spanish)** • Section Summary, Ch. 33, Sec. 2 **Mental Mapping booklet** • Outline Map 33, p. 127 **Guided Reading Audiotapes (English/Spanish)**, Ch. 33, Sec. 2 **Section Reading Support Transparencies**, Ch. 33, Sec. 2

ENRICHMENT/HONORS/PREAP

Teaching Resources
- **Unit 9**/Ch. 33
  - Critical Thinking, p. 48
- **Mental Mapping booklet**
  - Atlas Activity, p. 128
- **Social Studies Skills Handbook**
  - Study and Research Skills, pp. 94–108
- **World Geography Map and Photo Transparencies**
  - East Asia and the Pacific World: Maps and Photos
- **World Geography Videos**
  - Government and Citizenship: Southeast Asia, Tape 4
- **Companion Web site, www.phschool.com**
  - Chapter 33 Activities

Teaching Resources
- **Social Studies Skills Handbook**
  - Recognizing Bias, p. 47
- **Companion Web site, www.phschool.com**
  - Chapter 33 Activities

Teaching Resources
- **Social Studies Skills Handbook**
  - Identifying the Main Idea, p. 41
- **Companion Web site, www.phschool.com**
  - Chapter 33 Activities

ASSESSMENT

PRENTICE HALL ASSESSMENT SYSTEM

Core Assessment
- ExamView Test Bank booklet, Ch. 33
- ExamView Test Bank CD-ROM, Ch. 33

Standardized Test Preparation

Review and Reteach
- Review Book for World Geography, pp. 19–20

Practice and Assess
- Test-taking Strategies With Transparencies for High School
- Test-taking Strategy Poster
- Alternative Assessment booklet
- Test Prep Book for World Geography

Teaching Resources
- **Unit 9**/Ch. 33
  - Section Quizzes, pp. 44, 46
  - Test Forms A and B, pp. 50–55
- **Guide to the Essentials (English/Spanish)**
  - Chapter 33 Test
- **Spanish Resources**, Ch. 33
  - Section Quizzes, pp. 84–85
- **Mental Mapping booklet**
  - Chapter 33 Map Test, p. 129
- **Companion Web site, www.phschool.com**
  - Chapter 33 Self-Test

CUSTOMIZE FOR INDIVIDUAL NEEDS

Gifted and Talented
- Teacher's Edition, Customize for . . . , p. 705

Less Proficient Readers
- Guide to the Essentials (English), Ch. 33, Section Summaries
- Guided Reading Audiotapes (English), Ch. 33
- Section Reading Support Transparencies, Ch. 33
- Book on CD, Ch. 33
- Teacher's Edition, Reading Strategy, pp. 703, 708
- Teacher's Edition, Activity: Vocabulary, p. 707
- Teacher's Edition, Customize for . . . , p. 709

Students Acquiring English/ESL
- Guide to the Essentials (English/Spanish), Ch. 33
- Guided Reading Audiotapes (English/Spanish), Ch. 33
- Section Reading Support Transparencies, Ch. 33
- Book on CD, Ch. 33
- Teacher's Edition, Customize for . . . , p. 703

Less Proficient Writers
- Alternative Assessment, Writing Assignment Rubric, p. 6

MENTAL MAPPING

Point out that Southeast Asia lies in the southern part of Asia, east of India and south of China. Have students name the oceans and seas that surround the peninsulas and islands that make up Southeast Asia. (Indian Ocean, South China Sea, Pacific Ocean, Philippine Sea, Sulu Sea, Celebes Sea, Banda Sea, Java Sea, Timor Sea, Flores Sea, Arafura Sea, Coral Sea, Andaman Sea)

Mapping the Region Have students study the map on this page. Then instruct them to close their books and create a sketch map of Southeast Asia. You may also distribute the Chapter 33 Outline Map on page 127 of the Mental Mapping booklet in the Teaching Resources. Instruct students to lightly shade each country a different color. Then ask them to label the countries and bodies of water shown on this map. Students should keep their maps in their Atlas Portfolios in order to prepare for the Chapter 33 Map Test.

CHAPTER

33

*S*outheast Asia

Southeast Asia: POLITICAL

KEY

— National boundary
⊛ National capital
• Other city

Two-Point Equidistant Projection

0   400   800 mi
0   400   800 km

MYANMAR (BURMA) · LAOS · ⊛Hanoi · Vientiane⊛ · Yangon · THAILAND · Bangkok⊛ · CAMBODIA · Phnom Penh⊛ · VIETNAM · Ho Chi Minh City · Luzon · PHILIPPINES · Manila⊛ · Mindanao · BRUNEI · Bandar Seri Begawan⊛ · Kuala Lumpur⊛ · MALAYSIA · Singapore⊛ SINGAPORE · Sumatra · Borneo · Celebes · Moluccas · PAPUA NEW GUINEA · New Guinea · ⊛Port Moresby · Jakarta · Bandung · Java · Surabaja · EAST TIMOR · Bali · INDONESIA

Bay of Bengal · Andaman Sea · Gulf of Tonkin · Mekong · South China Sea · Gulf of Thailand · Strait of Malacca · Sulu Sea · Celebes Sea · Philippine Sea · PACIFIC OCEAN · Tropic of Cancer · Taiwan Strait · Equator · Banda Sea · Java Sea · Flores · Flores Sea · Arafura Sea · Torres Strait · Timor Sea · Coral Sea · INDIAN OCEAN

Go Online
PHSchool.com

For: More information about Southeast Asia and access to the Take It to the Net activities
Visit: phschool.com
Web Code: mjk-0034

---

eTeach

Be sure to check out this month's online forum with a Master Teacher to join in an exchange of teaching ideas. **www.phschool.com**

RESOURCE DIRECTORY

Teaching Resources

Unit 9, Chapter 33
• Section 1, Guided Reading and Review, p. 43
Guide to the Essentials (English/Spanish)
• Section Summary, Chapter 33, Section 1
Mental Mapping booklet
• Atlas Activity, p. 128
• Unit 9 Checklist, p. 115

Technology

Guided Reading Audiotapes (English/Spanish),
  Chapter 33, Section 1

Section Reading Support Transparencies,
  Chapter 33, Section 1
World Geography Map and Photo Transparencies
• East Asia and the Pacific World: Maps and Photos
Book on CD, Chapter 33
World Geography Videos
• Government and Citizenship: Southeast Asia, Tape 4
TeacherExpress™ CD-ROM, Chapter 33
Prentice Hall Presentation Pro CD-ROM, Chapter 33
Social Studies Skills Tutor CD-ROM
Companion Web site, www.phschool.com
• Chapter 33 Activities

1 Historical Influences on Southeast Asia

Reading Focus

- How has the migration of people into Southeast Asia over the centuries affected the culture of that region?
- How did Europeans change the economy, environment, and political boundaries of Southeast Asia?

Key Terms

barbarian

paddy

indigenous

Main Idea The cultures of India, China, Southwest Asia, and the West all influenced Southeast Asia.

Cultures A Buddhist monk stands within view of the Cambodian temple Angkor Wat.

Southeast Asia's location makes it one of the world's great geographic crossroads. Many groups of people from distant regions have met here to trade. The cultures of India, China, Southwest Asia, and the West all influenced Southeast Asia. This rich variety blended with the cultures of native Southeast Asians to create a diverse and distinct region.

Migration

The earliest inhabitants of mainland Southeast Asia probably migrated to the region from southern China and South Asia. Over thousands of years, other people slowly moved south from Central Asia and southern China into the region. Groups such as the Mons, Khmers (kuh MER z), and Thais eventually made their way down into the peninsula of Southeast Asia. They settled along the peninsula's rich river valleys and fertile coastal plains.

Indian Influence By the first century A.D., the Mons, Khmers, and other groups began to establish strongholds in Southeast Asia. No single group ever united the entire region, but various rich and powerful kingdoms did develop. Attracted by the wealth of these kingdoms, merchants from India sailed the coasts of Southeast Asia, bringing with them Hindu and Buddhist monks. Through their interaction with the people of Southeast Asia, these traders and monks greatly influenced life in the region.

Over the centuries, Indian culture and religion gradually blended with the culture of Southeast Asia. The people of Southeast Asia absorbed Hinduism and Buddhism into their existing religious beliefs. They adopted many Hindu myths and worshiped Hindu gods, but rejected other ideas such as the strict caste system. Southeast Asian rulers built palaces and temples in the Indian architectural style and dedicated them to Hindu gods. Others built Buddhist monasteries. Boys were encouraged to enter the monastery at an early age to learn to read and write. Although some became monks, the majority left the monastic life to marry.

◀ **The Mekong Delta** (photo left)

Chapter 33 ▪ Section 1   **701**

Objectives

Upon completion of Section 1, students should be able to:

- ◆ explain how the migration of people into Southeast Asia has affected the region's culture;
- ◆ describe how Europeans changed the economy, environment, and political boundaries of Southeast Asia.

National Geography Standards

The following National Geography Standards are highlighted in this section: 1, 2, 4, 6, 9, 10, 11, 12, 13, 14, 16, 17

Bellringer

Ask: **What do canned pineapple, tropical fish, sugar, cocoa, and rubber have in common?** (They are all exported from Southeast Asia.)

LESSON PLAN

1. Focus Tell students to consult a globe or a world map and imagine that they are aboard a European trading ship in the 1600s. Ask: **What geographical factors might influence you to stop in Southeast Asia?** (location, possible natural resources)

2. Instruct Write the headings *India, China, Southwest Asia,* and *Europe* on the board. Have students find examples of the influences each of these regions had on Southeast Asia. Write responses under the proper headings. Have students copy the chart to keep as a study aid.

3. Close/Reteach Ask students to write a paragraph summarizing how Europeans affected the physical geography and politics of Southeast Asia.

TEACHING TIP
From A Master Teacher

Local and World Economies Draw students' attention to the large array of goods such as sneakers, electronics, and clothing produced in Southeast Asia's low-wage assembly plants. These factories are financed by foreign investment. At the local scale, however, the majority of Southeast Asians still practice traditional subsistence agriculture. As economic opportunities in the region expand, the interaction of local and world economies creates an increasingly complex network of labor, transportation, and markets.

Pacing Suggestions

For 60-minute Blocks

You will want to vary activities.

- Ask students to complete the Map/Graph Skills activity on page 49 of the Unit 9 booklet. Review the answers. Have students use the World Almanac and other appropriate sources to determine the life expectancy and literacy rate of five additional nations not mentioned in the worksheet. Ask students to write a paragraph explaining what these statistics suggest about the nations of Southeast Asia.

Connecting With . . .

History Two women, the Trung sisters, led the Vietnamese struggle against Chinese rule in A.D. 39. Their armies freed 65 towns from the Chinese before the women were defeated. The Trung sisters are still celebrated in Vietnamese history.

Alternative Assessment

Introduce the Activity

Constructing a Time Line Ask students to choose one country in Southeast Asia and construct a time line marking the important events in its history. Distribute the Time Line Rubric found on page 12 of the Alternative Assessment booklet in the Prentice Hall Assessment System for students' reference.

Islam in Indonesia

Cultures The Muslim influence in Southeast Asia can be seen in this Indonesian junior high school, which is run according to Islamic principles.

Place *How did Islam first enter Southeast Asia?*

Buddhist influences remain strong in much of Southeast Asia. Buddhist monasteries and temples are often at the center of village life. Farmers turn to Buddhist monks for advice on daily life and sometimes for political leadership.

Muslim Influence Sometime between the 1200s and the 1400s, a new influence reached Southeast Asia. Traders from Arabia and India brought the Islamic religion to the region. Islam spread quickly along the trade routes. It reached the islands of Indonesia and spread as far east as the southern Philippines. Along with Buddhism and Hinduism, Islam became an important religion in the region. (See the religion map on page 642.) Islam created strong ties among the peoples of Malaysia, Indonesia, the southern Philippines, and other Muslim lands.

Chinese Influence Although many of the people who migrated to Southeast Asia came from China, the Chinese had little impact on the region. One reason was that the Chinese were

not interested in exporting their culture. They viewed themselves and their civilization as superior, and they were not eager to share their culture with foreigners. They considered foreigners to be **barbarians,** or people without manners or civilized customs.

There was one exception. Around 100 B.C., China took control of what is today the northern part of Vietnam. For over 1,000 years Vietnam remained under Chinese influence. Vietnamese language, religious beliefs, art, government, and agriculture—all were affected by Chinese culture to some degree. But the Vietnamese never lost their identity. They kept their own customs, and although many Chinese words entered their vocabulary, they continued to speak Vietnamese.

Europeans Bring Change

Eager to gain access to the silks, spices, and precious metals in Southeast Asia, Portuguese traders arrived in Southeast Asia in the 1500s and set up trading posts. The Spanish, Dutch, British,

RESOURCE DIRECTORY

Teaching Resources
Creative Teaching Activities, Learning About Batik, p. 35

Prentice Hall Assessment System
Alternative Assessment booklet
• Time Line Rubric, p. 12

Answer to Photo Caption

Traders from Arabia and India brought Islam to Southeast Asia.

and French soon followed. In the 1700s and 1800s, three changes in Europe caused these nations' colonies to expand deeper into Southeast Asia. First, Europeans acquired a taste for products such as coffee and tea that grew in tropical climates. Second, the rapidly expanding population in Europe led to an increased demand for these products. Third, the Industrial Revolution caused Europeans to look to Southeast Asia not only for the raw materials needed to produce factory-made goods, but for markets for these products as well. By the late 1800s, the Europeans had colonized all of Southeast Asia except for Thailand.

To take advantage of Southeast Asia's many natural resources, the Europeans drastically changed the region's physical and human geography. They cleared vast areas of forest and established plantations, or large farms, to grow cash crops such as coffee, tea, tobacco, and latex (raw rubber). They also encouraged rich, local landlords to grow rice for export. **Paddies,** the wet land on which rice is grown, spanned the deltas of the Irrawaddy, Chao Phraya, and Mekong

rivers as far as the eye could see.

Southeast Asian farmers had traditionally tended their own small plots of land. However, they could not compete with the large landowners. Many small farmers were forced to leave their land and go to work on foreign-owned plantations and in the paddies of wealthy Southeast Asians.

The Europeans sold factory-made goods to their colonies. They undercut local crafts by selling cloth, tools, and other products more cheaply. Unable to compete with factory-made goods, local artisans were forced out of business. As a result, the economies of Southeast Asia became

GL**O**BAL CONNECTIONS

Migration Starting in the mid-1970s, the forced migration of various Indochinese ethnic groups became a common occurrence in Southeast Asia. Changes in leadership in Cambodia, Vietnam, and Laos resulted in extensive ethnic purges. Hundreds of thousands of people from various Southeast Asian groups sought refuge in Thailand, the United States, and other countries.

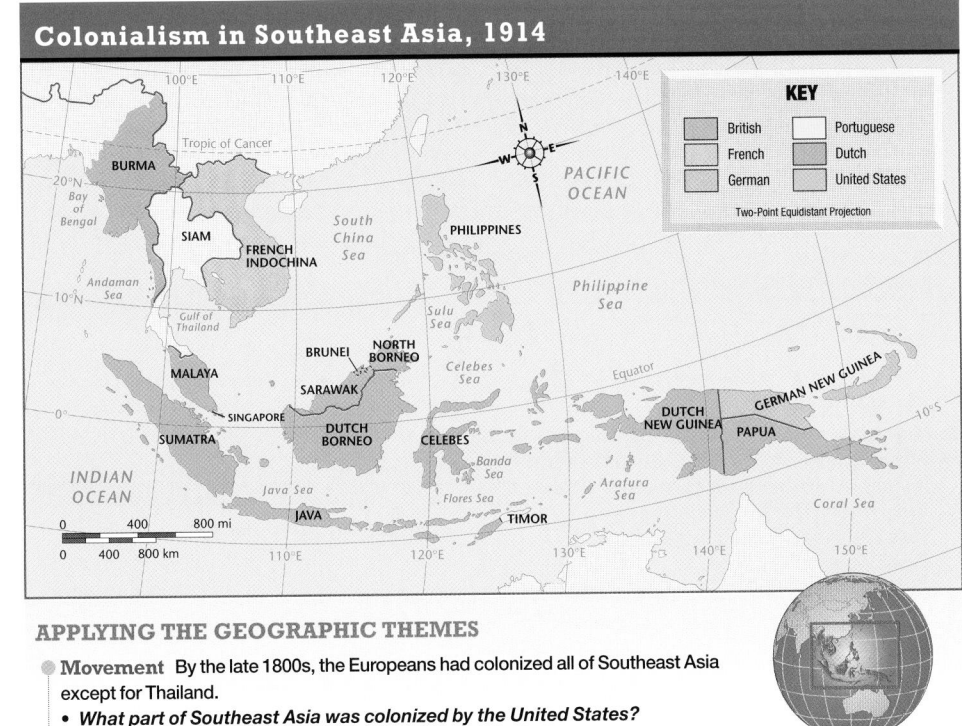

Colonialism in Southeast Asia, 1914

KEY
- British
- French
- German
- Portuguese
- Dutch
- United States

Two-Point Equidistant Projection

APPLYING THE GEOGRAPHIC THEMES

● **Movement** By the late 1800s, the Europeans had colonized all of Southeast Asia except for Thailand.
• *What part of Southeast Asia was colonized by the United States?*

Summarizing Main Ideas

Before students read the subsection Europeans Bring Change beginning on page 702, write the following sentence beginnings on the board. After students have read the section, ask them to complete the sentences. *The colonization of Southeast Asia brought Europeans many benefits, including . . .* (Possible answers: access to the region's products and natural resources and new markets for European manufactured goods) *European colonization affected Southeast Asia by . . .* (Possible answers: destroying forests, creating powerful plantations, forcing Southeast Asians to depend on Europe for manufactured goods, attracting immigrants from China and India, and increasing tensions between local ethnic groups)

CUSTOMIZE FOR...

Students Acquiring English/ESL

Comparing Influences Have students create a three-column chart that compares the Indian, Muslim, and Chinese influences on Southeast Asia. Students may use sentences, phrases, key words, or icons to record their information. Allow students to use their charts when they complete the Section 1 Assessment.

TEST PREPARATION

Have students use the map on this page to answer the following question.
By 1914, which country had colonized the eastern region of the Southeast Asian peninsula?
A   United States
B   France
C   Portugal
D   Great Britain

Answer to Map Caption
the Philippines

Asia's Key Crop

Economic Activities No crop is more important for feeding humanity than rice, especially in Asia where 90 percent of the world's rice is grown. Rice is a single species of grass, but more than 140,000 subspecies of rice are cultivated.

Human-Environment Interaction *How did European intervention change the pattern of rice growing in Southeast Asia?*

dependent on the industrialized nations for manufactured goods.

Europeans also financed the construction of inland roads and railroads. These new roadways carried crops and other goods to port cities for export to Europe. As these once slow, sleepy port cities began to grow rapidly, they attracted large numbers of people from China and India. Tensions sometimes developed between these new immigrants and **indigenous,** or native, Southeast Asians.

Colonization also greatly affected relations among different indigenous groups within Southeast Asia. When Europeans arrived in the region and carved out their own colonies, they paid little attention to existing ethnic boundaries. As a result, hostile groups often were united into one colony, while others, which had lived together peacefully for centuries, were separated. When the colonies finally became independent countries after World War II, many of them inherited deep ethnic conflicts.

SECTION 1 ASSESSMENT

1. **Key Terms** Define **(a)** barbarian, **(b)** paddy, **(c)** indigenous.

2. **Migration (a)** In what way did migrants to Southeast Asia affect the culture of the region? **(b)** How did these migrations influence Southeast Asian religion? **(c)** Why did Chinese immigrants have less of an influence on the people of Southeast Asia?

3. **Understanding the Past** What are three major changes that Europeans brought to Southeast Asia?

4. **Critical Thinking Identifying Main Ideas** How did location affect the development of culture in Southeast Asia?

Activity

Take It to the NET

Analyzing Data Use economic statistics from the Internet to create a graph about the economy of Southeast Asia. For each country, collect and record the following information: major industries, imports, exports, and annual per capita income. Visit the World Geography section of **www.phschool.com** for help in completing this activity.

Recognizing Propaganda

Propaganda consists of ideas or information that are spread deliberately to influence people's thoughts or actions. The information may be true or false. Propaganda can be used in many ways, such as to conduct campaigns for social reform, to win political elections, or to sell a particular commercial product.

Learn the Skill Use the poster, abstract, and the following steps to recognize propaganda.

1 *Identify the initial impact.* The propaganda poster below shows some of the different ethnic minorities in Vietnam. Record your initial response to the poster. Take note of what the image is trying to convince you to think or do. *What is the main message of the propaganda piece below?*

2 *Identify the use of propaganda techniques.* One technique that propagandists use is to supply only those facts that support a particular cause. A second technique is to use appealing images, which often are misleading. A third technique is to identify a cause with a famous person. *Which technique is used in the propaganda piece below? Explain.*

3 *Compare sources.* Conduct additional research for facts on the same topic. For this lesson we have provided an additional source for you. *How are ethnic relations in Vietnam according to the* New York Times *abstract?*

4 *Analyze the emotional appeal of the propaganda.* Decide how the image is presented in order to sway opinion or appeal to people. **(a)** *What does the propaganda poster lead you to believe about ethnic minorities in Vietnam?* **(b)** *How does this message compare with the information from the* New York Times *abstract?*

5 *Draw conclusions.* Decide what the purpose of the propaganda is and whom it was meant to influence. **(a)** *What is the purpose of the poster?* **(b)** *Do you think the poster will have a great impact on its audience? Explain.*

 Do It Yourself

Practice the Skill Find an example of propaganda in a newspaper, or a magazine, or from a television commercial. Then, use the steps in this Skills for Life lesson to analyze the propaganda.

Apply the Skill See Chapter 33 Review and Assessment.

Minorities in Vietnam

Unrest Among Minorities

Vietnam's authorities acknowledge that the wave of unrest in Central Highlands is more extensive than previously admitted, leading to several injuries and 20 arrests. . . . Government spokeswoman says protesters destroyed public buildings, including schools. . . . [Protesters were] angered over confiscation of their churches and breakup of religious services. . . .

—Source: www.nytimes.com, February 9, 2001, abstract

Vietnamese Propaganda

Teaching the Skill

After students have read the introductory paragraph, tell them to brainstorm a list of advertising campaigns that they consider particularly effective or interesting. Ask them what made each of the campaigns memorable. As you complete the lesson with the students, apply the Learn the Skill steps to the advertising campaigns that the students listed. As a concluding activity, ask students to decide whether the advertising campaigns are a form of propaganda.

Answers to Learn the Skill

1. The main message is the solidarity and unity among different Vietnamese ethnic women under communism.

2. The propaganda employs an appealing image. The women have their arms around each other and are smiling.

3. There is discontent among ethnic minorities.

4. (a) The poster suggests unity and affection among different Vietnamese ethnic groups. **(b)** The abstract seems to contradict the image.

5. (a) The purpose is to promote the idea of happiness under communism. **(b)** Answers will vary, but students may suggest that the audience knows the reality and will not be influenced by a poster that suggests the opposite.

Answers to Practice the Skill

Students' analyses should demonstrate a clear understanding and recognition of propaganda.

CUSTOMIZE FOR...

Gifted and Talented

Re-creating Historical Propaganda Arrange students in two teams. Ask them to research the controversy that raged among Americans when the United States acquired and assumed rule over the Philippines in 1898. Have both teams create propaganda posters, cartoons, editorials, and speeches: One should be in favor of U.S. imperialism, while the other should be opposed to it.

Objectives

Upon completion of Section 2, students should be able to:

◆ explain why Myanmar struggles with its national identity but Thailand does not;

◆ describe how years of conflict affected Vietnam, Laos, and Cambodia;

◆ explain what keeps the diverse nations of Indonesia and the Philippines united;

◆ list the natural resources that support the economies of Singapore, Malaysia and Brunei, and Papua New Guinea.

 National Geography Standards

The following National Geography Standards are highlighted in this section: 1, 3, 4, 5, 6, 9, 10, 11, 12, 13, 16, 17, 18

 Bellringer

Take a poll to find out how many students have heard of the Vietnam War and what they know about it.

LESSON PLAN

1. Focus Write the names of the countries of Southeast Asia on slips of paper and have each student choose a slip. Have students refer to the map on page 707 and sketch a rough map of the country they have chosen. Then have them identify each other's sketches.

2. Instruct List the names of the countries of Southeast Asia on the board. Have students use their texts to contribute facts about each country. Then ask them to form generalizations about each country's economic and political stability.

3. Close/Reteach Divide the class into groups and assign each group one Southeast Asian country. Instruct each group to briefly summarize how its country's interaction with other nations has affected its economy and government. Ask a spokesperson from each group to read the summaries to the class.

 # The Countries of Southeast Asia

Reading Focus

- **Why does Myanmar struggle with its national identity and Thailand does not?**
- **In what ways did years of conflict affect Vietnam, Laos, and Cambodia?**
- **What keeps the diverse nations of Indonesia and the Philippines united?**
- **What natural resources support the economies of Singapore, Malaysia and Brunei, and Papua New Guinea?**

Key Terms

insurgent

doi moi

heterogeneity

Main Idea Ethnic and political divisions have made a sense of unity difficult for many nations of Southeast Asia.

Government and Citizenship Citizens of Myanmar pass beneath a government billboard.

Most countries in Southeast Asia belong to the Association of Southeast Asian Nations (ASEAN). This organization, like the European Union, works to promote economic cooperation and peace among its members. Unfortunately, unity within many of these nations has often been hard to achieve. Although all of Southeast Asia is now independent, colonialism has left its mark on the region. In many cases, the factions that fought together to gain independence are having trouble learning to coexist and govern peacefully.

Myanmar

Myanmar, formerly called Burma, is a country about the size of Texas where more than 100 languages are spoken. About 68 percent of Myanmar's people are members of the Burman ethnic group and speak Burmese. The rest belong to a variety of ethnic groups and speak different languages. Sometimes people living in villages only miles apart may belong to completely different ethnic groups.

Throughout their history, these groups protected their cultural identities. When the British took control of the region in the late 1800s, they combined the people in Myanmar into a single political unit, but they made little attempt to unify them culturally. They allowed the people a great deal of autonomy. Partly for this reason, when Myanmar gained its independence in 1948, the new country lacked unity.

Since independence, various ethnic groups have fought against the government; some wanted to secede from the country; others tried to overthrow the government. Warfare with various ethnic **insurgents,** or people who rebel against their government, has greatly slowed Myanmar's economic growth.

Another cause of the weak economy is Myanmar's repressive military government. The leader in the fight for democracy in Myanmar is Aung San Suu Kyi (awng sahn soo chee). She has led opposition to the government for many years, even though she was under arrest from 1989 to 1995 and again in 2000. In 1991, she won the Nobel Peace Prize for her efforts to bring change to Myanmar without violence. Continuing her struggle, she helped organize a meeting of opposition politicians in 1996. Though the government took harsh measures to try to stop the meeting, it went ahead as planned. Said Aung San Suu Kyi:

66 Giving in to bullying is not good. We must have the courage to face the bully's challenge. I am very pleased and satisfied to see the people have real courage. 99

Thailand

The population of Thailand is not as divided as that of Myanmar. Though the population is made up of several groups, more than 85 percent of the people speak a dialect of Thai. Because of this cultural unity, as well as their long history as a free nation, Thailand's people have a strong national identity.

Preserving Independence Thailand is the one country in Southeast Asia that was not colonized by Europeans. King Mongkut and his son, whose reigns stretched from 1868 to 1910, maintained independence by signing treaties with the United States and several European nations. The Thai say that they are like bamboo that bends in the wind: they have been flexible

Southeast Asia: PHYSICAL-POLITICAL

KEY

Elevation		
Feet		Meters
14,000		4,270
7,000		2,135
1,500		457
700		213
(sea level) 0		0 (sea level)

⊛ National capital
• Major city
▲ Mountain

Two-Point Equidistant Projection

APPLYING THE GEOGRAPHIC THEMES

● **Location** Of the countries of Southeast Asia, five are located entirely on the Asian mainland. Other South Asian countries lie partially or entirely on islands.

• *What are the names of the five countries that are located entirely on the Asian mainland?*

Articles From NATIONAL GEOGRAPHIC

The following article may be used to extend the content in this section.

Swerdlow, Joel L., and Steve McCurry, photographer. "Burma: The Richest of the Poor Countries." *National Geographic*, Vol. 188, No. 1 (July 1995), pp. 70–97.

With one of the world's highest literacy rates and lowest standards of living, Burma (Myanmar) is a country of contrasts.

Before reading the subsection Progress Brings Change, ask students to think about Thailand's history since World War II. Instruct students to list two changes they think may have come to Thailand in recent years. Have them revise and add to their predictions after they read the subsection.

Alternative Assessment

Mid-Point Monitoring

Constructing a Time Line You may wish to monitor students' progress on their time lines. Confer with students to see if they have finished their research to determine which items to include on their time lines.

The New Thailand

Economic Activities Bangkok, Thailand's capital and largest city, is also the center of the nation's flourishing economy. Once known for its leisurely pace, Bangkok has grown into one of the largest cities in the world, with a population of more than 7 million.

Place *What are some of the important elements of Thailand's economic success?*

when dealing with foreigners in order to keep their independence.

Since World War II, Thailand has had close political ties to the United States. Threatened by the Communist revolution in China, it joined with the United States to stop Communist expansion in Southeast Asia. During the Vietnam War, Thailand allowed the United States to use its country as a base for air attacks against the Communists in Vietnam, Cambodia, and Laos.

Progress Brings Change Thailand's ability to bend with the wind has helped it to build one of the strongest economies in Southeast Asia. Until recently, Thailand's economy was dominated by agriculture, and rice was its main export. However, in the 1960s Thailand began to diversify its economy. Today it has industries that produce cement, food products, and textiles. Foreign companies operate plants that assemble machinery and electronic equipment. Manufactured goods now contribute more than twice as much to the economy as do agricultural products.

Tourism has become a major source of income for Thailand. In the last few decades, the tourist industry has grown significantly. Millions of foreign visitors flock to the country to enjoy its rich, varied culture, bringing with them billions of dollars annually.

Thailand's economic development has resulted in great changes. Bangkok, Thailand's capital, has become a transportation hub for the entire Southeast Asian region. Many international airlines serve this bustling city of skyscrapers, modern hotels, and noisy expressways. These modern structures stand in sharp contrast to the mysterious charm of traditional Bangkok, which one writer described in these words:

> 66 I still like Bangkok [because it is] a city of secrets. Not far from the railroad station, for example, stands a temple of ordinary exterior, Wat Trimit, containing an image of the Lord Buddha three meters high; it weighs five and a half tons—and is made of gold. Jewel merchants in simple shops may cover a desktop with a fortune in sapphires. . . . And behind the watery moat of the royal palace live the royal white elephants. 99

RESOURCE DIRECTORY

Teaching Resources
Social Studies Skills Handbook
• Identifying the Main Idea, p. 41

Answer to Photo Caption

Possible answers: Thailand's flexibility in dealing with foreign powers; the fact that the country was never colonized; diversification of its economy to include manufacturing and tourism industries

Unlike Myanmar, Thailand has gladly opened its doors to the world, reaching out to interact with many other countries. Spurred by this increased interdependence and its tradition of flexibility, Thailand has one of the most successful economies in Southeast Asia.

Vietnam, Laos, and Cambodia

Vietnam, Laos, and Cambodia are very different from one another ethnically. The overwhelming majority of the people in Vietnam are Vietnamese. In Cambodia, the vast majority belong to the Khmer ethnic group. Laos is ethnically more diverse. The country is home to Lao, Tai, Hmong, Yao, Mon, and Khmer, as well as Chinese and Vietnamese.

In other respects, Vietnam, Laos, and Cambodia have much in common. All of their cultures were influenced by India, and most of their people are Buddhists. As French colonies, the three countries together formed a region once known as French Indochina.

French influence in the area dates from the 1800s. By the early 1900s, Vietnam, Laos, and Cambodia had become French colonies. During World War II, from about 1940 to 1945, the Japanese took control of Indochina. But when the Japanese surrendered to the Allies in 1945, France was determined to regain its colonies.

Years of Conflict France's attempt to return to power in Indochina marked the beginning of a series of long and bloody wars in the area. In 1945, Ho Chi Minh, a Vietnamese leader, declared Vietnam's independence from France. Ho Chi Minh's forces fought a bitter and fierce war with the French. In 1954, the French were defeated.

After the war, a peace conference was held in Geneva, Switzerland. Instead of ending the conflict, however, the conference laid the foundation for more fighting by dividing Vietnam into two parts. North Vietnam was left to the Communists under Ho Chi Minh. South Vietnam was headed by Ngo Dinh Diem (NGO DIN DEE em), a pro-Western ruler.

The Communists in North and South Vietnam wanted to reunite the two countries. Another war soon began in which the United States

The Mekong River

Natural Resources Southeast Asians are trying to make use of resources offered by the Mekong. These woodcutters are looking for trees to sell in foreign markets.

Human-Environment Interaction *What other resources does a river offer?*

entered, hoping to keep South Vietnam free of Communist control.

Neighboring Laos and Cambodia were also drawn into the fighting when Communists in those countries provided a supply line to the Communist insurgents in South Vietnam. The North Vietnamese set up bases in Cambodia, and

Chapter 33 ▪ Section 2 **709**

Chapter 33 ▪ Section 2 **709**

Critical Thinking

Political Instability and Economics Use the following questions to help students see the link between political instability and economic growth: **What has been the economic result of Myanmar's political unrest?** (slow development) **How does Thailand's economy compare with Myanmar's?** (It is much stronger.) **How is Thailand's political history different from Myanmar's political history?** (Thailand was never colonized and has a history of cultural unity, which has greatly contributed to its political stability today.) **Why has Indonesia succeeded economically when Myanmar has not?** (Its numerous ethnic groups were united by strong government control.)

Daily Life

The Family The Vietnamese have a strong sense of family unity. They often live in extended families, with three generations living and working together. Ancestors are revered, since it is believed that a person's spirit lives on after death. Special days are set aside each year to honor the dead, who are given special offerings of food and clothing.

Southeast Asia and the United States
Trade Data

Country	Total Exports (billions of dollars)	Total Imports (billions of dollars)	Trade Balance (billions of dollars)
Brunei	3.00	1.40	1.60
Cambodia	1.05	1.40	−0.35
Indonesia	56.50	38.10	18.40
Laos	0.33	0.54	−0.21
Malaysia	94.40	76.90	17.50
Myanmar	1.80	2.20	−0.40
Papua New Guinea	1.80	1.02	0.78
Philippines	37.00	30.00	7.00
Singapore	122.00	116.00	6.00
Thailand	65.30	62.30	3.00
Vietnam	15.10	15.30	−0.20
United States	723.00	1,148.00	−425.00

Source: *The World Factbook*

CHART SKILLS

● **Global Trade Patterns** *What country in this table has the largest trade surplus? How might this country's location contribute to its high level of exports?*

● **Cooperation and Conflict** *What country has the lowest total exports? What political conditions might be affecting this country's economy?*

the struggle between the Communists and non-Communists in Laos and Cambodia intensified.

The United States withdrew from the war in 1973 and South Vietnam fell to the Communists in 1975. Vietnam was reunited one year later. Communists also gained control of the governments of Cambodia and Laos. In all three countries, the new governments killed huge numbers of non-Communists. In Cambodia, a brutal group called the Khmer Rouge (KMER ROUZH) murdered between 1 and 2 million people out of the total population of 7 million. Only an invasion by Vietnam in 1979 stopped the killings.

Prospects for the Future Astounding changes have taken place since Communist forces swept over South Vietnam in 1975. In 1986, Vietnam began a program of economic change called *doi moi* (dwa mwah). The keystone of

the program was attracting foreign investors. During the 1990s, Vietnam's economy boomed, growing 8 percent each year. It went from a once-starving nation to the world's second largest exporter of rice. Even companies from its former enemy, the United States, were pouring money into the Vietnamese economy as they scrambled to compete with European businesses.

The United States resumed official diplomatic relations with Vietnam in 1995, and the two nations signed a trade agreement in 2001. Vietnam's strategy of producing low-cost export goods has served it well, but competition from China makes its future uncertain. Furthermore, economic freedom in Vietnam has not yet brought about political freedom.

Laos and Cambodia have also loosened government controls on the economy. Both have seen economic growth over the last decade despite limited infrastructures.

Indonesia and the Philippines

Cultural **heterogeneity,** or lack of similarity, also challenges two other Southeast Asian nations. In Indonesia, more than 250 languages and dialects are spoken; in the Philippines, about 70 languages and dialects are spoken. These nations are also physically splintered. Indonesia has more than 13,660 islands, and the Philippines more than 7,100. What keeps countries with such variety united?

Indonesia Uniting Indonesia has required great effort. Indonesia has more than 228 million people living on islands spread over 3,200 miles (5,100 km) of ocean. Strong government, backed by the military, has maintained unity by using force and violating human rights. General Suharto ruled in this way for 32 years, until he resigned in 1998. In 1999, after much violence, the region of East Timor voted for independence and came under the administration of the United Nations.

Strong government rule has provided some benefits. Between 1966 and 1996, Indonesia's annual per capita income rose from $50 to $960—largely because of its oil resources. Indonesia, a member of OPEC, is a major producer of

Answers to Chart Skills

Indonesia; Indonesia is located in the center of an important trade route between Europe and East Asia.

Laos; Laos has only recently loosened government control of its economy.

petroleum. Oil has given Indonesia money to spend on roads, airports, and schools. As a result, illiteracy dropped from 61 percent in 1960 to 23 percent in 1990. The government has also focused on improving agriculture.

Indonesia experienced an economic slowdown when Asian economies soured in the late 1990s. Its large international debt has been a source of trouble, as have weaknesses in the banking system and government corruption.

The Philippines The Philippines experienced a long period of colonial rule. The Spanish ruled the Philippines for more than 300 years, until their defeat by the United States in the Spanish-American War in 1898. Independence from the United States came in 1946.

The people of the Philippines were strongly influenced by their colonial rulers. Spanish priests converted the Filipinos to the Roman Catholic religion. Today, about 83 percent of the current population of the Philippines is Roman Catholic. Many native Filipinos married Spanish people. This intermarriage spread the Spanish culture among various ethnic groups and helped to unite them.

The United States also had a great impact on the Philippines. It introduced a new educational system in which English was taught. Along with Filipino, English is an official language of the Philippines. The United States also introduced democracy to the country. Western cultural influences and a shared Asian heritage help give the people of the Philippines a sense of national unity.

The Philippines is now recovering from the Asian economic slowdown of the late 1990s. The country has a high birthrate of almost 30 per 1000 people, about twice the United States rate. The growth in population means that Filipinos do not have enough wealth, food, or work to go around. About 4 million Filipinos work overseas because they cannot find jobs at home.

GEOFacts

The Philippines lies on the typhoon belt in the Pacific Ocean. Five or six powerful storms strike the islands annually. The islands are also in the path of tsunamis, enormous tidal waves caused by undersea earthquakes.

Economic Hardship

Patterns of Settlement A rapidly growing population and economic fluctuations over the last decade have brought challenges to the Philippines. Many people move to the cities in search of better lives but can find housing only in slums like this one in Manila.

Place *How does this Manila slum compare to Bangkok, as shown on page 708?*

Articles From NATIONAL GEOGRAPHIC

The following article may be used to extend the content in this section.

Dahlby, Tracy, and Karen Kasmauski, photographer. "The New Saigon." *National Geographic*, Vol. 187, No. 4 (Apr. 1995), pp. 60–87.

Under Communist rule since 1975, Ho Chi Minh City is now experiencing the freedom of a liberated economy.

TEST PREPARATION

Have students read the subsection Prospects for the Future on the opposite page to complete the following statement.

The main goal of Vietnam's *doi moi* program was to —

A counteract Communist aggression
B improve Vietnam's economy
C compete with European businesses
D join ASEAN

Answer to Photo Caption

Possible answer: Bangkok appears to have newer, more modern buildings.

Economic Activities

Child Labor Human rights groups estimate that there may be as many as 250 million children worldwide, some of them as young as 5 years old, working full-time for low wages, with no chance to play or go to school. Many of these children work in Africa, Latin America, and Southeast Asia for foreign companies. Such companies use workers in countries where wages are low in order to lower their manufacturing costs. In 1999, the United States put legislation into effect that prohibits the import of goods made by children.

ACTIVITY

Group Work

Activity: Writing a news brief

Purpose: Instruct each group to develop a news brief that will report on an event or special-interest story involving Southeast Asia. (Examples: Vietnam's growing economy; the struggle against oppression in Myanmar)

Roles: Researchers, writers, and a newscaster

Result: The newscaster from each group reads the news brief to the class.

Answer to Photo Caption

Malaysia's proximity to the sea makes fishing an important economic activity.

Singapore

Singapore is Southeast Asia's smallest country. It consists of a single city located on one main island and more than fifty smaller surrounding islands. But this tiny country casts a big shadow because of its political and economic power.

Singapore's physical features and relative location played an important role in its success. It has a deep, natural, sheltered harbor. Its location at the southern tip of the Malay Peninsula places it in the center of an important trade route between Europe and East Asia.

From its beginning as a British trading post in 1819, Singapore prospered and attracted immigrants from Malaysia, China, and India. It became an independent country in 1965. Singapore's former leaders pushed through laws favorable to foreign investors. By keeping wages low, they attracted foreign companies eager to produce goods cheaply. Singapore actively courted high-tech companies and built a modern educational system to provide the highly skilled workers needed to work in high-tech industries.

Modern Singapore is a thriving center of international trade and an important manufacturing center. It is one of the world's busiest ports. Thousands of ships dock at Singapore each year carrying rubber, wood, petroleum products from Singapore's refineries, and many other goods. Industrial growth and high population density have contributed to air and water pollution. To minimize these problems, the government imposes strict controls on emissions and waste.

Malaysia and Brunei

Like Singapore, Malaysia and Brunei have strong economies that are not based on agriculture. Malaysia and Brunei are two of the wealthiest countries in Southeast Asia.

About 50 percent of Brunei's wealth comes from its large reserves of oil and natural gas. Income from these resources enabled Brunei to

Tradition and Change in Malaysia

Cultures Malaysia has had one of the world's fastest growing economies over recent years. Yet, traditional ways of life are still common in many parts of the nation.

Location *How does Malaysia's relative location benefit the economic activity shown in this photograph?*

RESOURCE DIRECTORY

Teaching Resources
Unit 9, Chapter 33
- Section 2 Quiz, p. 46
- Reviewing Main Ideas, p. 47
- Test Forms A and B, pp. 50–55

Spanish Resources
- Section 2 Quiz, p. 85

Guide to the Essentials (English/Spanish)
- Chapter 33 Test

Mental Mapping booklet
- Chapter 33 Map Test, p. 129

Simulations, Games, and Lab Activities
- Place Location Review Games, pp. 58–63

Social Studies Skills Handbook
- Study and Research Skills, pp. 94–108

Prentice Hall Assessment System
Alternative Assessment booklet
- Time Line Evaluation Form, p. 13

Technology
ExamView Test Bank CD-ROM, Chapter 33 Test
Companion Web site, www.phschool.com
- Chapter 33 Self-Test

modernize. Some remote villages now have electricity and running water. The government provides free schooling and medical care for citizens.

Malaysia supports a wide variety of economic activities. Machinery and transport equipment, oil, and other raw materials are its leading exports. As does Brunei, Malaysia uses its oil revenues to help develop manufacturing and improve agriculture.

Papua New Guinea

Like its larger neighbors, Papua New Guinea is ethnically diverse, with some 700 ethnic groups. It is actually part of two overlapping regions—Southeast Asia and Oceania. It seems to straddle two worlds—one traditional, the other modern.

More than 80 percent of Papua New Guinea's nearly 5 million people are engaged in agriculture. Villagers in the remote highlands still plant their crops with traditional tools. Communication is poor because there are no roads to many of the country's far-flung villages. Only 1 out of every 113 people has a telephone. Electricity reaches only a small percentage of the nation.

In sharp contrast, modern machines are used to mine great quantities of gold and copper ore in Papua New Guinea. In village stores, you will find modern goods such as canned beef, rice, and sugar imported from Japan and Australia. The prospects are that in the years ahead Papua New Guinea will become a more culturally integrated, modern consumer state.

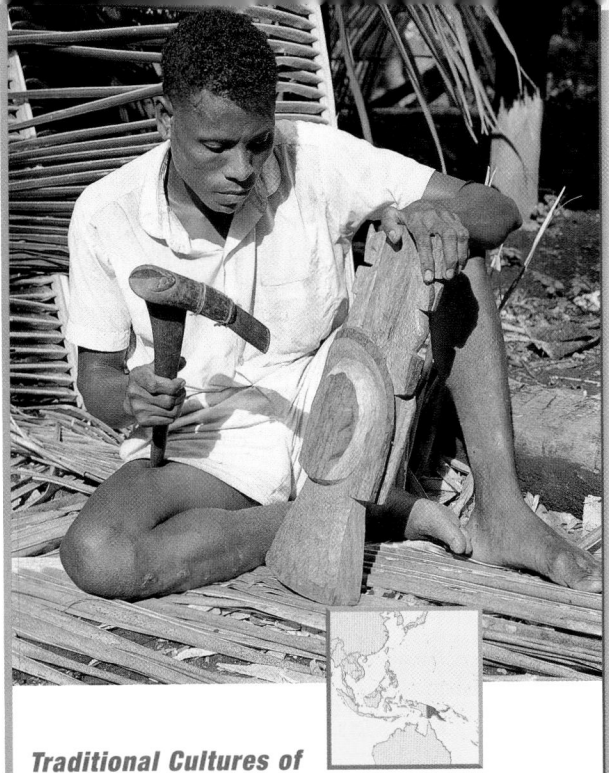

Traditional Cultures of Papua New Guinea

Cultures Papua New Guinea's forbidding physical geography has helped its traditional cultures survive. This woodcarver lives on one of the Trobriand Islands in the isolated Solomon Sea.

Place *Is the woodcarver's tool an example of traditional or modern technology? Explain.*

SECTION 2 ASSESSMENT

1. **Key Terms** Define **(a)** insurgent, **(b)** *doi moi*, **(c)** heterogeneity.

2. **Government and Citizenship** What problems do the citizens of Myanmar face that the citizens of Thailand do not?

3. **Cooperation and Conflict** How have Vietnam, Laos, and Cambodia recovered from years of war?

4. **Cultures** What constant challenges do Indonesia and the Philippines have to overcome?

5. **Natural Resources** What natural resources support the economies of **(a)** Singapore,

(b) Malaysia, **(c)** Brunei, and **(d)** Papua New Guinea?

6. **Critical Thinking Analyzing Information** Why would a Communist nation like Vietnam decide to invite investment by capitalist nations?

Activity

USING THE REGIONAL ATLAS

Review the Regional Atlas for East Asia and the Pacific World and this section. Prepare a brochure to promote investment in each country in the Southeast Asia region. Provide information to show how each country might have a bright economic future.

Creating a Chapter Summary

As a reteaching opportunity, pair a more able student with a less able student to complete this chapter summary.

Possible answers: **Myanmar** *Strength:* Movement for nonviolent change *Weakness:* Warfare among ethnic insurgents, Repressive military government *Plan:* Create a democratic government **Thailand** *Strength:* Strong national identity and economy, Interaction with other countries *Weakness:* None *Plan:* Maintain economic prosperity **Vietnam** *Strength:* Economy *Weakness:* Political repression *Plan:* Encourage foreign investment

Check students' charts for accuracy of answers for other nations.

Reviewing Key Terms

1–6. Students' sentences should show a clear understanding of each term.

Understanding Key Ideas

7. Hinduism, Buddhism, Christianity, and Islam
8. to take advantage of Southeast Asia's many natural resources
9. She won the prize for her nonviolent efforts to bring democracy to Myanmar.
10. Foreign companies operate plants in Thailand, tourism has become a major source of income, and Bangkok has become a transportation hub.
11. Communists in Laos and Cambodia provided a supply line to insurgents in South Vietnam, and the North Vietnamese set up bases in Cambodia.
12. It has greatly improved Vietnam's foreign relations.
13. There are not enough resources, food, or work for the growing population.

Critical Thinking and Writing

14. (a) Advantage: Location provided a diversity of trading partners. **(b)** Disadvantage: More powerful nations coveted resources and were able to invade and colonize the region.
15. Possible answer: Myanmar's economy could prosper in a politically peaceful environment.

714 Chapter 33

Creating a Chapter Summary

Copy this chart onto a piece of paper. Add rows for every nation in Southeast Asia. Then, complete the chart with details from the chapter. Some entries have been completed to serve as an example.

COUNTRY	STRENGTH	WEAKNESS	PLAN FOR THE FUTURE
MYANMAR			
THAILAND			• To maintain economic prosperity
VIETNAM	• Economy		

Take It to the NET
Chapter Self-Test For practice test questions for Chapter 33, go to the World Geography section of **www.phschool.com**.

Reviewing Key Terms

Use the key terms listed below to write sentences. Leave blanks where the key terms belong. Exchange sentences with those of a partner and fill in the blanks.

1. barbarian
2. paddy
3. indigenous
4. insurgent
5. *doi moi*
6. heterogeneity

Understanding Key Ideas

7. Cultures What religions spread to Southeast Asia from India, Southwest Asia, and Europe?
8. Environmental Change Why did the Europeans change the environment of Southeast Asia?
9. Government and Citizenship Why did Aung San Suu Kyi win the Nobel Peace Prize?
10. Global Trade Patterns Give three examples of how relationships with other nations have affected Thailand's economy.

11. Cooperation and Conflict How did Laos and Cambodia become involved in the Vietnam War?
12. Economic Activities How has *doi moi* affected Vietnam's relationship with other nations?
13. Population Growth Why is population growth a problem for the Philippines?

Critical Thinking and Writing

14. Drawing Conclusions (a) How is Southeast Asia's location as a geographic crossroad advantageous? **(b)** Why might its location be considered a disadvantage?
15. Predicting Consequences What might happen to Myanmar's economy if the political unrest there came to an end?
16. Identifying Relationships (a) Why was it beneficial for Thailand to ally itself with the United States? **(b)** What did the United States gain from the relationship?
17. Planning for the Future What are steps Papua New Guinea could take to modernize?

16. (a) Thailand remained free of Communist control and its economy prospered as a trading partner with the United States. **(b)** The United States built a base for air attacks in Thailand against the Communists in Vietnam, Cambodia, and Laos.
17. Mining profits could be used to build roads, provide electricity, or promote modern agricultural methods.

Applying Skills

Recognizing Propaganda Refer to the Skills for Life lesson on page 705 to answer these questions:

18. Why might a person, organization, or government use propaganda?

19. What are three main techniques of propagandists?

20. Who do you think is the intended audience for the propaganda piece provided in the skill lesson?

Drawing Conclusions Read the quotation below, and answer the following questions:

21. What modern technology has impacted the city of Bangkok?

22. What is one religion that is present in Bangkok?

23. What is one economic activity practiced in Bangkok?

24. How does the quotation suggest that Thailand has a monarch?

25. Do you think the author of this quotation is a citizen of Thailand or a visitor to the country? Explain your reasoning.

❝I still like Bangkok [because it is] a city of secrets. Not far from the railroad station, for example, stands a temple of ordinary exterior, Wat Trimit, containing an image of the Lord Buddha three meters high; it weighs five and a half tons—and is made of gold. Jewel merchants in simple shops may cover a desktop with a fortune in sapphires. . . . And behind the watery moat of the royal palace live the royal white elephants.❞

Test Preparation

Read the question and choose the best answer.

26. A major cause of the violence in many Southeast Asian countries is —

A limited natural resources

B ethnic diversity

C poor communication systems

D strong economies

Activities

USING THE **REGIONAL ATLAS**

Review the Regional Atlas for East Asia and the Pacific World and Chapter 33. Write a profile for each country in the region. List at least five details for each country, such as location, chief products, and natural resources.

MENTAL MAPPING

Study a map of Southeast Asia and its neighbors. Then, on a separate piece of paper, draw a sketch map of the area from memory. Label the following places on your map:

- Myanmar
- Indian Ocean
- The Philippines
- Thailand
- Cambodia
- Malaysia
- Papua New Guinea
- Vietnam
- Indonesia
- Pacific Ocean

Take It to the NET

Making Comparisons Visit Web sites of regional organizations such as the Association of Southeast Asian Nations (ASEAN) and the European Union. Compare the goals and influence of the two organizations. Visit the World Geography section of **www.phschool.com** for help in completing this activity.

Applying Skills

18. Possible answers: to conduct campaigns for social reform, to win elections, or to sell a particular product

19. supply only those facts that support a particular cause; use appealing images, which often are misleading; identify a cause with a famous person

20. Answers will vary, but some students may suggest the ethnic minorities in Vietnam.

21. the railroad

22. Buddhism

23. selling of jewels

24. The speaker mentions a royal palace.

25. Answers will vary but should be based on sound reasoning.

Test Preparation

26. B

Activities

Using the Regional Atlas
Students' profiles will vary but should include sufficient information for identification of the country.

Mental Mapping
Review students' maps for relative and absolute location.

Take It to the Net
Students' work should reflect sound research. Check students' work for accurate comparisons of the organizations selected.

MENTAL MAPPING

Games for Review See pages 58–63 of the Simulations, Games, and Lab Activities booklet for games to review place names in preparation for the Chapter 33 Map Test.

Chapter Map Test Students should use the completed outline maps and the Unit 9 Checklist in their Atlas Portfolios to prepare for the Chapter 33 Map Test. Point out to students that the test will cover only those place names on the Unit 9 Checklist.

Alternative Assessment

Final Evaluation

Constructing a Time Line Use the Time Line Evaluation Form on page 13 of the Alternative Assessment booklet in the Prentice Hall Assessment System to evaluate students' participation. Either teachers or students can complete the forms to indicate which level of work was achieved for each of the criteria. The evaluation should include specific examples and comments.

Resource Manager

Chapter-Level Resources	CORE INSTRUCTION	READING/SKILLS
	Teaching Resources 📘 **Unit 9**/Ch. 34 • Reviewing Main Ideas, p. 62 📖 **Mental Mapping booklet** • Unit 9 Checklist, p. 115 📖 **Simulations, Games, and Lab Activities** • Place Location Review Games, pp. 58–63 💿 **TeacherExpress™ CD-ROM**, Ch. 34 🖥 **Companion Web site,** **www.phschool.com** • eTeach	**Teaching Resources** 📘 **Unit 9**/Ch. 34 • Map/Graph Skills, p. 64 📖 **Mental Mapping booklet** • Outline Map 34, p. 130 💿 **Book on CD**, Ch. 34 💿 **Social Studies Skills Tutor CD-ROM**
1 Australia 1. Show how migration affected Australia's population and land use. 2. Explain why Australia's population is clustered in and around its major cities. 3. Describe how European settlers changed Australia's environment.	**Teaching Resources** 📘 **Unit 9**/Ch. 34 • Guided Reading and Review, p. 56 💿 **Prentice Hall Presentation Pro CD-ROM**, Ch. 34, Sec. 1	**Teaching Resources** 📖 **Guide to the Essentials (English/Spanish)** • Section Summary, Ch. 34, Sec. 1 📖 **Social Studies Skills Handbook** • Using the Compass Rose, p. 4 • Using Latitude and Longitude, p. 11 📼 **Guided Reading Audiotapes (English/Spanish)**, Ch. 34, Sec. 1 📄 **Section Reading Support Transparencies**, Ch. 34, Sec. 1
2 New Zealand and the Pacific Islands 1. Explain how New Zealand's European majority affected the Maori way of life and the economy of the region. 2. Describe the physical characteristics of the two types of Pacific Islands—high islands and low islands.	**Teaching Resources** 📘 **Unit 9**/Ch. 34 • Guided Reading and Review, p. 58 💿 **Prentice Hall Presentation Pro CD-ROM**, Ch. 34, Sec. 2	**Teaching Resources** 📖 **Guide to the Essentials (English/Spanish)** • Section Summary, Ch. 34, Sec. 2 📖 **Social Studies Skills Handbook** • Understanding Road Maps, p. 35 • Reading a Road Map, p. 36 📼 **Guided Reading Audiotapes (English/Spanish)**, Ch. 34, Sec. 2 📄 **Section Reading Support Transparencies**, Ch. 34, Sec. 2
3 Antarctica 1. Describe how Antarctica's climate and ice-covered terrain affect wildlife habitation and exploration. 2. Explain why many scientists consider Antarctica to be a land of valuable natural resources.	**Teaching Resources** 📘 **Unit 9**/Ch. 34 • Guided Reading and Review, p. 60 📖 **Creative Teaching Activities** • A Pacific Expedition, p. 36 💿 **Prentice Hall Presentation Pro CD-ROM**, Ch. 34, Sec. 3	**Teaching Resources** 📖 **Guide to the Essentials (English/Spanish)** • Section Summary, Ch. 34, Sec. 3 📖 **Social Studies Skills Handbook** • Reading a Contour Map, p. 30 📼 **Guided Reading Audiotapes (English/Spanish)**, Ch. 34, Sec. 3 📄 **Section Reading Support Transparencies**, Ch. 34, Sec. 3

ENRICHMENT/HONORS/PREAP

Teaching Resources

Unit 9/Ch. 34
- Critical Thinking, p. 63

Mental Mapping booklet
- Atlas Activity, p. 131

Social Studies Skills Handbook
- Study and Research Skills, pp. 94–108

World Geography Map and Photo Transparencies
- East Asia and the Pacific World: Maps and Photos
- How the Earth Works, Unit 9

World Geography Videos
- Physical Processes: The Pacific World and Antarctica, Tape 4

Companion Web site, www.phschool.com
- Chapter 34 Activities

Teaching Resources

Unit 9/Ch. 34
- Geography and World Literature, p. 71

Companion Web site, www.phschool.com
- Chapter 34 Activities

Companion Web site, www.phschool.com
- Chapter 34 Activities

Companion Web site, www.phschool.com
- Chapter 34 Activities

ASSESSMENT

PRENTICE HALL ASSESSMENT SYSTEM

Core Assessment

- ExamView Test Bank booklet, Ch. 34
- ExamView Test Bank CD-ROM, Ch. 34
- ExamView Test Bank CD-ROM, Unit 9

Standardized Test Preparation

Review and Reteach
- Review Book for World Geography, pp. 19–20

Practice and Assess
- Test-taking Strategies With Transparencies for High School

  Test-taking Strategy Poster

- Alternative Assessment booklet
- Test Prep Book for World Geography

Teaching Resources

Unit 9/Ch. 34
- Section Quizzes, pp. 57, 59, 61
- Test Forms A and B, pp. 65–70

Guide to the Essentials (English/Spanish)
- Chapter 34 Test

Spanish Resources, Ch. 34
- Section Quizzes, pp. 86–88

Mental Mapping booklet
- Chapter 34 Map Test, p. 132
- Unit 9 Map Test, p. 133

Companion Web site, www.phschool.com
- Chapter 34 Self-Test

CUSTOMIZE FOR INDIVIDUAL NEEDS

Honors/PreAP
- Teacher's Edition, Customize for . . . , p. 727

Less Proficient Readers
- Guide to the Essentials (English), Ch. 34, Section Summaries
- Guided Reading Audiotapes (English), Ch. 34
- Section Reading Support Transparencies, Ch. 34
- Book on CD, Ch. 34
- Teacher's Edition, Reading Strategy, pp. 720, 727, 734
- Teacher's Edition, Activity: Vocabulary, pp. 720, 729, 735
- Teacher's Edition, Customize for . . . , pp. 721, 725, 733

Students Acquiring English/ESL
- Guide to the Essentials (English/Spanish), Ch. 34
- Guided Reading Audiotapes (English/Spanish), Ch. 34
- Section Reading Support Transparencies, Ch. 34
- Book on CD, Ch. 34

Less Proficient Writers
- Alternative Assessment, Writing Assignment Rubric, p. 6

⊕ **MENTAL MAPPING**

Ask students to look at the map on this page. Point out Australia and New Zealand. Have students explain the locations of these two places in relation to other regions. (Example: Australia lies southeast of Asia and west of South America.)

Mapping the Region Have students study the map. Then instruct them to close their books and create a sketch map like the one on this page, or distribute the Chapter 34 Outline Map on page 130 of the Mental Mapping booklet. Have them shade each country a different color and add labels for the countries, cities, and bodies of water that are shown on the map. Students should keep their maps in their Atlas Portfolios in order to prepare for the Chapter 34 Map Test.

CHAPTER

34

The Pacific World and Antarctica

SECTIONS

1 Australia

2 New Zealand and the Pacific Islands

3 Antarctica

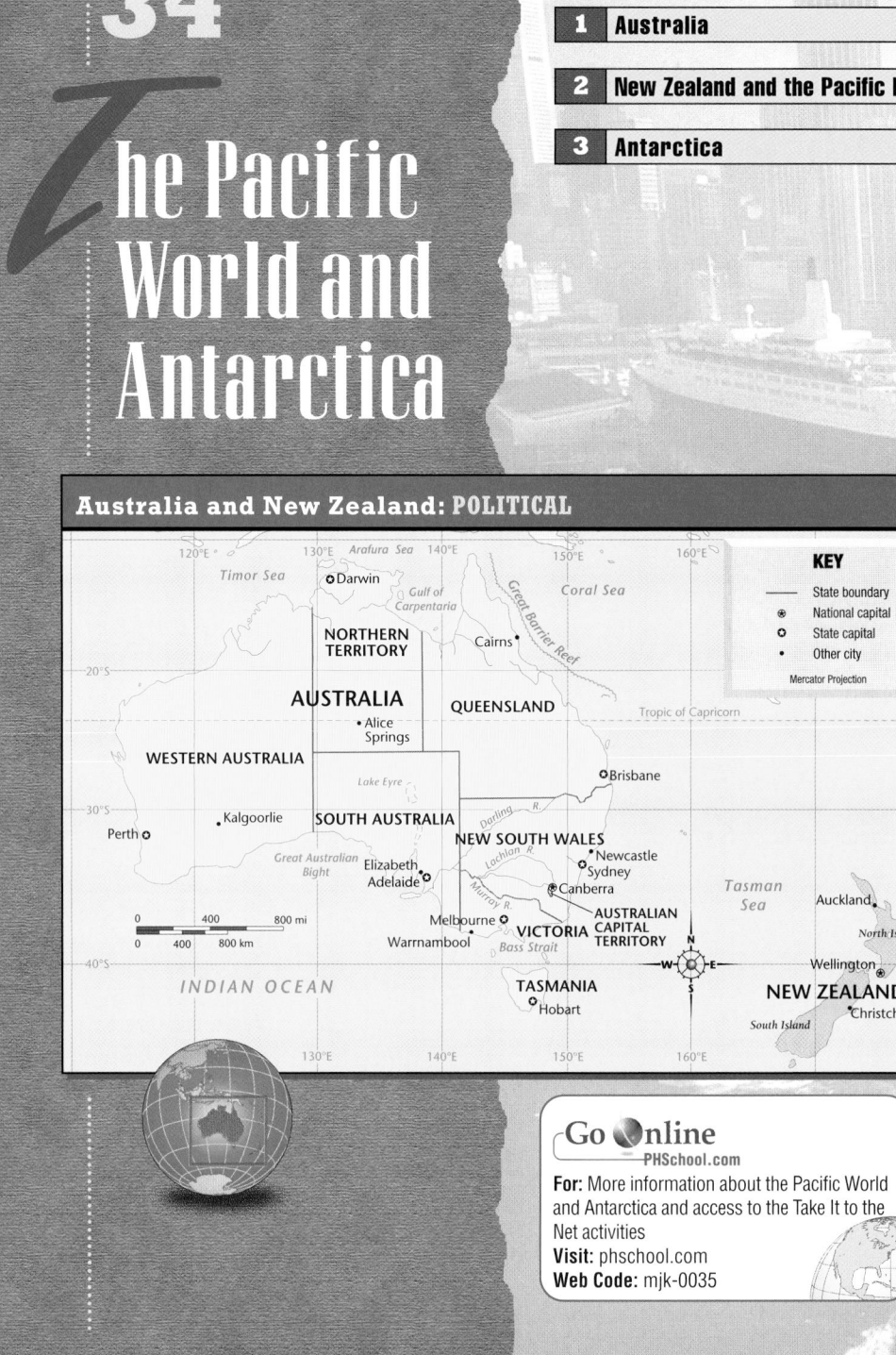

Australia and New Zealand: POLITICAL

KEY
— State boundary
⊛ National capital
◉ State capital
• Other city

Mercator Projection

Go Online
PHSchool.com

For: More information about the Pacific World and Antarctica and access to the Take It to the Net activities
Visit: phschool.com
Web Code: mjk-0035

🖥 **eTeach**

Be sure to check out this month's online forum with a Master Teacher to join in an exchange of teaching ideas. **www.phschool.com**

RESOURCE DIRECTORY

Teaching Resources
Unit 9, Chapter 34
• Section 1 Guided Reading and Review, p. 56
Guide to the Essentials (English/Spanish)
• Section Summary, Chapter 34, Section 1
Mental Mapping booklet
• Atlas Activity, p. 131
• Unit 9 Checklist, p. 115

Technology
Guided Reading Audiotapes (English/Spanish),
  Chapter 34, Section 1

Section Reading Support Transparencies
  Chapter 34, Section 1
World Geography Map and Photo Transparencies
• East Asia and the Pacific World: Maps and Photos
Book on CD, Chapter 34
World Geography Videos
• Physical Processes: The Pacific World and
  Antarctica, Tape 4
TeacherExpress™ CD-ROM, Chapter 34
Prentice Hall Presentation Pro CD-ROM, Chapter 34
Social Studies Skills Tutor CD-ROM
Companion Web site, www.phschool.com
• Chapter 34 Activities

1 Australia

Reading Focus

- How did various migrations to Australia affect population and land use?
- Why is Australia's population clustered in and around its major cities?
- How have European settlers changed Australia's environment?

Key Terms

Aborigine
lagoon
cyclone
outback
artesian well

 Main Idea Australia is a vast land with diverse physical characteristics and a relatively small population.

Ecosystems Golfers play alongside kangaroos, one of the many indigenous animals of Australia.

Australia is both a continent and a country. In area, it is the world's sixth largest country and the smallest, flattest, and—except for Antarctica—driest continent. About 19 million people live in Australia. That's only about 1 million more than live in New York. Yet, Australia is nearly as large in area as the entire United States. Why is such a vast land so underpopulated? To answer this question, you must look at Australia's climate, natural vegetation, and the patterns of settlement and land use.

A History of Migration

Scientists think that the first Australians, known as **Aborigines** (ab uh RIJ uh neez), crossed a land bridge from Southeast Asia to Australia about 50 thousand years ago. The Aborigines were nomadic hunters and gatherers. They lived in small groups and spoke as many as 250 distinct languages. While customs varied from one group to another, they shared some things in common, including a deep respect for nature and the land.

At some point the land bridge connecting Australia to Southeast Asia sank under the sea, leaving the Aborigines isolated from the rest of the world for thousands of years. Australia's isolation ended in 1770, however, when Captain James Cook landed on the east coast of Australia and claimed it for Great Britain.

European Settlement The European settlement of Australia began in earnest 18 years after Cook arrived. Britain quickly came to see Australia as a solution to the problem of its prisons, which were overcrowded with the poor. In 1787 the first group of prisoners boarded ships for the long journey to the southern continent. Many of them still wore leg irons when they arrived in Sydney Harbor.

During the next 80 years, more than 160,000 men, women, and children were transported from Britain to Australia's distant shores. After their sentences ended, many prisoners stayed in Australia. Other settlers from Britain joined them, looking for land on which to raise sheep and grow wheat.

Meanwhile, the Aborigines suffered tremendous losses, killed by European diseases or weapons. The number of Australians who are completely Aborigine in ancestry sank from 300,000 in the 1700s to only about 50,000 today.

◀ Sydney Harbor, Australia *(photo left)*

Chapter 34 ▪ Section 1 **717**

Objectives

Upon completion of Section 1, students should be able to:

- ◆ show how migration affected Australia's population and land use;
- ◆ explain why Australia's population is clustered in and around its major cities;
- ◆ describe how European settlers changed Australia's environment.

 ### National Geography Standards

The following National Geography Standards are highlighted in this section: 1, 3, 4, 5, 6, 8, 9, 10, 11, 12, 13, 14, 16, 17

 ### Bellringer

Mention that Australia's unofficial national anthem is "Waltzing Matilda." Ask: **What do you think the song is about?** (In Australian slang, a matilda is a bedroll, often the only possession of farmhands who wander the outback in search of work. The song glorifies their way of life.)

LESSON PLAN

1. Focus Direct students to the map of Australia on page 716 and point out Perth, Adelaide, Sydney, Melbourne, Canberra, Hobart, Darwin, and Brisbane. **What is similar about their locations?** (All are on or near the coast.)

2. Instruct Divide the class into pairs. Assign one of Australia's eight major cities to each pair. Have students use the text to find and list details about the city. Call one pair assigned for each city to locate its city on a wall map and read its list of information.

3. Close/Reteach Direct students to the Reading Focus questions on this page. Have them find and record the answers to each question.

TEACHING TIP
From A Master Teacher

Migration and Diffusion The themes of migration and diffusion emerge as powerful concepts in the study of Australia, New Zealand, and the Pacific Islands. The first migrants to New Zealand and other Pacific Islands spread from elsewhere in the Pacific. Later, migrants were pulled to Australia and New Zealand over great distances by the rich resources the region offered. Today, both Australia and New Zealand attract immigrants from Asia and the Pacific Islands.

Pacing Suggestions

 For 90-minute Blocks

You will want to vary activities.

- Assign each group a specific location in the region. Have them identify and research factors affecting the quality of life of local residents, such as transportation, language, culture, economy, communications, climate, and natural resources. Then have them prepare a presentation about the advantages and disadvantages of living in that location.

Chapter 34 ▪ Section 1 **717**

The Physical World

Wildlife Many of the world's marsupials are unique to Australia. These mammals give birth before the offspring are fully developed. The young are then nurtured in a pouch on the mother's abdomen until they mature. Kangaroos, wallabies, and wombats are just a few of Australia's marsupials. So is the ferocious Tasmanian devil, which lives in the rain forests of Tasmania.

Alternative Assessment

Introduce the Activity

Giving an Oral Presentation Ask students to conduct library research and prepare a 5- to 10-minute oral presentation about how the Aborigines of Australia or the Maori of New Zealand have adapted to the changes brought about by the presence of European immigrants and their descendants. Distribute the Oral Presentation Rubric found on page 20 of the Alternative Assessment booklet in the Prentice Hall Assessment System for student reference during the project.

Answer to Map Caption

The arid climate and sparse vegetation discourage settlement.

718 Chapter 34

Even while the Aborigine population was dwindling, the European population continued to grow, especially since the early 1900s. Until the end of World War II, most of Australia's immigrants came from Great Britain. After the war ended, large numbers of immigrants came from Greece, Italy, and other countries in southern and eastern Europe. Today, many immigrants come from the nearby countries of Southeast Asia. They come because of Australia's location in the Pacific Ocean and because of its high standard of living.

Patterns of Settlement Australia's hot, dry climate and forbidding interior have greatly affected the country's settlement and land use patterns. As immigrants entered Australia, they sought out the areas that had the mildest climates. Look for these regions on the climate map on page 719. Notice that the moist and mild climates are along the eastern and southeastern coasts, while the interior of the continent is extremely hot and dry.

Now look closely at the population density map on page 643. Notice that the vast majority of Australians live in cities located along the eastern and southeastern coasts—the so-called Urban Rim. In fact, 90 percent of Australia's population live within 100 miles (160 km) of the ocean. Commenting on the pattern of settlement in Australia, one author has noted:

> 66 In shape, Australia resembles a ragged square, but the real Australia where people live and work is a ribbon. 99

This, then, is the answer to the question about Australia's population. The population is

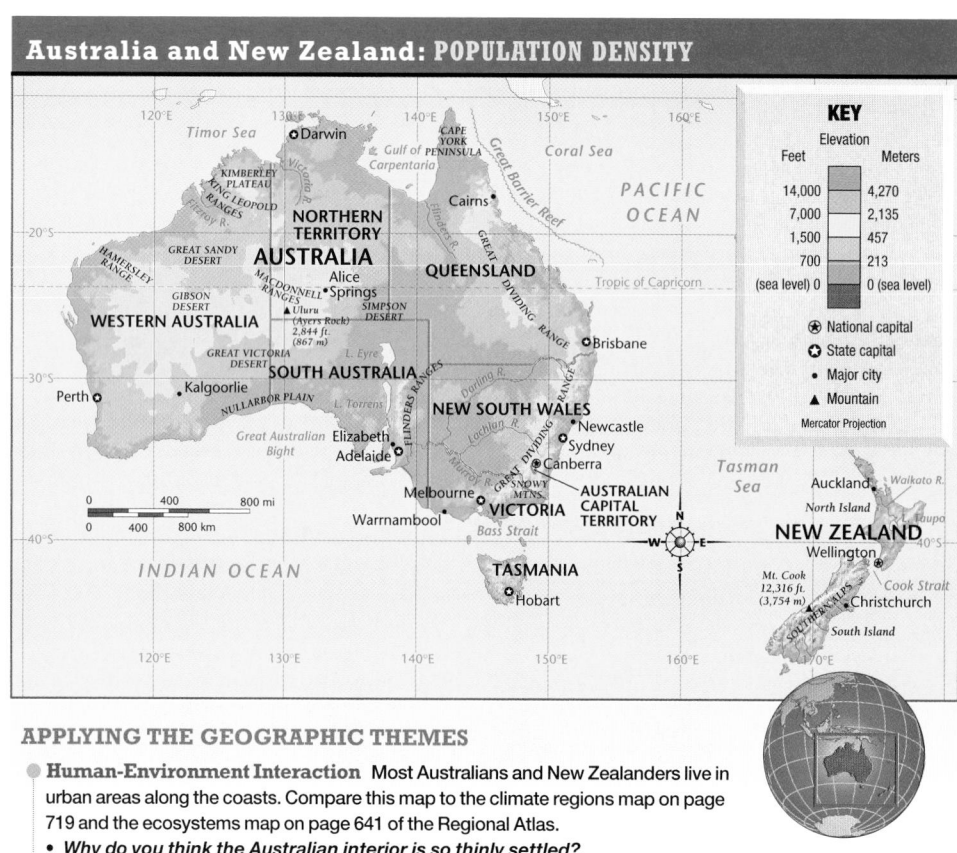

Australia and New Zealand: POPULATION DENSITY

KEY

Elevation	
Feet	Meters
14,000	4,270
7,000	2,135
1,500	457
700	213
(sea level) 0	0 (sea level)

⊛ National capital
✪ State capital
• Major city
▲ Mountain

Mercator Projection

APPLYING THE GEOGRAPHIC THEMES

● **Human-Environment Interaction** Most Australians and New Zealanders live in urban areas along the coasts. Compare this map to the climate regions map on page 719 and the ecosystems map on page 641 of the Regional Atlas.
  • *Why do you think the Australian interior is so thinly settled?*

718   Chapter 34 ▪ The Pacific World and Antarctica

RESOURCE DIRECTORY

Teaching Resources
Unit 9, Chapter 34
• Critical Thinking Activity, p. 63
• Geography and World Literature, My Brilliant Career, p. 71
Mental Mapping booklet
• Outline Map 34, p. 130
Social Studies Skills Handbook
• Using the Compass Rose, p. 4
• Using Latitude and Longitude, p. 11

Prentice Hall Assessment System
Alternative Assessment booklet
• Oral Presentation Rubric, p. 20

Australia and New Zealand: CLIMATE REGIONS

KEY

- Tropical wet
- Tropical wet and dry
- Semiarid
- Arid
- Mediterranean
- Humid subtropical
- Marine west coast

Mercator Projection

APPLYING THE GEOGRAPHIC THEMES

● **Regions** Rainfall is heaviest in the northern and eastern coastal regions of Australia.

• *What is Australia's largest climate region?*

small because relatively few people moved to the remote continent from other nations. Also, Australia's harsh climate discourages widespread settlement in the interior.

Major Cities

Australia's population clusters in and around the eight largest cities. These cities include the capitals of Australia's seven states, plus Canberra, the national capital. Each city derives its own distinct flavor from its location, its landscapes, and its varied people.

Perth and Adelaide The huge state of Western Australia sits astride the Great Sandy, Gibson, and Great Victoria deserts. This region is very sparsely populated, with less than two persons per square mile (less than one person per sq km). In this vast, empty area, Perth stands out

as one of the world's most remote cities. Located on the western coast of Australia, Perth is more than 1,400 miles (2,300 km) from the next major city. If you flew east from Perth along Australia's southern coast, you would spend hours looking at barren land and small, isolated towns—until you reached Adelaide. A city of 1 million people, Adelaide is the capital and major city of the state of South Australia.

Australia's Urban Rim Three of Australia's most important cities—Sydney, Melbourne, and Canberra—lie within the Urban Rim. Moist winds from the Pacific Ocean and the Tasman Sea rise and cool as they approach the highlands, depositing their moisture in frequent rains. This weather pattern makes the Urban Rim one of Australia's best-watered and most fertile regions.

Sydney is the capital of the state of New South Wales and is Australia's oldest and largest

BACKGROUND

The Global Economy

Industry in Perth Despite its remote location, Perth plays a central role in Australian industry. The city produces construction materials, including paint, plaster, sheet metal, cement, rubber, and steel. It is also the site of food processing plants and oil refineries.

TEST PREPARATION

Have students read the subsection Patterns of Settlement that begins on the opposite page to answer the following question. Which statement best describes the main idea of this subsection?

  A The population of Australia is small.

  B The climate along the eastern and southeastern coasts is moist and mild.

  Ⓒ The harsh climate of the interior has discouraged settlement there.

  D Australia resembles a ragged square in shape.

Answer to Map Caption

arid

READING STRATEGY

Visualizing

As students read, encourage them to visualize the ways in which Australia's cities and regions differ from each other physically. Invite students to sketch pictures of several places in Australia and write captions describing their distinct features.

BACKGROUND

Word Origin

Tasmania Tasmania was named for the Dutch explorer Abel Tasman, who discovered it in 1642. However, until 1856 it was known as "Van Diemen's Land," after the Dutch governor of the East Indies who authorized Tasman's voyage.

ACTIVITY

Vocabulary

Lagoon Refer to the Key Terms list on page 717. Write the following sentence on the board: *The Great Barrier Reef is separated from the mainland of Australia by a large lagoon.* Ask students to guess the meaning of *lagoon* from its context in the sentence. Have a volunteer look up the term in the Glossary and read its definition aloud.

BACKGROUND

The Physical World

Fragile Wonders Coral reefs like the Great Barrier Reef are among the most biologically diverse ecosystems on earth. They are also the most endangered. Corals grow at a rate of only a few inches a year. They need warm, crystal clear water in order to grow. Sediment created from onshore development and carried into the ocean by rivers can suffocate or bury the coral. Pollution, rising ocean temperatures, and overfishing, which destroy species beneficial to the reef, are also major concerns.

Answer to Photo Caption

Possible answer: access to commerce, trade, sports, and cultural events

720 Chapter 34

Melbourne

Urbanization In Australia's second-largest city, Melbourne, people use the Princess Bridge to cross over the Yarra River. Besides its reputation as a center of commerce and trade, Melbourne is also known for its sports and cultural events.
Movement *What are some reasons why people move to urban centers, such as Melbourne?*

city. Sydney's splendid harbor is laced with small coves and crowned by the Sydney Opera House, which looks from the water like sails billowing in the wind.

Melbourne, the capital of Victoria and Australia's second-largest city, has a long-standing rivalry with Sydney. In the late 1800s Melbourne overtook Sydney as the nation's largest city. Although Sydney regained this status in the 1900s,

720 Chapter 34 ▪ The Pacific World and Antarctica

RESOURCE DIRECTORY

Teaching Resources
Social Studies Skills Handbook
• Understanding Road Maps, p. 35
• Reading a Road Map, p. 36

---

the two cities continue to compete for trade and commerce. Melbourne's south-facing harbor is not as conveniently located for world markets as Sydney's. Still, the factories of the Melbourne area make it a major source of goods for Australia.

Canberra Australia's capital, Canberra, is the country's only major planned city. It lies in federal territory within New South Wales, about 100 miles (160 km) from the coast. Like Washington, D.C., and Ottawa, Ontario, Canberra's location was selected to balance competing political interests in different states.

The government of Australia, like Australian culture in general, is dominated by the models it inherited from the British. Australia has a parliament led by a prime minister and a cabinet. Unlike Great Britain, however, Australia has a written constitution that divides power between the federal government and the states.

Across the Bass Strait Hobart is the capital of the island state of Tasmania. This island hangs off the southeastern coast of Australia like a geographic punctuation mark. Tasmania was not always an island. About 12 thousand years ago, rising ocean levels covered the land that connected it to the mainland and created the Bass Strait.

The island of Tasmania is mountainous and heavily forested; Hobart is cradled in deep blue peaks. With only about 190,000 inhabitants, Hobart is much smaller than the mainland cities of Sydney or Melbourne.

The Sunshine Coast Showered with frequent rains from moist trade winds, the east coast of Queensland is Australia's wettest region. This region, which includes Queensland's capital city, Brisbane, is in the heart of Australia's vacation land. Known as the Sunshine Coast, its humid subtropical climate and many lovely beaches attract millions of tourists to the region each year.

North of Brisbane and the Sunshine Coast is the Great Barrier Reef, the largest coral reef in the world. The reef forms a **lagoon,** a shallow body of water with an outlet to the ocean, between itself and the mainland. The reef extends for 1,250 miles (2,010 km)—just about the length of the United States coast from Maine to North Carolina.

The Great Barrier Reef

Environmental Change The Great Barrier Reef is a natural barrier made of the bodies of living and dead coral. If damaged, a coral reef takes many years to regenerate. There are several human-made threats to the coral reefs, such as pollution, fishing, and the carelessness of people, who often walk on the reefs or break off pieces as souvenirs.

Human-Environment Interaction *What can humans do to better protect and preserve coral reefs?*

ACTIVITY

Group Work

Activity: Creating a travel poster
Purpose: Tell each group that its job is to create a travel poster for one of the eight Australian cities described in Section 1. They may illustrate the posters with drawings, words, or photographs from magazines.
Roles: Groups should include researchers and artists.
Result: Display the completed posters on the bulletin board.

The Tropical North The sparsely populated Northern Territory is mostly too hot and dry to support human activities. The state's capital, Darwin, however, lies on the northern coast, where the climate is tropical, with wet and dry seasons. Darwin is the closest Australian city to Asia. As flights to other cities become more frequent, it continues to grow. Darwin's location has some disadvantages, however. The city was bombed by the Japanese in World War II. Moreover, it has twice been leveled by **cyclones,** the Australian term for hurricanes. The threat of cyclones has influenced architecture in the area, with few buildings in Darwin rising higher than one or two stories.

Environmental Change

Nearly all of Australia west of the Great Dividing Range is arid plain or dry plateau. Australians often refer to the harsh wilderness region of the central and western plains and plateaus as the **outback.** The Aborigines were the first humans to live in the outback. They learned over time how fragile their environment was and felt a sacred obligation to protect it.

Aborigines and the Land The Aborigines had few material possessions. However, they did have a rich oral tradition that preserved their religious beliefs and explained how their ancestors created the world. Aboriginal creation stories teach that in a time long ago, known as the Dreamtime, the ancestors of all living things moved across the formless earth and created the natural world. The Dreamtime ancestors were usually in the form of animals, but sometimes they took the form of human beings. Big Bill Neidjie (NAY jee), an Aborigine elder, says that when humans were created, the ancestors gave them responsibility for taking care of the earth: "Now we have done these things, you make sure they remain like this for all time. You must not change anything."

Over countless generations, the Aborigines took this responsibility to heart. They handed down ancient knowledge about the sacred sites of each ancestor from parent to child as a priceless gift. Aboriginal artists left records of these and other stories on rock paintings and carvings. The Aborigines learned to take from the land what they needed to survive without destroying their precious earth.

Chapter 34 ▪ Section 1   **721**

CUSTOMIZE FOR...

Less Proficient Readers
Using Textual Cues Remind students that "however" is often used to mark a turning point. As students read the subsection The Tropical North, ask them to note where "however" is used and to explain how it marks turning points in the paragraph.

Answer to Photo Caption

Possible answers include taking steps to decrease pollution levels and exercising care when visiting the reef.

Science and Technology

Eucalyptus Australia's eucalyptus tree has become a familiar sight in many nations around the world. Also known as the Fever Tree, eucalyptus has been used to help fight malaria since the mid-1800s. The antiseptic oil from its leaves combats malarial fever and many other ills. However, the tree's most powerful antimalarial tool is its root system, which rapidly drains the marshy land where malaria-carrying mosquitoes breed. In Algeria and Italy, eucalyptus trees are credited with transforming wet, fever-ridden areas into dry, healthy environments. Other nations, including Egypt, Tahiti, South Africa, India, Brazil, and the United States, cultivate eucalyptus both for its drainage properties and for its oil.

The Global Economy

Changing Trade Patterns As a result of the shift in focus of global trade to the Pacific Rim nations, Australia and the rest of the Pacific region are now situated at the "top of the world." A region that was once described as being situated "down under" and later viewed as a "moat" separating the Eastern and Western Hemispheres is today envisioned as a link instead. Most of Australia's wheat, beef, sheep, and sugar is exported, with most of it going to countries in Asia.

GEOFacts

Australia's plant fossils provide evidence of a single ancient landmass that included Australia, Antarctica, Africa, South America, and India.

European Land Use The European settlers who came to Australia had a different view. They wanted to make the land produce something that could be sold for money. In 1851 gold was discovered in the outback of New South Wales and Victoria. In the gold rush that followed, Australians and new immigrants swarmed out of the cities, eager to join the search.

Today, gold is only one of many mineral resources that are mined in various locations throughout Australia. Other resources include coal, iron ore, copper, zinc, uranium, and lead. Australia is the leading exporter of bauxite, which is used to make aluminum. The area also has fairly large deposits of oil and natural gas both in the interior and offshore. Some of these resources are shown in the Regional Atlas on page 645.

Many gold seekers stayed on in Australia to build farms and sheep ranches. Today, huge sheep and cattle ranches, called stations, account for most of the economic activity in the outback. Many of these stations are enormous in area. For example, the Anna Creek cattle station in South Australia covers 12,000 square miles (31,000 square km), which is larger than many of the New England states. Ranchers round up livestock on the enormous stations by using helicopters to locate strays and then chasing them down with pickup trucks. Life on a station in the Australian outback can be difficult. Ranchers face dangerous working conditions, including high risk of heat exhaustion and dehydration in the hot, dry land.

Uluru: A Sacred Site

Cultures Aborigines (above) have gathered for a ceremony before Uluru, a site sacred to many Aborigines. Uluru (left), also called Ayers Rock, is the world's largest monolith, or single stone. Located in Australia's interior desert, it looms 1,142 feet (348 m) high and has a circumference of about 6 miles (9 km).

Human-Environment Interaction *What is the traditional relationship between the Aborigines and nature?*

Answer to Photo Caption

The Aborigines traditionally respect nature and take what they need without destroying the land.

Land Use in the Outback

Economic Activities
Only 6 percent of Australia's land is arable, or suitable for planting row crops. Yet, a great deal of land is suitable for grazing. Beef and wool taken from the nation's cattle and sheep are two of Australia's greatest exports.

Human-Environment Interaction *What conditions might make Australia's land nonarable?*

Sheep, or "jumbucks," are raised in the cooler plains regions of southeastern and southwestern Australia. Some sheep and lambs are raised primarily for their meat, but the fine, curly wool of merino (muh REE noh) sheep is the most important product. Australia is one of the world leaders in wool production.

Cattle are raised in the hotter northern and central regions of Australia, where the native grasses and shrubs provide enough food. Water for these stations comes mainly from **artesian wells.** These wells are bored deep into the earth to tap a layer of porous material filled with groundwater.

Growth in the Australian cattle industry reflects changes in both the supply and demand for beef. New breeds of cattle that thrive better in hot, dry weather have increased beef yields, making Australia one of the world's leading producers of cattle.

SECTION 1 ASSESSMENT

1. **Key Terms** Define **(a)** Aborigine, **(b)** lagoon, **(c)** cyclone, **(d)** outback, **(e)** artesian well.

2. **Migration** How did European migration affect the lives of the Aborigines?

3. **Patterns of Settlement** Why do the majority of Australia's major cities lie along the coast?

4. **Environmental Change (a)** How have Aborigines interacted with the environment of the outback? **(b)** How have European settlers changed the environment of the outback?

5. **Critical Thinking** **Defending a Position** Do you consider it fortunate or unfortunate that much of Australia remains unsettled? Explain your answer.

Activity

Creating a Chart Design and draw a chart of Australia's major cities, such as Perth, Adelaide, Sydney, Melbourne, Canberra, Hobart, Brisbane, and Darwin. Compare climate, vegetation, population density, economic activities, and points of interest. Then, write a paragraph that explains which city you would prefer to live in and why.

Articles From NATIONAL GEOGRAPHIC

The following article may be used to extend the content in this section.

Wolinkski, Cary, text and photographs. "Wildflowers of Western Australia." *National Geographic*, Vol. 187, No. 1 (Jan. 1995), pp. 68–69.

Western Australia's wildflowers are now protected by the government for their ecological, aesthetic, and medicinal value.

Answers to Section 1 Assessment

1. (a) Aborigine, p. 717 **(b)** lagoon, p. 720 **(c)** cyclone, p. 721 **(d)** outback, p. 721 **(e)** artesian well, p. 723

2. Many Aborigines were killed by European diseases or weapons.

3. The moist and mild coastal climates are more hospitable than the dry interior.

4. (a) Aborigines take from the land what they need to survive without destroying it. **(b)** Europeans have used the interior for mining and for sheep and cattle ranches.

5. Answers will vary. Students may value the natural environment as the Aborigines do, or they may express a preference for development of the outback. They should support their answers with reasoned arguments.

Activity Rubrics Share rubrics with students before they begin their charts.

Attempted The chart has few entries, contains factual errors, and is messy; the paragraph is incomplete.

Minimal The chart has several entries and contains few errors; the paragraph is complete but poorly written.

Adequate The chart has sufficient entries and contains no errors; the paragraph is well written.

Exemplary The chart has many entries, contains no errors, and is neatly executed; the paragraph is creative and very well written.

Answer to Photo Caption

Much of the land is too arid, the soil is rocky, and some areas are too mountainous to farm easily.

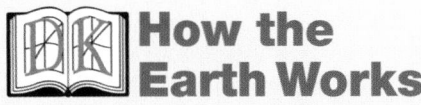

How the Earth Works

pp. 724–725

Objectives

Upon completion of this feature, students should be able to:

◆ describe the conditions in each of the ocean's vertical zones;

◆ identify the special features and phenomena that allow organisms to survive in the different vertical zones;

◆ explain how atolls are formed.

National Geography Standards

The following National Geography Standards are highlighted in this feature: 1, 2, 7, 8

Bellringer

Ask students to name as many organisms as they can that live in the ocean. Make a list of all of these organisms on the board.

LESSON PLAN

1. Focus Have students examine the chart of vertical zones on this page. Ask: **How many of those organisms did you name in the Bellringer activity?** Then have them list the animals they do not know. Discuss with the class the possible reasons certain animals are less familiar than others. (Animals that live deeper in the ocean are not seen in aquariums or zoos.)

2. Instruct Write *bioluminescence, eyespots, hydrothermal vents,* and *coral reef* on the board. Have students review the material on this page and the next to define each term. Then discuss how each feature or phenomenon supports ocean life.

3. Close/Reteach Have students choose one of the organisms in the vertical zone chart to learn more about. Ask them to do research in the library or on the Internet to find out about the organism's features and adaptations. Have them summarize why the organism lives in its particular part of the ocean.

How the Earth Works

Ocean Life

The world's oceans cover almost three quarters of the earth's surface and are home to a vast array of life. Below the surface, the oceans become increasingly cold and dark. Even so, plants and animals, ranging in size from giant whales to microscopic floating organisms called **plankton,** thrive at every depth. Some jellyfish and turtles float or swim near the surface. Whales and squid often live in the ocean's middepths. A whole host of strange-looking creatures swim or crawl around the darkest ocean depths.

Distribution of world's major oceans

BIOLUMINESCENCE
Some fish have special organs called photophores that give off a glow. In this process, called **bioluminescence,** fish use the light to recognize members of their own species or as lures for attracting prey.

Black snaggletooth fish

VERTICAL ZONES
Geographers divide the oceans into zones based on depth. Each zone is home to living things that are adapted to survive at that depth. For example, deep-water animals cope with darkness, very cold temperatures, and pressures that would crush a human. Some creatures can survive in more than one zone.

A school of chromis swims among the coral in Australia's Great Barrier Reef.

Life in the ocean zones

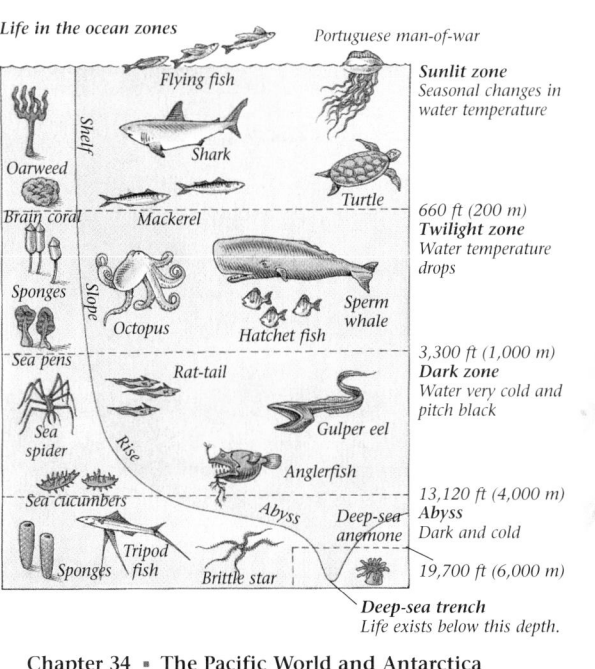

Flying fish
Portuguese man-of-war
Oarweed
Shark
Brain coral
Mackerel
Turtle
Sponges
Octopus
Hatchet fish
Sperm whale
Sea pens
Rat-tail
Gulper eel
Sea spider
Anglerfish
Sea cucumbers
Abyss
Deep-sea anemone
Tripod fish
Sponges
Brittle star

Sunlit zone
Seasonal changes in water temperature

660 ft (200 m)
Twilight zone
Water temperature drops

3,300 ft (1,000 m)
Dark zone
Water very cold and pitch black

13,120 ft (4,000 m)
Abyss
Dark and cold

19,700 ft (6,000 m)

Deep-sea trench
Life exists below this depth.

724 Chapter 34 ▪ The Pacific World and Antarctica

CORAL REEFS

A coral is a tubular animal with tentacles. Most corals attach to a surface and build reefs that can rise above sea level around islands and continents. Other reefs are ring-shaped **atolls** around a lagoon of shallow water. Atolls grow over millions of years.

Growth of a coral atoll

1. Coral starts to grow around a volcanic island.

2. The island sinks. Sand collects on the growing coral reef and forms land.

3. The island disappears. Vegetation grows on the atoll that remains.

HYDROTHERMAL VENTS

On the deep ocean floor, hot, mineral-rich water gushes from cracks, called **hydrothermal vents.** Bacteria feed on chemicals in this water, forming the basis of a food chain that does not rely on sunlight and plants. Giant tube worms, clams, and blind white crabs live around these vents.

Worms and crabs live near a hydrothermal vent.

Australian sea lions are marine mammals that breathe air, feed at sea, and breed on land.

SUNLIGHT ZONE

Sunlight supports the growth of algae, sea grasses, and other plants on which some sea creatures feed. Marine mammals, squid, fish, and other animals have to be strong swimmers to move in the surface currents. Sea grasses and coral reefs provide food, shelter, and breeding sites for a variety of creatures.

Jellyfish can swim, but they are also influenced by ocean currents.

Forcepsfish

False eyespot

BRIGHT COLORS

Many fish have bright colors that attract mates and confuse predators. Complex coloration makes it hard to detect the outline of a fish. Some fish have eyespots, or false eyes. As a predator attacks the false head, the fish darts off in the opposite direction.

Chapter 34   725

ASSESSMENT

1. **Key Terms** Define **(a)** plankton, **(b)** bioluminescence, **(c)** atoll, **(d)** hydrothermal vent.

2. **Ecosystems** Why does plant life grow near the ocean surface but not on the deep ocean floor?

3. **Physical Processes** How can the emergence of a volcano lead to the growth of coral and the formation of an atoll?

4. **Ecosystems** How are some fish specially adapted to attract prey or to escape predators?

5. **Critical Thinking Analyzing Processes** Suppose that changes in the environment cause a decline in the population of ocean plants and corals. How might that environmental change also cause damage to populations of fish, marine mammals, and other sea creatures?

Objectives

Upon completion of Section 2, students should be able to:

◆ explain how New Zealand's European majority affected the Maori way of life and the economy of the region;

◆ describe the physical characteristics of the two types of Pacific Islands—high islands and low islands.

 National Geography Standards

The following National Geography Standards are highlighted in this section: 1, 4, 5, 8, 9, 10, 11, 12, 16, 17

 Bellringer

Ask students what they envision when they hear the words *Pacific Islands.*

LESSON PLAN

1. Focus Ask students to hypothesize how Pacific Islanders earn a living. (Examples: fishing, tourist services, tropical agriculture) Point out that the economy of the Pacific Islands relies mostly on tourism. Ask students what they think is the basis of New Zealand's economy. (agriculture)

2. Instruct Have students draw an outline map of New Zealand and the Pacific Islands and mark the divisions between Micronesia, Melanesia, and Polynesia as on the map on page 729. Then ask them to use the information in the text to show how the region was populated by drawing arrows to show where the settlers came from.

3. Close/Reteach Have students make a three-column chart comparing the physical geography, people, and economy of New Zealand and the Pacific Islands.

2 New Zealand and the Pacific Islands

Reading Focus

- How has New Zealand's European majority affected the minority Maori group's way of life and sense of group identity and the economy of this region?
- What kinds of physical characteristics distinguish the two types of Pacific Islands—namely, the high islands and the low islands?

Key Terms

geyser

trust territory

| Main Idea | New Zealand and the Pacific Islands are distinct island groups spread across a wide ocean. |

Physical Characteristics High, rugged mountains add beauty to New Zealand's majestic landscape.

ritish naturalist Charles Darwin wrote these words as he sailed across the Pacific from Tahiti to New Zealand in 1835:

❝It is necessary to sail over this great ocean to comprehend its immensity. . . . [F]or weeks together, we meet with nothing but the same blue, profoundly deep, ocean. Even with the archipelagoes, the islands are mere specks, and far distant one from the other. Accustomed to looking at maps drawn on a small scale, where dots, shading, and names are crowded together, we do not rightly judge how infinitely small the proportion of dry land is to the water of this vast expanse.❞

The Pacific Ocean is, indeed, immense. At 70 million square miles (181 million sq km), the Pacific is more than twice the area of the Atlantic. Set in this watery expanse are the tiny islands of

the Pacific. South of the Pacific Islands and east of Australia lie the two comparatively larger islands that make up most of New Zealand.

New Zealand

New Zealand lies about 1,000 miles (1,600 km) east of Australia across the rough and windy Tasman Sea. Although New Zealand is part of the Pacific Islands, its physical and human characteristics are very different from those of the other islands.

Two Islands The backbone of New Zealand is a string of volcanic mountains formed along the border between the Australian and Pacific tectonic plates. These mountains form two large islands, called South Island and North Island. The two islands are quite distinct geographically.

North Island is narrow and hilly. Spread across the center is a plateau and an active geothermal region. Volcanoes and **geysers** (GY zers), hot springs that shoot jets of steam and

726 Chapter 34 ▪ The Pacific World and Antarctica

RESOURCE DIRECTORY

Teaching Resources

Unit 9, Chapter 34
- Section 2 Guided Reading and Review, p. 58

Guide to the Essentials (English/Spanish)
- Section Summary, Chapter 34, Section 2

Mental Mapping booklet
- Unit 9 Checklist, p. 115

Technology

Guided Reading Audiotapes (English/Spanish), Chapter 34, Section 2

Section Reading Support Transparencies, Chapter 34, Section 2

World Geography Map and Photo Transparencies
- East Asia and the Pacific World: Maps and Photos

Book on CD, Chapter 34

Social Studies Skills Tutor CD-ROM

Companion Web site, www.phschool.com
- Chapter 34 Activities

heated water into the air, fuel an active tourist industry.

New Zealand's highest mountains tower above South Island. Mystery novelist Ngaio (NY oh) Marsh, a native of New Zealand, described the scenery of these mountains—known as the Southern Alps—in this way:

> 66At their highest, they are covered by perpetual snow. Turbulent rivers cut through them, you can see these rivers twisting and glittering like blue snakes through deep gorges, spilling into lakes and pouring across plains to the coast. The westward flanks of the Alps are clothed in dark, heavy forest. It rains a lot over there: everything is lush and green.99

From Settlement to Today Perhaps referring to the rain and mist of the west, the first people to arrive in New Zealand called it Aotearoa—"Land of the Long White Cloud." The origin of these people, the Maori, is in dispute. Some scholars claim the Maori are a Polynesian people who came by canoe around A.D. 900. Others believe they came from the Malaysian Peninsula, or even from Peru.

Prior to European settlement of New Zealand in 1769, the Maori did not consider themselves a nation. They comprised many groups, each forming a highly ordered society with intricate rules of conduct and custom. Although they traded goods and shared a common culture, groups were fiercely territorial. Competition for choice cropland and fishing grounds often led to intergroup warfare. As time went by, however, more peaceful relations were established on the island. In 1840, the Maoris signed a treaty with the British. In exchange for certain land rights they agreed to accept British rule.

As European settlers moved onto their land, the Maori began to see themselves as a nation instead of individual competing groups. Though today the Maori number less than 10 percent of the population, they have their own political party, Mana Motuhake, which means "self-determination." They are currently attempting to reclaim lands that were once theirs in an effort to preserve their culture. In 1996, for example, the New Zealand government determined that a large area of North Island—nearly an entire province—had been taken from the Maori without any recognition of their rights.

Though the Maori are a vital force in New Zealand culture, they remain a minority. Some

READING STRATEGY

Summarizing Main Ideas

As students read the subsection From Settlement to Today, have them note important dates. Then have them create a time line based on the passage. Students may use key words or symbols to mark each event.

New Zealand's Shores

Understanding the Past English Captain James Cook arrives at Queen Charlotte's Sound in New Zealand in this painting attributed to J. Clevely. During the 1770s, Captain Cook became the first explorer to chart accurately the coast of New Zealand and the east coast of Australia.

Place *How did European exploration and settlement affect the lives of the Maori?*

Chapter 34 ▪ Section 2 **727**

CUSTOMIZE FOR...

Honors/PreAP

Maori Influence Have students work in pairs to find out how Maori culture has influenced the history and culture of New Zealand. Have each pair present its findings in a diagram.

Answer to Photo Caption

After Europeans moved onto their land, the Maori began to see themselves as a nation instead of as individual groups.

Word Origin

Kiwifruit Developed in New Zealand in the early 1900s from a vine found in China, the kiwifruit was originally known as the Chinese gooseberry. However, when exporters wanted to promote the fruit as a memorable New Zealand product later in the century, they renamed it "kiwifruit" after the flightless kiwi, New Zealand's rather round, brown-feathered national bird.

GE⊙Facts

Eighty percent of New Zealand's electricity is provided by hydropower.

79 percent of New Zealand's 3.7 million people are of European descent. The result of this mix of peoples is a national identity that is rooted in both its Polynesian and British past.

An Agricultural Economy The European settlers were largely responsible for developing the New Zealand economy, which is still in large part agricultural. Gentle plains slope down from the mountains on both islands of New Zealand. These plains have rich soils, and the marine west coast climate is ideal for farming. Dairy cattle graze on parts of North Island, and sheep are raised throughout the country.

Livestock are raised in New Zealand for many of the same reasons as in Australia. They are well suited to the local conditions, and their products can be shipped over thousands of miles to foreign markets. It is not practical to export milk from New Zealand. But butter and cheese can survive long journeys by boat or yield high enough prices to make the extra cost of air transportation worthwhile. Similarly, wool and frozen lamb and mutton from New Zealand reach buyers in Asia, Europe, and North America.

Kiwifruit are another New Zealand product commonly seen in American grocery stores. Today, New Zealand produces one quarter of the world's kiwifruit.

Urbanization Despite the importance of agriculture, the great majority of the people live in large cities along the coast. Three out of four New Zealanders live on North Island. Auckland (AWK luhnd), New Zealand's largest city, is located there. Auckland's northern latitude places it closer to other nations than any other major New Zealand city. Its airport and ocean port are the country's busiest. Auckland has also developed as a manufacturing center, and nearby farms make it an agricultural trade center.

On South Island lies New Zealand's second-largest city, Christchurch. The national capital, Wellington, overlooks Cook Strait, which separates North Island from South Island. Wellington's location on the strait symbolically unites the nation.

Wellington's Harbor

Global Trade Patterns New Zealand's economy depends on exporting many of its agricultural and industrial products. Wellington's location makes it an important link in the nation's overseas trade. It has a superb harbor and sits near the middle of the country.

Place *What are some of New Zealand's agricultural exports?*

Answer to Photo Caption
butter, cheese, wool, frozen lamb and mutton, kiwifruit

The Pacific Islands

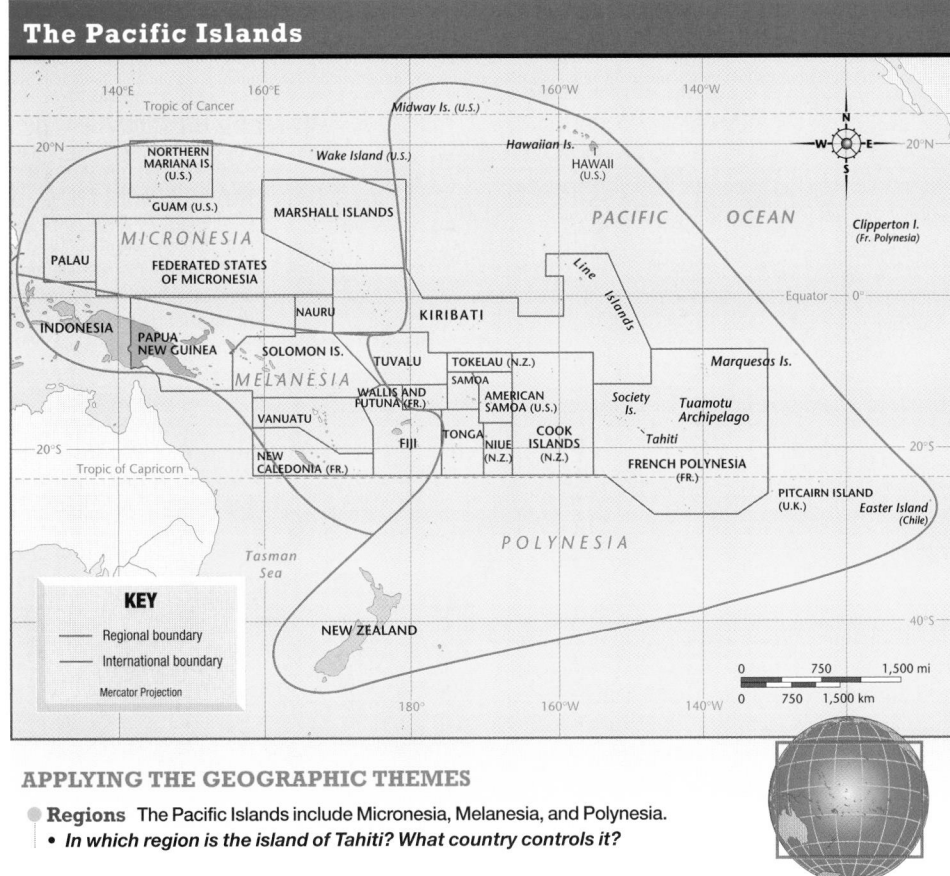

KEY
— Regional boundary
— International boundary

Mercator Projection

0   750   1,500 mi
0   750   1,500 km

APPLYING THE GEOGRAPHIC THEMES
● **Regions** The Pacific Islands include Micronesia, Melanesia, and Polynesia.
• *In which region is the island of Tahiti? What country controls it?*

The Pacific Islands

Like the two islands that form New Zealand, many of the Pacific Islands are of a type called high islands. Imagine a huge chain of underwater mountains in the Pacific Ocean. Where the tops of these mountains break the surface of the water, they create high islands. Because many of these islands lie along the boundary of the Australian and Pacific plates, they are capped by volcanoes. On some islands, volcanic cones rise several thousand feet above the ocean's surface.

Other islands in the Pacific are known as low islands. On ring-shaped islands called **atolls** (AH tawlz), coral reefs surround an inner lagoon. Atolls form most of the Marshall Islands and the islands of Kiribati (KIR uh bas). An atoll begins as a fringing reef in the warm, shallow waters

surrounding a volcanic island. When the volcanic cone falls below the ocean's surface, the coral continues to build up. Then, after millions of years, the volcano disappears, leaving only a ring of coral around a lagoon. Waves crashing over the coral break the top layer into sand. The sand piles up atop the coral and finally forms soil that can support plant and animal life.

Various Island Groups The Pacific Islands are divided into three groups: Micronesia, Melanesia, and Polynesia. Each group is shown on the map above. Melanesia was inhabited first—beginning more than 40,000 years ago—probably by people from Southeast Asia. Micronesia was settled between 3000 and 2000 B.C. by voyagers from the Philippines, Indonesia, and some of the islands north of New Guinea.

Articles From
NATIONAL GEOGRAPHIC

The following article may be used to extend the content in this section.

Vaughan, Roger, and James Standfield, photographer. "The Two Worlds of Fiji." *National Geographic*, Vol. 188, No. 4 (Oct. 1995), pp. 114–137.

The turbulent political environment of Fiji is set amidst a tranquil and tropical paradise.

TEST PREPARATION

Have students read the subsection The Pacific Islands on this page to answer the following question.
In what way are high islands and low islands similar?
A Both are snowcapped.
B Both may have volcanic origins.
C Both are shaped like underwater mountains.
D Both are ring-shaped.

Group Work

Activity: Preparing a debate

Purpose: Tell each group that it will debate the following statement: "Tourism should be discouraged in the Pacific Islands in order to preserve the cultural heritage of the native peoples." Each team chooses a pro or con position and works together to write an opening statement and three to five supporting statements.

Roles: Debaters, one student to act as class timer, and a moderator

Result: Groups should present their debates to the class, which judges the debates based on the validity and soundness of the arguments.

Life on Coral Reefs

Ecosystems The bruising force of the Pacific surf is softened by the coral reefs around many islands (left). This helps even small islands survive the hurricanes and storms that rage in the Pacific. A woman (below) harvests sea urchins on a protected, shallow shore.

Human-Environment Interaction *What becomes of the marine life caught by people in the Pacific Islands?*

The distinct culture and physical characteristics of the Polynesians developed over a long period of time when they were isolated in the Tonga and Samoa islands. From this base, the Polynesians explored and settled a huge region of the Pacific, mostly to the north and east. (See the map on page 729.) Today, Fiji has large numbers of Melanesians, and Polynesians. About one half of its 800,000 residents are descended from East Indians who were brought to the islands in the late nineteenth century to work on sugar plantations.

Economic Activities Many Pacific Islanders today make their living from farming or fishing. Coconut products, pineapples, bananas, skipjack (a kind of fish), and yellowfin tuna are some of the products exported from the Pacific Islands. Most people, however, live at a subsistence level. That is, they usually grow or catch only enough to feed themselves. Some high islands in Melanesia

GLOBAL CONNECTIONS

Environmental Change
The rise in sea level predicted by some scientists as a result of global warming presents a particular problem to Pacific Islanders. A rise of only 8 to 10 inches could make some low-lying islands uninhabitable.

and Polynesia can support cash crops such as rubber, coffee, and sugar cane. Minerals are extracted on a few islands—a large gold mine operates on Fiji, and New Caledonia has a nickel mine. In 1995, Marshall Islands officials rejected a proposal for a new kind of industry—storage of nuclear wastes—on Bikini Atoll. This atoll had been made radioactive by repeated United States nuclear tests in the 1940s and 1950s.

Pacific Island tourism is a growing industry. Vacationers in search of warm, sunny beaches and scenic beauty have increasingly headed for these islands as travel and communications have become faster and easier. Fiji, for instance, actively promotes tourism. Its airport is a stopping point for airplanes traveling between North America and Australia. In Tonga—an archipelago of 169

Answer to Photo Caption

The people doing the fishing eat most of the catch. In other words, much of the catch is used for subsistence rather than for export.

volcanic and coral islands—tourism is the primary source of hard currency on the 45 islands that are inhabited. In contrast, Western Samoa is scenic and well-situated with respect to air routes. The government, however, does not want a large tourist industry. It fears that visitors might change the indigenous culture.

Toward Independence Most of the world paid little attention to the Pacific Islands until World War II. During the war, Japanese and United States forces fought many bloody battles on the islands. Afterward, many islands became **trust territories,** or territories supervised by other nations. The United States oversees Guam and American Samoa.

Most of the Pacific Islands were granted independence in the 1960s and 1970s. Independence helped renew interest in native cultures among the people. Many new governments were based on traditional forms of leadership. Tonga, for example, chose to remain a kingdom. Samoa adopted a parliamentary system, but 47 of the 49 members of the assembly must be chiefs. Vanuatu is a fully representative democracy. Fiji has also had popular elections, but military coups occurred three times between 1987 and 2001.

Pacific Island nations struggle with economic development, as most rely solely on agriculture and tourism. In some nations, tensions between ethnic groups persist. Natural hazards also are common, including typhoons, earthquakes, volcanoes, and flooding.

Australia, the Pacific Islands, and the United States
Economic Data

Country	GDP per Capita (U.S. dollars)	GDP Growth Rate (percentage)	Unemployment (percentage)
Australia	24,000	2.3	8
Micronesia	2,000	2.0	8
Fiji	5,200	1.0	6
Marshall Islands	1,600	1.0	31
New Zealand	19,500	3.1	7
Palau	9,000	1.0	7
Samoa	3,500	6.0	NA
Solomon Islands	1,700	-10.0	NA
Vanuatu	1,300	2.7	NA
United States	36,300	0.3	4

Sources: *The World Factbook; Dorling Kindersley World Desk Reference*   NA = information not available.

CHART SKILLS

● **Planning for the Future** *What economic conditions might you find in the Solomon Islands? What figures led you to this conclusion?*

● **Economic Activities** *Which two nations in the Pacific world have the highest GDP per capita? What are some major economic activities of these nations?*

SECTION 2 ASSESSMENT

1. **Key Terms** Define **(a)** geyser, **(b)** trust territory.

2. **Economic Activities** **(a)** What culture groups make up the population of New Zealand? **(b)** How did these groups influence New Zealand's main economic activities?

3. **Physical Characteristics** **(a)** What is the origin of the difference between the high islands and the low islands of the Pacific Ocean? **(b)** What kinds of natural resources can be found on the Pacific Islands?

4. **Critical Thinking** **Solving Problems** How would you propose that the New Zealand government repay the Maori for the land illegally taken from them?

Activity

USING THE REGIONAL ATLAS

Review the Regional Atlas for East Asia and the Pacific World and this section. Plan a two-month trip to the Pacific Islands. Make a sample itinerary of the islands you would visit, the length of your stay in each place, the major differences among the islands, and the distances between them.

Teaching the Skill

Conduct a discussion noting that contour and topographic are two names for the same kind of map: one that shows changes in elevation, often over small areas. Tell students to think of themselves as looking down on a portion of the earth's surface when reading a topographic map. Focus on the term *contour* and help students follow the length of one contour line on the map. Use the questions in steps 1 to 4 in a class activity or as part of a homework assignment.

Answers to Learn the Skill

1. the height of a line; each line represents a specific elevation or height above sea level
2. (a) Mt. Orohena, at 7,352 feet (2,241 m) **(b)** about the same elevation
3. (a) near the top of Mt. Orohena **(b)** the lines are closer together **(c)** near the coast **(d)** the lines are farther apart
4. (a) start due east of Papeete and head due south **(b)** start from Papeete and head southeast

Answers to Practice the Skill

Students' paragraphs should demonstrate an understanding of how to read and interpret a contour map.

ACTIVITY

Reteach

Using Local Contour Maps Have students secure copies of local topographical or contour maps from the library or the Internet. Ask them to describe the general pattern of landforms in the area covered on the map and to note any physical or human-made landmarks that may have been added to the map. (Visual/Spatial)

A contour map, also known as a topographic map, shows variations in elevation and how dramatically those changes take place. Contour maps have many applications. For example, a hiker poised at the start of an unfamiliar mountain trail needs to know if a trail climbs steeply for the next mile or if the grade is a slow and steady rise. Will there be serious climbing involved, or can the hiker cover the distance at an easy pace?

Engineers also use contour maps when deciding where to build highways and dams. Police emergency medical personnel often consult topographic maps during search-and-rescue operations for people who are lost in the woods. A good topographic map can be used in all of these applications and help ensure the success and safety of a hike, a construction project, or a rescue mission.

Learn the Skill Use the contour map of Tahiti below and the following steps to learn to read a contour map.

1 *Understand what contour lines measure.* The lines on a topographic map are called *contour lines*. A contour line connects all points where elevation is equal. If you were to hike along one of the contour lines shown on this topographic map, you would always be at the same height above sea level. *Do contour lines measure the length of a line or the height of a line? Explain.*

2 *Understand contour-line labels.* Notice that the contour lines on this map of Tahiti are labeled with numbers. These numbers tell the elevation in feet along that contour line. **(a)** *What is the highest point on Tahiti?* **(b)** *Are Papeete and Matalea at about the same elevation or at different elevations?*

3 *Interpret the relationships among contour lines.* When a series of contour lines are close together, it means that the elevation of the land is changing rapidly. In other words, the terrain is steep. On the other hand, contour lines that are spread wide apart indicate that the elevation is changing slowly. If you were to hike along one of these contour lines, the land would be relatively flat. **(a)** *In Tahiti, where is the land steepest?*

(b) *How can you tell?* **(c)** *In Tahiti, where is the land more flat—near the top of Mt. Orohena or near the coast?* **(d)** *How can you tell?*

4 *Apply the data.* Once you understand how to read a topographic map, you can use the skill to help plan a hike. For example, a difficult climb would take you through territory where the contour lines are close together, whereas an easier hike would be a gradual ascent through territory where contour lines are farther apart. **(a)** *If you and a friend wanted to climb to the top of Mt. Orohena, how would you plot the most gradual ascent possible?* **(b)** *How would you plot a steeper climb?*

Do It Yourself

Practice the Skill Locate a contour map of a national park. Redraw the map. Plot a starting point. Then, trace a route to hike. In a short paragraph, explain your route and its level of difficulty.

Apply the Skill See Chapter 34 Review and Assessment.

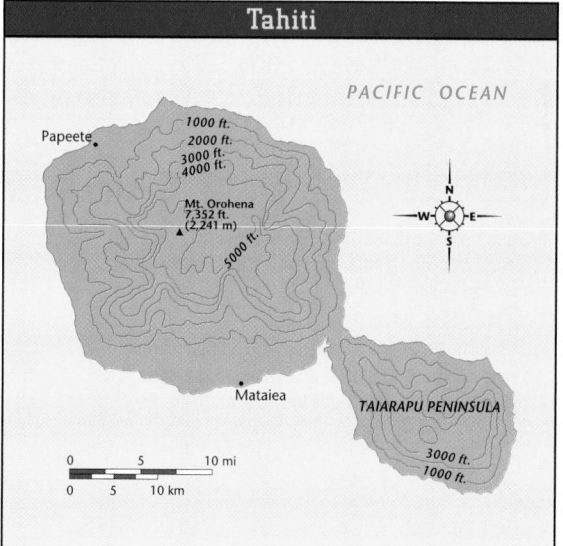

Tahiti

RESOURCE DIRECTORY

Teaching Resources

Unit 9, Chapter 34
• Section 3 Guided Reading and Review, p. 60
• Map/Graph Skills, p. 64

Guide to the Essentials (English/Spanish)
• Section Summary, Chapter 34, Section 3

Mental Mapping booklet
• Unit 9 Checklist, p. 115

Social Studies Skills Handbook
• Reading a Contour Map, p. 30

Technology

Guided Reading Audiotapes (English/Spanish), Chapter 34, Section 3

Section Reading Support Transparencies, Chapter 34, Section 3

World Geography Map and Photo Transparencies
• East Asia and the Pacific World: Maps and Photos

Book on CD, Chapter 34

Social Studies Skills Tutor CD-ROM, Analyzing and Interpreting a Special Purpose Map

Companion Web site, www.phschool.com
• Chapter 34 Activities

3 Antarctica

Reading Focus

- How do the climate and ice-covered terrain of the continent of Antarctica affect wildlife habitation and human exploration?
- Why do many scientists consider Antarctica to be a land of valuable natural resources?

Key Terms

crevasse
ice shelf
pack ice
convergence zone
krill

Physical Processes "Pancake ice" forms in the seas around Antarctica.

 Main Idea Antarctica is covered by several different forms of ice, which affect climate, wildlife habitation, and exploration.

On most world maps, Antarctica appears as a long, ragged strip of white that stretches across the southern boundary. In reality, however, Antarctica is a large, mushroom-shaped continent that accounts for nearly one tenth of the world's land. To be seen clearly on a map, Antarctica must occupy a central position. Therefore, only a south-polar projection like the one shown in the map on page 734 provides a true picture of Antarctica's shape and size.

Following a visit to Antarctica in the early 1980s, environmental historian Stephen Pyne had this to say about Antarctica:

> 66 Ice is the beginning of Antarctica and ice is its end. . . . Ice creates more ice, and ice defines ice. Everything else is suppressed. This is a world derived from a single substance, water, in a single crystalline state, snow, transformed into a lithosphere composed of a single mineral, ice. This is earthscape transfigured into icescape. 99

The Frozen Continent

As Pyne suggests, in a sense, Antarctica *is* ice. Ice covers the continent's rocks, and it alters the climate. The ice affects Antarctica's wildlife, because few plants and animals can survive in its frigid conditions. And, the ice has greatly limited human activity, leaving Antarctica as the only major landmass on the earth without permanent human settlements.

Dense Ice Sheets The ice covering Antarctica makes it, on average, the highest continent. It has an average elevation of 1.3 miles (2.1 km), compared to an average of 0.6 miles (1.0 km) for the rest of the world's land. The average thickness of the ice caps, or ice sheets, covering central regions of the South Pole ranges from 5,600 to 7,200 feet (1,700 to 2,200 m).

The weight of the Antarctic ice sheets is enormous. In many areas the ice creates so much pressure that the land surface actually sinks below sea level. If the ice were to melt, the land would rise 260 feet (80 m). In addition, the weight

Chapter 34 ▪ Section 3 **733**

Objectives

Upon completion of Section 3, students should be able to:

◆ describe how Antarctica's climate and terrain affect wildlife habitation and exploration;

◆ explain why many scientists consider Antarctica to be a land of valuable natural resources.

National Geography Standards

The following National Geography Standards are highlighted in this section: 1, 4, 5, 6, 7, 8, 9, 13, 15, 16, 17, 18

 Bellringer

Ask students if they would like to visit Antarctica. Have them explain why or why not.

LESSON PLAN

1. Focus Have students imagine what temperatures of less than -100°F (-73°C) would feel like. Ask several volunteers to try to describe how cold this would be. Point out that during the winter, this temperature is common in Antarctica. For this reason, most of the research conducted on the continent is done during the summer months.

2. Instruct Divide the class into small groups. Assign each group one of the following forms of ice: ice caps, glaciers, ice shelves, and pack ice. Have each group use the text to list the characteristics of the form of ice they have been assigned. Ask a spokesperson from each group to read the group's list.

3. Close/Reteach Write the title *Human Activities in Antarctica* enclosed in a rectangle on the board. Work with students to make a concept map on this topic. Draw lines from the title box to three boxes labeled *Early Exploration, Land Claims,* and *Scientific Research*. Have students suggest important facts that might be "mapped" under each subtopic.

CUSTOMIZE FOR...

Less Proficient Readers

Word Analysis Call students' attention to the word *crystalline* in the quoted passage on this page. Explain that something that is crystalline is like a crystal, is made of crystal, or has the structure of crystal. Have students describe crystals they have seen. Then ask them to list ways in which snow is crystalline.

Chapter 34 ▪ Section 3 **733**

Antarctica The word *Antarctica* means "opposite to the Arctic," which describes its position on the earth.

Visualizing

As students read the subsection Ice and the Climate, ask them to draw a diagram that shows the relationship between the sun's rays and the ice sheets in Antarctica. (The ice reflects the sun's rays rather than absorbing their heat.) Ask: **What is the result of this relationship?** (frigid temperatures)

of the ice sheets on the South Pole gives the earth a slightly lopsided pear shape.

Ice and the Climate The Antarctic ice sheets have a significant effect on both the continent's own climate and on weather patterns throughout the Southern Hemisphere. The ice reflects most of the sun's rays back into space rather than absorbing their heat, making temperatures frigid. The average annual temperature at one research station is –71°F (–57°C). One of the coldest temperatures ever recorded on the earth was measured at the same site: –128.6°F (–89.3°C).

While even the glare of six months of summer sun cannot melt them, the Antarctic ice caps do not grow rapidly. This is because very little snow falls. Like high plateaus on other continents, the region is quite dry, because air loses its moisture as it rises. Air becomes even drier as it gets colder. As a result, the South Pole sees less than 2 inches (5 cm) of precipitation each year. Even the most arid deserts of Africa and Asia usually get more precipitation than Antarctica.

Glaciers Moister and warmer conditions near the coast and in the Transantarctic Mountains

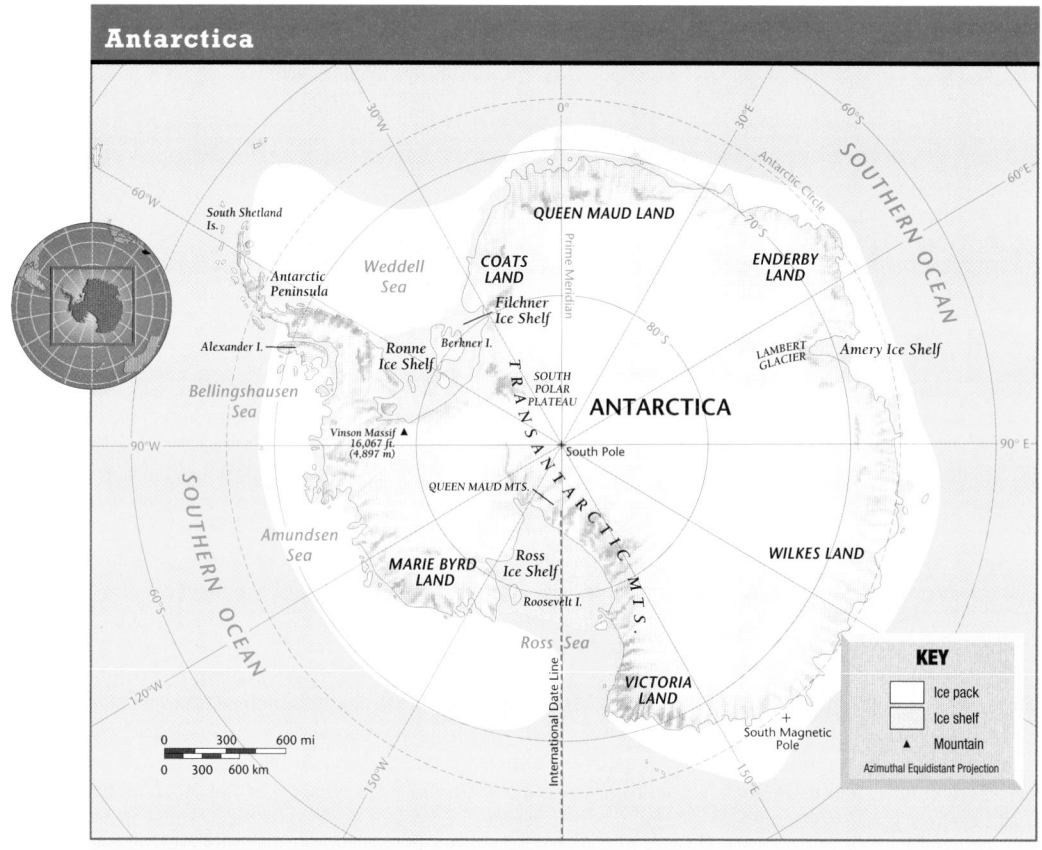

APPLYING THE GEOGRAPHIC THEMES

● **Place** Most of Antarctica lies south of 70°S latitude and is thickly covered with ice.
 • *Which mountain range cuts across the middle of the continent from east to west?*

RESOURCE DIRECTORY

Teaching Resources
Creative Teaching Activities
• A Pacific Expedition, p. 36

Technology
World Geography Map and Photo Transparencies
• East Asia and the Pacific World: Maps and Photos

Answer to Map Caption

Transantarctic Mountains

permit glaciers to flow over the land. Antarctic glaciers creep like giant, slow-moving frozen rivers, oozing down from the mountains and the edges of the ice sheet to the coast. The average annual glacial movement varies from about 360 to 3,600 feet (about 110 to 1,100 m). Glaciers provide the most convenient routes to the interior of the continent. However, travelers must beware of large cracks called **crevasses** that form in glacial ice.

Ice Shelves Antarctica's ice sheets and glaciers are so deeply frozen that the slowly creeping ice extends out over the ocean in several places and forms massive permanent extensions of ice called **ice shelves.** The larger shelves cover enormous areas of the Ross and Weddell seas; smaller shelves dot the coastline.

The ice on the shelves can be more than 6,000 feet (1,800 m) thick in many places. The shelves thin out as they extend farther into the ocean, however, leaving them brittle and easily broken. In a 35-day period in early 2002, more than 1,250 square miles (3,250 square km) of ice in a shelf broke off into thousands of icebergs on the Weddell Sea. Scientists believe that global warming threatens the future of many Antarctic ice shelves.

Pack Ice In the various seas surrounding Antarctica, icebergs mix with ice formed in the superchilled waters to form **pack ice.** Pack ice fringes most of the Antarctic continent. During the long winter, when the sun shines for only a few hours each day, the pack ice can extend more than 1,000 miles (1,600 km). In the summer, the outer reaches of the ice melt, and the pack ice extends only about one tenth as far into the ocean.

The edge of the winter pack ice is close to the **convergence zone.** This is the area where the frigid waters around Antarctica meet the warmer waters of the Atlantic, Pacific, and Indian oceans. This clash of warm and cold waters causes severe storms along Antarctica's coastline. The contrast in temperatures also mixes different layers of water along the edge of the pack ice. Nutrient-rich, deep waters rise to the surface, feeding millions of small shrimplike creatures called **krill.** The krill provide ample food for whales and fish. The fish, in turn, become food for seals, penguins, and other animals.

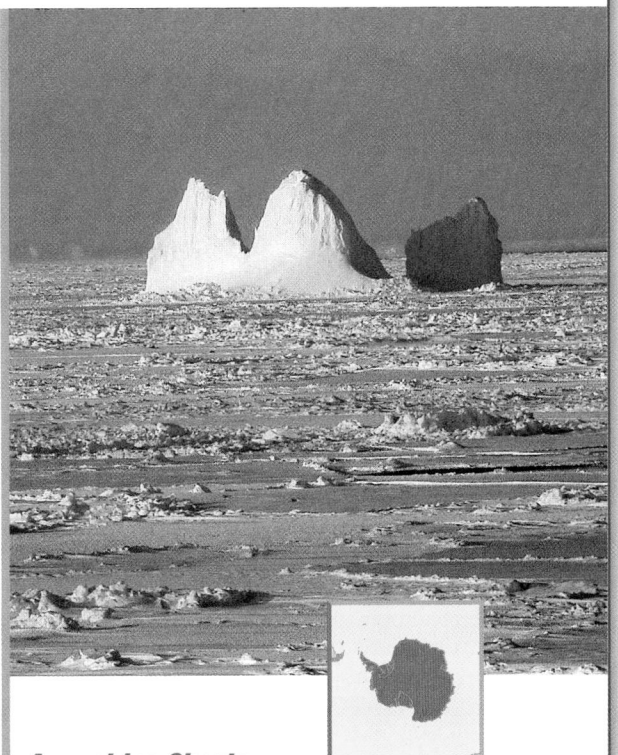

Annual Ice Sheets

Physical Processes Each winter the seas around Antarctica begin to freeze. By the end of the season this ice sheet covers an area twice the size of the United States. Then the Antarctic summer, weak as it is, melts the sheet away again.

Place *What geographic characteristics contribute to low precipitation levels in Antarctica?*

Interacting With the Land

Antarctica's unique physical geography makes its human geography different from that of any other continent. Because of its remote location and harsh natural conditions, it was the last of the world's continents to be discovered and explored. It remains uninhabited.

Antarctica was first sighted in the early 1820s by sailors from Russia, Great Britain, and the United States. Explorers reached the Ross Ice Shelf in the early 1840s. But the ice and cold prevented anyone from actually setting foot on the continent until 1895.

BACKGROUND

Word Origin

Iceberg The word *iceberg* comes from a Dutch word, *ijsberg,* which literally means "ice mountain."

ACTIVITY

Vocabulary

Convergence Zone Refer to the Key Terms list on page 733. Write the term *convergence zone* on the board. Ask students what *convergence* means (the act of moving together). Have students guess the meaning of *convergence zone* based on the meaning of *convergence* and then look it up in the Glossary to check the accuracy of their guesses.

TEST PREPARATION

Have students read the subsection Pack Ice on this page to answer the following question.

If waters did not mix in the convergence zone, which of the following would likely happen?

A The fish population near Antarctica would decrease.

B The ice packs would melt.

C Storms would occur off the coast of Antarctica.

D Different layers of water would mix.

Answer to Photo Caption

low precipitation levels due to combination of high plateau and dry rising air

Group Work

Activity: Writing journal entries
Purpose: Have students imagine that they are scientists doing research in Antarctica, such as conducting a geological survey or studying penguin populations. Have them prepare appropriate journal entries about their research and life in Antarctica in general. Encourage students to be imaginative.
Roles: All group members should contribute a journal entry and members should vote on a representative entry. Each group should select a spokesperson.
Result: Have the spokesperson read the group's entry to the class.

BACKGROUND

Connecting With . . .

Science Flying to the South Pole in the Antarctic winter is considered extremely dangerous. Low temperatures cause fuel to solidify, and visibility is often very bad. Nevertheless, in 1999 two flights were made to the South Pole in winter weather conditions. The flights helped save Dr. Jerri Nielsen, a researcher stationed there who had fallen seriously ill. The first flight dropped drugs that Nielsen required. Then the second flight landed in a blinding storm to rescue her from Antarctica so that she could receive treatment.

Answer to Photo Caption

Ice sheets could be broken into large fragments by tides and strong currents in the water. They could also be broken by powerful storms that occur along Antarctica's coast.

GLOBAL CONNECTIONS

International Cooperation

In 1961, twelve countries, including those that had claimed portions of Antarctica, signed the Antarctic Treaty. The treaty provided for the peaceful use of the continent and the sharing of scientific research. When the treaty expired in 1989, the 12 original nations, and 28 others, renewed it. They also added a section that prohibits any mining of Antarctica's mineral resources for 50 years.

Roald Amundsen of Norway and Robert Scott of Great Britain each led major expeditions across Antarctica's ice sheets. Both reached the South Pole in the Antarctic summer of 1911–1912, but Scott and his four companions died on their return trip. Further exploration of the interior began in the late 1920s, when airplanes were built that could withstand Antarctica's high winds and cold temperatures.

Slicing the "Pie" Antarctica's unusual conditions also affected the ways in which nations tried to make territorial claims. Many early explorers made claims in the hope of protecting areas rich in whales and seals. But, by the late 1880s, the world's most powerful nations agreed that land had to be occupied and actively governed for a national claim to be valid.

Through the first half of the twentieth century, Argentina, Australia, Chile, France, New Zealand, Norway, and the United Kingdom all claimed parts of Antarctica. Most of these countries' claims took the form of pie-shaped wedges that met at the South Pole. Two nations, the United States and the Soviet Union, refused to make any claims. They also refused to acknowledge the claims of other nations, arguing that actual settlement had not occurred.

Why did so many nations claim parts of Antarctica? One reason was national pride. Many countries wanted to expand their colonial empires to Antarctica's frontier or simply keep other countries from claiming large slices of the continent.

Antarctic Resources Another reason for territorial claims was to claim the ownership of resources. Demand for whales and seals had declined, but it was still possible to find valuable minerals under the ice. Geological discoveries in recent decades suggest that oil, gold, iron, and other minerals may well be present. Coal has already been found, but deposits remain untouched because it would cost too much to mine and transport them. Other minerals would cost even more to find and to exploit.

Sharing the Bounty By far, the greatest resource Antarctica has to offer is its wealth of scientific information. Scientists worked to convince the world that Antarctica needed to remain open to all countries that wanted to conduct research there. In 1961, twelve countries ratified

736

Open Water on an Icy Plain

Physical Processes The ice sheets around Antarctica sometimes split open, exposing the open water just a few feet below. These gaps make a natural route for icebreakers exploring the region.

Human-Environment Interaction *What forces might cause the ice to split open?*

RESOURCE DIRECTORY

Science Exploration

Science and Technology
Today's scientists meet the challenge of Antarctica's climate with cutting-edge technology. Early in the 1900s, however, explorers struggled toward the South Pole on sleds pulled by dogs and Manchurian ponies.

Human-Environment Interaction *Why is research on Antarctica so valuable?*

the Antarctic Treaty. This treaty provided for the peaceful use of the continent and the sharing of scientific research. The treaty banned military activity, nuclear explosions, and the disposal of radioactive waste. A number of other countries later signed the treaty, and several countries set up research stations on the continent. Throughout the years, amendments have been added to protect wildlife.

The continent is the key to a vast store of knowledge that many countries are now exploring and sharing. For example, one team of scientists has drilled deep into the Antarctic ice, extracting a sample called a core as they proceeded. This core includes ice that was formed over 450,000 years ago, and gives clues as to what earth's environment was like during each of those years. Deeper still, on the bedrock of the continent, lie lakes of liquid water that have been sealed beneath ice for half a million years. Scientists dream of finding ancient microscopic lifeforms alive in those lakes.

SECTION 3 ASSESSMENT

1. **Key Terms** Define **(a)** crevasse, **(b)** ice shelf, **(c)** pack ice, **(d)** convergence zone, **(e)** krill.

2. **Climates (a)** What kinds of ice are most prevalent on Antarctica? **(b)** How do they affect the continent's climate? **(c)** How does the climate of Antarctica affect exploration of the continent?

3. **Natural Resources (a)** What resources exist on Antarctica? **(b)** Which of these resources is considered the most valuable? **(c)** Why is it so valued?

4. **Critical Thinking Asking Geographic Questions** You are planning an expedition to the South Pole. Create a list of questions that you would ask someone who already has successfully completed such a trip.

Activity

Take It to the NET

Summarizing an Event Use the Internet to locate information about a visit to Antarctica by scientists. Report on the discoveries that the expedition team may have made during or after their visit. Share any photographs of the expedition with the class.

Articles From NATIONAL GEOGRAPHIC

The following article may be used to extend the content in this section.

Stevens, Jane Ellen, and Maria Stenzel, photographer. "Exploring Antarctic Ice." *National Geographic*, Vol. 189, No. 5 (May 1996), pp. 36–53.

Researchers study the unique forms of sea ice around Antarctica, searching for answers to questions about world climate.

Creating a Chapter Summary

As a reteaching opportunity, pair a more able student with a less able student to complete this chapter summary.

Causes: (1) In the late 1700s, Great Britain's prison system suffers greatly from overcrowding. (2) European settlers move onto Maori land in New Zealand. (3) The climate of the Pacific Islands is warm, and there are many beaches. (4) Scientists convince the world that Antarctica needs to remain open to all countries that want to conduct research there.
Effects: (1) More than 160,000 prisoners are transported to Australia. (2) The Maori begin to see themselves as a nation instead of individual, competing groups. (3) Pacific Island tourism is a growing industry. (4) An international treaty provides for the peaceful use of Antarctica.

Reviewing Key Terms

1–10. Students' sentences should show a clear understanding of each term.

Understanding Key Ideas

11. high standard of living; proximity to Southeast Asia
12. (a) The Dreamtime is the ancient time when the ancestors of all living things formed the world and gave humans responsibility for it. **(b)** Aborigines see caring for the land as a sacred trust.
13. Ranchers use helicopters and pickup trucks to survey their large stations and round up strays. Cattle ranchers drill artesian wells to provide water for their stations.
14. The North Island is narrow and hilly and has a central plateau with an active geothermal region. The South Island is mountainous with snowcapped peaks and dense forests.
15. Melanesia was probably settled by people from Southeast Asia. Micronesia was probably settled by voyagers from the Philippines, Indonesia, and some of the islands north of New Guinea.
16. (a) because most islands have few mineral resources or other industry **(b)** The government wants to avoid potential change that visitors might bring to the indigenous culture.

738 Chapter 34

Creating a Chapter Summary

On a sheet of paper, draw a flowchart like this one. Fill in the empty boxes with details from the chapter. Some information has been filled in to help you get started.

MIGRATIONS TO THE PACIFIC WORLD AND ANTARCTICA

CAUSE	EFFECT
• In the late 1700s, Great Britain's prison system suffers greatly from overcrowding.	•
•	• The Maori begin to see themselves as a nation instead of individual, competing groups.
• The climate of the Pacific Islands is warm, and there are many beaches.	•
•	• An international treaty provides for peaceful use of Antarctica.

Take It to the NET
Chapter Self-Test For practice test questions for Chapter 34, go to the World Geography section of **www.phschool.com**.

Reviewing Key Terms

Review the meaning of each key term below. Then, write a sentence for each.

1. Aborigine
2. lagoon
3. outback
4. artesian well
5. geyser
6. atoll
7. trust territory
8. pack ice
9. convergence zone
10. krill

Understanding Key Ideas

11. Migration What pull factors attract Southeast Asians to Australia today?
12. Cultures (a) Briefly explain the Aboriginal concept of the Dreamtime. **(b)** How does belief in the Dreamtime influence the Aborigines' relationship with the land?
13. Science and Technology How do Australian sheep and cattle ranchers use technology in their work?
14. Physical Characteristics How are the physical characteristics of New Zealand's North Island different from those of its South Island?
15. Understanding the Past How were the islands of Melanesia and Micronesia probably settled?
16. Economic Activities (a) Why is tourism an important industry in many of the Pacific Islands? **(b)** Why does the nation of West Samoa discourage tourism?
17. Climates What geographic factor makes Antarctica's ice caps drier than deserts in Africa and Asia?
18. Ecosystems If Antarctica has such a harsh environment, what accounts for the richness of its marine life?

Critical Thinking and Writing

19. Making Comparisons (a) How is Australia's government similar to that of Great Britain? **(b)** How is it different?
20. Identifying Relationships Why do the Maori, a minority group, have great influence in the decisions made by New Zealand's government?

---

17. The ice caps form a high plateau, and air loses moisture as it rises. Extreme cold makes the air even drier; thus, Antarctica sees less precipitation than the deserts.
18. The convergence zone causes layers of water to mix along the edge of the pack ice. Nutrient-rich deep water comes to the surface, providing food for krill. Whales and fish eat the krill; seals, penguins, and other animals eat the fish.

Critical Thinking and Writing

19. (a) Australia has a parliament led by a prime minister and a cabinet. **(b)** Australia has a written constitution that divides power between the federal government and the states.
20. They are the earliest known inhabitants of New Zealand; they have their own political party.

(Continued on next page.)

21. Sequencing What are the steps in the formation of an atoll?

22. Analyzing Causes and Effects How does the existence of the convergence zone affect the weather in Antarctica?

23. Predicting Consequences What might happen to Antarctica if a practical way were found to extract its natural resources?

Applying Skills

Reading a Contour Map Refer to the Skills for Life lesson on page 732 to answer these questions:

24. When a series of contour lines on a topographic map are close together, what information is being conveyed about elevation?

25. (a) Does the main island of Tahiti have a greater and steeper elevation than its peninsula? **(b)** How can you tell?

Analyzing a Photograph Study the photograph below, and answer the following questions:

26. Was this photo taken inside or outside a coral reef? Explain.

27. What other kinds of natural resources could a coral island provide?

28. What does the photograph suggest about the importance of machine power in this activity?

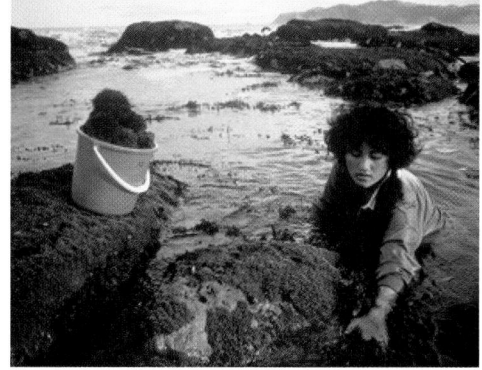

Test Preparation

Read the question and choose the best answer.

29. A major human characteristic that sets Antarctica apart from Australia, New Zealand, and the Pacific Islands is its —

A harsh and uninhabitable climate

B lack of natural resources

C popularity as a tourist attraction

D international treaty to share data

Activities

USING THE REGIONAL ATLAS

Review the Regional Atlas for East Asia and the Pacific World. Then, prepare a set of questions that compare and contrast Australia, New Zealand, the Pacific Islands, and Antarctica. Exchange questions with a partner. Answer the questions.

 MENTAL MAPPING

Study a map of East Asia and the Pacific World. Then, on a separate piece of paper, draw two sketch maps—one of the Pacific World and one of Antarctica—from memory. Label the following places on your maps:

- Australia
- New Zealand
- Tasmania
- Indian Ocean
- Fiji
- Tahiti
- Antarctica
- Transantarctic Mountains
- South Pole
- Ross Ice Shelf

Take It to the NET

Making Investments Which countries or parts of this region have economic activities that would interest foreign investors? Identify two investments in this region on the Internet. Then, explain your choices in a short essay. Visit the World Geography section of **www.phschool.com** for help in completing this activity.

 MENTAL MAPPING

Games for Review See pages 58–63 of the Simulations, Games, and Lab Activities booklet for games to review place names in preparation for the Chapter 34 and Unit 9 Map Tests.

Chapter Map Test Students should use their completed outline maps and the Unit 9 Checklist to prepare for the Chapter 34 Map Test.

Unit Map Test To prepare for the Unit 9 Map Test, students should study the location of all the place names on the Unit 9 Checklist.

Alternative Assessment

Final Evaluation

Giving an Oral Presentation Use the Oral Presentation Evaluation Form on page 21 of the Alternative Assessment booklet in the Prentice Hall Assessment System to evaluate students' presentations. Either teachers or students can complete the forms to indicate which level of work was achieved for each of the criteria. The evaluation should include specific examples and comments.

Critical Thinking and Writing (cont.)

21. A reef develops around a volcano that juts out of the sea; the volcanic cone falls under the water; the coral continues to build up on the reef; the volcano disappears, leaving a ring of coral around a lagoon; waves break the top layer of coral into sand; the sand breaks down into soil.

22. The clash of water temperatures there causes severe coastal storms.

23. Possible answers: Its environment might be endangered; nations might fight for control over the region.

Applying Skills

24. The slope of the land is steep.

25. (a) yes **(b)** There are more contour lines on the main island, and the lines are closer together. Also, the line labels verify higher elevation.

26. Inside. The water appears shallow and calm, protected from the ocean beyond.

27. Possible answers: fish and other marine life, coconuts, minerals

28. The woman is harvesting sea urchins by hand, suggesting that machine power is not very important in this activity.

Test Preparation
29. D

Activities

Using the Regional Atlas
Make sure that questions and answers are accurate. You may wish to work with students to create an in-class game that tests their knowledge.

Mental Mapping
To check their work, have students compare their maps to those in the Regional Atlas.

Take It to the Net
Students' responses should be explained clearly and should demonstrate an understanding of various countries' natural resources or economic activities.

TEST PREPARATION

Use this sample exam to help your students prepare for standardized tests.

You might want to remind your students of the following:

Tips for Test Taking

1. Read the directions carefully.

2. Read each question carefully.

3. For multiple choice questions, try to answer the question before you look at the choices. Read all the choices. Then, eliminate those that are absolutely incorrect.

4. For short answer questions, be sure to answer the question completely if there is more than one part.

5. Answer the easy questions first. Then, go back to the ones that will take more time.

6. Pace yourself. Be sure to set aside enough time for the writing questions.

Write answers on a separate sheet of paper.

Multiple Choice

Use the passage <u>and</u> your knowledge of social studies to answer the following question.

> A young man should serve his parents at home and be respectful to elders outside his home. He should be earnest and truthful, loving all. . . . After doing this, if he has energy to spare, he can study literature and the arts.

1 The person most likely to have made this statement was —

 A Chiang Kai-shek

 B Confucius

 C Deng Xiaoping

 D Mao Zedong

2 In order to weaken the power of the Uighurs in Xinjiang province, the Chinese government has encouraged migration into the area by —

 A Han Chinese

 B women

 C Buddhists

 D Tibetans

3 How has the creation of Special Economic Zones in southeast China affected the city of Beijing?

 A Beijing has grown more prosperous due to high tax rates imposed on businesses in the Southeast.

 B The extension of the Silk Road has caused people to move to way stations near oases.

 C Investment in Beijing has decreased, and many people apply for permission to move to the Southeast.

 D Government support for local minority cultures has increased.

4 Which of these was a geographic factor that contributed to Japan's decision to build an overseas empire?

 A Destruction of most cities by volcanic eruptions and other natural hazards

 B Isolation due to strong monsoon winds that made trade difficult

 C Influence of ocean currents on climate

 D Limited natural resources such as raw materials and land

Use the graph <u>and</u> your knowledge of social studies to answer the following question.

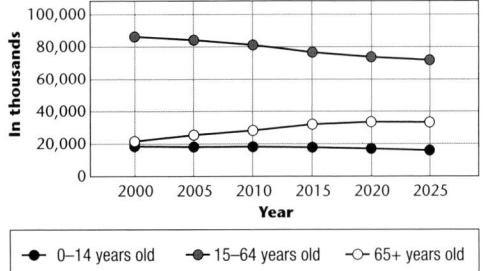

Projected Population Changes in Japan

Source: Japan National Institute of Population and Social Security Research

5 Based on the information in this graph, how are population changes likely to affect Japan's economy?

 A Health care costs for retired workers will increase.

 B Health care costs for retired workers will decrease.

 C Enrollment in primary and secondary schools will increase.

 D More people will work in industries than in services.

PRENTICE HALL
ASSESSMENT SYSTEM

Diagnose and Prescribe
 • Profile student skills with Diagnostic Tests A&B.
 • Address student needs with program materials identified in the test.

Review and Reteach
 • Provide cumulative content review with the Review Book.

Practice and Assess
 • Build test-taking skills with Test-Taking Strategies on Transparencies.

6 Why would commercial farming be unlikely to succeed in southwestern China?

A The region is densely populated, and there is little undeveloped land.

B Nomadic herders have overgrazed the land.

C The region is too cold, dry, and mountainous for farming.

D Although the climate is good for farming, the remoteness of the region would make transporting crops too costly.

7 Economic and political differences between North Korea and South Korea have led to —

A greater enthusiasm in North Korea for Western culture

B dramatically different standards of living in the two nations

C migration from South Korea to North Korea

D increased agricultural development in North Korea

8 How did European colonization affect economies in Southeast Asia?

A The development of large plantations forced small landowners out of business.

B Southeast Asian crafts found new markets in Europe, encouraging artisans.

C Immigration slowed as Europeans restricted the movement of Chinese and Indian workers.

D Battles over Thailand destroyed the nation's economy.

9 How are goods and services most likely to be produced in Singapore?

A Subsistence agriculture

B Market-oriented agriculture

C Cottage industries

D Commercial industries

10 How did land use in Australia differ between the Aborigines and European settlers?

A The Aborigines emphasized large-scale agriculture, whereas Europeans emphasized small farms.

B The Aborigines built sheep and cattle stations, whereas Europeans moved from one area to another and established few permanent settlements.

C The Aborigines felt responsible for taking care of the earth, whereas Europeans felt that natural resources were a source of wealth.

D The Aborigines mined for gold and other minerals, whereas Europeans refused to take anything from the land.

Writing Practice

11 The deepest ocean zone lacks sunlight and plant life. Why are a variety of creatures able to thrive in those conditions?

12 **(a)** Why did the United States and the Soviet Union refuse to make claims to Antarctica? **(b)** Would this decision be more likely to help or to hinder regional activities by the two nations? Explain.

13 **(a)** What parts of East Asia are most densely populated? **(b)** What factors do you think account for that density?

Test Preparation Answers

Multiple Choice

1 B

2 A

3 C

4 D

5 A

6 C

7 B

8 A

9 D

10 C

Writing Practice

11 At great ocean depths, hydrothermal vents discharge heat and chemicals into the water; bacteria feed on those chemicals. The bacteria, in turn, become the basis of a food chain that encompasses several marine animals, including species of worms, clams, and crabs.

12 **(a)** Both the United States and the Soviet Union agreed with the idea that Antarctica could be claimed by a nation only if that nation occupied and actively governed the land. Because of its harsh physical geography, Antarctica is essentially uninhabited. **(b)** Possible answer: This decision would enable American and Russian scientists to conduct research in Antarctica without fear of international conflicts.

13 **(a)** Japan, South Korea, and eastern China are the most densely populated parts of East Asia. **(b)** In general, large populations live in these regions because they tend to have mild temperatures, adequate rainfall, and easy access to the ocean for fishing and trade.

Table of
COUNTRIES

The following Table of Countries provides important geographic, economic, and political data for the countries of the world. Countries are listed alphabetically within regions, which are listed in the same order as they appear in the text.

When taken together, the data provide an overview of a country's level of development, or general quality of life. The table includes the following information for each country:

- *Capital city* is the seat of government.
- *Land area* is given in square miles.
- *Population* estimate is given in millions. For example, a population of 26. 3 means 26.3 million people.
- *Birthrate* is given for each 1,000 of population. For example, a birthrate of 36 means that for every 1,000 people, 36 babies are born each year.
- *Death rate* is for each 1,000 of population.
- *Annual growth rate,* the speed at which a country's population is increasing per year, is given as a percentage. To find the actual number of

Country	Capital City	Land Area (sq miles)	Population (millions)	Birthrate	Death Rate
				(per 1,000 population)	
WORLD		51,789,516	6,067.0	22	9
MORE DEVELOPED		19,814,583	1,184.0	11	10
LESS DEVELOPED		31,974,933	4,883.0	25	9
LESS DEVELOPED (Excl. China)		28,278,833	3,619.0	29	9

The United States and Canada

Country	Capital City	Land Area (sq miles)	Population (millions)	Birthrate	Death Rate
Canada	Ottawa	3,849,670	30.7	12	7
United States	Washington, D.C.	3,717,796	290.3	14	9

Latin America

Country	Capital City	Land Area (sq miles)	Population (millions)	Birthrate	Death Rate
Antigua and Barbuda	Saint John's	170	0.07	17	6
Argentina	Buenos Aires	1,073,514	36.3	20	8
Bahamas	Nassau	5,359	0.3	21	5
Barbados	Bridgetown	166	0.3	15	8
Belize	Belmopan	8,865	0.2	31	6
Bolivia	La Paz, Sucre	424,162	7.8	31	10
Brazil	Brasília	3,300,154	176.0	21	9
Chile	Santiago	292,135	14.8	18	6
Colombia	Bogotá	439,734	38.6	25	6
Costa Rica	San José	19,730	3.6	23	4
Cuba	Havana	42,803	11.2	13	7
Dominica	Roseau	290	0.07	17	6
Dominican Republic	Santo Domingo	18,815	8.7	26	6
Ecuador	Quito	109,483	12.3	23	5
El Salvador	San Salvador	8,124	5.8	27	6
Grenada	Saint George's	131	0.1	28	5

people by which a population is increasing each year, multiply the country's population by its annual growth rate.

- *Projected population* in 2025 is given in millions.
- *Infant mortality rate* refers to the number of infants out every thousand born who will die before their first birthday.
- *Population under age 15* is given as a percentage of the total population.
- *Population over age 65* is given as a percentage of the total population.
- *Life expectancy* refers to the average number of

years that a person can be expected to live.
- *Urban population* is the percentage of the population living in places considered urban, usually having at least 2,000 people.
- *Per capita GDP*, given in United States dollars, represents the total value of goods and services produced within a country in a year, divided by the country's total population.
- *NA* indicates that information is not available.

Sources: *Encarta World Atlas; World Population Data Sheet of the Population Reference Bureau, Inc.; CIA World Factbook*

Annual Population Growth Rate (percentage)	Projected Population 2025 (millions)	Infant Mortality Rate (per 1,000 births)	Population Under Age 15 (percentage)	Population Over Age 65 (percentage)	Life Expectancy (years)	Urban Population (percentage)	Per Capita GDP (U.S. dollars)
1.4	7,810.0	57	31	7	68	45	4,890
0.1	1,236.0	8	19	14	75	75	19,480
1.7	6,575.0	63	34	5	64	38	1,260
1.9	5,144.0	69	37	4	62	40	1,450
1.1	38.0	6	20	13	79	77	20,070
0.9	335.4	7	22	13	77	77	36,300
0.4	0.07	21	26	6	71	37	7,700
1.3	48.4	19	28	10	75	89	9,110
1.4	0.04	19	28	6	74	84	13,200
0.1	0.3	17	23	10	75	38	6,600
2.4	0.4	32	42	4	69	46	2,830
2.0	12.0	64	39	5	61	62	1,030
0.9	209.6	36	30	5	63	80	7,400
1.3	18.0	10	28	7	75	84	5,270
1.9	58.3	25	33	5	70	74	2,390
2.0	5.3	13	34	5	76	50	2,750
0.4	11.7	8	22	10	76	75	2,300
−1.3	0.07	9	27	10	78	71	3,290
1.6	11.8	44	35	4	70	61	1,860
1.9	17.8	32	36	4	72	60	1,660
1.6	8.4	29	37	5	70	46	1,900
0.8	0.2	11	43	5	71	34	3,110

Country	Capital City	Land Area (sq miles)	Population (millions)	Birthrate (per 1,000 population)	Death Rate (per 1,000 population)
Guatemala	Guatemala City	42,042	12.0	36	7
Guyana	Georgetown	83,000	0.7	19	9
Haiti	Port-au-Prince	10,714	7.0	33	14
Honduras	Tegucigalpa	43,278	5.9	32	7
Jamaica	Kingston	4,243	2.6	21	6
Mexico	Mexico City	756,062	98.6	25	5
Nicaragua	Managua	50,193	4.6	36	6
Panama	Panama City	29,158	2.7	22	8
Paraguay	Asunción	157,046	5.3	32	5
Peru	Lima	496,224	26.1	27	6
Saint Kitts-Nevis	Basseterre	139	0.04	23	9
Saint Lucia	Castries	239	0.2	23	6
Saint Vincent and the Grenadines	Kingstown	151	0.1	19	5
Suriname	Paramaribo	63,039	0.4	23	21
Trinidad and Tobago	Port-of-Spain	1,981	1.3	15	8
Uruguay	Montevideo	68,498	3.3	17	9
Venezuela	Caracas	352,143	22.8	23	5

Western Europe

Country	Capital City	Land Area (sq miles)	Population (millions)	Birthrate	Death Rate
Austria	Vienna	32,378	8.2	10	10
Belgium	Brussels	11,787	10.3	10	10
Denmark	Copenhagen	16,637	5.3	12	11
Finland	Helsinki	130,560	5.1	11	10
France	Paris	212,934	60.2	12	9
Germany	Berlin	137,830	82.4	9	11
Greece	Athens	50,950	10.7	10	9
Iceland	Reykjavík	39,768	0.2	15	7
Ireland	Dublin	27,135	3.7	14	9
Italy	Rome	116,320	56.8	9	10
Liechtenstein	Vaduz	62	0.03	13	7
Luxembourg	Luxembourg	999	0.4	11	9
Malta	Valletta	124	0.4	12	7
Netherlands	Amsterdam, The Hague	15,768	16.2	12	9
Norway	Oslo	125,050	4.4	13	10
Portugal	Lisbon	35,514	9.9	11	10
Spain	Madrid	195,363	39.1	10	10
Sweden	Stockholm	173,730	8.9	12	11
Switzerland	Bern	15,942	7.3	11	9
United Kingdom	London	94,548	59.0	12	11

Central Europe and Northern Eurasia

Country	Capital City	Land Area (sq miles)	Population (millions)	Birthrate	Death Rate
Albania	Tirana	11,100	3.3	21	8
Belarus	Minsk	80,154	10.4	10	14
Bosnia and Herzegovina	Sarajevo	19,741	3.4	9	12
Bulgaria	Sofia	42,822	8.2	8	13

Annual Population Growth Rate (percentage)	Projected Population 2025 (millions)	Infant Mortality Rate (per 1,000 births)	Population Under Age 15 (percentage)	Population Over Age 65 (percentage)	Life Expectancy (years)	Urban Population (percentage)	Per Capita GDP (U.S. dollars)
2.7	22.3	48	43	4	66	39	1,690
−0.5	0.7	49	31	5	62	36	920
1.5	10.2	99	43	4	51	35	380
2.3	8.6	42	42	3	65	45	2,600
0.7	3.4	14	32	7	75	50	1,620
1.8	141.6	26	36	4	72	74	9,000
2.9	8.1	42	44	3	67	63	430
1.6	3.8	24	32	6	75	56	3,080
2.7	9.9	57	40	5	72	54	2,000
2.0	39.2	43	37	5	70	72	2,620
1.2	0.06	18	33	6	68	43	6,050
1.1	0.2	17	34	5	72	30	3,790
0.6	0.2	16	31	6	74	44	2,460
0.8	0.5	27	33	5	71	50	820
−1.3	1.1	19	28	7	71	72	4,510
0.7	3.9	14	24	13	76	91	6,110
1.8	32.5	28	34	5	73	86	3,840
0.2	7.8	5	17	16	77	64	25,550
0.1	9.5	6	17	17	77	97	23,800
0.5	5.3	5	17	15	76	85	32,180
0.2	5.0	4	19	15	77	64	23,310
0.4	57.8	6	19	16	79	75	23,760
0.04	75.4	5	16	16	77	87	25,490
0.4	10.5	7	16	17	78	60	11,740
0.5	0.3	5	24	12	79	92	27,020
0.4	3.9	6	22	11	76	58	20,490
−0.1	50.4	6	14	18	78	67	19,910
0.9	0.04	5	19	11	78	19	NA
1.2	0.4	5	18	15	78	89	40,840
0.6	0.4	8	21	12	78	90	8,860
0.5	15.9	5	18	14	78	89	23,080
0.4	4.6	5	20	16	78	74	34,820
−0.1	9.0	7	17	15	76	37	10,270
0.1	36.8	7	15	16	78	77	13,530
0.3	9.2	4	19	17	79	83	25,720
0.2	7.1	5	17	15	79	62	36,010
0.23	60.0	6	19	16	77	89	21,800
0.1	4.3	45	33	6	69	38	3,800
−0.1	10.2	14	20	13	68	72	8,200
3.6	3.5	31	18	12	63	42	1,800
−0.6	7.3	13	17	16	72	69	6,200

Country	Capital City	Land Area (sq miles)	Population (millions)	Birthrate (per 1,000 population)	Death Rate (per 1,000 population)
Croatia	Zagreb	21,830	4.7	10	11
Czech Republic	Prague	30,448	10.3	9	11
Estonia	Tallinn	17,413	1.4	9	14
Hungary	Budapest	35,919	10.2	11	14
Latvia	Riga	24,942	2.4	8	16
Lithuania	Vilnius	25,174	3.6	11	13
Macedonia	Skopje	9,927	2.0	16	8
Moldova	Chisinau	13,012	4.5	14	12
Poland	Warsaw	124,807	38.6	10	10
Romania	Bucharest	92,042	22.4	9	12
Russia	Moscow	6,592,819	145.0	10	15
Slovakia	Bratislava	18,923	5.4	10	10
Slovenia	Ljubljana	7,819	2.0	9	10
Ukraine	Kiev	233,089	50.1	10	16
Yugoslavia	Belgrade (Serbia), Podgorica (Montenegro)	39,448	11.2	11	11

Central and Southwest Asia

Country	Capital City	Land Area (sq miles)	Population (millions)	Birthrate (per 1,000 population)	Death Rate (per 1,000 population)
Armenia	Yerevan	11,506	3.4	14	9
Azerbaijan	Baku	33,436	7.9	22	9
Bahrain	Manama	266	0.6	22	3
Cyprus	Nicosia	3,571	0.7	14	8
Georgia	Tbilisi	26,911	5.1	12	14
Iran	Tehran	630,575	69.0	31	6
Iraq	Baghdad	169,266	21.7	37	7
Israel	Jerusalem	8,131	3.6	20	6
Jordan	Amman	4,444	4.4	35	4
Kazakhstan	Astana	1,049,151	16.8	17	10
Kuwait	Kuwait City	6,880	1.9	21	2
Kyrgyzstan	Bishkek	760,641	4.5	22	9
Lebanon	Beirut	4,015	3.5	23	7
Oman	Muscat	82,031	2.4	38	4
Qatar	Doha	4,247	0.7	17	4
Saudi Arabia	Riyadh	829,996	20.8	38	5
Syria	Damascus	71,498	16.7	38	6
Tajikistan	Dushanbe	55,251	6.0	28	8
Turkey	Ankara	299,158	64.6	21	5
Turkmenistan	Ashgabat	188,456	4.3	26	9
United Arab Emirates	Abu Dhabi	32,278	2.3	19	3
Uzbekistan	Tashkent	172,741	23.8	24	8
Yemen	Sanaa	203,849	16.4	43	10

Africa

Country	Capital City	Land Area (sq miles)	Population (millions)	Birthrate (per 1,000 population)	Death Rate (per 1,000 population)
Algeria	Algiers	919,591	30.5	28	6
Angola	Luanda	481,351	10.9	44	17
Benin	Porto-Novo	43,483	6.1	46	13

Annual Population Growth Rate (percentage)	Projected Population 2025 (millions)	Infant Mortality Rate (per 1,000 births)	Population Under Age 15 (percentage)	Population Over Age 65 (percentage)	Life Expectancy (years)	Urban Population (percentage)	Per Capita GDP (U.S. dollars)
0.1	4.3	8	17	15	74	57	8,300
-0.1	10.1	7	17	14	74	66	14,400
-1.0	1.2	14	19	14	69	74	10,000
-0.2	9.4	10	18	14	71	65	12,000
-1.4	2.0	17	19	15	67	73	7,800
-0.5	3.4	15	20	13	69	73	7,600
0.7	2.2	19	24	9	73	61	4,400
0.1	4.8	44	25	10	64	53	2,550
-0.1	40.1	9	21	12	74	64	8,800
-0.3	21.4	18	19	13	71	57	6,800
-0.3	138.8	20	20	13	67	77	3,030
0.1	5.7	10	21	11	73	60	11,500
-0.1	1.9	5	17	13	75	52	16,000
-0.6	45.1	21	19	14	67	71	4,200
0.1	10.7	19	21	13	74	58	2,250
-0.4	3.4	41	26	8	67	69	430
0.7	9.4	82	32	6	63	56	580
2.1	0.9	16	31	3	75	91	9,830
0.7	1.0	8	25	10	77	55	10,990
-0.9	4.7	51	22	12	65	59	970
2.0	111.9	49	43	4	68	60	1,530
3.2	52.6	62	44	3	67	75	NA
1.9	7.8	8	28	10	78	91	16,810
2.5	8.2	33	43	3	73	72	1,580
-0.2	18.6	58	29	7	64	60	1,400
0.4	6.1	75	36	6	64	39	380
4.1	3.6	11	32	2	77	97	16,790
1.6	4.8	32	30	6	71	88	3,610
3.5	5.3	26	41	2	71	79	5,670
3.8	1.2	18	26	2	74	92	11,620
3.4	50.4	41	43	2	70	84	7,000
3.2	31.7	38	46	3	68	53	1,200
1.3	9.6	112	41	5	65	32	340
1.6	89.7	38	31	6	73	72	2,980
1.6	6.5	73	39	4	61	45	960
1.8	3.4	15	32	2	75	85	16,710
1.3	34.3	71	38	5	64	42	1,060
3.3	40.4	72	48	3	60	35	350
2.1	47.7	45	38	4	69	57	1,610
2.8	21.6	132	45	3	48	32	660
3.3	13.5	100	48	2	54	40	370

Country	Capital City	Land Area (sq miles)	Population (millions)	Birthrate (per 1,000 population)	Death Rate (per 1,000 population)
Botswana	Gaborone	224,606	1.4	32	21
Burkina Faso	Ouagadougou	105,792	11.3	46	18
Burundi	Bujumbura	10,745	5.5	42	17
Cameroon	Yaoundé	183,568	15.0	42	14
Cape Verde	Praia	1,556	0.4	35	7
Central African Republic	Bangui	240,533	3.4	39	17
Chad	N'Djamena	495,753	7.4	44	17
Comoros	Moroni	861	0.5	41	10
Congo	Brazzaville	132,046	2.7	39	16
Côte d'Ivoire	Yamoussoukro	124,502	15.4	42	16
Democratic Republic of the Congo	Kinshasa	905,351	49.0	47	15
Djibouti	Djibouti	8,958	0.4	42	15
Egypt	Cairo	386,660	74.7	27	8
Equatorial Guinea	Malabo	10,830	0.5	39	13
Eritrea	Asmara	45,405	3.8	43	13
Ethiopia	Addis Ababa	426,371	58.4	45	21
Gabon	Libreville	103,347	1.2	28	13
Gambia	Banjul	4,363	1.3	43	13
Ghana	Accra	92,100	18.5	33	11
Guinea	Conakry	94,927	7.5	41	18
Guinea-Bissau	Bissau	13,946	1.2	39	16
Kenya	Nairobi	224,081	28.3	32	14
Lesotho	Maseru	11,718	2.1	32	13
Liberia	Monrovia	43,000	2.8	42	7
Libya	Tripoli	679,359	5.7	44	7
Madagascar	Antananarivo	226,656	14.5	42	14
Malawi	Lilongwe	45,745	9.8	40	24
Mali	Bamako	478,838	10.1	50	19
Mauritania	Nouakchott	395,954	2.5	45	15
Mauritius	Port Louis	788	1.2	19	7
Morocco	Rabat	172,413	29.1	26	6
Mozambique	Maputo	309,494	17.5	44	18
Namibia	Windhoek	318,259	1.6	36	20
Niger	Niamey	489,189	9.7	53	23
Nigeria	Abuja	356,954	133.9	42	13
Rwanda	Kigali	10,170	8.0	39	19
São Tomé and Príncipe	São Tomé	371	0.2	44	8
Senegal	Dakar	75,954	9.7	44	11
Seychelles	Victoria	174	0.08	20	7
Sierra Leone	Freetown	27,699	5.1	46	17
Somalia	Mogadishu	246,201	6.8	47	19
South Africa	Pretoria	471,444	42.8	26	12
Sudan	Khartoum	967,464	33.6	40	11
Swaziland	Mbabane	6,703	1.0	41	21
Tanzania	Dar es Salaam, Dodoma	364,900	30.6	41	17
Togo	Lomé	21,927	4.9	45	10
Tunisia	Tunis	63,170	9.4	20	5
Uganda	Kampala	93,066	22.2	49	19
Zambia	Lusaka	290,583	9.5	45	23
Zimbabwe	Harare	150,873	11.0	31	20

Annual Population Growth Rate (percentage)	Projected Population 2025 (millions)	Infant Mortality Rate (per 1,000 births)	Population Under Age 15 (percentage)	Population Over Age 65 (percentage)	Life Expectancy (years)	Urban Population (percentage)	Per Capita GDP (U.S. dollars)
1.1	1.6	59	42	4	40	65	3,310
2.7	21.4	109	48	3	46	17	230
3.5	10.5	101	47	3	46	8	600
2.8	29.1	77	46	3	51	46	650
1.5	0.5	48	46	6	71	57	1,060
2.0	5.5	106	44	4	47	40	300
2.7	14.4	117	44	3	48	23	220
3.1	1.2	85	43	3	60	31	370
2.2	4.2	103	43	3	47	60	850
2.4	27.8	96	47	2	46	45	720
2.2	105.7	104	48	3	49	29	130
1.5	0.8	102	43	3	51	82	1,400
1.9	103.4	69	36	4	62	43	1,250
2.6	0.9	93	43	4	54	45	1,160
3.4	8.4	79	43	3	55	18	740
2.2	98.8	126	46	3	41	16	700
1.5	1.8	85	33	6	57	52	4,470
3.4	2.7	77	46	3	54	30	340
2.1	28.2	78	43	3	57	37	380
0.8	13.1	129	43	3	46	31	560
2.3	2.1	112	42	3	49	22	230
1.7	34.8	59	44	3	48	40	1,000
1.9	2.7	78	40	5	54	25	470
5.8	6.5	103	45	4	60	46	NA
3.7	14.2	56	49	3	65	86	NA
2.8	29.3	91	45	3	53	28	250
1.7	10.9	134	46	3	37	14	250
3.2	22.6	122	47	3	47	28	250
2.5	5.4	78	47	2	50	54	450
1.2	1.5	17	16	6	71	41	3,830
1.9	43.2	53	36	5	69	53	1,230
0.8	17.5	120	46	2	45	33	170
1.6	3.3	67	44	4	42	38	2,020
3.0	20.4	114	48	2	42	19	190
2.5	206.4	72	45	3	51	45	340
2.5	12.2	113	45	3	42	6	1,000
3.1	0.3	55	48	4	64	44	320
3.3	22.5	61	48	3	57	45	520
0.7	0.09	17	30	6	71	57	6,940
4.0	11.0	129	45	3	49	35	170
4.4	15.2	126	44	3	46	26	550
0.01	34.0	52	35	5	56	58	3,180
2.7	64.8	73	45	2	56	33	1,360
2.0	1.6	103	46	3	39	33	550
2.1	50.7	97	45	3	46	26	610
3.5	11.7	80	48	2	59	32	340
1.4	12.8	33	32	6	73	63	2,050
2.9	33.5	93	51	2	43	13	1,200
2.1	16.2	93	49	3	37	44	410
1.1	12.4	62	44	3	39	33	780

Table of Countries

Country	Capital City	Land Area (sq miles)	Population (millions)	Birthrate	Death Rate
				(per 1,000 population)	

South Asia

Country	Capital City	Land Area (sq miles)	Population (millions)	Birthrate	Death Rate
Afghanistan	Kabul	251,772	28.7	42	17
Bangladesh	Dhaka	55,598	138.4	29	11
Bhutan	Thimphu	18,147	2.1	37	15
India	New Delhi	1,269,340	1,049.7	26	9
Maldives	Male	116	0.3	40	6
Nepal	Kathmandu	56,826	26.5	36	10
Pakistan	Islamabad	307,375	150.7	34	11
Sri Lanka	Colombo	25,332	19.7	18	6

East Asia

Country	Capital City	Land Area (sq miles)	Population (millions)	Birthrate	Death Rate
Brunei	Bandar Seri Begawan	2,228	0.3	25	5
Cambodia	Phnom Penh	69,900	15.0	42	17
China	Beijing	3,696,100	1,284.0	16	7
Indonesia	Jakarta	735,355	231.0	23	8
Japan	Tokyo	145,869	126.0	10	8
Korea, North	P'yŏngyang	46,541	21.2	15	16
Korea, South	Seoul	38,324	46.4	16	6
Laos	Vientiane	91,429	5.3	41	13
Malaysia	Kuala Lumpur	127,317	20.9	27	5
Mongolia	Ulan Bator	604,826	2.6	24	8
Myanmar	Yangon	261,228	47.3	29	13
Papua New Guinea	Port Moresby	178,703	4.6	32	10
Philippines	Manila	115,830	77.7	28	7
Singapore	Singapore	239	3.5	14	5
Taiwan	Taipei	13,969	22.3	13	6
Thailand	Bangkok	198,116	60.0	17	7
Vietnam	Hanoi	128,066	76.2	22	7

The Pacific World

Country	Capital City	Land Area (sq miles)	Population (millions)	Birthrate	Death Rate
Australia	Canberra	2,988,888	18.6	14	7
Federated States of Micronesia	Palikir	270	0.1	28	6
Fiji	Suva	7,054	0.8	23	6
Marshall Islands	Majuro	69	0.06	45	7
New Zealand	Wellington	104,452	3.6	15	8
Palau	Koror	178	0.02	21	8
Samoa	Apia	1,097	0.2	30	6
Solomon Islands	Honiara	11,158	0.4	37	4
Vanuatu	Port-Vila	4,707	0.2	29	8

Annual Population Growth Rate (percentage)	Projected Population 2025 (millions)	Infant Mortality Rate (per 1,000 births)	Population Under Age 15 (percentage)	Population Over Age 65 (percentage)	Life Expectancy (years)	Urban Population (percentage)	Per Capita GDP (U.S. dollars)
3.4	48.0	144	43	3	47	21	NA
2.1	180.6	68	37	3	61	19	340
2.1	3.3	112	40	4	52	6	520
1.5	1,408.3	61	35	5	63	27	400
3.4	0.6	41	47	3	68	27	1,340
2.3	42.6	76	41	3	58	11	220
2.0	211.7	78	42	4	62	35	480
0.8	24.1	16	28	6	73	23	810
2.4	0.5	23	33	4	72	70	17,510
2.5	22.8	107	45	3	48	22	290
0.9	1,407.7	27	26	7	72	32	740
1.5	288.0	39	31	4	68	37	1,070
0.2	119.9	4	15	16	81	78	33,230
−0.1	26.1	88	26	6	51	62	NA
1.0	54.3	8	22	6	74	83	9,620
2.8	9.8	92	45	3	54	22	360
2.1	34.2	22	36	3	71	55	4,540
1.5	3.6	66	37	4	62	62	340
1.7	68.1	78	37	4	55	27	NA
2.3	7.6	57	40	3	58	17	1,030
2.1	120.5	35	40	4	66	56	1,120
1.2	4.2	4	21	7	79	100	31,040
0.7	25.3	7	21	8	75	77	NA
1.0	70.3	31	24	6	69	21	2,540
1.4	103.9	36	35	5	68	20	320
0.9	22.2	5	21	12	80	85	24,000
3.3	0.1	35	32	4	68	28	2,000
1.3	1.1	17	34	3	66	41	5,200
3.9	0.2	45	50	2	65	69	1,600
1.0	4.4	6	23	12	78	86	19,500
2.0	0.02	19	27	5	68	NA	9,000
2.3	0.4	33	40	4	69	21	3,500
3.2	0.8	24	45	3	72	18	1,700
2.1	0.3	61	39	3	61	19	1,300

Land Area Comparison Maps

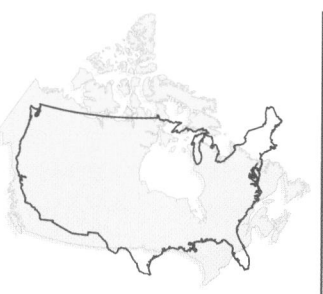

United States and Canada

United States
= 3,717,796 sq mi
Canada
= 3,849,670 sq mi

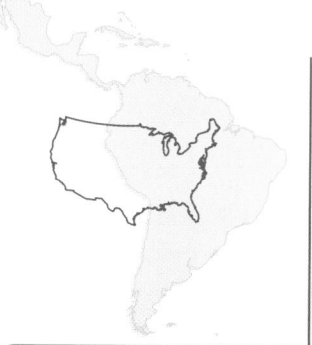

United States and Latin America

United States
= 3,717,796 sq mi
Latin America
= 7,941,950 sq mi

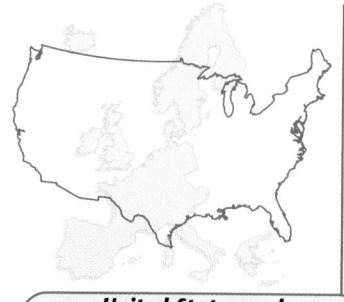

United States and Western Europe

United States
= 3,717,796 sq mi
Western Europe
= 1,433,422 sq mi

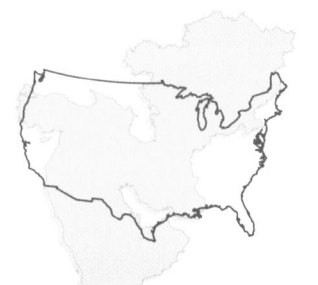

United States and Central and Southwest Asia

United States
= 3,717,796 sq mi
Central and Southwest Asia
= 4,648,298 sq mi

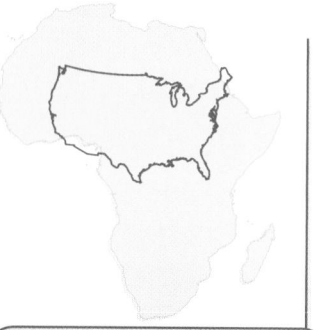

United States and Africa

United States
= 3,717,796 sq mi
Africa
= 11,698,105 sq mi

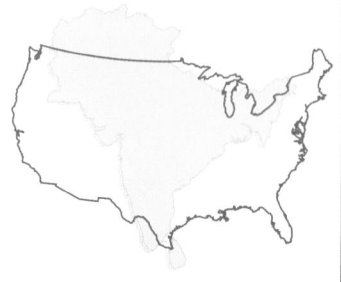

United States and South Asia

United States
= 3,717,796 sq mi
South Asia
= 1,984,506 sq mi

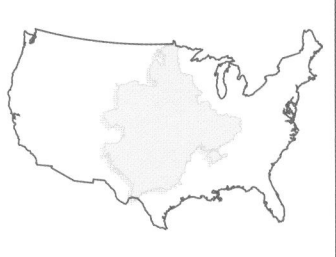

**United States and
Central and Eastern Europe**

United States
= 3,717,796 sq mi
Central and Eastern Europe
= 848,610 sq mi

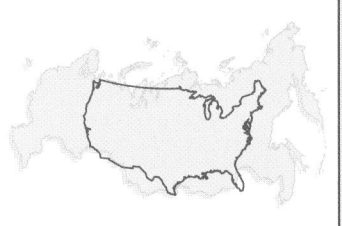

United States and Russia

United States
= 3,717,796 sq mi
Russia
= 6,592,819 sq mi

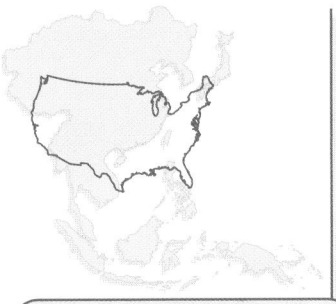

United States and East Asia

United States
= 3,717,796 sq mi
East Asia
= 6,275,758 sq mi

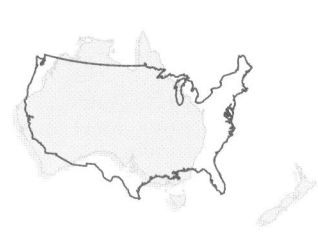

**United States and
the Pacific World**

United States
= 3,717,796 sq mi
Pacific World
= 3,305,506 sq mi

GAZETTEER

Berlin (53°N, 13°E) The capital city of Germany, p. 289

Bern (47°N, 7°E) The capital city of Switzerland, p. 289

Bhutan A country in South Asia, p. 591

Biscay, Bay of A part of the Atlantic Ocean bordered by France to the north and east, and Spain to the south, p. 291

Black Sea A landlocked sea between Europe and Asia, connected to the Mediterranean Sea by the Bosporus, p. 34

Bogotá (5°N, 75°W) The capital and largest city of Colombia in South America, p. 205

Bolivia A country in South America, p. 205

Bombay *See* **Mumbai**

Bosnia and Herzegovina A country in Eastern Europe, p. 373

Bosporus A narrow strait between the Black Sea and the Sea of Marmara, p. 441

Boston (42°N, 71°W) The capital and largest city of Massachusetts, p. 127

Bothnia, Gulf of An arm of the Baltic Sea, extending between Finland and northern Sweden, p. 291

Botswana A country in southern Africa, p. 507

Brahmaputra River A major South Asian river, flowing from the Himalayas through Bangladesh and into the Bay of Bengal, p. 593

Brasília (16°S, 48°W) The capital city of Brazil, p. 205

Bratislava (48°N, 17°E) The capital city of Slovakia (Slovak Republic), p. 373

Brazil The largest country in South America, p. 205

British Columbia A western province of Canada, along the Pacific coast, p. 180

Brunei (Negara Brunei Darussalam) A country on the northern coast of the island of Borneo in Southeast Asia, p. 635

Brussels (51°N, 4°E) The capital city of Belgium, p. 289

Bucharest (44°N, 26°E) The capital and largest city of Romania, p. 373

Budapest (48°N, 19°E) The capital city of Hungary, p. 373

Buenos Aires (34°S, 59°W) The capital city of Argentina, p. 205

Bulgaria A country in Eastern Europe, p. 373

Burkina Faso A country in West Africa, p. 507

Burma *See* **Myanmar**

Burundi A country in East Africa, p. 507

C

Cairo (30°N, 31°E) The capital city of Egypt, p. 507

Calcutta *See* **Kolkata**

Calgary (51°N, 114°W) A major city in Alberta, Canada, p. 127

California The most populous state in the United States, located on the Pacific Ocean coast, p. 142

Cambodia A country on the Indochina Peninsula in Southeast Asia, p. 635

Cameroon A country in Central Africa, p. 507

Canada A country in North America, consisting of ten provinces and three territories, p. 127

Canadian Shield A large horseshoe-shaped formation of exposed bedrock around the southern end of Hudson Bay, p. 129

Canberra (35°S, 149°E) The capital city of Australia, p. 635

Cape of Good Hope (34°S, 18°E) Cape in the Republic of South Africa, p. 509

Cape Horn (56°S, 67°W) Cape in Tierra del Fuego, Chile, the southern extremity of South America, p. 207

Cape Town (34°S, 18°E) A major city in the nation of South Africa, p. 507

Cape Verde A chain of fifteen islands in the Atlantic Ocean, off the west coast of Africa, p. 507

Caracas (10°N, 67°W) The capital and largest city of Venezuela in South America, p. 205

Caribbean Sea Part of the western Atlantic Ocean, p. 207

Carpathian Mountains A major mountain system of Central and Eastern Europe, a continuation of the Alps, p. 375

Casablanca (34°N, 8°W) The largest city in the North African nation of Morocco, p. 507

Cascade Range A mountain range extending from northern California in the United States into southern British Columbia, Canada, p. 129

Caspian Sea A landlocked saltwater sea, which lies in Northern Eurasia, p. 375

Caucasus Mountains A mountain range in Northern Eurasia and Turkey, p. 375

Central African Republic A country in Central Africa, p. 507

Central America The part of Latin America that comprises the seven republics of Guatemala, Honduras, El Salvador, Nicaragua, Costa Rica, Panama, and Belize, p. 236

Central Siberian Plateau A major plateau in Siberia between the Lena and Yenisei rivers, p. 375

Chad A country in Central Africa, p. 507

Chad, Lake A large freshwater lake in north central Africa, p. 509

Chicago (42°N, 88°W) A major city in Illinois in the midwestern United States, p. 127

Chile A country in South America, p. 205

China A country occupying most of the mainland of East Asia, p. 635

Coast Ranges A series of mountain ranges along the Pacific coast of North America, extending from Baja California in the south to Alaska in the north, p. 129

Colombia A country in South America, p. 205

Colorado A mountainous state in the western part of the United States, p. 142

Colorado River A major river in western North America, flowing from central Colorado into the Gulf of California, p. 129

Comoros An island nation between the East African coast and the island of Madagascar, p. 507

Congo A country in Central Africa, p. 507

Congo (Zaire) River A major river of Central Africa, flowing into the Atlantic Ocean, p. 509

Connecticut A state in the northeast region of the United States, p. 142

Copenhagen (56°N, 12°E) The capital city of Denmark, p. 289

Corsica A French island in the Mediterranean Sea west of Italy, p. 291

Costa Rica A country in Central America, p. 205

Côte d'Ivoire A country in West Africa, p. 507

Crete A Greek island in the Mediterranean Sea, p. 291

Croatia A country in Eastern Europe, p. 373

Cuba An island country that is the largest of the Caribbean islands, p. 205

Cyprus An island country in the eastern Mediterranean Sea, p. 439

Czech Republic A country in Eastern Europe, p. 373

D

Dakar (15°N, 17°W) The capital and largest city of the West African nation of Senegal, p. 507

Dallas (33°N, 97°W) A major city in Texas, in the southern United States, p. 127

Danube River A river in Central and Eastern Europe, flowing from Germany east to the Black Sea, p. 375

Darling River A major river in eastern Australia, p. 637

Dead Sea A saltwater lake on the border of Israel and Jordan, the lowest point on the earth's surface, p. 441

Deccan Plateau The plateau in southern India between the Eastern and Western Ghats, p. 593

Delaware A small state in the northeastern United States, p. 142

Delhi (29°N, 77°E) A major city located in northwestern India, p. 591

Democratic Republic of the Congo (formerly the country of Zaire) A country in Central Africa, p. 507

Denmark A country in northern Europe, p. 289

Denver (40°N, 105°W) The capital and largest city of Colorado, in the western United States, p. 127

District of Columbia Identical to the city of Washington, D.C., located on the Potomac River between Maryland and Virginia, p. 127

Djibouti A country in East Africa, p. 507

Dnieper River A major river of Eastern Europe that flows into the Black Sea, p. 375

Dniester River A major river of southeastern Europe that flows through Moldova and into the Black Sea, p. 375

Dominican Republic A country in the Caribbean Sea on the island of Hispaniola, p. 205

Don River A major river of European Russia that flows into the Black Sea, p. 375

Dublin (53°N, 6°W) The capital city of the Republic of Ireland, p. 289

E

East China Sea An arm of the Pacific Ocean east of mainland China and north of Taiwan, p. 637

Eastern Ghats A mountain chain in southern India on the eastern side of the Deccan Plateau, p. 593

Ecuador A country in South America, p. 205

Edinburgh (56°N, 3°W) The capital city of Scotland, p. 306

Egypt A country in northern Africa, p. 507

El Salvador The smallest country in Central America, p. 205

England *See* **United Kingdom**

English Channel A strait between England and France, connecting the Atlantic Ocean and the North Sea, p. 291

Equatorial Guinea A country in Central Africa, p. 507

Erie, Lake One of the Great Lakes of the United States, p. 129

Eritrea A country in East Africa, p. 507

Estonia A country in Northern Eurasia, p. 373

Ethiopia A country in East Africa, p. 507

Euphrates River A river flowing from Turkey south through Syria and Iraq, p. 441

Europe The world's second-smallest continent, a peninsula of the Eurasian landmass bounded by the Arctic Ocean, the Atlantic Ocean, the Mediterranean Sea, and Asia, p. 34

Everest, Mt. The world's tallest mountain, in the Himalayas, p. 593

F

Fiji A country consisting of an island group in the southern Pacific Ocean, p. 729

Finland A country in northern Europe, p. 289

Florida A populous state in the southern part of the United States, p. 142

France A country in Western Europe, p. 289

French Guiana (Department of Guiana) An overseas department of France in South America, p. 205

French Polynesia A country in the South Pacific Ocean roughly midway between Australia and South America, p. 729

G

Gabon A country in Central Africa, p. 507

Gambia A country in West Africa, p. 507

Ganges River A river in northern India and Bangladesh, flowing from the Himalayas to the Bay of Bengal, p. 593

Gaza A strip of land at the southeastern end of the Mediterranean Sea, formerly part of Egypt, occupied by Israel from 1967 until 1994, p. 439

Gdańsk (54°N, 19°E) A seaport city in northern Poland, p. 388

Genoa (44°N, 9°E) A major seaport city in northwestern Italy, p. 355

Georgia A state in the southern United States, p. 142

Georgia, Republic of A country in the Caucasus region of Asia, p. 439

Germany A country in Europe, p. 289

Ghana A country in West Africa, p. 507

Gibraltar A British colony at the southern tip of Spain, p. 289

Gibraltar, Strait of The narrow passage of open water connecting the Mediterranean Sea and the Atlantic Ocean, p. 291

Glasgow (56°N, 4°W) The largest city in Scotland, p. 304

Gobi Desert A desert in Mongolia and northern China, p. 637

Great Barrier Reef The long series of coral reefs running along the northeastern coast of Australia, p. 637

Great Indian Desert A large desert in northwestern India, p. 593

Great Lakes A group of five large lakes—Superior, Michigan, Huron, Erie, and Ontario—in central North America, p. 127

Great Plains The broad fertile plain descending east from the base of the Rocky Mountains in central North America, p. 129

Great Rift Valley A long depression running from Jordan in southwestern Asia to Mozambique in southeastern Africa, p. 508

Great Salt Lake A large, salty lake in the Great Basin region, p. 129

Great Sandy Desert A desert in western Australia, p. 637

Greater Antilles A group of islands in the Caribbean Sea, p. 207

Greece A country in Mediterranean Europe, p. 289

Greenland A large, self-governing island in the northern Atlantic Ocean, part of Denmark, pp. 16–17

Guatemala A country in Central America, p. 205

Guinea A country in West Africa, p. 507

Guinea, Gulf of A part of the Atlantic Ocean along the western coast of Africa, p. 509

Guinea-Bissau A country in West Africa, p. 507

Gulf Coast In the southern United States, the coastal region bordering the Gulf of Mexico, p. 162

Guyana A country in South America, p. 205

H

Hague, The (52°N, 4°E) A city in the Netherlands, headquarters of the International Court of Justice, p. 289

Haiti A country in the Caribbean Sea on the island of Hispaniola, p. 205

Hamburg (54°N, 10°E) A major seaport city in Germany, p. 332

Hanoi (21°N, 106°E) The capital and one of the largest cities of Vietnam, p. 635

Havana (23°N, 82°W) The capital city of Cuba, p. 205

Hawaii A state in the United States made up of several islands in the central Pacific Ocean, p. 142

Helsinki (60°N, 25°E) The capital city of Finland, p. 289

Himalayas A mountain system of south central Asia, extending along the border between India and Tibet and through Pakistan, Nepal, and Bhutan, p. 593

Hindu Kush A mountain range in Afghanistan, p. 593

Hiroshima (34°N, 132°E) A seaport city in Japan, on the island of Honshu, p. 680

Hispaniola An island in the Caribbean Sea, divided between Haiti on the west and the Dominican Republic on the east, p. 207

Ho Chi Minh City (11°N, 106°E) Formerly called Saigon, the largest city of Vietnam, p. 635

Honduras A country in Central America, p. 205

Hong Kong (22°N, 114°E) Formerly a British crown colony in East Asia, it became part of the People's Republic of China in 1997, p. 635

Honolulu (21°N, 158°W) The capital and largest city of Hawaii, in the United States, p. 127

Hormuz, Strait of A narrow passage of water between the Persian Gulf and the Gulf of Oman, p. 441

Huang He A river in northern China, p. 637

Hudson Bay An inland sea in the Northwest Territories, Canada, p. 129

Hungary A country in Eastern Europe, p. 373

Huron, Lake One of the Great Lakes of central North America, p. 129

I

Iberian Peninsula A peninsula in southwestern Europe, shared by Spain and Portugal, p. 62

Iceland An island country in the northern Atlantic Ocean, close to the Arctic Ocean, p. 289

Idaho A state in the western United States, p. 142

Illinois A state in the midwestern region of the United States, p. 142

India A large country occupying most of the Indian subcontinent in South Asia, p. 591

Indian Ocean The world's third-largest ocean, lying between Africa, Asia, and Australia, p. 34

Indiana A state in the midwestern part of the United States, p. 142

Indochina Peninsula The southeastern peninsula of Asia, surrounded by the South China Sea and the Andaman Sea, p. 62

Indo-Gangetic Plain A major plain of South Asia, in northeastern India, p. 593

Indonesia A country in Southeast Asia consisting of many islands, including Sumatra, Java, Sulawesi (Celebes), Bali, and the western half of New Guinea, p. 635

Indus River A river in South Asia, starting in Tibet and flowing through India and Pakistan to the Arabian Sea, p. 593

Ionian Sea An arm of the Mediterranean Sea, between Greece and southern Italy, p. 289

Iowa A state in the midwestern region of the United States, p. 142

Iran A country in Southwest Asia, p. 439

Iran, Plateau of A major plateau of Southwest Asia, east of the Zagros Mountains, p. 441

Iraq A country in Southwest Asia, p. 439

Ireland A country in northern Europe, occupying part of an island lying west of Great Britain in the Atlantic Ocean, p. 289

Irrawaddy River A major river of southeastern Asia, running south through Myanmar, into the Andaman Sea, p. 637

Irtysh River A major Siberian river, starting in the Altai Mountains and flowing into the Ob River, p. 375

Islamabad (33°N, 73°E) The capital of Pakistan, p. 591

Israel A country in Southwest Asia, p. 439

Istanbul (41°N, 29°E) A seaport city in northwestern Turkey on the Bosporus; formerly Constantinople, p. 439

Italy A boot-shaped country in southern Europe, including the islands of Sicily and Sardinia, p. 289

J

Jakarta (6°S, 107°E) The capital and largest city of Indonesia, p. 635

Jamaica An island country in the Caribbean Sea, p. 205

Japan An island country in the Pacific Ocean off the east coast of Asia, consisting of four main islands—Honshu, Hokkaido, Kyushu, and Shikoku, p. 635

Japan, Sea of (East Sea) An arm of the Pacific Ocean between Japan and the Asian mainland, p. 637

Java Sea A sea among the islands between the Indian and Pacific oceans, south of Borneo, p. 637

Jerusalem (32°N, 35°E) The capital city of Israel, holy to Jews, Christians, and Muslims, p. 439

Johannesburg (26°S, 28°E) The largest city in the Republic of South Africa, p. 507

Jordan A country in Southwest Asia, p. 439

Jordan River A river in Southwest Asia, starting in Syria and flowing to the northern end of the Dead Sea, forming the border between Israel and Jordan, p. 441

K

Kabul (34°N, 69°E) The capital and largest city of Afghanistan, p. 591

Kalahari A desert plateau in southern Africa, p. 509

Kamchatka Peninsula A peninsula of northeastern Asia pointing into the Pacific Ocean, p. 375

Kansas A state in the midwestern United States, p. 142

Karachi (25°N, 67°E) The largest city of Pakistan, p. 591

Karakoram Range A major chain of mountains at the meeting point of Pakistan, India, and China, p. 593

Kara Kum A desert of Central Asia, south of the Aral Sea and east of the Caspian Sea, p. 441

Kathmandu (28°N, 85°E) The capital and largest city of Nepal, p. 591

Kazakhstan A country in Central Asia, p. 439

Kentucky A southern state in the United States with a long northern border on the Ohio River, p. 142

Kenya A country in East Africa, p. 507

Kiev (50°N, 31°E) The capital and largest city of Ukraine, p. 373

Kilimanjaro, Mt. The highest mountain of Africa, located in Tanzania, p. 509

Kinshasa (4°S, 15°E) The capital and largest city of the Democratic Republic of the Congo, p. 507

Kirgiz Steppe A plain of Central Asia, north of the Aral Sea, p. 441

Kolkata (Calcutta) (22°N, 88°E) One of the largest cities in India, located by the Bay of Bengal, p. 591

Korean Peninsula A peninsula of eastern Asia, surrounded by the Sea of Japan and the Yellow Sea, p. 637

Kuril Islands A chain of islands running north from Japan toward the Kamchatka Peninsula, p. 375

Kuwait A country on the Persian Gulf in Southwest Asia, p. 439

Kuwait City (29°N, 47°E) The capital and a seaport city of Kuwait, p. 439

Kyrgyzstan A country in Central Asia, p. 439

L

Lagos (6°N, 3°E) The capital and largest city of Nigeria, p. 507

Laos A country on the Indochina Peninsula in Southeast Asia, p. 635

Latin America The culture region that includes Mexico, Central America, South America, and some of the Caribbean Islands, p. 202

Latvia A country in Northern Eurasia, p. 373

Lebanon A country in Southwest Asia on the eastern end of the Mediterranean Sea, p. 439

Lena River A major Siberian river, flowing north into the Arctic Ocean, p. 375

Lesotho A country in Southern Africa, completely surrounded by the Republic of South Africa, p. 507

Lesser Antilles A group of islands in the Caribbean Sea, p. 238

Liberia A country in West Africa, p. 507

Libya A country in northern Africa, p. 507

Liechtenstein A country in Western Europe, p. 289

Lima (12°S, 77°W) The capital and largest city of Peru, in South America, p. 205

Lisbon (39°N, 9°W) The capital and a seaport city of Portugal, p. 289

Lithuania A country in Northern Eurasia, p. 373

London (52°N, 0°) The capital city of the United Kingdom of Great Britain and Northern Ireland, p. 289

Los Angeles (34°N, 118°W) A seaport city in California in the southwestern United States, p. 127

Louisiana A southern state in the United States with a long border on the Gulf of Mexico, p. 142

Luxembourg A country in Western Europe, p. 289

M

Macao (22°N, 114°E) A major city on the east coast of mainland Asia, p. 635

Macedonia A former republic of Yugoslavia, p. 373

Mackenzie River A major river of Canada, flowing through the Northwest Territories and into the Arctic Ocean, p. 129

Madagascar An island country off the southeast coast of Africa in the Indian Ocean, p. 507

Madras (13°N, 80°E) A major city of India, located on the southeast coast, p. 591

Madrid (40°N, 4°W) The capital city of Spain, p. 289

Magellan, Strait of A narrow passage of water between Tierra del Fuego and the South American mainland, p. 207

Maine One of the northeastern states in the United States, p. 142

Malacca, Strait of A narrow passage of water between the Malay Peninsula and the island of Sumatra, p. 637

Malawi A country of southeastern Africa, p. 507

Malay Peninsula A peninsula in Southeast Asia, comprising West Malaysia and part of Thailand, p. 637

Malaysia A country in Southeast Asia, p. 635

Maldives A country consisting of a chain of islands in the Indian Ocean southwest of India, p. 591

Mali A country in West Africa, p. 507

Malta An island country in the Mediterranean Sea, p. 289

Manila (15°N, 121°E) The capital of the Philippines, p. 635

Manitoba A province of Canada, located between Saskatchewan and Ontario, p. 180

Marseille (43°N, 5°E) A major seaport city in southeast France, p. 289

Marshall Islands An island nation in the central Pacific Ocean, p. 729

Maryland A state on the Atlantic coast of the United States, p. 142

Massachusetts One of the New England states in the northeastern United States, p. 142

Mauritania A country in West Africa, p. 507

Mauritius An island nation in the Indian Ocean, east of Madagascar, p. 507

Mecca (21°N, 40°E) Islam's holiest city, in western Saudi Arabia, p. 439

Medina (24°N, 40°E) Islam's second-holiest city, in western Saudi Arabia, p. 439

Mediterranean Sea A large sea separating Europe and Africa, p. 291

Mekong River A major river of southeastern Asia, flowing through Indochina and into the South China Sea, p. 637

Melbourne (38°S, 145°E) Australia's second-largest city, p. 635

Mexico A country in North America, p. 205

Mexico City (19°N, 99°W) Capital and largest city of Mexico; largest urban area in the world, p. 205

Mexico, Gulf of An arm of the Atlantic Ocean, east of Mexico and south of the United States, p. 127

Miami (26°N, 80°W) The largest city in Florida, in the southern United States, p. 127

Michigan A state in the midwestern United States, p. 142

Michigan, Lake One of the Great Lakes of central North America, p. 129

Micronesia A nation of many islands in the central Pacific Ocean, p. 729

Middle East *See* **Southwest Asia**

Milan (46°N, 9°E) A city in northwestern Italy, p. 289

Minneapolis (45°N, 93°W) The largest city of Minnesota and a major city of the Midwest region of the United States, p. 127

Minnesota A state in the midwestern region of the United States, sharing a border with Canada, p. 142

Minsk (54°N, 28°E) The capital and largest city of Belarus in Eastern Europe, p. 373

Mississippi A southern state in the United States with a border on the Gulf of Mexico, p. 142

Mississippi River A river in the central United States, flowing from Minnesota south into the Gulf of Mexico, p. 129

Missouri A state in the midwestern part of the United States, p. 142

Missouri River A river in the central United States, p. 129

Moldova A country in Northern Eurasia, p. 373

Monaco A country in Western Europe, p. 289

Mongolia A country in East Asia, p. 635

Montana A large western state on the Great Plains of the United States, p. 142

Montenegro A republic of Yugoslavia in southeastern Europe, p. 373

Montreal (46°N, 74°W) A city in the province of Quebec in eastern Canada, p. 127

Morocco A country in northern Africa, p. 507

Moscow (55°N, 37°E) The capital city of Russia, p. 373

Mouths of the Ganges The delta region of the Ganges River in eastern India and Bangladesh, p. 593

Mozambique A country in southern Africa, p. 507

Mumbai (Bombay) (19°N, 73°E) The largest city in India, p. 591

Munich (48°N, 12°E) A city in southeastern Germany, p. 289

Murray River A major river of Australia, p. 637

Myanmar A country in Southeast Asia; formerly Burma, p. 635

Nagasaki (33°N, 130°E) A seaport city on the west coast of Japan, p. 680

Nairobi (1°S, 36°E) The capital and largest city of Kenya, p. 507

Namib A desert in southern Africa, p. 509

Namibia A country in southern Africa, p. 507

Narmada River A river in South Asia, flowing into the Arabian Sea, p. 593

Nebraska A state in the Midwest of the United States, p. 142

Nepal A country in South Asia, p. 591

Netherlands A country in Western Europe, p. 289

Netherlands Antilles Two groups of islands in the Caribbean Sea, p. 238

Nevada A western state in the United States, largely in the Great Basin, p. 142

New Brunswick A Maritime Province of Canada, located south of the mouth of the St. Lawrence River, p. 180

New Delhi (29°N, 77°E) The capital city of India, p. 591

New Hampshire One of the northeastern states in the United States, p. 142

New Jersey The most densely populated state in the United States, p. 142

New Mexico A western state in the United States, p. 142

New Orleans (30°N, 90°W) A major seaport city in Louisiana in the southern United States, p. 127

New York The second most populous state in the United States, p. 142

New York City (41°N, 74°W) A major seaport city in the state of New York in the northeastern United States, p. 127

New Zealand A country in the southwest Pacific Ocean, consisting of two major islands, p. 635

Newfoundland A Maritime Province of Canada and the easternmost Canadian province, p. 180

Nicaragua, Lake A lake in the Central American nation of Nicaragua, p. 207

Nicaragua A country in Central America, p. 205

Niger A country in West Africa, p. 507

Niger River A river in West Africa, flowing from Guinea into the Gulf of Guinea, p. 509

Nigeria A country in West Africa, p. 507

Nile River A river in east and northeast Africa, the longest in the world, flowing north into the Mediterranean Sea, p. 509

North America The world's third-largest continent, consisting of Canada, the United States, Mexico, and many islands, p. 34

North Carolina A southern state along the Atlantic coast of the United States, p. 142

North Dakota A state in the Midwest of the United States, p. 142

North European Plain A broad plain in Europe, extending through parts of Russia, Belarus, and Ukraine, p. 375

North Korea A country in East Asia, p. 635

North Sea An arm of the Atlantic Ocean between Great Britain and the European mainland, p. 291

Northern Ireland *See* **United Kingdom**

Northwest Territories A northern territory of Canada, bordered in part by Hudson Bay and the Arctic Ocean, p. 180

Norway A country in northern Europe, p. 289

Nova Scotia One of Canada's Maritime Provinces, located east of New Brunswick, p. 180

Nyasa, Lake A major lake in southeastern Africa along the borders of Malawi, Tanzania, and Mozambique, p. 509

Ob River A major Siberian river, flowing from the Altai Mountains and into the Arctic Ocean, p. 375

Ohio A state in the midwestern part of the United States, with a long border on the Ohio River, p. 142

Ohio River A major North American river, flowing from the Allegheny Mountains into the Mississippi River, p. 129

Okeechobee, Lake A large lake in Florida in the southern United States, p. 162

Okhotsk, Sea of An arm of the Pacific Ocean between the Kamchatka Peninsula and the Asian mainland, p. 375

Oklahoma A state in the Midwest of the United States, p. 142

Oman A country in Southwest Asia on the Arabian Peninsula, p. 439

Oman, Gulf of An arm of the Indian Ocean between mainland Asia and the southeastern tip of the Arabian Peninsula, p. 441

Ontario The most populous of Canada's provinces, located between Quebec and Manitoba, p. 180

Ontario, Lake One of the Great Lakes of central North America, p. 129

Orange River A river in southern Africa, flowing west into the Atlantic Ocean, p. 509

Oregon A western state on the Pacific coast of the United States, p. 142

Orinoco River A South American river, flowing through Venezuela and into the Atlantic Ocean, p. 207

Osaka (35°N, 135°E) One of the largest cities in Japan, p. 635

Oslo (60°N, 11°E) The capital city of Norway, p. 289

Ottawa (45°N, 76°W) The capital city of Canada, located in the province of Ontario, p. 127

P

Pacific Ocean A large body of water, bounded by North and South America on the east and Asia and Oceania on the west, and stretching from the Arctic to the Antarctic, p. 34

Pakistan A country in South Asia, p. 591

Palestine (32°N, 35°E) A historical region at the eastern end of the Mediterranean Sea, p. 471

Pamirs A mountainous area in southeastern Tajikistan, p. 441

Panama (9°N, 80°W) The capital and a seaport city of the Republic of Panama, p. 205

Panama, Isthmus of A narrow strip of land linking South and Central America and separating the Atlantic and Pacific oceans; site of the Panama Canal, p. 207

Panama, Republic of A country in Central America, p. 205

Panama Canal An important shipping canal across the Isthmus of Panama, linking the Caribbean Sea (hence the

Atlantic Ocean) to the Pacific Ocean, p. 238

Papua New Guinea A country in Southeast Asia, p. 635

Paraguay A country in South America, p. 205

Paraguay River A major river of South America, rising in Brazil and flowing south into the Atlantic Ocean, p. 207

Paraná River A river of South America, flowing into the Paraguay River, p. 207

Paris (49°N, 2°E) The capital city of France, p. 289

Pennsylvania A state in the northeastern part of the United States, p. 142

Persian Gulf An arm of the Arabian Sea, p. 441

Peru A country in South America, p. 205

Philadelphia (40°N, 75°W) A city in Pennsylvania in the northeastern United States, p. 127

Philippine Sea A part of the Pacific Ocean east of the Philippines and north of New Guinea, p. 637

Philippines An island country in Southeast Asia, p. 635

Phnom Penh (12°N, 105°E) The capital and largest city of Cambodia, p. 635

Phoenix (33°N, 112°W) The capital and largest city of Arizona in the United States, p. 127

Pindus Mountains A range of mountains in central and northern Greece, p. 291

Poland A country in Eastern Europe, p. 373

Portugal A country in southwestern Europe, p. 289

Prague (50°N, 14°E) The capital city of the Czech Republic, p. 373

Prince Edward Island One of Canada's Maritime Provinces and the smallest of the provinces, p. 180

Puerto Rico An island commonwealth of the United States in the Caribbean Sea, p. 205

P'yŏngyang (39°N, 126°E) The capital and largest city of North Korea, p. 635

Pyrenees A mountain range in southwestern Europe forming the border between France and Spain, p. 291

Q

Qatar A country in Southwest Asia on the Arabian Peninsula, p. 439

Quebec The largest of Canada's provinces, located in the eastern part of the country, p. 180

Quebec City (47°N, 71°W) The capital city of the province of Quebec in eastern Canada, p. 127

Quito (1°S, 79°W) The capital of Ecuador and one of its largest cities, p. 205

R

Red Sea A narrow sea separating northeastern Africa from the Arabian Peninsula, connected to the Mediterranean Sea by the Suez Canal and to the Indian Ocean by the Gulf of Aden, p. 441

Réunion An island in the Pacific Ocean east of Madagascar, p. 507

Rhine River A river in Western Europe, starting in Switzerland and flowing north through Germany to the Netherlands, p. 291

Rhône River A river in Western Europe, starting in Switzerland and flowing south through France into the Mediterranean Sea, p. 291

Rhode Island The smallest state in the United States, located in the Northeast, p. 142

Riga (57°N, 24°E) The capital and largest city of Latvia, p. 373

Rio de Janeiro (23°S, 43°W) A major city in Brazil, p. 205

Rio Grande A river of North America, known in Mexico as the Río Bravo, flowing from the Rocky Mountains to the Gulf of Mexico, p. 129

Rocky Mountains A mountain system in North America, p. 129

Romania A country in Eastern Europe, p. 373

Rome (42°N, 12°E) The capital city of Italy, p. 289

Rub' al-Khali (Empty Quarter) A desert on the Arabian Peninsula, p. 441

Russia A country in Northern Eurasia, p. 373

Rwanda A country in East Africa, p. 507

S

Sahara A desert in northern Africa, p. 509

St. Lawrence River A major North American river, flowing from Lake Ontario into the Atlantic Ocean, p. 129

St. Louis (38°N, 90°W) A major city of Missouri in the midwestern United States, p. 127

St. Petersburg (60°N, 30°E) Formerly called Leningrad, one of the largest cities of Russia, p. 373

Samoa An island nation in the South Pacific, p. 729

San Francisco (38°N, 122°W) A seaport city in California in the western United States, p. 127

San Juan (18°N, 67°W) The capital and largest city of Puerto Rico, p. 205

San Marino A country in north central Italy, p. 289

Santiago (33°S, 71°W) The capital city of Chile, p. 205

São Francisco River A river of eastern Brazil, rising in the Brazilian Highlands and flowing into the Atlantic Ocean, p. 207

São Paulo (24°S, 46°W) The largest city in Brazil, p. 205

São Tomé and Príncipe An island nation off the coast of western Africa, p. 507

Sarajevo (44°N, 18°E) The capital city of Bosnia and Herzegovina, p. 373

Sardinia An Italian island in the Mediterranean Sea west of Italy, p. 291

Saskatchewan A province on the Great Plains of Canada, p. 180

Saudi Arabia A country in Southwest Asia occupying most of the Arabian Peninsula, p. 439

Scandinavia A region in northern Europe consisting of Norway, Sweden, Denmark, and sometimes Finland, Iceland, and the Faroe Islands, p. 291

Scandinavian Peninsula A peninsula of northwestern Europe surrounded by the Baltic, North, and Norwegian seas, p. 62

Scotland *See* **United Kingdom**

Seattle (48°N, 122°W) The largest city in Washington, one of the western United States, p. 127

Seine River A river in northern France, flowing through Paris and emptying into the English Channel, p. 291

Senegal A country in West Africa, p. 507

Senegal River A river in West Africa, p. 509

Seoul (38°N, 127°E) The capital and largest city of South Korea, p. 635

Serbia A republic of Yugoslavia, in southeastern Europe, p. 373

Shanghai (31°N, 121°E) A large city in eastern China and one of the world's leading seaports, p. 635

Siberia A resource-rich region of Russia, extending east across northern Asia from the Ural Mountains to the Pacific coast, p. 375

Sicily An Italian island in the Mediterranean Sea, p. 291

Sierra Leone, Republic of A country in West Africa, p. 507

Sierra Madre A rugged mountain system in Mexico, including the Sierra Madre Oriental (East), the Sierra Madre Occidental (West), and the Sierra Madre del Sur (South), p. 207

Sierra Nevada A mountain range in California in the western United States, p. 129

Singapore An island country in Southeast Asia, p. 635

Slovakia (Slovak Republic) A country in Eastern Europe, p. 373

Slovenia A country in Eastern Europe, p. 373

Solomon Islands A nation of islands in the South Pacific, north of the Coral Sea, p. 635

Somalia A country in East Africa, p. 507

South Africa A country in southern Africa, p. 507

South America The world's fourth-largest continent, bounded by the Caribbean Sea, the Atlantic Ocean, and the Pacific Ocean and linked to North America by the Isthmus of Panama, p. 34

South Carolina A southern state on the Atlantic coast of the United States, p. 142

South Dakota A state in the Midwest of the United States, p. 142

Southern Ocean A large body of water extending from the coast of Antarctica north to 60 degrees south latitude, p. 34

South Korea A country in East Asia, p. 635

Spain A country in southwestern Europe, p. 289

Sri Lanka An island country off the southeast coast of India, p. 591

Stockholm (59°N, 18°E) The capital city of Sweden, p. 289

Sudan A country in East Africa, p. 507

Suez Canal A shipping canal across the Isthmus of Suez, connecting the Mediterranean Sea and the Indian Ocean through the Gulf of Suez and the Red Sea, p. 509

Superior, Lake The largest of the Great Lakes in central North America, p. 129

Suriname A country in South America, p. 205

Swaziland A country in southern Africa, p. 507

Sweden A country in northern Europe, p. 289

Switzerland A country in Western Europe, p. 289

Sydney (34°S, 151°E) The capital of New South Wales, a state of Australia, p. 635

Syria A country in Southwest Asia, p. 439

Syrian Desert A desert in Southwest Asia, p. 441

T

Taipei (25°N, 121°E) The capital and largest city of Taiwan, p. 635

Taiwan An island country off the southeast coast of the People's Republic of China, p. 635

Tajikistan A country in Central Asia, p. 439

Takla Makan Desert A large desert in western China, p. 637

Tallinn (59°N, 25°E) The capital and largest city of Estonia, p. 373

Tanganyika, Lake A lake in eastern Africa, along the borders of Tanzania and Burundi, p. 509

Tanzania A country in East Africa, p. 507

Tashkent (41°N, 69°E) The capital and largest city of Uzbekistan in Central Asia, p. 439

Tasman Sea An arm of the Pacific Ocean, located between Australia and New Zealand, p. 729

Taurus Mountains A mountain chain in southern Turkey, p. 441

Tbilisi (42°N, 45°W) The capital and largest city of Georgia, in the Caucasus region of Asia, p. 439

Tehran (36°N, 52°E) The capital city of Iran, p. 439

Tennessee A state in the southern part of the United States, p. 142

Texas A large state in the southern part of the United States, located along the Rio Grande, p. 142

Thailand A country in Southeast Asia, p. 635

Tien Shan A mountain system in central Asia, p. 637

Tigris River A river in Turkey and Iraq, p. 441

Togo A country in West Africa, p. 507

Tokyo (36°N, 140°E) The capital and largest city of Japan, on the island of Honshu, p. 635

Toronto (44°N, 79°W) The largest city in Canada and capital of the province of Ontario, p. 127

Tripoli (34°N, 13°E) The capital and largest city of Libya, p. 507

Tunis (37°N, 10°E) The capital and largest city of Tunisia, p. 507

Tunisia A country in northern Africa, p. 507

Turkey A country in Europe and Southwest Asia, p. 439

Turkmenistan A country in Central Asia, p. 439

Tyrrhenian Sea An arm of the Mediterranean Sea, west of the Italian Peninsula, p. 291

U

Uganda, Republic of A country in East Africa, p. 507

Ukraine A country in Northern Eurasia, formerly a republic of the Soviet Union, p. 373

United Arab Emirates A country in Southwest Asia on the eastern coast of the Arabian Peninsula, p. 439

United Kingdom of Great Britain and Northern Ireland An island country of Western Europe, consisting of England, Scotland, Wales, and Northern Ireland, p. 289

United States of America A country in North America, consisting of forty-eight contiguous states, the District of Columbia, and Alaska and Hawaii, p. 127

Ural Mountains A mountain system in Northern Eurasia, forming part of the border between Europe and Asia, p. 375

Uruguay A country in South America, p. 205

Utah A western state in the United States, p. 142

Uzbekistan A country in Central Asia, p. 439

V

Vancouver (49°N, 123°W) A major seaport city in western Canada, p. 127

Vanuatu A nation made up of many islands, formerly called New Hebrides, in the Pacific Ocean, east of the Coral Sea, p. 635

Vatican City The independent papal state contained within the city of Rome, Italy; headquarters of the Roman Catholic Church, p. 289

Venezuela A country in South America, p. 205

Venice (45°N, 12°E) A seaport city located on more than one hundred islands in the Lagoon of Venice in northern Italy on the Adriatic Sea, p. 355

Vermont A state in the New England region of the United States, p. 142

Victoria, Lake The largest lake in Africa, located along the Tanzania-Uganda border, p. 509

Vienna (48°N, 16°E) The capital city of Austria, p. 289

Vietnam A country in Southeast Asia, p. 635

Vilnius (55°N, 25°E) The capital and largest city of Lithuania, p. 373

Virginia A southern state along the Atlantic coast of the United States, p. 142

Vladivostok (43°N, 132°E) A port city on the Pacific coast and Russia's largest city in the Far East, p. 414

Volga River A river in Russia, rising near Moscow and flowing into the Caspian Sea, p. 375

W

Wales *See* **United Kingdom**

Warsaw (52°N, 21°E) The capital city of Poland, p. 373

Washington A northwestern state along the Pacific coast of the United States, p. 142

Washington, D.C. (39°N, 77°W) The capital city of the United States, p. 127

West Virginia A mountainous state in the eastern part of the United States, p. 142

Western Dvina River A river flowing from Russia, west through Belarus and Latvia, into the Baltic Sea, p. 375

Western Siberian Lowland A major lowland between the Ural Mountains and the Central Siberian Plateau, p. 375

White Sea An arm of the Arctic Ocean in far northwestern Russia, p. 414

Wisconsin A midwestern state in the United States, p. 142

Wyoming A western state in the United States, p. 142

Y

Yangzi River A major river in China, p. 637

Yellow Sea An arm of the Pacific Ocean between the Korean Peninsula and mainland China, p. 637

Yemen A country in southwest Asia on the Arabian Peninsula, p. 439

Yenisei River A major Siberian river, flowing north into the Arctic Ocean, p. 375

Yeravan (40°N, 44°E) The capital and largest city of Armenia, p. 439

Yucatán Peninsula A low, flat peninsula in southeastern Mexico, p. 207

Yukon River A major North American river, flowing from the Yukon Territory of Canada, through Alaska and into the Bering Sea, p. 129

Yukon Territory Located in the far northwest of Canada, bordered in part by Alaska and the Arctic Ocean, p. 180

Z

Zagreb (46°N, 16°E) The capital city of Croatia, p. 373

Zagros Mountains A mountain system in southern and western Iran, p. 441

Zambezi River A river in southern Africa, flowing east into the Indian Ocean opposite Madagascar, p. 509

Zambia A country in southern Africa, p. 507

Zimbabwe A country in southern Africa, p. 507

GLOSSARY

PRONUNCIATION KEY

Symbol	Key Words
a	asp, fat, parrot
ā	ape, date, play, break, fail
ä	ah, heart, father, cot
e	wealth, ten, berry
ē	even, meet, money, flea, grieve
i	is, hit, mirror
ī	ice, bite, high, sky
ō	open, tone, go, boat
ô	all, horn, law
oo	look, pull, moor, wolf
o͞o	ooze, tool, crew, rule
yoo	cure, furious
yo͞o	cute, few, globule
oi	oil, point, toy
ou	out, crowd, plow
u	up, cut, color, flood
ʉr	urn, fur, deter, irk
ə	a as in ago
	e as in agent
	i as in sanity
	o as in comply
	u as in focus
ər	perhaps, murder
zh	azure, leisure, beige
ŋ	ring, anger, drink

A

abdicate To surrender one's office, throne, or authority, pp. 423, 652

Aborigine (ab′ə rij′ə nē′) An original inhabitant; one of the original inhabitants of Australia, p. 717

absolute location The position on the earth in which a place can be found, p. 39

acid rain Rain whose high concentration of chemicals, usually from industrial pollution, pollutes water, kills plant and animal life, and eats away at the surface of stone and rock; a form of chemical weathering, pp. 53, 382

acupuncture The ancient Chinese practice of inserting fine needles at specific body points to cure disease or to ease pain, p. 669

aftershock Tremor that occurs after an earthquake, p. 245

agricultural revolution The change from nomadic hunting and gathering to farming that took place about 8000 B.C., p. 438

alluvial plain A broad expanse of land along riverbanks, consisting of rich, fertile soil left by floods, p. 592

altiplano (al′ti plä′nō) A plateau region located in the Andes of Bolivia and Peru, p. 273

anarchy Political disorder and violence; lawlessness, p. 484

ancestor worship The belief that respecting and honoring one's ancestors will cause them to live on in the spirit world after death, p. 550

animism The religious belief that such things as the sky, rivers, and trees contain gods or spirits, p. 550

annex To formally incorporate into a country or state the territory of another, pp. 126, 407

apartheid (ə pär′tāt′) Formerly in the Republic of South Africa, the policy of strict racial segregation, p. 575

aqueduct A large pipe or channel designed to transport water from a remote source over a long distance, p. 174

archipelago (är′kə pel′ə gō′) A group of islands, p. 246

artesian well A well that is drilled deep enough to tap a layer of porous material filled with groundwater, p. 723

atheism The belief that God does not exist, p. 668

atmosphere The layer of gases, water vapor, and other substances above the earth, p. 45

atoll (a′tôl) A ring-shaped coral island surrounding a lagoon, p. 725

authoritarian Descriptive of a system of government in which the leaders hold all political power, p. 103

autonomous region A political unit with limited self-government, p. 664

autonomy independence, p. 456

avalanche A sudden fall of a mass of ice and snow, p. 245

ayatollah A religious leader among Shiite Muslims, p. 498

B

balkanize To break up into small, mutually hostile political units, as occurred in the Balkans after World War I, p. 398

barbarian A person without manners or civilized customs, p. 702

barter The exchange of goods without money, p. 559

basin irrigation In Egypt, a system by which water and silt were controlled by embankments and time-released to irrigate farmlands, p. 527

bauxite A mineral used in making aluminum, p. 268

bayou A marshy inlet or outlet of a lake or a river, p. 162

bazaar An open-air market; a street lined with shops and stalls, p. 524

bedrock The solid rock underlying the earth's surface, p. 184

bioluminescence The process by which some fish and other organisms give off light, p. 724

biome (bī´ōm) The term used to describe a major type of ecosystem that can be found in various regions throughout the world, p. 77

biosphere The world of plants, animals, and other living things in earth's land and waters, p. 45

birthrate The number of live births each year per 1,000 people, p. 89

black market The system of selling goods and services outside of official channels, p. 430

blight A plant disease, p. 316

blizzard A heavy snowfall accompanied by strong winds, p. 627

bog An area of wet, spongy ground, p. 310

boycott To refuse to purchase or use a product or service as an expression of disapproval, p. 608

buffer A protective zone between two countries, p. 672

buffer state A country that separates two hostile countries, p. 622

bullet train A high-speed train, p. 646

C

campesino (käm´pe sē´nō) In Latin America, a tenant farmer or farm worker, p. 270

canal An artificial waterway, p. 145

canopy The uppermost layer of a forest where tree branches meet, p. 210

canton A political division or state; one of the states in Switzerland, p. 342

canyon A deep valley with vertical sides that have been eroded by river water, p. 465

capital Wealth in the form of money or property owned or used in business, p. 529

caravan A large group of merchants who join together to travel in safety, p. 532

carnivore A meat-eating animal, pp. 81, 578

cash crop A farm crop grown for sale and profit, p. 229

caste system A social hierarchy in which a person possesses a distinct rank in society that is determined by birth, p. 614

caudillo A Latin American military dictator, p. 204

cay (kē) A small, low island or coral reef, p. 206

cede To transfer or give up, p. 126

chaparral A type of natural vegetation that is adapted to Mediterranean climates; small evergreen trees and low bushes, or scrub, pp. 80, 444, 512

character of a place The physical and human characteristics that help to distinguish a place from other places, p. 40

charpoy A wooden bed frame with knotted string in place of a mattress, p. 615

chemical weathering The process by which the actual chemical structure of rock is changed, usually when water and carbon dioxide cause a breakdown of the rock, p. 53

chernozem A rich topsoil found in the Russian steppes and other mid-latitude grasslands, pp. 417, 461

civil war A conflict between opposing groups of citizens of the same country, p. 126

civilization An advanced culture, p. 438

climate The term used for the weather patterns that an area typically experiences over a long period of time, p. 63

cloud A mass of tiny particles of water and dust floating in the atmosphere, p. 74

collective farm A government-owned farm managed by workers who share the profits from their produce, p. 395

colonialism The system by which countries set up colonies to secure sources of raw materials and markets for their products, p. 506

colony A territory separated from but subject to a ruling power, p. 126

columnar rock Volcanic rock that split into columns as lava cooled, p. 360

command economy An economic system that is controlled by a single central government, pp. 104, 216, 423

commercial farming The raising of crops and livestock for sale in markets, p. 116

commercial industry A large-scale manufacturing operation that employs many people and produces large quantities of goods, p. 117

communism A system of government in which the government controls the means of production, determining what goods will be made, how much workers will be paid, and how much items will cost, p. 372

compulsory Required, p. 300

concession A privilege or exemption granted by a government, p. 634

confederation A system of government in which individual political units keep their sovereignty but give limited power to a central government, pp. 102, 331

coniferous Cone-bearing; a type of tree able to survive long, cold winters, with long, thin needles rather than leaves, pp. 80, 198

conquistador Name for the Spanish explorers who claimed land in the Americas for Spain, p. 204

continent Any of the seven large landmasses of the earth's surface: Africa, Antarctica, Asia, Australia, Europe, North America, and South America, p. 45

continental climate The type of climate found in the great central areas of continents in the Northern Hemisphere; characterized by cold, snowy winters and warm or hot summers, p. 69

continental divide A boundary or area of high ground that separates rivers flowing toward opposite sides of a continent, p. 128

continental drift theory The idea that continents slowly shift their positions due to movement of the tectonic plates on which they ride, p. 47

convergence zone An area of severe storms where the frigid waters circulating around Antarctica meet the warmer waters of the Atlantic, Pacific, and Indian oceans, p. 735

coral The rocklike skeletons of tiny sea animals, p. 206

coral island An island formed by the skeletal remains of tiny sea animals and the sand and sediment piling on top of them, p. 247

cordillera (kôr´dil yer´ə) A related set of separate mountain ranges, p. 270

core The earth's center, consisting of very hot metal that is dense and solid in the inner core and molten, or liquid, in the outer core, p. 44

cottage industry A small-scale manufacturing operation using little technology, often located in or near people's homes. pp. 116, 618

coup (kōo) The sudden overthrow of a ruler or government, often involving violent force or the threat of force, p. 548

crater lake A body of water that occupies a bowl-shaped depression around the opening of an extinct or dormant volcano, p. 361

crevasse (krə vas´) A deep crack in glacial ice, p. 735

crust The solid, rocky, surface layer of the earth, p. 44

cultural convergence The contact and interaction of one culture with another, pp. 97, 204

cultural diffusion The process by which people adopt the practices of their neighbors, p. 288

cultural divergence The restriction of a culture from outside influences, pp. 98, 316

culture The way of life that distinguishes a people, for example, government, language, religion, customs, and beliefs, p. 87

culture hearth A place in which important ideas begin and thereafter spread to surrounding cultures, p. 90

customs Fees charged by a government on imported goods, p. 193

cyclone A violent, rotating windstorm, p. 721

czar An emperor of Russia, p. 422

D

decentralize To transfer government power to smaller regions, p. 338

deciduous Leaf-shedding; a type of tree that sheds its leaves during one season, p. 79

deforestation The process of stripping the land of its trees, pp. 262, 544, 625

delta The land that forms at the mouth of some rivers by soil that is dropped as the river slows and enters the sea, p. 523

demilitarized zone A strip of land on which troops or weapons are not allowed, p. 694

democracy A system of government in which the people are invested with the power to choose their leaders and determine government policy, p. 103

desalination The process of removing salt from seawater so that it can be used for drinking and irrigation, pp. 448, 488

desertification The transformation of arable land into desert either naturally or through human intervention, pp. 463, 544

dialect A variation of a spoken language that is unique to a region or community, p. 329

dictatorship A system of government in which absolute power is held by a small group or one person, p. 103

diffusion The process by which a cultural element is transmitted from one group or individual to another, p. 97

dike An embankment of earth and rock built to hold back water, p. 337

diversify To increase the variety of, p. 408

doi moi The economic change begun by Vietnam in 1986, p. 710

domestication The process of training and breeding animals for use by humans, p. 372

double cropping In farming, growing more than one crop a year on the same land, p. 661

downsize To fire an employee in order to reduce costs, p. 691

drainage basin The entire area of land that is drained by a major river and its tributaries, p. 128

drip irrigation A process by which precisely controlled amounts of water drip directly onto plants from pipes, thus preserving precious water resources in dry areas, p. 476

dry farming A farming technique that leaves land unplanted every few years in order to gather moisture, p. 350

E

earthquake A shaking of the ground caused by sudden movements in the earth's crust, p. 244

ecosystem The interaction of plant life, animal life, and the physical environment in which they live, p. 77

ecotourism Tourism that encourages environmental awareness and has little effect on the ecosystem, p. 263

ejido (e hē´dô) Farmland owned collectively by members of a rural community, p. 229

El Niño A warm ocean current off South America's northwestern coast that influences global weather patterns, p. 208

embankment dam A wall of soil and rock to hold back water, p. 621

embargo A severe restriction of trade with other countries, p. 486

emigrant A person who leaves a country to live elsewhere, p. 89

enclave A country completely surrounded by another country, p. 580

entrepreneur A go-getter individual who starts and builds a business, p. 399

epicenter The point on the earth's surface directly above the focus of an earthquake, p. 245

equinox Either of the two times each year (spring and fall) when day and night are of nearly equal length everywhere on earth, p. 65

erosion The movement of weathered materials, including gravel, soil, and sand, usually caused by water, wind, and glaciers, pp. 54, 464

escarpment A steep cliff that separates two level areas of differing elevations, pp. 255, 508

estuary The wide mouth of a river, where freshwater river currents meet salt water, p. 278

ethnic group People who share such things as culture, language, and religion, p. 380

ethnocracy A system of government in which one ethnic group rules over others, p. 571

Eurasia The name some geographers suggest should be used for the landmass of Europe and Asia, p. 374

euro The common currency used by member nations of the European Union, p. 298

exodus A mass migration from a region, p. 675

export An item that is sent out of the country for sale, p. 117

falaj system In the Arabian Peninsula, an ancient system of underground and surface canals, p. 492

fall line Imaginary line between the Appalachian Mountains and the Atlantic coastal plain, where rivers and streams form waterfalls and rapids as they descend from higher elevations to the coastal plain, p. 163

favela A slum community in a Brazilian city, p. 256

federation A government structure in which some powers are given to the national government and other powers are reserved for more local governments, p. 102

fellaheen Egyptian peasants (sing. fellah), p. 523

fertile Able to produce abundantly, p. 305

Fertile Crescent A region in the Middle East where farming and the first civilizations developed, p. 482

fjord (fyôrd) A narrow valley or inlet from the sea, originally carved out by an advancing glacier and filled by melting glacial ice, p. 318

forage Food for grazing animals, p. 544

formal region A group of places that have similar attributes, for example, a political region, p. 41

fossil fuel Any one of several nonrenewable mineral resources formed from the remains of ancient plants and animals and used for fuel, p. 109

free enterprise An economic system that allows individuals to own, operate, and profit from their own businesses in an open, competitive market, p. 147

front The boundary between two masses of air that differ in density or temperature, p. 68

functional region A group of places connected by movement, for example, the region drained by the Amazon River and its tributaries, p. 41

fundamentalism A set of religious beliefs based on a strict interpretation of a sacred text, p. 461

gasohol A fuel mixture of gasoline and ethanol, p. 261

gaucho (gou´chō) A cowboy who herded cattle in the pampas of Argentina and Uruguay, p. 279

GDP per capita The total value of goods and services produced within a country in a year, divided by the country's total population, p. 216

genocide The systematic killing or intentional destruction of a people, p. 457

geography The study of the earth's surface and the processes that shape it, the connections between places, and the complex relationships between people and their environments, p. 35

geothermal energy Energy produced from the earth's intense interior heat, pp. 111, 319

geyser (gī´zər) A natural hot spring that shoots a column of water and steam into the air, p. 726

ghetto A section of a city in which a particular minority group is forced to live, p. 390

GIS A geographic information system, which uses computer technology to collect and analyze data about the earth's surface in order to solve geographic problems, p. 37

glacier A huge, slow-moving mass of snow and ice, pp. 56, 465

glasnost A policy of openness introduced in the Soviet Union in the late 1980s, p. 425

glen A narrow valley, p. 311

graben (grä´bən) A long, narrow area that has dropped between two faults, p. 362

grain elevator A tall building equipped with machinery for loading, cleaning, storing, and discharging grain, p. 169

grain exchange A place where grain is bought and sold as a commodity, p. 169

gross domestic product (GDP) The total value of goods and services produced within a county in a year, including the domestic output of foreign firms and excluding the output of domestic firms in foreign countries, p. 118

gross national product (GNP) The total value of a nation's goods and services, including the output of domestic firms in foreign countries and excluding the domestic output of foreign firms, p. 143

growing season In farming, the average number of days between the last frost of spring and the first frost of fall, p. 167

guerrilla (gə ril´ə) A member of an armed force that is not part of a regular army; relating to a form of warfare carried on by such an independent armed force, p. 241

hacienda (hä´sē en´də) A large Spanish-owned estate in the Americas, often run as a farm or a cattle ranch, p. 228

harambee A policy of cooperation adopted in Kenya after independence to encourage economic growth, p. 567

hemisphere A half of the earth; the Equator divides the Northern and Southern hemispheres; the Prime Meridian divides the Eastern and Western hemispheres, p. 39

herbivore A plant-eating animal, pp. 81, 578

heterogeneity A lack of similarity, p. 710

hibernation The dormant state in which an animal's bodily functions slow to a minimum, p. 199

hierarchy Rank according to function, p. 151

hinterland The area served by a metropolis, p. 151

Holocaust The execution of 6 million Jews in Nazi concentration camps during World War II, p. 390

homogeneous (hō´mō jē´nē əs) Having a similar nature; uniform in structure or quality, p. 685

hub A central point of concentrated activity and influence, p. 351

humus The organic material that results when plants and animals that live in the soil die and decay, pp. 167, 420

hurricane A destructive tropical storm that forms over the Atlantic Ocean, usually in late summer and early fall, with winds of at least 74 miles (119 km) per hour, p. 208

hydroelectric power Electricity that is generated by moving water, p. 620

hydrosphere The water contained in oceans, lakes, rivers, and under the ground, p. 45

hydrothermal vent A crack in the ocean floor from which hot, mineral-rich water gushes, p. 725

I

ice shelf A massive extension of glacial ice over the sea, often protruding hundreds of miles, p. 735

ideogram In written language, a character or symbol that represents an idea or thing, p. 667

immigrant A person who moves into a country, p. 89

import An item that is brought into the country for sale, p. 117

Impressionism A style of art where painters try to catch visual impressions made by color, light, and shadows, p. 329

indigenous Native to or living naturally in an area or environment, p. 704

Industrial Revolution The shift from human power to machine power, pp. 126, 288

infant mortality The number of children per 1,000 live births who die within the first year, p. 384

inflation A sharp, widespread rise in prices, p. 332

infrastructure The basic support facilities of a community or country, such as roads and bridges, power plants, and schools, pp. 245, 490

inhabitable Able to support permanent residents, p. 364

inland delta An area of lakes, creeks, and swamps away from the ocean, p. 545

inland sea A sea that is almost completely surrounded by land, p. 376

insurgent A person who rebels against his or her government, p. 706

intensive farming Farming that requires a great deal of labor, p. 644

International Monetary Fund (IMF) An agency of the United Nations that provides loans to countries for development projects, p. 553

irrigation The watering of farmland with water drawn from reservoirs or rivers, pp. 223, 621

isthmus (is´məs) A narrow strip of land having water on each side and joining two larger bodies of land, p. 237

J

joint family system In India, the custom of housing all members of an extended family together, p. 616

K

krill Small, shrimplike creatures; food for whales and fish, p. 735

L

lagoon A shallow body of water separated from the sea by coral reefs or sandbars, p. 720

land degradation Reduction in the productive potential of the land, p. 516

land redistribution A policy by which land is taken from those who own large amounts and redistributed to those who have little or none, pp. 229, 583

landlocked Almost or entirely surrounded by land; cut off from the sea, p. 544

landslide A sudden drop of a mass of land on a mountainside or hillside, p. 245

latifundio (lat´ə fun´dē ō) A large commercial farm owned by a private individual or a farming company, p. 229

lava Magma, or molten rock from the earth's mantle, that breaks through the surface of the earth during volcanic activity, p. 360

leaching The dissolving and washing away of nutrients in the soil, p. 516

leeward Facing away from the wind, p. 247

life expectancy The number of years an individual is expected to live as determined by statistics, p. 384

light industry The production of small consumer goods such as clothing and appliances, p. 657

lignite A soft, brownish-black coal, p. 334

literacy The ability to read and write, p. 134

lithosphere The surface features of the earth, including soil, rocks, and landforms, p. 45

llano A grassy plain, p. 269

loam Soil that is a mixture of clay, silt, and sand, p. 421

lock An enclosed section of a canal, in which a ship may be raised or lowered by raising or lowering the level of the water in that section, p. 183

loess (lō´es´) Fine-grained, mineral-rich loam, dust, or silt deposited by the wind, p. 55

M

malnutrition Disease caused by a lack of food or an unbalanced diet, pp. 567, 623

mandate A commission from the League of Nations authorizing a nation to govern a territory, p. 471

mangrove A tropical tree that grows in swampy ground along coastal areas, p. 162

mantle A thick layer of mostly solid rock beneath the earth's crust that surrounds the earth's core, p. 44

maquiladora (mä kē´lə dôr´ə) A factory in Mexico, along the United States border, that assembles goods for export, p. 231

maritime Bordering on or near the sea; relating to navigation or shipping, p. 181

market economy An economic system in which decisions about production, price, and other economic factors are determined by the law of supply and demand, pp. 104, 216

martial law The law administered during a period of strict military control, p. 658

maternal mortality The number of women who died due to pregnancy and childbirth complications per 100,000 live births, p. 384

mechanical weathering The actual breaking up or physical weakening of rock by forces such as ice and roots, p. 52

medina The old section of a North African city, usually centered around a mosque, p. 534

megalopolis (meg´ə läp´ə lis) A very large city; a region made up of several large cities and their surrounding areas, considered to be a single urban complex, p. 159

mercenary A professional soldier hired by a foreign country, p. 558

mestizo (me stē´zō) A person of mixed European and Native American heritage, p. 212

metropolitan area A major city and its surrounding suburbs, p. 148

migrant worker A worker who travels from place to place, working where extra help is needed to cultivate or harvest crops, p. 229

militarism The glorification of the military and a readiness for war, p. 689

militia A citizen army, p. 484

minaret A tall, slender tower attached to a mosque, p. 446

mixed economy A system combining different degrees of government regulation, pp. 105, 320

monarchy A system of authoritarian government headed by a monarch—a king, queen, shah, or sultan—whose position is usually inherited, p. 103

monotheism The belief in one God, p. 438

monsoon A seasonal shift in the prevailing winds that influences large climate regions, p. 594

moor Broad, treeless, rolling land, often poorly drained and having patches of marsh and peat bog, p. 310

moraine (mə rān´) A ridgelike mass of rock, gravel, sand, and clay carried and deposited by a glacier, p. 56

mosque An Islamic place of religious worship, p. 446

muezzin (myo͞o ez´in) In Islam, a crier who calls the faithful to prayer five times each day from a minaret, p. 446

mulatto (mə lät´ō) A person of mixed African and European ancestry, pp. 212, 268

multiethnic Composed of many ethnic groups, p. 380

multiplier effect The effect an investment has in multiplying related jobs throughout the economy, p. 399

N

NAFTA North American Free Trade Agreement, which phased out trade barriers among the United States, Canada, and Mexico, pp. 194, 230

national identity A people's sense of what makes them a nation, p. 389

nationalism Pride in one's nation; the desire of a cultural group to rule themselves as a separate nation, pp. 457, 607

nationalize To bring a business under state control, p. 330

natural resource A material in the natural environment that people value and use to satisfy their needs, p. 109

navigable Deep and wide enough to allow the passage of ships, p. 349

neutral Not taking sides in a war, p. 342

nomad A person who travels from place to place, p. 448

nomadic herding The practice of moving flocks to different pastures throughout the year, p. 516

nonaligned nation A nation that adopted neutrality during the Cold War, p. 590

nonrenewable resource A natural resource that cannot be replaced once it is used, p. 109

nonviolent resistance The policy of opposing an enemy or oppressor by any means other than violence, p. 608

nuclear energy A type of energy produced by fission— the splitting of uranium atoms in a nuclear reactor, releasing stored energy, p. 111

O

oral history History passed down by word of mouth, p. 514

ore A rocky material containing a valuable mineral, p. 308

organic matter Matter derived from living plants and animals and their remains, p. 420

outback Remote, sparsely settled, arid, rural country, especially the central and western plains and plateaus of Australia, p. 721

ozone layer A band of ozone gas in the atmosphere that absorbs the sun's harmful ultraviolet rays, p. 75

P

pack ice Floating sea ice formed by a mix of icebergs with other ice formed in superchilled ocean waters, p. 735

paddy Irrigated or flooded land on which rice is grown, p. 703

pampas A grasslands region in Argentina and Uruguay, pp. 206, 279, 578

páramo (par´ə mo´) A plateau in the Andes of Ecuador, p. 273

partition A division into separate parts, p. 609

peat Spongy material containing waterlogged and decaying mosses and plants, sometimes dried and used as fuel, p. 315

peninsula A strip of land that juts out into an ocean, p. 221

per capita Per person, p. 138

perception A viewpoint that is influenced by one's own culture and experiences, p. 41

perceptual region A group of places that is defined by people's feelings and attitudes, p. 41

perennial irrigation An irrigation system that provides necessary water to the land throughout the year, p. 527

perestroika (pər´ə stroi´kə) In the former Soviet Union, a policy of economic restructuring, p. 425

perishable good A product that does not stay fresh for long, p. 343

permafrost A layer of soil just below the earth's surface that stays permanently frozen, pp. 82, 418

photosynthesis The process by which plants make food from carbon dioxide and release oxygen, p. 74

piedmont A region of rolling foothills, p. 278

plankton Microscopic floating organisms, p. 724

plantation A large estate farmed by many workers, p. 260

plateau An area of high, flat land, pp. 221, 508

plate tectonics The theory that the earth's outer shell is composed of a number of large, unanchored plates, or slabs of rock, whose constant movement explains earthquakes and volcanic activity, p. 46

plume A very hot spot in the earth's mantle, p. 361

poaching Illegal hunting, p. 444

polder An area of low-lying land that has been reclaimed from the sea, p. 337

population density The average number of people living in a given area, pp. 87, 518

potash (pät´ash´) A mineral used in explosives and fertilizer, p. 476

prairie A temperate grassland characterized by a great variety of grasses, pp. 81, 578

precipitation All the forms of water that fall to earth from the atmosphere, including rain and snow, p. 67

predator An animal that feeds upon other animals, p. 198

prevailing westerlies The constant flow of air from west to east in the temperate zones of the earth, p. 292

primary economic activity An economic activity that takes or uses natural resources directly, such as fishing or mining, p. 115

privatization The process of selling government-owned industries and businesses to private owners, p. 394

proliferation An increase in the number of something, p. 696

protectorate An area that has its own government but is controlled by an outside power, p. 438

province A territory governed as a political division of a country, p. 181

provisional government A temporary government pending permanent arrangements, p. 672

purdah (pʉr´də) The practice among Hindu and Muslim women of covering the face with a veil when outside the home, p. 616

pyrethrum A pesticide produced from certain flowers, p. 567

Q

quaternary economic activity An economic activity that focuses on the acquisition, processing, and sharing of information, such as education or research, p. 117

quota A fixed quantity, p. 692

R

rain shadow An area of reduced rainfall on the leeward side of high mountains, pp. 68, 130

recession An extended decline in business activity, p. 330

refugee A person who flees his or her country to escape danger or unfair treatment, p. 544

regolith Weathered rock, p. 420

reincarnation The belief that the soul of a human being or animal goes through a series of births, deaths, and rebirths, p. 614

relative location The position of a place in relation to another place, p. 39

relief The differences in elevation, or height, of the landforms in any particular area, p. 45

Renaissance The revival of art, literature, and learning that took place in Europe during the fourteenth, fifteenth, and sixteenth centuries, pp. 288, 357

renewable resource A natural resource that the environment continues to supply or replace as it is used, p. 109

reparation Money paid for war damages, p. 332

reservoir A natural or artificial lake used to collect water for human needs, p. 527

revolution One complete orbit of the earth around the sun. The earth completes one revolution every $365\frac{1}{4}$ days, or one year, p. 64

Ring of Fire A ring of volcanic mountains surrounding the Pacific Ocean, p. 49

rotation The spinning motion of the earth, like a top on its axis, as it travels through space, p. 64

ruble The currency of Russia, p. 430

rural Of, or characteristic of, the countryside, p. 90

Sahel The region in Africa just south of the Sahara, p. 506

sanction An action taken by the international community to punish a country for unacceptable behaviors, p. 575

sandstorm A windstorm that blows hot air, dust, and grit, p. 524

sari A brightly colored cloth, worn by many Indian women, that is draped over the body like a long dress, p. 616

savanna A tropical grassland with scattered trees, located in the warm lands near the Equator, pp. 81, 512, 578

scavenger An animal that eats the remains of animals that have died or been killed, p. 579

sea stack A pillar of rock formed over time by wave action and erosion, p. 465

secede To withdraw formally from membership in a political or religious organization, p. 191

secondary economic activity An economic activity in which people use raw materials to produce or manufacture new products of greater value, p. 116

secular Worldly, not relating to religion, p. 497

sediment Particles of soil, sand, and gravel carried and deposited by wind or water, pp. 54, 464

segregation The separation of the races, p. 575

seismic activity Earthquakes and volcanic eruptions, p. 354

seismic wave Vibration caused by movement of tectonic plates, p. 245

seismograph An instrument that measures and records movement in the earth's crust, p. 682

self-determination The right of a people to decide their own political future, p. 472

selva (sel´və) A forested region in Ecuador, Peru, and Bolivia, p. 273

separatism A movement to win political, religious, or ethnic independence from another group, p. 190

sertão (ser tī ō) An interior plateau in Brazil with poor soil and uncertain rain, p. 255

shah The title of the former ruler of Iran, p. 498

shifting agriculture The practice of farming a site until the soil is exhausted, then moving on to a new site, p. 543

sinkhole A hole formed when limestone is dissolved, causing the land above to collapse, p. 224

sirocco A hot, dry wind from northern Africa, p. 350

soil The thin layer of loose material in which plants grow, p. 420

soil creep The process by which soil moves gradually and constantly downhill because of gravity, p. 420

soil horizon Each distinct layer that forms as soil develops, p. 420

solar energy Energy produced by the sun, p. 111

solstice Either of the two times a year when the sun appears directly overhead at the Tropics of Cancer and Capricorn, p. 65

souk A market in an Arab community, p. 534

sovereignty A country's freedom and power to decide on policies and actions, p. 101

soviet In the former Soviet Union, any one of various governing councils, p. 423

sphere of influence An area or country that is politically and economically dominated by, though not directly governed by, another country, p. 651

standard of living A person's or group's level of material well-being, as measured by education, housing, health care, and nutrition, p. 136

steppe (step) A temperate grassland found in Europe and Asia, pp. 378, 417, 578

storm surge A wall of water that overwhelms coastal regions when a tropical storm strikes land, p. 627

strategic value Importance of a place or thing for nations planning military actions, p. 569

striations Marks characterizing glaciated areas of rocks, p. 128

strip mining The process whereby miners strip away the surface of the earth to lay bare the mineral deposits, p. 345

structural adjustment program A program to reform the structure of an economy, p. 553

subcontinent A large landmass forming a distinct part of a continent, p. 592

subsidence A geological phenomenon in which the ground in an area sinks, p. 356

subsistence economy *See* **traditional economy**

subsistence farming Farming that provides only enough for the needs of a family or a village, pp. 116, 229

suburb A residential area outside a central city, p. 134

sultanate A state ruled by a sultan, p. 590

summit The highest point of a mountain or similar elevation, p. 290

Sunbelt The southern and southwestern states of the United States, from the Carolinas to southern California, characterized by a warm climate and, recently, rapid population growth, p. 164

taiga Thinly scattered, coniferous forests found in Europe and Asia, pp. 378, 416

tariff A tax imposed by a government on imported goods, pp. 194, 692

telecommunication Communication by electronic means, p. 146

terrace In farming, a flat, narrow ledge of land, usually constructed in hilly areas to increase the amount of arable land, p. 644

tertiary economic activity An economic activity in which people do not directly gather or process raw materials but pursue activities that serve others; service industry, pp. 117, 309

theocrat Someone who claims to rule by religious or divine authority, p. 663

timber line The boundary in high elevations above which continuous forest vegetation cannot grow, p. 273

tornado A funnel-shaped cloud of violently rotating air, p. 627

totalitarianism A system of government in which a central authority controls all aspects of society, p. 103

trade deficit The situation in which a country imports more than it exports, p. 450

trade surplus The situation in which a country exports more than it imports, p. 450

traditional economy An economic system in which families produce goods and services for their own use, with little surplus and exchange of goods; also known as a subsistence economy, pp. 103, 217

tributary A river or stream that flows into a main river, p. 128

tropical cyclone A storm that originates over a tropical ocean and whirls around a low-pressure center, p. 627

tropical storm A storm with winds of at least 39 miles (63 km) per hour, p. 208

troposphere The layer of the atmosphere closest to land, p. 74

trust territory A dependent colony or territory supervised by another country by commission of the United Nations, p. 731

tsunami (tsoō nä´mē) A huge wave caused primarily by a disturbance beneath the ocean, such as an earthquake or a volcanic eruption, pp. 244, 364

tundra A region where temperatures are always cool or cold and only specialized plants can grow, pp. 82, 172, 378, 416

typhoon A destructive tropical storm that forms over the Pacific Ocean, pp. 613, 683

U

unitary system A system of government in which one central government holds most of the political power, p. 102

urbanization The growth of city populations, p. 90

velvet revolution A revolution without bloodshed, which took place in Czechoslovakia during the late 1980s, p. 394

villagization A political movement by which rural people are forced to move to towns and work on collective farms, p. 572

volcano An opening in the earth's crust from which molten rock escapes to the surface, p. 360

W

wadi (wä´dē) A usually dry riverbed or gully that temporarily holds water from a sudden downpour, pp. 464, 531

warlord A local leader with a military following, p. 652

water power Energy produced from falling water to move machinery or generate electricity, p. 111

watershed A dividing ridge between two basins, p. 557

weather The condition of the bottom layer of the earth's atmosphere in one place over a short period of time, p. 63

weathering The chemical or mechanical process by which rock is gradually broken down, eventually becoming soil, p. 52

white flight The departure of white people from a region, p. 581

wind Air in motion, p. 626

windward Facing the wind, p. 247

World Bank An agency of the United Nations that provides loans to countries for development projects, p. 553

yurt A round tent made of a wooden framework and covered with felt or skins, p. 462

Zionist A member of a movement known as Zionism, founded to promote the establishment of an independent Jewish state, p. 472

Glossary

SPANISH GLOSSARY

A

abdicate/abdicar Renunciar a un cargo, trono o autoridad, págs. 423, 652

aborigine/aborigen Persona originario del lugar donde vive; término que se refiere a los habitantes autóctonos de Australia, pág. 717

absolute location/ubicación absoluta Lugar exacto donde se encuentra algo en la Tierra, pág. 39

acid rain/lluvia ácida Lluvia cuya alta concentración de substancias químicas, generalmente producidas por la contaminación industrial, contamina el agua, destruye las plantas y los animales, y desgasta las superficies rocosas; tipo de meteorización química, págs. 53, 382

acupuncture/acupuntura Práctica de introducir agujas finas en partes determinadas del cuerpo para curar enfermedades o calmar el dolor, pág. 669

aftershock/temblor secundario Movimiento de tierra que ocurre después de un terremoto, pág. 245

agricultural revolution/revolución agrícola Paso de la economía de caza y recolección entre los pueblos nómadas a la agricultura y los asentamientos permanentes, ocurrido hacia el año 8000 a. de C., pág. 438

alluvial plain/llano aluvial Gran extensión de terreno a lo largo de las riberas de los ríos, compuesta de tierra fértil que acarrea el agua de las inundaciones, pág. 592

altiplano/altiplano Término que se refiere a las mesetas que se encuentran en los Andes de Bolivia y Perú, pág. 273

anarchy/anarquía Desorden político y violencia; carencia de leyes, pág. 484

ancestor worship/culto a los antepasados Creencia según la cual el respeto y las ceremonias dedicadas a los antepasados hacen que éstos sigan viviendo en el mundo de los espíritus después de la muerte, pág. 550

animism/animismo Creencia religiosa según la cual dioses o espíritus se encuentran en objetos o lugares tales como el cielo, los ríos y los árboles, pág. 550

annex/anexar Incorporar formalmente al territorio de un país o estado el territorio de otro, págs. 126, 407

apartheid/apartheid Régimen político de la República de Sudáfrica que estaba basado en una estricta segregación racial, pág. 575

aqueduct/acueducto Tubería o canal de grandes dimensiones que sirve para transportar agua a gran distancia, pág. 174

archipelago/archipiélago Grupo de islas, pág. 246

artesian well/pozo artesiano Foso cavado a suficiente profundidad para perforar una capa de material poroso lleno de agua subterránea, pág. 723

atheism/ateísmo La creencia de que Dios no existe, pág. 668

atmosphere/atmósfera La capa de gases, vapor de agua y otras substancias que envuelve a la Tierra, pág. 45

atoll/atolón Isla de coral en forma de anillo con una laguna interior, pág. 725

authoritarian/autoritario Sistema de gobierno en el que los dirigentes imponen su poder de forma absoluta, pág. 103

autonomous region/región autónoma Unidad política con poderes limitados para gobernase a sí misma, pág. 664

autonomy/autonomía Independencia, pág. 406

avalanche/alud Masa de hielo y nieve que se derrumba súbitamente, pág. 245

ayatollah/ayatolá Líder religioso entre los musulmanes chiítas, pág. 498

B

balkanize/balcanizar Fragmentarse en pequeñas unidades políticas enfrentadas entre sí, como ocurrió en los Balcanes después de la Segunda Guerra Mundial, pág. 398

barbarian/bárbaro Persona de costumbres rudas, inculta y grosera, pág. 702

barter/trueque Intercambio de bienes sin la intervención del dinero, pág. 559

basin irrigation/cuenca de irrigación En Egipto, un sistema para irrigar las tierras de cultivo mediante el cual se controlaban el agua y los sedimentos con muros de contención y se dejaban correr durante lapsos precisos, pág. 527

bauxite/bauxita Mineral utilizado en la producción de aluminio, pág. 268

bayou/bayou Entrada o salida cenagosa de un río o lago, pág. 162

bazaar/bazar Mercado al aire libre, pág. 524

bedrock/lecho de rocas Las rocas sólidas que yacen inmediatamente debajo de la superficie terrestre, pág. 184

bioluminescence/bioluminiscencia Proceso por el cual algunos peces y otros organismos emiten luz, pág. 724

biome/bioma Término para referirse a los principales ecosistemas que hay en las diversas regiones del mundo, pág. 77

biosphere/biosfera El mundo de las plantas, animales y otros seres vivos que habitan los medios terrestres y acuáticos de la Tierra, pág. 45

birthrate/índice de natalidad Número de personas nacidas en un año por cada 1,000 habitantes, pág. 89

black market/mercado negro Tráfico de productos y servicios por medios no autorizados, pág. 430

blight/añublo Enfermedad de las plantas de cereales, pág. 316

blizzard/ventisca Borrasca de nieve acompañada de fuertes vientos, pág. 627

bog/tremedal Zona de suelos húmedos de consistencia blanda, pág. 310

boycott/boicotear Rehusar a comprar a consumir un producto o servicio en señal de desaprobación, pág. 608

buffer/zona de amortiguación Zona protectora entre dos países, pág. 672

buffer state/estado amortiguador País que separa dos países enemigos, pág. 622

bullet train/tren bala Tren de alta velocidad, pág. 646

C

campesino/**campesino** Término que se refiere a la persona que trabaja y vive en el campo en América Latina, pág. 270

canal/canal Vía navegable artificial, pág. 145

canopy/bóveda Capa superior del bosque formada por las copas de los árboles que se juntan, pág. 210

canton/cantón División política o estado; cada una de las divisiones administrativas de Suiza, pág. 342

canyon/cañón Valle profundo de paredes verticales, producto de la erosión del agua del río, pág. 465

capital/capital Bienes en forma de dinero o propiedades que se tienen o se usan en los negocios, pág. 529

caravan/caravana Grupo grande de mercaderes que se unen para viajar con seguridad, pág. 532

carnivore/carnívoro Animal que se alimenta de carne, págs. 81, 578

cash crop/cultivo comercial Cultivo cuya finalidad es vender los productos y obtener ganancias, pág. 229

caste system/sistema de castas Jerarquía social determinada por nacimiento, en la que una persona tiene un rango específico dentro de la sociedad, pág. 614

caudillo/**caudillo** Término que se refiere a un dictador militar en América Latina, pág. 204

cay/cayo Pequeña isla rasa o arrecife de coral, pág. 206

cede/ceder Transferir, dejar de ofrecer resistencia, pág. 126

chaparral/chaparral Tipo de vegetación adaptada a los climas mediterráneos; pequeños árboles y arbustos bajitos de hojas perennes, págs. 80, 444, 512

character of a place/carácter de un lugar Características físicas y humanas que distinguen a un lugar y lo hacen único, pág. 40

charpoy/*charpoy* Cama que consiste en un marco de madera con cuerdas anudadas en vez de colchón, pág. 615

chemical weathering/meteorización química Proceso de alteración de la estructura química de la roca que se desintegra por acción del agua y el dióxido de carbono, pág. 53

chernozem/chernozem Suelo superficial negro de las estepas rusas y otras tierras de pastoreo, págs. 417, 461

civil war/guerra civil Conflicto entre grupos enemigos de un mismo país, pág. 126

civilization/civilización Cultura avanzada, pág. 438

climate/clima Término que se refiere a los patrones del tiempo atmosférico que se dan en una región durante un largo período, pág. 63

cloud/nube Masa de partículas diminutas de agua y polvo que flota en la atmósfera, pág. 74

collective farm/granja colectiva Granja del gobierno, administrada por los trabajadores, quienes se reparten las ganancias obtenidas de los productos agrícolas, pág. 395

colonialism/colonialismo Sistema por el cual los países fundaban colonias para apropiarse de fuentes de materia prima y de mercados para sus productos, pág. 506

colony/colonia Territorio separado, pero al mismo tiempo sujeto a una potencia gobernante, pág. 126

columnar rock/roca columnar Roca volcánica que se fracciona en columnas cuando la lava se enfría, pág. 360

command economy/economía centralizada Sistema económico controlado por un único gobierno central, págs. 104, 216, 423

commercial farming/agricultura comercial Explotación agrícola y cría de ganado para la venta en mercados externos, pág. 116

commercial industry/industria comercial Producción a gran escala que emplea a muchas personas y genera gran cantidad de productos, pág. 117

communism/comunismo Sistema de gobierno en el que es el gobierno quien controla los medios de producción, decide qué artículos se producen, cuánto devengan los trabajadores y cuánto cuestan los productos, pág. 372

compulsory/forzoso Obligatorio, pág. 300

concession/concesión Privilegio o exención que otorga un gobierno, pág. 634

confederation/confederación Sistema de gobierno basado en unidades políticas autónomas que dan poderes limitados a un gobierno central, págs. 102, 331

coniferous/conífero Que produce conos; tipo de árbol capaz de sobrevivir largos y fríos inviernos, y que tiene agujas largas y finas en vez de hojas, págs. 80, 198

conquistador/conquistador Término que se asocia con los exploradores españoles que ocuparon tierras en América y las declararon propiedad de España, pág. 204

continent/continente Cada una de las siete grandes extensiones de tierra firme que hay en nuestro planeta: África, Antártida, Asia, Australia, Europa, América del Norte y América del Sur, pág. 45

continental climate/clima continental Clima propio de las grandes regiones centrales de los continentes del hemisferio Norte; se caracteriza por tener inviernos fríos con nieve y veranos templados o calurosos, pág. 69

continental divide/divisoria continental Línea de división o zona de tierras altas que separa ríos que fluyen en direcciones opuestas en un continente, pág. 128

continental drift theory/teoría de la deriva de los continentes Teoría según la cual las masas continentales se desplazan lentamente debido al movimiento de las placas tectónicas sobre las que yacen, pág. 47

convergence zone/zona de convergencia Área de fuertes tormentas donde convergen las heladas aguas que bordean la Antártida y corrientes cálidas de los océanos Atlántico, Pacífico e Índico, pág. 735

coral/coral Esqueletos calcáreos de minúsculos animales marinos, pág. 206

coral island/isla de coral Isla formada por los restos de esqueletos de minúsculos animales marinos y por la arena y el sedimento que se acumulan encima de éstos, pág. 247

cordillera/cordillera Cadena de montañas enlazadas entre sí, pág. 270

core/núcleo Centro de la Tierra, compuesto de metal sumamente caliente, que es denso y sólido en la parte más interna y fundido, o en estado líquido, en la más externa, pág. 44

cottage industry/industria casera Actividades de producción en pequeña escala que requieren de poca tecnología, por lo general ubicadas en casas particulares o cerca de ellas, págs. 116, 618

coup/golpe de estado Derrocamiento súbito de un gobernante o un gobierno, generalmente por medios violentos o con la amenaza de usar medios violentos, pág. 548

crater lake/laguna de cráter Masa de agua que ocupa una depresión en la boca de un volcán extinto o inactivo, pág. 361

crevasse/fisura Grieta profunda en hielo glaciar, pág. 735

crust/corteza Capa sólida y rocosa que constituye la superficie de la Tierra, pág. 44

cultural convergence/convergencia cultural Contacto e interacción de una cultura con otra, págs. 97, 204

cultural diffusion/adopción cultural Proceso por el cual un grupo de gente adquiere las costumbres de otro grupo, pág. 288

cultural divergence/divergencia cultural La oposición de una cultura a influencias externas, págs. 98, 316

culture/cultura Modo de vida que caracteriza a un pueblo, por ejemplo, su gobierno, lenguaje, religión, costumbres y creencias, pág. 87

culture hearth/foco de cultura Lugar donde nacen ideas importantes que más tarde se difunden a otras culturas vecinas, pág. 90

customs/derechos de aduana Pago de impuestos que impone un gobierno sobre los artículos importados, pág. 193

cyclone/ciclón Fuerte vendaval, como un torbellino, pág. 721

czar/zar Emperador de Rusia, pág. 422

D

decentralize/descentralizar Transferir el poder del gobierno central a pequeñas regiones, pág. 338

decidouos/caducifolio De hoja caduca; tipo de árbol que pierde las hojas durante una estación, pág. 79

deforestation/deforestación Proceso de despojar árboles y plantas de un terreno, págs. 262, 544, 625

delta/delta Terreno de la desembocadura de algunos ríos formado con la tierra que depositan las aguas al penetrar el mar, pág. 523

demilitarized zone/zona desmilitarizada Franja de terreno donde no se admite la presencia de tropas o armamento, pág. 694

democracy/democracia Sistema de gobierno en el que los ciudadanos tienen el poder de elegir a sus gobernantes y decidir las políticas del gobierno, pág. 103

desalination/desalinización Proceso de eliminar la sal del agua del mar para aprovecharla como agua potable y en irrigación, págs. 448, 488

desertification/desertización Transformación de tierras arables en desiertos debido a procesos naturales o por la intervención humana, págs. 463, 544

dialect/dialecto Variedad de una lengua que se da en una región o comunidad determinada, pág. 329

dictatorship/dictadura Sistema de gobierno en el que un pequeño grupo o una persona retienen el poder absoluto, pág. 103

diffusion/difusión Proceso por el cual se transmite un elemento cultural de un grupo o individuo a otro, pág. 97

dike/dique Estructura construida para controlar el nivel y el recorrido del agua, pág. 337

diversify/diversificar Aumentar la variedad, pág. 408

doi moi/doi moi Reforma económica iniciada en Vietnam en 1986, pág. 710

domestication/*domesticación* Proceso de entrenamiento y crianza de animales para beneficio de los humanos, pág. 372

double cropping/cultivo doble En agricultura, cultivar más de una cosecha al año en el mismo terreno, pág. 661

downsize/reducción de plantilla Despido de empleados para reducir los costos, pág. 691

drainage basin/cuenca hidrográfica Región que es bañada por un río importante y sus tributarios, pág. 128

drip irrigation/riego por goteo Proceso de irrigación mediante un sistema de goteo por tubos, que hacen llegar el agua directamente a las plantas; de este modo se preservan los escasos recurso de agua en las zonas áridas, pág. 476

dry farming/cultivo seco Técnica de cultivo en la que se deja de sembrar la tierra cada año o cada dos años para acumular humedad, pág. 350

E

earthquake/terremoto Sacudimiento del suelo causado por movimientos súbitos de la corteza terrestre, pág. 244

ecosystem/ecosistema La interacción entre las formas de vida vegetal y animal y el entorno físico donde viven, pág. 77

ecotourism/ecoturismo Turismo cuya finalidad es crear una conciencia sobre el medio ambiente y causar un mínimo impacto en el ecosistema, pág. 263

ejido/ejido Campo que pertenece a todos los integrantes de una comunidad rural, pág. 229

El Niño/El Niño Corriente marina templada de la costa noroeste de América del Sur que influye en los patrones del tiempo atmosférico a nivel global, pág. 208

embankment dam/muro de contención Muro de tierra y roca para contener el agua, pág. 621

embargo/embargo Restricción severa al comercio con otros países, pág. 486

emigrant/emigrante Persona que deja un país para vivir en otro, pág. 89

enclave/enclave Territorio rodeado completamente por otro país, pág. 580

entrepreneur/empresario Persona con iniciativa que funda y desarrolla un negocio, pág. 339

epicenter/epicentro Punto de la superficie terrestre situado directamente encima del foco de un terremoto, pág. 245

equinox/equinoccio Uno de los dos días del año (primavera y otoño) en que el día es igual de largo que la noche en toda la Tierra, pág. 65

erosion/erosión Desgaste y desplazamiento de materiales de la superficie terrestre, como piedras, suelo y arena, producto generalmente de la acción del agua, el viento y los glaciares, págs. 54, 464

escarpment/escarpa Declive pronunciado que separa dos áreas planas de distinta altitud, págs. 255, 508

estuary/estuario La desembocadura ancha de un río donde se juntan corrientes de agua dulce con el agua de mar, pág. 278

ethnic group/grupo étnico Grupo de personas que comparten elementos tales como la cultura, el lenguaje y la religión, pág. 380

ethnocracy/etnocracia Sistema de gobierno en el que un grupo étnico domina a los otros, pág. 571

Eurasia/Eurasia Nombre que algunos geógrafos proponen para referirse a la masa terrestre que comprende Europa y Asia, pág. 374

euro/euro Moneda de las naciones integrantes de la Unión Europea, pág. 298

exodus/éxodo Emigración en masa de la población de una región o país, pág. 675

export/producto de exportación Artículo enviado al extranjero para su venta, pág. 117

F

falaj **system/sistema** *falaj* En la península de Arabia, antiguo sistema de canales de agua subterráneos y superficiales, pág. 492

fall line/línea geográfica de descenso Línea imaginaria entre los montes Apalaches y la llanura costera del Atlántico, donde se forman cascadas y rápidos al descender los ríos y arroyos de las altas elevaciones a la llanura costera, pág. 163

favela/favela Barrios de extrema pobreza en las ciudades de Brasil, pág. 256

federation/federación Estructura de gobierno en la que el gobierno nacional retiene ciertos poderes y otros poderes se reservan a los gobiernos locales, pág. 102

fellaheen/felás Campesinos egipcios, pág. 523

fertile/fértil Capacidad de producir en abundancia, pág. 305

Fertile Crescent/Medialuna de las Tierras Fértiles Región del Oriente Medio donde nacieron la agricultura y las primeras civilizaciones, pág. 482

fjord/fiordo Valle formado originalmente por el avance de un glaciar y lleno del agua derretida de los glaciares, pág. 318

forage/forraje Comida para ganado, pág. 544

formal region/región formal Grupo de lugares que tienen atributos semejantes, por ejemplo, una región política, pág. 41

fossil fuel/combustible fósil Cualquiera de los recursos minerales no renovables formados a partir de los restos de plantas y animales de otras eras y aprovechados como combustible, pág. 109

free enterprise/libre empresa Sistema económico que permite a cada individuo poseer, operar y obtener ganancias de su propio negocio en un mercado abierto y competitivo, pág. 147

front/frente Límite entre dos masas de aire de distinta densidad y temperatura, pág. 68

functional region/región funcional Grupo de lugares vinculados por un flujo o movimiento, por ejemplo, la región bañada por el río Amazonas y sus tributarios, pág. 41

fundamentalism/fundamentalismo Creencias religiosas basadas en una interpretación estricta de un texto sagrado, pág. 461

G

gasohol/gasoil Combustible mezcla de gasolina y etanol, pág. 261

gaucho/gaucho Vaquero de las pampas de Argentina y Uruguay, pág. 279

GDP per capita/PIB per cápita El valor total de los productos y servicios producidos en un país durante un año, dividido por la población total del país, pág. 216

genocide/genocidio Destrucción intencional de un pueblo, pág. 457

geography/geografía Estudio de la superficie de la Tierra y de los procesos que le dan forma, las conexiones entre los lugares y las relaciones entre la población y el medio ambiente, pág. 35

geothermal energy/energía geotérmica Energía producida por el intenso calor de las entrañas de la Tierra, págs. 111, 319

geyser/géiser Fuente termal natural de la que surte una columna de agua y vapor, pág. 726

ghetto/gueto Zona de una ciudad donde vive marginada una minoría, pág. 390

GIS/SIG Sistema de información geográfica, un sistema computarizado que reúne y analiza datos referentes a la superficie terrestre a fin de resolver problemas geográficos, pág. 37

glacier/glaciar Masa enorme de hielo y nieve que se desplaza lentamente, págs. 56, 465

glasnost/glasnost Política de apertura introducida en la Unión Soviética a finales de la década de 1980, pág. 425

glen/cañada Valle angosto, pág. 311

graben/graben Fosa larga y angosta que se abre entre dos fallas, pág. 362

grain elevator/silo de cereales Edificio alto equipado con maquinaria para cargar, limpiar, almacenar y descargar granos, pág. 169

grain exchange/bolsa de cereales Lugar donde se compran y venden cereales como productos de mercancía, pág. 169

gross domestic product (GDP)/producto interno bruto (PIB) El valor total de los productos y servicios producidos en un país durante un año, que incluye la producción total de las compañías extranjeras en el país y excluye la producción total de las compañías nacionales en el extranjero, pág. 118

gross national product (GNP)/producto nacional bruto (PNB) El valor total de los productos y servicios de un país, que incluye la producción total de las compañías nacionales en países extranjeros y excluye la producción total de las compañías extranjeras en el país, pág. 143

growing season/temporada de cultivo En agricultura, el promedio de días comprendidos entre la última helada de la primavera y la primera helada del otoño, pág. 167

guerrilla/guerrillero Integrante de un grupo armado independiente compuesto por civiles, no por soldados del ejército, pág. 241

H

hacienda/hacienda Una propiedad española de gran extensión en las Américas, dirigida normalmente como finca agrícola o ganadera, pág. 228

harambee/harambee Política de cooperación adoptada en Kenya después de la independencia para estimular el desarrollo económico, pág. 567

hemisphere/hemisferio Mitad de la superficie de la esfera terrestre; el ecuador divide el hemisferio norte del hemisferio sur; el meridiano de Greenwich divide el hemisferio oriental del hemisferio occidental, pág. 39

herbivore/herbívoro Animal que se alimenta de plantas, págs. 81, 578

heterogeneity/heterogeneidad La falta de semejanza, pág. 710

hibernation/hibernación Estado latente en el que las funciones del organismo de un animal disminuyen hasta un mínimo grado, pág. 199

hierarchy/jerarquía Rango o categoría de acuerdo a la función, pág. 151

hinterland/interior (de un país) zona que está bajo la influencia de una metrópolis, pág. 151

Holocaust/Holocausto La ejecución de 6 millones de judíos en campos de concentración nazis durante la Segunda Guerra Mundial, pág. 390

homogeneous/homogéneo De naturaleza semejante; de estructura o calidad uniforme, pág. 685

hub/centro de labores Punto central de actividades e influencia concentrada, pág. 351

humus/humus Material orgánico formado cuando plantas y animales que viven en la tierra mueren y se descomponen, págs. 167, 420

hurricane/huracán Tormenta devastadora que se forma en el océano, generalmente a fines del verano o a comienzos del otoño, con fuertes vientos que soplan como mínimo a 74 millas (119 km) por hora, pág. 208

hydroelectric power/potencia hidroeléctrica Electricidad generada por la fuerza del agua, pág. 620

hydrosphere/hidrosfera El agua de todos los océanos, lagos y ríos y las fuentes subterráneas de nuestro planeta, pág. 45

hydrothermal vent/fisura hidrotérmica Grieta en el suelo oceánico de la cual mana agua caliente rica en minerales, pág. 725

I

ice shelf/capa de hielo polar Masa espesa de hielo glacial que se forma en las costas polares y que puede medir cientos de millas de largo, pág. 735

ideogram/ideograma En la lengua escrita, un carácter o símbolo que representa una idea o cosa, pág. 667

immigrant/inmigrante Persona que llega a un país que no es el suyo para establecerse, pág. 89

import/producto de importación Artículo introducido a un país para su venta, pág. 117

Impressionism/impresionismo Movimiento artístico en el que los pintores trataban de plasmar las impresiones visuales producidas por el color, la luz y las sombras, pág. 329

indigenous/indígena Originario de un país, zona o medio ambiente, pág. 704

Industrial Revolution/Revolución Industrial Cambio que se dio en el sistema de producción del trabajo manual a la mecanización, págs. 126, 288

infant mortality/mortalidad infantil El número de niños que mueren en el primer año de vida de cada 1,000 nacimientos, pág. 384

inflation/inflación Alza acentuada y generalizada de los precios, pág. 332

infrastructure/infraestructura Conjunto de bienes y servicios básicos necesarios para el funcionamiento de un país, como carreteras, puentes, centrales de energía y escuelas, págs. 245, 490

inhabitable/habitable Capacidad de acoger a residentes permanentes, pág. 364

inland delta/delta interior Zona de lagos, riachuelos y pantanos lejos del mar, pág. 545

inland sea/mar interior Mar rodeado casi por completo de superficie terrestre, pág. 376

insurgent/insurgente Persona que se subleva contra su gobierno, pág. 706

intensive farming/agricultura intensiva Cultivo que requiere de mucha mano de obra, pág. 644

International Monetary Fund (IMF)/Fondo Monetario Internacional (FMI) Agencia de las Naciones Unidas que otorga préstamos a los países para proyectos de desarrollo, pág. 553

irrigation/irrigación Acción de regar los terrenos cultivables con agua de embalses o ríos, págs. 223, 621

isthmus/istmo Franja angosta de tierra rodeada de agua por ambos lados y que une dos masas extensas de tierra, pág. 237

J

joint family system/sistema de familias mancomunadas En la India, costumbre de albergar en un mismo lugar a todos los integrantes de una familia extendida, pág. 616

K

krill/kril Criaturas marinas pequeñas, semejantes a los camarones; alimento de las ballenas y peces, pág. 735

L

lagoon/laguna Masa de agua de menor dimensión, separada del mar por arrecifes de coral o bancos de arena, pág. 720

land degradation/degradación del suelo Disminución en la producción potencial de un terreno, pág. 516

land redistribution/redistribución de la tierra Política según la cual se expropia terreno a los que poseen grandes extensiones para redistribuirlo entre los que tienen poca tierra o ninguna, págs. 229, 583

landlocked/rodeado de tierra Rodeado casi o completamente de tierra; totalmente aislado del mar, pág. 544

landslide/deslizamiento Caída precipitada de una masa de tierra por una ladera, pág. 245

latifundio/latifundio Granja comercial de gran extensión, de propiedad de un individuo o una compañía, pág. 229

lava/lava Magma o roca derretida del manto terrestre, que brota a la superficie durante la actividad volcánica, pág. 360

leaching/lixiviación Proceso en que se disuelven y son arrastrados por el agua los nutrientes que contiene la tierra, pág. 516

leeward/sotavento Orientado de espaldas a la dirección que lleva el viento, pág. 247

life expectancy/esperanza de vida Los años que se espera que viva un persona, calculados según las estadísticas, pág. 384

light industry/industria ligera Producción de bienes de consumo de menor importancia, tales como ropa y aparatos caseros, pág. 657

lignite/lignito Carbón blando de color marrón negruzco, pág. 334

literacy/alfabetismo Saber leer y escribir, pág. 134

lithosphere/litosfera Características de la corteza exterior sólida de la Tierra, como la tierra, las rocas y los accidentes geográficos, pág. 45

llano/llano Campo plano extenso con pastizales, pág. 269

loam/greda Materia del suelo compuesta de arcilla, limo y arena, pág. 421

lock/esclusa Sección encerrada de un canal de navegación que se llena o se vacía para cambiar el nivel del agua, pág. 183

loess/loes Greda, polvo o cieno depositado por el viento, de grano fino y rico en minerales, pág. 55

M

malnutrition/desnutrición Enfermedad causada por la falta de alimentación o una dieta desequilibrada, págs. 567, 623

mandate/mandato Potestad conferida por la Liga de las Naciones que autoriza a una nación a gobernar un territorio menos poderoso, pág. 471

mangrove/mangle Árbol tropical que crece en suelos pantanosos de las zonas costeras, pág. 162

mantle/manto Capa intermedia entre la corteza terrestre y el núcleo de la Tierra, compuesta de roca sólida, pág. 44

maquiladora/maquiladora Fábrica en México, junto a la frontera de Estados Unidos, que ensambla productos para su exportación, pág. 231

maritime/marítimo Que bordea o está situado en el mar; relativo a la navegación y las embarcaciones, pág. 181

market economy/economía de mercado Sistema económico en el que las decisiones sobre la producción, los precios y otros factores económicos están determinados por la ley de la oferta y la demanda, págs. 104, 216

martial law/ley marcial Ley impuesta en períodos de control militar estricto, pág. 658

maternal mortality/mortalidad materna El número de mujeres que mueren de cada 100,000 nacimientos, como consecuencia del embarazo y complicaciones del parto, pág. 384

mechanical weathering/meteorización mecánica Proceso de desgaste o debilitamiento físico de la roca por acción de fuerzas como el hielo o las raíces, pág. 52

medina/medina La sección antigua de las ciudades de África del Norte, generalmente con una mezquita en el centro, pág. 534

megalopolis/megalópolis Ciudad gigantesca; región compuesta de varias ciudades y sus zonas aledañas, considerada como un mismo complejo urbano, pág. 159

mercenary/mercenario Soldado a sueldo contratado por un país extranjero, pág. 558

mestizo/mestizo Persona con ascendencia europea y nativo americana mezcladas, pág. 212

metropolitan area/área metropolitana Área comprendida por una ciudad principal y sus suburbios, pág.148

migrant worker/trabajador itinerante Labriego que se desplaza de un sitio a otro para trabajar donde se necesite mano de obra, ya sea para sembrar o cosechar la tierra, pág. 229

militarism/militarismo Preponderancia de los militares y propensión a entrar en guerra, pág. 689

militia/milicia Ejército compuesto por civiles, pág. 484

minaret/minarete Torre alta y delgada de una mezquita, pág. 446

mixed economy/economía mixta Sistema que combina diversos niveles de reglamentación del gobierno, págs. 105, 320

monarchy/monarquía Sistema de gobierno autoritario encabezado por un monarca (rey, reina, sha o sultán) cuyo trono es heredado, pág. 103

monotheism/monoteísmo La creencia en un solo Dios, pág. 438

monsoon/monzón Viento que cambia de dirección periódicamente e influye en extensas regiones climáticas, pág. 594

moor/tremedal Terreno pantanoso carente de árboles y con abundante turba, pág. 310

moraine/morrena Masa de roca, grava, arena y arcilla en forma de cresta, transportada y depositada por un glaciar, pág. 56

mosque/mezquita Edificio donde los musulmanes practican sus ceremonias religiosas, pág. 446

muezzin/muecín Musulmán que convoca a los fieles desde un minarete para orar cinco veces al día, pág. 446

mulatto/mulato Persona con mezcla de antepasados de África y otros lugares, págs. 212, 268

multiethnic/multiétnico Compuesto por muchos grupos étnicos, pág. 380

multiplier effect/efecto multiplicador El efecto que tiene una inversión de hacer proliferar ocupaciones relacionadas entre sí por toda la economía, pág. 399

NAFTA/TLC Tratado de Libre Comercio, o acuerdo que eliminó las barreras comerciales entre los Estados Unidos, Canadá y México, págs. 194, 230

national identity/identidad nacional Lo que le da a un pueblo el sentido de ser una nación, pág. 389

nationalism/nacionalismo Orgullo que se siente por el propio país; aspiración de un grupo cultural de constituirse y gobernarse como una nación autónoma, págs. 457, 607

nationalize/nacionalizar Hacer que pasen a depender del Estado propiedades industriales particulares, pág. 330

natural resource/recurso natural Material proveniente del medio ambiente que los seres humanos valoramos y aprovechamos para satisfacer nuestras necesidades, pág. 109

navigable/navegable Lo suficientemente profundo o ancho para permitir el paso de las embarcaciones, pág. 349

neutral/neutral Que no toma partido entre partes enfrentadas en guerra, pág. 342

nomad/nómada Persona que vive desplazándose de un lugar a otro, pág. 448

nomadic herding/pastoreo errante Práctica de desplazar el ganado por distintos pastos a lo largo del año, pág. 516

nonaligned nation/nación no alineada Nación neutral durante la guerra fría, pág. 590

nonrenewable resource/recurso no renovable Recurso natural que no se puede restituir después de ser utilizado, pág. 109

nonviolent resistance/resistencia no violenta Política de oponerse a un enemigo u opresor por cualquier medio excepto la violencia, pág. 608

nuclear energy/energía nuclear Tipo de energía producida por fisión, es decir, por la división de átomos de uranio en un reactor nuclear para liberar energía almacenada, pág. 111

oral history/historia oral Historia que se transmite verbalmente, pág. 514

ore/mena Material rocoso del que se extrae un mineral valioso, pág. 308

organic matter/materia orgánica Materia derivada de las plantas, animales vivos y sus despojos, pág. 420

outback/llanura desértica Término que designa la vasta región árida y abrupta de Australia, pág. 721

ozone layer/capa de ozono Franja de gas ozono de la atmósfera que absorbe los rayos ultravioleta dañinos del sol, pág. 75

P

pack ice/banquiza de hielo Hielo marino formado por una mezcla de icebergs y otros témpanos flotantes en aguas supergélidas del mar, pág. 735

paddy/arrozal Terreno irrigado o inundado donde se cultiva arroz, pág. 703

pampas/**pampas** Término que se refiere a las regiones de llanuras extensas y sin árboles en Argentina y Uruguay, págs. 206, 279, 578

páramo/**páramo** Término que se refiere a la meseta de los Andes del Ecuador, pág. 273

partition/partición División en partes; separación; fraccionamiento, pág. 609

peat/turba Material esponjoso formado de residuos descompuestos de musgos y plantas acumulados en sitios pantanosos, que cuando se seca puede aprovecharse como combustible, pág. 315

peninsula/península Una parte de la superficie terrestre que sobresale del océano, pág. 221

per capita/per cápita Por persona, pág. 138

perception/percepción Punto de vista que está influido por la propia cultura y la propia experiencia, pág. 41

perceptual region/región de percepción Grupo de lugares que está definido por los sentimientos y actitudes de sus habitantes, pág. 41

perennial irrigation/irrigación perenne Sistema de irrigación que suple el agua necesaria para la tierra durante todo el año, pág. 527

perestroika/*perestroika* En la antigua Unión Soviética, política de reestructuración económica, pág. 425

perishable good/producto perecedero Producto que no permanece fresco por mucho tiempo, pág. 343

permafrost/permahielo Capa de suelo inmediatamente debajo de la corteza terrestre que permanece congelada, págs. 82, 418

photosynthesis/fotosíntesis Proceso por el cual las plantas fabrican su alimento a partir de bióxido de carbono y liberan oxígeno, pág. 74

piedmont/tierras bajas Región inferior de los montes y sierras, pág. 278

plankton/plancton Organismo microscópico flotante, pág. 724

plantation/plantación Propiedad con extensos terrenos cultivables donde laboran muchos agricultores, pág. 260

plate tectonics/tectónica de placas Teoría según la cual la corteza externa de la Tierra está compuesta de varias placas extensas y flotantes, o losas de roca, cuyo movimiento constante explica los terremotos y la actividad volcánica, pág. 46

plateau/meseta Planicie extensa situada a considerable altura sobre el nivel del mar, págs. 221, 508

plume/plúmula Punto extremadamente caliente en el manto terrestre, pág. 361

poaching/caza ilícita Entrar en propiedad ajena para cazar ilícitamente, pág. 444

polder/pólder Zona pantanosa de las tierras bajas que han sido recobradas del mar, pág. 337

population density/densidad de población Promedio de habitantes que viven en un área determinada, págs. 87, 518

potash/potasa cáustica Mineral empleado para fabricar explosivos y como fertilizante, pág. 476

prairie/pradera Campo llano de una zona templada caracterizado por la gran variedad y abundancia de pastos, págs. 81, 578

precipitation/precipitación Todas las formas de agua que caen a la Tierra de la atmósfera, incluidas la lluvia y la nieve, pág. 67

predator/depredador Animal que caza animales de otra especie para su subsistencia, pág. 198

prevailing westerlies/vientos alisios del NE y SE La corriente constante de aire que sopla de oeste a este en las zonas templadas de la Tierra, pág. 292

primary economic activity/actividad económica primaria Actividad económica que toma o consume recursos naturales directamente, como la pesca o la minería, pág. 115

privatization/privatización Transferencia de industrias y empresas del gobierno a manos de propietarios privados, pág. 394

proliferation/proliferación Acción de multiplicarse algo en abundancia, pág. 696

protectorate/protectorado Territorio que tiene su propio gobierno pero está controlado por una potencia externa, pág. 438

province/provincia Territorio gobernado como división política de un país, pág. 181

provisional government/gobierno provisional Gobierno transitorio en espera de acuerdos permanentes, pág. 672

purdah/*purdah* Costumbre de las mujeres hindúes y musulmanes de taparse el rostro con un velo cuando están fuera de casa, pág. 616

pyrethrum/piretrina Pesticida producido a partir de ciertas flores, pág. 567

Q

quaternary economic activity/actividad económica cuaternaria Actividad económica que se centra en la adquisición, procesamiento y difusión de la información, tales como la educación y la investigación, pág. 117

quota/cuota Cantidad fija, pág. 692

R

rain shadow/zona al abrigo de las lluvias Zona en las altas montañas donde caen muy pocas precipitaciones por quedar a sotavento, págs. 68, 130

recession/recesión Descenso prolongado en la actividad económica, pág. 330

refugee/refugiado Persona que busca refugio fuera de su país para escapar del peligro o de un tratamiento injusto, pág. 544

regolith/regolito Roca meteorizada, pág. 420

reincarnation/reencarnación La creencia de que el alma de un ser humano o un animal pasa por una serie de nacimientos, muertes y renacimientos, pág. 614

relative location/ubicación relativa Localización de un lugar con relación a otro, pág. 39

relief/relieve Cambios de elevación o altitud del terreno en una determinada zona, pág. 45

Renaissance/Renacimiento Florecimiento del arte, la literatura y el conocimiento que tuvo lugar en Europa en los siglos XIV, XV y XVI, págs. 288, 357

renewable resource/recurso renovable Recurso natural que el medio ambiente suple o restituye continuamente a medida que se consume, pág. 109

reparation/indemnización Dinero pagado como desagravio por los daños sufridos por ejemplo en una guerra, pág. 332

reservoir/embalse Lago natural o artificial donde se contiene el agua para consumo humano, pág. 527

revolution/revolución Vuelta completa de la Tierra alrededor del Sol. La Tierra completa una revolución cada 365$\frac{1}{4}$ días, lo cual equivale a un año, pág. 64

Ring of Fire/Anillo de Fuego Círculo de montañas volcánicas que bordean el océano Pacífico, pág. 49

rotation/rotación Movimiento giratorio de la Tierra sobre su propio eje, como si fuera un trompo, a medida que se desplaza por el espacio, pág. 64

ruble/rublo Moneda de Rusia, pág. 430

rural/rural Perteneciente a o característico del campo, pág. 90

S

Sahel/Sahel Región de África al sur del Sahara, pág. 506

sanction/sanción Pena que impone la comunidad internacional para castigar a un país por comportamientos no aceptables, pág. 575

sandstorm/tormenta de arena Vendaval que arrastra aire caliente, polvo y arena, pág. 524

sari/sari Prenda típica de color vivo que llevan las mujeres hindúes envuelta en el cuerpo como una túnica larga, pág. 616

savanna/sabana Llanura extensa con escasos árboles, localizada en las zonas cálidas cercanas al ecuador, págs. 81, 512, 578

scavenger/carroñero Animal que se alimenta de los despojos de otros animales, pág. 579

sea stack/pilar marino Bloque de rocas formadas por la erosión de las olas marinas, pág. 465

secede/escindirse Retirarse formalmente de una organización política o religiosa, pág. 191

secondary economic activity/actividad económica secundaria Actividad económica en la que se consumen materias primas para producir o fabricar nuevos productos de mayor valor, pág. 116

secular/secular Mundano, que no está vinculado a la religión, pág. 497

sediment/sedimento Pequeñas partículas de tierra, arena y grava que el agua transporta y deposita en el suelo, págs. 54, 464

segregation/segregación Separación de las razas, pág. 575

seismic activity/actividad sísmica Terremotos y erupciones volcánicas, pág. 354

seismic wave/onda sísmica Vibración causada por el movimiento de las placas tectónicas, pág. 245

seismograph/sismógrafo Instrumento que mide y registra los movimientos de la corteza terrestre, pág. 682

self-determination/autodeterminación El derecho de un pueblo de decidir su propio destino político, pág. 472

selva/**selva** Región de bosques muy tupidos, tales como los que se encuentran en Ecuador, Perú y Bolivia, pág. 273

separatism/separatismo Movimiento social que lucha por obtener la independencia política, religiosa o étnica de otro grupo, pág. 190

sertão/**sertão** Región del Brasil de suelos estériles y escasas lluvias, pág. 255

shah/sha Título del antiguo gobernante de Irán, pág. 498

shifting agriculture/cultivos de rotación Práctica de cultivar un terreno hasta agotar el suelo para luego pasar a cultivar otro, pág. 543

sinkhole/dolina Boquete que se abre al disolverse la piedra caliza, que hace que se caiga el terreno de encima, pág. 224

sirocco/siroco Viento cálido y seco que sopla en el norte de África, pág. 350

soil/tierra Capa delgada del suelo de materia desmenuzada donde crecen las plantas, pág. 420

soil creep/solifluxión Proceso por el cual el suelo se desliza lenta y continuamente por acción de la gravedad, pág. 420

soil horizon/horizonte del suelo Una capa diferenciable de tierra que va quedando a medida que se forma el suelo, pág. 420

solar energy/energía solar Energía producida por el Sol, pág. 111

solstice/solsticio Uno de los dos días del año cuando el Sol está perpendicular en los Trópicos de Cáncer y Capricornio, pág. 65

souk/zoco Mercado de una comunidad árabe, pág. 534

sovereignty/soberanía La libertad y el poder de un país para decidir su política y acciones, pág. 101

soviet/soviet Uno de los diversos órganos de gobierno en la antigua Unión Soviética, pág. 423

sphere of influence/esfera de influencia Área o país política y económicamente dominado por otro país, aunque no sea gobernado por éste directamente, pág. 651

standard of living/nivel de vida Nivel de bienestar material de una persona o grupo, medido según la educación, la vivienda, los servicios de salud y la nutrición, pág. 136

steppe/estepa Término que se refiere a los terrenos llanos y extensos sin cultivar, que se encuentran en las zonas templadas de Europa y Asia, págs. 378, 417, 578

storm surge/ola ciclónica Pared de agua que inunda las regiones costeras cuando una tormenta tropical toca tierra, pág. 627

strategic value/valor estratégico Importancia que tiene un lugar o una cosa para las naciones que planean acciones militares, pág. 569

striations/estriaciones Surcos que caracterizan las partes de la roca sometidas a la acción de los glaciares, pág. 128

strip mining/minería a cielo abierto Proceso de despejar los mineros la superficie de un terreno para dejar al descubierto depósitos de minerales, pág. 345

structural adjustment program/programa de ajuste estructural Programa para reformar la estructura de una economía, pág. 553

subcontinent/subcontinente Extensa masa de tierra que forma una parte diferenciada de un continente, pág. 592

subsidence/subsidencia Fenómeno geológico en el que se hunde paulatinamente el suelo en un área, pág. 356

subsistence economy/economía de subsistencia Véase **economía tradicional**

subsistence farming/agricultura de subsistencia Cultivo que provee sólo lo suficiente para suplir las necesidades de una familia o población, págs. 116, 229

suburb/suburbio Zona residencial en las afueras de una ciudad central, pág. 134

sultanate/sultanía Territorio gobernado por un sultán, pág. 590

summit/cumbre Punto más alto de una montaña o una elevación semejante, pág. 290

Sunbelt/*Sunbelt* Los estados del sur y sudeste de los Estados Unidos comprendidos entre las Carolinas y el sur de California, caracterizados por tener un clima cálido y, recientemente, un rápido crecimiento de la población, pág. 164

T

taiga/taiga Bosques coníferos y dispersos de Europa, Asia y América, págs. 378, 416

tariff/arancel Impuesto del gobierno a los artículos importados, págs. 194, 692

telecommunication/telecomunicación Transmisión de mensajes por medios electrónicos, pág. 146

terrace/terraza En agricultura, macizo angosto de tierra sostenido por muros de piedra y barro que van paralelos a la pendiente natural del terreno, generalmente construido en zonas montañosas para disponer de más tierras arables, pág. 644

tertiary economic activity/actividad económica terciaria Actividad económica en la que no se acopian ni se procesan directamente materias primas, sino que se realizan actividades en servicio de otros; industria de servicios, págs. 117, 309

theocrat/teócrata Persona que afirma gobernar por autoridad religiosa o divina, pág. 663

timber line/límite de vegetación arbórea Límite en grandes elevaciones sobre el cual no crece vegetación continua de bosque, pág. 273

tornado/tornado Viento impetuoso que forma un torbellino con forma de embudo, pág. 627

totalitarianism/totalitarismo Sistema de gobierno en el que una autoridad central controla todos los aspectos de la sociedad, pág. 103

trade déficit/déficit comercial Situación en la que un país importa más de lo que exporta, pág. 450

trade surplus/superávit comercial Situación en la que un país exporta más de lo que importa, pág. 450

traditional economy/economía tradicional Sistema económico en el que las familias producen productos y servicios para su propio consumo, con muy pocos excedentes y escaso intercambio de productos; conocida también como economía de subsistencia, págs. 103, 217

tributary/tributario Río o arroyo que desemboca en un río principal, pág. 128

tropical cyclone/ciclón de los trópicos Tormenta que se origina en un océano tropical y sopla alrededor de un centro de baja presión, pág. 627

tropical storm/tormenta tropical Tormenta con vientos como mínimo de 39 millas (63 km) por hora, pág. 208

troposphere/troposfera La capa de la atmósfera más cercana a la superficie terrestre, pág. 74

trust territory/territorio en fideicomiso Colonia o territorio dependiente que es supervisado por otro país por encargo de las Naciones Unidas, pág. 731

tsunami/tsunami Enorme onda marina causada por una alteración geológica del fondo del océano, tales como un maremoto o una erupción volcánica, págs. 244, 364

tundra/tundra Región abierta y llana donde siempre hace frío y donde se dan muy pocas plantas, págs. 82, 172, 378, 416

typhoon/tifón Tormenta tropical destructora que se forma en el océano Pacífico, págs. 627, 683

U

unitary system/sistema unitario Sistema de gobierno en el que un solo gobierno central sustenta todo el poder político, pág. 102

urbanization/urbanización Crecimiento de la población urbana, pág. 90

V

velvet revolution/revolución blanca Revolución sin derramamiento de sangre, la cual ocurrió en Checoslovaquia a finales de la década de 1980, pág. 394

villagization/aldeización Movimiento político que obliga a los habitantes de zonas rurales a desplazarse hacia los pueblos para trabajar en granjas colectivas, pág. 572

volcano/volcán Abertura en la corteza terrestre por donde salen a la superficie rocas derretidas, pág. 360

W

wadi/rambla Cauce o cañada normalmente seca que contiene provisionalmente agua de lluvias caudalosas repentinas, págs. 464, 531

warlord/señor de la guerra Líder local de gran influencia con seguidores militares, pág. 652

water power/energía hidroeléctrica Energía producida por la fuerza de una caída de agua para mover maquinaria o generar electricidad, pág. 111

watershed/divisoria de aguas Cresta que separa dos cuencas hidrográficas, pág. 557

weather/tiempo atmosférico Condición que se da en la capa inferior de la atmósfera sobre un determinado lugar por un breve período, pág. 63

weathering/meteorización Proceso químico o mecánico por el cual la roca se desgasta paulatinamente hasta transformarse en tierra, pág. 52

white flight/desplazamiento de población blanca Traslado de la población de raza blanca de una región a otra, pág. 581

wind/viento Aire en movimiento, pág. 626

windward/barlovento Orientado de cara a la dirección en que sopla el viento, pág. 247

World Bank/Banco Mundial Agencia de las Naciones Unidas que otorga préstamos a los países para proyectos de desarrollo, pág. 553

yurt/yurta Tienda redonda hecha con un marco de madera cubierto con fieltro o pieles, pág. 462

Zionist/sionista Integrante del movimiento Sionista, fundado para promover la fundación de un estado judío independiente, pág. 472

Items in black type refer to the Student Edition pages; items in blue refer to the Teacher's Edition pages.

The Index includes references not only to the text but to maps, charts, and pictures as well. A page number followed by *m*, such as 591*m*, refers to a map. Page numbers with *c, g,* or *p* after them refer to charts, graphs, or pictures.

also names of individual countries
European Community, 195, 339
European Union, 288, 298*p*, 309, 317, 339, 352, *352,* 355, 358, 362, 394
evaluating conclusions, 419. *See also* social studies skills
evaluating sources on the Internet, 243. *See also* social studies skills
Everglades, 132, 132*p*
exports, 117–118; of Azerbaijan, 450*c*; of Egypt, 528; farm, 144; of Israel, 451*c*; of Kazakhstan, 450*c*; of Mexico, 224*c*; of Saudi Arabia, 451*c*; of South Africa, 575*c*; of the United States, 224*c*, 451*c*; of West Africa, 547. *See also* trade
Exxon Valdez (oil tanker), *67*

factories. *See* industry
falaj **system,** 492
Falkland Islands, 281
fall line, 163
Falun Gong, 669
family, 96, 491, *515,* 533, 616, 666, 668*p*, *710*
family farms, 144
famine, 159, 316, 569, 651
farming, in Canada, 182; cash crops, 229; in Central America, 240; in Central Asia, 462; in China, 663; commercial, 116, 117*p*; under Communists, 395, 424, 651*p*, 654–655, 656–657; *in the desert, 81;* double cropping, 661; dry, *82,* 350; in East Asia, 644*p*; as economic activity, 116, 116*p*, 117*p*; in Egypt, 523, 525*p*, 528; *family, 144;* in Greece, 362; intensive, 644*p*; in Iran, 498*p*; in Japan, 116, 681, 681*p*; by Native Americans, 143, 163; in Oman, 492; in Pakistan, 620–621, 620*p*; in Poland, 389, 389*p*; in Russia, 430; in the Sahel, 543–544; *slash-and-burn agriculture, 240;* in Slovakia, 395; in South Africa, 574; in Southeast Asia, 644*p*, 703; subsistence, 116, *116,* 229, 240, 260, 516, 574; in Switzerland, 343; in Syria, 485; in Tanzania, 572; technology in, 168–169; tenant farmers, 270; in Ukraine, 409; in the United States, 116, 117*p*, 143–144, 143*p*; in Western Europe, 288; in Yemen, 492; in Zimbabwe, 582–583, 583*p*. *See also* agriculture
farming collectives, 654
faults, 45–46, 50*c*, *245*
favelas, 256–257, 260, 262
Fedchenko Glacier, 460
Federal-Aid Highway Act (1956), 150
federal government, *101,* 102, *102*
federalism, 102
federation, 102
fellaheen, 523, 524
Fertile Crescent, 438, 482, *483*
feudalism, 423
Fever Tree, 722
fiber optics, 146
Fiji, 730, 731, 731*c*
Finland, 289*m*, 291*m*, 307*c*; climate, 292, 293*m*; economic activities of, 299*m*; ecosystems, 294, 295*m*; education in, 300*c*; languages of, 297*m*; literacy rate, 300*c*; natural resources of, 299*m*; population density, 297*m*
fire, 97
firths, 310
fishing, 158, 173, 215*m*, 268, 276*p*, 351*p*, *445,* 695
fjords, *293,* 318, 318*p*, *319*
flood plain, 54
floods, 623
Florida, 132, 132*p*, 142*m*, 161, 162, 162*m*, *162,* 164, 165, 165*p*, 250
food, 249; of China, 661; of Croatia, 401; fast *food, 430;* of Mexico, 229; regional, 165
food distribution, 89
food processing, 169
foot-and-mouth disease, 280, 298*p*

foraging, 544
foreign investment, 661–662, 674*p*, 710*c*
forest ecosystems, 78–80, 78*m*–79*m*, 80*p*, 132, 132*p*, 133*m*, 144, 169*c*, 378*p*, 556
forestry, 173, 182, 215*m*
formal regions, 41
Fort Worth, Texas, 165
fossil fuels, 109–111, 110*p*, 144–145, 144*c*
Four Modernizations, 656–657
Fox, Vicente, 228*p*
France, 289*m*, 291*m*, 324*m*, 327*m*, *327,* 736; Algeria and, 533, 536; Canadian colonies of, 189–190, 190*p*; climate, 292, 293*m*; culture of, 329–330; economic activities of, 299*m*, 325–328, 325*p*, 330, 330*c*; economy of, 330, 330*c*; ecosystems, 294, 295*m*; education in, 300*c*; Germany and, 329, 331–332; government of, 330; *Guiana Space Center, 268;* history of, 288, 328–329, 328*p*; industry in, 327–328; influence in Southeast Asia, 703, 703*m*, 709; invasions against, 328; language of, 297*m*, 328, 329; Lebanon and, 483; literacy rate in, 300*c*; market economy of, 325; national identity of, 325; natural resources of, 299*m*; Norman invaders, 315; Pacific Islands and, 731; physical characteristics of, 290*p*, 326–327, 326*p*; population density, 297*m*; population of, 329*c*; refugees to, 334*g*; regions of, 325–328, 327*m*; Sykes-Picot Agreement, 470–471; Syria and, 471; Tunisia and, 533; vineyards of, 325–326, 326*p*; *weather, 326;* in World War I, 470
Franco-Prussian War, 331–332
Franks, 328
free enterprise, 147, 147*p*, 396–397, 397*p*, 674–675
free market system, 397, 429
Free Trade Agreement, 194
Freetown, Sierra Leone, 547
French and Indian War, 190
French Canadians, 190, *190*
French Guiana, 205*m*, 207*m*, 209*m*, 211*m*, *213m,* 215*m*, 266*m*, 267–268, 267*p*
French Indochina, 709
French Revolution, 329
French Riviera, 327
frontal precipitation, 68, 69*c*
frost wedging, 52–53, 53–54
Fujian province, 661
Fujimori, Alberto, 275
Fulani people, 546, 552, 553*p*
functional regions, 41
fundamentalist religion, 461, *461*

Gabon, 540*m*, 542*m*, 555, 556*c*
Gambia, 540*m*, 542*m*, 547, 548*c*
Gandhi, Mohandas, 590, 607–609, *613*
Ganges River, 614, 617*p*, 618, 622
gasohol, 261–262, *261*
gasoline, 150
gasoline emissions, 235
gathering, 115
gauchos, 279, *279, 280p*
Gaul, 328
Gaza Strip, 479, *479,* 481
GDP. *See* gross domestic product
Geiranger Fjord, 318*p*
genetic engineering, 336
Geneva Convention, 343
Genghiz Khan, 676
Genoa, Italy, 356
genocide, 457
Geographia (Ptolemy), *39*
geographic concepts, 37–38
geographic information systems, 37, 604–605
geographic tools, 35–38, 36*c*
geography, definition of, 35; five themes of, 38–42
geology, 621
Georgia (Republic of), 439*m*, 441*m*, 454*m*,

455–456, 455*p*, 456*m*, 457*c*; climate of, 442, 443*m*; economic activities of, 449*m*; ecosystems, 445*m*; natural resources of, 449*m*; population density, 447*m*
Georgia (United States), 142*m*, 162*m*
geothermal energy, 111, 319
German language, 335
Germany, 289*m*, 291*m*, 332*m*; climate of, 292, 293*m*, 333; economic activities of, 299*m*; economy of, 332, 335; ecosystems, 294, 295*m*; France and, 329, 331–332; industry of, 334; languages of, 297*m*; natural resources of, 299*m*, 334; physical characteristics of, 290*p*, 333–335; population density, 297*m*; population of, 329*c*; refugees to, 334*g*; Soviet Union and, 333, 424; technology in, 335*p*; unification of, 331, 333, 333*p*; in World War I, 332, 470; in World War II, 288, 332, 334, 390, 473
geysers, 51, 51*p*, 726–727
Ghana, 506, 540*m*, 542, 542*m*, 547, 548*c*, 550
ghettos, 390, *390*
Gibran, Kahlil, 484
Gibson Desert, 719
Gift of the Nile, 523
GIS. *See* geographic information systems
Giza, Egypt, 522*m*, 522*p*, 530*p*
glacial caves, 57
glaciers, 56–57, 56*p*, 57*p*, *128,* 184*p*, 734–735
Glasgow, Scotland, 311
glasnost, 425
glen, 311
Global Connections, AIDS virus, 570; climates, 66; coastal cities, 536; cooperation and conflict, 194, *241,* 328, *343,* 401, 473, *479, 535, 601,* 608; cultures, 165, 257, 270, 299, 363, *457;* economic activities, *110,* 344, 526, 553, 575, *654, 712;* ecosystems, *379;* environmental change, *67,* 396, *557,* 730; global trade patterns, 240, *257,* 270, 390, 428, *449,* 479, *691,* 695; government and citizenship, *101, 275, 425,* 675; international cooperation, 736, 737; migration, 159, *187,* 190, 230, 703; natural hazards, 49, 49*p*, *209,* 683; natural resources, 174, *224, 517;* Olympic Games, 657; petroleum, 479; *religion, 410;* science and technology, *37, 137,* 146, 280, 334, 570, 618, *618, 645, 722;* tourism, 567; *understanding the past, 306;* urbanization, *568*
global economy, 54, 66, 104, 150, 159, 186, 239, 273, 344, 350, 352, 383, 397, 410, 517, 526, 566, 601, 645, 675, 695, 719, 722
global positioning system, 37
Global ReLeaf, 396
global trade patterns, 118*p*, 240; of China, 656*p*, 657; coffee, *257,* 270; Columbian Exchange, 163*c*; economic activities and, 117–118, 118*p*; of Egypt, 528–529; exports, 117–118; fishing, 276*p*, 695; imports, 117–118; of Japan, 691; London and, 307; of New Zealand, 728, 728*p*; Panama Canal, 237*p*; petroleum, 428, 479, 494
global warming, 64, 65, 73, 73p, 111, 730
globalization, 607
GNP. *See* gross national product
Gobi Desert, 62*m*, 662, 663*p*, 676
Golan Heights, 485
gold, 110, 145, 172, 215*m*, 506, 516, 722
Golden Horde, 422
Gorbachev, Mikhail, 424–425, *425*
Gore, Al, 141
government and citizenship, of Africa, 514*m*; of Algeria, 536–537; of Argentina, 280; of Australia, 720; authority of, 102–103; of Bhutan, 624*p*; of Brazil, 260–261; of Central America, 240–242; of China, 102*p*, 654*p*; Communist, 98, 372; of Democratic Republic of the Congo, 558–559; of Egypt, 525–526; elongated states, 275; *federal system, 101;* of France, 330; of Italy, 356; of Japan, 691–692; of Kenya, 567–568, 567*p*;

krill, 735
Kumar, Ashwini, 609
Kunlun Shan, 636
Kura River, 457
Kurdistan, 487
Kurds, 486, 487, 497
Kushite civilization, 506, 569
Kuwait, 439*m*, 441*m*, 443*m*, 445*m*, 447*m*, 449*m*, 471*m*, 480*c*, 486, 488, 489, 489*m*
Kyoto, Japan, 87*p*, 687
Kyrgyzstan, 454*m*, 457*c*, 460–463, 461*m*
Kyushu, Japan, 636*p*, 681, 683
Kyzyl Kum Desert, 440, 460

L

lagoon, 720, 720, 721*p*, 729
Lagos, Nigeria, 90*c*, 518*c*
Lake Baikal, 108*m*, 374*p*, 416
Lake Erie, 54
Lake Nasser, 527, 527*p*
Lake Nicaragua, 239
Lake Nyasa, 580
Lake Ontario, 183
Lake Superior, 183
Lake Titicaca, 275
Lake Victoria, 108*m*, 509, 565, 571, 572
lakes, 69, 108*m*, 374*p*
land bridge, 717; degradation, 516*p*; reclamation, 340; redistribution, 229, 583
land redistribution, 583, 583
land use, 223; economic activities, 115–117; energy resources, 110–111; global trade patterns, 117–118; natural resources, 109–110; in the Netherlands, 338
landforms, 36*c*, 40, 45; of Brazil, 255, 256*m*; of Canada, 181, 184, 184*p*; of Central America, 237–239, 238*m*; chemical weathering and, 53; climate and, 70; of South America, 268; of the United States, 167, 167*p*; water bodies and, 46*c*
landlocked, 544, 544
Landsat program, 37
landscape, 97*f*; of Brazil, 255; of Canada, 128; of Caribbean islands, 246–248; of Central America, 237–239; of Central Asia, 460–461; of Central Europe, 374; of East Asia, 636; of Egypt, 523–524; of England, 305–306; of Germany, 333–334; of Ireland, 315; of Japan, 681–682; of Kenya, 565; of Latin America, 206; of Mexico, 221, 223–224; of Netherlands, 337–338; of Nordic nations, 318–320; of North Africa, 531; of Northern Eurasia, 374; of Poland, 389; of Russia, 415–416; of Scotland, 310–311; of South America, 272–273, 278–279; of South Asia, 592; of Southwest Asia, 440; of United States, 128, 157, 161, 172; of Wales, 312; of Western Europe, 290
languages, 328, 335; of Africa, 532–533; of ancient Egypt, 525; of Asia, 461, 469; of the Baltic States, 406; of Belgium, 338; of Central America, 239; of China, 667, 667*p*; culture and, 91, 92*m*–93*m*; dialects of, 329; of Ecuador, 274; of Egypt, 525; English, 297; of Europe, 297*m*; of France, 329; of the Guianas, 267; of India, 599; of Ireland, 315; of Korea, 693; lingua franca, 350; of Luxembourg, 339; of Nordic nations, 320; of Pakistan, 621; of Paraguay, 279; of Peru, 274; of the Philippines, 711; of Portugal, 353*m*; of South Africa, 574; of Spain, 351–352, 353*m*; Spanish, 229; Swahili, 570; of Switzerland, 342; of Venezuela, 268; of Wales, 312; written, 401
Laos, 635*m*, 636*p*, 637*m*, 639*m*, 641*m*, 643*m*, 645*m*, 700*m*, 703*m*, 707*m*, 709–710, 709*p*, 710*c*
Laozi, 668
Lapps, 115
latifundio, 229
Latin America, climate of, 208, 208*c*, 208*p*,

209*m*; cultures of, 212, 212*c*, 212*p*; economic activities of, 215*m*; economy of, 214*p*, 216–217, 216*c*, 217*c*; ecosystems of, 210, 210*p*, 211*m*; environment of, 214*p*; history of, 204; location of, 202, 202*m*; physical characteristics of, 206, 206*c*, 206*p*; the plaza, 215; population density of, 213*m*; regional atlas, 205*m*, 207*m*, 209*m*, 211*m*, 213*m*, 215*m*; technology of, 214*p*. *See also* Brazil; Caribbean; Central America; South America
latitude, 39, 39, 65, 66–67, 66*m*, 67*m*
Latvia, 373*m*, 375*m*, 377*m*, 379*m*, 381*m*, 383*m*, 388*m*, 406–408, 406*p*, 407*m*, 423
Laviera, Tato, 251
law of supply and demand, 104, 104*c*
leaching, 516
lead, 145, 215*m*
League of Nations, 471
Lebanon, 439*m*, 441*m*, 468*m*, 471, 471*m*, 480*c*, 483–485, 483*m*; in Arab League, 473; climate of, 442*g*, 443*m*; economic activities of, 449*m*; ecosystems, 445*m*; history of, 438; independence in, 471; Israel and, 480, 484; natural resources of, 449*m*; Palestinian refugees in, 479; population density of, 447*m*
Lee Teng-hui, 674
leeward, 248
Lena River, 416
Lenin, V. I., 423
Leningrad, Russia, 423*p*
Lesotho, 564*m*, 566*m*, 575*c*, 580
Lesser Antilles, 238*m*, 246, 247
level of development, 104, 118–119, 119*p*
Lewis, Flora, 325, 333
Li Hongzhi, 669
Liberia, 540*m*, 542*m*, 547, 548, 548*c*
Libya, 522*m*, 527*c*, 531, 532*m*, 533, 534, 534*p*, 535–536, 535*p*, 535
Libyan Desert, 523
lichen, 82, 378*p*
Liechtenstein, 289*m*, 291*m*, 297*m*, 299*m*, 324*m*, 329*c*
life expectancy, 384, 384*c*, 385, 385*c*; in India, 619; in Russia, 430; in South America, 274*c*; in the United States, 274*c*; in Venezuela, 268
lignite, 334, 334
limited self-government, 664
lingua franca, 350
Lisbon, Portugal, 352
literacy rate, 134; in Egypt, 527*c*; in Finland, 300*c*; in France, 300*c*; in India, 616*p*, 619; in Italy, 301*c*; in Japan, 686*c*, 690*p*; in Oman, 492*p*; in Pakistan, 621; in Portugal, 353; in Russia, 428*c*; in Turkey, 496; in the United Kingdom, 301*c*; in the United States, 301*c*. *See also* education
lithosphere, 45
Lithuania, 372, 373*m*, 375*m*, 377*m*, 379*m*, 381*m*, 383*m*, 388*m*, 406–408, 407*m*, 423
Little Ice Age, 56
Liverpool, 306
llamas, 275*p*
Llano Estacado, 269
llanos, 269
local government, 102
location, 39–40, 39*p*; of Africa, 504; of Antarctica, 632; of Australia, 632; of Baltic States, 406–407; of Central Europe, 370; of cities, 148; of East Asia, 632; of Egypt, 523; of Horn of Africa, 564*m*, 569–570; of London, 307; of North Africa, 532; of Northern Eurasia, 370; of Portugal, 349; of South Asia, 588; of Spain, 349; of West Africa, 547; of Western Europe, 286
Loch Ness monster, 311
lochs, 310
Lockerbie, Scotland, 535
lock, 183–184, 183*p*, 183
loess, 55, 660, 660
logging industry, 186, 186*p*

London, England, 306–307, 306*m*
Long March, 652–653, 652*p*, 653*m*
longitude, 39, 39
Lorraine, France, 327
Los Angeles, 90*c*, 152, 174
lost cities, 223
Louisiana, 41, 142*m*, 161, 162, 162*m*, 163–164, 165, 190
Louisiana Purchase, 144
L'Ouverture, Toussaint, 204
Low Countries, 337–339, 337*p*, 338*m*, 339*p*
low islands, 729
lumber industry, 144, 186
Lutheran Church, 320
Luxembourg, 289*m*, 291*m*, 293*m*, 295*m*, 297*m*, 299*m*, 329*c*, 338*m*, 339, 339*p*

M

Macao, 675
Macedonia, 362, 373*m*, 375*m*, 377*m*, 379*m*, 381*m*, 383*m*, 388*m*, 399*m*, 400, 402, 403*p*, 403
Machu Picchu, 32, 33*p*
Madagascar, 564*m*, 566*m*, 575*c*
Madeira Islands, 353
Madrid, Spain, 351
Magellan, Ferdinand, 207
Maghreb Desert, 532
Maghreb nations, 522*m*, 531–534, 531*p*, 532*m*, 533*p*, 534*p*, 536–537, 536*p*, 537*p*
magma, 45
Magyar people, 372, 396
Maine, 142*m*, 157, 157*p*, 158*m*
majority rule, 575–576
making a diagram, 520. *See also* social studies skills
making and analyzing climate graphs, 302. *See also* social studies skills
making and analyzing political maps, 140. *See also* social studies skills
making and analyzing population pyramids, 218. *See also* social studies skills
making and analyzing thematic maps, 76, 76*m*. *See also* social studies skills
making decisions, 530. *See also* social studies skills
making inferences, 226. *See also* social studies skills
making valid generalizations, 171. *See also* social studies skills
malaria, 722
Malawi, 564*m*, 566*m*, 575*c*, 580
Malay Peninsula, 62*m*, 707*m*
Malaysia, 635*m*, 637*m*, 639*m*, 640*p*, 641*m*, 643*m*, 645*m*, 700*m*, 702, 707*m*, 710*c*, 712–713, 712*p*
Mali, 506, 540*m*, 540*p*, 542–543, 542*m*, 545, 545*c*, 545*p*, 546, 546*p*
Mali River, 512*p*
malnutrition, 567, 567, 623
Malta, 352*c*
Mana Motuhake, 727
Manchuria, 634, 688
mandate, 471, 471
Mandela, Nelson, 575–576, 576*p*
Mandingo people, 546
manganese, 456
mangroves, 162, 623
Manitoba, 180*m*, 182*m*, 185–186
manufacturing, 116–117, 148, 215*m*, 261, 261*p*. *See also* industry
Mao Zedong, 652*p*, 653–656, 655, 665
Maori people, 727–728
maps, ancient, 39; contour, 732*m*; economic, 452; political, 140; recognizing patterns in, 114, 114*m*; skill lessons, 10–15; thematic, 76, 76*m*
maquiladoras, 231, 231*p*
Mardi Gras, 165
Margrethe (queen of Denmark), 320
Mariana Trench, 37

national identity, 389, 685

national parks, 174

National Water Carrier, 476

nationalism, 457, 607

Nationalist People's party, 652

Nationalist Republic of China, 652

Native Americans, 143, 163, 204, 212, 212p, 227–228, 229, 274

Native Canadians, 187, 189, 189p, 191

NATO, 362, 401, 402, 403

natural gas, 109–111, 138, 144c, 173, 188

natural hazards, 45–46, 111, 206, 221–222, 239, 244, 360, 364, 682, 683, 711; earthquakes, 46, 49, 245, 441, 682; El Niño, 209; tsunami, 364; typhoon, 639, 683; volcanoes, 45, 50, 247, 363

natural phenomena, 637

natural resources, 100, 174, 517; of Africa, 517m, 535, 535p, 556–558; of the Andean countries, 273; of Antarctica, 736; of Asia, 449m, 461, 601m, 645m, 709p; of Australia, 645m; of Canada, 137m, 186, 186p, 187–188, 188p, 193, 194p; of China, 645m; distribution of, 111; of Egypt, 523–524; energy sources, 110–111, 110p; of England, 308; of Europe, 299m, 383m; of Germany, 334; of Israel, 477; of Kenya, 565, 565p; of Moldova, 411p; nonrenewable resources, 109–110, 557–558; of Nordic nations, 318–319; of Northern Eurasia, 383m; of Pakistan, 620–621, 620p; petroleum, 224; of the Philippines, 645m; of Poland, 389; primary economic activities and, 115–116, 115p, 116p, 117p; recycling programs and, 109p, 110; renewable resources, 109, 557; of the Sahel, 545–546, 545p; of Switzerland, 343; of Taiwan, 645m; of Thailand, 645m; of the United States, 137m, 143–145, 144g, 158, 163–164, 172–173, 172p; of Vietnam, 645m

Nazca Plate, 46, 47m

Nazi party, 288, 332, 390, 473

Nebraska, 142m, 144, 168m

Negev Desert, 81, 476, 476m, 476

Nehru, Jawaharlal, 607

Neidjie, Big Bill, 721

Nepal, 589p, 591m, 592, 593m, 595m, 597m, 599m, 601m, 606m, 624, 625c, 635m, 637m, 639m, 641m, 643m, 645m

Neruda, Pablo, 275

Netherlands, 289m, 291m, 337–338, 337p, 338m; climate of, 292, 293m; colonies of, 634; economic activities of, 299m; ecosystems, 294, 295m; history of, 288; influence in Southeast Asia, 702–703, 703m; land reclamation in, 340; languages of, 297m; natural resources of, 299m; population, 329c; population density, 296, 297m, 338

Netherlands Antilles, 246, 249

neutral country, 342

Neva River, 376p

Nevada, 142m, 172, 173m, 174, 222

New Brunswick, 180m, 181, 182m, 182

New Caledonia, 635m, 637m, 639m, 641m, 643m, 645m, 730

New Delhi, India, 618

New England, 144

New Hampshire, 142m, 158m, 159

New Jersey, 142m, 158m

New Mexico, 142m, 173m, 174, 222, 269

New Orleans, Louisiana, 41, 91, 149, 151, 165

New South Wales, 719–720

New Spain, 227–228

New York, 142m, 158m; moraines in, 56; physical characteristics of, 157; recycling in, 136, 136p

New York, New York, 130, 130c, 149, 150, 151, 160, 479; migration to, 250; urbanization in, 90c, 159p

New York Stock Exchange, 105p

New Zealand, 111, 632m, 634, 635m, 636, 637m, 638, 639m, 640, 641m, 643m, 645m, 716m, 718m, 719m, 726–728, 726p, 728, 731c, 736

Newfoundland and Labrador, 180m, 181, 182, 182m, 191

Ngo Dinh Diem, 709

Niagara Falls, 54, 194p

Nicaragua, 204, 205m, 207m, 209m, 211m, 213m, 215m, 236m, 237, 238m, 239, 241, 241, 242

nickel, 215m

Nielsen, Dr. Jerri, 736

Niger, 514p, 540m, 542m, 545, 545c, 546

Niger River, 108m, 542, 545

Nigeria, 506, 540m, 542m, 548c, 553, 558; economic activities, 553p, 554p; government of, 553–554; migration in, 552–553, 552p; patterns of settlement in, 552, 552p; petroleum in, 553, 554p; population density of, 518c; population of, 99c, 518c; regions of, 552; religion in, 553

Nihon, 682

Nile River, 108m, 483, 506, 508, 508p, 523, 523p, 527–528, 527p

Nippon, 682

nomadic herding, 446p, 448p, 516, 533–534, 676

nonaligned nations, 590

nonmaterial culture, 90

nonphonetic, 667

nonrenewable resources, 109–110, 557–558

nonviolent resistance, 608

NORAD. *See* North American Aerospace Defense Command

Norden. *See* Nordic nations

Nordic nations, 304m, 307c, 318–321, 318p, 319m, 329c. *See also* Denmark; Finland; Iceland; Norway; Sweden

Norgay, Tenzing, 624

North Africa, 506, 522m; Arabs in, 532–533; climate of, 531; cooperation and conflict in, 532–533; economic activities of, 531p, 533p, 536p; family in, 533; Islam in, 532–533; languages of, 532–533; location of, 532; migration in, 532; natural resources in, 535, 535p; patterns of settlement in, 533; physical characteristics of, 531; trade, 532; urbanization in, 534; wadis, 531. *See also* Algeria; Egypt; Libya; Morocco; Tunisia

North America, 34m, 69, 77p, 79–80, 81. *See also* Canada; Mexico; United States

North American Aerospace Defense Command (NORAD), 194

North American Free Trade Agreement (NAFTA), 194, 230

North American Plate, 46, 47m, 221

North Atlantic Current, 69

North Atlantic Drift, 292m

North Atlantic Treaty Organization (NATO), 333

North Carolina, 55, 142m, 162m

North China Plain, 661

North Dakota, 142m, 168m

North European Plain, 290p, 325, 333, 389

North German Plain, 333

North Island, 726–727

North Korea, 635m, 637m, 639m, 641m,

643*m*, 645*m*, 680*m*, 686*c*, 693–696, 694*m*, 696*p*
North Pole, 64*c*, 65, 319
North Sea, 333, 334, 338
North Vietnam, 709
North Yemen, 491
Northern Eurasia, 373*m*; climate of, 376–377*m*; culture of, 380, 380*p*; economy of, 382, 382*p*, 383*m*; ecosystems of, 378, 378*p*, 379*m*; environment of, 382, 382*p*; ethnic groups in, 380*p*; health care in, 384, 384*c*, 385, 385*c*; history of, 372; lakes in, 374*p*; location of, 370, 374; migration in, 380; natural resources of, 383*m*; physical characteristics of, 374, 374*p*; political systems in, 372; population density of, 381*m*; religion of, 380, 380*p*; rivers in, 374*p*; technology of, 382, 382*p*
Northern Hemisphere, 39
Northern Ireland, 91, 306*m*, 314, 315–317, 316*p*
northern lights, 319
Northwest Territories, 187
Norway, 289*m*, 291*m*, 293, 307*c*, 318–321, 318*p*, 319*m*, 319, 736; climate of, 292, 293*m*; economic activities of, 299*m*; ecosystems, 294, 295*m*; languages of, 297*m*; natural resources of, 299*m*; population density, 297*m*
Nova Scotia, 180*m*, 181, 182, 182*m*, 182, 190
nuclear energy, 111
nuclear power, 409
Nuclear Non-Proliferation Treaty, 696
Nunavut, 187, 187

O

oasis, 524
Ob River, 416
Obasanjo (Nigerian president), 554
occupational groups, 151*c*
Oceania, 730
ocean pollution, 67
oceans, 724–725; currents of, 66, 67, 67*m*; effect on climate, 69; erosion and, 55
Odyssey **(Homer),** 365, 365
Odzala National Park, 557
Ogallala aquifer, 169
Ohio, 142*m*, 167, 168*m*, 170
Ohio River, 149
oil, 109–111. *See also* petroleum
oil supply, 150
Oklahoma, 142*m*, 161, 162, 162*m*, 163–164
Oklahoma City, Oklahoma, 479
Old Faithful, 51, 51*p*
Olmec culture, 91
Olympic Games, 657
Omaha, Nebraska, 169
Oman, 439*m*, 441*m*, 443*m*, 445*m*, 447*m*, 449*m*, 468*m*, 480*c*, 489*m*, 492, 492*p*, 493*p*
Omsk, Russia, 418*p*
Ontario, 180*m*, 182*m*, 183–184, 183, 191
OPEC. *See* Organization of Petroleum Exporting Countries
oral history, 514*p*
oranges, 162
Oregon, 142*m*, 144, 173*m*
Organization of Petroleum Exporting Countries (OPEC), 224, 489
organizing data into tables, 60. *See also* social studies skills
origami, 684
Orinoco River, 269
Orkney Islands, 290*p*
orographic precipitation, 68, 69*c*
orthodox, 478
Orthodox Christianity, 380*p*, 410, 422
Ossentian ethnic group, 456
Ottawa, Ontario, 184
Ottawa River, 184
Ottoman Empire, 372, 438, 469–471, 470*p*, 496

Ottoman Turks, 469, 525
outback, 721
Outer Banks, 55
overgrazing, 41, 544
oxygen, 75
Oyashio Current, 683

P

Pacific Coastal Plain, 238–239
Pacific Islands, 729–731, 729*m*, 730*p*, 731*c*
Pacific Ocean, 34*m*, 68, 635*m*, 637*m*, 726
Pacific Plate, 46, 47*m*, 221
Pacific Rim, 691, 722
pack ice, 735
paddies, 703, 704*f*
Pahlavi, Mohammad Reza, 498
Pakistan, 90*c*, 591*m*, 593*m*, 596*p*, 606*m*, 620–621, 621*p*, 621, 625*c*; climate regions, 595*m*; communications in, 602*c*; economic activities of, 601*m*; ecosystems, 597*m*; history of, 590; India and, 609, 610; languages, 599*m*; natural resources, 601*m*; physical characteristics of, 592; population density, 599*m*; population of, 99*c*, 625*c*; poverty in, 602
Palau, 731*c*
Palestine, 438, 469, 471–474, 471*m*, 473
Palestinian Liberation Organization (PLO), 479–481, 479, 484
Palestinian refugees, 473*p*, 474, 478–481, 478*p*, 479*p*, 481*p*, 482, 484
Palestinians, 480
Pamir-Alai Mountains, 460
pampas, 81, 206, 279, 281*p*
Pan Am Flight 103, 535
Pan American Games, 270
Panama, 205*m*, 207*m*, 209*m*, 211*m*, 213*m*, 215*m*, 236, 237, 238*m*, 239, 242*c*, 250
Panama Canal, 237, 237*p*, 239, 250
Panara tribe, 258
Pangaea, 47, 48*m*
Papua New Guinea, 635*m*, 637*m*, 639*m*, 641*m*, 643*m*, 645*m*, 700*m*, 707*m*, 710*c*, 713, 713*p*
Paraguay, 205*m*, 207*m*, 209*m*, 211*m*, 213*m*, 215*m*, 217, 266*m*, 274*c*, 278, 279, 279*p*, 279
Paraguay River, 278, 279
parallels, 39
páramos, 273
Paraná River, 278, 279*p*
Paris, France, 287*p*, 325, 329–330
Paris Basin, 325
Parthenon, 40
Patagonia, 279
patterns of settlement, 36*c*, 38, 90, 212, 212*p*; in Australia, 718–719; commuters, 150*p*; in Egypt, 524; in Greece, 362*p*; in Nigeria, 552, 552*p*; in North Africa, 533; in the Philippines, 711*p*; pollution, 390; of Portugal, 352; in the Sahel, 545, 545*p*; of Southwest Asia, 469*p*; in Spain, 351; trade balance, 118; trade routes, 118; trade surplus, 450, 710*c*; of West Africa, 547; wool, 280*p*. *See also* migration
Pearl Harbor, 689
Pearson, Lester, 195
peat, 315
Peloponnese Mountains, 362
Pemex, 230
peninsula, 62*m*, 221, 291
peninsulares, 227, 228
Pennsylvania, 142*m*, 157, 158, 158*m*
Pentagon, 479, 622
People and Geography, 112–113, 178–179, 234–235, 340–341, 404–405, 494–495, 562–563, 612–613, 670–671
People's Republic of China, 634, 654
per capita income, 317
perception, 41
perceptual regions, 41
perennial irrigation, 527, 528

perestroika, 425
permafrost, 82, 418
Perón, Eva, 280
Perón, Juan Domingo, 280
Perry, Matthew C., 687
Persia, 469, 497
Persian Gulf, 438, 470, 483
Persian Gulf War, 486–487, 487*p*
Perth, Australia, 719, 719
Peru, 32, 204, 205*m*, 207*m*, 208, 208*c*, 209*m*, 211*m*, 213*m*, 215*m*, 266*m*, 272, 273, 274–275, 274*c*, 275*p*
Peru current, 209, 272
Peter the Great, 422
petroleum, 109, 138*c*, 139*c*, 144*c*, 215*m*, 224, 517, 689; in Africa, 516, 556*c*; in Alaska, 173, 175*p*; in Algeria, 536; in Arabian Peninsula, 488*p*; in Azerbaijan, 458, 459*p*; in British Isles, 307*c*; in Canada, 186, 188, 188*p*; in Ecuador, 274; in Egypt, 528, 529*g*; in Indonesia, 711; in Iraq, 486–487; in Libya, 535, 535*p*; in Mexico, 224, 224*p*, 230; in Nigeria, 553, 554*p*; in Nordic nations, 307*c*; in Persian Gulf, 438; in Russia, 428; in Saudi Arabia, 451*c*; in Southwest Asia, 479; in the United States, 163–164, 307*c*; in Venezuela, 269
Philadelphia, Pennsylvania, 149, 160
Philip II (king of Spain), 351
Philippine Plate, 47*m*
Philippines, 90*c*, 632*m*, 634, 635*m*, 637*m*, 637, 639*m*, 641*m*, 643*m*, 645*m*, 700*m*, 702, 707*m*, 710*c*, 711, 711*p*, 711
physical characteristics, 36*c*, 38, 40, 44–45; of Africa, 508, 508*p*, 531; of Asia, 440, 460–461, 636, 636*p*; of Australia, 636; of Canada, 128, 128*p*, 129*m*; of Egypt, 523–524; of Europe, 290, 374, 374*p*; of Hungary, 396; of Italy, 358*p*; of Japan, 681–682; of Jordan, 482*p*; of Kenya, 565, 565*p*, 566*m*; of Latin America, 206, 206*c*, 206*p*; of Mexico, 221–225, 221*p*, 222*m*, 223*m*; of the Mississippi River, 170, 170*p*; of Nepal, 592; of New Zealand, 636, 726–727, 726*p*; of Northern Eurasia, 374, 374*p*; of Pakistan, 592; of Poland, 389; of Russia, 415–416, 415*p*; of Slovakia, 395*p*; of South Africa, 573; of the United States, 128, 128*p*, 129*m*, 157–158
physical processes, 36*c*, 38, 45–46, 56–57, 56*p*
piedmont, 278
Pillars of Hercules, 536
Piraeus, Greece, 363
Pittsburgh, Pennsylvania, 151, 159
place, 40, 40*p*
plains, 45, 374*p*
planning for the future, 340–341, 494–495; in the Arabian Peninsula, 489–490; in Egypt, 528*p*; in India, 616; in Japan, 691–692; in Kenya, 568; in Korea, 696; in Portugal, 352–353; in Russia, 425–426; in the Sahel, 544–546; in South Africa, 576
plant life, 77–78
plant succession, 78
plantations, 116, 163, 240, 250, 255, 256, 260
plate movement, 48–49, 49*p*, 50*c*
plate tectonics, 46–47, 47*m*, 47, 48*m*, 49*p*, 50*c*, 221, 362
Plateau of Tibet, 636
plateaus, 45, 221, 349, 508, 557
plaza, 215
PLO. *See* Palestinian Liberation Organization
Po River, 356
points of view, 126, 153, 314
Poland, 372, 373*m*, 377*m*, 378*p*, 379*m*, 381*m*, 383*m*, 384, 384*c*, 388*m*, 389–391, 389*p*, 390*m*
polar climate, 70*m*–71*m*; easterlies, 66*m*; ice cap, 73; zones, 65
polder, 337
policy planner, 193

ACKNOWLEDGMENTS

The people who made up the *World Geography: Building a Global Perspective* team—representing design services, editorial, editorial services, electronic publishing technology, manufacturing & inventory planning, market research, marketing services, online services & multimedia development, planning & budgeting, product planning, production services, project office, publishing processes, and rights & permissions—are listed below. Bold type denotes the core team members.

Staff Credits Mary Aldridge, Margaret Antonini, Helene Avraham, **Jim Doris**, Marlies Dwyer, Libby Forsyth, **Joe Galka, Holly Gordon, Katharine Graydon**, Diana Hahn, Beth Hyslip, Bob Landgraf, Carol Lavis, **Kathleen Mercandetti, Carrie O'Connor**, Mark E. O'Malley, Ray Parenteau, Robert Prol, Ryan Richards, Kirsten Richert, Elaine Soares, Annette Simmons, Robin Sullivan, Wendy Svec

Additional Credits Greg Abrom, Ernest Albanese, Diane Alimena, Penny Baker, John Carle, Rui Camarinha, Martha Conway, Kathy Gavilanes, Xavier W. Niz, Mike Ginsberg, Patricia Jarden, Vickie Menanteaux, Art Mktchyan, Ken Myett, Jeremy Naidus, Bruce Rolff, Mildred Schulte, Melissa Shustyk

How the Earth Works Earth's Atmosphere Taken from *Earth*, published by Dorling Kindersley Limited. © Dorling Kindersley Limited, 2000, pp. 10–11. **Coniferous Forests** Taken from *Nature Encyclopedia*, published by Dorling Kindersley Limited. © Dorling Kindersley Limited, 1998, pp. 78–79. **Effects of Earthquakes** Taken from *Volcano & Earthquake*, published by Dorling Kindersley Limited. © Dorling Kindersley Limited, 2000, pp. 46–47, 56–57. **Effects of Volcanoes** Taken from *Volcano & Earthquake*, published by Dorling Kindersley Limited. © Dorling Kindersley Limited, 2000, pp. 14–15, 22, 34–35, 39, 40–41. **Soil** Taken from *Dictionary of the Earth*, published by Dorling Kindersley Limited. © Dorling Kindersley Limited, 1994, pp. 130–132; *Ecology* published by Dorling Kindersley Limited. © Dorling Kindersley Limited, 2000, pp. 22–23; *Earth*, published by Dorling Kindersley Limited. © Dorling Kindersley Limited, 2000, pp. 52–53. **Erosion** Taken from *Earth*, published by Dorling Kindersley Limited. © Dorling Kindersley Limited, 2000, pp. 54–55; *Dictionary of the Earth*, published by Dorling Kindersley Limited. © Dorling Kindersley Limited, 1994, pp. 112–113, 123. **Grasslands** Taken from *Nature Encyclopedia*, published by Dorling Kindersley Limited. © Dorling Kindersley Limited, 1998, pp. 84–85. **Winds and Storms** Taken from *Weather*, published by Dorling Kindersley Limited. © Dorling Kindersley Limited, 2000, pp. 38–39, 44–45. **Ocean Life** Taken from *Nature Encyclopedia*, published by Dorling Kindersley Limited. © Dorling Kindersley Limited, 1998, pp. 68–69, 72–73, 188.

Maps maps.com

Charts and Graphs Ernest Albanese, Kenneth Batelman

Photos Frequently cited sources are abbreviated as follows: DK, Dorling Kindersley Media Library; MP, Magnum Photos; NGIC, National Geographic Image Collection; PE, Pearson Education; PR, Photo Researchers, Inc.; WC, Woodfin Camp & Associates.

Cover NOAA i l. NOAA i m. NOAA i l. NOAA v t.r. © Jack Fields/PR v b. © 2000 Nigel Francis/The Stock Market vi t.r. © Stone vi b. Sandy Felsenthal/CORBIS vii Ary Diesendruck/Stone viii b. © IFA Bilderteam/eStock, Photo viii t. © Yann Layma/Stone ix t.r. (1) Michael Rosenfeld/Stone ix t.r. (1) Liaison Agency ix b. Homer Sykes/WC x Steve Vidler/eStock Photo xi t.r. H. Edward Kim/NGIC xi b. SuperStock xii t.l. SuperStock 26 t.r. © DK 26 b.l. © DK 26 m.l. Hope Ryden/NGIC 26 b.r. Eff Foott/Bruce Coleman, Inc. 26–27 m.m. Heather Angel/Natural Visions 27 t.r. Robert Gill; Papilio/CORBIS 27 b.r. © Dorling Kindersley/Frank Greenaway 32–33 Bates Littlehales/NGIC 34 George Mobley/NGIC 35 © Vince Streano/Stone 37 Kevin Kelley/CORBIS 38 James Blair/NGIC 39 Steve Raymer/NGIC 40 Stone 41 Michael E. Long/NGIC 42 Tomaszewski/NGIC 44 Steve Raymer/NGIC 49 © Georg Gerster/Comstock, Inc. 51 © Nicholas DeVore III/Photographers Aspen 52 © Paul Chesley/Photographers Aspen 53 © Kurgan-Lisne/Liaison Agency 54 l. © Cameron Davidson/Comstock, Inc. 54 r. © Gilles Rigoulet/Cosmos/Matrix 55 © Steven C. Wilson/Entheos 56–57 © Robert Knight/Stone 62 NOAA/NGIC 63 CORBIS 65 b.l. Dean Conger/NGIC 65 m.r. Dean Conger/NGIC 73 Peter Bull/ © DK 74 t.l. © Wayne Lawler/PR 74 t.r. NASA 74 b.r. © John Heseltine/Science Photo Library/PR. 74 b.l. Nicholas Hall/DK 75 m.l. Stephen Bull/DK 75 t.l. Stephen Bull/DK 75 b.r. © PR 75 t.r. NASA Goddard Space Flight Center 77 Thomas Abercrombie/NGIC 80 © The Stock Market/Sergio Pitamitz 81 © Paul Chesley/Photographers Aspen 82–83 Michael Medford/The Image Bank 86 Rich Iwasaki/Stone 87 Thomas Nebbia/NGIC 97 © PR 98 Thomas Nebbia/WC 100 © Reuters/Jeff Christensen/Archive Photos 101 Winfield I Parks Jr./NGIC 102 David & Peter Turnley/CORBIS 103 C. Renault/Liaison Agency 105 AP/Wide World Photos 107 Thomas Nebbia/WC 108 James Blair/NGIC 109 James Amos/NGIC 110 m.r. Jodi Cobb/NGIC 110 b. George F. Mobley/NGIC 112 Wolfgang Kaehler 113 b.l. Agence France Presse/CORBIS 113 t.r. © 1995 Bruno Barbey/MP 115 Frank & Helen Schreider/NGIC 116 David Austen/WC 117 Cotton Coulson/WC 118 Jose Galvez/PhotoEdit 119 Sandy Felsenthal/CORBIS 121 James Amos/NGIC 124–125 Bill Ross/WC 125 Bill Ross/WC 128 t.l. © Bill Brooks/Masterfile Stock Image Library 128 m.r. © 2000 Nigel Francis/The Stock Market 130 l. © Garry D. McMichael/PR 130 r. © Garry Black/Masterfile Stock Image Library 132 t.l. SuperStock 132 m.r. © George D. Lepp/PR 132 b.l. © Ted Wood/Stone 134 t.l. Rob Crandall/Stock Boston 134 b.l. © David R. Frazier Photolibrary 134 m.m. Cary Wolinsky/Stock Boston 136 t.l. © Mitch Kezar/Stone 136 m.r. George Hall/WC 136 b.l. Ed Bailey/AP/Wide World Photos 138 b.r. Corel Professional Photos CD-ROM™ 138 l. Corel Professional Photos CD-ROM™ 138–139 t.r. image © 2001 PhotoDisc, Inc. 138–139 m. PE 139 t.r. image © 2001 PhotoDisc, Inc. 139 l. Corel Professional Photos CD-ROM™ 139 m. Pearson Education 139 b.r. Corel Professional Photos CD-ROM™ 142 © Doris De Witt/Stone 143 Paul A. Souders/CORBIS 145 Ted Spiegel/Black Star 146 Property of AT&T Archives. Reprinted with permission of AT&T 147 © Bob Daemmrich/Stock Boston/PictureQuest 148 © Peter Pearson/Stone 149 Maggie Steber/Aurora & Quanta 150 © Don Spiro/Stone 156 Eastcott Momatiuk/WC 157 B. Anthony Stewart/NGIC 159 Nicholas DeVore III/Photographers Aspen 160 Leonard Lee Rue III 161 John Elk III/Stock Boston 164 SuperStock 165 Stuart Cohen/Comstock, Inc. 166 t. Sisse Brimberg/NGIC 166 m. Pearson Education/Prentice Hall 167 George Gerster/Comstock, Inc. 170 James L. Stanfield/NGIC 172 © David Stoecklein/The Stock Market/Corbis 174 l. CORBIS 174 r. Phillip James Corwin/CORBIS 175 Steven L. Raymer/NGIC 178 © Gilbert Grant/PR 179 l. © Newman & Floweb/PR 179 r. © Peter Yates/PR 180 George F. Mobley/NGIC 181 © The Stock Market/Randy Ury 184 David Hiser/Photographers Aspen 185 David Alan Harvey/NGIC 186 © Gordon Fisher/Stone 187 David Hiser/Photographers Aspen 188 l. Todd Buchanan/NGIC 188 r. © Al Harvey/Masterfile Stock Image Library 189 David Hister/Photographers Aspen 190 Sisse Brimberg/NGIC 193 Ottmar Bierwagen Photo/Spectrum Stock 194 James P. Blair/NGIC 197 © Gordon Fisher/Stone 198 t.r. © DK 198 m.r. © DK/Matthew Ward 198 m.b. © DK 198–199 W. Wisniewski/Frank Lane Picture Library 199 m.l. (1) Cyril Laubscher/ © DK 199 t.l. © DK/Malcolm McGregor 199 m.m. © Stone 199 m.r. © DK 199 b.r. Joe McDonald/CORBIS 199 m.l. (2) Peter Chadwick/ © DK 202–203 Mireille Vautier/WC 206 l. Chip & Rosa Maria de la Cueva Peterson 206 r. © Will & Deni McIntyre/Stone 208 Ilkka Olimonen/CORBIS Sygma 208 b. JPL/NASA 210 t.l. Brian Parsley/Stone 210 m.r. Kevin Schafer/CORBIS 210 b.l. Robert Frerck/Odyssey Productions/Chicago 212 t. Ary Diesendruck/Stone 212 b. Porterfield/Chickering/PR 214 t.r. Robert Frerck/Odyssey Productions/Chicago 214 m.l. © Les Stone/Sygma CORBIS 214 b.r. Mireille Vautier/WC 220 Peter Menzel 221 PhotoDisc, Inc. 224 Robert Frerck/Odyssey Productions/Chicago 225 Kenneth Garrett/NGIC 226 Robert Frerck/WC 227 David Hiser/Photographers Aspen 228 l. Courtesy of the Library of Congress 228 r. © Henry Romeros/Reuters NewMedia/CORBIS 229 SuperStock 230 PE/PH School 231 Joel Sartore 234 © PR 235 Guillermo Gutierrez/AP/Wide World Photos 236 Jodi Cobb/NGIC 237 © Will & Deni McIntyre/PR 239 Joseph J. Scherschel/NGIC 240 Tomasz Tomaszewski/NGIC 241 El Diario De Hoy/Sipa 244 b. Reuters/Jorge Silva/Archive Photos 244 m.r. The Granger Collection, New York 245 m.l. Bettman/CORBIS 245 b.r. Andrew Green/ © DK 245 t.r. Bruce Coleman, Inc. 245 t.l. Lenny Ignelzi AP/Wide World Photos 246 Catherine Karnow/WC 248 t. © Joe Viesti/The Viesti Collection 248 m.r. © Joel Simone/Stone 249 James P. Blair/NGIC 251 SuperStock 253 Joseph J. Scherschel/NGIC 254 Loren McIntyre 255 © Luiz C. Marigo/Peter Arnold, Inc. 258 Loren McIntyre 259 Kevin Kelley/CORBIS 260 © Stephanie Maze/Material World 261 Stephanie Maze/NGIC 263 © Luiz C. Marigo/Peter Arnold, Inc. 266 © Hans Strand/Stone 267 Carol Lee/St. Croix 269 Robert W. Madden/NGIC 271 Sam Abell/NGIC 272 Steve Vidler/eStock, Photo 273 Mireille Vautier/WC 275 A. Ramey/WC 276 © Peter Menzel 278 Joe Viesti/The Viesti Collection 279 Loren McIntyre 280 Stephanie Maze/WC 281 James Blair/NGIC 286–287 © Paul Chesley/Stone 290 t.l. © Michael Marten/Science Photo Library/PR 290 m.r. © IFA Bilderteam/eStock, Photo 290 b.l. Photographers Consortium/eStock, Photo 292 t.r. (1) Peter Bull/ © DK 292 t.r. (2) Peter Foreman/Stockscotland.com 292 m.l. image © 2001 PhotoDisc, Ltd. 292 b.r. Chad Ehlers/International Stock Photography, Ltd. 294 m.r. Catherine Slade/ © DK 294 t.l. © H. Reinhard/Okapia/PR 294 b.l. Randall Hyman 296 m.r. Adam Woolfitt/WC 296 t.l. Wolfgang Kaehler 298 t.l. © Siegfried Tauqueur/eStock Photo 298 m.r. (1) Michael Rosenfeld/Stone 298 b.l. AFP/CORBIS 298 m.r. (2) Liaison Agency 300 m. Ken Karp/PE/PH School 300–301 t.l. (1) PE 300–301 t.l. (2) PE 300–301 t.r. (2) PE 300–301 t.r. (1) PE 301 b.r. PE 304 © Janet Gill/Stone 305 Michael Yamashita/WC 308 Annie Griffiths Belt 309 © Mike

McQueen/Stone **310** © Yann Layma/Stone **311** Winfield I. Parks, Jr./NGIC **312** Sam Abell/NGIC **313** A. Howarth/WC **315** Slide File/eStock, Photo **316** Stuart Franklin/MP **317** AP/Wide World Photos/John Cogill **318** Picture Finders Ltd./eStock, Photo **320** Paul A. Souders/CORBIS **321** Tomaz Tomaszewski/NGIC **324** Volkmar Wentzel/NGIC **325** Marc Garanger/CORBIS **326** © Michael Busselle/Stone **328** Adam Woolfitt/CORBIS **331** SuperStock **333** Lester Sloan/WC **335** © Michael Rosenfeld/Stone **336** PE/PH School **336** PE/PH School **337** © Manfred Wehlig/Stone **339** © Porterfield/Chickering/PR **340** t.l. SuperStock **340** m.b. Andrew Beckett/ © DK **341** D. Davis/Art Directors & TRIP Photo Library **342** © Nicholas DeVore III/Stone **344** l. Photo Klopfenstein Adelboden Schweiz **344** r. Photo Klopfenstein Adelboden Schweiz **345** Adam Woolfitt/CORBIS **348** © Kathleen Campbell/Stone **349** Stephen G. St. John/NGIC **351** David Alan Harvey/NGIC **354** © Charlie Waite/Stone **356** Sam Abell/NGIC **357** l. O. Louis Mazzatenta/NGIC **357** r. Augustus Prima Porta. Braccio Nuovo, Vatican Museums Collection. Scala/Art Resource, NY **358** William Albert Allard/NGIC **360** b.l. Ingo Arndt/The Viesti Collection, Inc. **360** m.l. © F. Le Diascorn/Rapho/PR **360** m.m. Andre Jenny/Unicorn Stock Photos **360–361** m.m. Phyllis Picardi/International Stock Photography, Ltd. **361** m.r. © DK **361** b.r. (1) © DK **361** b.r. (2) © DK **361** t.r. NOAA/Frank Spooner Pictures/Liaison Agency **361** m.m. Wolfgang Kaehler **362** SuperStock **364** Wolfgang Kaehler **365** © Mark Segal/Stone **367** Wolfgang Kaehler **370–371** © Anthony Cassidy/Stone **374** m.r. Archive Photos **374** b.l. TRIP/B Turner **374** t.l. A. Woolfitt/Robert Harding Picture Library **376** t.l. Serguel Fedorov/WC **376** m.r. Geoggrey Clifford/WC **378** t.l. © M.K. Ranjitsina/PR **378** m.r. Sovfoto/Eastfoto **378** b.l. © B&C Alexander/PR **380** t.l. Mimi Cotter/International Stock Photography, Ltd. **380** m.r. Dean Conger/NGIC **380** b.l. Chuck Szymanski/International Stock Photography, Ltd. **382** b.l. © DK **382** t.l. Peter Essick/NGIC **382** m.r. Frank Siteman/PhotoEdit **384–385** r. Corel Professional Photos CD-ROM™ **384–385** l. PE/PH College **384–385** m. Corel Professional Photos CD-ROM™ **385** b. Courtesy Medical City Dallas Hospital **388** Nick Haslam/Hutchinson Library **389** © Jack Fields/PR **391** Leonard Freed/MP **393** James Stanfield/NGIC **395** © Brett Baunton/Stone **396** Gavin Hellier/Stone **397** Tomasz Tomaszewski/NGIC **398** © Sue Cunningham/SCP **400** Nicole Bengiveno/NGIC **401** TRIP/H. Sayer **402** L. Freed/Mp **403** Luc Delahaye/MP **406** Jeff Greenberg/Archive Photos **408** Gerd Ludwig/Visum Archiv **410** Jeff Greenberg/Unicorn Stock Photos **411** Trip/V. Kolpakov **414** Steve Raymer/NGIC **415** Sovfoto/Eastfoto **416** Trip D. McDonald/The Viesti Collection **418** Sovfoto/Eastfoto **420** m.m. Andrew Green/ © DK **420–421** b. © PR **421** m.l. Clive Streeter/ © DK **421** t.l. Frank Greenaway/ © DK **421** t.r. Andreas Einsiedel/ © DK **421** m.r. Mike Saunders/ © DK **421** b.r. © DK **422** Corel Professional Photos CD-ROM™ **423** Brown Brothers **424** David King Collection **426** ©Reuters NewMedia Inc./CORBIS **427** Sovfoto/Eastfoto **430** l. Express Newspapers/J717/Archive Photos **430** r. Sovfoto/Eastfoto **431** Sovfoto/Eastfoto **433** David King Collection **436–437** Thomas Abercrombie/National Geographic Society **440** t.l. NASA **440** m.r. Homer Sykes/WC **440** b.l. Serguei Fedorov/WC **442** t.l. SuperStock **442** b.l. AFP/CORBIS **444** m.r. Sovfoto/Eastfoto/PictureQuest **444** t.l. SuperStock **444** b.l. P. Prasanov/Ardea London **446** b.l. James L. Stanfield/NGIC **446** t.l. © Gerd Ludwig/Visum Archiv **446** m.r. R&S Michaud/WC **448** b.r. Joan Iaconetti **448** t.r. © Ed Kashi **448** m.l. Anthony Howarth/WC **449** Guido Rossi/The Image Bank **450–451** m.m. (3) © The Stock Market/Douglas Mesney **450–451** m.m. (1) Corel Professional Photos CD-ROM™ **450–451** r. PE **452** © DK **454** Sovfoto/Eastfoto **455** © Jeremy Nicholl/Katz/WC **458** Trevor Page/Hutchison Library **459** © 1994 Berry/MP **460** © Buddy Mays/International Stock Photography, Ltd. **462** m.r. Sharmil Zhumatov/CORBIS **462** t.l. Sharmil Zhumatov/CORBIS **463** Christopher Rennie/TRIPP Photographic Library **464** t.r. Wolfgang Kaehler **464** m.r. James Stevenson/ © DK **464–465** b. Wolfgang Kaehler **465** m.m. © DK **465** t.r. W. Kenneth Hamblin **465** t.l. (1) Mike Saunders/ © DK **465** b.r. © Michael Marten/Science Photo Library/PR **465** m.l. (1) Mike Saunders/ © DK **465** m.l. (2) Mike Saunders/ © DK **468** Robert Azzi/WC **469** Barry Iverson/WC **470** Vladpans/eStock Photo **472** Robert Capa/MP **473** George Rodger/MP **474** Bettman/CORBIS **475** A. Ramey/WC **477** m.r. Hulton Getty/Archive Photos **477** b.r. © M. Milner/CORBIS Sygma **478** Joanna Pinneo/Aurora & Quanta **479** Annie Griffiths Belt **480** Peter Turnley/Black Star **481** © Facelly/Sipa **482** Charles & Josette Lenars CORBIS **484** A. C. Lefevre/Liaison Agency **485** Barry Iverson/WC **486** © Georg Gerster/PR **487** ©AFP/CORBIS **488** Kevin McKiernan/Sipa **491** Robert Azzi/WC **492** James Stanfield/NGIC **493** Earth Observation Satellite Company **494** Robert Azzi/WC **495** David Young Wolff/PhotoEdit **496** Robert Frerck/WC **498** © Fred Maroon/PR **504–505** © Sybil Sassoon/Robert Harding Picture Library **508** t.r. Robert Caputo/Stock Boston **508** t.l. © DK **508** b.l. Steve Vidler/eStock Photo **508** t.l. © DK **510** t.l. Georg Gerster/Comstock, Inc. **510** m.r. Jean Gaumy/MP **510** b.l. © M&E Bernheim/WC **512** t.l. © Michael Yamashita/WC **512** m.r. © Trip/M Jelliffe/The Viesti Collection, Inc. **512** b.l. McGuire/Anthro-Photo **514** m.r. SuperStock **514** b.r. © J. Bertrand Eastock Photo/eStock Photo **516** t.l. Patrick Robert/CORBIS Sygma **516** m.r. Peter Essick/Aurora & Quanta Productions **516** b.l. Frank Lane Picture Agency/CORBIS **518–519** t.r. (2) Corel Professional Photos CD-ROM™ **518–519** t.r. (1) Corel Professional Photos CD-ROM™ **518–519** t.l. (1) Stone **518–519** t.l. (2) © The Stock Market/Torlief Svensson **519** b.r. PE/PH College **520** © DK **521** © DK **522** Winfield I. Parks, Jr./NGIC **523** © Tim Thompson **525** Robert Caputo/Stock Boston **525** inset The National Geographic Society

Film Library **526** Gerhardt Liebmann/ © PR **527** © Ed Kashi **528** Winfield I. Parks, Jr./NGIC **530** Vanni Archive/CORBIS **531** SuperStock **533** Wolfgang Kaehler **534** m.r. © Barry Iverson/WC **534** b. James L. Stanfield/NGIC **535** © Jim Holland/Black Star **536** © Abbas/MP **537** James L. Stanfield/NGIC **539** © Jim Holland/Black Star **540** Steve McCurry/MP **541** Joanna Pinneo **544** © Georg Gerster/PR **545** James L. Stanfield/NGIC **546** Betty Press/WC **547** Michael Dwyer/Stock Boston **549** Patrick Robert/CORBIS Sygma **550** Gerald Buthaud/WC **552** M. Bertinetti/PR **553** The Hutchison Library **554** Gilbert/CORBIS Sygma **555** Robert Caputo/Aurora **557** Robert Caputo/NGIC **558** Robert Caputo/Aurora **559** George Mulala/Reuters/Archive Photos **562** b.r. Wolfgang Kaehler **562–563** b. R.E. Barber/Unicorn Stock Photo **563** t.r. Michele & Tom Grimm/International Stock Photography, Ltd. **564** James P. Blair/NGIC **565** © Tim Davis/PR **567** Peter Jordan/Liaison Agency **568** Stuart Cohen/Comstock, Inc. **569** Scott Peterson/Liaison Agency **571** Robert Caputo/Aurora **572** Hans Paul/LEH/WC **573** Jonathan Blair/CORBIS **574** Henner Frankenfeld/Anthony Bannister's Photo Library **576** Mike Hutchings/AP Wide World Photos **580** David Young-Wolff/PhotoEdit **581** Andre Penner/Liaison Agency **582** James L. Stanfield/NGIC **583** Ian Murphy/Stone **588–589** James P. Blair/NGIC **592** t.l. Barry Bishop/NGIC **592** m.r. Paul Almasy/CORBIS **592** b.l. Harry Gruyaert/MP **594** t.r. James Blair/NGIC **594** m.l. Wolfgang Kaehler **596** t.l. Eric Dragesco/Ardea London **596** m.r. Wolfgang Kaehler **596** b.l. Jehangir Gazdar/WC **598** t.l. Steven J. Raymer/NG **598** m.r. Raghu Rai/MP **598** b.l. Steve McCurry/MP **600** t.l. Bruno Barbey/MP **600** b.l. Dinodia/The Viesti Collection **600** m.r. H. Mahidhar/Dinodia Picture Agency **602–603** m. image © 2001 PhotoDisc, Inc. **602–603** t.r. (1) P Crowther/S Carter/Stone **602–603** t.r. (2) image © 2001 PhotoDisc, Inc. **602–603** t.l. (1) image © 2001 PhotoDisc, Inc. **603** b.r. Corel Professional Photos CD-ROM™ **603** t.l. (2) PE/PH College **606** Steve McCurry/MP **607** © Van Bucher/PR **608** Anis Hamdani/Liaison Agency **609** James L. Stanfield/NGIC **610** Raghu Rai/MP **612** t.r. © DK **612** b.l. Warren Faidley/International Stock Photography, Ltd. **613** m.t. Richard Corey/Liason Agency **613** m.l. AFP/CORBIS **613** t.l. © Warren Faidley/International Stock Photography, Ltd. **613** m.m. Reuters/Archive Photos **613** t.r. Courtesy of Naval Research Laboratory/NOAA **613** m.r. (2) Courtesy of Naval Research Laboratory/NOAA **613** m.r. (1) Courtesy of Naval Research Laboratory/NOAA **613** b.r. (1) Courtesy of Naval Research Laboratory/NOAA **613** b.r. (2) Courtesy of Naval Research Laboratory/NOAA **614** Frank Grant/International Stock Photography, Ltd. **616** James P. Blair/NGIC **617** David Sutherland/Stone **618** l. Steve McCurry/MP **618** r. Steve McCurry/MP **620** Luca Tettoni/The Viesti Collection **621** Steve Malnes/Stock Boston **622** Stephen Dupont/CORBIS **623** James P. Blair/NGIC **624** James L. Stanfield/NGIC **626** Bill Bachman/PhotoEdit **627** Wolfgang Kaehler **632–633** Dean Conger/NGIC **636** t.l. Michael Yamashita/WC **636** m.r. © David Ball/CORBIS/The Stock Market **636** b.l. © Mark A. Johnson/CORBIS/The Stock Market **638** b.l. Georg Gerster/Comstock, Inc. **638** m.r. AP/Wide World Photos **640** t.l. James P. Blair/NGIC **640** m.r. Marc Bernheim/WC **640** b.l. Craig Lovell/The Viesti Collection, Inc. **642** b.l. CORBIS/The Stock Market **644** t.l. Hiroji Kubota/MP **644** m.r. Michael Yamashita/WC **644** b.l. TIMESPACE/The Viesti Collection, Inc. **646–647** t.l. (2) Corel Professional Photos CD-ROM™ **646–647** t.l. (1) Corel Professional Photos CD-ROM™ **646–647** m.m. Corel Professional Photos CD-ROM™ **646–647** t.r. (2) Corel Professional Photos CD-ROM™ **646–647** t.r. (1) Jeff Greenberg/Omni-Photo Communications, Inc. **647** b.r. SuperStock **650** Georg Gerster/Comstock, Inc. **651** O. Louis Mazzatenta/NGIC **652** Sovfoto/Eastfoto **654** Cary Wolinsky/Stock Boston **655** Paolo Koch/PR **656** m.r. James L. Stanfield/NGIC **656** b. H. Edward Kim/NGIC **658** Stuart Franklin/MP **659** Dean Conger/NGIC **661** Bruce Dale/NGIC **662** Earl & Nazima Kowall/CORBIS **663** George Gerster/Comstock, Inc. **664** Wong How Man/NGIC **665** Franklin Stuart/MP **667** H. Edward Kim/NGIC **668** t.l. James L. Stanfield/NGIC **668** m.r. James L. Stanfield/NGIC **669** © Dennis Cox/China Stock **670** Kelly Mooney/CORBIS **671** Earl Kowall/CORBIS **672** © Stone **673** Jodi Cobb/NGIC **674** Jodi Cobb/NGIC **675** Jodi Cobb/NGIC **680** Chad Ehlers/Stone **681** Kyodo News International Inc. **684** Paul Chesley/NGIC **685** Michael Yamashita/WC **687** SuperStock **688** Laurie Platt Winfrey, Inc. **689** (1). Jodi Cobb/NGIC **689** r. SuperStock **690** Richard Kalvar/MP **691** Karen Kasmauski/WC **692** Michael Yamashita/WC **693** AP/Wide World Photos/Ahn Young-joon **695** Alain Evrard/Robert Harding Picture Library, Ltd. **696** Yann Layma/Stone **700** Michael Yamashita/WC **701** David Alan Harvey/NGIC **702** James L. Stanfield/NGIC **704** Jean Claude Lejeune/Stock Boston **705** © AFP/CORBIS **706** Steve McCurry/MP **708** Jodi Cobb/NGIC **709** Michael Yamashita/WC **711** © Jean Higgins/Unicorn Stock Photos LLC **712** Robert Harding Picture Library **713** Eric Smith/TRIP Photographic Library **716** Robert W. Madden/NGIC **717** Tony Freeman/PhotoEdit **720** SuperStock **721** David Austen/WC **722** m.r. Michael Jensen/Auscape **722** b. Jennie Jones/Comstock, Inc. **723** Joseph J. Schershel/NGIC **724** t.r. © DK **724** b.l. John Woodcook/ © DK **724** m.m. Norbert Wu **724–725** m.b. Red Bavendam/Peter Arnold, Inc. **725** m.m. Norbert Wu **725** t.r. © Kelvin Aitken/Peter Arnold, Inc. **725** t.l. © DK **725** m.r. Ron Sefton/Bruce Coleman, Inc. **725** b.r. Ed Robinson/Tom Stack & Associates **726** SuperStock **727** Parker Gallery, London/Archive Photos **728** Eastcott/Momatiuk/WC **730** t. David Hiser/Stone **730** m.r. John Eastcott & Momatiuk Yva/NGIC **733** Maria Stenzel/NGIC **735** Maria Stenzel/NGIC **736** Maria Stenzel/NGIC **737** Maria Stenzel/NGIC **739** John Eastcott & Momatiuk Yva/NGIC

800   Acknowledgments